Agriculture in the United States

A Documentary History

WAYNE D. RASMUSSEN is an Agricultural Historian in the Economic Research Service, United States Department of Agriculture, Washington, D.C. He received his Ph.D. in 1950 from George Washington University. In 1973, Dr. Rasmussen was awarded the Distinguished Service award of the United States Department of Agriculture. He is the editor of *Readings in the History of American Agriculture* (1960), and co-author of *Century of Service: The First 100 Years of the United States Department of Agriculture* (1963), and *The Department of Agriculture* (1972).

Agriculture in the United States

A Documentary History

Edited by

Wayne D. Rasmussen

National Economic Analysis Division
United States Department of Agriculture

Volume 4

Random House   New York

Reference Series Editors:

William P. Hansen
Fred L. Israel

FIRST EDITION

9 8 7 6 5 4 3 2 1

MANUFACTURED IN THE UNITED STATES OF AMERICA

Library of Congress Cataloging in Publication Data

Rasmussen, Wayne David, 1915-   comp.
  Agriculture in the United States.

1. **Agriculture — United States — History — Sources.**
I.   Title.
S441.R33   630′.973   74–9643
ISBN 0-394-49979-4   Vol. 4

Contents

VOLUME FOUR

The Second American Agricultural Revolution, 1941-1973

Introduction

The second American agricultural revolution, triggered by World War II, has seen major changes in land use, farm policies, agricultural production, farm management, and farm life. When World War II began, the United States and its allies were fortunate in that the nation had substantial quantities of grain and cotton in storage, largely as a result of the price support programs. Even before the Japanese attack at Pearl Harbor, the United States was supplying food to Great Britain and the U.S.S.R. The Secretary of Agriculture called for increased production of many commodities in 1941, and Congress, in the Steagall Amendment, provided for price supports for additional commodities.

In 1943, a War Food Administration, working within the Department of Agriculture, was established. Virtually all production controls were removed, and very substantial increases in production were achieved. Within the United States, food prices were controlled along with others, and a number of foods were rationed. Farm machinery was rationed, fertilizers and insecticides were under priority control, and labor was recruited, trained, and assigned to areas where needed. Workers were brought in from Mexico and other nations. Internationally, a Combined Food Board was established to allocate food supplies among the nations of the free world.

During the war, much land which had been in conservation programs was planted to crops. The value of conservation seemed to be proven, because the land was available when needed and in a condition to yield abundantly. After the war and the period of postwar shortages, conservation programs were reinstituted.

The war saw an acceleration of the long-term trend towards a decline in the farm population and in the number of farms, and an increase in the average size of farms. In 1940, the farm population was 31 million of a total of 132 million. In 1950, the totals were 23 million and 151 million, while in 1972, they were 10 million and 208 million. In 1940, there were 6 million farms in the nation, averaging 167 acres each. The figures for 1950 were 5.4 million and 213; and for 1973, 2.8 million and 385.

These matters were and are of concern to many Americans. The trends seemed to be continuing in the 1970's, although many experts felt that the family farm, that is, the farm which hired no more than one and one-half manyears of labor each year, will survive. Similarly, although there is debate as to land use in the United States, there appears, according to experts, to be "enough land for tomorrow."

In the years immediately after World War II, questions of price support revolved around the levels at which supports should be maintained. Parity prices, based upon the ratio between prices paid for goods needed for production and prices received for farm products, were set by law at 90 percent for many commodities for the duration of the war and for two years after. Thereafter, Congress, in a series of bitterly-fought laws, dropped price supports, for the most part, for perishable products, and reduced those for storable or basic commodities. Finally, in the 1970's, after sharp rises in farm prices in the market, support prices for several major commodities were established in relation to market prices rather than in relation to prices paid by farmers.

During the late 1940's, but particularly during the 1950's, surplus farm products, financed by price support loans, piled up in warehouses. Public Law 480, signed on July 10, 1954, made some of these surpluses available to aid in the agricultural development of less-developed nations. In 1961, President Kennedy directed the Secretary of Agriculture to expand the program of food distribution to needy people — another use for the surpluses. Finally, in 1972, the surpluses, as well as normal stocks in storage, were virtually wiped out by a very large sale of wheat to the USSR and by sales to other nations.

The distribution of food to needy persons, either directly or through a revived food stamp program, which had ended during World War II, became a matter of controversy during the 1950's. A food stamp program, essentially a means of subsidizing food purchases by the needy, got underway in the 1960's, but its adequacy was in question. In 1969, President Nixon stated that he was going to use the food stamp program to aid America's needy. As a result, legislation was passed strengthening the plan. In the summer of 1974, some 13½ million Americans were being helped by food stamps.

While food stamps reach rural as well as urban poor, it was argued from the 1950's on that additional programs were needed to overcome rural poverty. A disproportionate number of the nation's poor resided in rural areas. For example, the President's National Advisory Commission, in *The People Left Behind*, reported that in 1964, 25 percent of the rural population was poor, compared with 15 percent of the urban people.

In 1955, the Department of Agriculture proposed locally-oriented programs for the development of industry and other activities in some of the nation's poorer rural counties. Efforts of varying intensity have continued, but the problem has proven difficult. One difficulty, though, that plagued agriculture before World War II, has virtually disappeared. Tenancy, particularly share-cropping, has almost come to an end, partly through government programs, but mainly because of the mechanization of agriculture, including cotton production.

The decline in tenancy, like the increase in the size of farms and their decline in number, was, in a broad sense, a result of the second American agricultural revolution. This revolution saw the virtual completion of the changeover from animal to mechanical power. As Dieffenbach and Gray show, the tractor was improved over a period of years, with many models available in the 1920's and 1930's. However, it was not until 1954 that the number of tractors exceeded the number of horses and mules on American farms. The number of tractor on farms more than doubled between 1940 and 1950, even though the number of farms declined.

The tractor permitted the mechanization of many other farm operations. Tomato production and hay making are examples. However, the agricultural revolution was not the result of adapting some one tool or technique. Rather, it came through farmers adopting what has been called a "package" of agricultural technology, which usually includes machines, improved (often hybrid) seeds and breeding stock, careful tillage, fertilizer, productive use of water through irrigation or drainage, the application of chemicals to control weeds, fungi, and insects, the widespread use of conservation practices, and the balanced feeding of livestock. The package idea is actually a systems approach to the problems of increasing agricultural productivity. In many instances, particular problems are solved by adapting advanced technology from other fields. The conquest of the screw-worm by Edward F. Knipling, as shown in an article by Gall, is an excellent example.

Much of the technology going into the package had been developed between World War I and World War II. However, as Johnson states in *Changes in American Farming:* " . . . the production-increasing potentialities of improvements that were made over a decade, and that normally would have been diverted gradually into the production stream, were held back by the drought and depression of the 1930's."

During World War II, higher prices, with high levels of price support guaranteed for two years after the end of the war, and a seemingly unlimited demand for farm products, combined with a shortage of farm labor and appeals from the government to increase production, led farmers to adopt technological advances. With the end of the war, continued demand for food for foreign relief and governmental price supports encouraged farmers to greatly increase their use of mechanical power and machinery, fertilizer, feed and seed, and other production items. And, with the end of the war, these became readily available. Industry, the state experiment stations, and the Department of Agriculture continued with research that would increase productivity per man hour, per acre, and per unit of means of production or inputs. Innovations were adopted by farmers almost as soon as they were made available.

Farm productivity, measured as an index of output per unit of input, with 1967 as 100, increased from 73 to 109 from 1950 to 1972. On a similar basis, the index of farm production per hour of farm labor increased from 35 to 131. While total farm production or output was increasing from 73 to 111, land used for crops was declining from 111 to 99 and labor used in all farm work was declining from 208 to 85. So far as actual acreage is concerned, 345 million acres of crops were harvested in 1950, compared with 296 in 1972. These data indicate that an agricultural revolution had occurred, with the tremendous increases in productivity coming from the adoption of a technology which was replacing both land and labor.

Farmers who adopted the new technology, increased the size of their farms, and produced for the market — that is, commercial farmers — experienced a general upward trend in income and a rising standard of living after World War II. At the same time, they held to traditional rural values. Most farmers, according to a study by Rasmussen and Baker, believed that farming was an occupation essential to the well-being of the nation, that it permitted independence, and that it provided a favorable environment for the family.

Even though they cherish traditional rural values, many farmers are uncertain about the future of family farming. They are concerned about large capital requirements, long hours and hard work, and the continued migration of young people away from the farm.

Scientists and economists differ as to the future of American agriculture. An eminent scientist wrote in 1970: "Continuing development and application of technology in production of food, fiber, and forest products can supply the next generation abundantly." One danger, discussed by J.T. Bonnen, is that with the marked decline in farm population, agricultural interests will have less influence in government. At the same time, there is conflict among rural organizations. Thus, there may be less support in the future for agricultural research and experimentation.

Large exports of American grain in 1972 led to speculation as to whether or not there had been a fundamental deterioration in the world food situation. The next year, Don Paarlberg, Director of Agricultural Economics in the Department of Agriculture, citing projections to 1980, stated that world demands for grain would probably be met. In 1974, he stated that he was cautiously optimistic about prospects to 1985. As reasons, he cited the "Green Revolution" in the less-developed nations, and the fact that only 3.4 billion acres are now being cultivated out of a possible 7.8 billion, all of which get enough rainfall to make a crop and are within 50 miles of a possible means of transportation.

Even though the demand for farm products remains high, there are other problems. An agricultural economist at the University of Missouri, Harold F. Breimyer, has published a number of papers on the future structure of agriculture. He sees agriculture threatened by a prospective retarded rate of growth in the economy, by pressures to divert land to nonfarm uses, by uncertainties as to government policy, and by the threat of nonfarm capital controlling the land and agriculture.

A study prepared in the Economic Projections Group of USDA's Economic Research Service in mid-1974, forecast an increase in harvested cropland in 1980 and 1985, but suggested that not all potential cropland would be used. The production of major crops would increase by 1985 by one-third to one-half over 1973. Increased crop yields would contribute the biggest part of the increase.

Potentials for increasing crop and livestock production over the next decades include wider application of high-level management skills; hybrid varieties of wheat, barley, and soybeans; higher protein content in grains; insect-resistant plant varieties; improved breeding practices for beef cattle; multiple births in beef cattle; greater feeding efficiency; and double cropping.

Some forecasters have seen all farming in the hands of three or four corporations by 2000, with practices being almost entirely mechanized. Others have seen increased irrigation, soilless or hydroponic farming, the desalting of sea water, the use of plankton as food, and the growing of edible protein on petroleum as necessary to maintain the world population of the future.

Farming in the United States was begun many centuries ago by the American Indians. Their crops and practices have been adopted and changed and new crops and animals have been acclimated by European immigrants for some four hundred years. In the two hundred years since American farmers made the United States independent, the nation has seen two agricultural revolutions. During that period of time, in spite of dire predictions, famines throughout the world have become fewer and less intense, in part because of the productivity of the American farmer. Even though population is pressing against natural resources throughout the world, most economists and scientists suggest that world food supplies will meet demand, even though there may be hardships within particular areas, during the next 25 or even 50 years.

Historically, changes in farming over the part two hundred years have been so great that the Revolutionary War soldier-farmer would recognize only a few of the tools and none of the machines on today's farm. While changes will continue over the next fifty years, food will be produced primarily on the land by farmers responsible for their own decisions as it has been for the past two hundred years.

Land Use and Tenure

The Family Farm, 1958

From Kenneth L. Bachman and Jackson V. McElveen, "Trends in Kinds and Sizes of Farms," U.S. Department of Agriculture, *Yearbook*, 1958 (Washington, 1958), pp. 302–09.

Many persons have been worried about the changes that have been coming fast in the kinds and sizes of American farms.

As a Nation, we grew up believing in the values of farm life; in farming as a small, family enterprise; in the farmer's independence, self-sufficiency, and mental and physical strength.

Now, in less than a generation, we have seen the changes a technological revolution has made in our agriculture. Farms have become bigger and fewer. Fewer boys grow up on farms. Fewer families live on farms.

Farmers now produce primarily for the market and buy from the store much of their eggs and milk.

Many wonder whether family farms are giving way to large-scale employer units. Some fear that "factories in the field," which separate management and labor, and accumulations of land in relatively few, large holdings may be a result of the revolution in farming.

Others question whether the increasing investment needed and the larger cash costs that are associated with modern, highly specialized, commercially oriented agriculture will make it impossible for operators of family farms to compete in the adoption of new techniques.

In short, can the family farm survive? We cannot answer that question, for the answer depends on developments whose outcome we cannot foresee and on forces that we cannot or are unwilling to change. All we can do is to describe the forces.

They are part of the great social and economic change in the Nation. More jobs in nonfarm industries, trades, and service have led to shifts from farm to nonfarm occupations and have thereby facilitated the combination of farms. Shifts in concentrations of population and markets, changes in eating habits, and developments in processing and transporting farm products have affected the types of farming.

Present trends in the sizes of farms became evident before the First World War. By 1910 the settlement of western lands was virtually complete — the climax of a historical marvel in mass migration. Although the number of farms continued to increase until 1920, land frontiers were giving way to even greater technological frontiers.

The 1920's marked the beginning of the long and continuous transition from animal power to tractor power. The number of farms has declined steadily since 1920. Farming has moved toward greater specialization. Integration of production with financing, supply, or marketing functions has risen. Nonfarm employment has grown in importance: More than a fourth of all farm operators worked at off-farm jobs 100 or more days in 1954. That is more than twice the proportion of operators who worked off the farm in 1930.

In looking at the trends that have taken place since 1920, we will need to distinguish between the commercial farms — those operated primarily for income — and farms that serve mainly as part-time farming and residential units.

We estimate about a third of all farms were operated as part-time or residential units in 1958. These farms have increased both in number and as a proportion of all farms. The number of commercial farms has declined substantially. There were 4.7 million commercial farms in 1930 — fewer than 3 million in 1958.

The Census of Agriculture provides the only source of comprehensive data on trends in kinds and sizes of farms. While 1954 is the most recent year for which census data are available, the indications are that the trends have continued since 1954.

We here deal primarily with commercial farms, which account for practically all — about 98 percent — of the market sales by farmers and for most of the farmland, machinery, and other capital investments.

As commercial farmers shifted from animal to tractor power and began making use of a steady stream of improved farm machines, they and their families found they could handle larger acreages of crops and care for greater numbers of livestock. This is the essence of the process of consolidation of land into fewer commercial farms, which has progressed through depression and prosperity.

The commercial farms, although fewer in number, are larger in acreage — half again as large on the average in 1958 as in 1940 — and in volume of products they sell. Not all are large farms, of course. Their average acreages range from a few acres to several thousand acres. What has happened is that there are now more farms of larger acreages and fewer farms of small acreages.

Among certain types of farms, however, acreage is becoming a minor factor in determining the size of operation. A large poultry farm, for instance, may have few acres, and a relatively small acreage of irrigated land may produce much more than a large acreage of dry rangeland.

The volume of farm products sold probably is the best indicator of the change in size. In terms of 1954 prices, the average volume of sales of commercial farmers has more than doubled since 1940.

During the 25-year period that ended in 1954, farms with a volume of farm products sold of 5 thousand dollars or more (in terms of 1954 dollars) grew in number. They comprised fewer than one-fifth of the farms in 1930 and about two-fifths in 1954. Farms that sold products worth at least 10 thousand dollars more than doubled in number.

Nearly all the commercial farms that did decline in number were those that produced less than 2,500 dollars' worth of products. This drop occurred both under the depressed economic conditions of the 1930's and during the prosperous postwar years. The rate of change has been much faster during the later years. Very likely these small farmers left for better jobs outside agriculture or else seized the chance to enlarge their farm business.

Much of the current concern about larger farms stems from the fact that increased mechanization of farming tends to induce larger operating units. The salient effect of mechanization on agriculture has been to cut the amount of work. Machines enable a given farmwork force to handle larger acreages and more livestock. It paves the way for increasing the size of farms.

Changes in the size of a farm have been closely related to mechanization of farm operations and improvements in technology. In wheat farming, significant increases in the size of farm occurred largely during the 1930's and early 1940's. Back of this increase was the development of the modern tractor and combine. In work capacity, the tractor could easily do the work of 20 to 25 horses. As the combine replaced horse-drawn binders, two men could do the harvest work that had previously required 12 to 15 men.

In the Corn Belt there was a steady stream of improved machines during this period, including the tractor, cornpicker, and now the picker-sheller, which picks, husks, and shells the corn. Added to this are the technical developments that have increased yields, such as hybrid corn and fertilizer. These developments have enabled the farmer in the Corn Belt to expand his operations in two directions — to handle more acres and to get a larger production per acre.

More recently, mechanization has become widespread in the Cotton Belt. The use of cotton strippers in Texas and Oklahoma and cottonpickers in the Delta and irrigated areas and the mechanization of preharvest operations have permitted a marked expansion in the production and acres of cotton that can be handled by one person. A 1-row cottonpicker can cover as much as 8 acres a day and harvest as much as 10 bales of cotton.

The evidence we have, however, does not indicate that the wage-operated, industrial type of farm is increasing. The rate of growth in size of commercial farms has been geared closely to the pace of invention and farmers' adoption of laborsaving and yield-increasing innovations.

The average farmworker today produces 2.5 times more than his counterpart of a generation ago did. If we use this increase in a worker's output as a reflection of the difference in farm techniques in the two periods, we can view changes in size of farms over time in terms of today's farming techniques.

Such a measure has been applied to farms grouped by the value of the products they sell. Farms are classified as large scale, family scale, and small scale. Large-scale farms, as shown by this measure, are those that would produce a volume of products of more than 25 thousand dollars, with today's techniques and prices.

Small-scale farms would be those that would have a volume of sales of less than 2,500 dollars. The large-scale farms in general can be viewed as the farms that have a greater volume of business than could ordinarily be handled by the farm operator and members of his family. Small-scale farms can be viewed as those having a volume of business too small to employ a full-time worker who uses average farming practices.

Family farms, considered in this way, appear to be holding their own. The number of operations that are larger than family size has gone down. Although their number declined along with the overall decline in the total number of commercial farms, family farms, and large-scale farms make up about the same proportion of commercial farms in 1958 as they did a quarter century earlier.

There has been no tendency toward increasing concentration of farmland or market sales in the larger units. Farmland and market sales since 1930 have been divided in approximately similar proportions between the large-scale and the family farms. There has been evidence since 1940 that operators of family farms have made a slight gain over those of large-scale farms in controlling land and market sales.

The much larger scale of operation on our commercial farms has not meant any significant tendency toward a general development of an industrial type of organization in agriculture. Estimated requirements for hired labor per commercial farm in 1958 were at approximately the 1930 level.

A problem in farm management — and one that has ordinarily been a limiting factor in the size of farm operations — is the supervision of labor in a variety of different farm tasks. These tasks are usually dispersed both within and without the boundaries of the farm. They vary with the seasons as well as the enterprises, and day-to-day modifications are the rule rather than the exception.

Mechanization has not appreciably reduced the number of specific farm tasks to be performed. Thus it has not increased the capacity of management for supervision of more farmworkers. Rather, it has reduced the need for so many farmworkers and enabled farmers to supervise a greater quantity of other farm resources.

The number and importance of family farms have been affected largely by the many adjustment problems that are found on the smaller units in commercial agriculture rather than by the encroachment of large-scale farming.

Operators of the larger farms have more nearly kept abreast of new machines and techniques. Their more favorable financial situations afforded greater freedom of choice. Because they depend mainly on hired labor to operate their farms, the rising farm wages that have resulted from the competition of nonfarm jobs stimulated the adoption of mechanical equipment as a substitute for labor.

Technological improvements in production practices have been associated with increasing disparity between the largest and smallest sizes of commercial farms. The substantial shift of farm families from commercial to part-time farming and the migration of others from agriculture to nonfarm occupations have resulted in no appreciable improvement in the farm organization of many small units that remain in commercial agriculture.

Operators of the smaller farms have been faced with the reality that mechanization could not increase incomes unless it was accompanied either by increases in the size of farm or reorganization of the farm. There was no strong economic incentive to substitute machinery for labor as long as family members remained at home.

Small-scale farms — those with a volume of business too small to employ a full-time worker using average farming practices — have apparently grown in importance as a proportion of the commercial farms. Apparently a more serious problem than the threat of domination by large-scale farms exists in the failure of many farmers to take full advantage of developments in mechanization and technology.

Changes in kinds of farms also are significant.

American agriculture has always been and will probably remain an industry in which individual units commonly carry on several enterprises. Diversification of enterprises makes for fuller use on most farms of land and labor resources. But the increase in the size of farms since 1930 has not meant more enterprises. Farmers instead have tended to concentrate on fewer enterprises.

During the depression and the production-control programs of the 1930's, little change occurred in the average number of enterprises on each farm. A definite trend has been evident since 1940, however. The number of major enterprises dropped by about a fourth during and since the war.

Many farmers since 1940 have eliminated small home-use enterprises, such as a family milk cow, a small flock of chickens, or the home orchard.

Other farmers have stopped producing feed for workstock and other livestock. The number of farmers reporting production of corn, for example, has reduced by about two-fifths sine 1940. Increased purchases of gasoline, more use of tractors, and purchase of larger amounts of feed have replaced the feed enterprises on many farms.

At the same time, some farmers have found it profitable to specialize in commercial production of a few enterprises. Specialization in cotton farming, dairy farming, fruit and vegetable farming, and poultry farming has increased significantly.

What has happened to the poultry enterprise is a good illustration. Only two-fifths as many farmers sold chickens in 1940 as in 1958. But during this period the number of farms with flocks of 400 or more chickens more than doubled.

As farms have become mechanized, farmers often are in the position of either enlarging an enterprise to permit efficient utilization of buildings, machinery, and equipment, or of cutting it out entirely. Modern machinery costs so much that it encourages farmers to develop enterprises on a scale that permits relatively full use of the machinery and equipment.

Most farm machines encourage some degree of specialization. An instance is in the Great Plains, where many farmers found that the use of a tractor increased the advantage in growing crops rather than in, say, dairying. New harvesters encourage production of small grains in some areas rather than the production of small grains and row crops at the same time. Milking machines and bulk tanks encourage larger herds of dairy cows, but they do not increase directly the advantage of raising the feed on the farm.

Not all trends have been in the direction of increased specialization, however. Soybeans have become an additional crop on many farms in the Corn Belt. A greater percentage of the farmers grew tobacco in 1958 than in 1940.

Certain factors in buying supplies and in marketing also work in the direction of farm specialization. Farmers who produce large amounts of such products as broilers, milk, and vegetables can buy and sell more economically in quantity. The cost of assembly often can be reduced. A more uniform product may be possible. Feed may be bought more cheaply.

Changes have occurred in both costs of farming and the structure of the market for farm products. These have affected the organization of production and marketing functions, and, in turn, may influence both the sizes and kinds of farms in the future.

The use of such things as modern machinery, commercial fertilizers, and scientifically mixed feeds increases the farmers' cash outlays. This intensifies problems of finance. Markets for farm products have become highly specialized, demanding products of more exacting quality and in more uniform quantity throughout the seasons.

These and other developments in some situations have encouraged supply and marketing organizations to make contracts with farmers. These contracts usually involve agreements with respect to financing and purchase of supplies and sale of the product. Integration of production with related functions sometimes has meant that the operator gives up some management functions with respect to production methods, size of enterprise, and markets that used to be associated with the farmer.

The tendency toward vertical integration is most evident in some of the fruits and vegetables and in broiler production. Much of our fruit, vegetables, and poultry is produced on large, highly specialized farms. From class I farms — those that sell more than 25 thousand dollars' worth of farm products — we get about one-third of our poultry, more than one-half of our fruit, and one-half of our vegetables. In appraisal of this trend, however, one should bear in mind that the number of farmers who specialize in poultry, fruit, and vegetable production is not large. Only about 6 percent of the farms are classified in these types, and they account for about 15 percent of the value of farm products sold.

What is the meaning of these changes in the sizes and kinds of farms?

Do they have implications for the future?

We need first to summarize and explain some of the basic reasons for the trends that have characterized farming since 1940.

Of first importance has been the availability of the technological innovations that increased a worker's output. Especially significant to the enlargement of the family farm were the mechanical inventions that encourage replacement of labor with capital. Many of the larger farmers found that they could reduce their hired labor considerably when they shifted to tractor operations and bought a combine, a cornpicker, or a milking machine.

Equally basic has been the rising standard of living in the United States and the availability of off-farm employment opportunities. These two things have provided an incentive for mechanization and for higher incomes in agriculture and have afforded alternatives for those who prefer other occupations.

In the future, commercial farms will continue to grow in size, as measured both in terms of acreage and output. Machines that further reduce labor requirements are continuing to be developed. Even more important, the number of farms that are smaller than is generally considered an economic unit indicates that there is considerable room for further mechanization and adjustments in farm size. The chances for the survival of small, low-income farms in a high-wage, full-employment economy are not bright. Family farms that are large enough to utilize modern machinery can be expected to continue to hold their own.

The rate of increase in size of farm will be affected by economic conditions. Agriculture each year is becoming more closely tied to the general economy. Opportunities to enlarge farms will be related to employment conditions in nonfarm occupations. Shifts in the types of farms will be related closely to the relatively large increases in the demands for livestock and fruit and vegetable products we foresee. That in turn may affect the trends toward specialization and vertical integration.

An additional aspect affecting the changes in sizes of farms revolves around the types of technological development that are forthcoming.

Some people believe that in the coming quarter century, innovations that increase crop and livestock yields may be more important than those that further reduce labor needs. These may provide more opportunities for development on small farms and encourage family farm operation. On the other hand, irrigation and other changes in methods of production in some situations may greatly simplify management decisions, reduce the problems of supervising hired farmworkers, and work to the advantage of large-scale operations.

Getting into farming may be more difficult for the young man of tomorrow. Problems of financing and ownership take on increased significance.

Capital investments in agriculture have gone up greatly. In the past quarter century, the average investment per worker in agriculture more than trebled. In 1958, more than 18 thousand dollars of capital is associated with the average farmworker, as compared with less than 5 thousand dollars in 1930. A question of real concern is whether able young men with limited funds can get the capital needed for modern mechanized farming.

In the South, changes in the size of farms will be more closely tied to changes in the number of management units. With only a quarter of a million sharecropper units now classed as commercial farms, a further reduction will not be as large a factor in the next quarter century as it was in the past quarter century.

If the trends toward vertical integration continue, for example, they may exert a pull in the direction of larger farms in order to retain producer bargaining power and management responsibilities. Or, with other arrangements, a greater integration of production with the financing, supply, or marketing functions could bring some of the advantages of technical efficiency to small operations. Cooperative financing, marketing, and purchasing of farm supplies and products are being tried in some areas.

In the broad perspective of our whole agriculture, there appears to be little evidence that efficient family farms cannot survive with larger farms. Trends indicate that the scales to date have probably been tilted in the other direction. For the future, much will depend on the developments in institutions, educational services, financing, and farm policies.

Management of Indian Lands

From M. Wilfred Goding, "The Management of Tribal Lands," U.S. Department of Agriculture, *Yearbook*, 1958 (Washington, 1958), pp. 96–102.

Federal responsibility for the management of Indian lands is essentially that of a trustee.

Actual tenure of the Indian holdings is in a wide variety of forms, tribal and individual, which range from indeterminate use rights to fee simple.

The lands subject to trust that Indians use, control, or own total 53,376,000 acres in the United States — 39,465,000 acres of tribal land, 13,328,000 acres of individual allotted land, and 583,000 acres of Government-owned land used in the administration of Indian affairs.

Nearly all these lands share two characteristics, which in one form or another have attached to Indian lands since early colonial days. They are protected against alienation and encumbrance. They are exempt from State and local taxation.

The Indian holdings nevertheless have been reduced continuously. Much of the reduction was inevitable, for at the beginning of white settlement in America some 800 thousand Indians held the whole continent by occupancy and use. The impact of succeeding tides of aggressive, land-hungry settlers, many of whom were beyond or without moral or other law, could result only in large-scale dispossession of the Indian occupants, who held or claimed large areas under nonintensive uses and under no right except that of aboriginal use.

Indian title, based on aboriginal occupancy, was officially recognized and protected by the Colonial Governments. England and Spain reserved to the Crown or the Colonies the sole right to negotiate with the Indians for the transfer of their lands.

The first colonists who showed concern for Indian rights and welfare apparently hoped to integrate the Indians into the colonial settlements. Massachusetts Bay Colony as early as 1633 invited the Indians to the settlements to accept individual land allotments on condition that they "shall there live civily and orderly."

This policy was soon frustrated because the Indians lacked the colonists' ideas about protecting property interests. They were not inclined to clear the land and follow the white settlers' agricultural pursuits. They were cheated in land transactions because land to them was not a commodity to be bought and sold for profit.

The Colonial Governments recognized the need to protect Indian property interests by prohibiting land purchases by individuals without the specific consent of the Governments.

This policy was followed when the United States, under the Confederation, issued a proclamation in 1783 prohibiting all persons "from making settlements on lands inhabited or claimed by Indians without the limits or jurisdiction of any particular state, and from purchasing or receiving any gift or cession of such lands or claims without the express authority and direction of the United States in Congress assembled."

Indian lands have been at the focal point of the relationship of the United States with the Indian population from the beginning of the Government. Article I, section 8, of the Constitution provides that Congress shall have the power "to regulate commerce with foreign nations, and among the several States, and with the Indian tribes." This constitutional provision recognized the Indian tribes as quasi-sovereign "domestic nations." In fact, the first treaty entered into by the United States, antedating the Constitution, was with the Delaware Indians in 1778.

The early attempts to bring the Indians into the landholding economy of the colonial frontier were followed by a policy of removing the Indian population from the frontier settlement areas: If the Indian could not be integrated, he was to be isolated.

The sharp trading of individuals and continuing efforts of many to separate the Indians from their lands caused resentment and bloody reprisals. The increasing movement of population to the west of the Appalachians resulted in intensified conflict, which the Government attempted to resolve by treating with the Indian tribes for relinquishment of their holdings and movement to western lands.

The policy of removing the Indians from the settlement areas east of the Mississippi reached a climax during the administration of President Jackson with the compulsory and tragic movement of the Cherokee Nation.

The forced movement of the Cherokee Nation from their traditional lands in the Southeast to the Indian Territory was probably the darkest page in the history of our Indian relations. The issues involved not only the Federal Government and the Indians. The State of Georgia initiated and pressed the removal under the terms of the compact of 1802 with the Federal Government, whereby the area now forming Alabama and Mississippi was transferred to the United States in consideration, in part, for the purchase and extinction of Indian title to all land within the State of Georgia.

The Supreme Court decision in 1831 in the case of the Cherokee Nation *v.* Georgia left the Indians in a weak position for the protection of their traditional rights. It denied the jurisdiction of the Supreme Court on the technical grounds that the tribe was not a sovereign entity. This undermined the basic legal validity of all "treaties" with Indian tribes.

The next year, however, the Court ruled that the whole intercourse with the Indian tribes was vested in the United States and that the Cherokee Nation was a distinct community occupying a defined territory in which the laws of Georgia had no force. It was of this decision that President Jackson is reported as having remarked that, "John Marshall has made his decision, now let him enforce it." Jackson declined to enter the jurisdictional controversy and gave the Indians the choice of emigrating or complying with State law.

The Indian tribes by 1840 had surrendered nearly all of the territory east of the Mississippi, except a few reservations in Minnesota, Wisconsin, Michigan, North Carolina, and New York and the holdings of a few small groups, survivors of once powerful tribes, who maintained their ancient ways in scattered settlements throughout the Eastern States. The country west of the Mississippi, except for some settlements in Louisiana, Arkansas, and Missouri, was legally and actually Indian country at that time.

The years between 1851 and 1880, when new waves of settlers moved westward, mark the period of the fiercest armed conflict with the tribes that attempted to hold their own. Most of the Indian reservations were established then.

In general, the Indians were guaranteed permanent title to a reservation — land reserved for Indian use — in return for relinquishing to the United States large areas of land they claimed. Despite the extinguishment of Indian occupancy rights to vast areas, however, the settlers still coveted the undeveloped lands within the reserved areas. New treaties with Indian tribes diminished the area of such reservations for cash payments, annuities, or other considerations.

It has been estimated that by 1858 more than 581 million acres had been acquired by the United States in more than 400 treaties at a cost of less than 50 million dollars.

Negotiation of treaties with Indian tribes ceased in 1871.

The policy of "individualizing" ownerships of Indian land was initiated with the General Allotment Act of 1887. Friends of the Indians believed that the only way the Indians could retain their land was for each family to be allotted a portion of the reservation area in severalty. These advocates believed that a share of individual land was all the Indian needed to become a successful independent farmer.

At the outset the act provided for the allotment of 160 acres to the head of each family. Lesser amounts were allotted to single persons and minor children, and issuance of patents in fee was to be withheld for 25 years. As the trust periods have run out, they have been periodically extended by special legislation. Reservation land not required to meet the allotments was to be purchased by the Government and opened to homestead settlement.

The Government, however, failed to provide the equipment and the vocational training necessary to make the Indians successful farmers. Many Indians were physically not able to undertake farming. Others did not know how or wish to learn to farm. Their lives, outlook, and inheritance were all against it; to try to force them into farming was to demand the impossible of many of them.

The allotment system eventually became a device for transferring Indian land to white settlers. Indians in 1887 owned about 138 million acres of land.

When the allotment system was brought to an end in 1934, their lands had shrunk to about 52 million acres.

More than 59 million acres had been sold as "surplus" land. Nearly 23 million acres were sold by the original allottees. About 4 million acres were sold on behalf of the Indian heirs.

Of the lands remaining in Indian ownership, only 4 million acres were farming land, more than 45 million acres were classified as grazing lands, and the rest was timbered, swamp, or miscellaneous land types.

The distribution, as well as the value, of the remaining lands varied widely among the tribal groups. An example: 20 million acres, nearly half of the remaining grazing lands, were composed of the Navajo, Papago, and Pueblo Reservations in the Southwest. The allotting process applied to the best and most accessible farmlands. The result was that about 93 percent of the agricultural land and about 30 percent of the better grazing land went into individual allotments.

A serious byproduct of the allotting process was the scattering of holdings in uneconomic units, particularly in the Great Plains. This pattern of land tenure became more complicated when the original allottees died and the allotment descended in undivided interests to the heirs. Often it was possible only to sell the land, lease it, or not to use it at all.

Partly because of the complications as to heirs, leasing was first permitted by an act in 1892 in order to meet hardship situations. All restrictions on leasing were removed later. The Congress in 1902 authorized the sale of an ancestor's allotment by the heirs in an effort to solve the increasing complications of the land-tenure pattern.

Despite outright sale of much of these lands and many efforts later to consolidate and rationalize the pattern of landownership, the administration of the "heirship lands" remains a difficult aspect of Indian land management. It is estimated that more than 65 percent of all allotted lands remaining under Federal trust are now in heirship status.

The cost of administration is burdensome, but no ready, fully acceptable solution has been found. Some persons advocate that a major financing program be established to buy such lands for tribal account, but no funds have been appropriated for this purpose in recent years. In some areas the tribal organizations have been using tribal funds to purchase the splitup allotment interests. Elsewhere corporate-type tribal-land enterprises have been established to take title to such lands by issuing shares in the enterprise in exchange for the individual holdings.

The Indian Reorganization Act of 1934 stopped all further allotments. It authorized land purchase and the restoration of ceded lands to the tribes and established a revolving loan fund to make possible more effective use of the land base. At the same time, sales of Indian lands were generally stopped, and a policy of retaining both tribal and allotted land for the use of Indians was emphasized. This shift in basic policy halted the long trend toward disposal of Indian lands. Indian holdings increased by nearly 4 million acres in the next several years. The new policy caused individual hardships, however, and, because exceptions were so limited, seriously curtailed the basic property rights of many competent Indian citizens. The policy was modified in 1948 to permit the competent Indian to retain or dispose of his property as he desired.

The problems of the Government as trustee for the landholdings of the Indians today arise from the complexities inherent in the nature of the lands involved, the diversity and multiplicity of the ownership interests, and the status of Indians as individuals and groups in the social and economic framework of the larger community.

It would be relatively simple if the responsibility could be discharged by the judicious determination of the competency of Indian individuals to manage their business affairs and thereby end the trust status. The Indian lands then would lose their special attributes. They could be alienated and would no longer be tax exempt. Understandably, some Indians are not inclined to press for a declaration that would result in the termination of such a privileged status.

The mixed-ownership pattern of lands on many reservations also presents problems of land-use management. An Indian owner of allotted land might have his personal interests advanced by an outright sale and termination of the trust, but it would be detrimental to the management and use of adjoining tribal lands.

The present sales policy is based on congressional statutory enactments that permit the sale of Indian lands. When an Indian makes an application under the applicable law for the sale of his trust or restricted land, the Bureau of Indian Affairs must comply with such a request if the facts indicate the action would be in the best interests of the Indian owner. The Government has no equitable right to deny arbitrarily such an application.

Before a sale is approved, an examination is made of the applicant's reasons for desiring a sale and his plans for using the money after he receives it. Indians in debt who cannot handle their affairs may be required to help prepare a budget before the sale of their land is approved to insure that the money from the sale will be used for their benefit.

The Bureau in 1955–1957 sold 927,926 acres owned by individual Indians in response to written requests by the Indian owners; 292,488 acres were turned over to Indians who applied for fee patents and satisfied the Bureau of their competency to manage their affairs; and 122,414 acres of mixed tribal and individual Indian land have been taken by the Government for flood-control purposes with full compensation to the owners.

Even more difficult policy matters are entailed in the sale or liquidation of unallotted tribal lands. These are the lands held in common that can be sold only after specific authorization by the Congress.

The policy of restoring and increasing tribal holdings, which resulted from enactment of the Indian Reorganization Act of 1934, found much favor and acceptance. However, such a policy was contrary to the desire of the majority of some Indian groups to terminate the trusteeship of the Federal Government and to liquidate their holdings.

Not all Indian groups accepted the philosophy underlying that act. A number of tribes had long emphasized their desire to "terminate" the Federal trust relationship. Increasing land values have stimulated the desire of many tribal members to sell their holdings. The Congress, by concurrent resolution in 1953, enunciated a policy directed toward termination of Federal supervision as soon as possible.

That was followed by the enactment of several bills to terminate the Federal trust for a number of tribal groups, of which the Klamath Termination Act of 1954, relating to the Klamath Indians of southern Oregon, was typical. It provides that an appraisal be made of all tribal property and that each member of the tribe be given an opportunity to sever his tribal affiliation and withdraw his share of the tribal property or to remain and participate in a tribal management plan. As much of the tribal property as may be necessary to reimburse the withdrawing members will be sold. In any event, the Federal trust relationship was to cease at the end of 4 years. Because execution of this act has encountered unforeseen complexities and presented certain policy issues that have not been fully resolved, the termination date was extended for 2 years by the Congress in 1957.

The high value of the Klamath Reservation timberlands is a strong inducement for many tribal members to sell their holdings. These lands, which have been managed as a unit under modern sustained-yield principles, are a major resource base for the economy of the area. Much concern is expressed that the partitioning and sale of the forest lands will result in destructive use. In order to avoid such a result, attention has been given to ways of proceeding under the act so as to assure continued conservation management. There is much support among residents of the area for acquisition of the lands by the Federal Government. This and other proposals were placed before the Congress.

Along with the sales of Indian land during the intervening years, there also have been acquisitions. More than 1 million acres were added in 1955–1957 to tribal holdings throughout the country as a result of congressional enactments and administrative acts by the Department of the Interior.

A total of 818,277 acres was restored to ownership of the Colville Tribe of Washington in 1956. The restored land was originally ceded to the Government by the tribe as "surplus" at the time the reservation was allotted. The tribe subsequently requested the restoration of the unallotted surplus. That was accomplished by legislation in 1956. The land is held in trust by the United States for the tribe on the same basis as other reservation lands.

The second largest addition to tribal holdings was the purchase by the Navajo Tribe of a ranch of 98 thousand acres in Arizona. The land is held by the tribe in fee simple title and is not in Federal trusteeship, but it represents a substantial increase in acreage available for use by the Navajos. The Pueblo of Zia added 41,216 acres, and the Pueblo of Jamez added 36,352 acres to their holdings. Both are in New Mexico.

Other acquisitions were for the Seminoles in Florida, the Yavapai Tribe of Arizona, the Kanosh Band in Utah, the Blackfeet and Flathead Indians in Montana, and the Shoshone and Arapahoes in Wyoming.

Purchases made by the Bureau in trust for individual Indians during the period account for nearly 20 thousand additional acres.

Indian lands held in trust by the Federal Government are administered for the use and benefit of the Indian owners in accordance with the policies followed by the Department of the Interior in managing the public lands under its jurisdiction. Accepted principles of conservation are the basis for specific treatment of forest lands, rangelands, irrigable lands, and general farmlands.

An increasing source of income to some Indians and tribes has been from mineral leasing. The total income from gas and oil on all reservations amounted to 41,007,075 dollars in 1956, and 2,881,532 dollars were received for other minerals.

The forest lands amount to an estimated 16 million acres. About 6 million acres are considered commercial forest land, more than half of which is in the Pacific Coast and northern Rocky Mountain States. About one-fourth is in the Southwest. Most of the rest is in the Lake States.

Most of the timber is sold as standing timber on the open market. Tribal sawmills operate on three reservations to utilize the annual harvest. The tribe is paid the fair market value of the stumpage used.

All phases of forest management and protection are supervised by employees of the Bureau of Indian Affairs. They designate the timber to be cut, measure the volume, collect payments, and distribute the receipts to the Indian owners. The Indian owners are encouraged to participate in the development of plans for managing the estate. The consent of the owners is obtained before timber is sold. In 1956, 643,440,000 board-feet of timber were sold for 14,123,806 dollars.

Total administrative expenses for the fiscal year 1956 for Indian forestry operations amounted to 1,713,292 dollars, of which 505,246 dollars came from Indian tribal funds and 1,208,046 dollars from appropriated funds.

Rangelands amount to about 44 million acres, inclusive of forest lands grazed by livestock. They are managed so as to bring the maximum return to the Indian owners consistent with sustained production of forage. Indian owners are encouraged to use the range for grazing their own livestock. About 75 percent of the range is so used. General grazing regulations were adopted in 1931 to limit the grazing of each unit to the estimated capacity. Management methods have been improved steadily.

Cash receipts for the use of Indian rangelands in 1956 amounted to 2.8 million dollars. The value of grazing privileges on tribal lands and of the use of allotted land by the owners thereof was 3,475,000 dollars in 1956. Federal expenditures for range management amounted to 566 thousand dollars; and 600 thousand dollars were spent to develop watering places.

More than 2,170,000 acres of farmland and rangeland were covered by various conservation treatment works in 1956, and 11,069 farm and range conservation plans were completed during the year. The soil and moisture conservation budget for 1958 was 4,638,000 dollars. About 80 percent of the conservation expenditures are borne by Indian landowners. The estimated return for the conservation investment is 21.56 dollars for every dollar of Federal conservation funds expended and 2.86 dollars for every dollar of such expenditure from all sources.

Irrigation works and facilities to increase the productivity of Indian lands were first undertaken by the Bureau of Indian Affairs 90 years ago on the Colorado River Reservation in Arizona. About 850 thousand acres, comprising 300 irrigation systems ranging from 100 acres to more than 120 thousand acres in 11 States, have been irrigated. About 190 thousand Indians live on these irrigated lands.

The construction or expansion of three major irrigation projects was under way or projected in 1958 — the Colorado River Reservation in Arizona (65 thousand acres), the Navajo project in Colorado and New Mexico (113 thousand acres), and the Michaud unit of the Fort Hall project in Idaho (21 thousand acres).

Irrigation systems in use in 1958 provided about 3 acres per capita for Indians in the arid regions. Full development of all potentially irrigable Indian lands in the West would provide about 6.5 acres per capita. Under present law, construction charges assessed against Indian-owned lands within any Government irrigation project are deferred while the lands remain in Indian ownership.

The total annual cost of operating and maintaining the projects is approximately 3.8 million dollars, of which 800 thousand dollars is met by Federal appropriations. The rest comes from receipts from the water users and revenues from power. The part provided by the Federal Government is reimbursable in accordance with law and is provided to cover the share of costs for Indian landowners who cannot make such payments.

Recommendations of the Public Land Law Review Commission

From Public Land Law Review Commission, *One Third of the Nation's Land; A Report to the President and to the Congress* (Washington, 1970), pp. 1–7.

Feeling the pressures of an enlarging population, burgeoning growth, and expanding demand for land and natural resources, the American people today have an almost desperate need to determine the best purposes to which their public lands and the wealth and opportunities of those lands should be dedicated. Through the timely action of Congress, and through the work of this Commission, a rare opportunity is offered to answer that need.

For reasons that we will detail, we urge reversal of the policy that the United States should dispose of the so-called unappropriated public domain lands. But we also reject the idea that merely because these lands are owned by the Federal Government, they should all remain forever in Federal ownership.

We have also found that by administrative action the disposal policy, although never "repealed" by statute, has been rendered ineffective. In the absence of congressional guidelines, there has been no predictable administrative policy.

We, therefore, recommend that:

The policy of large-scale disposal of public lands reflected by the majority of statutes in force today be revised and that future disposal should be of only those lands that will achieve maximum benefit for the general public in non-Federal ownership, while retaining in Federal ownership those whose values must be preserved so that they may be used and enjoyed by all Americans.

While there may be some modest disposals, we conclude that at this time most public lands would not serve the maximum public interest in private ownership. We support the concepts embodied in the establishment and maintenance of the national forests, the National Park System, the National Wildlife Refuge System, and the parallel or subsidiary programs involving the Wilderness Preservation System, the National Riverways and Scenic Rivers Systems, national trails, and national recreation areas.

In recent years, with very few exceptions, all areas that have been set aside for specific use have been given intensive study by both the legislative and executive branches and have been incorporated in one of the programs through legislative action. We would not disturb any of these because they have also been subjected to careful scrutiny by state and local governments as well as by interested and affected people.

Based on our study, however, we find that, generally, areas set aside by executive action as national forests, national monuments, and for other purposes have not had adequate study and there has not been proper consultation with people affected or with the units of local government in the vicinity, particularly as to precise boundaries. Although the Department of the Interior and the Bureau of Land Management classified lands under the temporary Classification and Multiple Use

Act of 1964, we believe that in many cases there was hasty action based on preconceived determinations instead of being based on careful land use planning. In addition, there are many areas of the public domain that have never been classified or set aside for specific use.

We, therefore, recommend that:

An immediate review should be undertaken of all lands not previously designated for any specific use, and of all existing withdrawals, set asides, and classifications of public domain lands that were effected by Executive action to determine the type of use that would provide the maximum benefit for the general public in accordance with standards set forth in this report.

The result of these reviews will be the delineation of lands that should be retained in Federal ownership and those that could best serve the public through private ownership. For those to be retained in Federal ownership, there will be a further breakdown indicating which ones should be set aside for special-purpose use — which may or may not include several different uses.

As intimated above, our studies have also led us to the conclusions that the Congress has largely delegated to the executive branch its plenary constitutional authority over the retention, management, and disposition of public land; that statutory delegations have often been lacking in standards or meaningful policy determinations; that the executive agencies, understandably, in keeping with the operation of the American political system, took the action they deemed necessary to fill this vacuum through the issuance of regulations, manuals, and other administrative directives; and that the need for administrative flexibility in meeting varying regional and local conditions created by the diversity of our public lands and by the complexity of many public land problems does not justify failure to legislate the controlling standards, guidelines, and criteria under which public land decisions should be made.

We, therefore, recommend that:

Congress should establish national policy in all public land laws by prescribing the controlling standards, guidelines, and criteria for the exercise of authority delegated to executive agencies.

Many types of public land have been reserved by executive action for governmental uses, such as defense installations and atomic energy testing areas. The result has been to materially restrict or preclude their availability for recreation and resource development purposes. In other cases, withdrawals and reservations have severely limited permissible types of uses on tremendous acreages of public land in order to further administrative land policies.

We find that when proposed land uses are passed on by the Congress, they receive more careful scrutiny in the executive branch before being recommended; furthermore, in connection with congressional action, the general public is given a better opportunity to comment and have its views considered. We conclude that Congress should not delegate broad authority for these types of actions.

We, therefore, recommend that:

Congress assert its constitutional authority by enacting legislation reserving unto itself exclusive authority to withdraw or otherwise set aside public lands for specified limited-purpose uses and delineating specific delegation of authority to the Executive as to the types of withdrawals and set asides that may be effected without legislative action.

Our studies have convinced us that, with respect to lands retained in Federal ownership, the rules and regulations governing their use, to the extent that they exist, have not been adequate to fulfill the purpose; that they were promulgated without proper consultation with, and participation by, either those affected or the general public; that existing regulations are cumbersome; and that the procedures for users or other interested parties to exercise their rights to seek or oppose the grant of interests in public land are likewise cumbersome as well as expensive with no assurance of objective, impartial consideration of appeals from, or objections to, decisions by land managers.

We, therefore, recommend that:
Public land management agencies should be required by statute to promulgate comprehensive rules and regulations after full consideration of all points of view, including protests, with provisions for a simplified administrative appeals procedure in a manner that will restore public confidence in the impartiality and fairness of administrative decisions. Judicial review should generally be available.

In pursuing our work, we took cognizance of the fact that between 1965, when we started our work, and the year 2000, the population of the United States will have grown by over 100 million people. The public lands can, must, and will contribute to the well-being of our people by providing a combination of many uses. Some of these will help to take care of the increasing leisure time that Americans of the future will have, while others must help in furnishing the added amounts of food, fiber, and minerals that the larger numbers of people will require.

Under existing statutes and regulations, there is no assurance that the public lands retained in Federal ownership will contribute in the manner that will be required. We find that the absence of statutory guidelines leaves a void which could result in land managers withholding from public use public lands or their resources that may be required for a particular time; that even if land managers plan to make specific goods and services available to the public, there are no long-range objectives or procedures that will assure fulfillment of a program; and that the absence of statutory guidelines for the establishment of priorities in allocating land uses causes unnecessary confusion and inconsistent administration.

We, therefore, recommend that:
Statutory goals and objectives should be established as guidelines for land-use planning under the general principle that within a specific unit, consideration should be given to all possible uses and the maximum number of compatible uses permitted. This should be subject to the qualification that where a unit, within an area managed for many uses, can contribute maximum benefit through one particular use, that use should be recognized as the dominant use, and the land should be managed to avoid interference with fulfillment of such dominant use.

Throughout our work we were aware of the evergrowing concern by the

American people about the deterioration of the environment. We share that concern and have looked in vain to find assurance in the public land laws that the United States, as a landowner, had made adequate provision to assure that the quality of life would not be endangered by reason of activities on federally owned lands. We find to the contrary that, despite recent legislative enactments, there is an absence of statutory guidelines by which land management agencies can provide uniform, equitable, and economically sound provision for environmental control over lands retained in Federal ownership.

We, therefore, recommend that:
Federal statutory guidelines should be established to assure that Federal public lands are managed in a manner that not only will not endanger the quality of the environment, but will, where feasible, enhance the quality of the environment, both on and off public lands, and that Federal control of the lands should never be used as a shield to permit lower standards than those required by the laws of the state in which the lands are located. The Federal licensing power should be used, under statutory guidelines, to assure these results.

Every landowner is concerned with the return that he receives for the use of his land or for the revenue he receives from products produced on that land. United States citizens, collectively the owners of the public lands, are similarly concerned. We ascertained from the many witnesses that we heard that the concern of some is that the United States has not been receiving the maximum dollar return; the concern of others is that the United States has been trying to receive too much of a dollar return; while the concern of still others is that the United States is uneven in its efforts to obtain monetary return from its public lands.

From our review, we find that there is a great diversity in public land policy on fees and charges for the various goods and services derived from the public lands; that the fee structures vary among commodities and among agencies administering the public lands; that objectives for the pricing of goods and services are unclear; and that the absence of comprehensive statutory guidelines has created a situation in which land managers are unable to provide uniform equitable treatment for all.

We, therefore, recommend that:
Statutory guidelines be established providing generally that the United States receive full value for the use of the public lands and their resources retained in Federal ownership, except that monetary payment need not represent full value, or so-called market value, in instances where there is no consumptive use of the land or its resources.

Many of those who appeared before the Commission testified to the drastic results that sometimes flow from the uncertainty of tenure and the insecurity of investment of public land users. Studies prepared for the Commission confirm this, despite the fact that not only individuals and companies but many communities are wholly or partially dependent for their economic life on the public lands and their resources.

We, therefore, recommend that:
Statutory provision be made to assure that when public lands or their resources are

made available for use, firm tenure and security of investment be provided so that if the use must be interrupted because of a Federal Government need before the end of the lease, permit, or other contractual arrangement, the user will be equitably compensated for the resulting losses.

The United States need not seek to obtain the greatest monetary return, but instead should recognize improvements to the land and the fact that the land will be dedicated, in whole or in part, to services for the public as elements of value received.

Having determined that there should be no wholesale disposition of the public lands, we turned our attention to the impact that the retention in Federal ownership would have on other levels of government. In doing this, we made an intensive review of existing programs.

Revenue-sharing programs were established for the purpose of compensating state and local governments for the fact that certain types of lands would not be going into private ownership and, therefore, onto the tax rolls. Nonetheless, we find that such programs actually have no relationship to the burdens imposed on state and local governments by the retention of public lands in Federal ownership. The continuation of the general United States policy of providing for transfer to private ownership of virtually all of the public lands would not have required consideration of a comprehensive program to compensate state and local governments for the burdens imposed by Federal ownership of public lands since such ownership was then transitory. The establishment of new programs in recent years and the administration of the public land laws generally has resulted in millions of acres of land being set aside for permanent retention by the Federal Government throughout the 50 states with concomitant unpredicted burdens on state and local governments. The potential retention of additional millions of acres of public domain lands as a result of the review recommended by this Commission requires that we reexamine the obligations and responsibilities of the United States as a landowner in relation to state and local governments upon which continuing burdens will be placed. We find further that any attempt to tie payments to states and local governments to receipts generated from the sale or use of public lands or their resources causes an undue emphasis to be given in program planning to the receipts that may be generated. We, therefore, recommend that:

The United States make payments in lieu of taxes for the burdens imposed upon state and local governments by reason of the Federal ownership of public lands without regard to the revenues generated therefrom. Such payments should not represent full tax equivalency and the state and local tax effort should be a factor in determining the exact amount to be paid.

The statute establishing the Public Land Law Review Commission stated that, "those laws, or some of them, may be inadequate to meet the current and future needs of the American people." Our review has led us to the conclusion that the laws are indeed inadequate, first, because of the emphasis on disposition, second, because of the absence of statutory guidelines for administration, as discussed above, and third, because the disposition laws themselves are obsolete and not geared to the present and future requirements of the Nation. With the exception of the temporary Public Land Sale Act, which will expire 6 months after submission of the final report by this Commission, there is no statute permitting the sale of public domain lands in any large tracts for residential, commercial, or industrial use, and we find that the statute for the sale of small tracts has not worked well.

Accordingly, we find that it is necessary to modify or repeal all of the public domain disposition laws and replace them with a body of law that will permit the orderly disposition of those lands that can contribute most to the general welfare by being placed in private ownership.

We, therefore, recommend that:

Statutory authority be provided for the sale at full value of public domain lands required for certain mining activities or where suitable only for dryland farming, grazing of domestic livestock, or residential, commercial, or industrial uses, where such sale is in the public interest and important public values will not thereby be lost.

In the mid-1860's, statutory provision was made for the use of public lands as sites for new towns. Our studies reveal that relatively few new towns are established on public lands through the townsite laws.

We find that the need for the establishment of new towns to provide for a portion of the anticipated population growth and the parallel growth of industry by the year 2000 will be, realistically, challenging and difficult to fulfill. Compounding the problem are the mounting difficulties facing the large existing cities. While we find that the problems of urban areas cannot be solved by transplanting large numbers of people to the public land areas, we also find that the public lands offer an opportunity for the establishment of at least some of the new cities that will be required in the next 30 years, and that, in many instances, they offer the only opportunity for the expansion of existing communities.

We, therefore, recommend that:

Legislation be enacted to provide a framework within which large units of land may be made available for the expansion of existing communities or the development of new cities.

Until some experience has been gained in the various mechanisms that might be utilized and a national policy adopted concerning the establishment of new cities generally, Congress should consider proposals for the sale of land for new cities on a case-by-case basis.

Our inquiries and studies have revealed that there are many instances where all concerned will agree that public domain land previously incorporated within a national forest could best serve the public interest by being transferred to private ownership. We find, however, that the present procedures for the accomplishment of such transfer, requiring as they do an exchange for other lands, are cumbersome, administratively burdensome, and unnecessarily expensive to both the Government and the private party, inordinately time consuming, and result in the acquisition of land that may not, in fact, be needed by the United States any more than the land of which it is disposing through the exchange process.

We, therefore, recommend that:

Statutory authority be granted for the limited disposition of lands administered by the Forest Service where such lands are needed to meet a non-Federal but public purpose, or where disposition would result in the lands being placed in a higher use than if continued in Federal ownership.

The administration of some programs, such as recreation, can be accomplished just as well, if not better, by state and local government units; in other instances, Federal public lands are required for construction of schools and other buildings that provide state or local government services.

We find that it is in the best interest of all concerned to encourage state and local governments to assume complete responsibility for the maximum number of programs that those levels of government can and will administer and to acquire title to the required land in order to permit the proper level of investment to be made.

We, therefore, recommend that:
Legislation be enacted to provide flexible mechanisms, including transfer of title at less than full value, to make any federally owned lands available to state and local governments when not required for a Federal purpose if the lands will be utilized for a public purpose.

Throughout our studies and inquiries, we compared the policies, practices, and procedures applicable to the public lands as defined in the statute establishing the Public Land Law Review Commission with the policies, practices, and procedures applicable to other types of lands where such other lands were managed in conjunction with or had characteristics similar to public lands concerning which this Commission with the policies, practices, and procedures applicable to other types of lands where such other lands were managed in conjunction with or had characteristics similar to public lands concerning which this Commission was charged with responsibility of making recommendations. We also take note of the fact that within the definition of lands in our Organic Act, there are both "public domain" and "acquired" lands as discussed elsewhere in this report.

We find that there is no logical basis for distinguishing between public domain and acquired lands or between lands defined as "public lands" and all other federally owned lands.

We, therefore, recommend that:
Generally, in both legislation and administration, the artificial distinctions between public domain and acquired lands of the Federal Government should be eliminated.

We find that the division of responsibility for the development of policy and the administration of public lands among Congressional Committees and several Federal departments and agencies has led to differences, contradictions, and duplications in policies and programs. Not only have these factors been administratively burdensome, but they have also been the source of confusion to citizens dealing with the Government.

We, therefore, recommend that:
Responsibility for public land policy and programs within the Federal Government in both the legislative and executive branches should be consolidated to the maximum practicable extent in order to eliminate, or at least reduce, differences in policies concerning the administration of similar public land programs.

We submit the foregoing findings and basic recommendations as a statement of principles that should govern the retention and management or disposition of federally owned lands. In the chapters that follow, we will develop detailed background in specific subject areas, along with more detailed recommendations designed to implement the basic principles enunciated in the foregoing recommendations.

In arriving at these recommendations and those that follow, we made each decision on the basis of what we consider to be the maximum benefit for the general public, in accordance with the statutory charge to the Commission as cited in the Preface.

We have not defined in any one place what we consider to be "the maximum benefit for the general public." Nor have we defined a set of criteria that will lead all persons to the same conclusion as to what is the maximum benefit for the general public. These are tasks that are perhaps best left to sociologists, philosophers, and others. But, we did study the problem and found, in the end, that our work was eased and made more meaningful by adopting a convenient categorization of broadly justifiable, unexceptionable, yet often conflicting, interests within the totality of the general public.

Obviously, the general public is made up of many persons and groups with conflicting aims and objectives. Stated another way, it may be said that there are several "publics" which, in the aggregate, make up the general public with respect to policies for the public lands. Perhaps this categorization of identifiable interests would be useful in other areas of public policy, too. In any case, we found it useful in our work and applied it to all of our decisions. The six categories of interests we recognized are:

The national public: all citizens, as taxpayers, consumers, and ultimate owners of the public lands are concerned that the lands produce and remain productive of the material, social, and esthetic benefits that can be obtained from them.

The regional public: those who live and work on or near the vast public lands, while being a part of and sharing the concerns of the national public, have a special concern that the public lands help to support them and their neighbors and that the lands contribute to their overall well-being.

The Federal Government as sovereign: the ultimate responsibility of the Federal Government is to provide for the common defense and promote the general welfare and, in so doing, it should make use of every tool at its command, including its control of the public lands.

The Federal Government as proprietor: in a narrower sense, the Federal Government is a landowner that seeks to manage its property according to much the same set of principles as any other landowner and to exercise normal proprietary control over its land.

State and local government: most of the Federal lands fall within the jurisdiction limits of other levels of governments, which have responsibility for the health, safety, and welfare of their constituents and, thus, an interest in assuring that the overriding powers of the Federal Government be accommodated to their interests as viable instruments in our Federal system of government.

The users of public lands and resources: users, including those seeking economic gain and those seeking recreation or other noneconomic benefits, have an interest in assuring that their special needs, which vary widely, are met and that all users are given equal consideration when uses are permitted.

The Commission in each of its decisions gave careful consideration to the interests of each of the several "publics" that make up the "general public." Distinguishing among these interests required that the Commission specifically consider each of them and, thus, assure that the decisions of the Commission, to the best of its ability, reflect all of the interests of the general public.

In applying the procedure that we did, in each case it was possible to see which interest is affected most. This is not only useful in the decision making process but provides a healthy atmosphere in which all parties interested can be assured that consideration has been given to them.

We, therefore, recommend that:
In making public land decisions, the Federal Government should take into consideration the interests of the national public, the regional public, the Federal Government as the sovereign, the Federal proprietor, the users of public lands and resources, and the state and local governmental entities within which the lands are located in order to assure, to the extent possible, that the maximum benefit for the general public is achieved.

Premises

Fundamental premises are beliefs set forth in the foregoing underlying principles as well as in the implementing recommendations that follow. These are:

1. Functioning of Government in a manner that reflects the principles set forth in the Constitution.

In adhering to this principle, we seek to give recognition particularly to these specific principles:

Congress, elected by and responsive to the will of the people, makes policy; the executive branch administers the policy. Maintenance of a strong Federalism. The Federal Government not only recognizes the importance of state and local governments in the Federal system but affirmatively supports and strengthens their roles to the maximum extent possible. The Federal Government protects the rights of individual citizens and assures that each one is dealt with fairly and equitably.

2. Balancing of all major interests in order to assure maximum benefit for the general public.

No one of the interests we have identified should benefit to the unreasonable detriment of another unless there is an overriding national interest present.

3. Providing responsible stewardship of the public lands and their resources.

Environmental values must be protected as major permanent elements of public land policy. Public lands must be available to meet a diversity of expanding requirements without degradation of the environment and, where possible, enhancement of the environment.
Better planning will provide increased efficiency in the allocation of resources and the investment of funds.
Guidelines must be established to provide for priorities in reducing conflicts among users and resolving conflicts when they arise.

4. In addition to serving national requirements, the public lands must serve regional and local needs.

In many areas, consideration must be given to dependence of regional and local social and economic growth upon public lands and land policy.

In planning the use of public lands, the uses of nonpublic lands must be given consideration.

Land Use in 1970

From Lloyd E. Partain, "Enough Land for Tomorrow," U.S. Department of Agriculture, *Yearbook*, (Washington, 1970), pp. 189–96.

We are learning to produce more and more on fewer and fewer acres.

There are several reasons for this. We are applying research findings about genetics, fertilizers and other soil amendments, and controlling insects, weeds, and plant and animal diseases. We have learned to mechanize an increasing number of farm operations. Farmers and ranchers, individually and in groups, are better managers than ever. And we have learned more about conservation — about managing and using our soil and water.

Phenomenal production, especially in the last quarter century, makes it possible to use land for purposes other than production of food and fiber. Demands for other uses which doubtlessly will increase in the future will be met only if we accelerate our program of natural resource conservation, development, and management.

Our natural resource base not only is the strength of our agriculture, but also provides space and conditions for many other uses wanted and needed by the whole population. Thanks to the most efficient agriculture ever developed, we can provide land for purposes besides producing food and fiber.

We have the land for recreation development and use; for parks and wildlife refuges; for wilderness; for second homes in the mountains, in the woods, on a lake, or at the seashore; and for the other amenities of living an affluent society demands. Land can be made available to disperse industry, for highways and other travel facilities, and for military and other national defense and special uses.

But we must realize that as competition for land and water increases, food and fiber — people's vital needs — will always have first claim upon these resources.

Obviously, using farmland indiscriminately for purposes other than farming can prevent us from producing enough food and fiber. By doing more research and using resource management and conservation practices on land, including using water wisely, we can be sure of meeting the increasing and varied demands on our resources. We must also consider that farm, forest, recreational, residential, industrial, and other land is being used more and more intensely. This helps meet resource demands but increases the need for conservation treatment.

In view of resource demands, our future depends on policies and programs for conserving, developing, and managing soil, water, forests, and related resources. In determining policies and setting up programs, we must consider that the conservation job is not done so long as we keep using these resources more and more intensely.

For a future program to be effective, we must know about the availability and condition of our land and water resources. Fortunately, data and information are available in the National Inventory of Soil and Water Conservation Needs, which describe the use and condition of our privately owned rural land. Revised data as of base year 1967 were being prepared for publication as this article was written.

U.S. Department of Agriculture agencies participating in this 3-year study are: the Agricultural Research Service, Agricultural Stabilization and Conservation Service, Economic Research Service, the Farmers Home Administration, Extension Service, Forest Service, Soil Conservation Service, and the Statistical Reporting Service.

The Soil Conservation Service has the leadership for this inventory.

Representatives of land-grant universities, State agencies, and interested county organizations also participated, as well as the Bureau of Indian Affairs of the Interior Department.

The study is a county-by-county inventory of land use and conservation treatment needs of non-Federal rural land, including watershed project needs. Some of the figures listed here from the inventory may be changed slightly when data have been analyzed completely.

The current inventory shows a total of 1.4 billion acres of non-Federal rural land in the 50 States, of which 437.6 million acres are cropland, 481.9 million pasture and rangeland, 462.3 million forest, and 56.2 million in other miscellaneous uses.

Comparing these figures with a similar 1958 inventory, we find that we now have 10.1 million fewer acres in cropland, 3.5 million fewer in pasture and range, 9.6 million more in forest, and 10.8 million fewer in "other" uses. Almost 15 million acres have been shifted from farming to nonfarming uses in the last decade. Most of this land has gone to urban and other built-up uses; some has become Federal nonfarm land; and some has been covered by ponds, lakes, and reservoirs.

Cropland acreage has been decreasing since 1950. It had risen to 480 million acres by 1920 and stayed near that level until 1950, except for a brief drop in the late 1930's and early 1940's associated with drought and a wartime manpower shortage. Cropland acreage decreased from 478 million acres in 1950 to 437 million in 1967 and is still decreasing. The average annual decrease in cropland has been almost 2.5 million acres per year since 1950.

During this time production per acre has increased about 3 percent a year due to such things as fertilizers, pesticides, better technology including soil and water conservation practices, and less use of lower grade land.

Some of the significant changes in land use have resulted from the Nation's resource conservation program. This aspect of recent land use history is not as well known or generally understood as are figures about decreased acreage in crops.

These changes have come about because better crops and pasture can be grown on land where good drainage, erosion and flood prevention, irrigation, and weed and brush control practices have been applied.

There have been substantial shifts in land use in many areas, such as concentrating crops on fertile, more level, productive soils, and growing grass and trees on hilly, less productive soils once used for crops.

The amount of food and fiber we can produce on fewer acres seems even more impressive if we consider that we have been meeting the needs of an ever-increasing population with an improving standard of living. Moreover, we can export a substantial amount of what we produce.

Few will doubt that we could not have made such records without public programs including research, extension education, technical assistance, cost-sharing and loans, and stabilization of the production and marketing processes. And industries supplying man-made inputs needed in modern agricultural production, processing, and distribution have contributed a great deal to the most efficient agriculture ever known.

Perhaps the greatest benefit of this efficiency goes to the American consumer, whose real food cost not only is lower than that in any other nation but is the lowest in history. Today we spend on the average less than 17¢ out of each dollar of take-home pay, for food. We spent more than 25¢ a quarter of a century ago.

Efficient agriculture, made possible by public programs and the American farmer's ingenuity, deserves the interest and support of every citizen.

As we look to the future we must remember that our land and water space is finite. For the most part all land suitable for food and fiber production is being used. This has happened relatively recently.

Since, from all indications, demand for the products of the land will increase, natural resource management of the future must be more selective and often more intensive. Even after years of enlightenment and experience in conservation and resource management, much remains to be done and it must be done quickly.

Details of the current National Inventory of Soil and Water Conservation Needs show where we have been and where we must go in managing resources.

Only 36 percent of the land in the inventory has been adequately treated with soil and water conservation practices and measures. By major uses, the amounts adequately treated are: 36 percent of the cropland, 29 percent of rangeland, 28 percent of pastureland, 38 percent of forest land, and 71 percent of "other" land.

Of the 278 million acres of U.S. cropland needing soil and water conservation treatment, about 4 percent should be used for other purposes. This is land that is too steep, has soils that are too thin, or has other characteristics that make it unsuited for crop production.

Cultural and mechanical practices are needed on 64 percent of the cropland to hold soil losses to an acceptable minimum. Terraces, stripcropping, and water diversions are needed on 22 percent of the cropland to reduce erosion by wind and water.

About 29 percent of the 40.5 million acres of irrigated cropland is adequately treated, and 12 percent needs only cultural measures such as effective use of crop residues and good tillage practices. This means that on 41 percent of irrigated cropland, irrigation and water management are good. Most needed on the remaining 59 percent is better irrigation, primarily to prevent too much water loss and to use water more efficiently.

About 29 percent of non-Federal rangeland is adequately treated according to current conservation standards. Five percent of the remaining land cannot be treated because of soil, topography, or climate conditions.

The many different plants on native rangeland make it valuable for several secondary uses compatible with producing forage and grazing for domestic livestock. Well managed range benefits big game animals and other wildlife which find a large part of their habitat on rangeland and related grazing land.

Often range treatment and conservation practices can be changed to improve wildlife habitat yet still meet the primary objective of livestock production. For many rangeland owners and managers, producing game is a primary objective and livestock grazing is secondary. Livestock and game usually can be companion crops.

Our wide expanse of native grazing land — interspersed with ridges, escarpments, and water courses, and having many different kinds of plants, topography, domestic animals, and wildlife — invites a growing number of recreationists. More and more rangeland owners and managers operate their enterprises as guest ranches for part of the year. Some provide lodging and guide services to earn extra income from hunters and fishermen.

In determining conservation needs and in applying practices, both primary and secondary uses of grazing land should be considered.

Of the nearly 102 million acres of pastureland, 70 million need conservation treatment to improve vegetation and to supply forage needed on farms and ranches. About 28.2 million acres are adequately treated. Nearly 3 million acres should be converted to forest or to another noncropland use, and on another 1.3 million acres conservation treatment is not feasible. Most pastures are on soils that can be treated and managed effectively.

The Conservation Needs Inventory covers forest that is not in National Forests or on other public land of the United States. The Nation's private forest resources are 2½ times as large in area as all public forest land. Of the total 462.3 million acres, 398.2 million acres are called commercial forest and the remaining 64.1 million acres noncommercial. Conservation treatment is needed on 71 percent of the privately owned commercial forest land.

On some privately owned noncommercial forest land, forest needs to be reestablished or reinforced to protect watersheds, benefit wildlife, or hide the scars of past misuse.

A part of the National Inventory of Soil and Water Conservation Needs deals with watersheds. In this part, 19,194 upstream watersheds ranging up to 250,000 acres were identified.

In some of these watersheds the U.S. Department of Agriculture is assisting local sponsoring organizations under authority of the Watershed Protection and Flood Prevention Act (Public Law 566 as amended — 83rd Congress). The kind and extent of upstream watershed problems needing action — beyond land conservation action discussed earlier — were estimated for each watershed.

Flood plains in these 19,194 watersheds comprise about 134 million acres, of which 129 million are rural and 5 million in urban areas. This kind of information about flood plain land has not been available before.

Problems needing project action include floodwater and sediment damages on 92.7 million acres of agricultural land and 2.8 million acres of urban land. On 72.8 million acres project action is needed to treat severe erosion damage. Better drainage is needed on 65.4 million acres, and another 16.7 million acres need to be irrigated.

Multiple-purpose development is an effective way to meet resource needs in a watershed area: water supply and control facilities are combined with flood-prevention measures. There is a need and potential for developing rural water supplies in 5,540 watersheds, recreation in 12,396, better fish and wildlife in 13,059, and water quality control in 8,778.

The significance of these data and this information about conservation needs on rural land goes beyond problems of producing food and fiber. This information and similar studies — such as timber resource inventories, water supply and water management investigations, and other studies of basic natural wealth — show the importance of resource management. From these studies it is evident that resource management can be the key to solving many problems of future competition for land and water.

Competition for land and water becomes stiff as more people demand more parks and playgrounds, more wilderness and wildlife sanctuaries, and other uses which seem essential and desirable for modern living. Tomorrow's resource management must try to meet these demands so far as possible. We are fortunate that to a great extent we can allot resources to these and other uses. In many situations these uses are compatible with farming, ranching, and commercial forestry.

To best satisfy the interests of all people concerned, resource management must be considered fully in community, area, regional, and national development plans and action programs.

People must realize that to meet the needs of a growing population at a higher standard of living, we must limit the areas of natural resources that we lock up merely for preservation. In many situations, multiple use will have to prevail over single use. As demand for land and water resources grows, the price we pay for limited use or nonuse will be greater.

Fortunately, with our stewardship, scientific know-how, and resource management, we can meet most of the foreseeable demands for our land and water resources in an orderly manner.

Land Use Planning

From *Progressive Farmer* (April, 1973), pp. 52, 102.

Legislation under consideration at national and state levels in regard to land use planning appears destined to run head-on into the traditional philosophy that a man's land is his to do with as he pleases. Land use planning is society's way of saying that the general public has an interest in the use of land — whether it is privately or publicly owned.

Land use planning has been defined as "a process to see that land is used and managed for optimum private and public benefit, for both short-term and long-range needs."

Since agriculture is the largest landowner — controlling about 1.3 billion acres or 59% of the land area in the United States — farmers and ranchers have an important stake in influencing the types of policies and the way they are carried out.

While various forms of land use control have been practiced for a century or more in this country — such as urban zoning — interest is now at a new high.

A growing population has increased the demand for land for homesites, highways and airports, industrial expansion, and parks and recreation areas. This surging demand for land has brought on undesirable effects of urban sprawl; "ribbon" development along freeways; traffic congestion around airports, parks, and recreation areas; and sight and sound pollution.

At the same time, increasing environmental concerns are pressuring for regulation of development in "ecologically fragile" areas. Included in such areas are flood plains, coastal lands, woodlands, scenic areas, wildlife habitats, and along rivers and lakefronts.

Hot debate is raging, too, in regard to use of public lands. Ranchers are pitted against recreation enthusiasts, environmentalists against mining and timber interests, and sportsmen against wildlife protection groups.

Agriculture also has had cause to become concerned as each year for the past decade more than a million acres of farm and ranch land has been moved into nonfarm uses.

As the city spills over into the countryside, many producers who would prefer to continue farming are forced out. They're either pressured by exorbitant taxes or complaints and nuisance suits filed against them by nonfarm neighbors.

In light of these developments, there has been a gradual upsurge in the view that some form of land use planning is essential. It is generally expected that Congress and many states will pass legislation this session that will set in motion the mechanisms for state and regional involvement in land use planning.

With so many differing values as to what uses of land are in the public's interest to regulate, agricultural people need to become involved early in the development of policies and plans. Once on the books, laws are hard to change — no matter how unfair or impractical they may be.

A poll of farmers and ranchers undoubtedly would show overwhelming opposition to land use planning. The very term produces mental pictures of "Big Government" looking over their shoulders. There is fear that they will be told how they may farm, what size barn they can build, and to whom they can sell their property.

Those who have studied existing and proposed land use legislation maintain this is not the purpose at all. Most land use decisions are of purely local interest, they say. Decisions will continue to be made at the local level by boards or commissions made up of local people who represent various local interests.

The Federal Government would set overall goals, priorities, and guidelines and encourage states to develop programs to deal with land use problems of more than local impact. In such a group would be critical environmental areas; areas impacted by airports and major highway interchanges; and development of land of regional benefit. The Federal Government would be directly involved in regulating use of public lands.

Carl Farler, University of Arkansas economist, cites an example to explain the difference between land use policy and planning. "The national policy might be to get more acres out of cropland and into grassland for beef production or to increase recreation acres. These policies wouldn't dictate to an individual farmer how he can use his land," Farler says. "On the other hand, a county planning commission could influence an individual producer's land use by zoning the area in which his farm lies for agricultural use, thereby keeping the land from being developed for residential or industrial uses," Farler explained.

Zoning, commonly used in urban areas to regulate construction and land uses, has been used to some extent in rural areas. Restrictions have been placed on uncontrolled development of sanitary landfills, dumping grounds, and undesirable commercial businesses such as taverns. Some question whether use of zoning to regulate agricultural use of land is constitutional.

Many authorities on land use planning doubt that agricultural zoning will be used to any great extent except around expanding urban areas and along major transportation networks. And they maintain that agricultural zoning will not infringe on any producer's right to decide how to manage his farm, so long as his use does not endanger public health or welfare.

Tax policies can be used to influence land use. By taxing land on the basis of its farm productive value instead of its market or speculative value, a community can encourage its continued use for agricultural purposes. If the land is sold or developed for different use, the owner may be required to pay "roll-back" taxes.

Other forms of land use regulation would include agreements between buyer and seller restricting future uses of property and use of public easements. Some states restrict the amount of soil sediment that a landowner may permit to run off his farm.

One of the most likely methods to be used to control rural land use is one that farmers have been using for decades — only they didn't call it by that name. Since the early 1930's, Federal subsidies have been used to shift production from one crop to another, to reduce erosion, to keep land in conserving uses, and to fertilize and lime grassland. Soil and water conservation programs have resulted in a shift of 24 million acres of cropland to grassland. Another 3.2 million acres have shifted to woodland and wildlife and recreation land.

Of course, there will be some situations where the only solution may be for the Government to buy the land, either to put it into a public park, recreation area, or wildlife refuge or to resell to private interests with strict limitations on how it may be used.

You will find no consensus among agriculturists concerning land use planning. H. F. Breimyer, University of Missouri economist, says: "Land use controls will not hurt, but will help the farmers who want to stay in farming. Only the farmers who want to make their money by speculation will be harmed. Those farmers want to farm at minimum tax costs, and get all the benefits of speculation. They ask too much, and they will be disappointed."

"With proper local participation, land use planning and zoning can be useful tools in protecting agriculture from some of the undesirable side effects arising from rapid land use change," adds Farler.

J. T. Woodson, president of the Texas Farm Bureau, agrees that there are certain advantages if planning is properly done and private rights are zealously safeguarded.

"However, we have come to the conclusion that the potential loss of private property rights far outweighs any other consideration," he says. "For this reason, we must oppose land use planning at the Federal and state level with all our strength."

Many farm groups and individuals are determined to fight "tooth and nail" against any land use laws. Others are taking the more pessimistic attitude that land use legislation is inevitable, and that the best approach is to work for the fairest and most workable policy possible.

Federal Farm Policies

The Brannan Plan, 1949

From *Congressional Record,* May 5, 1949.

Since making my farm-program recommendations, the committee's comments and public discussion seem to have centered on three broad questions. These deal with cost, how the proposed program would operate, and the degree of Government control involved. With your permission, I should like to take up these questions a little more fully than has been possible heretofore.

First, let us look at the cost question.

As you know, this question involves many values in addition to dollars. We can and will use certain dollar illustrations, but, as your own experience will verify, our economy is so complex and dynamic that it has never been possible to make accurate dollar estimates in advance for price-support operations.

It has been said that the production payments called for in my proposal would be costly and that the cost must be estimated now. Yet title II of the Agricultural Act of 1948 provides for the same kind of payments, and no estimates of the cost of that legislation were ever requested or made prior to its adoption.

Title I of the act of 1948 continued the wartime level of price supports, yet no cost estimates were called for or considered at the time of its adoption, even on potatoes, for which we were then carrying out the most expensive price-support operation in history.

The same point could be made about earlier legislation. New bills and amendments have been enacted year after year on the basis of needs and the benefits to be derived. Actual results have been measured against actual costs, which is the only valid comparison.

My recommendations contemplate the operation of price-support programs through the Commodity Credit Corporation, as they are being operated today. And as you know, Congress does not appropriate in advance for the CCC because, for a host of obvious reasons, the dollar requirements cannot be estimated accurately in advance. But Congress has a very effective control over costs. It controls authorizations and appropriations. If a particular program results in a greater outlay than the Congress is willing to continue, the Government's commitment may be changed for ensuing years. No program can cost more, over a period of years, than the Congress makes available.

Another point we need to keep in mind as we deal with the cost question is that we must always make comparisons. It helps no one to compare the costs of one program against no program at all. The American people have already taken the position that the farmer should have adequate returns, and until a better method is brought to light the farm price support method is the one we should use. We have such a program in operation now. We have legislation on the books that is scheduled to go into effect next year. We have had considerable experience in the past.

Due to our expanded productive capacity and the possibility that our foreign markets will diminish, costs under any effective program may increase. The least expensive program in the public interest, for the long run, will be that which encourages the greatest and most efficient consumption of farm commodities which would otherwise be surplus. These facts must be taken into account as we consider the recommended program. An absolute figure without comparisons is bound to be misleading and to give substance to the fallacious arguments of the enemies of price-support legislation.

The real core of the question of cost is how effective we choose to make our program. Obviously, we are not going to get something for nothing in this farm-program business, any more than anywhere else.

In my statement of April 7, I laid before you my views on the public need for a strong farm income and price-support system. I said it can serve the interests of all the people by helping to prevent depression, build bigger markets for industrial goods and jobs for workers, maintain high-level production of farm commodities, conserve natural resources, maintain reserves for national security, strengthen the rural commodity, and provide consumers increased supplies at attractive prices.

A program that will effectively contribute toward these ends is worth a considerable public investment.

But let us not try to kid anybody — either the farmer or the general public. Any program which is so designed that the public investment is always sure to be small is going to be an ineffective program at the very time a strong program is needed. It is not likely to give adequate service of the kinds I have listed, either to the farmer or to the general public.

What is adequate?

An eastern financial journal says that my proposal ''promises to farmers more than they are entitled to.'' That is a matter of opinion which the Congress is going to settle. But let me emphasize this question: In the public interest, how far down do you dare let farm income slide?

Farm prices already have come down 15 percent since the beginning of last year. The prices paid by farmers have stayed close to their peak level and are currently only about 2 percent under last summer's level. The purchasing power of what the farmer sells has come down to the lowest point since 1942.

(e) Section 322 (a) of such Act, as so amended (relating to corn marketing quotas), is amended by adding at the end thereof the following: "With respect to the 1950 crop of corn the determination and proclamation required by this section may be made, notwithstanding the foregoing, at any time prior to February 1, 1950, using 1949 as 'such calendar year' for the purposes of (1) and (2) of the preceding sentence."

(f) Section 328 of such Act, as so amended (relating to corn acreage allotments), is amended by striking out "reserve supply level" and inserting in lieu thereof "normal supply".

SEC. 410. Section 4 of the Act of March 8, 1938, as amended (15 U.S.C., 1946 edition, 713a–4), is amended by substituting a colon for the period at the end of the next to the last sentence thereof and adding the following: "*Provided,* That this sentence shall not limit the authority of the Corporation to issue obligations for the purpose of carrying out its annual budget programs submitted to and approved by the Congress pursuant to the Government Corporation Control Act (31 U.S.C., 1946 edition, sec. 841)."

SEC. 411. Section 32, as amended, of the Act entitled "An Act to amend the Agricultural Adjustment Act, and for other purposes", approved August 24, 1935 (U.S.C., title 7, sec. 612c), is amended by inserting before the last sentence thereof the following: "The sums appropriated under this section shall be devoted principally to perishable nonbasic agricultural commodities (other than those designated in title II of the Agricultural Act of 1949) and their products."

SEC. 412. Determinations made by the Secretary under this Act shall be final and conclusive: *Provided,* That the scope and nature of such determinations shall not be inconsistent with the provisions of the Commodity Credit Corporation Charter Act.

SEC. 413. This Act shall not be effective with respect to price support operations for any agricultural commodity for any marketing year or season commencing prior to January 1, 1950, except to the extent that the Secretary of Agriculture shall, without reducing price support theretofore undertaken or announced, elect to apply the provisions of this Act.

SEC. 414. Section 302 of the Agricultural Adjustment Act of 1938, as amended, and any provision of law in conflict with the provisions of this Act are hereby repealed.

SEC. 415. (a) Except as modified by this Act or by Public Law 272, Eighty-first Congress, sections 201 (b), 201 (d), 201 (e), 203, 207 (a), and 208 of the Agricultural Act of 1948 shall be effective for the purpose of taking any action with respect to the 1950 and subsequent crops upon the enactment of this Act. If the time within which any such action is required to be taken shall have elapsed prior to the enactment of this Act, such action shall be taken within thirty days after the enactment of this Act.

(b) No provision of the Agricultural Act of 1948 shall be deemed to supersede any provision of Public Law 272, Eighty-first Congress.

(c) Section 301 (b) (10) of the Agricultural Adjustment Act of 1938, as amended, by section 201 (d) of the Agricultural Act of 1948, is amended (1) by striking out of subparagraph (A) the following: "cotton,", (2) by striking out of subparagraph (A) the following: "30 per centum in the case of cotton;", and (3) by adding at the end thereof the following subparagraph:

"(C) The 'normal supply' of cotton for any marketing year shall be the estimated domestic consumption of cotton for the marketing year for which such normal supply is being determined, plus the estimated exports of cotton for such marketing year, plus 30 per centum of the sum of such consumption and exports as an allowance for carry-over."

(d) Section 301 (b) (16) of the Agricultural Adjustment Act of 1938, as amended by section 201 (e) of the Agricultural Act of 1948 is amended (1) by striking out of subparagraph (A) the following: "cotton,", and (2) by adding the following subparagraph:

"(C) 'Total supply' of cotton for any marketing year shall be the carry-over at the beginning of such marketing year, plus the estimated production of cotton in the United States during the calendar year in which such marketing year begins and the estimated imports of cotton into the United States during such marketing year."

(e) Sections 201 (c), 205, 206, and 207 (c) of the Agricultural Act of 1948 are hereby repealed.

SEC. 416. In order to prevent the waste of food commodities acquired through price support operations which are found to be in danger of loss through deterioration or spoilage before they can be disposed of in normal domestic channels without impairment of the price support program, the Secretary of Agriculture and the Commodity Credit Corporation are authorized, upon application by the Munitions Board or any other Federal agency and on such terms and under such regulations as may be deemed in the public interest, to make such commodities available to any such agency for use in making payment for commodities not produced in the United States. Any such commodities which are not disposed of pursuant to the foregoing sentence may be made available by the Secretary and the Commodity Credit Corporation at the point of storage at no cost, save handling and transportation costs incurred in making delivery from the point of storage, as follows in the order of priority set forth: First, to school-lunch programs; and to the Bureau of Indian Affairs and Federal, State, and local public welfare organizations for the assistance of needy Indians and other needy persons; second, to private welfare organizations for the assistance of needy persons within the United States; third, to private welfare organizations for the assistance of needy persons outside the United States.

SEC. 417. (a) Section 41 of the Farm Credit Act of 1933 (U.S.C., title 12, sec. 1134c) is amended by adding at the end thereof the following:

"Notwithstanding any limitations or conditions imposed by law, but subject to the availability of funds, each Bank for Cooperatives shall have power and authority to make separate loans to cooperative associations as defined in the Agricultural Marketing Act, as amended, for the purpose of financing the construction of structures for the storage of agricultural commodities (other than structures to provide refrigerated cold storage or structures in areas in which existing privately owned storage facilities for the commodity concerned are adequate) in amounts up to a maximum of 80 per centum of the cost of such structures, as approved by the Bank for Cooperatives to whom application is made for the loan: *Provided,* That the cooperative association which has applied for any loan shall have furnished to the Bank for Cooperatives an appropriate commitment from the Commodity Credit Corporation that the Commodity Credit Corporation will lease or guarantee utilization of not less than 75 per centum of the storage space contained in such structures when completed for a period of at least three years if such structures are not addi-

With this $230,000,000 a production payment to farmers could be made on 21,000,000,000 pounds of hogs in the approximate sum of $1.10 per hundred, live weight (or more if payments were made only on marketings). In other words, the price of hogs, live weight, in the market place could be reduced by $1.10 before it would cost this Government 1 cent more money than it would be obligated to pay under the purchase method. This $1.10 is about 7 percent of the $16.50 assumed support level. If a 7 percent reduction could be carried all the way through to the re-tail level, it would be possible to reduce the consumer's price of pork by about 7 percent and at the same time give him access to the finished pork product from 1,000,000,000 pounds of live hogs. Perhaps this example is an oversimplification. There are many factors which might influence the final conclusion in a small way in either direction. But we do believe it summarizes the essential facts.

Beef, Lambs, and Chickens

I don't suppose anyone on the committee expects us to be in a program of supporting the price of beef cattle and lambs in the near future, but if and when we are, the operation would be analogous to the hog example I have just given. This would also be true with respect to chickens.

Eggs

If we undertook to maintain egg consumption at about the present levels, it appears that an annual commercial movement of about 4,000,000,000 dozen eggs would be required. Let us assume that production or marketings exceed the 4,000,000,000 dozen figure by 300,000,000 dozen eggs. What would be the cost under the present purchase program?

Based on our experience over the last two seasons, the surplus of 300,000,000 dozen purchased as dried eggs would probably cost the CCC about $120,000,000. However, this is again only the initial cost. Additional costs would be incurred because of transportation, storage, and other charges, which might well run another $52,000,000. Since little or no prospective outlets are available for these eggs, the entire inventory would represent a potential loss to the Government.

Under the production-payment plan, this cost of $172,000,000 would allow a production payment of about 4 cents a dozen on the 4,300,000,000 dozen eggs available for the commercial market. This ought to permit a decline in retail prices in excess of 4 cents a dozen and give consumers access to the additional 300,000,000 dozen eggs.

Milk and Milk Products

Under the proposed program with regard to milk and its products, we would continue full use of present marketing agreements and orders, extend those pro-grams as and when producers and handlers desire, and continue to use purchases of dairy products as a price-support method wherever this method would be most economical and otherwise consistent with the public interest.

We would not, however, make purchases for which we could not find ac-ceptable outlets.

We would use the purchase method mainly to relieve spot surpluses and seasonal problems which could be met most efficiently in this way.

The Board of Directors of the Commodity Credit Corporation recently estimated that $20,000,000 may be required in this type of operation between now and the end of this calendar year. We are just coming into the flush milk-producing season and it is imperative that we make the best possible arrangements to discharge the CCC obligation to support this commodity.

Whenever any large-scale operation becomes necessary, we should use the production-payment method. As a rule, this would cost the Government about the same amount as would purchases and would make more milk and milk products available to consumers at lower prices than would otherwise be the case. It would also call for a greater consumption of our grain and forage production.

As I previously indicated, the payment method could be used, if Congress so decided, not merely to support prices but directly to encourage greater production and consumption of milk. Prices of fluid or class I milk to consumers over the country these past few months have ranged between 22 cents in several eastern cities to a low of 14 cents in one of the major Midwest cities. In a 4-quart container, milk is now selling in grocery stores in Chicago at 16¼ cents a quart.

To the extent that the objective is to increase consumption of milk by lowering the price to the level which will secure the greatest consumption, it may be necessary to use additional sums of money and relate the payments to costs of production, the support operation and the reduced price to consumers.

For whatever assistance it may be to the committee, here is one guide estimate. If a payment of 1 cent were made on every quart of class I milk consumed in fluid form the cost to the Federal Government would be around $150,000,000 per year. It is obvious, however, that to achieve the desired result such a payment would not be necessary on much in excess of one-half of the milk so consumed.

Potatoes

While the demand for the main livestock items is relatively elastic, this is evidently not true of potatoes. Small changes in market supplies cause much greater changes in market prices. I believe a satisfactory production payment program can be operated for a great deal less money than we have been spending on potatoes.

When the CCC has fulfilled its obligations under the existing law to support the price of potatoes for the marketing season of 1948, it will have expended approximately $225,000,000. This program will have maintained the price to producers at an average of $1.75 per bushel for grade A potatoes. The total production last year was 445,000,000 bushels. Therefore, in order to maintain this level, it will be necessary to withdraw from the market and dispose of approximately 123,000,000 bushels. With the use of $225,000,000, we could have reduced the price of sales for commercial purposes to about $1 per bushel and retained the farm return at the support level. Consumers would have benefited accordingly.

Let me make it very clear that, in my opinion, the major portion of the potatoes withdrawn from the market during the 1948 season represents excessive and unjustified production, which by the use of production payments, acreage allotments, or marketing quotas, or marketing agreements and orders, should be eliminated in future years so that such losses to the Government on a single crop would not be incurred.

There are other commodities now receiving support, both storables and nonstorables, for which we have made no comparisons, and the general factors would be the same as those previously discussed. Some will continue to be supported.

Some of the commodities not now under support are of sufficient importance to the income of some sections of the country and are of sufficient importance to the national diet that it is conceivable that, at some date in the future, support prices should be made available to them under appropriate circumstances. But to estimate those kinds of factors now does not in my opinion, come within the realm of practicability.

For these reasons and the others already discussed, to estimate the over-all cost of the program would serve no useful purpose.

Another misunderstanding of my recommendations which I should like to clear up has to do with the amount of Government control involved.

This is somewhat related to the cost question. On the one hand, we hear that a program will be too costly, and on the other hand, we hear it said that if we place limits or conditions upon the amount of price support, this is regimentation. The two arguments conflict. It should be clearly understood that the only so-called Government controls involved in my recommendations are those which limit the amount of the Government's commitment to farmers.

I state categorically:

1. That my recommendations call for absolutely no form of authority or control not contemplated by title II of the Agricultural Act of 1948.

2. That the legislation I have recommended is less restrictive than any so far enacted by virtue of the fact that it offers more encouragement to the abundant consumption and production of farm products and, thereby, offers more protection against surpluses. This program would increase inducements for desirable adjustments without ordering them.

3. That the present legal right of producers to accept or reject by referendum any proposed mandatory limitation upon their marketing should not be infringed. As you know, a farm marketing quota program cannot be put into effect for any commodity unless at least two-thirds of the producers voting in a referendum have accepted such regulation. The Secretary cannot even propose such a mandatory limit except under carefully defined conditions which safeguard the public interest.

Farmers fought for the legal rights they now have to impose marketing limits upon themselves. In the view of those who did so, these rights represent an extension, not an infringement, of their freedom. I adhere to this principle.

For the record, let me give you the citations to provisions of title II, Agricultural Act of 1948, and preceding legislation, which carry every type of authority to which my own recommendations refer. Unless otherwise noted, the citations will refer to title II, Agricultural Act of 1948.

Production payments: Section 202 (a).

Acreage allotments and marketing quotas: Sections 311 et seq., Agricultural Adjustment Act of 1938; sections 203–208 of title II.

Marketing agreements and orders: First provided in section 8, Agricultural Adjustment Act of 1933; also see Congressional Record of July 7, 1948 (94

CONGRESSIONAL RECORD A4620) for confirmation that it was the intent of title II, Agricultural Act of 1948, that the Secretary have authority to condition price support for certain commodities upon there being in effect marketing agreements or orders regulating the marketing of such commodities.

Soil conservation as a condition required for price support: See section 8, Soil Conservation and Domestic Allotment Act. When the farmer's income was supported in part through payments under this act, full payment to a farmer was conditioned upon observance of soil-conserving and soil-building practices. See also section 202 (a), title II. This lists compliance with production goals as a condition for price support. Under this provision, by administrative determination, a particular acreage of soil-conserving crops would be a production goal upon which price support could be conditioned.

Parenthetically, let me say that with a realistic income and price support in effect, the farmer should be able to operate with more regard to soil conservation than he otherwise could. This is another reason why I regard this recommendation as a fair one.

Limitation of amount of price support per farm: In principle, this is not different from limitations upon the size of conservation payments (see sec. 8 (e) of the Soil Conservation and Domestic Allotment Act and the appropriations for such act in the Department of Agriculture Appropriation Acts for 1948 and 1949). Nor is it different in principle from limitations upon private use of the public domain such as irrigation water and grazing lands.

With regard to the recommended conditions and limits as a whole, let me make this one observation: Price supports are granted by the public in the public interest, not as a matter of inherent right. The public has also established certain other policy objectives in the field of agriculture. In my opinion, it is entirely proper that the program should connect up the various policy objectives that are naturally interrelated.

The Agricultural Act of 1949

From 63 Statutes at Large 1041.

Title I — Basic Agricultural Commodities

SEC. 101. The Secretary of Agriculture (hereinafter called the "Secretary") is authorized and directed to make available through loans, purchases, or other operations, price support to cooperators for any crop of any basic agricultural commodity, if producers have not disapproved marketing quotas for such crop, at a level not in excess of 90 per centum of the parity price of the commodity nor less than the level provided in subsections (a), (b), and (c) as follows:

(a) For tobacco (except as otherwise provided herein), corn, wheat, and rice, if the supply percentage as of the beginning of the marketing year is:

The level of support shall be not less than the following percentage of the parity price:

Not more than 102	90
More than 102 but not more than 104	89
More than 104 but not more than 106	88
More than 106 but not more than 108	87
More than 108 but not more than 110	86
More than 110 but not more than 112	85
More than 112 but not more than 114	84
More than 114 but not more than 116	83
More than 116 but not more than 118	82
More than 118 but not more than 120	81
More than 120 but not more than 122	80
More than 122 but not more than 124	79
More than 124 but not more than 126	78
More than 126 but not more than 128	77
More than 128 but not more than 130	76
More than 130	75

(b) For cotton and peanuts, if the supply percentage as of the beginning of the marketing year is:	The level of support shall be not less than the following percentage of the parity price:
Not more than 108	90
More than 108 but not more than 110	89
More than 110 but not more than 112	88
More than 112 but not more than 114	87
More than 114 but not more than 116	86
More than 116 but not more than 118	85
More than 118 but not more than 120	84
More than 120 but not more than 122	83
More than 122 but not more than 124	82
More than 124 but not more than 125	81
More than 125 but not more than 126	80
More than 126 but not more than 127	79
More than 127 but not more than 128	78
More than 128 but not more than 129	77
More than 129 but not more than 130	76
More than 130	75

(c) For tobacco, if marketing quotas are in effect, the level of support shall be 90 per centum of the parity price.

(d) Not withstanding the foregoing provisions of this section —

(1) if producers have not disapproved marketing quotas for such crop, the level of support to cooperators shall be 90 per centum of the parity price for the 1950 crop of any basic agricultural commodity for which marketing quotas or acreage allotments are in effect;

(2) if producers have not disapproved marketing quotas for such crop, the level of support to cooperators shall be not less than 80 per centum of the

parity price for the 1951 crop of any basic agricultural commodity for which marketing quotas or acreage allotments are in effect;

(3) the level of price support to cooperators for any crop of a basic agricultural commodity, except tobacco, for which marketing quotas have been disapproved by producers shall be 50 per centum of the parity price of such commodity; and no price support shall be made available for any crop of tobacco for which marketing quotas have been disapproved by producers;

(4) the level of price support for corn to cooperators outside the commercial corn-producing area shall be 75 per centum of the level of price support to cooperators in the commercial corn-producing area;

(5) price support may be made available to noncooperators at such levels, not in excess of the level of price support to cooperators, as the Secretary determines will facilitate the effective operation of the program.

(e) Not withstanding any of the provisions of this Act, section 2 of the Act of July 28, 1945 (59 Stat. 506) shall continue in effect.

Title II — Designated Nonbasic Agricultural Commodities

SEC. 201. The Secretary is authorized and directed to make available (without regard to the provisions of title III) price support to producers for wool (including mohair), tung nuts, honey, Irish potatoes, milk, butterfat, and the products of milk and butterfat as follows:

(a) The price of wool (including mohair) shall be supported through loans, purchases, or other operations at such level, not in excess of 90 per centum nor less than 60 per centum of the parity price therefor, as the Secretary determines necessary in order to encourage an annual production of approximately three hundred sixty million pounds of shorn wool;

(b) The price of tung nuts, honey, and early, intermediate, and late Irish potatoes, respectively, shall be supported through loans, purchases, or other operations at a level not in excess of 90 per centum nor less than 60 per centum of the parity price therefor;

(c) The price of whole milk, butterfat, and the products of such commodities, respectively, shall be supported at such level not in excess of 90 per centum nor less than 75 per centum of the parity price therefor as the Secretary determines necessary in order to assure an adequate supply. Such price support shall be provided through loans on, or purchases of, the products of milk and butterfat.

Title III — Other Nonbasic Agricultural Commodities

SEC. 301. The Secretary is authorized to make available through loans, purchases, or other operations price support to producers for any nonbasic agricultural commodity not designated in title II at a level not in excess of 90 per centum of the parity price for the commodity.

SEC. 302. Without restricting price support to those commodities for which a marketing quota or marketing agreement or order program is in effect, price support shall, insofar as feasible, be made available to producers of any storable nonbasic agricultural commodity for which such a program is in effect and who are complying with such program. The level of such support shall not be in excess of 90 per centum of the parity price of such commodity nor less than the level provided in the following table:

If the supply percentage as of the beginning of the marketing year is:	The level of support shall be not less than the following percentage of the parity price:
Not more than 102	90
More than 102 but not more than 104	89
More than 104 but not more than 106	88
More than 106 but not more than 108	87
More than 108 but not more than 110	86
More than 110 but not more than 112	85
More than 112 but not more than 114	84
More than 114 but not more than 116	83
More than 116 but not more than 118	82
More than 118 but not more than 120	81
More than 120 but not more than 122	80
More than 122 but not more than 124	79
More than 124 but not more than 126	78
More than 126 but not more than 128	77
More than 128 but not more than 130	76
More than 130	75

Provided, That the level of price support may be less than the minimum level provided in the foregoing table if the Secretary, after examination of the availability of funds for mandatory price support programs and consideration of the other factors specified in section 401 (b), determines that such lower level is desirable and proper.

SEC. 303. In determining the level of price support for any nonbasic agricultural commodity under this title, particular consideration shall be given to the levels at which the prices of competing agricultural commodities are being supported.

Title IV — Miscellaneous

SEC. 401. (a) The Secretary shall provide the price support authorized or required herein through the Commodity Credit Corporation and other means available to him.

(b) Except as otherwise provided in this Act, the amounts, terms, and conditions of price support operations and the extent to which such operations are carried out, shall be determined or approved by the Secretary. The following factors shall be taken into consideration in determining, in the case of any commodity for which price support is discretionary, whether a price-support operation shall be undertaken and the level of such support and, in the case of any commodity for which price support is mandatory, the level of support in excess of the minimum level prescribed for such commodity: (1) the supply of the commodity in relation to the demand therefor, (2) the price levels at which other commodities are being supported and, in the case of feed grains, the feed values of such grains in relation to corn, (3) the availability of funds, (4) the perishability of the commodity, (5) the importance of the commodity to agriculture and the national economy, (6) the ability to dispose of stocks acquired through a price-support operation, (7) the need for offsetting temporary losses of export markets, and (8) the ability and willingness of producers to keep supplies in line with demand.

(c) Compliance by the producer with acreage allotments, production goals and marketing practices (including marketing quotas when authorized by law), prescribed by the Secretary, may be required as a condition of eligibility for price support.

(d) The level of price support for any commodity shall be determined upon the basis of its parity price as of the beginning of the marketing year or season in the case of any commodity marketed on a marketing year or season basis and as of January 1 in the case of any other commodity.

Sec. 402. Notwithstanding any other provision of this Act, price support at a level in excess of the maximum level of price support otherwise prescribed in this Act may be made available for any agricultural commodity if the Secretary determines, after a public hearing of which reasonable notice has been given, that price support at such increased level is necessary in order to prevent or alleviate a shortage in the supply of any agricultural commodity essential to the national welfare or in order to increase or maintain the production of any agricultural commodity in the interest of national security. The Secretary's determination and the record of the hearing shall be available to the public.

Sec. 403. Appropriate adjustments may be made in the support price for any commodity for differences in grade, type, staple, quality, location, and other factors. Such adjustments shall, so far as practicable, be made in such manner that the average support price for such commodity will, on the basis of the anticipated incidence of such factors, be equal to the level of support determined as provided in this Act. Middling seven-eighths inch cotton shall be the standard grade for purposes of parity and price support.

Sec. 404. The Secretary, in carrying out programs under section 32 of Public Law Numbered 320, Seventy-fourth Congress, approved August 24, 1935, as amended, and section 6 of the National School Lunch Act may utilize the services and facilities of the Commodity Credit Corporation (including but not limited to procurement by contract), and make advance payments to it.

Sec. 405. No producer shall be personally liable for any deficiency arising from the sale of the collateral securing any loan made under authority of this Act unless such loan was obtained through fraudulent representations by the producer. This provision shall not, however, be construed to prevent the Commodity Credit Corporation or the Secretary from requiring producers to assume liability for deficiencies in the grade, quality, or quantity of commodities stored on the farm or delivered by them, for failure properly to care for and preserve commodities, or for failure or refusal to deliver commodities in accordance with the requirements of the program.

Sec. 406. The Secretary shall, insofar as practicable, announce the level of price support for field crops in advance of the planting season and for other agricultural commodities in advance of the beginning of the marketing year or season (January 1 in the case of commodities not marketed on a marketing year or season basis), but the level of price support so announced shall not exceed the estimated maximum level of price support specified in this Act, based upon the latest information and statistics available to the Secretary when such level of price support is announced; and the level of price support so announced shall not be reduced if the maximum level of price support when determined, is less than the level so announced.

Sec. 407. The Commodity Credit Corporation may sell any farm commodity owned or controlled by it at any price not prohibited by this section. In determining sales policies for basic agricultural commodities or storable nonbasic commodities, the Corporation should give consideration to the establishing of such policies with respect to prices, terms, and conditions as it determines will not discourage or deter manufacturers, processors, and dealers from acquiring and carrying normal inventories of the commodity of the current crop. The Corporation shall not sell any basic agricultural commodity or storable nonbasic commodity at less than 5 per centum above the current support price for such commodity, plus reasonable carrying charges. The foregoing restrictions shall not apply to (A) sales for new or byproduct uses; (B) sales of peanuts and oilseeds for the extraction of oil; (C) sales for seed or feed if such sales will not substantially impair any price-support program; (D) sales of commodities which have substantially deteriorated in quality or as to which there is a danger of loss or waste through deterioration or spoilage; (E) sales for the purpose of establishing claims arising out of contract or against persons who have committed fraud, misrepresentation, or other wrongful acts with respect to the commodity; (F) sales for export; (G) sales of wool; and (H) sales for other than primary uses.

Sec. 408. For the purposes of this Act —

(a) A commodity shall be considered storable upon determination by the Secretary that, in normal trade practice, it is stored for substantial periods of time and that it can be stored under the price-support program without excessive loss through deterioration or spoilage or without excessive cost for storage for such periods as will permit its disposition without substantial impairment of the effectiveness of the price-support program.

(b) A "cooperator" with respect to any basic agricultural commodity shall be a producer on whose farm the acreage planted to the commodity does not exceed the farm acreage allotment for the commodity under title III of the Agricultural Adjustment Act of 1938, as amended, or in the case of price support for corn to a producer outside the commercial corn-producing area, a producer who complies with conditions of eligibility prescribed by the Secretary. For the purpose of this subsection, a producer shall not be deemed to have exceeded his farm acreage allotment unless such producer knowingly exceeded such allotment.

(c) A "basic agricultural commodity" shall mean corn, cotton, peanuts, rice, tobacco, and wheat, respectively.

(d) A "nonbasic agricultural commodity" shall mean any agricultural commodity other than a basic agricultural commodity.

(e) The "supply percentage" as to any commodity shall be the percentage which the estimated total supply is of the normal supply as determined by the Secretary from the latest available statistics of the Department of Agriculture as of the beginning of the marketing year for the commodity.

(f) "Total supply" of any nonbasic agricultural commodity for any marketing year shall be the carry-over at the beginning of such marketing year, plus the estimated production of the commodity in the United States during the calendar year in which such marketing year begins and the estimated imports of the commodity into the United States during such marketing year.

(g) "Carry-over" of any nonbasic agricultural commodity for any marketing year shall be the quantity of the commodity on hand in the United States at the beginning of such marketing year, not including any part of the crop or production of such commodity which was produced in the United States during the calendar year then current. The carry-over of any such commodity may also include the quantity of such commodity in processed form on hand in the United States at the beginning of such marketing year, if the Secretary determines that the inclusion of such processed quantity of the commodity is necessary to effectuate the purposes of this Act.

(h) "Normal supply" of any nonbasic agricultural commodity for any marketing year shall be (1) the estimated domestic consumption of the commodity for the marketing year for which such normal supply is being determined, plus (2) the estimated exports of the commodity for such marketing year, plus (3) an allowance for carry-over. The allowance for carry-over shall be the average carry-over of the commodity for the five marketing years immediately preceding the marketing year in which such normal supply is determined, adjusted for surpluses or deficiencies caused by abnormal conditions, changes in marketing conditions, or the operation of any agricultural program. In determining normal supply, the Secretary shall make such adjustments for current trends in consumption and for unusual conditions as he may deem necessary.

(i) "Marketing year" for any nonbasic agricultural commodity means any period determined by the Secretary during which substantially all of a crop or production of such commodity is normally marketed by the producers thereof.

(j) Any term defined in the Agricultural Adjustment Act of 1938, shall have the same meaning when used in this Act.

SEC. 409. (a) Section 301 (a) (1) (B) of the Agricultural Adjustment Act of 1938, as amended by the Agricultural Act of 1948 (defining "adjusted base price"), is amended by adding at the end thereof the following: "As used in this subparagraph, the term 'prices' shall include wartime subsidy payments made to producers under programs designed to maintain maximum prices established under the Emergency Price Control Act of 1942."

(b) Section 301 (a) (1) (C) of such Act, as so amended (defining "parity index"), is amended (1) by inserting after the word "buy" a comma and the following: "wages paid hired farm labor", and (2) by inserting after "such prices" a comma and the word "wages".

(c) Section 301 (a) (1) of such Act, as so amended, is amended by adding at the end thereof the following new subparagraph:

"(G) Notwithstanding the foregoing provisions of this section, the parity price for any basic agricultural commodity, as of any date during the four-year period beginning January 1, 1950, shall not be less than its parity price computed in the manner used prior to the enactment of the Agricultural Act of 1949."

(d) Section 301 (b) (10) (A) of such Act, as so amended (defining "normal supply"), is amended by striking out "7 per centum in the case of corn" and inserting in lieu thereof "10 per centum in the case of corn".

(e) Section 322 (a) of such Act, as so amended (relating to corn marketing quotas), is amended by adding at the end thereof the following: "With respect to the 1950 crop of corn the determination and proclamation required by this section may be made, notwithstanding the foregoing, at any time prior to February 1, 1950, using 1949 as 'such calendar year' for the purposes of (1) and (2) of the preceding sentence."

(f) Section 328 of such Act, as so amended (relating to corn acreage allotments), is amended by striking out "reserve supply level" and inserting in lieu thereof "normal supply".

SEC. 410. Section 4 of the Act of March 8, 1938, as amended (15 U.S.C., 1946 edition, 713a–4), is amended by substituting a colon for the period at the end of the next to the last sentence thereof and adding the following: "*Provided,* That this sentence shall not limit the authority of the Corporation to issue obligations for the purpose of carrying out its annual budget programs submitted to and approved by the Congress pursuant to the Government Corporation Control Act (31 U.S.C., 1946 edition, sec. 841)."

SEC. 411. Section 32, as amended, of the Act entitled "An Act to amend the Agricultural Adjustment Act, and for other purposes", approved August 24, 1935 (U.S.C., title 7, sec. 612c), is amended by inserting before the last sentence thereof the following: "The sums appropriated under this section shall be devoted principally to perishable nonbasic agricultural commodities (other than those designated in title II of the Agricultural Act of 1949) and their products."

SEC. 412. Determinations made by the Secretary under this Act shall be final and conclusive: *Provided,* That the scope and nature of such determinations shall not be inconsistent with the provisions of the Commodity Credit Corporation Charter Act.

SEC. 413. This Act shall not be effective with respect to price support operations for any agricultural commodity for any marketing year or season commencing prior to January 1, 1950, except to the extent that the Secretary of Agriculture shall, without reducing price support theretofore undertaken or announced, elect to apply the provisions of this Act.

SEC. 414. Section 302 of the Agricultural Adjustment Act of 1938, as amended, and any provision of law in conflict with the provisions of this Act are hereby repealed.

SEC. 415. (a) Except as modified by this Act or by Public Law 272, Eighty-first Congress, sections 201 (b), 201 (d), 201 (e), 203, 207 (a), and 208 of the Agricultural Act of 1948 shall be effective for the purpose of taking any action with respect to the 1950 and subsequent crops upon the enactment of this Act. If the time within which any such action is required to be taken shall have elapsed prior to the enactment of this Act, such action shall be taken within thirty days after the enactment of this Act.

(b) No provision of the Agricultural Act of 1948 shall be deemed to supersede any provision of Public Law 272, Eighty-first Congress.

(c) Section 301 (b) (10) of the Agricultural Adjustment Act of 1938, as amended, by section 201 (d) of the Agricultural Act of 1948, is amended (1) by striking out of subparagraph (A) the following: "cotton,", (2) by striking out of subparagraph (A) the following: "30 per centum in the case of cotton;", and (3) by adding at the end thereof the following subparagraph:

"(C) The 'normal supply' of cotton for any marketing year shall be the estimated domestic consumption of cotton for the marketing year for which such normal supply is being determined, plus the estimated exports of cotton for such marketing year, plus 30 per centum of the sum of such consumption and exports as an allowance for carry-over."

(d) Section 301 (b) (16) of the Agricultural Adjustment Act of 1938, as amended by section 201 (e) of the Agricultural Act of 1948 is amended (1) by striking out of subparagraph (A) the following: "cotton,", and (2) by adding the following subparagraph:

"(C) 'Total supply' of cotton for any marketing year shall be the carry-over at the beginning of such marketing year, plus the estimated production of cotton in the United States during the calendar year in which such marketing year begins and the estimated imports of cotton into the United States during such marketing year."

(e) Sections 201 (c), 205, 206, and 207 (c) of the Agricultural Act of 1948 are hereby repealed.

SEC. 416. In order to prevent the waste of food commodities acquired through price support operations which are found to be in danger of loss through deterioration or spoilage before they can be disposed of in normal domestic channels without impairment of the price support program, the Secretary of Agriculture and the Commodity Credit Corporation are authorized, upon application by the Munitions Board or any other Federal agency and on such terms and under such regulations as may be deemed in the public interest, to make such commodities available to any such agency for use in making payment for commodities not produced in the United States. Any such commodities which are not disposed of pursuant to the foregoing sentence may be made available by the Secretary and the Commodity Credit Corporation at the point of storage at no cost, save handling and transportation costs incurred in making delivery from the point of storage, as follows in the order of priority set forth: First, to school-lunch programs; and to the Bureau of Indian Affairs and Federal, State, and local public welfare organizations for the assistance of needy Indians and other needy persons; second, to private welfare organizations for the assistance of needy persons within the United States; third, to private welfare organizations for the assistance of needy persons outside the United States.

SEC. 417. (a) Section 41 of the Farm Credit Act of 1933 (U.S.C., title 12, sec. 1134c) is amended by adding at the end thereof the following:

"Notwithstanding any limitations or conditions imposed by law, but subject to the availability of funds, each Bank for Cooperatives shall have power and authority to make separate loans to cooperative associations as defined in the Agricultural Marketing Act, as amended, for the purpose of financing the construction of structures for the storage of agricultural commodities (other than structures to provide refrigerated cold storage or structures in areas in which existing privately owned storage facilities for the commodity concerned are adequate) in amounts up to a maximum of 80 per centum of the cost of such structures, as approved by the Bank for Cooperatives to whom application is made for the loan: *Provided,* That the cooperative association which has applied for any loan shall have furnished to the Bank for Cooperatives an appropriate commitment from the Commodity Credit Corporation that the Commodity Credit Corporation will lease or guarantee utilization of not less than 75 per centum of the storage space contained in such structures when completed for a period of at least three years if such structures are not additions to existing structures, or two years if such structures are additions to existing structures."

(b) Section 34 of the Farm Credit Act of 1933 (U.S.C., title 12, sec. 1134j) is amended by adding at the end thereof the following:

"Notwithstanding any limitations or conditions imposed by law, but subject to the availability of funds, the Central Bank for Cooperatives shall have power and authority to make separate loans to cooperative associations as defined in the Agricultural Marketing Act, as amended, for the purpose of financing the construction of structures for the storage of agricultural commodities (other than structures to provide refrigerated cold storage or structures located in areas in which existing privately owned storage facilities for the commodity concerned are adequate) in amounts up to a maximum of 80 per centum of the cost of such structures, as approved by such bank: *Provided,* That the cooperative association which has applied for any loan shall have furnished to such bank an appropriate commitment from the Commodity Credit Corporation that the Commodity Credit Corporation will lease or guarantee utilization of not less than 75 per centum of the storage space contained in such structures when completed for a period of at least three years if such structures are not additions to existing structures, or two years if such structures are additions to existing structures."

SEC. 418. (a) Sections 353, 354, 355, and 356 of the Agricultural Adjustment Act of 1938, as amended, are amended to read as follows:

"Apportionment of National Acreage Allotment

"SEC. 353. (a) The national acreage allotment of rice for each calendar year shall be apportioned by the Secretary among the several States in which rice is produced in proportion to the average number of acres of rice in each State during the five-year period immediately preceding the calendar year for which such national acreage allotment of rice is determined (plus, in applicable years, the acreage diverted under previous agricultural adjustment and conservation programs) with adjustments for trends in acreage during the applicable period.

"(b) The State acreage allotment shall be apportioned to farms owned or operated by persons who have produced rice in any one of the five calendar years immediately preceding the year for which such apportionment is made on the basis of past production of rice by the producer on the farm taking into consideration the acreage allotments previously established for such owners or operators; abnormal conditions affecting acreage; land, labor, and equipment available for the production of rice; crop rotation practices; and the soil and other physical factors affecting the production of rice: *Provided,* That if the State committee recommends such action and the Secretary determines that such action will facilitate the effective administration of the Act, he may provide for the apportionment of the State acreage allotment to farms on which rice has been produced during any one of such period of years on the basis of the foregoing factors, using past production of rice on the farm and the acreage allotments previously established for the farm in lieu of past production of rice by the producer and the acreage allotments previously established for such owners or operators. Not more than 3 per centum of the State acreage allotment shall be apportioned among farms operated by persons who will produce rice during the calendar year for which the allotment is made but who have not produced rice in any one of the past five years, on the basis of the applicable apportionment factors set forth herein: *Provided,* That in any State in which allotments are established for farms on the basis of past production of rice on the farm such percentage of the State acreage allotment shall be apportioned among the farms on which rice is to be planted during the calendar year for which the apportionment is made but on which rice was not planted during any of the past five years, on the basis of the applicable apportionment factors set forth herein.

"(c) Notwithstanding any other provisions of this Act —

"(1) if farm acreage allotments are established by using past production of rice on the farm and the acreage allotments previously established for the farm in lieu of past production of rice by the producer and the acreage allotments previously established for owners or operators, the State acreage allotment shall be apportioned among counties in the State on the same basis as the national acreage allotment is apportioned among the States and the county acreage allotments shall be apportioned to farms on the basis of the applicable factors set forth in subsection (b) of this section: *Provided,* That the State committee may reserve not to exceed 5 per centum of the State allotment, which shall be used to make adjustments in county allotments for trends in acreage and for abnormal conditions affecting plantings;

"(2) any acreage planted to rice in excess of the farm acreage allotment shall not be taken into account in establishing State, county, and farm acreage allotments.

"*Marketing Quotas*

"SEC. 354. (a) Whenever in any calendar year the Secretary determines that the total supply of rice for the marketing year beginning in such calendar year will exceed the normal supply for such marketing year by more than 10 per centum, the Secretary shall not later than December 31 of such calendar year proclaim such fact and marketing quotas shall be in effect for the crop of rice produced in the next calendar year.

"(b) Within thirty days after the date of the issuance of the proclamation specified in subsection (a) of this section, the Secretary shall conduct a referendum by secret ballot of farmers engaged in the production of the immediately preceding crop of rice to determine whether such farmers are in favor of or opposed to such quotas. If more than one-third of the farmers voting in the referendum oppose such quotas the Secretary shall, prior to the 15th day of February, proclaim the result of the referendum and such quotas shall become ineffective.

"*Amount of Farm Marketing Quota*

"SEC. 355. The farm marketing quota for any crop of rice shall be the actual production of rice on the farm less the normal production of the acreage planted to rice on the farm in excess of the farm acreage allotment. The normal production from such excess acreage shall be known as the 'farm marketing excess': *Provided,* That the farm marketing excess shall not be larger than the amount by which the actual production of rice on the farm exceeds the normal production of the farm acreage allotment if the producer establishes such actual production to the satisfaction of the Secretary.

"Penalties and Storage

"SEC. 356. (a) Whenever farm marketing quotas are in effect with respect to any crop of rice, the producer shall be subject to a penalty on the farm marketing excess at a rate per pound equal to 50 per centum of the parity price per pound for rice as of June 15 of the calendar year in which such crop is produced.

"(b) The farm marketing excess of rice shall be regarded as available for marketing and the amount of penalty shall be computed upon the normal production of the acreage on the farm planted to rice in excess of the farm acreage allotment. If a downward adjustment in the amount of the farm marketing excess is made pursuant to the proviso in section 355, the difference between the amount of the penalty computed upon the farm marketing excess before such adjustment and as computed upon the adjusted marketing excess shall be returned to or allowed the producer.

"(c) The person liable for payment or collection of the penalty shall be liable also for interest thereon at the rate of 6 per centum per annum from the date the penalty becomes due until the date of payment of such penalty.

"(d) Until the penalty on the farm marketing excess is paid, postponed, or avoided, as provided herein, all rice produced on the farm and marketed by the producer shall be subject to the penalty provided by this section and a lien on the entire crop of rice produced on the farm shall be in effect in favor of the United States.

"(e) The penalty on the farm marketing excess on any crop of rice may be avoided or postponed by storage or by disposing of the commodity in such other manner, not inconsistent with the purposes of this Act, as the Secretary shall prescribe, including, in the discretion of the Secretary, delivery to Commodity Credit Corporation or any other agency within the Department. The Secretary shall issue regulations governing such storage or other disposition. Unless otherwise specified by the Secretary in such regulations, any quantity of rice so stored or otherwise disposed of shall be of those types and grades which are representative of the entire quantity of rice produced on the farm. Upon failure so to store or otherwise dispose of the farm marketing excess of rice within such time as may be determined under regulations prescribed by the Secretary, the penalty on such excess shall become due and payable. Any rice delivered to any agency of the Department pursuant to this subsection shall become the property of the agency to which delivered and shall be disposed of at the direction of the Secretary in a manner not inconsistent with the purposes of this Act.

"(f) Subject to the provisions of subsection (g) of this section, the penalty upon the farm marketing excess stored pursuant to this section shall be paid by the producer at the time and to the extent of any depletion in the amount so stored except depletion resulting from some cause beyond the control of the producer or from substitution of the commodity authorized by the Secretary.

"(g) (1) If the planted acreage of the then current crop of rice for any farm is less than the farm acreage allotment, the amount of the commodity from any previous crop of rice stored to postpone or avoid payment of the penalty shall be reduced by an amount equal to the normal production of the number of acres by which the farm acreage allotment exceeds the acreage planted to rice.

"(2) If the actual production of the acreage of rice on any farm on which the acreage of rice is within the farm acreage allotment is less than the normal production of the farm acreage allotment, the amount of rice from any previous crop stored to postpone or avoid payment of the penalty shall be reduced by an amount which, together with the actual production of the then current crop will equal the normal production of the farm acreage allotment: *Provided,* That the reduction under this paragraph shall not exceed the amount by which the normal production of the farm acreage allotment less any reduction made under paragraph (1) of this subsection is in excess of the actual production of the acreage planted to rice on the farm.''

(b) Section 301 (b) (1) (B) of the Agricultural Adjustment Act of 1938, as amended, is amended by inserting after the word ''cotton'' a comma and the word ''rice''.

(c) Section 301 (b) (9) of the Agricultural Adjustment Act of 1938, as amended, is amended by inserting after the comma following the word ''cotton'' the word ''rice''.

SEC. 419. Section 344 (f) (3) of the Agricultural Adjustment Act of 1938, as amended by Public Law 272, Eighty-first Congress, is amended (i) by striking the figure ''10'' in the first sentence and inserting therefor the figure ''15'', and (ii) by striking the figure ''30'' in the proviso and inserting therefor the figure ''20''.

Approved October 31, 1949.

Rural Telephone Act of 1949

From 63 Statutes at Large 948.

Be it enacted by the Senate and House of Representatives of the United States of America in Congress assembled, That it is hereby declared to be the policy of the Congress that adequate telephone service be made generally available in rural areas through the improvement and expansion of existing telephone facilities and the construction and operation of such additional facilities as are required to assure the availability of adequate telephone service to the widest practicable number of rural users of such service. In order to effectuate this policy, the Rural Electrification Act of 1936 is amended as hereinafter provided.

SEC. 2. The Rural Electrification Act of 1936 is amended by inserting at the beginning thereof the caption: ''TITLE I''.

SEC. 3. Section 2 of the Rural Electrification Act of 1936 is amended by inserting after the word ''service'' the words ''and for the purpose of furnishing and improving telephone service in rural areas''; and by inserting after the words ''electrification of'' the words ''and the furnishing of adequate telephone service in''.

SEC. 4. (a) Subsection (a) of section 3 of the Rural Electrification Act of 1936 is amended by inserting after the words ''or systems'' the words ''and for the purpose of financing the improvement, expansion, construction, acquisition, and operation of facilities to render telephone service''.

(b) Subsection (c) of section 3 of the Rural Electrification Act of 1936 is amended by striking out the words "or the purposes of this Act" and by inserting in lieu thereof the words "for loans for rural electrification pursuant to sections 4 and 5 of this title".

(c) Subsection (d) of section 3 of the Rural Electrification Act of 1936 is amended by inserting after the words "available for" the words "rural electrification".

(d) Subsection (e) of section 3 of the Rural Electrification Act of 1936 is amended by inserting after the word "sums" in the proviso the words "for rural electrification loans".

(e) Section 4 of the Rural Electrification Act of 1936 is amended by inserting after the words "to make loans" the words "for rural electrification".

(f) Sections 7 and 12 of the Rural Electrification Act of 1936 are amended by inserting after the words "section 4" wherever they appear therein the words "or section 201".

SEC. 5. The Rural Electrification Act of 1936 is further amended by adding the following new title:

"Title II

"SEC. 201. From such sums as are from time to time made available by the Congress to the Administrator for such purpose, pursuant to section 3 of the Rural Electrification Act of 1936, as amended, the Administrator is authorized and empowered to make loans to persons now providing or who may hereafter provide telephone service in rural areas and to cooperative, nonprofit, limited dividend, or mutual associations. Except as otherwise provided by this title, such loans shall be made under the same terms and conditions as are provided in section 4 of said Act, for the purpose of financing the improvement, expansion, construction, acquisition, and operation of telephone lines, facilities, or systems to furnish and improve telephone service in rural areas: *Provided, however,* That the Administrator, in making such loans, shall give preference to persons providing telephone service in rural areas, and to cooperative, nonprofit, limited dividend, or mutual associations: *And provided further,* That for a period of one year from and after the effective date of this title applications for loans received by the Administrator from persons who on the effective date of this title are engaged in the operation of existing telephone service in rural areas shall be considered and acted upon before action is taken upon any application received from any other person for any loan to finance the furnishing or improvement of telephone service to substantially the same subscribers. The Administrator in making such loans shall, insofar as possible, obtain assurance that the telephone service to be furnished or improved thereby will be made available to the widest practical number of rural users. When it is determined by the Administrator to be necessary in order to furnish or improve telephone service in rural areas, such loans may be made for the improvement, expansion, construction, acquisition, and operation of telephone lines, facilities, or systems without regard to their geographical location. The Administrator is further authorized and empowered to make loans for the purpose of refinancing outstanding indebtedness of persons furnishing telephone service in rural areas: *Provided,* That such refinancing shall be determined by the Administrator to be necessary in order to furnish and improve telephone service in rural areas: *And provided further,* That such refinancing shall constitute not more than 40 per centum of any loan made under this title. Loans under this section shall not be made unless the Administrator finds and certifies that in his judgment the security therefor is reasonably adequate and such loan will be repaid within the time agreed, nor shall such loan be made in any State which now has or may hereafter have a State regulatory body having authority to regulate telephone service and to require certificates of convenience and necessity to the applicant unless such certificate from such agency is first obtained. In a State in which there is no such agency or regulatory body legally authorized to issue such certificates to the applicant, no loan shall be made under this section unless the Administrator shall determine (and set forth his reasons therefor in writing) that no duplication of lines, facilities, or systems, providing reasonably adequate services will result therefrom.

"SEC. 202. Nothing contained in this Act shall be construed to deprive any State commission, board, or other agency of jurisdiction, under any State law, now or hereafter effective, to regulate telephone service which is not subject to regulation by the Federal Communications Commission, under the Communications Act of 1934, including the rates for such service.

"SEC. 203. (a) As used in this title, the term 'telephone service' shall be deemed to mean any communication service whereby voice communication through the use of electricity between the transmitting and receiving apparatus, is the principal intended use thereof, and shall include all telephone lines, facilities, or systems used in the rendition of such service; but shall not be deemed to mean telegraph services or facilities, or radio broadcasting services of facilities within the meaning of section 3 (o) of the Communications Act of 1934, as amended.

"(b) As used in this title, the term 'rural area' shall be deemed to mean any area of the United States not included within the boundaries of any incorporated or unincorporated city, village, or borough having a population in excess of one thousand five hundred inhabitants."

Approved October 28, 1949.

Agricultural Trade Development and Assistance Act 1954

From 68 Statutes at Large 454.

Be it enacted by the Senate and House of Representatives of the United States of America in Congress assembled, That this Act may be cited as the "Agricultural Trade Development and Assistance Act of 1954".

SEC. 2. It is hereby declared to be the policy of Congress to expand international trade among the United States and friendly nations, to facilitate the convertibility of currency, to promote the economic stability of American agriculture and the national welfare, to make maximum efficient use of surplus agricultural commodities in furtherance of the foreign policy of the United States, and to stimulate and facilitate the expansion of foreign trade in agricultural commodities produced in the United States by providing a means whereby surplus agricultural commodities in excess of the usual marketings of such commodities may be sold through private trade channels, and foreign currencies accepted in payment therefor. It is further the policy to use foreign currencies which accrue to the United States under this Act to expand international trade, to encourage economic development, to purchase strategic materials, to pay United States obligations abroad, to promote collective strength, and to foster in other ways the foreign policy of the United States.

Title 1 — Sales for Foreign Currency

SEC. 101. In furtherance of this policy, the President is authorized to negotiate and carry out agreements with friendly nations or organizations of friendly nations to provide for the sale of surplus agricultural commodities for foreign currencies. In negotiating such agreements the President shall —

(a) take reasonable precautions to safeguard usual marketings of the United States and to assure that sales under this Act will not unduly disrupt world prices of agricultural commodities;

(b) take appropriate steps to assure that private trade channels are used to the maximum extent practicable both with respect to sales from privately owned stocks and from stocks owned by the Commodity Credit Corporation;

(c) give special consideration to utilizing the authority and funds provided by this Act, in order to develop and expand continuous market demand abroad for agricultural commodities, with appropriate emphasis on underdeveloped and new market areas;

(d) seek and secure commitments from participating countries that will prevent resale or transshipment to other countries, or use for other than domestic purposes, of surplus agricultural commodities purchased under this Act, without specific approval of the President; and

(e) afford any friendly nation the maximum opportunity to purchase surplus agricultural commodities from the United States, taking into consideration the opportunities to achieve the declared policy of this Act and to make effective use of the foreign currencies received to carry out the purposes of this Act.

SEC. 102. (a) For the purpose of carrying out agreements concluded by the President hereunder, the Commodity Credit Corporation, in accordance with regulations issued by the President pursuant to subsection (b) of this section, (1) shall make available for sale hereunder at such points in the United States as the President may direct surplus agricultural commodities heretofore or hereafter acquired by the Corporation in the administration of its price support operations, and (2) shall make funds available to finance the sale and exportation of surplus agricultural commodities from stocks owned by the Corporation or pledged or mortgaged as security for price support loans or from stocks privately owned if the Corporation is not in a position to supply the commodity from its owned stocks: *Provided,* That to facilitate the use of private trade channels the Corporation, even though it is in a position to supply the commodity, may finance the sale and exportation of privately owned stocks if the Corporation's stocks are reduced through arrangements whereby the private exporter acquires the same commodity of comparable value or quantity from the Commodity Credit Corporation. In supplying commodities to private exporters under such arrangements Commodity Credit Corporation shall not be subject to the sales price restriction in section 407 of the Agricultural Act of 1949, as amended.

(b) In order to facilitate and maximize the use of private channels of trade in carrying out agreements entered into pursuant to this Act, the President may, under such regulations and subject to such safeguards as he deems appropriate, provide for the issuance of letters of commitment against funds or guaranties of funds supplied by the Commodity Credit Corporation and for this purpose accounts may be established on the books of any department, agency, or establishment of the Government, or on terms and conditions approved by the Secretary of the Treasury in banking institutions in the United States. Such letters of commitment, when issued, shall constitute obligations of the United States and moneys due or to become due thereunder shall be assignable under the Assignment of Claims Act of 1940. Expenditures of funds which have been made available through accounts so established shall be accounted for on standard documentation required for expenditures of Government funds.

SEC. 103. (a) For the purpose of making payment to the Commodity Credit Corporation to the extent the Commodity Credit Corporation is not reimbursed under section 105 for commodities disposed of and costs incurred under titles I and II of this Act, there are hereby authorized to be appropriated such sums as are equal to (1) the Corporation's investment in commodities made available for export under this title and title II of this Act, including processing, packaging, transportation, and handling costs, and (2) all costs incurred by the Corporation in making funds available to finance the exportation of surplus agricultural commodities pursuant to this title. Any funds or other assets available to the Commodity Credit Corporation may be used in advance of such appropriation or payments, for carrying out the purposes of this Act.

(b) Transactions shall not be carried out under this title which will call for appropriations to reimburse the Commodity Credit Corporation, pursuant to subsection (a) of this section, in amounts in excess of $700,000,000.

SEC. 104. Notwithstanding section 1415 of the Supplemental Appropriation Act, 1953, or any other provision of law, the President may use or enter into agreements with friendly nations or organizations of nations to use the foreign currencies which accrue under this title for one or more of the following purposes:

(a) To help develop new markets for United States agricultural commodities on a mutually benefiting basis;

(b) To purchase or contract to purchase strategic and critical materials, within the applicable terms of the Strategic and Critical Materials Stockpile Act, for a supplemental United States stockpile of such materials as the President may determine from time to time under contracts, including advance payment contracts, for supply extending over periods up to ten years. All strategic and critical materials acquired under authority of this title shall be placed in the above named supplemental stockpile and may be additional to the amounts acquired under authority of the Strategic and Critical Materials Stockpile Act. Materials so acquired shall be released from the supplemental stockpile only under the provisions of section 3 of the Strategic and Critical Materials Stockpile Act;

(c) To procure military equipment, materials, facilities, and services for the common defense;

(d) For financing the purchase of goods or services for other friendly countries;

(e) For promoting balanced economic development and trade among nations;

(f) To pay United States obligations abroad;

(g) For loans to promote multilateral trade and economic development, made through established banking facilities of the friendly nation from which the foreign currency was obtained or in any other manner which the President may deem to be appropriate. Strategic materials, services, or foreign currencies may be accepted in payment of such loans;

(h) For the financing of international educational exchange activities under the programs authorized by section 32 (b) (2) of the Surplus Property Act of 1944, as amended (50 U.S.C. App. 1641 (b)).

Provided, however, That section 1415 of the Supplemental Appropriation Act, 1953, shall apply to all foreign currencies used for grants under subsections (d) and (e) and for payment of United States obligations involving grants under subsection (f) and to not less than 10 per centum of the foreign currencies which accrue under this title: *Provided, however,* That the President is authorized to waive such applicability of section 1415 in any case where he determines that it would be inappropriate or inconsistent with the purposes of this title.

SEC. 105. Foreign currencies received pursuant to this title shall be deposited in a special account to the credit of the United States and shall be used only pursuant to section 104 of this title, and any department or agency of the government using any of such currencies for a purpose for which funds have been appropriated shall reimburse the Commodity Credit Corporation in an amount equivalent to the dollar value of the currencies used.

SEC. 106. As used in this Act, "surplus agricultural commodity" shall mean any agricultural commodity or product thereof, class, kind, type, or other specification thereof, produced in the United States, either privately or publicly owned, which is or may be reasonably expected to be in excess of domestic requirements, adequate carryover, and anticipated exports for dollars, as determined by the Secretary of Agriculture.

SEC. 107. As used in this Act, "friendly nation" means any country other than (1) the U.S.S.R., or (2) any nation or area dominated or controlled by the foreign government or foreign organization controlling the world Communist movement.

SEC. 108. The President shall make a report to Congress with respect to the activities carried on under this Act at least once each six months and at such other times as may be appropriate and such reports shall include the dollar value, at the exchange rates in effect at the time of the sale, of the foreign currency for which commodities exported pursuant to section 102 (a) hereof are sold.

SEC. 109. No transactions shall be undertaken under authority of this title after June 30, 1957, except as required pursuant to agreements theretofore entered into pursuant to this title.

Title II — Famine Relief and Other Assistance

SEC. 201. In order to enable the President to furnish emergency assistance on behalf of the people of the United States to friendly peoples in meeting famine or other urgent relief requirements, the Commodity Credit Corporation shall make available to the President out of its stocks such surplus agricultural commodities (as defined in section 106 of title I) f.o.b. vessels in United States ports, as he may request, for transfer (1) to any nation friendly to the United States in order to meet famine or other urgent relief requirements of such nation, and (2) to friendly but needy populations without regard to the friendliness of their government.

SEC. 202. The President may authorize the transfer on a grant basis of surplus agricultural commodities from Commodity Credit Corporation stocks to assist programs undertaken with friendly governments or through voluntary relief agencies: *Provided,* That the President shall take reasonable precaution that such transfers will not displace or interfere with sales which might otherwise be made.

SEC. 203. Not more than $300,000,000 (including the Corporation's investment in the commodities) shall be expended for all transfers, including delivery on board vessels in United States ports, under this title. The President may make such transfers through such agencies including intergovernmental organizations, in such manner, and upon such terms and conditions as he deems appropriate; he shall make use of the facilities of voluntary relief agencies to the extent practicable.

SEC. 204. No programs of assistance shall be undertaken under the authority of this title after June 30, 1957.

Title III — General Provisions

SEC. 301. Section 407 of the Agricultural Act of 1949 is amended by adding at the end thereof the following: "Notwithstanding the foregoing, the Corporation, on such terms and conditions as the Secretary may deem in the public interest, shall make available any farm commodity or product thereof owned or controlled by it for use in relieving distress (1) in any area in the United States declared by the President to be an acute distress area because of unemployment or other economic cause if the President finds that such use will not displace or interfere with normal marketing of agricultural commodities and (2) in connection with any major disaster determined by the President to warrant assistance by the Federal Government under Public Law 875, Eighty-first Congress, as amended (42 U.S.C. 1855). Except on a reimbursable basis, the Corporation shall not bear any costs in connection with making such commodity available beyond the cost of the commodities to the Corporation in store and the handling and transportation costs in making delivery of the commodity to designated agencies at one or more central locations in each State."

SEC. 302. Section 416 of the Agricultural Act of 1949 is amended to read as follows:

"SEC. 416. In order to prevent the waste of commodities acquired through price-support operations by the Commodity Credit Corporation before they can be disposed of in normal domestic channels without impairment of the price-support program or sold abroad at competitive world prices, the Commodity Credit Corporation is authorized, on such terms and under such regulations as the Secretary may deem in the public interest: (1) upon application, to make such commodities available to any Federal agency for use in making payment for commodities not produced in the United States; (2) to barter or exchange such commodities for strategic or other materials as authorized by law; (3) in the case of food commodities to donate such commodities to the Bureau of Indian Affairs and to such State, Federal, or private agency or agencies as may be designated by the proper State or Federal authority and approved by the Secretary, for use in the United States in nonprofit school-lunch programs, in the assistance of needy persons, and in charitable institutions, including hospitals, to the extent that needy persons are served; and (4) to donate any such food commodities in excess of anticipated disposition under (1), (2), and (3) above to nonprofit voluntary agencies registered with the Committee on Voluntary Foreign Aid of the Foreign Operations Administration or other appropriate department or agency of the Federal Government and intergovernmental organizations for use in the assistance of needy persons outside the United States. In the case of (3) and (4) above the Secretary shall obtain such assurance as he deems necessary that the recipients thereof will not diminish their normal expenditures for food by reason of such donation. In order to facilitate the appropriate disposal of such commodities, the Secretary may from time to time estimate and announce the quantity of such commodities which he anticipates will become available for distribution under (3) and (4) above. The Commodity Credit Corporation may pay, with respect to commodities disposed of under this section, reprocessing, packaging, transporting, handling, and other charges accruing up to the time of their delivery to a Federal agency or to the designated State or private agency, in the case of commodities made available for use within the United States, or their delivery free alongside ship or free on board export carrier at point of export, in the case of commodities made available for use outside the United States. For the purpose of this section the terms 'State' and 'United States' include the District of Columbia and any Territory or possession of the United States.''

SEC. 303. Whenever the Secretary has reason to believe that, in addition to other authorized methods and means of disposing of agricultural commodities owned by the Commodity Credit Corporation, there may be opportunity to protect the funds and assets of the Commodity Credit Corporation by barter or exchange of such agricultural commodities for (a) strategic materials entailing less risk of loss through deterioration or substantially less storage charges, or (b) materials, goods or equipment required in connection with foreign economic and military aid and assistance programs, or (c) materials or equipment required in substantial quantities for offshore construction programs, he is hereby directed to use every practicable means, in cooperation with other Government agencies, to arrange and make, through private trade channels, such barters or exchanges or to utilize the authority conferred on him by section 4 (h) of the Commodity Credit Corporation Charter Act, as amended, to make such barters or exchanges. Agencies of the United States Government procuring such materials, goods or equipment are hereby directed to cooperate with the Secretary in the disposal of surplus agricultural commodities by means of barter or exchange. Strategic materials so acquired by the Commodity Credit Corporation shall be considered as assets of the Corporation and other agencies of the Government, in purchasing strategic materials, shall purchase such materials from Commodity Credit Corporation inventories to the extent available in fulfillment of their requirements. The Secretary is also directed to assist, through such means as are available to him, farmers' cooperatives in effecting exchange of agricultural commodities in their possession for strategic materials.

SEC. 304. The President shall exercise the authority contained herein (1) to assist friendly nations to be independent of trade with the U.S.S.R. or nations dominated or controlled by the U.S.S.R. for food, raw materials and markets, and (2) to assure that agricultural commodities sold or transferred hereunder do not result in increased availability of those or like commodities to unfriendly nations.

Sec. 305. All Commodity Credit Corporation stocks disposed of under title II of this Act and section 416 of the Agricultural Act of 1949, as amended, shall be clearly identified by, as far as practical, appropriate marking on each package or container as being furnished by the people of the United States of America.

Approved July 10, 1954.

Pure Foods

From Charles W. Crawford, "The Long Fight for Pure Foods," U.S. Department of Agriculture, *Yearbook,* 1954 (Washington, 1954) pp. 211–20.

The first laws prohibiting tampering with foods and selling unwholesome provisions were enacted in ancient times. Early Mosaic and Egyptian laws governed the handling of meat. Greek and Roman laws attempted to prevent the watering of wine. In 200 B.C. India provided for the punishment of adulterators of grains and oils. In the same era China had agents to prohibit the making of spurious articles and the defrauding of purchasers. Most of our food laws, however, came to us as a heritage from our European forebears.

In early times foods were few and very simple, and trade existed mostly through barter. Such cheating as did occur was crude and easily detected by the prospective buyer. In the Middle Ages traders and merchants began to specialize and united themselves into guilds. One of the earliest was called the Pepperers — the spice traders of the day. The Pepperers soon absorbed the grocers and in England got a charter from the king as the Grocers' Company. They set up an ethical code designed to protect the integrity and quality of the spices and other foods sold. Later they appointed a corps of food inspectors to test and certify the merchandise sold to and by the grocers. These men were the first public food inspectors of England. Later on they became officers of the crown, and King Henry III made them custodians of the official weight standards.

Pepper is a good example of the trade practices that brought about the need for the food inspectors. The demand for pepper was widespread, as much for its perservative action as for its value as a condiment. Its price was high; it was handled by various people during its long journey from the Spice Islands to the grocer's shelf. Each handler had opportunity to debase it; the grinders had the best chance, and made the most of it, since adulterants could not be detected in the ground spices by methods then available. Worthless barks and seeds, iron ore, charcoal, nutshells and olive pits, and coconut shell at times were ground along with the pepper berries.

Bread was another food that offered temptation to unscrupulous bakers. The most common cheat was short weight, but at times the flour used contained ground dried peas or beans. In fact, sharp practices by members of the Bakers' Guild brought about the passage of the first protective food law on record. Known as the

Assize of Bread, it was proclaimed by King John of England in 1202. A quotation from the law, rewritten into modern English, shows the type of punishment meted to violators:

"If any default be found in the bread of a baker of this city, the first time let him be drawn upon a hurdle, from the Guild hall to his own house, through the greatest streets, where the most people are assembled, and through the streets which are most dirty, the false loaf hanging from his neck; if a second time he shall be found committing the same offense, he shall be placed in a pillory, and remain there at least an hour."

A third offense banished him from his Guild. At times the magistrate ordered a bakery to be torn down and the culprit banished from the city.

In the fifteenth century the explorers opened up the era of colonial expansion. New luxuries — such as tea, coffee, chocolate, and sugar — began to arrive at home ports. Some of these commodities, coffee and tea in particular, seem to have been adulterated from the beginning. They came from countries whose traders had developed skillful and novel methods of adulteration. The Chinese suppliers added to tea destined for export such things as dried leaves from other plants, sand, clay, and even dried spent tea leaves ingeniously dyed and rolled to look like freshly dried tea. The importers further stretched the tea with leaves from their own trees (completely unlike tea leaves) and spent tea leaves from their coffee houses and inns.

Coffee has a similar history; chicory, roasted turnips, barley, acorns, beans, and mahogany sawdust were used as adulterants.

The crown's first interest in this situation came from its loss of excise revenues; more tea and coffee were being served in England than had been taxed at the ports. A law passed in 1718 imposed a fine of 20 pounds for adding foreign substances to coffee.

The nineteenth century in England brought developments in the central processing of foods and with it new forms of adulteration, some of them definitely dangerous to health, such as mineral pigments in candy and spices; and opium, nux vomica, and picrotoxin added to beer to conceal the addition of water. Publication of the scientific findings in the popular and medical journals resulted in the appointment of a committee of Parliament to investigate the extent of such adulteration, both dangerous to health and to the consumer's purse. This resulted in the enactment in 1860 of the Adulteration to Food and Drink Act, the first general food law of England.

The first general food laws in the United States were enacted by the States, Massachusetts leading the way in 1784. California enacted a pure food and drink law in 1850, a year after the Gold Rush. Most of the States had Laws of this type by 1900, along with additional laws on special foods, many of them enacted to protect the farmers' basic commodities from competition with adulterated wares. Conditions paralleled those in nineteenth century England. New York inspectors in 1875 found 52 percent of the butter, 56 percent of the olive oil, and 64 percent of the brandy they examined to be adulterated. A Boston Health Department report in 1880 stated that 46 percent of the colored candies sampled contained lead chromate.

Little uniformity existed under the State laws; foods legal in one State might be banned by its neighbors.

The State chemists were among the first to advocate a Federal law to bring order into the chaos.

The pioneer who waged the most effective fight for Federal pure food laws was Dr. Harvey W. Wiley, who came from Indiana in 1883 to be chief chemist of the United States Department of Agriculture. Long interested in the composition of foods, he immediately assigned some of his staff to the problems of food adulteration. Soon a series of Government bulletins emerged; the most important was the 1,417-page Chemistry Bulletin 13, issued in 10 parts from 1887 to 1902, as *Foods and Food Adulterants*.

The first Federal food and drug bill was introduced into Congress in 1879, but the real fight for such legislation began about 1900 and lasted until the law was enacted 6 years later.

By that time the factory preparation of food had become big business, with each manufacturer a law unto himself, as far as the Federal Government was concerned. He could put whatever he chose into his wares, and his only labeling guides were his conscience and his competitor's practices. Few processors knew or cared about sanitation in those days, and commercial refrigeration was in its infancy.

Dr. Wiley, a born crusader, took his message to the public. He became a popular speaker before women's clubs and other organized groups. Reporters began to write front-page stories, which aroused consumers to the danger to their own health inherent in the debased foods of the day. Particularly interesting to the public were reports on the progress of Dr. Wiley's "poison squad," a group of young chemists who volunteered to be "guinea pigs" for a full year and eat nothing but the food prepared in the Bureau of Chemistry laboratories with measured doses of the chemicals prevalent in the prepared food of that period — formaldehyde, benzoate of soda, boric acid, and salicylates. Dr. Wiley became popularly known as "Old Borax."

Stories about medicines in national magazines alarmed every mother and homemaker — reports of infants' soothing sirups containing morphine and opium, of people who became narcotic addicts from the use of medicines with an innocent appearance, of women's tonics that depended on alcohol for their bracing effects, of the tragic consequences to those depending on the cure-all promises of the patent medicines on every drugstore shelf.

In 1906 a chapter in Upton Sinclair's *The Jungle* aroused the public with its graphic exposé of revolting conditions in the Chicago stockyards and packinghouses.

Mark Sullivan, in *Our Times,* wrote:

"The women of the country were ripe for the crusade. Enough of them had lived through the transition from home and village food-industry, to large-scale corporation food-industry, to know the taste, odor, and sight of pure products of nature; and to recognize that in what they were now obliged to buy, and what they could not avoid feeding their children, there were elements new and mysterious, and therefore disquieting. These women, by the support they gave Doctor Wiley, by the pressure they brought upon Congress — without votes, without ever thinking they needed votes — did a work greater than anything that women accomplished or attempted during the eight years after women got the suffrage in 1919."

From 1879, when the first Federal pure food bill was introduced, until the law was finally enacted, Congress considered 103 food bills. It passed a tea importation act in 1883, and in 1890 acts prohibiting the *importation* of adulterated food and the certification of certain meat products processed for exportation. In 1891 and 1895 it extended meat inspection to partial protection of domestic consumers by requiring inspection of animals for disease before slaughter.

Despite bitter opposition, the crusade was finally ended when Congress passed the Food and Drugs Act and the Meat Inspection Act. Both were signed on June 30, 1906, by President Theodore Roosevelt, who had fought valiantly for their passage.

Both laws went to the Department of Agriculture for enforcement by the Bureaus, which had small staffs to administer the limited laws enacted in the 1890's — the Food and Drugs Act to the Bureau of Chemistry and the Meat Inspection Act to the Bureau of Animal Industry.

The enforcement of the Food and Drugs Act, which went into effect in 1907, was a stunning blow to the doctrine of *caveat emptor*. Both the Bureau of Chemistry and the affected industries recognized that the new slogan was to be "public interest comes first."

During the first year, before any cases were prosecuted in the courts, the Bureau set up a series of laboratories throughout the country, supplementing the port laboratories already in operation to keep any adulterated foreign products from entering the country. A corps of inspectors was appointed to collect samples of the foods and drugs shipped in interstate commerce. Chemists at Washington headquarters were busy devising new chemical and microscopic methods to supplement the woefully few then available for objective tests of the samples deluging the laboratories.

The industries, too, were putting their houses in order to live with the new law. Labels had to be changed to declare chemical preservatives in processed foods, and to give consumers other information the law required for intelligent purchasing. Almost immediately the processors encountered buyer resistance to foods labeled as containing chemicals that the public suspected would do them no good. The Bureau of Chemistry sent experts into the field to demonstrate how foods could be preserved without chemicals by employing adequate sanitation and suitable raw stock. The processors who adopted those practices found a new, enthusiastic market and prospered. Many others fell into line, preferring to abandon preservatives rather than to declare them on their labels.

In general, factory conditions improved during this period, for it was an era of awakening to the concepts of modern sanitation. The sanitary requirements in meatpacking establishments and the suggestions of Food and Drug inspectors in the plants to which they were admitted (the law did not compel their admission) played no small part in the trend toward the production of cleaner food. Seizures of unfit products in the channels of trade also encouraged more attention to sanitation.

Some compromises had to be made to enact the 1906 law, but for its time it was a good law — the strongest in the world. However, the era of food industrialization had just begun. By the turn of the century there had been a marked change from home production to bulk distribution. The next 25 years brought the package age — not only a change from the cracker barrel to the sealed carton, but from the delicatessen tray to jars and cans. These foods were better protected from contamination, but their contents were concealed from the inspection of the purchaser. More informative labeling was in order.

Other protections to the food consumer were needed, also — official standards defining the composition of basic food products, compulsory sanitary inspection of factories, heavier penalties for illegal practices, a ban on inherent poisons in food as well as added ones.

Stronger controls were needed in the drug field, also, and there was no Federal regulation of therapeutic devices and cosmetics, despite the injurious nature of many products on the market.

Some of the early deficiencies were pointed out by the chief chemist of the Bureau of Chemistry soon after the 1906 act went into effect, and others from year to year as conditions developed that required greater consumer protection.

Meanwhile, a separate enforcement agency was formed in 1927. It employed the staff of the Bureau of Chemistry assigned to administer the Food and Drugs Act. First known as the Food, Drug, and Insecticide Administration, its name was changed in 1931 to the Food and Drug Administration.

President Franklin D. Roosevelt gave a new impetus in 1933 to the reforms the Food and Drug officials had been calling for. A 5-year struggle for a stronger and more inclusive law finally culminated in passage of the Copeland bill in 1938. The best features of the 1906 act were retained, but the new law covered new conditions that had developed and put teeth into the enforcement provisions that had proved weak in the past.

There was little crusading in newspapers and periodicals for the passage of this stronger law such as that which had played so important a part in enactment of the Wiley bill in 1906.

Consumer groups, particularly the large national women's organizations, took up the fight, just as they had done for the first national law a generation earlier. They aroused public thinking on this subject in the cities, towns, and villages throughout the land, despite the general apathy of the press.

The Food, Drug, and Cosmetic Act of 1938 stands today, amended as weaknesses revealed by court decisions or changing conditions (such as the development of antibiotics, which required predistribution testing) were pointed out to Congress. This continuous process of keeping the law alive to the needs of the public should preclude another complete overhaul such as that necessary in 1938.

The new law made instantly effective the provisions designed to protect the public against dangerous drugs, devices, and cosmetics. As originally enacted, the statute was to become fully effective on June 25, 1939. This date was extended by amendment to January 1940, for the new labeling provisions and certain other requirements, with restricted authorization for additional postponements until July 1, 1940. Its complete coverage followed by a day the transfer of the Food and Drug Administration from the Department of Agriculture to the Federal Security Agency. All of the powers vested in the Secretary of Agriculture in the enforcement of the Food, Drug, and Cosmetic Act, the Tea Act, the Caustic Poison Act, the Import Milk Act, and Filled Milk Act were concurrently transferred to the Federal Security Administrator. In 1953 this Agency became the Department of Health, Education, and Welfare.

Where do we stand today in the fight for pure foods? The American public has the best and safest food in its history. We are no longer dependent on geographical location or season to have an abundant choice of nutritious food at any grocery store in the land. We cannot afford to be complacent, however, as we view the advances of the past half century. Most food is perishable or subject to the depredations of insects or rodents at some stage in its processing or distribution. Constant changes in producing and processing methods require comparable development in the regulatory field. There is wide variation among the industries subject to Federal food laws. Some are highly advanced technologically, with excellent control over the factors that lead to violative food, and others still employ methods unsuited to the protection of foods for human consumption.

With only a few hundred inspectors and analysis to cover the operations of 96,000 establishments that are producing and warehousing the commodities subject to the Federal Food, Drug, and Cosmetic Act, spot checking is the only course available. Violations involving direct danger to health receive first consideration in planning enforcement operations. Filth and decomposition are next in importance — and first in the amount of enforcement time actually allotted. Economic cheats affect the consumer's pocketbook, but they can be given relatively little attention. Coverage of the first two categories is woefully incomplete. It is possible to examine and inspect only a small fraction of 1 percent of the total production each year.

Conditions in food factories as a whole have shown progressive improvement throughout the history of enforcement of Federal food laws. The procurement of fit raw materials continues to be a problem. Milk and grain, for example, originate in thousands of farms that ordinarily make no interstate shipments. They are delivered to small collection centers — elevators or cream stations — and the intermingling of lots continues until large deliveries are made to the processors, whose business may be nationwide. The problem is to improve handling and storage conditions at the farms, then to protect the products at each step of the way. Such precautions are equally needed for our fresh produce, which is sometimes handled in city wholesale markets under reprehensible sanitary conditions. The Federal pure food laws can never substitute for adequate local protection of our food.

Another limitation of food protection today, under laws against false labeling and advertising, is the inability to curb the practice of nutritional quackery. Self-styled nutritionists are distorting the facts of the real advances of the science of nutrition and menacing the health of ailing and misinformed persons by making unwarranted therapeutic claims for various "food supplements." People who should be spending their money for readily available and adequate foods, and for competent medical care, frequently divert it to the faddist items promoted by food quacks. This tribe of nutritional pitchmen base their sales talk on myths about soil depletion, misconceptions regarding food processing, and falsely alarming exaggerations about "sub-clinical deficiencies" in the diet.

The food quack has something to sell, but usually he is fully enough aware of Federal laws to keep his claims and promises off food labels. He frequently confines his false teachings to books, magazine articles, and oral promotion which cannot be linked with a commercial scheme of distributing the product. The purchasing public must set up its own defenses against such exploitation.

On the chemical front, the fight for pure foods has been waged in two major battles. The first was a struggle against the recognized poisons used in and on our foods in the past. After passage of the 1906 law, widespread use of formaldehyde and boric acids to preserve foods was soon abandoned. The chief chemist reported in 1909 that a large number of prominent manufacturers had "entirely abandoned the use of any kind of preservatives and openly announced their adhesion to the doctrine that drugs should not be placed in foods."

Arsenic was found in early samples of baking powder, confectioners' glaze, and a few other processed foods, added inadvertently because it was so commonly used in the manufacture of phosphates and phosphoric acid and other commercial preparations purchased by food processors. The primary fight against arsenic and lead occurred in the late 1920's and during the 1930's when those chemicals were widely used as orchard sprays to control insect damage. After turbulent protests against seizures of fruits bearing excess residues when they reached the market, the growers installed washing equipment recommended by State and Federal officials and found that with the exercise of adequate precautions on spray schedules and removal of residues above the informal tolerances set by the Secretary of Agriculture, they could still protect their crops without violating the pure food laws.

Stronger provisions to prohibit or control the known poisons that might contaminate foods were included in the 1938 act. Soon after the new law went into effect, however, and before all of its regulatory provisions could be employed, the Second World War began. With it came an accelerated development of chemicals needed for military supplies in all parts of the world. The second struggle in the cause of pure foods was against chemicals with unknown potentialities.

New insecticides, new packaging and preservative materials, and many other necessary adjuncts of modern warfare were accepted after preliminary tests showed they were safe for emergency use — a calculated risk. There was not time for the 2- or 3-year chronic toxicity tests, without which a pharmacologist could not venture an opinion as to long-range safety in the diet of the general public. Such tests were in progress, but most of the new materials were restricted to temporary military purposes, and permanent, unrestricted use in a civilian economy was a problem of the future.

The end of the war released not only these chemicals but many other new substances developed for technical purposes but later adapted to food uses. Much progress has been made in the study of their long-range effect if ingested day by day in our food supply but there is still much to be learned about them. Additional products continue to appear, much more rapidly than the Food and Drug Administration can study them.

A succession of obviously poisonous additives have been removed from the markets — beer containing fluorine; soft drinks, wine, beer, salad dressings, and sirups containing monochloracetic acid and the quaternary ammonium compounds; frozen peaches with thiourea added as an antioxidant; cheese wrapped in papers impregnated with dehydroacetic acid to prevent spoilage; and numerous other foods containing substances that have been proved deleterious and not required in good production or manufacturing practice. The courts have ruled that it is not necessary to prove that such added poisons are present in the food in injurious amounts. The Government has the burden of proof that the substance is deleterious — and this may take several years of investigation, while the product is being used, with the public serving as "guinea pigs."

In December 1952 a circuit court ruled that the Government may exclude ingredients from standardized foods if there is doubt as to their safety. The court said: "One making a rule for the future which in practical effect will determine whether millions of people shall eat something every day may reasonably refuse to subject the general public to even slight risks and small deceptions."

The Congress, through the Select Committee on Chemicals in Foods, held hearings in 1951 and 1952 to determine whether the public is receiving adequate protection from chemicals used in foods. In a report issued in 1952, it concluded that the Food, Drug, and Cosmetic Act should be amended to require that new chemicals in food be cleared for safety in advance of distribution, similar to the practice established by law in 1938 for new drugs. This would place on the producer the responsibility for establishing evidence of safety.

The Second World War brought a great change in the insecticides and pesticides used to protect food crops. Arsenic, lead, and fluorine, the poisonous sprays of the past, gave way to DDT and its newer cousins. Hearings were conducted by the Federal Security Agency from January to September 1950 to establish residue tolerances for all of the substances required in the production of all classes of food crops. In investigating the problems of poisoning pests without poisoning people, the Food and Drug Administration has received the close cooperation of the Public Health Service, several units of the Department of Agriculture, and many State agencies.

The 1938 act gave a new impetus to sanitation in our food supply. It expanded the definition of adulteration to include production or storage under insanitary conditions that *may* result in contamination with filth. Previously, actions against filthy foods had to be based on contamination that could be detected in the product of the market place. Sanitary inspection of factories gained a new importance in food regulation — not only as an enforcement tool, but also for its educational value.

FDA inspectors invite the management to accompany them during the factory inspection and, when it is completed, leave a written report to the management on observations of insanitary conditions. Usually their constructive suggestions are adopted, and if objectionable products are on hand they are not shipped for human food use. A minority disregard the inspectors' warnings and suffer subsequent seizures of their goods and criminal prosecutions for continued carelessness in preparing food for the use of human beings.

Approximately 80 percent of the court actions involving foods each year are based on filth or decomposition. Major causes have been contamination by insects and rodents, and the use of unfit materials, such as decomposed or high-sediment milk, fruits and vegetables with the spoiled parts not adequately trimmed, and fish and eggs frozen after decomposition had set in.

The effectiveness of FDA's efforts toward a cleaner food supply was threatened by two court decisions. The first temporary setback came in February 1947, when the Supreme Court refused to review an appellate court decision which denied Federal jurisdiction over foods that became contaminated during storage after interstate shipment. An amendment in June 1948 closed this breach in the statute, and assured jurisdiction over adulteration and misbranding of interstate goods until they are delivered to the consumer.

The second came late in 1952 with a Supreme Court ruling that the language of the statute did not give the Government the right to make factory inspections without permission of the owner or manager. The immediate reaction of responsible producers was to invite continued factory inspections, making it abundantly clear that they were a burden only to careless and willful violators rather than to producers with pride in the quality of their merchandise. Early in 1953 amendments to correct this serious threat to law enforcement were introduced into Congress by members of both political parties. The President, in his State of the Union address, urged prompt action to restore FDA's factory inspection powers. Spokesmen of most of the trade associations of the food, drug, and cosmetic industries assured their support of prompt remedial legislation. This was enacted in August 1953.

To protect consumers against economic cheats, the 1906 Food and Drugs Act prohibited shipment of foods adulterated with inferior ingredients, and misbranded with false labeling. The 1938 law provided that labels should be informative — the whole truth, rather than merely a prohibition against dishonest claims of composition.

One of the most important sections of the new law provided for establishing of legal definitions and standards for foods, wherever in the opinion of the Secretary they are needed to "promote honesty and fair dealing in the interest of consumers." The statute calls for a very democratic process in establishing such standards, with every interested party, producer and consumer alike, invited to participate in public hearings and to comment on the proposed standards before the specifications for each item are determined. After such standards become final, foods failing to comply are in violation of the act and are subject to court action.

Food standards are the cornerstone of effective protection of consumers against many economic food cheats. They likewise protect the honest manufacturer and dealer from unfair competition. The standard is a yardstick for the manufacturer and the law-enforcement official alike. While the housewife may not know the exact specifications for any standardized food, she can be confident when she buys a standardized food by name. She knows the law-abiding manufacturer follows the specifications, and that the Government has an effective basis for legal action against the cheating or careless minority that does not comply.

Water is still the commonest adulterant of foods. Court actions in 1952 involved watered oysters, low-fat butter, and frozen turkeys with an average of a quart of water injected into the flesh before freezing. In other instances a 7- to 10-percent ice glaze was produced on poultry by packing wet birds in plastic bags before freezing.

The greatest incidence of fraudulent adulterations came in wartime when food was scarce and many items were rationed. Substitutes and "extenders" appeared on the market, some in disguise and others legally labeled for what they were. Such things appeared on the market as "victory butter," containing only 30 percent butterfat instead of the 80 percent the law demands; an eggless egg substitute; coffee diluted with roasted cereals and even the exhausted grounds found in precontrol days; french dressing devoid of salad oil; and coconut-peanut candy with corn flakes substituted for the coconut and processed wheat for the peanuts. Any product labeled "olive oil" was suspect, for the adulteration of olive oil is an ancient pursuit, even when there is a free flow of imports. Rationing of food oils induced many a mineral oil substitute — a good example of an economic adulteration with a direct bearing on public health. Spices, always subject to adulteration, became much more of a problem when imports of many items were cut off.

Throughout those trying times, however, the general integrity of our food supply was maintained. Enforcement was aimed to insure honest labeling and no concessions were made for expediency that would lower public confidence. As a result, there were few problems in resuming the higher standards of a postwar economy, although high prices prevalent since that period have been tempting to the unscrupulous to take any advantage of the buyer.

There will always be a regulatory problem in the economic adulteration field as long as one product closely resembles another selling at a higher price. A recent example has been the conviction of horsemeat racketeers who removed all required labeling and markings from horsemeat to sell it at triple the price as beef. In a somewhat similar fraud, "butterleggers" surreptitiously repackaged oleomargarine and labeled it as butter, selling for more than twice as much.

The Federal Food, Drug, and Cosmetic Act covers animal feeds and veterinary remedies as well as products for human use. These controls are of great value to the farmer. He depends on the labeled protein content of feeds to determine both the price he should pay and the feeding schedules he should adopt. He is also protected from worthless animal and poultry remedies which, if used, may result in serious loss of stock that could be saved with proper medication.

The story of the fight for pure foods would not be complete without recognition of the part played by the men behind the lines — the chemists, microanalysts, biologists, bacteriologists, and pharmacologists who have developed the objective evidence that has made possible the progress of the past half century. Before a pharmacologist can test the effects of minute daily doses of a substance on laboratory animals, the chemist must develop methods to isolate and measure them. The bacteriologist must study the effects of bacterial contamination of foods, how it occurs, and how it can be prevented. The biochemist has basic responsibilities in the nutritional value of foods, not only in devising testing methods, but in guiding administrative decisions as to enrichment of products and the validity of labeling claims.

In the struggle for pure food, the Food and Drug Administration has had valiant allies in other Federal groups, in State and local enforcement officers, and in the responsible elements of the regulated industries.

The Bureau of Animal Industry, fortified by the Meat Inspection Act of June 30, 1906, continued its elimination of diseased animals brought to slaughter, but added to it post mortem examinations by veterinarians, of slaughtered animals and parts. It was also provided sanitary controls over slaughtering houses and supervision of all meat condemned by its inspectors. All unprocessed meat shipped in interstate commerce now bears the stamp "U.S. Inspected and Passed," and processed meat products are labeled "U.S. Inspected and Passed by Department of Agriculture."

The Public Health Service of the Department of Health, Education, and Welfare establishes uniform sanitary codes used by local health departments in the control of the sanitation of restaurants, and has a comprehensive program to reduce or prevent pollution of the Nation's waters.

State and city officials enforce their own laws and ordinances controlling products distributed within State lines, and work closely with Federal control officials in the planning and operation of food-protective measures that neither could accomplish alone.

Last, but not least, has been the constructive work of the food industry to produce better, purer foods. Its members have drawn themselves into associations which have improved their products, both by sanitation campaigns and collective research to solve technical problems common to all. Most American food manufacturers today have the will and the know-how to produce the pure foods that the public wants. They accept the Food, Drug, and Cosmetic Act as a blueprint of their obligations to the Nation's consumers. *(Charles W. Crawford.)*

Agricultural Act of 1954

From 68 Statutes at Large 897.

Title 1 — Set Aside of Agricultural Commodities

SEC. 101. The Commodity Credit Corporation shall, as rapidly as the Secretary of Agriculture shall determine to be practicable, set aside within its inventories not more than the following maximum quantities and not less than the following minimum quantities of agricultural commodities or products thereof heretofore or hereafter acquired by it from 1954 and prior years' crops and production in connection with its price support operations:

Commodity	Maximum quantity	Minimum quantity
Wheat (bushels)	500,000,000	400,000,000
Upland Cotton (bales)	4,000,000	3,000,000
Cottonseed oil (pounds)	500,000,000	0
Butter (pounds)	200,000,000	0
Nonfat dry milk solids (pounds)	300,000,000	0
Cheese (pounds)	150,000,000	0

Such quantities shall be known as the "commodity set-aside".

SEC. 102. Quantities of commodities shall not be included in the commodity set-aside which have an aggregate value in excess of $2,500,000,000. The value of the commodities placed in the commodity set-aside, for the purpose of this section, shall be the Corporation's investment in such commodities as of the date they are included in the commodity set-aside, as determined by the Secretary.

SEC. 103. (a) Such commodity set-aside shall be reduced by disposals made in accordance with the directions of the President as follows:

(1) Donation, sale, or other disposition for disaster or other relief purposes outside the United States pursuant to and subject to the limitations of title II of the Agricultural Trade Development and Assistance Act of 1954;

(2) Sale or barter (including barter for strategic materials) to develop new or expanded markets for American agricultural commodities, including but not limited to disposition pursuant to and subject to the limitations of title I of the Agricultural Trade Development and Assistance Act of 1954;

(3) Donation to school-lunch programs;

(4) Transfer to the national stockpile established pursuant to the Act of June 7, 1939, as amended (50 U.S.C. 98–98h), without reimbursement from funds appropriated for the purposes of that Act;

(5) Donation, sale, or other disposition for research, experimental, or educational purposes;

(6) Donation, sale, or other disposition for disaster relief purposes in the United States or to meet any national emergency declared by the President; and

(7) Sale for unrestricted use to meet a need for increased supplies at not less than 105 per centum of the parity price in the case of agricultural commodities and a price reflecting 105 per centum of the parity price of the agricultural commodity in the case of products of agricultural commodities.

The President shall prescribe such terms and conditions for the disposal of commodities in the commodity set-aside as he determines will provide adequate safeguards against interference with normal marketings of the supplies of such commodities outside the commodity set-aside. Strategic materials acquired by the Commodity Credit Corporation under paragraph (2) of this subsection shall be transferred to the national stockpile established pursuant to the Act of June 7, 1939, as amended, and the Commodity Credit Corporation shall be reimbursed for the value of the commodities bartered for such strategic materials from funds appropriated pursuant to section 8 of such Act of June 7, 1939, as amended. For the purpose of such reimbursement, the value of any commodity so bartered shall be the lower of the domestic market price or the Commodity Credit Corporation's investment therein as of the date of such barter, as determined by the Secretary of Agriculture.

(b) The quantity of any commodity in the commodity set-aside shall be reduced to the extent that the Commodity Credit Corporation inventory of such commodity is reduced, by natural or other cause beyond the control of the Corporation, below the quantity then charged to the commodity set-aside.

Sec. 104. (a) The Corporation shall have authority to sell, without regard to section 103 (a) (7) hereof, any commodity covered by the commodity set-aside for the purpose of rotating stocks or consolidating inventories, any such sale to be offset by purchase of the same commodity in a substantially equivalent quantity or of a substantially equivalent value:

(b) Dispositions pursuant to this title shall not be subject to the pricing limitations of section 407 of the Agricultural Act of 1949, as amended.

Sec. 105. The quantity of any commodity in the commodity set-aside or transferred from the set-aside to the national stockpile established pursuant to the Act of June 7, 1939, as amended (50 U.S.C. 98–98h) shall be excluded from the computation of "carryover" for the purpose of determining the price support level for such commodity under the Agricultural Act of 1949, as amended, and related legislation, but shall be included in the computation of total supplies for purposes of acreage allotments and marketing quotas under the Agricultural Adjustment Act of 1938, as amended, and related legislation. Until such time as the commodity set-aside has been completed, such quantity of the commodity as the Secretary shall determine between the maximum and minimum quantities specified in section 101 of this Act shall be excluded from the computations of "carryover" for the purpose of determining the price support level, but shall be included in the computation of total supplies for purposes of acreage allotments and marketing quotas, for the 1955 crop of the commodity, notwithstanding that the quantity so excluded may not have been acquired by the Corporation and included in the commodity set-aside.

SEC. 106. The Commodity Credit Corporation shall keep such records and accounts as may be necessary to show, for each commodity set-aside, the initial and current composition, value (in accordance with section 102), current investment, quantity disposed of, method of disposition, and amounts received on disposition.

SEC. 107. In order to make payment to the Commodity Credit Corporation for any commodities transferred to the national stockpile pursuant to section 103 (a) (4) of this Act, there are hereby authorized to be appropriated amounts equal to the value of any commodities so transferred. The value of any commodity so transferred, for the purpose of this section, shall be the lower of the domestic market price or the Commodity Credit Corporation's investment there of the date of transfer to the stockpile, as determined by the Secretary of Agriculture.

Title II — Amendments to Agricultural Act of 1949, as Amended, and Related Legislation

SEC. 201. (a) Section 101 (d) (6) of the Agricultural Act of 1949 is amended to read as follows:

"(6) Except as provided in subsection (c) and section 402, the level of support to cooperators shall be not more than 90 per centum and not less than 82½ per centum of the parity price for the 1955 crop of any basic agricultural commodity with respect to which producers have not disapproved marketing quotas; within such limits, the minimum level of support shall be fixed as provided in subsections (a) and (b) of this section."

(b) Section 101 (d) of the Agricultural Act of 1949 (7 U.S.C., sec. 1441 (d) is amended by adding at the end thereof the following new paragraph:

"(7) Where a State is designated under section 335 (e) of the Agricultural Adjustment Act of 1938, as amended, as outside the commercial wheat-producing area for any crop of wheat, the level of price support for wheat to cooperators in such State for such crop of wheat shall be 75 per centum of the level of price support to cooperators in the commercial wheat-producing area."

SEC. 202. Section 101 (f) of the Agricultural Act of 1949, as amended, is amended by deleting in the first sentence thereof everything following the word "except" and inserting in lieu thereof the following: "that, notwithstanding any of the foregoing provisions of section 101 of this Act, the level of support to cooperators for the 1955 and each subsequent crop of extra long staple cotton, if producers have not disapproved marketing quotas therefor, shall be the minimum level specified in section 101 (b) of this Act for the supply percentage for extra long staple cotton as of the beginning of the marketing year for the crop."

SEC. 203. (a) Section 201 of the Agricultural Act of 1949 (7 U.S.C. 1446), as amended, is amended (1) by deleting "Irish potatoes," from the first sentence thereof, and (2) by deleting from subsection (b) thereof "tung nuts, honey, and early, intermediate and late Irish potatoes" and inserting in lieu thereof "tung nuts and honey".

(b) Section 5 of the Act of March 31, 1950 (7 U.S.C. 1450), as amended by section 5 (a) of Public Law 290, Eighty-third Congress, is repealed.

SEC. 204. (a) The production and use of abundant supplies of high quality milk and dairy products are essential to the health and general welfare of the Nation: a dependable domestic source of supply of these foods in the form of high grade dairy herds and modern, sanitary dairy equipment is important to the national defense; and an economically sound dairy industry affects beneficially the economy of the country as a whole. It is the policy of Congress to assure a stabilized annual production of adequate supplies of milk and dairy products, to promote the increased use of these essential foods; to improve the domestic source of supply of milk and butterfat by encouraging dairy farmers to develop efficient production units consisting of high-grade, disease-free cattle and modern sanitary equipment; and to stabilize the economy of dairy farmers at a level which will provide a fair return for their labor and investment when compared with the cost of things that farmers buy.

(b) Section 201 (c) of the Agricultural Act of 1949, as amended, is amended to read as follows:

"(c) The price of whole milk, butterfat, and the products of such commodities, respectively, shall be supported at such level not in excess of 90 per centum nor less than 75 per centum of the parity price therefor as the Secretary determines necessary in order to assure an adequate supply. Such price support shall be provided through loans on, or purchases of, milk and the products of milk and butterfat, and for the period ending March 31, 1956, surplus stocks of dairy products owned by the Commodity Credit Corporation may be disposed of by any methods determined necessary by the Secretary. Beginning September 1, 1954, and ending June 30, 1956, not to exceed $50,000,000 annually of funds of the Commodity Credit Corporation shall be used to increase the consumption of fluid milk by children in non-profit schools of high school grade and under."

(c) In order to prevent the accumulation of excessive inventories of dairy products the Secretary of Agriculture shall undertake domestic disposal programs under authorities granted in the Agricultural Adjustment Act of 1938 and the Agricultural Act of 1949, as amended, or as otherwise authorized by law.

(d) Title II of the Agricultural Act of 1949, as amended, is amended by adding at the end thereof the following:

"SEC. 202. As a means of increasing the utilization of dairy products, (including for purposes of this section, milk) upon the certification by the Administrator of Veterans' Affairs or by the Secretary of the Army, acting for the military departments under the Department of Defense's Single Service Purchase Assignment for Subsistence, or their duly authorized representatives that the usual quantities of dairy products have been purchased in the normal channels of trade —

"(a) The Commodity Credit Corporation until December 31, 1956, shall make available to the Administrator of Veterans' Affairs at warehouses where dairy products are stored, such dairy products acquired under price-support programs as the Administrator certifies that he requires in order to provide butter and cheese and other dairy products as a part of the ration in hospitals under his jurisdiction. The Administrator shall report monthly to the Committees on Agriculture of the Senate and House of Representatives and the Secretary of Agriculture the amount of dairy products used under this subsection.

"(b) The Commodity Credit Corporation until December 31, 1956, shall make available to the Secretary of the Army, at warehouses where dairy products are stored, such dairy products acquired under price-support programs as the Secretary of the Army or his duly authorized representative certifies can be utilized in order to provide additional butter and cheese and other dairy products as a part of the ration of the Army, Navy, or Air Force, and as a part of the ration in hospitals under the jurisdiction of the Department of Defense. The Secretary of the Army shall report every six months to the Committees on Agriculture of the Senate and the House of Representatives and the Secretary of Agriculture the amount of dairy products used under this subsection.

"(c) Dairy products made available under this section shall be made available without charge, except that the Secretary of the Army or the Administrator of Veterans' Affairs shall pay the Commodity Credit Corporation the costs of packaging incurred in making such products so available.

"(d) The obligation of the Commodity Credit Corporation to make dairy products available pursuant to the above shall be limited to dairy products acquired by the Corporation through price-support operations and not disposed of under provisions (1) and (2) of section 416 of this Act, as amended."

(e) As a means of stabilizing the dairy industry and further suppressing and eradicating brucellosis in cattle the Secretary is authorized to transfer not to exceed $15,000,000 annually for a period of two years from funds available to the Commodity Credit Corporation to the appropriation item "Plant and Animal Disease and Pest Control" in the Department of Agriculture Appropriation Act, 1955, for the purpose of accelerating the brucellosis eradication program, for the purpose of increasing to not to exceed $50 per head of cattle the amount of the indemnities paid by the Federal Government for cattle destroyed because of brucellosis in connection with cooperative control and eradication programs for such disease in cattle entered into by the Secretary under the authority of the Act of May 29, 1884, as amended, for the purpose of increasing the number of such indemnities, and for the purpose of defraying any additional administrative expenses in connection therewith. There is hereby authorized to be appropriated annually such sums as may be necessary to reimburse the Commodity Credit Corporation for expenditures pursuant to this section.

(f) The Secretary of Agriculture is directed to make a study of the various methods of production control and of the various methods of price support which could be made applicable to milk and butterfat and their products, including programs to be operated and financed by dairymen; and to submit to Congress on or before the 3d day of January, 1955, a detailed report thereof showing among other things the probable costs and effects of each type of operation studied and the legislation, if any, needed to put it into effect. The purpose of the study and report is to develop basic material which can be used by Congress in formulating an improved agricultural program for milk and butterfat and their products. Alternative programs are to be submitted for consideration by Congress and for possible submission to a referendum of dairy farmers. The Secretary may conduct such hearings and receive such statements and briefs in connection with such study as he deems appropriate.

SEC. 206. Section 401 (c) of the Agricultural Act of 1949, as amended (7 U.S.C. 1421), is amended by adding, at the end thereof, the following: "In administering any program for diverted acres the Secretary may make his regulations applicable on an appropriate geographical basis. Such regulations shall be administered (1) in semiarid or other areas where good husbandry requires maintenance of a prudent feed reserve in such manner as to permit, to the extent so required by good husbandry, the production of forage crops for storage and subsequent use either on the farm or in feeding operations of the farm operator, and (2) in areas declared to be disaster areas by the President under Public Law 875, Eighty-first Congress, in such manner as will most quickly restore the normal pattern of their agriculture."

SEC. 207. Section 401 of the Agricultural Act of 1949, as amended, is amended by adding thereto the following new subsection:

"(e) Whenever any price support or surplus removal operation for any agricultural commodity is carried out through purchases from or loans or payments to processors, the Secretary shall, to the extent practicable, obtain from the processors such assurances as he deems adequate that the producers of the agricultural commodity involved have received or will receive maximum benefits from the price support or surplus removal operation."

SEC. 208. Notwithstanding the provisions of section 407 of the Agricultural Act of 1949, as amended, or of any other law, the Commodity Credit Corporation is authorized until March 1, 1955, to sell at the point of storage any feed grain owned by the Corporation at 10 per centum above the current support price for the commodity.

SEC. 209. Section 408 (b) of the Agricultural Act of 1949 (7 U.S.C., sec. 1428 (b)) is amended by inserting "or wheat" after "corn", and by inserting "or wheat-producing" after "corn-producing".

Title III — Amendments to Agricultural Adjustment Act of 1938, and Related Legislation

SEC. 301. Section 301 (a) (1) (E) of the Agricultural Adjustment Act of 1938, as amended (U.S.C., 1952 edition, title 7, sec. 1301 (a) (1) (E)), is amended as follows:

"SEC. 301 (a) (1) (E). Notwithstanding the provisions of subparagraph (A), the transitional parity price for any agricultural commodity, computed as provided in this subparagraph, shall be used as the parity price for such commodity until such date after January 1, 1950, as such transitional parity price may be lower than the parity price, computed as provided in subparagraph (A), for such commodity. The transitional parity price for any agricultural commodity as of any date shall be —

"(i) its parity price determined in the manner used prior to the effective date of the Agricultural Act of 1948, less

"(ii) 5 per centum of the parity price so determined multiplied by the number of full calendar years which, as of such date, have elapsed after January 1, 1949, in the case of nonbasic agricultural commodities, and after January 1, 1955, in the case of the basic agricultural commodities."

SEC. 302. Section 301 (b) of the Agricultural Adjustment Act of 1938, as amended (7 U.S.C. 1301 (b)), is amended:

(a) By striking out in paragraph 10 (A) the language "10 per centum in the case of corn" and "15 per centum in the case of wheat" and inserting in lieu thereof

"15 per centum in the case of corn" and "20 per centum in the case of wheat", respectively;

(b) By amending paragraph (13) (A) to read as follows:

"(A) 'Normal yield' for any county, in the case of corn or wheat, shall be the average yield per acre of corn or wheat for the county during the ten calendar years in the case of wheat, or the five calendar years in the case of corn, immediately preceding the year in which such normal yield is determined, adjusted for abnormal weather conditions and, in the case of wheat, for trends in yields. Such normal yield per acre for any county need be redetermined only when the actual average yield for the ten calendar years in the case of wheat, or the five calendar years in the case of corn, immediately preceding the calendar year in which such yield is being reconsidered differs by at least 5 per centum from the actual average yield for the ten years in the case of wheat, or the 5 years in the case of corn, upon which the existing normal yield per acre for the county was based."; and

(c) By amending the first sentence of paragraph (13) (E) to read as follows:
" 'Normal yield' for any farm, in the case of corn, wheat, cotton, or peanuts, shall be the average yield per acre of corn, wheat, cotton, or peanuts, as the case may be, for the farm, adjusted for abnormal weather conditions and, in the case of wheat, but not in the case of corn, cotton, or peanuts, for trends in yields, during the ten calendar years in the case of wheat, and five calendar years in the case of corn, cotton, or peanuts, immediately preceding the year in which such normal yield is determined."

SEC. 303. Part II of subtitle B of title III of the Agricultural Adjustment Act of 1938, as amended (7 U.S.C., ch. 35, subch. II, subtitle B, pt. II), is amended by striking out the designation "MARKETING QUOTAS — CORN" and inserting in lieu thereof the words "ACREAGE ALLOTMENTS — CORN".

SEC. 304. Sections 322 to 325, inclusive (7 U.S.C. 1322 to 1325), and section 326 (7 U.S.C. 1326), insofar as it is applicable to corn, of the Agricultural Adjustment Act of 1938, as amended, are hereby repealed, and section 327 thereof (7 U.S.C. 1327), is hereby amended to read as follows:

"*Proclamation of Commercial Corn-Producing Area*

"SEC. 327. Not later than February 1 of each calendar year, the Secretary shall ascertain and proclaim the commercial corn-producing area."

SEC. 305. The first sentence of section 328 of the Agricultural Adjustment Act of 1938, as amended (7 U.S.C. 1328), is amended by striking out the word "ten" and inserting in lieu thereof "five", by striking out the language "and trends in yield", and by striking out the word "or" and inserting in lieu thereof "and corn".

SEC. 306. Section 329 (a) of the Agricultural Adjustment Act of 1938, as amended (7 U.S.C. 1329), is amended by striking out the word "ten" and inserting in lieu thereof "five".

SEC. 307. Section 332 of the Agricultural Adjustment Act of 1938, as amended, is amended to read as follows:

"SEC. 332. Not later than May 15 of each calendar year the Secretary shall ascertain and proclaim the national acreage allotment for the crop of wheat produced in the next succeeding calendar year."

SEC. 308. Section 334 of the Agricultural Adjustment Act of 1938, as amended, is amended by adding at the end thereof a new subsection as follows:

"(f) Any part of any 1955 farm wheat acreage allotment on which wheat will not be planted and which is voluntarily surrendered to the county committee shall be deducted from the allotment to such farm and may be reapportioned by the county committee to other farms in the same county receiving allotments in amounts determined by the county committee to be fair and reasonable on the basis of past acreage of wheat tillable acres, crop rotation practices, type of soil, and topography. If all of the allotted acreage voluntarily surrendered is not needed in the county, the county committee may surrender the excess acreage to the State committee to be used for the same purposes as the State acreage reserve under subsection (c) of this section. Any allotment transferred under this provision shall be regarded for the purposes of subsection (c) of this section as having been planted on the farm from which transferred rather than on the farm to which transferred, except that this shall not operate to make the farm from which the allotment was transferred eligible for an allotment as having wheat planted thereon during the three-year base period: *Provided,* That notwithstanding any other provisions of law, any part of any 1955 farm acreage allotment may be permanently released in writing to the county committee by the owner and operator of the farm, and reapportioned as provided herein. Acreage surrendered, reapportioned under this subsection, and planted shall be credited to the State and county in determining future acreage allotments."

SEC. 309. Section 335 of the Agricultural Adjustment Act of 1938, as amended, is amended —

(a) by striking out of subsection (a) "July 1" following the words "not later than" and inserting in lieu thereof "May 15"; and

(b) by adding at the end there of the following new subsection:

"(e) If, for any marketing year, the acreage allotment for wheat for any State is twenty-five thousand acres or less, the Secretary, in order to promote efficient administration of this Act and the Agricultural Act of 1949, may designate such State as outside the commercial wheat-producing area for such marketing year. No farm marketing quota or acreage allotment with respect to wheat under this title shall be applicable in such marketing year to any farm in any State so designated; and no acreage allotment in any other State shall be increased by reason of such designation. Notice of any such designation shall be published in the Federal Register.

SEC. 310. (a) Section 344 (f) (6) of the Agricultural Adjustment Act of 1938, as amended, is amended by changing the first sentence to read as follows:

"(6) Notwithstanding the foregoing provisions of this subsection except paragraph (3), if the county committee recommends such action and the Secretary determines that such action will result in a more equitable distribution of the county allotment among farms in the county, the county acreage allotment, less the acreage reserved under paragraph (3) of this subsection, shall be apportioned to farms on which cotton has been planted in any one of the three years immediately preceding the year for which such allotment is determined, on the basis of the acreage planted to cotton on the farm during such three-year period, adjusted as may be necessary for abnormal conditions affecting plantings during such three-year period: *Provided,* That the county committee may in its discretion (A) apportion such county allotment by first establishing minimum allotments in accordance with paragraph (1) of this subsection and by allotting the remaining acreage to farms other than those receiving an allotment under paragraph (1) (B) in accordance with the foregoing provisions of this paragraph and (B) limit any farm acreage allotment established under the provisions of this paragraph for any year to an acreage not in excess of 50 per centum of the cropland on the farm, as determined pursuant to the provisions of paragraph (2) of this subsection: *Provided further,* That any part of the county acreage allotment not apportioned under this paragraph by reason of the initial application of such 50 per centum limitation shall be added to the county acreage reserve under paragraph (3) of this subsection and shall be available for the purposes specified therein.

(b) Section 344 (m) (2) of the Agricultural Adjustment Act of 1938, as amended, is amended by striking out "1954 or 1955" wherever they appear therein.

SEC. 311. (a) Section 348 of the Agricultural Adjustment Act of 1938, as amended, is amended effective with the 1955 crops to read as follows:

"SEC. 348. (a) Any person who knowingly harvests any basic agricultural commodity on his farm which has been determined by the Secretary to be in excess of the farm acreage allotment for such commodity for the farm for such year under this title shall not be eligible for any payment for such year under the Soil Conservation and Domestic Allotment Act, as amended.

"(b) Persons applying for any payment of money under the Soil Conservation and Domestic Allotment Act, as amended, shall file with the application a statement of facts showing eligibility under this section."

(b) Section 374 of the Agricultural Adjustment Act of 1938, as amended, is amended by striking out the last sentence of subsection (b) thereof and adding the following new subsection:

"(c) If the acreage determined to be planted to any basic agricultural commodity on the farm is in excess of the farm acreage allotment, the Secretary shall by appropriate regulations provide for a reasonable time prior to harvest within which such planted acreage may be adjusted to the farm acreage allotment."

SEC. 312. Section 371 of the Agricultural Adjustment Act of 1938, as amended (7 U.S.C. 1371), is hereby amended:

(a) By amending subsection (b) to read as follows:

"(b) If the Secretary has reason to believe that, because of a national emergency or because of a material increase in export demand any national acreage allotment for corn or any national marketing quota or acreage allotment for wheat, cotton, rice, peanuts, or tobacco should be increased or terminated, he shall cause an immediate investigation to be made to determine whether the increase or termination is necessary in order to effect the declared policy of this Act or to meet such emergency or increase in export demand. If, on the basis of such investigation, the Secretary finds that such increase or termination is necessary, he shall immediately proclaim such finding (and if he finds an increase is necessary, the amount of the increase found by him to be necessary) and thereupon such quota or allotment shall be increased, or shall terminate, as the case may be."

(b) By adding in subsection (c) after the words "marketing quota", wherever they appear therein, the words "or acreage allotment", and

(c) By deleting subsection (d) therefrom.

Sec. 313. Public Law 74, Seventy-seventh Congress (7 U.S.C. 1330, 1340), as amended, shall not be applicable to corn.

Sec. 314. Notwithstanding any other provision of law, in areas where a summer fallow crop rotation of wheat is a common practice the 1955 wheat acreage allotment for any farm on which such rotation was practiced with respect to the 1952 and 1953 crops of wheat shall not be less than 50 per centum of (1) the average acreage planted for the production of wheat for the calendar years 1952 and 1953 plus (2) the average of the acreage summer fallowed during the calendar year 1951 for the seeding of wheat for 1952 and the acreage summer fallowed during the calendar year of 1952 for the seeding of wheat for 1953, adjusted in the same ratio as the national average seedings for the production of wheat during the calendar years 1952 and 1953 bears to the national acreage allotment for wheat for the 1955 crop, taking into consideration the adjustments made for crop rotation practices pursuant to the regulations pertaining to farm acreage allotments for the 1955 crop of wheat issued by the Secretary: *Provided,* That, except for farms on which at least 90 per centum of the acreage seeded for the production of wheat for the calendar years 1952 and 1953 was seeded on land which was summer fallowed during the years 1951 and 1952, respectively, and for which a definite and regular alternate wheat and summer fallow crop rotation practice has been determined under the aforesaid regulations, the acreage determined under this section to which the national adjustment factor is applied shall not exceed 50 per centum of the cropland on the farm well suited for the production of wheat: *Provided further,* That no acreage shall be included under (1) or (2) which the Secretary, by appropriate regulations, determines will become an undue erosion hazard under continued farming: *Provided further,* That the acreage determined under this section to which the national adjustment factor is applied shall not exceed six hundred and forty acres, with the acres in excess of six hundred and forty acres, if any, to be adjusted by the adjustment factor for the county. To the extent that the allotment to any county is insufficient to provide for such minimum farm allotments, the Secretary shall allot such county such additional acreage (which shall be in addition to the county, State, and National acreage allotments otherwise provided for under the Agricultural Adjustment Act of 1938, as amended) as may be necessary in order to provide for such minimum farm allotments.

Sec. 315. The Secretary of Agriculture is directed to make a study of the various two-price systems of price support and marketing which could be made applicable to rice and to submit to Congress on or before March 1, 1955, a detailed report thereon. The Secretary may conduct such hearings and receive such statements and briefs in connection with such study as he deems appropriate.

Title IV — Amendments to Agricultural Marketing Agreement Act of 1937

Sec. 401. The Agricultural Adjustment Act (of 1933), as amended, and as reenacted and amended by the Agricultural Marketing Agreement Act of 1937, as amended, is further amended as follows:

(a) Section 2, as amended (7 U.S.C. 602), is amended by adding the following new subsection:

"(4) Through the exercise of the powers conferred upon the Secretary of Agriculture under this title, to establish and maintain such orderly marketing conditions for any agricultural commodity enumerated in section 8c (2) as will provide, in the interests of producers and consumers, an orderly flow of the supply thereof to market throughout its normal marketing season to avoid unreasonable fluctuations in supplies and prices."

(b) Section 8c (2), as amended (7 U.S.C. 608c (2)), is amended to read as follows:

"(2) Orders issued pursuant to this section shall be applicable only to the following agricultural commodities and the products thereof (except canned or frozen grapefruit, the products of naval stores, and the products of honeybees), or to any regional, or market classification of any such commodity or product: Milk, fruits (including filberts, almonds, pecans and walnuts but not including apples, other than apples produced in the States of Washington, Oregon, and Idaho, and not including fruits, other than olives and grapefruit, for canning or freezing), tobacco, vegetables (not including vegetables, other than asparagus, for canning or freezing), soybeans, hops, honeybees and naval stores as included in the Naval Stores Act and standards established thereunder (including refined or partially refined oleoresin): *Provided,* That no order issued pursuant to this section shall be effective as to any grapefruit for canning or freezing unless the Secretary of Agriculture determines, in addition to other findings and determinations required by this Act, that the issuance of such order is approved or favored by the processors who, during a representative period determined by the Secretary, have been engaged in canning or freezing such commodity for market and have canned or frozen for market more than 50 per centum of the total volume of such commodity canned or frozen for market during such representative period."

(c) Section 8c (6), as amended (7 U.S.C. 608c (6)), is amended:

(1) By deleting the provisions immediately preceding paragraph (A) thereof and inserting in lieu thereof the following:

"(6) In the case of the agricultural commodities and the products thereof, other than milk and its products, specified in subsection (2) orders issued pursuant to this section shall contain one or more of the following terms and conditions, and (except as provided in subsection (7)), no others:"

(2) By adding the following new paragraphs at the end thereof:

"(H) providing a method for fixing the size, capacity, weight, dimensions, or pack of the container, or containers, which may be used in the packaging, transportation, sale, shipment, or handling of any fresh or dried fruits, vegetables, or tree nuts: *Provided, however,* That no action taken hereunder shall conflict with the Standard Containers Act of 1928 (15 U.S.C. 257–257i);

"(I) establishing or providing for the establishment of marketing research and development projects designed to assist, improve, or promote the marketing, distribution, and consumption of any such commodity or product, the expense of such projects to be paid from funds collected pursuant to the marketing order."

(d) Section 8c (7) (C), is amended by adding at the end thereof: "There shall be included in the membership of any agency selected to administer a marketing order applicable to grapefruit for canning or freezing one or more representatives of processors of the commodity specified in such order."

(e) Section 8 as amended, is further amended by adding a new section 8e reading as follows:

"8e. Notwithstanding any other provision of law, whenever a marketing order issued by the Secretary of Agriculture pursuant to section 8c of this Act contains any terms or conditions regulating the grade, size, quality, or maturity of tomatoes, avocados, limes, grapefruit, green peppers, Irish potatoes, cucumbers, or eggplants produced in the United States the importation into the United States of any such commodity during the period of time such order is in effect shall be prohibited unless it complies with the grade, size, quality, and maturity provisions of such order or comparable restrictions promulgated hereunder: *Provided,* That this prohibition shall not apply to such commodities when shipped into continental United States from the Commonwealth of Puerto Rico or any Territory or possession of the United States where this Act has force and effect: *Provided further,* That whenever two or more such marketing orders regulating the same agricultural commodity produced in different areas of the United States are concurrently in effect, the importation into the United States of any such commodity shall be prohibited unless it complies with the grade, size, quality, and maturity provisions of the order which, as determined by the Secretary of Agriculture, regulates the commodity produced in the area with which the imported commodity is in most direct competition. Such prohibition shall not become effective until after the giving of such notice as the Secretary of Agriculture determines reasonable, which shall not be less than three days. In determining the amount of notice that is reasonable in the case of tomatoes the Secretary of Agriculture shall give due consideration to the time required for their transportation and entry into the United States after picking. Whenever the Secretary of Agriculture finds that the application of the restrictions under a marketing order to an imported commodity is not practicable because of variations in characteristics between the domestic and imported commodity he shall establish with respect to the imported commodity such grade, size, quality, and maturity restrictions by varieties, types, or other classifications as he finds will be equivalent or comparable to those imposed upon the domestic commodity under such order. The Secretary of Agriculture may promulgate such rules and regulationsas he deems necessary, to carry out the provisions of this section. Any person who violates any provision of this section or of any rule, regulation, or order promulgated hereunder shall be subject to a forfeiture in the amount prescribed in section 8a (5) or, upon conviction, a penalty in the amount prescribed in section 8c (14) of the Act, or to both such forfeiture and penalty."

Title V — Amendments to Soil Conservation and Domestic Allotment Act

SEC. 501. Section 8 of the Soil Conservation and Domestic Allotment Act, as amended (16 U.S.C. 590h), is amended:

(a) By striking out of subsection (a) "January 1, 1955" and "December 31, 1954", wherever they appear therein, and inserting in lieu thereof "January 1, 1957" and "December 31, 1956", respectively;

(b) By adding at the end of subsection (a) the following:

"During the period prior to January 1, 1957, the Secretary shall carry out the purposes specified in section 7 (a) through State action as rapidly as adequate

State laws are enacted and satisfactory State plans are submitted. Notwithstanding the foregoing provisions of this section and section 7, the provisions of this section with respect to the State, county, and local committees of farmers shall continue in full force and effect for purposes other than the administration of State plans.'';

(c) By striking out of the second paragraph of subsection (b) the language "at not to exceed a fair price fixed in accordance with regulations to be prescribed by the Secretary" and by adding at the end of such paragraph the following new sentence: "The price at which purchase orders for any conservation materials or services are filled may be limited to a fair price fixed in accordance with regulations prescribed by the Secretary."

SEC. 502. Section 15 of the Soil Conservation and Domestic Allotment Act, as amended (16 U.S.C. 590o), is amended by adding at the end thereof the following:

"Notwithstanding the foregoing provisions of this section and the provisions of section 7 (g), programs of soil building practices and soil- and water-conserving practices shall be based on a distribution of the funds available for payments and grants among the several States in accordance with their conservation needs, as determined by the Secretary, except that the proportion allocated to any State shall not be reduced by more than 15 per centum from the distribution of such funds for the next preceding program year. In carrying out such programs, the Secretary shall give particular consideration to conservation problems on farm lands diverted from crops under acreage allotment programs and to the maintenance of a proper balance between soil conserving and soil depleting crops on the farm."

SEC. 503. Nothing contained in section 8 (b) of the Soil Conservation and Domestic Allotment Act, as amended, or in any other provision of law, shall be construed to authorize the Secretary of Agriculture to impose any limitations upon the number of terms for which members of county committees established under such section may be reelected.

Title VI — Agricultural Attaches

SEC. 601. For the purpose of encouraging and promoting the marketing of agricultural products of the United States and assisting American farmers, processors, distributors, and exporters to adjust their operations and practices to meet world conditions, the Secretary of Agriculture shall acquire information regarding the competition and demand for United States agricultural products, the marketing and distribution of said products in foreign countries and shall be responsible for the interpretation and dissemination of such information in the United States and shall make investigations abroad regarding the factors affecting and influencing the export of United States agricultural products, and shall conduct abroad any other activities including the demonstration of standards of quality for American agricultural products for which the Department of Agriculture now has or in the future may have such standards, as he deems necessary. Nothing contained herein shall be construed as prohibiting the Department of Agriculture from conducting abroad any activity for which authority now exists.

SEC. 602. (a) To effectuate the carrying out of the purposes of this title, the Secretary of Agriculture is authorized to appoint such personnel as he determines to be necessary and, with the concurrence of the Secretary of State, to assign such personnel to service abroad, and the Secretary of Agriculture may place not to exceed eight positions in grade 16 and two in grade 17 of the General Schedule of the Classification Act of 1949, as amended, in accordance with the standards and procedures of that Act and such positions shall be in addition to the number authorized in section 505 of that Act.

(b) Officers or employees assigned or appointed to a post abroad pursuant to this title shall have the designation of Agricultural Attaché or other titles or designations, which shall be jointly agreed to by the Secretary of State and the Secretary of Agriculture.

(c) Upon the request of the Secretary of Agriculture, the Secretary of State shall regularly and officially attach the officers or employees of the United States Department of Agriculture to the diplomatic mission of the United States in the country in which such officers or employees are to be assigned by the Secretary of Agriculture, and shall obtain for them diplomatic privileges and immunities equivalent to those enjoyed by Foreign Service personnel of comparable rank and salary.

(d) The President shall prescribe regulations to insure that the official activities of persons assigned abroad under this title are carried on (1) consonant with United States foreign policy objectives as defined by the Secretary of State; (2) in accordance with instructions of the Secretary of Agriculture with respect to agricultural matters; and (3) in coordination with other representatives of the United States Government in each country, under the leadership of the Chief of the United States Diplomatic Mission.

Sec. 603. The Secretary of Agriculture may, under such rules and regulations as may be prescribed by the President or his designee, provide to personnel appointed or assigned by the Secretary of Agriculture under this title or other authority allowances and benefits similar to those provided by title IX of the Foreign Service Act of 1946. Leaves of absence for personnel under this title shall be on the same basis as is provided for the Foreign Service of the United States by the Annual and Sick Leave Act of 1951 (5 U.S.C. 2061).

Sec. 604. (a) The reports and dispatches prepared by the officers appointed or assigned under this title shall be made available to the Department of State, and may be made available to other interested agencies of the Government, and the agricultural reports and dispatches and related information produced by officers of the Foreign Service shall be available to the Secretary of Agriculture.

(b) The Secretary of State is authorized upon request of the Secretary of Agriculture to provide office space, equipment, facilities, and such other administrative and clerical services as may be required for the personnel affected by this title. The Secretary of Agriculture is authorized to reimburse or advance funds to the Secretary of State for such services.

Sec. 605. Provisions in annual appropriation Acts of the Department of State facilitating the work of the Foreign Service of the United States shall be applicable under rules and regulations prescribed by the President or his designee to activities pursuant to this title.

Sec. 606. The Secretary of Agriculture may make rules and regulations necessary to carry out the purposes of this title and may cooperate with any Department or agency of the United States Government, State, Territory, or possession or any organization or person. In any foreign country where custom or practice requires payment in advance for rent or other service, such payment may be authorized by the Secretary of Agriculture.

SEC. 607. (a) For the fiscal year 1955 so much of the Department of State and Department of Agriculture unexpended balances of appropriations, allocations, and other funds employed, held, used, available, or to be made available, in connection with the functions covered by this title as the Director of the Bureau of the Budget or the Congress by appropriation or other law shall determine shall be transferred to or established in accounts under the control of the Department of Agriculture, and there are hereby authorized to be established such additional accounts as may be necessary for this purpose.

(b) There are hereby authorized to be appropriated to the Department of Agriculture such amounts as may be necessary for the purpose of this title.

(c) For the fiscal year 1955 funds which become available for the purposes of this title may be expended under the provisions of law, including current appropriation Acts, applicable to the Department of State: *Provided,* That the provisions of section 571 (d) of the Foreign Service Act of 1946, as amended, with respect to the source of payment for Foreign Service officers and employees shall not apply to personnel employed under this title. Obligations incurred by the Department of State prior to September 1, 1954, with respect to functions affected by this Act, shall be paid from appropriations available to the Department of State.

SEC. 608. Nothing in this title shall be construed to affect personnel employed by or funds available to the Foreign Operations Administration or programs conducted under its authorities.

Title VII — National Wool Act of 1954

SEC. 701. This title may be cited as the "National Wool Act of 1954."

SEC. 702. It is hereby recognized that wool is an essential and strategic commodity which is not produced in quantities and grades in the United States to meet the domestic needs and that the desired domestic production of wool is impaired by the depressing effects of wide fluctuations in the price of wool in the world markets. It is hereby declared to be the policy of Congress, as a measure of national security and in promotion of the general economic welfare, to encourage the annual domestic production of approximately three hundred million pounds of shorn wool, grease basis, at prices fair to both producers and consumers in a manner which will have the least adverse effects upon foreign trade.

SEC. 703. The Secretary of Agriculture shall, through the Commodity Credit Corporation, support the prices of wool and mohair, respectively, to the producers thereof by means of loans, purchases, payments, or other operations. Such price support shall be limited to wool and mohair marketed during the period beginning April 1, 1955, and ending March 31, 1959. The support price for shorn wool shall be at such incentive level as the Secretary, after consultation with producer representatives, and after taking into consideration prices paid and other cost conditions affecting sheep production, determines to be necessary in order to encourage an annual production consistent with the declared policy of this title: *Provided,* That the support price for shorn wool shall not exceed 110 per centum of the parity price therefor. If the support price so determined does not exceed 90 per centum of the parity price for shorn wool, the support price for shorn wool shall be at such level, not in excess of 90 per centum nor less than 60 per centum of the parity price therefor, as the Secretary determines necessary in order to encourage an annual production of approximately three hundred and sixty million pounds of shorn wool. The support prices for pulled wool and for mohair shall be established at such levels, in relationship to the support price for shorn wool, as the Secretary determines will maintain normal marketing practices for pulled wool, and as the Secretary shall determine is necessary to maintain approximately the same percentage of parity for mohair as for shorn wool. The deviation of mohair support prices shall not be calculated so as to cause it to rise or fall more than 15 per centum above or below the comparable percentage of parity at which shorn wool is supported. Notwithstanding the foregoing, no price support shall be made available, other than through payments, at a level in excess of 90 per centum of the parity price for the commodity. The Secretary shall, to the extent practicable, announce the support price levels for wool and mohair sufficiently in advance of each marketing year as will permit producers to plan their production for such marketing year.

SEC. 704. If payments are utilized as a means of price support, the payments shall be such as the Secretary of Agriculture determines to be sufficient, when added to the national average price received by producers, to give producers a national average return for the commodity equal to the support price level therefor: *Provided,* That the total of all such payments made under this Act shall not at any time exceed an amount equal to 70 per centum of the accumulated totals, as of the same date, of the gross receipts from specific duties (whether or not such specific duties are parts of compound rates) collected on and after January 1, 1953, on all articles subject to duty under schedule 11 of the Tariff Act of 1930, as amended. The payments shall be made upon wool and mohair marketed by the producers thereof, but any wool or mohair produced prior to January 1, 1955, shall not be the subject of payments. The payments shall be at such rates for the marketing year or periods thereof as the Secretary determines will give producers the support price level as herein provided. Payments to any producer need not be made if the Secretary determines that the amount of the payment to the producer or all producers is too small to justify the cost of making such payments. The Secretary may make the payment to producers through the marketing agency to or through whom the producer marketed his wool or mohair: *Provided,* That such marketing agency agrees to receive and promptly distribute the payments on behalf of such producers. In case any person who is entitled to any such payment dies, becomes incompetent, or disappears before receiving such payment, or is succeeded by another who renders or completes the required performance, the payment shall, without regard to any other provisions of law, be made as the Secretary may determine to be fair and reasonable in all the circumstances and provided by regulation.

SEC. 705. For the purpose of reimbursing the Commodity Credit Corporation for any expenditures made by it in connection with payments to producers under this title, there is hereby appropriated for each fiscal year beginning with the fiscal year ending June 30, 1956, an amount equal to the total of expenditures made by the Corporation during the preceding fiscal year and to any amounts expended in prior fiscal years not previously reimbursed: *Provided, however,* that such amounts appropriated for any fiscal year shall not exceed 70 per centum of the gross receipts from specific duties (whether or not such specific duties are parts of compound rates) collected during the period January 1 to December 31, both inclusive, preceding the beginning of each such fiscal year on all articles subject to duty under schedule 11 of the Tariff Act of 1930, as amended. For the purposes of the appraisal under the Act of March 8, 1938, as amended (15 U.S.C. 713a-1), the Commodity Credit Corporation shall establish on its books an account receivable in an amount equal to any amount expended by Commodity Credit Corporation in connection with payments pursuant to this title which has not been reimbursed from appropriations made hereunder.

SEC. 706. Except as otherwise provided in this title, the amounts terms, and conditions of the price support operations and the extent to which such operations are carried out shall be determined or approved by the Secretary of Agriculture. The Secretary may, in determining support prices and rates of payment, make adjustments in such prices or rates for differences in grade, quality, type, location, and other factors to the extent he deems practicable and desirable. Determinations by the Secretary under this title shall be final and conclusive. The facts constituting the basis for any operation, payment, or amount thereof when officially determined in conformity with applicable regulations prescribed by the Secretary shall be final and conclusive and shall not be reviewable by any other officer or agency of the Government.

SEC. 707. The term "marketing year" as used in this title·means the twelve-month period beginning April 1 of each calendar year or, for either wool or mohair, such other period, or periods for prescribed areas, as the Secretary may determine to be desirable to effectuate the purpose of this title.

SEC. 708. The Secretary of Agriculture is authorized to enter into agreements with, or to approve agreements entered into between, marketing cooperatives, trade associations, or others engaged or whose members are engaged in the handling of wool, mohair, sheep, or goats or the products thereof for the purpose of developing and conducting on a National, State, or regional basis advertising and sales promotion programs for wool, mohair, sheep, or goats or the products thereof. Provision may be made in such agreement to obtain the funds necessary to defray the expenses incurred thereunder through pro rata deductions from the payments made under section 704 of this title to producers within the production area he determines will be benefited by the agreement and for the assignment and transfer of the amounts so deducted to the person or agency designated in the agreement to receive such amounts for expenditure in accordance with the terms and conditions of the agreement. No agreement containing such a provision for defraying expenses through deductions shall become effective until the Secretary determines that at least two-thirds of the producers who, during a representative period determined by the Secretary, have been engaged, within the production area he determines will be benefited by the agreement, in the production for market of the commodity specified therein approve or favor such agreement or that producers who, during such representative period have produced at least two-thirds of the volume of such commodity produced within the area which will be benefited by such agreement, approve or favor such agreement. Approval or disapproval by cooperative associations shall be considered as approval or disapproval by the producers who are members of, stockholders in, or under contract with such cooperative association of producers. The Secretary may conduct a referendum among producers to ascertain their approval or favor. The requirements of approval or favor shall be held to be complied with if two-thirds of the total number of producers, or two-thirds of the total volume of production, as the case may be, represented in such referendum, indicate their approval or favor.

SEC. 709. Section 201 of the Agricultural Act of 1949 (7 U.S.C., sec. 1446) is amended effective April 1, 1955, (i) by deleting from the first sentence thereof the phrase "wool (including mohair)," and (ii) by deleting subsection (a) thereof relating to the support of wool and mohair.

SEC. 710. (a) The third sentence of section 2 (a) of the Commodity Exchange Act, as amended, is amended by inserting "wool," after the comma following "(Irish potatoes)".

(b) The amendment made by this section shall become effective sixty days after the date of enactment of this Act.

Approved August 28, 1954.

Need for Rural Development

From Development of Agriculture's Human Resources (Washington, 1955) pp. 1–2, 4–6, 12–20.

SUMMARY AND RECOMMENDATIONS

One of the important farm problems in this country is the development of human resources in agriculture. Farm families with low earnings make up more than a fourth of all the farm families. In the United States, in 1950 there were roughly 5.4 million farm operator families in all. Out of these, about 1.5 million had cash incomes under $1,000 (table 1). Most of these families are on small farms.

President Eisenhower, in submitting his recommendations for a new program to the Congress in January 1954, stated that the Secretary of Agriculture in cooperation with the National Agricultural Advisory Commission would "give further special attention to the problems peculiar to small farmers."

In line with this directive, a review has been made of this problem. This report has been prepared for the Secretary of Agriculture by the United States Department of Agriculture. The purpose is to improve programs already in operation, develop others which are feasible, and suggest further proposals which the Congress may consider.

The procedure has been to review such programs as are in effect in each key area and develop suggestions to improve them. Task forces have been set up, drawn from various government departments and private groups. These have studied various aspects of the problem as will be indicated in this report.

The approach to this problem is here regarded as primarily educational and developmental. There appear to be some direct aids in the way of credit, improved opportunities for off-farm employment, and the like, which can be offered. But it is considered that what ever is done must be done within the American philosophy that each individual make his own decisions and set his own goals. Government has responsibility in keeping open the channels of opportunity.

TABLE 1 — *Number of farm operator familites with specific characteristics, classified by net family income, United States, 1950*[1]

Type of farm family	Total	Net cash family income from all sources	
		Under $2,000	Under $1,000
	Thousands	*Thousands*	*Thousands*
All farm operator families	5,379	2,849	1,513
Farm operator families on small farms[2]	3,287	2,145	1,269
Farm operator families on small farms with heads under 65.	2,680	1,691	943
Families with operator working off-farm 100 days or more.	1,091	404	156
Families with operator working off-farm less than 100 days.	1,589	1,287	787

[1]Derived from "Farms and Farm People," A Special Cooperative Report, U.S. Department of Commerce and U.S. Department of Agriculture, June, 1953.

[2]Farms where the gross sales of farm products were less than $2,500 in 1949.

Obviously, this must be a long-range program.

Some improvements have been going on. Some farmers have enlarged and improved their farm operations. Others have found off-farm jobs. Numbers of small, low-income farms have declined. These trends need to be stepped up. The proportion of our farm families on small, low-income farms remains large.

It may be stated as a broad premise that most of the large group of farmers on low-income farms have not shared much in the great advance of agricultural techniques. Many such farms are too small to fit the mechanized farming of the present day. Some of the soils are unproductive. Some of the farmers are old or incapacitated. On the other hand, the large numbers of able-bodied men and women in this group present a challenge to official and private agencies to point the way, if possible, to better incomes and living.

There are nearly a thousand counties in the United States where more than half of the farmers are mainly dependent on the income from small, poorly paying farms. What they are up against, in innumerable cases, is lack of enough good land, lack of equipment, lack of credit facilities, and often lack of the management information and skill which might open wider opportunity to them. In other cases, part- or full-time off-farm employment may be their best opportunity. With better information, training, sometimes credit, sometimes job opportunities off the farm, they can achieve a reasonably good living. They can thereby contribute a larger part to the community and national welfare.

Any substantial reorganization in the areas of limited opportunity is bound to be a long-term process. The job is a large one and is to be undertaken with a sense of persistent effort and of necessary continuity.

As an example, the Mississippi Agricultural Experiment Station recently estimated that the efficient reshaping of farm resources in the Mississippi uplands would mean larger farms and probably double the amount of capital. It also would involve a 60-percent reduction in the number of farm workers. Such changes would take time. The challenge is how to permit the speeding up of solutions already underway by education and by the practical application of credit, employment services, and other facilities which may be brought to bear by official or private agencies.

Of course, the changes in these low-income areas are tied to broader changes which are at work so widely in the whole American economy. The shift from an agricultural to an industrial society has brought a vast demand for industrial workers, and at the same time mechanization has lessened the need for as many workers as formerly on the farms. There has been a considerable movement from farms to urban industry. As output per farm worker goes on increasing, still fewer hands will be needed in agriculture for some time to come, which means a further movement from farm to town, especially from the low-income areas.

Even if our number of farmers were to remain stable during this 1950–60 decade, the mathematical fact is that a fourth of farm-reared young men would have to be working off farms. In low-income areas this proportion may be a third to a half.

But a technological revolution is taking place on our farms and the hours of labor needed to supply our food needs is decreasing. Perhaps half of our farm youth will desire full- or part-time, off-farm employment during this present decade.

The Approaches

Obviously the greatest need on the low-income farms is the opportunity for greater earnings. In attaining this goal more educational, developmental, and other services are needed. It is these services which may do most to improve the outlook for the coming generation — a consideration of importance when the long-time nature of this problem and its solution is understood.

One part of the problem centers around the older people or those partially incapacitated. For these, probably little practical aid can be given outside the range of welfare and social security services. The recent legislation broadening the coverage of social security will apply very helpfully in this field. In 1950 there were more than 300,000 aged operators on farms with incomes of less than $1,000. In some cases a son or relative helps out with the work or care on these places. But the number of cases as a whole are numerous enough to constitute a moving humanitarian problem.

With respect to the younger, able-bodied farmers in these areas, the chances for enlarging their earnings seem to lie in two general directions: First, by way of more capital, more land, better management and better information on crops and livestock; second, by way of more off-farm job opportunity. Vocational training and other informational and educational aids will help them either in farming or in nonfarm jobs.

The principal changes in these areas will be made by the young people, many of whom have not yet completed their education. It is important that these young people have opportunities for vocational training for both agricultural and nonagricultural pursuits. A sound program must be aimed to help them to help themselves.

Increased Productivity in Agriculture. — Farm technological developments make possible larger farms, improved production practices, and new systems of farming in several of the low-income areas.

Programs for increasing productivity in commercial farming in low-income farm areas must differ from educational programs in other areas. Efforts to improve productivity in commercial farming must be carried out hand in hand with efforts to broaden opportunities for nonfarm employment. Educational approaches must be adapted to reach people with little formal school training and small financial reserves. Technical assistance and advisory programs must be integrated with credit programs necessary to finance adoption of improved practices.

Improved Prospects in Part-Time Farming and Nonfarm Jobs. — Opportunities of this type need to be expanded. Important in this are developments to increase industrialization, part-time farming, nonfarm employment opportunities, and economic mobility.

Expanded and improved information services on job opportunities locally and outside the area should be made available. Measures should be taken to bring low-income farm areas into full consideration in industrial expansion. Services should be made available to assist low-income farmers in determining the merits of part-time farming, both as a more or less permanent activity and as a transitional step to full-time farm or nonfarm work.

Increased Opportunities for Training. — The long-term outlook for improved living in these areas depends largely on the young people now growing up there. Yet only a small percentage have a high school education, and vocational training is seldom within easy access. This limited education and training is a handicap to making the adjustments needed for improving living standards in the areas.

Defense Resources. — The Nation will be strengthened, both for peacetime and defense production, if the problems of low-income farmers are met. Improved education and technical skills, especially in low-income areas, are in the national interest. Need for improved health facilities and better diets is shown by the number of young men not suitable for military service. The move to decentralize industry and locate it in areas of abundant rural labor can be important in defense strategy and will bring supplemental income to families on small farms.

General Recommendations

1. Federal and State services together should develop and expand technical assistance and extension work with low-income and part-time farmers. During 1955 experimental programs should be launched in a number of counties to gain experience in new approaches.

2. Private as well as cooperative lending agencies should be encouraged to adopt lending policies which would extend more intermediate-term credit to worthy borrowers who are developing their farms.

3. More Farmers Home Administration funds should be made available for intermediate credit to supplement private and cooperative sources. These loans, supported by management guidance and technical services, would assist low-income farmers to become soundly established in a successful system of farming.

4. A State-Federal research program should be undertaken to canvass the

problems of such areas and explore approaches. This would give a factual picture of the needs with respect to farming adjustments, local opportunities for off-farm work, improved vocational training and related aspects in community improvement.

5. State and regional meetings should be held by land-grant colleges, credit agencies, and other groups in cooperation with the U.S. Department of Agriculture with the objective of developing programs adapted to local needs.

6. State employment services should improve their services to facilitate employment in farm and off-farm jobs in low-income rural areas.

7. Areas of rural underemployment should be identified and included as part of the labor market services to make occupational adjustments easier.

8. The Department of Agriculture should work with the Office of Defense Mobilization and other agencies on the program of dispersing defense industries, with a view to setting up criteria whereby regions with underemployed rural labor can be recognized as sources of labor supply.

9. Steps should be taken to develop more educational and vocational training opportunities needed by farm families with restricted economic opportunities. Revised formulas for grants in aid for vocational education should be considered. All possible ways of improving educational programs and of making them more readily available to farm people should be explored. Special attention should be given to factors that motivate farm people and to developing greater individual and family interest in getting a better education.

10. The Department of Agriculture and the Department of Health, Education, and Welfare should encourage and appropriately assist States and communities to set up experimental vocational training programs as pilot studies in typical low-income areas. These programs should be designed to increase the individual opportunities to prepare for farm and off-farm employment.

11. The Department of Agriculture and State colleges of agriculture should encourage farm leaders to take part in the State conferences on education that are now being developed in connection with the White House Conference on Education scheduled for November 1955.

12. Inclusion of farmers under the social security program beginning in 1955 was an important step aimed at giving more family security, especially for low-income farmers. Steps should be taken to see that all rural people know how to qualify under the program, and how to use the social security payments to get maximum benefits.

13. Improved health should be promoted. Some of the most urgent needs are better nutrition, development and use of voluntary health insurance, recruitment of medical personnel (especially nurses), promotion and establishment of clinics and other facilities.

14. Trade area programs and community development programs have been effective in increasing incomes and raising living standards. Farm, business, and other leadership should assume local responsibility and unite in efforts to develop agriculture's human resources.

These and other steps are discussed in the sections that follow.

THE MAJOR PROBLEM AREAS

Farms with low income are found in all parts of the country, but such farms are most numerous in areas of dense rural settlement with high birth rates, where there are few outside jobs, and where topography or other obstacles hinder the use of modern machinery. In some places the land is overcrowded, so to speak. The abundance of hand labor has tended to reduce the incentive for making adjustments which would give the farms higher earning power per worker.

*　　*　　*

In the "serious" areas are 1,100,000 farms. (See table 5.) Nine-tenths of them had farm sales of less than $2,500. Half of these farmers were dependent largely on their farm income and were under 65 years of age.

The value of land and buildings is less than $5,000, on the average. In 1950 only a fourth of all farms in the "serious" areas had tractors. Many farms are too small to use such machinery effectively. Although there are some good soils, much of the land is hilly or eroded or of low fertility.

TABLE 5. — *Number of farms and percentage of specified types with less than $2,500 gross sales of farm products, generalized problem areas compared with the remainder of the United States, 1950.*

Area	All farms	Farms with less than $2,500 gross sales		
		Total number	With operators of working age and primarily dependent upon farming	with operators over 65 or dependent on other income
	Thousands	*Thousands*	*Thousands*	*Thousands*
Generalized problem areas...............	2,474	2,059	983	1,076
Serious....................................	1,105	999	488	511
Substantial	619	502	259	244
Moderate	750	557	236	321
Appalachian	719	610	250	360
Southern Piedmont and Coastal Plains.........................	604	493	244	249
Southeastern Hilly	389	349	202	147
Mississippi Delta	210	161	110	51
Sandy Coastal Plains of Arkansas, Louisiana, and Texas....................................	186	159	67	92
Ozark-Ouachita Mountains and border.............................	185	158	70	88
Northern Lake States...................	103	72	29	43
Northwestern New Mexico	9	8	3	4
Cascade and Rocky Mountain areas	69	49	10	39
Remainder of the United States	2,905	1,228	381	847

Generalized Problem Areas
Area 1 — *Appalachian Mountains, Valleys, and Plateaus*

Largely mountainous country and broken plateaus. Good tillable land is scanty but the farm population is large. Until recent years large parts of the area have been rather isolated. Burley and dark tobacco farms are the most common commercial types, but the average tobacco allotment is very small. Livestock farms are a close second in number, followed by general farming.

Industrial jobs are spotted in the area but have been good in parts of the Tennessee and Ohio River Valleys. The decline of the coal industry, especially in the Cumberland Plateau, has seriously cut the off-farm income for many small farmers.

Migration of people out of this area has been heavy since 1940. However, farm families are large, with more children than could be absorbed in agriculture even if the size of total farm population remained steady.

Area 2 – Southern Piedmont and Coastal Plains

This large area extends from central Virginia to southeastern Louisiana, with two divisions, the Piedmont and Coastal Plain. The Piedmont is rolling or hilly; most of its soils have been abused and are naturally low in plant nutrients but respond to soil and water conservation practices. The Coastal Plain is much more level. Its upper portions are similar in soil type to the Piedmont, but the lower portions are mostly poorly drained sand and muck soils.

Cotton and flue-cured tobacco are the major crops. Peanuts dominate in smaller sections. In the last 30 years tobacco production has expanded while cotton has shrunk. The farm population is nearly 40 percent nonwhite.

Major sections of the Piedmont have offered industrial employment, especially in textiles; but this has not been true of the Coastal Plain, except in the port areas.

Area 3 — Southeastern Hilly Area

This represents largely the coastal plain west of the Appalachians and east of the Mississippi River. Topography ranges from prairie to low hills. Soil conditions are similar to those in interior portions of area 2. Cotton is the major source of cash income on three-fourths of the farms.

Average value of land and buildings was only $4,500 in 1950, lower than in any other area. About four-fifths of all commercial farms are in the low-production category. Off-farm work has been hardly worth noting until recent years. Forty percent of the farm population is nonwhite. Nearly half of the commercial farmers are tenants.

Area 4 — Mississippi Delta

Farm income in the flood plain of the Mississippi averages more than $1,000, highest of the problem areas. But levels of living are commonly low and more than half the farms are in the low-production category.

This area is different in that it is well endowed with fertile soil, not subject to erosion. The crops grown, cotton, rice, and sugar cane, are raised under plantation type of operation, 40 percent of the land being in multiple-unit operations. Seventy percent of all farmers are tenants, with 40 percent sharecroppers. Part-time and residential farming are much less important here than in other areas.

The pull of employment elsewhere plus the use of laborsaving machinery in cotton production have resulted in a steady decline in number of sharecropper families, and have changed the status of others. Average education of farm adults is only 5.5 years, lower than in any other area.

Area 5 — Southwestern Sandy Coastal Plain

The soils of the westernmost part of the old Cotton Belt were long devoted to cotton and corn, but produce those crops poorly in comparison with other areas. Since 1930 much of the land has been taken out of cultivation and livestock has assumed major importance. The farm population has declined very rapidly. More than half of all farms in the area are now residential or part-time. Mechanization has been slow except in central Oklahoma.

Some of the land is being reforested and lumber products are important. Petroleum is also important. Other industries are largely lacking. Thirty percent of the farm population is nonwhite.

Area 6 — Ozark-Ouachita Mountains and Border

This highlands area has many physical and population characteristics of the Appalachian country. Its cash crop has been cotton, however, instead of tobacco. Less than half the land is in farms and only a fraction of that is cropland. The great majority of farmers are owners.

Dairy, livestock, and poultry have become of increasing importance, especially in the northern portion, but nearly half the farms are residential or part-time and more than seven-tenths of the rest are small scale commercial. Migration away from the area has been heavy.

Area 7 — Northern Lake States

This territory was settled mainly as a lumbering and mining area. With the gradual exhaustion of the timber after 1900, and with the decline of certain mining areas, farming developed. But the soils are shallow and infertile, the season is short, and distance to markets is a problem. About half the farms are low in production. Dairying is the most common type of farming. Through some abandonment of farming, rural zoning, resort development, and reforestation conditions have improved.

Area 8 — Northwestern New Mexico

This is a dry and mountainous country through which runs the Continental Divide. Most of the farms are in the upper Rio Grande Valley east of the divide and on the Indian reservations to the west. Only a third of the farms produce enough to be called commercial farms. Most of the rest are residential farms, but many of these are run by young and middle-aged men who have less than 100 days of off-farm work in a year. The land here is little different from other parts of the Southwest.

Most of the farm people, especially in the Rio Grande Valley, are poorly educated, farming small irrigated acreages for home use. The majority of them speak Spanish. The remainder are largely Indian, many of whom are illiterate and do not speak English. More than 90 percent own their own land. Families are large. Health conditions are poor.

Area 9 — Cascade and Northern Rocky Mountains

This embraces most of the land west of the Cascade Mountains in Oregon and Washington, plus northernmost portions of the Rocky Mountains in Washington and Montana. Most of the land is in forest or has been cut over. Most of the low-income families are on poor soil and adverse terrain.

Nearly a fourth of these farmers are 65 years old, or older, a higher proportion than in any other area. Only a fourth are under 45 years of age, a very low proportion. Educational levels are good, higher than the national average. Nearly half the farms are part-time or residential.

Though farm income averages less than $1,000, fewer than half the commercial farms are low-production farms. Dairying is the principal enterprise in the Cascade areas, while cattle ranches are the most common type in the Rockies. In the western portion of the area, nonfarm population growth and industrial development have been heavy since 1940.

RESEARCH AND EXTENSION

In the past, research and extension activities have not reached many of these low-income people effectively (table 6). One reason has been lack of appeal to low-income farmers of the generalized type of services commonly provided. Another has been that solutions for this problem are peculiarly dependent upon an integrated attack upon all the facets of the problem: that is, those aspects which are concerned with nonfarm employment, credit and financial management, industrial jobs, and vocational training.

TABLE 6 — *Percentage of farmers who had adopted certain recommended practices by value of gross sales, Washington County, Ky., 1950* [1]

	Annual value of crops and products sold			
	Under $1,000	$1,000– $2,499	$2,500– $3,999	$4,000 or more
	Percent	*Percent*	*Percent*	*Percent*
Artificial breeding	3	7	21	33
Ladino clover	9	16	36	56
Kentucky 31 fescue	12	16	33	55
Calf vaccination	16	20	38	48
Bluestone-lime	35	56	78	76
Tobacco fertilization (1,000 pounds per acre or more)	55	58	75	76
Soil testing	9	14	35	48

[1] For each practice, the percentages are based on the number of farmers having the enterprise to which the practice applies.

Source: "Communication and the Adoption of Recommended Farm Practices." Ky. Agri. Expt. Sta.. Progress Report 22. November 1954.

Taken in conjunction with appropriate moves along the foregoing lines, it is believed that the recommendations to expand extension services, technical assistance, and research activities would help solve the low-income problem.

Extension and Technical Assistance — Present Situation

Extension services and technical assistance in production, conservation, and home management are available in most low-income counties. These services have helped many individuals in these areas. Low-income people have, however, frequently made less use of these facilities than farmers who have more productive businesses, who are generally more receptive to new ideas, and whose incomes permit them to undertake additional investment or some measure of experimentation (table 7). For the most part, extension personnel are fully employed in meeting the requests of those who seek assistance.

The use of extension services by low-income farmers has grown in recent years. Several States have greatly improved their programs in many counties in these areas. Much attention and thought have been given to better approaches but workers and funds have been lacking for a broad, vigorous program of the type required to work effectively with these farmers. Further development and expansion of these extension programs is needed.

During the past year Federal funds for extension have been increased by about 20 percent. Most of this increase (85 percent) is being used in the counties to explore or expand farm and home planning activities. This has permitted new work in many of the low-income counties. But available local funds are not plentiful in many counties having numerous low income farms and this has seriously limited the services available to these farmers.

TABLE 7. — *Percentage of farmers who reported use of selected channels of farming information, by value of gross sales, Washington County, Ky., 1950*

Channel of communication	Annual value of crops and products sold			
	Under $1,000 (N = 77)[1]	$1,000– $2,499 (N = 164)	$2,500– $3,999 (N = 81)	$4,000 or more (N = 64)
	Percent	*Percent*	*Percent*	*Percent*
Agricultural agency representatives	27	46	81	88
Farm meetings	9	26	46	64
Farm bulletins.....................................	20	36	65	78
Circular letters from county agent..............	56	70	93	92

[1] N = Number of farmers in each group.

Source: "Communication and the Adoption of Recommended Farm Practices." Ky. Agri. Expt. Sta.. Progress Report 22. November 1954.

Soil and water conservation districts have been organized in all low-income areas. Data from the Soil Conservation Service indicate that for the country as a whole, the distribution of assistance by size of farms corresponds to farm size distributions reported by the census of 1950.

Extension and Technical Assistance — Recommendations

1. Special funds should be provided to set up during the next year or so pilot technical assistance and extension programs in a sufficient number of counties in each low-income area to cover the range of different conditions. Special attention should be given to needs of the young people. In these pilot organizations, consideration should be given to: Setting up county and community committees with a broad base of participation; assembling materials for analysis or planning through cooperative efforts by all agencies concerned; using farm and home management specialist teams to work with individual farmers; exploring methods of working with farm people of limited opportunities; and developing community programs and goals.

2. In the pilot programs additional qualified personnel should be employed for farm and home planning and on-site technical assistance. Personnel should also be able to introduce such changes in methods as may be needed to reach the people involved. Planning should include development of efficient marketing and buying channels.

3. Over the longer term, additional county and community development committees should be organized in all areas where there are significant numbers of low-income farms. These committees should include not only farmers but also representatives of public and private credit agencies, local businesses, employment services, conservation agencies, and extension, vocational, and other educational services. Such committees could help develop local action to increase farm and home efficiency and productivity.

4. In the appropriation of special Federal funds for extension activities to help solve problems of low-income farm people, it is recommended that the basis of allocation recognize: (a) The numbers of low-income farms, and (b) the aggregate income base of each State. A part of the funds might be set up so they could be allocated directly to the States for special projects.

5. It is suggested that the Department of Agriculture take the initiative in bringing about State and regional conferences of leaders in agricultural education, technical assistance, credit, and research. The purpose of such a conference would be to discuss the closely interrelated interests in these fields in the problems of improving the productivity and incomes of farms in the low-income areas.

Suggested Approaches in Pilot Counties

County and community program development committees should be set up to consider the total problem of the area and what can be done about it. These activities would include evaluating alternatives in community development, considering farm enterprises to be encouraged, and setting up a program for special assistance to individual families in developing their own farms.

Any agricultural program in this field must be an integral part of the overall development program for the community or county. It should be an integrated approach. This will mean enlistment of services relating to nonfarm employment, vocational training and guidance, as well as technical services in agricultural conservation and development.

Based upon the preliminary work in a county a special program could be organized to work intensively with interested families who have opportunities to enlarge their farm incomes.

This kind of assistance is intended to help develop a well-balanced farm business, to help plan a wise use of income for living, and to help meet the problem of financing changes. Personal aid is required in helping families think through and work out plans in line with their own resources and values. Also required is an expansion of credit and technical services provided by State and Federal agricultural services and private enterprise.

Regular extension services should also be strengthened in these areas. In counties where additional personnel are being placed, it should be possible to work intensively on farm and home planning activities with at least 50 families a year individually, and perhaps more on a group basis. Advances made by families which have received special help will be noted and followed by other families.

To start with, some work might be done with families on specific problems which affect the farm as a whole. The procedure would be to budget particular changes which affect costs and returns, not only with respect to the specific item, but also as to effects on other parts of the farm business. What a family learns in this way about how to budget and make decisions can be applied to any problem that comes along.

Most of such work would be done with small groups of families who enroll for a series of meetings. This approach would encourage discussion among individuals on problems they have in common, and give opportunity for each family to work on a rather complete program for its own farm. Visits by the group could be made to some of the farms. Followup arrangements would help carry out their plans.

This individualized approach to farm planning is probably the most effective way to help those families who have major adjustments to make and who will need financial help to make them.

Extension and research also should give emphasis to assembly and dissemination of facts relating to the possibilities for increasing efficiency and incomes by low-income farmers working together to meet common problems. Small farmers frequently can cooperate advantageously in the use of equipment and other facilities including such things as farm machinery, electricity, credit, and other facilities. Fuller use of custom services can be helpful. Savings also frequently can be made by combining the sales in marketing farm products and combining purchasing power in securing farm supplies.

Research — Situation and Recommendations

In recent years most agricultural research has been applied to technical problems of production and marketing. Only limited research effort has been directed toward: Fitting farm units to the changing economic environment; the processes of change in farming, farm population, and levels of living; or the efficient use and extension of credit, and changes in land tenure. These types of research are especially important in low-income areas.

In the period before World War II considerable research of this type was carried on. Often this research can serve as a valuable background in an expanded research effort of this type.

Research activities here suggested are directed toward providing information needed to carry out extension work and technical assistance with low-income families. Additional specialized studies are also needed; these are discussed in other sections of this report.

1. Studies should be undertaken, in addition to those already made, to establish the facts concerning the combinations of resources which will increase incomes and improve levels of family living. Such studies would comprise analysis of soils and related physical resources including the completion of soil surveys where these are not now available. The studies also should include analysis of capabilities and attitudes, of conditions in health and education, and of financial and tenure problems which affect low-income people.

The studies would emphasize the evaluation of farming systems, size of operation, and home management which would provide a satisfactory income and level of living to the farm family. They would include an evaluation of income prospects in part-time farming and off-farm employment as well as commercial farming.

One aspect of this work might be a number of pilot research farms. On such farms new practices and enterprises or combinations could be tested in the setting of a farm business as a whole.

All such research presupposes a high degree of teamwork between scientists in various fields affecting agriculture. The results would provide guides to credit agencies as well as to extension workers.

2. Studies should be undertaken in these areas on practices of lending agencies, including repayment terms; also on the amount of credit likely needed to upgrade farmers' earnings. Suggestions should be developed for guidance of private and government lenders.

3. Studies are needed to determine why farm families cooperate or fail to cooperate in improvement programs and to determine possible new ways and approaches for working with those who have been unreceptive in the past.

4. Studies should be undertaken of how the change to an efficient higher income agriculture will affect the area economy, and how it will affect the levels of living attained by the population. These lines of study would cover population changes, off-farm job prospects, and marketing problems.

5. Research should be undertaken to determine the leasing arrangements and provisions that would be most equitable under the altered farming systems. It should determine the extent to which prevalent leasing arrangements stand in the way of adjustments to higher incomes.

6. Research is needed on production and marketing, covering both the long- and short-term prospects for supply and demand, for the United States and local areas. These would help in determining the most practicable farming systems for the low-income areas.

AGRICULTURAL SERVICES FOR PART-TIME FARMERS

Part-time farming is growing in this country. Off-farm work is one means by which families with low incomes can add to their earnings. However, many families still have only a low income after whatever off-farm earnings they can get. Some consideration, therefore, should be given to services which can be supplied to part-time farms.

What is a part-time farm? The census has a definition. It is a farm with sales of from $250 to $1,199 in a year, with the operator working off the farm 100 days or more, or where the family income from off-farm work exceeds the value of farm sales. In 1949 the census reported 639,000 such part-time farms in the United States, of which 326,000 had cash family incomes of less than $2,000 (fig. 4). In the latter group there were 272,000 operators under 65 years of age. These farms averaged 16.2 acres of harvested crops and $612 worth of products sold per farm.

Residential farms, so-called, are a closely allied group. Such a farm is used primarily as a home and is only incidentally a farm business. The census defines such a farm as one having less than $250 of products sold in a year. Such farms showed an average of only 6.1 acres of cropland, and only $82 worth of products sold. There are some residential farmers, however, who may be interested in expanding their farm operations and who thus come more definitely within the scope of this study.

Many of the suggestions applying to low-income farmers generally also apply to part-time farmers. These involve especially: Properly adapted extension programs, better credit service, and needed research. In making these suggestions, it is recognized that some of them are already being carried out in some States. Several good local studies have been made. Some counties are doing an excellent job in providing extension service for part-time farmers. However, in some areas where the need is greatest there has been the least activity of this kind.

Extension Programs for Part-time Farmers

For some low-income families in this category information about the home and the production of food for the family may be sufficient. Others will need help in planning and managing their farm to make it more profitable. Many boys and girls in part-time farm families belong to 4-H Clubs and the wives to home demonstration clubs.

Agricultural Act of 1958

From 72 Statutes at Large 988.

Title I — Cotton

Program for 1959 and 1960

SEC. 101. The Agricultural Act of 1949, as amended, is amended by adding the following new section:

"SEC. 102. Notwithstanding any other provisions of law —

"(a) for each of the 1959 and 1960 crops of upland cotton the Secretary of Agriculture is authorized and directed to offer the operator of each farm for which an allotment is established under section 344 of the Agricultural Adjustment Act of 1938, as amended, a choice of (A) the farm acreage allotment determined pursuant to section 344 of the Agricultural Adjustment Act of 1938, as amended, and price support determined pursuant to section 101 of this Act (the amount of cotton estimated to be produced on the additional acres allotted to producers selecting choice (B) for such year being taken into account in computing such support), except that for the 1959 crop the level of support shall be not less than 80 per centum of parity, or (B) the farm acreage allotment determined pursuant to section 344 of the Agricultural Adjustment Act of 1938, as amended, increased by not to exceed 40 per centum (such increased acreage allotment to be the acreage allotment for the farm for all purposes) and price support at a level which is 15 per centum of parity below the level of support established for producers who elect choice (A). Any person operating more than one farm, in order to be eligible for choice (B), must elect choice (B) for all farms for which he is operator. Not later than January 31 the Secretary shall determine and announce on the basis of his estimate of the supply percentage and the parity price as of the following August 1, the price support level for producers who elect choice (A) and choice (B) respectively, and such price support levels shall be final. As soon as practicable after such announcement, the Secretary shall cause the operator (as shown on the records of the county committee) of each farm for which an allotment is established under section 344 of the Agricultural Adjustment Act of 1938, as amended, to be notified of the alternative levels of price support and the alternative acreage allotments available for his farm. The operator of each farm shall, within the time prescribed by the Secretary, notify the county committee in writing whether he desires the increased acreage allotment and the level of price support prescribed in choice (B) to be effective for the farm. If the operator fails to so notify the county committee within the time prescribed, he shall be deemed to have chosen the acreage allotment and the price support level prescribed in choice (A). The choice elected by the operator shall apply to all the producers on the farm. Notwithstanding the foregoing provisions of this subsection, the Secretary may permit the operator of a farm for which choice (B) is in effect to change to choice (A) where conditions beyond the control of the farm operator, such as excessive rain, flood, or drought, prevented the planting of acreage to cotton or having cotton acreage available for harvest on the farm in accordance with the plans of such operator in selecting choice (B). The additional acreage required to be allotted to farms under this section shall be in addition to the county, State, and national acreage allotments and the production from such acreage shall be in addition to the national marketing quota. The additional acreage authorized by this section shall not be taken into account in establishing future State, county, and farm acreage allotments. Notwithstanding any other provision of law, no farm participating in any cotton acreage reserve program established for 1959 under the Soil Bank Act shall receive an increased acreage allotment under the provisions of this section for 1959. Notwithstanding the provisions of section 344 (m) (2) any farm cotton acreage allotment increased as the result of the selection of choice (B) may not be released and reapportioned to any other farm. Price support shall be made available under this paragraph only to cooperators and only if producers have not disapproved marketing quotas for the crop.

"(b) for each of the 1959 and 1960 crops of upland cotton, price support shall be made available to producers who elect choice (A) through a purchase program. Price support shall be made available to producers who elect choice (B) through loans, purchases, or other operations.

"(c) the Commodity Credit Corporation is directed, during the period beginning August 1, 1959, and ending July 31, 1961, to offer any upland cotton owned by it for sale for unrestricted use at not less than 10 per centum above the current level of price support prescribed in choice (B)."

Price Support for 1961 and Subsequent Years

SEC. 102. (a) The Agricultural Act of 1949, as amended is amended by adding a new section 103 as follows:

"SEC. 103. Notwithstanding the provisions of section 101 of this Act, price support to cooperators for each crop of upland cotton, beginning with the 1961 crop, for which producers have not disapproved marketing quotas shall be at such level not more than 90 per centum of the parity price therefor nor less than the minimum level prescribed below as the Secretary determines appropriate after consideration of the factors specified in section 401 (b) of this Act. For the 1961 crop the minimum level shall be 70 per centum of the parity price therefor, and for each subsequent crop the minimum level shall be 65 per centum of the parity price therefor. Price support in the case of noncooperators and in case marketing quotas are disapproved shall be as provided in section 101 (d) (3) and (5)."

Acreage Allotments and Marketing Quotas

SEC. 103. The Agricultural Adjustment Act of 1938, as amended, is amended as follows:

(1) Section 342 is amended by striking out the third sentence and by changing the period at the end of the second sentence to a colon and adding the following: "*Provided*, That beginning with the 1961 crop, the national marketing quota shall be not less than a number of bales equal to the estimated domestic consumption and estimated exports (less estimated imports) for the marketing year for which the quota is proclaimed, except that the Secretary shall make such adjustment in the amount of such quota as he determines necessary after taking into consideration the estimated stocks of cotton in the United States (including the qualities of such stocks) and stocks in foreign countries which would be available for the marketing year for which the quota is being proclaimed if no adjustment of such quota is made hereunder, to assure the maintenance of adequate but not excessive stocks in the United States to provide a continuous and stable supply of the different qualities of cotton needed in the United States and in foreign cotton consuming countries, and for purposes of national security; but the Secretary, in making such adjustments, may not reduce the national marketing quota for any year below (i) one million bales less than the estimated domestic consumption and estimated exports for the marketing year for which such quota is being proclaimed, or (ii) ten million bales, whichever is larger."

(2) Section 342 is further amended by adding at the end thereof the following: "Notwithstanding any other provision of this Act, the national marketing quota for upland cotton for 1959 and subsequent years shall be not less than the number of bales required to provide a national acreage allotment for each such year of sixteen million acres."

(3) Section 347 (b) is amended by changing the period at the end of the second sentence to a colon and adding the following: "*Provided*, That beginning with the 1961 crop of extra long staple cotton, such national marketing quota shall

be an amount equal to (1) the estimated domestic consumption plus exports for the marketing year which begins in the next calendar year, less (2) the estimated imports, plus (3) such additional number of bales, if any, as the Secretary determines is necessary to assure adequate working stocks in trade channels until cotton from the next crop becomes readily available without resort to Commodity Credit Corporation stocks."

(4) The second sentence of section 344 (a) is amended by striking the word "five" and substituting the word "four".

Minimum Farm Allotments

SEC. 104. (a) Section 344 (b) of the Agricultural Adjustment Act of 1938, as amended, is amended by inserting before the period at the end thereof a colon and the following: *"Provided,* That there is hereby established a national acreage reserve consisting of three hundred and ten thousand acres which shall be in addition to the national acreage allotment; and such reserve shall be apportioned to the States on the basis of their needs for additional acreage for establishing minimum farm allotments under subsection (f) (1), as determined by the Secretary without regard to State and county acreage reserves (except that the amount apportioned to Nevada shall be one thousand acres). For the 1960 and succeeding crops of cotton, the needs of States (other than Nevada) for such additional acreage for such purpose may be estimated by the Secretary, after taking into consideration such needs as determined or estimated for the preceding crop of cotton and the size of the national acreage allotment for such crop. The additional acreage so apportioned to the State shall be apportioned to the counties on the basis of the needs of the counties for such additional acreage for such purpose, and added to the county acreage allotment for apportionment to farms pursuant to subsection (f) of this section (except that no part of such additional acreage shall be used to increase the county reserve above 15 per centum of the county allotment determined without regard to such additional acreage). Additional acreage apportioned to a State for any year under the foregoing proviso shall not be taken into account in establishing future State acreage allotments. Needs for additional acreage under the foregoing provisions and under the last proviso in subsection (e) shall be determined or estimated as though allotments were first computed without regard to subsection (f) (1)."

(b) Section 344 (e) of the Agricultural Adjustment Act of 1938, as amended, is amended by inserting before the period at the end thereof a colon and the following: *"Provided further,* That if the additional acreage allocated to a State under the proviso in subsection (b) is less than the requirements as determined or estimated by the Secretary for establishing minimum farm allotments for the State under subsection (f) (1), the acreage reserved under this subsection shall not be less than the smaller of (1) the remaining acreage so determined or estimated to be required for establishing minimum farm allotments or (2) 3 per centum of the State acreage allotment; and the acreage which is required to be reserved under this proviso shall be allocated to counties on the basis of their needs for additional acreage for establishing minimum farm allotments under subsection (f) (1), and added to the county acreage allotment for apportionment to farms pursuant to subsection (f) of this section (except that no part of such additional acreage shall be used to increase the county reserve above 15 per centum of the county allotment determined without regard to such additional acreages)."

(c) Section 344 (f) of the Agricultural Adjustment Act of 1938, as amended, is amended by changing paragraph (1) to read as follows:

"(1) Insofar as such acreage is available, there shall be allotted the smaller of the following: (A) ten acres; or (B) the acreage allotment established for the farm for the 1958 crop."

(d) The first sentence of section 344 (f) (6) of such Act is amended to read as follows: "Notwithstanding the provisions of paragraph (2) of the subsection, if the county committee recommends such action and the Secretary determines that such action will result in a more equitable distribution of the county allotment among farms in the county, the remainder of the county acreage allotment (after making allotments as provided in paragraph (1) of this subsection) shall be allotted to farms other than farms to which an allotment has been made under paragraph (1) (B) of this subsection so that the allotment to each farm under this paragraph together with the amount of the allotment of such farm under paragraph (1) (A) of this subsection shall be a prescribed percentage (which percentage shall be the same for all such farms in the county) of the average acreage planted to cotton on the farm during the three years immediately preceding the year for which such allotment is determined, adjusted as may be necessary for abnormal conditions affecting plantings during such three-year period: *Provided,* That the county committee may in its discretion limit any farm acreage allotment established under the provisions of this paragraph for any year to an acreage not in excess of 50 per centum of the cropland on the farm, as determined pursuant to the provisions of paragraph (2) of this subsection: *Provided further,* That any part of the county acreage allotment not apportioned under this paragraph by reason of the initial application of such 50 per centum limitation shall be added to the county acreage reserve under paragraph (3) of this subsection and shall be available for the purposes specified therein."

(e) The amendments made by this section shall be effective beginning with the 1959 crop.

SEC. 105. Effective beginning with the 1959 crop, section 344 (f) of the Agricultural Adjustment Act of 1938, as amended, is amended by adding at the end thereof the following new paragraph:

"(7) (A) In the event that any farm acreage allotment is less than that prescribed by paragraph (1), such acreage allotment shall be increased to the acreage prescribed by paragraph (1). The additional acreage required to be allotted to farms under this paragraph shall be in addition to the county, State, and national acreage allotments and the production from such acreage shall be in addition to the national marketing quota.

"(B) Notwithstanding any other provision of law

"(i) the acreage by which any farm acreage allotment for 1959 or any subsequent crop established under paragraph (1) exceeds the acreage which would have been allotted to such farm if its allotment had been computed on the basis of the same percentage factor applied to other farms in the county under paragraph (2), (6), or (8) shall not be taken into account in establishing the acreage allotment for such farm for any crop for which acreage is allotted to such farm under paragraph (2), (6), or (8); and acreage shall be allotted under paragraph (2), (6), or (8) to farms which did not receive 1958 crop allotments in excess of ten acres if and only if the Secretary determines (after considering the allotments to other farms in the county for such crop compared with their 1958 allotments and other relevant factors) that equity and justice require the allotment of additional acreage to such farm under paragraph (2), (6), or (8).

"(ii) the acreage by which any county acreage allotment for 1959 or any subsequent crop is increased from the national or State reserve on the basis of its needs for additional acreage for establishing minimum farm allotments shall not be taken into account in establishing future county acreage allotments, and

"(iii) the additional acreage allotted pursuant to subparagraph (A) of this paragraph (7) shall not be taken into account in establishing future State, county, or farm acreage allotments."

Method of Determining Farm Allotments

SEC. 106. Section 344 (f) of the Agricultural Adjustment Act of 1938, as amended, is amended by adding at the end thereof the following new paragraph:

"(8) Notwithstanding the foregoing provisions of paragraphs (2) and (6) of this subsection, the Secretary may, if he determines that such action will facilitate the effective administration of the provisions of the Act, provide for the county acreage allotment for the 1959 and succeeding crops of cotton, less the acreage reserved under paragraph (3) of this subsection, to be apportioned to farms on which cotton has been planted in any one of the three years immediately preceding the year for which such allotment is determined, on the basis of the farm acreage allotment for the year immediately preceding the year for which such apportionment is made, adjusted as may be necessary (i) for any change in the acreage of cropland available for the production of cotton, or (ii) to meet the requirements of any provision (other than those contained in paragraphs (2) and (6)) with respect to the counting of acreage for history purposes."

Retention of Surrendered Acreage in County

SEC. 107. Paragraph (2) of section 344 (m) of the Agricultural Adjustment Act of 1938, as amended, is amended by striking out the period at the end of the second sentence of such paragraph and inserting in lieu thereof the following "; but no such acreage shall be surrendered to the State committee so long as any farmer receiving a cotton acreage allotment in such county desires additional cotton acreage."

Standard Grade

SEC. 108. Section 3 (a) of the Act of August 29, 1949, Public Law 272, 81st Congress, and the last sentence of section 403 of the Agricultural Act of 1949, as amended, are hereby repealed. This section shall become effective with the 1961 crop.

CCC Sales Restrictions

SEC. 109. Section 407 of the Agricultural Act of 1949, as amended, is amended by substituting a colon for the period at the end of the third sentence and adding at the end thereof the following: "*Provided,* That effective with the beginning of the marketing year for the 1961 crop, the Corporation shall not sell any upland or extra long staple cotton for unrestricted use at less than 15 per centum above the current support price for cotton plus reasonable carrying charges, except that the Corporation may, in an orderly manner and so as not to affect market prices unduly, sell for unrestricted use at the market price at the time of sale a number of bales of cotton equal to the number of bales by which the national marketing quota for such marketing year is reduced below the estimated domestic consumption and exports for such marketing year pursuant to the provisions of section 342 of the Agricultural Adjustment Act of 1938, as amended.''

Cotton Export Program

SEC. 110. Nothing in this Act shall be construed to affect or modify the provisions of section 203 of the Agricultural Act of 1956, and any cotton owned or acquired by the Commodity Credit Corporation under any price support program may be used for the purpose of carrying out the cotton export program provided for in section 203 of the Agricultural Act of 1956.

Split Grades

SEC. 111. Section 403 of the Agricultural Act of 1949, as amended, is amended by adding at the end thereof the following sentence: ''Beginning with the 1959 crop, in adjusting the support price for cotton on the basis of grade, the Secretary shall establish separate price support rates for split grades and for full grades substantially reflecting relative values.''

Title II — Corn and Feed Grains

Referendum

SEC. 201. Title I of the Agricultural Act of 1949, as amended, is further amended by adding at the end of such title the following:

''SEC. 104. (a) Not later than December 15, 1958, the Secretary shall conduct a referendum of producers of corn in 1958 in the commercial corn-producing area for 1958 to determine whether such producers favor a price support program as provided in subsection (b) of this section for the 1959 and subsequent crops in lieu of acreage allotments as provided in the Agricultural Adjustment Act of 1938, as amended, and price support as provided in section 101 of the Agricultural Act of 1949, as amended.

''(b) Notwithstanding any other provision of law, if less than a majority of the producers voting in the referendum conducted pursuant to subsection (a) hereof favor a price support program as provided in this subsection (b), the following provisions of law shall become inoperative:

''Discontinuance of Acreage Allotments on Corn

''(1) The Agricultural Adjustment Act of 1938, as amended, is amended by adding the following new section:

'' 'SEC. 330. Notwithstanding any other provision of law, acreage allotments and a commercial corn-producing area shall not be established for the 1959 and subsequent crops of corn.'

"*Price Support*

"(2) The Agricultural Act of 1949, as amended, is amended by adding the following new section:

" 'SEC. 105. (a) Notwithstanding the provisions of section 101 of this Act, beginning with the 1959 crop, price support shall be made available to producers for each crop of corn at 90 per centum of the average price received by farmers during the three calendar years immediately preceding the calendar year in which the marketing year for such crop begins, adjusted to offset the effect on such price of any abnormal quantities of low-grade corn marketed during any of such year: *Provided,* That the level of price support for any crop of corn shall not be less than 65 per centum of the parity price therefor.

" '(b) Beginning with the 1959 crop, price support shall be made available to producers for each crop of oats, rye, barley, and grain sorghums at such level of the parity price therefor as the Secretary of Agriculture determines is fair and reasonable in relation to the level at which price support is made available for corn, taking into consideration the feeding value of such commodity in relation to corn, and the other factors set forth in section 401 (b) hereof.'

"(3) Section 101 (d) (4) of the Agricultural Act of 1949, as amended, is repealed effective with the 1959 crop."

Title III — Rice

Minimum National and State Acreage Allotments

SEC. 301. Section 353 (c) (6) of the Agricultural Adjustment Act of 1938, as amended, is amended by striking out "1957 and 1958" in each place it occurs therein, and inserting "1957 and subsequent years".

Price Support

SEC. 302. (a) Section 101 (a) of the Agricultural Act of 1949, as amended, is amended, effective beginning with the 1959 crop —

(1) by striking out "wheat, and rice" and inserting "and wheat"; and

(2) by adding at the end thereof the following new paragraph: "For rice of the 1959 and 1960 crops, the level of support shall be not less than 75 per centum of the parity price. For rice of the 1961 crop the level of support shall be not less than 70 per centum of the parity price. For the 1962 and subsequent crops of rice the level of support shall be not less than 65 per centum of the parity price."

Title IV — Wool

SEC. 401. Section 703 of the National Wool Act of 1954 (68 Stat. 910) is amended by striking out "March 31, 1959" and inserting in lieu thereof "March 31, 1962".

SEC. 402. The first proviso in section 704 of such Act (68 Stat. 911) is amended by striking out "specific" the first time it appears therein, and by striking out "(whether or not such specific duties are parts of compound rates)".

SEC. 403. The proviso in section 705 of such Act (68 Stat. 911) is amended by striking out "specific" the first time it appears therein, and by striking out "(whether or not such specific duties are parts of compound rates)".

Title V — Miscellaneous

SEC. 501. The Agricultural Adjustment Act of 1938, as amended, is amended by adding after section 377 the following new section:

"SEC. 378. (a) Notwithstanding any other provision of this Act, the allotment determined for any commodity for any land from which the owner is displaced because of acquisition of the land for any purpose, other than for the continued production of allotted crops, by any Federal, State, or other agency having the right of eminent domain shall be placed in an allotment pool and shall be available only for use in providing allotments for other farms owned by the owner so displaced. Upon application to the county committee, within three years after the date of such displacement, or three years after the enactment of this section, whichever period is longer, any owner so displaced shall be entitled to have established for other farms owned by him allotments which are comparable with allotments determined for other farms in the same area which are similar except for the past acreage of the commodity, taking into consideration the land, labor, and equipment available for the production of the commodity, crop-rotation practices, and the soil and other physical factors affecting the production of the commodity: *Provided,* that the acreage used to establish or increase the allotments for such farms shall be transferred from the pool and shall not exceed the allotment most recently established for the farm acquired from the applicant and placed in the pool. During the period of eligibility for the making of allotments under this section for a displaced owner, acreage allotments for the farm from which the owner was so displaced shall be established in accordance with the procedure applicable to other farms, and such allotments shall be considered to have been fully planted. After such allotment is made under this section, the proportionate part, or all, as the case may be, of the past acreage used in establishing the allotment most recently placed in the pool for the farm from which the owner was so displaced shall be transferred to and considered for the purposes of future State, county, and farm acreage allotments to have been planted on the farm to which allotment is made under this section. Except where paragraph (c) requires the transfer of allotment to another portion of the same farm, for the purpose of this section (1) that part of any farm from which the owner is so displaced and that part from which he is not so displaced shall be considered as separate farms; and (2) an owner who voluntarily relinquishes possession of the land subsequent to its acquisition by an agency having the right of eminent domain shall be considered as having been displaced because of such acquisition.

"(b) The provisions of this section shall not be applicable if (1) there is any marketing quota penalty due with respect to the marketing of the commodity from the farm acquired by the Federal, State, or other agency or by the owner of the farm; (2) any of the commodity produced on such farm has not been accounted for as required by the Secretary; or (3) the allotment next established for the farm acquired by the Federal, State, or other agency would have been reduced because of false or improper identification of the commodity produced on or marketed from such farm or due to a false acreage report.

"(c) This section shall not be applicable, in the case of cotton, tobacco, and peanuts, to any farm from which the owner was displaced prior to 1950, in the case of wheat and corn, to any farm from which the owner was displaced prior to 1954, and in the case of rice, to any farm from which the owner was displaced prior to 1955. In any case where the cropland acquired for nonfarming purposes from an owner by an agency having the right of eminent domain represents less than 15 per centum of the total cropland on the farm, the allotment attributable to that portion of the farm so acquired shall be transferred to that portion of the farm not so acquired.

"(d) Sections 313 (h), 334 (d), 344 (h), 353 (f), and 358 (h) of the Agricultural Adjustment Act of 1938, as amended, are repealed, but any transfer or reassignment of allotment heretofore made under the provisions of these sections shall remain in effect, and any displaced farm owner for whom an allotment has been established under such repealed sections shall not be eligible for additional allotment under subsection (a) of this section because of such displacement."

SEC. 502. Section 405 of the Agricultural Act of 1949 is amended by adding at the end thereof the following: "There is authorized to be included in the terms and conditions of any such nonrecourse loan a provision whereby on and after the maturity of the loan or any extension thereof Commodity Credit Corporation shall have the right to acquire title to the unredeemed collateral without obligation to pay for any market value which such collateral may have in excess of the loan indebtedness."

SEC. 503. Section 201 (b) of the Agricultural Act of 1949, as amended, is amended by changing the semicolon at the end thereof to a colon and adding the following: "*Provided,* That in any crop year in which the Secretary determines that the domestic production of tung oil will be less than the anticipated domestic demand for such oil, the price of tung nuts shall be supported at not less than 65 per centum of the parity price therefore".

Extend Veterans and Armed Services Milk Program

SEC. 504. (a) The first sentence of section 202 (a) of the Agricultural Act of 1949, as amended (7 U.S.C. 1446a), is amended by striking out "1958" and inserting in lieu thereof "1961".

(b) Subsection (b) of section 202 of the Agricultural Act of 1949 (7 U.S.C. 1446a) is amended by striking out "1958" and inserting in lieu thereof "1961", by striking out "of the Army, Navy, or Air Force, and as a part of the ration" and inserting in lieu thereof "(1) of the Army, Navy, Air Force, or Coast Guard, (2)", and by inserting before the period at the end of the first sentence of such subsection the following: ", and (3) of cadets and midshipmen at, and other personnel assigned to, the United States Merchant Marine Academy".

SEC. 505. Commodity Credit Corporation is authorized, on such terms as the Secretary of Agriculture may approve, to donate cotton acquired through its price support operations to educational institutions for use in the training of students in the processing and manufacture of cotton into textiles.

Approved August 28, 1958.

Five Secretaries Look at Agricultural Policy

From *Agriculture in an Uneasy World*, pp. 3–22. East Lansing, Michigan: Michigan Agricultural Experiment Station and Michigan Cooperative Extension Service, 1961. Reprinted by permission of the Michigan Agricultural Experiment Station.

Introductory Remarks by President John A. Hannah of Michigan State University

Just 106 years ago this month — on February 12, 1855 — Michigan State University was founded by far-sighted men who believed deeply that higher education should be related to the practical affairs of life.

In 1855, we were a nation of about 31 million people. Eighty percent of those people lived in rural areas, and most of them were living on small, self-sufficient farms. There were large gaps between the levels of living in urban areas and those available to most farm people.

Higher education was limited largely to private universities which trained doctors, lawyers, ministers, and teachers and the sons of wealthy families for genteel lives. With the founding of the Michigan Agricultural College, all this was changed; opportunities for higher education were opened to the children of farmers and others who did the nation's work, and we began to apply the discoveries of science to the problems of working people, farmers, and city folks alike.

Today — in 1961 — less than 10 percent of our people are actively engaged in farm production. It has been suggested that this change means that agriculture is no longer as important as it once was. Nothing could be further from the truth. Vast changes *have* taken place in our society; agriculture has participated in these changes, and precipitated many of them; this University continues to be a proud participant in educating for these changes. As agriculture has changed, this University has changed its program to meet the new challenges, but Michigan State has never for a moment weakened in its interest in farms and farm people, nor wavered in its determination to do its best in the service of agriculture.

Far from declining in importance, the agricultural industry is actually increasing in importance by nearly any measure one might apply.

The present population of the United States exceeds 180 million·people, and they are better fed than ever before — probably the best fed of any people in history, thanks to agriculture.

Not only has the output of agriculture grown, but also the relative importance of agriculture to other sectors of our economy. Just three decades ago — the time span covered by the service of our distinguished speakers today — farmers spent a little more than 4 billion dollars annually for farm operating expenses. Mostly, those were purchases from non-farm sectors of the economy. Today, those expenditures are nearly 20 billion dollars annually, or nearly five times as much.

The vast changes in our society mean, among other things, that agriculture now includes much more than farming. Nearly 40 percent of the persons employed in the United States are engaged in producing food and fiber, processing and distributing farm products, or producing products used by farmers on their farms.

Changes in agriculture appear to come at an increasing pace. These changes have never been without strain, but in the late 1920's the stresses upon farmers became so great that widespread pressures developed for greater direct federal intervention to improve farm prices, farm incomes, and the well-being of farm people. Thus the role of the Secretary of Agriculture took on a new importance and a new dimension. This role has not diminished in importance over the past three decades, nor is it likely to diminish in the future.

The opportunity to meet and to listen to the five men who have held this important Cabinet post in succession during the past 28 years is truly a unique opportunity. As a university proud of its role in increasing the understanding of public problems and of its long history of service to agriculture, Michigan State University is proud to present the five former Secretaries of Agriculture to discuss *Agriculture in an Uneasy World*.

Remarks by Henry A. Wallace

Chairman Hannah has asked each of the five former Secretaries of Agriculture to cover the same three points in 12 minutes.

First I would say that every Secretary of Agriculture must have a fixed goal. In my case I wanted the farmers to get equality of bargaining power and parity of income while at the same time increasing soil fertility and feeding the people of the USA and the world more abundantly. I could never forget the masthead motto of the farm paper of which I had been Editor for many years, "GOOD FARMING, CLEAR THINKING, RIGHT LIVING."

Of course every Secretary wants the conditions of living and the opportunities for education on the farm to improve. Therefore, every Secretary wants greater security of tenure but no diminution in the speed of adopting modern technologies.

In 1933 when I became Secretary, the situation was so desperate that the farm organizations, many insurance companies and even the U.S. Chamber of Commerce were behind me in getting action legislation from the Congress.

I had fought for the McNary Haugen Bill and its Equalization fee when my father was Secretary of Agriculture. Therefore, I was in close contact with farm organization leaders. These people looked on me as a special pleader for their cause. But I felt I had to be more than that.

Moreover, I found what every Secretary of Agriculture knows, that I had to reckon with the Budget Bureau, with the Secretary of State, with the Secretary of Treasury, with the House and Senate Committees on Agriculture and the House and Senate sub-committees on agricultural appropriations. And above all there was the need for loyalty to the President's over-all program. A Secretary soon discovers that Senators and Congressmen often sympathize much more with high pressure, special interest groups, than with the President's program as set forth in either legislative requests or budget askings. Sometimes there is discord even in the Cabinet family.

The cross currents probably put the Secretary of Agriculture in more uncomfortable and difficult positions than any other cabinet officer. He must balance off a large number of conflicting forces. He usually ends up by pleasing no one completely.

My second four minutes are supposed to center around the changes that have taken place since I ceased being Secretary of Agriculture in 1940.

The War made temporarily irrelevant my Ever Normal Granary legislation of 1938 which was based on crop loans at 52 to 75 percent of parity. Great war needs rapidly used up the supplies accumulated in the Ever Normal Granary and the farmers were assured of a good price for everything they raised. The farmers responded so terrifically, partly because of price incentive, partly because of patriotism and largely because of very rapid improvements in seed, fertilizer, machinery and management — that post war surpluses rapidly accumulated.

When I left the agricultural post in 1940, one worker on the land could support 10 people. Today one farm worker can support 25 people. In other words, farm workers since 1940 have been increasing their efficiency at the rate of 4.3 percent a year. For the 60 years before 1940, farm worker efficiency increased at the rate of only 1.2 percent annually. Population in the USA and the World at the present time is increasing at the rate of only 1.6 percent annually.

No one can say that the American farm worker is not doing his share of carrying the world's burden.

The one large area where the American genius for organization and efficient, hard work shines forth most clearly in definite superiority over all other large nations is in agriculture. Russia will overtake us in many industrial fields before she begins to catch up with us in agricultural efficiency. Here we are supreme and are likely to remain that way for a long time.

Where else can one farm worker feed 25 people with abundant supplies of good food containing excellent proteins from animal sources as well as a variety of fruits and vegetables? From the standpoint of health, most citizens of the USA get too many calories rather than too little.

If they pay too much, that is not the farmers' fault. During the past 13 years farm net income has gone down more than 35 percent whereas non-farm income has gone up more than 60 percent. Prior to World War II the income of livestock farmers went up and down almost precisely in step with the total pay rolls of labor. Since 1946, pay rolls of labor have left livestock farm income far, far behind.

It is much more difficult for a Secretary of Agriculture to sponsor continuous wage increases for city labor in 1961 than it was in 1935 or even 1946. The bargaining power of labor has out-distanced the bargaining power of the farmer. The gap between what the consumer pays and what the farmer gets continually widens. The Secretary of Agriculture must more and more appeal to the Secretary of Labor and labor leaders for labor statesmanship in the general interest.

In 1932, agricultural surpluses were built up partly because of low purchasing power on the part of our unemployed and partly because of unemployment over-seas. Today only a small part of our surplus is due to unemployment at home. The surpluses accumulated during the past 10 years are due largely to rapidly expanding technology.

The problem is to turn these vast surpluses into a blessing instead of a curse. Public law 480, passed in 1954, is one mechanism for doing this. We can use our vast surpluses either as a weapon in the cold war or to develop backward nations to a point where they can help themselves. We can store vast quantities in places where they can be protected from fall-out both in this country and abroad. A strategic reserve is all-important. I felt this in 1939. I feel it many times as strongly in 1961.

Lastly, looking ahead 10 years I feel that all Secretaries of Agriculture will have to recognize that government is in the agricultural business to stay.

I do not like it. Farmers do not like it. But how are farmers to get equality of bargaining power without help from the government? The bargaining power of both corporations and labor comes largely from government. If minimum wages are guaranteed, farmers will insist on minimum prices. They will never get parity of income as defined during the campaign. If they could be sure of half that amount year in and year out, they would be lucky. As long as there are subsidies, direct or indirect, either of power or money to non-farm groups, farmers will want their equalizer.

The Secretary of Agriculture in the future will be subject to greater pulling and hauling than any previous Secretary. His only safety will be in defining his goal in such a manner that when he lays down his office he can feel:

1. He has done his part to improve the soil of the USA.

2. His use of government power has enabled the farmers of the USA to feed the people of our country well, while at the same time farmers have been able to bargain more successfully in the market place.

3. His use of government surpluses and surplus legislation have made our beloved country safer at home and abroad.

4. He has maintained the forward march of agricultural technology.

5. He has increased the pride of the farmers in their calling.

6. He has cooperated with his fellow cabinet members in serving the welfare of the world.

7. He has convinced city people that food surpluses properly used are a blessing and that agricultural welfare is vital to city welfare.

8. He has convinced the State Department of the dominance of the agricultural problem in all of the crowded, undeveloped nations of the world.

In order to give life to these eight goals, he must get the best judgment of:

1. The farm organization leaders.

2. The land grant college technicians and farm management experts.

3. Key men from Congress.

4. Farm economists in the USDA.

5. Agriculturally minded men in the State Department.

6. Commodity and cooperative leaders who are well posted on the details of the great surplus crops produced on 20 million or more acres.

7. Experts in the Livestock-feed grain complex.

There will be many conflicts as many selfish interests collide. In 1935 we tried to reconcile these conflicts county by county, state by state, and region by region. That might well be done again against the background of 1961 realities.

It is quite possible that philosophers and historians at the end of the year 1999, looking back over the Twentieth Century as they prepare to greet the Twenty-First Century, will say:

"The USA failed because she failed to understand the earth shaking potentialities in the nationalistic aspirations of the people in the crowded, under developed areas. She could have used her agricultural surplus and agricultural technology to prevent much of that destructive violence which has stained the last four decades of the most bloody century in all history. She did not bring together the best brains to meet that problem and act accordingly."

The statesmanship of the Secretaries of Agriculture and State during the next three Administrations will largely determine whether or not this judgment of doom will be passed upon our beloved country.

Remarks by Claude R. Wickard

What are the considerations and problems that are important to the Secretary of Agriculture as he serves as a Cabinet officer? Put in its simplest terms, why does a Secretary of Agriculture do the things he does sometimes?

I am sure that there were literally millions of people who wondered why I acted like I did when I was Secretary of Agriculture. I do not doubt that many such people are in this audience today.

What a Secretary of Agriculture does or does not do directly affects about all of our citizens, at least to some degree. The majority of our citizens develop decided opinions about what he does or does not do.

In my case I suspect that many wondered if I even knew what I was trying to do. Perhaps I should start by describing what I thought my job was. I thought my job, always within the policies of the President, was to advocate or undertake those measures which would, so far as possible, fill the nation's needs for food and fiber. Some of the President's policies were clear. Others were implied.

For example, if I thought additional funds were required, I could not ask the Congress to appropriate such funds until the Director of the Budget told me that the request was in keeping with the President's program.

When I became Secretary, I had more opportunity to learn about the gravity of the War in Europe. But I sensed that the President did not think it wise to make any statements about our becoming involved directly in the War.

I was much concerned when the 1940 December pig report indicated the farmers were going to make a drastic reduction in hog production because hogs were so cheap. I recalled how, as a young farmer, I was asked to increase my production during World War I. As Secretary, I made an announcement that I thought farmers would find it more profitable to increase hog production than to decrease it. I carefully made no reference to the War. My announcement was greeted with widespread protest. Resolutions were passed asking that I vacate the chair that I had scarcely had time to warm. Fortunately, hog prices soon started to advance and the protests died down.

This was just a foretaste of things to come. Within a few months, I was asking increases in most commodities. Farmers in turn asked me to see that they received the necessary equipment and materials. Steel and rubber were particularly critical. Farmers complained that their sons were being drafted into the armed services and that other farm laborers were leaving for the higher wages in the War plants.

With the advent of price controls, farmers felt that their prices were being held down more than those of other essential industries and more than wages were. In all these matters the farmers had the strong support of the Congress, but not so in the executive branch of the government where the attention was centered on the production of planes, tanks and guns. Many times I was told that my requests for materials or manpower for the farmers should be disregarded because we had too much food already. Many of my associates were suspicious that I was merely reflecting the unwarranted requests of farmers and their friends in Congress.

Poor food distribution, hoarding, sharply higher consumer incomes and fewer items other than food to buy made rationing of a few food items necessary. Rationing was unheard of in America. People became frightened.

Then both consumers and producers pointed their fingers at me as the one to blame for what they feared would be food shortages. Oddly enough some of my associates in the executive branch of the government now felt that I had not been as aggressive as I should have been in seeing that more food was produced.

You can see that, if nothing else, I was impartial. I succeeded in getting everyone angry with me.

But in spite of all the difficulties, American farmers broke all records for production.

We shipped twice as much food to our allies as we did in the first World War. Our Armed Services were twice as large and we fed them much better. Our civilians ate more food per person. The nutritive value of their diets was much higher than ever before, even in peace time.

Many factors made this production record possible. We had good reserves at the start. Farmers and their families worked hard. Through the Extension Service and the local USDA committees, we were able to reach farmers quickly and effectively to tell them of the nation's needs.

But there was yet another factor which I call the American Agricultural Revolution. It had started rather inconspicuously some years before with the advent of such things as the tractor, hybrid corn, liming, fertilization, and better research and extension services.

It was this Agricultural Revolution which helped us through the War, the rehabilitation of Western Europe after the War and the Korean conflict. It is the basic cause of what we think of as our present farm problem.

During the last 20 years, we have increased our total agricultural production 47 percent; our production per acre 44 percent and our production per worker 200 percent. Industry cannot boast of such increases in efficiency. Our production has been increasing annually about 4 percent faster than our population.

The most important task of the present Secretary and those to come later will be to do what they can to see that the Agricultural Revolution which was created by our advanced research, our ingenuity, our superior educational processes and our American system of farming, is not allowed to destroy these same forces which created it.

This can happen if American farmers are forced or even encouraged to continue producing for a market that does not exist.

Basically, the problem is to bring production and effective demand into balance.

We devoutly hope that everything practicable is done to make our abundance available to hungry people at home and abroad. Action which has been taken within the last 10 days to use more of our surpluses to feed the families of the unemployed is most commendable. The same can be said for the recently proposed food for peace program. There can be no better way of reducing our huge stockpiles of grain.

There are some limiting factors on the amount of agricultural products that we can move through regular commercial sales channels. Even if food is cheap, we

Americans refuse to eat much more than 1500 pounds per capita, per year, and our doctors tell us that is too much. We hope that research will find new uses for agricultural products, but the fact is that at present, industry is increasing the substitution of industrial products for farm products.

We farmers are glad that there has been a 50 percent increase in our exports during the past few years, but we must not forget that dumping our farm products on the international market at low prices and easy terms is costly to our taxpayers and very irritating to the producers of these products in other countries.

If we cannot rely upon an increasing demand at home or abroad to absorb our increasing production, we must turn to some means of holding down the increase in production. Fundamentally there are just two ways of reducing production. One is by what is termed free market prices. The other is through a national program which will enable farmers to make the proper adjustments cooperatively.

I have no doubt that if farm prices go low enough and stay low enough, there will be a reduction in production. How low or how long I do not know, but apparently much lower and longer than we have previously experienced.

I do know that when prices go down, we farmers will sacrifice in our homes; we will default on our obligations; we will let our buildings deteriorate and we will otherwise reduce expenditures, so as to be able to buy the good seed, the fertilizer, the fuel, the feed additives and other things which will enable us to maintain or even increase our production. We will do this in the hope that we can hold on to our farms and homes until things get better. But if prices stay low enough long enough, such efforts will prove futile.

I call this the bankruptcy route and I don't believe the nation can afford it. Economic chaos would creep through the rural communities of America. Our present pattern of owner-operation of our farms would be disrupted. This system and the American Agricultural Revolution it made possible have made American farmers the most efficient in the world and in turn have given American consumers the best diet in the world at the lowest cost in terms of their income. American factory workers are expending about 24 percent of their wages for food now as compared with 41 percent 20 years ago.

The communistic nations are having severe problems in food production. There have been estimates that as high as 60 million Chinese may die this year of malnutrition or diseases caused by malnutrition. The Chinese leaders say that unfavorable weather is the chief cause of their difficulty. They recently announced a purge.

Premier Khrushchev recently announced a purge also because of the failure of the Russian food program. He blamed the weather, poor management and the "figurers." This latter may be the equivalent of our economists who always make good whipping boys when things go wrong.

The Russians and the Chinese have been trying to change their system of farming from an owner-operator system to a communal system. Knowing farmers as I do, I can't help surmising that this attempted change may also be a large factor in their food production difficulties.

Despite the fact that in recent years we have had the greatest exodus of people from the land ever known, we still have too many left. This is not a farm problem. It is just part of a national problem of finding productive work and security for millions of our citizens wherever located. This national problem is even more difficult and more important than the farm problem. It constitutes a sharp challenge to our economic and political systems.

To be successful in reducing production, the free price plan — the bankruptcy plan — must ultimately reduce the amount of land under cultivation, or the intensity of its cultivation, or both. I am convinced that this method is undesirable and potentially dangerous. The sensible thing is to use a government program to achieve the same result in an orderly manner. I refer to a land retirement program.

Such a program would reduce the wasting of human, soil, mineral and other important resources involved in producing for a market that does not exist. In fact it would conserve our soil and water resources. It would tend to shift much of our land now under cultivation to reforestation and to watershed cover to which it is better adapted.

Such a program would promote the use of better farming methods rather than making their use impossible. It would make it possible for rural communities to have better, rather than poorer, educational and training facilities for the youth in these areas. It would make it possible for rural communities to continue to be a much needed economic, social and political stabilizing influence in our nation. It would preserve, rather than destroy, the kind of farming system which has met the needs of the nation so well in the past and which is the best guarantee that such needs will be met in the future.

The chief responsibility of the Secretary of Agriculture is to give us the leadership which will help us achieve the results which I have just listed.

Remarks by Clinton P. Anderson

I have been asked to comment briefly on each of three topics: What are the considerations and problems that are important to the Secretary of Agriculture as he serves as a Cabinet officer? Put in its simplest terms, why does a Secretary of Agriculture do the things he does sometimes? What are the considerations that cause him to react in this way?

The first thing a Cabinet member must understand — and never forget — is that he is a part of "the administration." This means he is an integral part of the Executive Branch of Government. He is held accountable *indirectly* through the President of the United States rather than *directly* by the voters.

As a consequence, he is subject to all the pressures that come to focus on the Executive Branch of Government. And, because the President is the unquestioned captain of the Executive team — *and each Cabinet member serves at the will and pleasure of the President* — the eventual impact of these pressures on a Cabinet officer is essentially the same in their effect as they are on the President himself.

This is in sharp contrast to the function of Congress — and the role of the individual members of the U.S. Senate and House of Representatives.

With the exception of the conduct of foreign affairs, the Congress has the primary policy-making function in our government. You have no doubt heard the expression, "The President proposes — the Congress disposes." The drafters of the Constitution wisely provided that it be this way.

Initially, members of the Congress get permission of the voters in their respective districts, or states, to represent them. Then each member of Congress is held personally accountable at each subsequent election for his acts of commission or omission.

All citizens should understand that the Secretary of Agriculture is primarily an "administrative officer" in the Executive Branch of Government. I'm afraid there is widespread confusion on this point. I sincerely hope the appearance on this program of five former administrative heads of this particular government agency — the U.S. Department of Agriculture — doesn't divert attention from where the primary responsibility for government farm policy determination *really* rests — namely, with the Congress and the farmers' own organizations.

In 1949 I stated my attitude on the role of farm organizations in farm policy formulation as follows:

"I want to see farm legislation developed by farmers through their own farm organizations in cooperation with the members of Congress who are sincerely interested in the long-time interests of farmers and who are determined to fit a sound farm program into our free enterprise system."

In preparation for my participation in today's programs, I reread the hearings conducted in 1947–48 by the Senate and House committees on agriculture.

In retrospect I'm glad that my testimony, and that of my associates in the USDA, reflected our clear realization that, although the Department could and should make recommendations, the responsibility for making *policy* rests squarely on the Legislative Branch of the government — the Congress.

I sincerely believe that our clear-cut recognition of this important concept was one of the main reasons that the testimony of the general farm organizations in 1947–48 reflected substantial agreement on postwar price support policy. Instead of coming forth with a specific plan, I insisted that the Congress and the general farm organizations shoulder their rightful responsibility in policy formulation. This they did. The Agricultural Act of 1948 — that part which was not a plain one-year extension of existing law — providing for price supports related to the supply-demand situation and a modernized parity formula, was the direct outgrowth of these efforts. It is a shame that this legislation wasn't allowed to become operative at the time of its passage. Many subsequent surplus problems would have been avoided — or substantially reduced.

In the Department's testimony at that time, we suggested a high degree of flexibility, both as to support levels and methods; we preferred to have loan and purchase operations limited to storable commodities; and we sought reasonable upper and lower support levels. These recommendations are still valid.

What are the changes that have taken place in these considerations and problems that impinge upon a Secretary of Agriculture from the time that the individuals concerned served to the present; and what further changes does he see that are likely to cause Secretaries of Agriculture to react differently over the next decade?

Important changes have occurred since 1947–49. For example —

Farm output per man hour has nearly doubled;

Total farm output has increased 30 percent;

Farm output per unit of input has increased by one-fourth;

Feed consumption per 100 pounds of broilers produced has declined 25 percent;

Output of all livestock and livestock products per hour of labor has increased more than 50 percent;

The rate of increase in farm output per hour of labor has been about 2½ times the rate of increase for non-farm workers.

All of this reflects our great technical triumph. We have expanded our productivity through the development and widespread use of new machinery, chemical fertilizers, insecticides, improved varieties of plants, and higher yielding livestock. In effect, we have substituted brainpower for brawn, and this has revolutionized our agriculture. It has raised our productive capacity to such an unprecedented high level that it is the envy of all the world. The output of each farm worker in the United States is, on the average, enough to supply himself and 23 other persons, as compared with only about a dozen other persons just before World War II. Nowhere else in the world does the level of output per farm worker even approach this average.

We are indeed blessed by the great productivity in our agriculture and the ability of our farm people to produce. From this source we have been able to derive and maintain much of the strength we as a nation need in this troubled world. Unfortunately, however, we still have to learn how to master the capabilities of our agriculture to produce. Farm output is still being maintained at, and in some instances above, the record high levels that were reached to meet the unprecedented war and post-war requirements. Surpluses have piled up, and farm income has suffered. The serious imbalance that has come to dominate our agriculture stands before all of us as a challenge which we can and must conquer.

As acreage is cut, farm production climbs. As income-depressing farm surpluses become larger, the percentage of farmers to the total population becomes smaller. This situation presents an ominous warning to anyone concerned with high *per family* farm income.

As one who served as Secretary of Agriculture in the OPA days, I believe I understand the built-in pressures for distributing benefits equitably — with "equitable" defined as "equal." This may be a necessary method of rationing, but it's an unsatisfactory way of determining per family farm income.

Looking ahead for the next decade, what should we do, taking into account the national and international problems and pressures that are likely to influence policy actions?

I would approach the future with essentially the same outlook I had in 1947 when I recommended that the Congress adopt a practical policy for American agriculture — a policy of organized, sustained and realistic abundance.

It is most unfortunate that in agricultural program discussions during the recent post-war years, the country has had its attention focused primarily on the question of price supports — whether they should be rigid or flexible. The great argument largely ignored the fact that price supports by themselves do not provide the complete and effective kind of farm program needed by our agriculture and the national economy.

The farm problem is far more than a problem of surpluses and the threat of surpluses. It is also a problem of people and land — people who have certain cherished hopes and aspirations they would like to see come true, and land that should be used wisely for the satisfaction of human wants now and in the future.

There is a crying need for all of these aspects of the farm problem to be brought into real focus so that we may regain our perspective and take up the challenge that we face.

In dealing with the problems of agriculture and its people, we must first decide, as a *Nation*, what kind of agriculture we really want. We can decide between a democratic world of abundance and a regimented world of scarcity. When that decision is reached, we then must be willing and ready to do what it takes to bring about such an agriculture and be prepared to stand the cost of getting it done.

As I envision the kind of world in which we live, we have no practical alternative but to accept the fact that our agriculture must be one of abundance. We therefore must learn to live with it — to organize our agriculture's capability for abundance, to sustain it, and to make it conform to the realities of demand, national and world conditions, and the progress of science and technology.

In the final analysis, this means producing what our people really want — what our domestic and export markets are able to absorb with reasonable supplies for normal carryover and necessary reserves for any contingencies that might arise. It means creating a pattern of agricultural production which uses our resources wisely and provides the basis for sustaining abundance.

There is no mistaking the fact that adjustment is needed in agriculture from the pattern that has evolved during the recent war and post-war years. In bringing about this adjustment, we face the dilemma of doing this without hurting the farmer — of trying to maintain and improve living conditions for farm people in the face of increasing improvement in technology in farm production.

Looking back over the record of what has transpired, it well could be said that the Agricultural Act of 1948 was not too bad a piece of legislation. It still is not too bad, providing the clutter that has been added to it is cleaned up. It needs to be brought up to date, and there is also need for essential flexibility for sound decision-making.

Many of the commodity problems are fairly well confined. For the most part, these are in wheat and the feed grains, including corn. These are the commodities on which we need to focus more attention. To deal with the problems that affect them, we need to develop more flexible arrangements than have been available up to now.

What is required is not so much a detailed legislative formula, but the development of the kind of flexibility that will permit the managers or administrators of the program to make needed decisions under the broad guidelines of Congressional intent. We also need competent administration and a will to administer proper programs despite the pressures. Experience in agriculture shows that when Congress writes a specific formula into law it is only building up its own pressures.

Overall, we need a more realistic and forward-looking approach to our agricultural and rural problems. Fundamentally, the broad requirements for such an approach have not changed much over the past decade and a half. My own feeling is that a policy of organized, sustained and realistic abundance still makes sense for this country's agriculture and its people; and it also makes sense if we are to accept and carry out our responsibilities of leadership in the world of nations.

Remarks by Charles F. Brannan

It was not until after the so-called "great depression" in the late 1920s and the election of Franklin Roosevelt in 1932 that the Department of Agriculture assumed a major role in the economic affairs of the country. True, it was that farmers had long been a political force, but their expression of political power had seldom been influenced by farm economics, prior to the 1932 election.

With the enactment of the first AAA legislation and greater emphasis upon farm price problems and soil conservation, the department began to assume a significant role in the daily operations of farmers and ranchers. It also began to perform some services for consumers, although only incidentally concerning itself with the prices consumers paid for food.

About this time, the capability of the American farmer to produce increasingly greater quantities of food and fiber was beginning to be a factor in the economic life of the nation. Economists told us that the recent depression had started on the farm and later spread into industries and the cities.

At the same time, problems of distribution and marketing of our farm products began to appear. In the late 1920s and early 1930s, many of the nation's citizens were experiencing malnutrition and hardship in the face of abundant supplies.

None of these problems have wholly disappeared. Some have worsened. The Secretaries of Agriculture present here today have all been confronted with the problems which have arisen out of our capability to produce food abundantly and our apparent lack of ability to move this abundance into the hands of consumers at home and abroad.

May I say here, parenthetically, that this is one of the few nations on the face of the earth to be confronted with problems of continuing ample supplies of almost all kinds of food and fiber, and I often think how much better off we are to be worrying about abundance than about scarcity.

There has been no major difference of opinions between or within political parties about the pursuit of basic research into all of the unknowns of plant and animal life related to production. Nor has there been any great difference of opinion about the need for applied research. Likewise, there has been almost unanimous agreement that farmers must be encouraged to preserve the future productive capability of their lands against the ever growing demands of the figure.

Most of the serious policy problems about which there has been dispute have related to how our federal government can effectively and at reasonable cost, encourage and sustain farmers in their effort to produce ample supplies of food without depressing their own prices and, thereby, economically destroying themselves. Farmers are ever confronted by the so-called law of supply and demand. I use the word "law" with some hesitation because this "law" is more honored in its violations and manipulations, by those who dominate many market places, than by its free application.

So far, we have been speaking of the many economic factors of production and marketing with which Secretaries of Agriculture are confronted as they discharge their duties as a Cabinet officer. Now, I hope it might aid us to understand why the Secretaries of Agriculture, past, present and in the future, have reacted or will react to their problems, if we were to review the organic legal relationships between a member of the Cabinet, the President and the Congress.

There is little, if any, Constitutional basis for any Cabinet position, from Secretary of State to Department of Health, Education and Welfare.

The word "Cabinet" does not appear in the Constitution and there is no language in the Constitution or the Acts of Congress which formalizes such a body. The existence of a Cabinet, as we understand it today, rests solely upon the language of Article II, Section 2 of the Constitution which, in the course of describing the powers of the President provides, "he may require the opinions in writing of the principal officers in each of the executive branches upon any subject relative to the duties of their respective offices."

It will be observed that the formation of the Cabinet is not remotely suggested by this language. Nevertheless, the subject was discussed at length during the Constitutional Convention. Early in the sessions Gouverneur Morris introduced a proposal for a "Council of State" to be composed of the Chief Justice and five heads of executive departments. He proposed that the President might submit any matter to the discussion of the Council and require written opinions of them. But, he emphasized that the Chief Executive "shall in all cases exercise his own judgment, and either conform to such opinions or not as he may think proper."

Alexander Hamilton expressed the apprehension of the Constitutional Convention about such a Council when he said, "a council to a magistrate, who is himself responsible for what he does, is generally nothing better than a clog upon his good intentions, is often the instruments and accomplices of his bad, and is almost always a cloak to conceal his faults."

On the other side of the argument, George Washington wrote, "the impossibility that one man should be able to perform all the great business of the state I take to have been the reason for instituting the great departments and appointing officers therein to assist the Supreme Magistrate in discharging the duties of his trust."

To this day no law requires the President to create a Cabinet; or, having appointed one, to convene it in session or accept its views. Nor is he prevented from dissolving his Cabinet or of disposing of any or all of its members whenever he sees fit. True, the President may appoint executive department heads "only by and with the advice and consent of the Senate," but he may terminate their services at will.

We, at this table, had only to read the language of our respective Certificates of Appointment to be sharply reminded of the fact that we each served "at the will of the President for the time being."

Thus, in the final analysis, the Secretary of Agriculture carries out the policies of the President of the United States, using the administrative authority, funds, resources and personnel which the Congress, from time to time, makes available to the executive branch of government for these purposes.

The ultimate authority and responsibility is the President's. The Cabinet officer, for all practical purposes, is the President's agent and representative for carrying out the assignments given to the executive branch by the Congress.

Thus, in the performance of his duties, the Secretary of Agriculture is, first of all, circumscribed by the policies of the administration of which he is a part.

Second, he can go no further than the Congress authorizes.

How much any Secretary may influence the policy decisions of his President depends upon the two men concerned. But the final responsibility rests with the President.

I refer to these facts, not to excuse any deed or apparent policy of Secretaries past, present or future, to which any of you may or will take exception, but rather in the interest of fuller understanding.

In my judgment, the broad agricultural policy of this government has been constant since the days of Franklin Roosevelt. It is well stated in the opening paragraphs of the AAA legislation.

So, also, the farm problems which confront this government have not basically changed. They involve the distribution of our abundance, domestically and also throughout the world for the achievement of the ultimate objective of all mankind — namely, a peaceful world in which all men will have a reasonable opportunity to develop their intellectual and spiritual potentialities. We continue to fail in this responsibility so long as our abundance remains unused or undevoted to this end.

Somehow this government has fallen far short, both on the domestic and world front, in applying this God-given abundance to the purpose and objective for which, in my humble judgment, He gave us the skills and resources to produce it.

It is the responsibility of the Secretary of Agriculture to so use the laws and resources at his disposal to make certain that there is always an ample supply of food on hand for our domestic needs, in peace and in emergencies, for our foreign trade and now for use in supporting the free peoples of the world in the contest with Communism for the minds of men.

If there was a major failure in the supply of food in this country, the economic impact would be almost immeasurable on every other industry and every individual. Perhaps a few of the farmers who were fortunate enough to produce a crop would temporarily benefit. But we know that even they would soon be confronted with price ceilings as was the case during and following World War II.

In addition, the Secretary of Agriculture is today charged with a greater responsibility to consumers than he has ever been heretofore.

It is impossible for consumers to reconcile ever mounting prices for their daily bread with the ever decreasing prices to the farmer who produces the essential ingredients of their daily bread. Above all, it is impossible for any of us to reconcile the $6 billion annual cost of operating the Department of Agriculture the past few years, and its resultant tax burden, with the negative results or absence of any benefits to both farmers and consumers.

These are the problems of the present and future Secretaries of Agriculture and I know we wish for them the strong supporting arm of providence in their search for solutions.

Remarks by Ezra T. Benson

In these prepared remarks we have been asked to answer three questions. First, why does a Secretary of Agriculture do the things he does? Any of us could talk about this for hours. Let me say that I believe all of us as Secretaries acted in what we sincerely felt was the best interest of agriculture and the whole nation.

Well-intentioned men reach different solutions — make different decisions — not because they lack sincerity, but because different backgrounds and different philosophies lead them to see facts in different lights.

My own actions stemmed from a basic philosophy which I expressed in a statement of principles a few days after becoming Secretary. I believe firmly that our freedom is a God-given blessing, vouchsafed to us under the Constitution — that it is more precious than life itself — and that it must be continually guarded, lest we lose it bit by bit to Big Government.

I believe that the primary objective of agriculture is to provide consumers with high quality food and fiber *at prices that give farmers a fair and steady return in the market place.*

I believe that the sound method of achieving this objective is not through government price fixing but through adequate programs of research, education, and market development.

I believe that price supports can be a valuable tool for the farmer if properly used and not abused. Their original purpose was and still is good — a device to facilitate orderly marketing. Their improper use results in loss of markets, the accumulation of surpluses in government warehouses and high costs to the taxpayers.

I believe that government should strive to help the individual and the group to help themselves, rather than to try to legislate prosperity for them.

And, I believe, finally, that the supreme test of any government policy in agriculture or outside of it should be:

> "How will this affect the character,
> morale, and well-being of our people."

A planned and subsidized economy weakens initiative, discourages industry, destroys character and demoralizes the people — and surely is not good for America.

These were the principles which we tried conscientiously to follow. They were the foundation upon which my actions as Secretary were based.

In following one's principles one does not operate in a vacuum, but in the rough and tumble of Washington politics. This involved some give and take in striving to achieve our goals.

For example, in the battle for flexible price supports in 1954, we did not get all that we asked. But we have managed in these eight years to make substantial progress towards realistic support levels which have resulted in improved markets for farmers.

Most of you know, especially my distinguished colleagues here, that the quest for flexibility in support levels did not originate with me. Let us turn back to 1948 and recall that supporters of flexibility included:

Both political parties,

Major farm organizations including the National Farmers Union.

President Truman, who urged it in a message to Congress, and Members of Congress who approved it in the Agricultural Act of 1948.

Why does the Secretary act as he does? Because he believes, or should believe, that his actions are right.

The second question comes down to this: What changes affecting agriculture have taken place during my years in office? The answer is: Some of the most amazing changes in U.S. world history.

The technological revolution in agriculture intensified until it became almost a scientific explosion. Whereas in 1952 one farm worker, on the average, provided food and fiber for 17 persons, now he provides for 25 persons. When I visited Russia last year I found that one peasant produces only enough for 4 or 5 comrades.

The weather certainly had an influence on farm output. Never, I venture, have we had such favorable growing conditions as we've seen in the past three or four years. And these followed severe drought which was a problem that faced us in the early years.

The combination of farmer efficiency, technical advances and good weather added up to the most amazing upsurge in agricultural productivity ever known in this country. In eight years production per man-hour of work in agriculture rose 63 percent — some three times as fast as the rate of productivity increase in non-agricultural industry.

The trend towards bigger farms and fewer farmers continued as a by-product of the technological revolution. The movement off the farm slackened from the record numbers of the previous seven years. We introduced the Rural Development Program to help farmers make these adjustments in their own best interests.

All of these changes affect agriculture in the present and will affect it in the future.

We came into office, as you know, at a time of great upheaval. The prices of farm products had been falling for two years, price controls had caused a black market in beef and there was strong resistance to ending them. Many areas of the country were suffering from severe and long continued drought, a shortage of storage capacity was close at hand, and the value of our farm exports in fiscal 1953 was at a postwar low of $2.8 billion. CCC investment in many commodities was going up — and dairy products were running into serious surplus.

Though these were small problems, perhaps, when contrasted with world peace and national defense, they had far-reaching importance. A sound agriculture is vital to a sound national economy. A sound national economy is the very basis of a strong defense. And, of course, a strong U.S. defense is the foundation of world peace.

We have made much progress toward a sounder agriculture. We have made some of the adjustments in price support levels needed to improve markets and reduce surpluses. Beef, pork, poultry, and dairy products have shown their ability to make sound adjustments. Last year was a rather favorable year for cattle and hogs. It was a year of record high income for dairy producers. 1960 was a better year for poultry than 1959. We have made progress in helping cotton and corn work their way toward better markets.

But the big commodity problem is wheat, and the problem will only be solved with far-reaching new legislation.

In other areas, agricultural exports have almost doubled since 1953. Both the volume and the value of exports last year set a new record of almost $4.8 billion.

We have vastly expanded agricultural research — appropriations have increased 171 percent. Farmers applied more conservation to their farms than in any other eight-year period in history. Much progress has been made in programs to protect small watersheds and prevent floods.

Many new programs were brought into existence. The Rural Development Program is now under way, or in the planning stage, in 350 counties in 39 states and Puerto Rico. This program of adjustment is the first real concerted effort to deal with the special needs of farmers, who for a variety of reasons find themselves in severest economic difficulty.

The Food for Peace Program is putting U.S. food and fiber to good use around the world in the interest of peace. We exported a grand total of $30.4 billion in farm products in this last Administration.

Our agricultural exports during 1960, I repeat, reached new all-time highs for value and quantity. About 70 percent of this total represented commercial sales and the balance was shipped under special export programs. No nation in the world has ever exported such quantities of food and natural fibers.

Besides providing record high exports of the past eight years, the Food for Peace Program is donating food for over 20 million U.S. citizens and some 62 million persons in 92 foreign countries.

The Great Plains Conservation Program, started in 1956, is improving agricultural stability on 13 million acres.

The Conservation Reserve Program has taken 29 million acres of farm land out of surplus production — while adding greatly to the conservation of soil, water, forests, and wildlife resources.

And I could go on.

Question number three concerns the future.

Based on a lifetime of experience as a farmer and in farm related activities, including eight years as Secretary, this is what I think needs to be done in the best interests of our farm people, the nation, and the free world.

First, the "Food for Peace" program should be continued and expanded where feasible. Remarkable use has been made of our surplus stocks through special export programs, but there are additional steps that can be taken. Food is serving humanitarian needs in foreign lands, aiding in economic development, and promoting the cause of peace and freedom.

Second, programs of research to develop new foreign and domestic markets, including new industrial uses, for our farm products should be vigorously pushed forward.

Third, laws should be enacted to improve the price support mechanism by providing levels of price support that will allow farm commodities to move into regular marketing channels, and at the same time afford adequate price protection.

Fourth, the use of farmland should be further adjusted in accordance with needs by such a program as an expanded Conservation Reserve.

Fifth, the Rural Development Program should be emphasized and expanded as rapidly as is feasible. We can help our small farmers make the adjustments which they want and need to improve their standard of living.

I would emphasize that as Secretary of Agriculture there are many more joys than disappointments — many more achievements than frustrations. In spite of the inevitable controversy it is a wonderful opportunity to serve people who are the salt of the earth — American farmers and ranchers.

For eight years I have had the privilege of serving all the people of the United States as a member of President Eisenhower's team. I cannot begin to express my admiration for the people of this land as they have revealed themselves to me during these eight years.

I have faith in the people of the United States.

May a kind Providence give our new leaders the vision and courage necessary:

To keep this land strong so that we may always be free.

To keep our nation free so that we may live at peace.

To keep America at peace so that we may serve all mankind with charity.

To serve humanity with charity so that the promise of this choice land may be fulfilled.

God grant it may be so.

Question and Answer Session

Question — Mr. Soth:

I would like to direct my first question to Mr. Wallace. You said that you thought government was in agriculture to stay and you thought farmers needed the power of government . . . I'd like to explore that a little further. I assume that you mean some kind of supply control, that farmers need help from government in controlling the production of their products. How far do you think we need to go with controls?

Answer — Mr. Wallace:

I think we should go the minimum necessary to deal with key points. I think the feed-grain livestock complex in particular is a key point. With regard to self adjusting products like eggs or broilers, I am very skeptical about government stepping in, except in cases of very unusual need. But at the same time, I do recognize that with the human stomach as it is, a very small surplus can cause a very great damage to the farmer without doing any good to the consumer. I do think that we need to call in the very best brains to consider what could be done to eliminate that damage done to farmers. I think, for instance, of the large number of New Jersey egg producers who went out of production last year. Was that a good thing or not?

Question — Mr. Streeter:

Everyone agrees that we're producing about 5 to 7 percent too much of a few things and I'd like to ask each of these Five Secretaries which mechanism he would choose for bringing the supply of these things that are in over production down to a more desirable level. There are about three choices that anyone mentions. One is to let price do it, another is to take sufficient land out of production; and the third one, that we're hearing quite a lot about recently, is to have market quotas to control what farmers are allowed to sell. I wonder which one of these routes these gentlemen would favor?

Answer — Mr. Benson:

I think the record indicates that our attempts to fix prices and control production in agriculture have failed rather miserably. We need to place our emphasis on research, education, and market development and permit price to play more nearly its role in helping to direct production and consumption. Four-fifths of agriculture is free today, and is in fairly good balance. That doesn't mean that we can move in the direction I have indicated *immediately*. It will take time, but I do believe that we need to place our emphasis on markets, on research, on education, and put *less* emphasis on government action. It seems to me the economics of the farm problem are rather simple, it's the politics of the problem that is baffling. What farmers really need is *less* government in agriculture, *less politics* in agriculture.

Answer — Mr. Brannan:

Well, you know I am sure that every group in the nation would say the same thing for itself. I am sure that all of the bankers would say, ''We need less government in banking,'' but if you ask them do you need the government to take care of somebody else's business, they'd probably say, ''Well I think there are some problems over there that the government ought to take care of.'' When we come down to the final analysis of a situation in which our country is capable of producing more than it absorbs in normal channels of trade and commerce, then, in my opinion, *history* has told us that the government must step into the operation of marketing and production. After all, the government isn't somebody over there. I am a part of it, and each and every one of you is a part of it. Whether or not you get good government in agriculture or anything else depends upon whether or not you supply it good participation at your level. So, lets not separate ourselves from our government and say this is something bad that I have nothing to do with. Finally, I think if we ask our government to provide an opportunity for orderly marketing of our farm products at reasonable prices in the market place, then farmers should not hesitate to accept reasonable regulations or controls of either their production or their marketing. This has been the philosophy of our government ever since the AAA; nobody has attacked it forthrightly and I don't think they will in a long time.

Answer — Senator Anderson:

Well, I think I would try to find out where the trouble is and then go to that spot, rather than to the place where the trouble isn't. For instance, cotton; we had about 10 million bales produced in 1957 and we had about 15 million bales produced in 1959. But the 15 million bales in 1959 didn't hurt us as much as the 10 million bales in '57 . . . so it isn't always large production that causes trouble. We had a more realistic cotton program in 1959 and we moved cotton in unprecedented quantities under that program. Our wheat program is out of line . . . our feed grain program is bad; we ought to spend our time on those programs and leave cotton and rice alone which seem to get along pretty well. It might not be too bad an idea to cut our $250 million in soil conservation payments which are being used to improve land while other land is being put to rest under another program. I don't think it makes too much sense to take out a whole lot of land in an Acreage Reserve program and then stimulate people to fertilize the remaining land by offering $250 million in payments. I think we ought to decide what we need and spend time on that.

Answer — Mr. Wickard:

I believe the question is, if we are producing 5 percent more than we can dispose of at a satisfactory price, what can we do about it. There is just one place to begin and that is with the land itself. We must have some kind of an orderly land retirement program which will preserve the American farming system that has meant so much to us and this entire world.

Answer — Mr. Henry Wallace:

I feel very strongly that it *is* important for the farmer to have equality in bargaining power and I would agree completely with Secretary Benson — if there were no labor unions, if there were no corporations, if there were no subsidies for ships, if there were no subsidies for magazines. I long for that primitive existence myself; I'm made that way. I hate to see government intervene, but we are not living in that kind of world which the American farmer really longs for. As a matter of fact, we're living in the kind of world in which perhaps the best occupation farmers could be engaged in would be the growing of geese to produce feathers for feather-bedding, both in labor and in industry.

Question — Mr. Hathaway:

Senator Anderson and several other of our distinguished speakers have indicated a good deal of satisfaction with flexibility of the type included in the Agricultural Act of 1948. However, Mr. Brannan recommmended that new legislation be passed soon after taking office. I wonder if he would like to outline why he thought changes were necessary and whether he still feels that those changes were desirable?

Answer —Mr. Brannan:

Well, Dr. Hathaway, and ladies and gentlemen, if you're expecting me to say that I now disavow the Brannan plan, you can change your mind. I do not. While I think the act of '48 had a great deal of virtue, I still think that there was room for improvement. It needed greater flexibility, as Senator Anderson defined it here this afternoon; flexibility in means and methods of dealing with the many problems which confront a Secretary of Agriculture when he undertakes to provide some stability in the market place for a very wide variety of crops, from the quickly perishable to the almost indestructible storables, such as cotton. It did need additional provisions. I think the effort to provide them was sound, as I think subsequent efforts to adapt the law to the problems as they developed were sound. I don't think you can freeze any law and say we should never do anything else about it. If that were true the Congress probably wouldn't need to convene very often.

Answer — Senator Anderson:

In all fairness to Mr. Brannan it ought to be pointed out that the Congress and the farm organizations worked on the Agricultural Act of 1948, but immediately after the 1948 election in which there were some surprises, the demand came to let the administration bring up a program. That has been followed consistently ever since and I think it is bad. They wanted Mr. Benson to come up with some cure-all for everything; now they're going to ask poor Orville Freeman, who has had very little agricultural experience, to solve the whole problem. Now this thing comes back to the Congress and the farm organizations, and if they don't come in with some leadership I think it's wrong to say, "well, let the new Secretary come out with a complete and comprehensive program." And when he tries to do it he catches it from every direction.

Answer — Mr. Benson:

If we had a few more members in the Congress like Senator Anderson it would be a lot easier for Secretaries of Agriculture. I'd just like to say this. We can produce more than we can consume of almost anything in this country, if there is the government imposed price incentive to induce that production. When government gets into the pricing field we're usually in difficulty. I think the best thing the government can do is to withdraw from it and put their emphasis in other areas.

Answer — Mr. Wallace:

With regard to price being a determinant of production, I happened to be in the seed corn business in 1932, and we put out seed corn on the basis of getting back half of the amount of the increase over what ordinary corn produced. We got very substantial amounts of corn, and we sold a great bit of it at 10¢ a bushel at the nearest elevator and some for 6¢ a bushel. Did that low price control production? I leave it to you — does low price control production in these great basic crops? In the case of eggs I grant it. In the case of potatoes I grant it, in the case of many of the horticultural crops I grant it, but when you take these great basic crops does it control production? You in Michigan don't know too much about these. In Iowa, Indiana, Illinois, Nebraska, Kansas, South Dakota and Minnesota they know a lot about them and they know that price does not control production to any great extent there. In addition, I wish to say that there is such a thing as responsibility to the soil, responsibility to future generations. Under the uncontrolled production situation in 1930–32, we were mining the soil and not putting anything back. I think it is important to think about the soil, and I have no apologies to make to anyone with regard to the 1938 Act which set the prices from 52 to 75 percent. It was a disaster protection.

Answer — Mr. Wickard:

I am a farmer, and know how I react as a farmer and how my fellow farmers react. When prices go down we will sacrifice our homes, we will let our buildings and our equipment deteriorate, we will do all the things we can in order to have enough money to buy the good seed and fertilizer and feed additives and all the other things to keep up our production. That is all we as individual farmers can do. Don't forget that fundamental thing — lower prices induce farmers to increase their production because they have to increase their volume as individuals in order to meet overhead in farming. I hope that there are some farmers in this audience who will agree with me on that particular thing.

Another very fundamental thing in this agricultural picture — we don't want a scarcity program in the United States; the consumers don't want it; we couldn't afford it. We want to have reserves for our protection and everybody else's. But let's not charge that bill up to the farmers who produce them. Food is an expensive reserve and surely belongs to the entire nation as much as our defense stock pile which we build up for the protection and safety of the free world.

Question — Mr. Grinnell:

This question came from a Kalamazoo county reader. As long as we have a surplus of food to pile up in storage won't small farmers need to find a place in industry? Mr. Brannan would you care to comment or make a prediction?

Answer — Mr. Brannan:

Well, there has been a trend toward increase in size of farms, and that increase has lent some substantial pressure. I am not one who contends for small farms or that we should freeze the farm size at its 1900 level, or its 1920 average, or its 1940 average. I think farms have been increasing in size just naturally and normally as we go along and as we get better machinery and are better able to use our available labor resources. It is not the small farmer in actuality who contributes a great bulk of our production. Therefore, a change in size of farms is not going to solve the so-called surplus problem. Actually, I do not believe that a surplus problem exists in this country nor in this world. Maybe that's another speech or another statement, but I do not believe we have excessive supplies of anything. We have a scarcity of understanding and *will* to use our God given abundance for the purposes for which I think He gave it to us.

Answer — Mr. Benson:

I think we have in the United States the most efficient farmers in all the world. And because of that all of our people benefit and are blessed. I have been in countries within the last year where 40 to 50 percent of the total labor force is busy trying to produce enough food and fiber for the rest of the population. In those countries, they don't have refrigerators, stoves, automobiles, and consumer goods like we have here. Because our farmers are so efficient, it requires a smaller number to operate our farms. That means that there are more people available to do other things — to make radios and TV sets and kitchen equipment which contribute to our high standard of living. I don't believe we want to do anything that will impede progress toward greater efficiency. Our farms are still family-type operations, 96 percent of them, the same as they were 30 years ago. They're becoming somewhat larger, but they are still family-type operations and they are more efficient than they have ever been. The small farm problem is one of adjustment and serious adjust-ment. That's why the Rural Development Program was initiated, to help farmers on small units make the adjustments which they must make in their own best interest.

Question — Mr. Soth:

I would like to ask Mr. Benson a question. You say that farmers should get their fair return in the market place, and that you don't think the government should engage in price fixing. What do you think about the government buying up $9 billion worth of grain, keeping if off the market, disposing of it overseas and thereby protecting farm incomes as we have been doing in recent years? Let me go just a little bit further. You say that four-fifths of agriculture is free from government intervention. But isn't it true that this policy we have been following under you — piling up the grain, storing it, and disposing of it overseas — hasn't that protected all agriculture? Hasn't that been good for agriculture?

Answer — Mr. Benson:

The old legislation under which we have been operating, gave us no choice but to take over the commodities — that was written in the law. Many of these support levels have been at points above competitive level so that products could not move into consumption. Therefore, commodities moved into government warehouses and the warehouses, of course, are not markets. With a flexible price support system, and we had it at the end of the war as Congress intended, we would not have built up surpluses. The commodities would move into consumption, our markets would expand rather than contract. In 1954 we had lost about 60 percent of our cotton market abroad simply because we priced cotton out of the world market, and it had accumulated in government warehouses. We must be competitive in all of our commodities, in price, in quality, and in promotion. If we're not competitive then we lose markets.

Question — Mr. Soth:

Well, what would have happened to farm income in these last few years if we hadn't had these programs?

Answer — Mr. Benson:

I think in the long run you don't help farm income by accumulating great surpluses and letting them hang over the market year after year. They're bound to have a bad effect unless the government is going to take over the market completely and fix prices.

Question — Mr. Soth:

You're not answering my question. What would have happened to farm income in the last eight years if we hadn't had these programs?

Answer — Mr. Benson:

As a matter of fact, in the areas where we didn't have government programs — government interference — we have had better markets than we have in the other areas. There no doubt was some help during the period of adjustment because we got no change in the legislation.

Question — Mr. Soth:

Well, economists who have studied this question, Land Grant College economists and government economists, say that net farm income would have been one-third lower if we hadn't had these programs. Is this true?

Answer — Mr. Benson:

Some economists indicate that overall farm income would have been $2 billion more had it not been for government interference in the field of crops — so what are you going to do?

Question — Mr. Wallace:

I just wondered if I could reverse the tables and ask a question of a member of the panel? I would like to ask Mr. Soth if it is true that we are spending $40 billion a year on military and perhaps have accumulated some $100 billion or more in the way of military hardware all over the world? Is it too much to ask from the point of the overall security of the nation to have the same mental attitude with regard to our agricultural surplus? Is it too much, as we survey the necessary security of our nation, to have $9 billion of crops stored in this county and abroad in the form of food? Is it too much to have $15 billion stored? We have had a regular drum fire from city editors with regard to the utter iniquity of consumers paying any cost of these farm programs. You belong to one of these city papers. I don't know that your city paper has been guilty of saying this, but I just wonder if it is wrong to have as much as $15 billion agricultural surplus from the standpoint of the welfare of the country, in view of the dangers involved, and in view of how much has been accumulated in the form of military hardware? What do you think? What is real security? That's what I am asking.

Answer — Mr. Soth:

Well, if I understand the question correctly, it's whether we have been subsidizing agriculture too heavily in light of the world situation and what we spend on military goods. My answer is no, and I think too often we discuss this problem of agricultural subsidies in terms of the total USDA budget, most of which goes to city people and a fairly small part of it, less than half, really goes for subsidies to farm people. Two to three billion dollars per year as compared with $40 billion for defense, I don't think that's exorbitant at all. I think it is a very good thing that we have had these subsidies for agriculture in recent years.

Question — Mr. Streeter:

Mr. Wickard, as a livestock farmer, and knowing the livestock farmers of the corn belt as you do, do you think that livestock farmers want or can tolerate production controls for livestock, dairy or poultry? My second question is do they even want controls on feed grains?

Answer — Mr. Wickard:

To answer the first part of your question, I think back to the early days of the New Deal and the idea of controlling the production of livestock. I don't think that farmers want any control of livestock or feed grains. Furthermore, I don't think it is practical. I believe Secretary Wallace made the same statement. We are producing more feed grains right now than we are consuming and I would just simply start with the land itself — controlling livestock output back where the feed grains are produced.

Question — Mr. Hathaway:

There have been several mentions of greater use of our farm abundance abroad. Practically, what can we do that hasn't been done in recent years in this regard, and why hasn't it been done?

Answer — Mr. Benson:

I mentioned earlier that our exports last year were at an all time high in dollar value and in volume. We have had a tremendous increase in our exports abroad, we have developed new markets, we have had an expansion of markets. I think we have not reached the saturation point, but I do feel that it is going to take some real effort and some real work and real promotion abroad to further increase our exports, but I think it can be done. We have developed some new markets, for example, in the case of poultry, markets which did not exist previously. We're now selling some $50 million worth of dressed poultry a year to Germany and $12 to $15 million to Switzerland which are new markets. We have expanded markets for dairy products and wheat products abroad through introduction of a school lunch program and other market development projects. I think we must keep working at this. I think we can further expand our markets at home and abroad, but it is going to take real effort.

Answer — Mr. Brannan:

The question goes beyond the development of normal markets. The question is whether or not there are uses for this food in our effort to win the support of the free peoples and the many millions of uncommitted peoples of the world. Food is one of the real effective weapons for peace. The Food for Peace legislation which is on the books should be grossly expanded to use our surplus products. We could do so with less money than we are using now to store them. This is the area in which we must very carefully explore the use of these great resources.

Answer — Senator Anderson:

I would like to point out that I had the responsibility for food right after the war when we were to feed many people of other lands. We have a great surplus of wheat now, but then it was so scarce that we almost had to ration ourselves. We had to put our total stocks of wheat in this country down to 75 million bushels when the millers all told me it would never come below 200 million bushels. We sacrificed in order to take care of people in other countries who were hungry. Now, if we could send them something when wheat was scarce why can't we send them something when wheat is in surplus?

Answer — Mr. Wallace:

I admire Secretary Benson's very strenuous efforts to utilize Public Law 480 to export large quantities of food products. Since 1954 I understand that pretty close to $4 billion worth has been sent abroad. We have just begun to utilize this extraordinary power represented by this vast supply of food.

I don't think we begin to realize the utter importance . . . I say utter, utter, utter importance of this surplus in saving the free world. The government does enter in there, and I think, Senator Anderson, that you wanted to make sure that this surplus is used with the greatest of intelligence. Not to hurt Canada, not to hurt Argentina, not to hurt Australia; through the United Nations we can make sure that these countries are included, too.

Answer — Mr. Benson:

There has never been such an effort put into the movement of surpluses abroad and gifts to needy people as we have experienced during recent years. For example, our food products that are in surplus are made available, without limitation as to quantity, to all churches, relief, and welfare organizations in other countries. However, there are some limitations that don't appear on the surface. For example, we run into some opposition when we move quantities of wheat into some countries because farmers say it is going to depress their prices. We run into cases where they don't have sufficient port facilities to unload the boats, and when they get them unloaded they don't have the storage capacity or the transportation inside the country. That's why under P.L. 480 there is provision made to take foreign currencies in exchange for these commodities, then loan the currencies back for economic development. In that economic development, they build transportation and port facilities in order that they might be able to handle more of these needed commodities. I agree with Secretary Wallace, we ought to do everything in our power to make our abundance available to needy people around the world. The record that has been made, I think all will agree, is outstanding. That doesn't mean that we shouldn't try to do better, and I wish Secretary Freeman and his associates every success.

Negroes and the Farm Programs

From U.S. Commission on Civil Rights, Equal Opportunity in Farm Programs, (March, 1965), pp. 3–7.

For decades the general economic, social, and cultural position of the southern Negro farmer and rural resident in relation to his white neighbor has steadily worsened. Whether measured in terms of value of products sold, level of living, land and home ownership, or schooling, most of the 4.7 million Negroes living in southern rural areas are seriously disadvantaged when compared with rural white southerners.

Each census enumeration of population and agriculture has reflected the fact that the Negro farmers have not participated fully in the benefits of government programs and the progress of American agriculture. The continuing reliance of Negroes on cotton, tobacco, and peanuts in an economy where white farmers are rapidly diversifying to other farm enterprises has been shown in Government reports issued every 5 years. Statistics have attested to the shrinking acreage farmed by Negroes. Every 10 years the census has reported a widening gap in income, education, and housing between southern rural whites and Negroes.

Although small farmers, without regard to race, are rapidly decreasing in number and although economic pressures appear to be forcing a reduction in number and an increase in size of farms, there is unmistakable evidence that racial discrimination has served to accelerate the displacement and impoverishment of the Negro farmer.

For more than 100 years — and particularly during the past 30 years — the U.S. Department of Agriculture has administered federally financed programs designed to improve almost every aspect of the lives of low-income farm and rural families. Although other political, social, and economic factors have simultaneously operated to the disadvantage of the rural southern Negro, it should be a matter of national concern that the gap between Negro and white rural residents in the South has increased during the very period when the programs of the Department were helping thousands of rural white families to achieve substantial gains in income, housing, and education. As the group most depressed economically, most deprived educationally, and most oppressed socially, Negroes have been consistently denied access to many services, provided with inferior services when served, and segregated in federally financed agricultural programs whose very task was to raise their standard of living.

The Commission's analysis of four major U.S. Department of Agriculture programs has clearly indicated that the Department has generally failed to assume responsibility for assuring equal opportunity and equal treatment to all those entitled to benefit from its programs. Instead, the prevailing practice has been to follow local patterns of racial segregation and discrimination in providing assistance paid for by Federal funds. At the same time, the Department has not developed adequate procedures for evaluating the degree to which its programs reach Negro as well as white rural residents.

One result of this failure of responsibility has been the perpetuation of a double standard for southern Negroes and whites affected by the Department's programs. In the Cooperative Extension Service this has led to the creation of separate and unequal administrative structures providing inferior services to Negro farmers, youth, and homemakers. In the Farmers Home Administration, it has meant a different kind of service to the two races, with Negro farmers receiving for the most part subsistence loans with limited supervision, while white farmers received supervised loans for capital expenditures. In the Soil Conservation Service, the result has been little service at all to many Negro landowners in areas where no Negro staff members are employed.

As applied to staff, the double standard has taken various forms in the programs studied. These have included failure to recruit, employ, or upgrade Negroes, or to permit them to serve white farmers; isolation of Negroes in separate offices or at segregated meetings; and providing Negro staff members with inservice training of shorter duration and inferior content than that given white staff members. In State extension services Negro staff members have often been required to provide to Negro farmers technical services outside their area of training, while white farmers have received assistance from speicalists in these areas.

In some programs, effective service to Negroes has been made dependent upon the number of Negroes employed, on the untenable theory that Negro farmers should be served only by Negro staff. This concept has worked to the detriment of both Negro rural families and Negro staff. Operating under this concept, these programs have failed to reach the Negro rural residents most in need of them because of inadequate numbers of Negro staff. At the same time, restricting Negro employees to serving only Negroes has further limited professional development and promotional opportunities.

Underlying much of the failure to provide equal service to Negro farmers in the South has been the preconception, found in the agricultural agencies, that Negro farmers have limited needs, capabilities, and aspirations. Starting with a view that Negores cannot improve as farmers, many programs have not trained Negroes in the new technology nor encouraged them to diversify, to acquire larger acreage, or to make their small acreage more productive.

Relegated to a separate, inferior, and outdated agricultural economy, too many Negroes have sunk to lower levels of subsistence. When they failed as farmers and became landless, unskilled laborers, the Deparment has not helped them and their children make the transition to a new way of life.

One of the most serious obstacles barring Negro farmers from the benefits of the Department's programs has been the consistent exclusion of Negroes from the local decision-making process which controls the dispensing of these benefits. Negroes have not been appointed to State and local committees by the Department of Agriculture.

Prior to 1964, except in a few all-Negro towns, Negroes have not been candidates for locally elected committees. Almost without exception, Negroes do not join white farmers in making plans for the community. Originally built into the programs to assure flexibility and responsiveness to grassroots needs, these local controls have been used in the South to establish and maintain racial differentials in the kinds and amounts of Federal aid available to farmers. Far from discouraging such undemocratic practices in its programs, the Department itself has generally conformed to the discriminatory regional pattern.

The current unanimity of all branches of the Federal Government on the necessity for equal opportunity and equal treatment in the administration of Federal programs leaves no room for uncertainty concerning the aims of national policy as they relate to the Department of Agriculture. Some of the problems found in the Commission's study of the Department's programs will be reached by the requirement of Title VI of the Civil Rights Act of 1964 that federally assisted programs be administered without segregation or discrimination. Differential service, training, awards and activities, segregated offices, meetings, training, and competitions are outlawed by Title VI and the regulations of the Department of Agriculture issued thereunder. These regulations generally require immediate compliance, though the State extension services have been permitted a period of adjustment during which States must make necessary changes in offices, staffing and program.

In addition to the Civil Rights Act, the Federal Government has had a longstanding policy against the discrimination in employment which was found so prevalent in the agencies of the Department. Under Executive Order 10925, the policy prohibits segregated assignment of responsibilities and offices, limited promotion opportunities, and exclusion of Negroes from employment in other than menial capacities. Also, a White House directive against official participation by Federal employees in segregated meetings provides a clear mandate for conducting the educational and informational activities of the Department on a nondiscriminatory basis.

In enacting the Economic Opportunity Act of 1964, the Congress stated a further national objective: to eliminate "poverty in the midst of plenty in this Nation by opening to everyone the opportunity for education and training, the opportunity to work, and the opportunity to live in decency and dignity." The economically and socially deprived Negroes of the rural South stand in great need of such opportunities.

Federal laws and policies require the termination of segregation and discrimination in federally financed and administered agricultural programs. If the Department of Agriculture is to make its full contribution to the Nation's effort to revitalize rural America and to combat rural poverty, it must engage in a thoroughgoing critical evaluation of its programs. No rural renaissance is likely for the southern Negro so long as these programs continue to isolate him through entrenched discriminatory practices.

It is the Commission's belief that few of the economic problems now burdening the rural South can be solved until basic changes are made in the Federal programs designed to help bring about solutions. These changes must include the elimination of the segregated structuring of services, the removal of racial limitations on opportunity, and the inclusion in the decision-making process of broad sections of the population previously denied participation. Until these long-deferred changes are made, the South will continue to place a brake upon its own progress and that of the Nation.

Food and Agriculture Act of 1965

From 79 Statutes at Large 1187.

Title I — Dairy

SEC. 101. The Agricultural Adjustment Act, as reenacted and amended by the Agricultural Marketing Agreement Act of 1937, as amended, is further amended by striking in subparagraph (B) of subsection 8c(5) all of clause (d) and inserting in lieu thereof a new clause (d) to read as follows:

(d) a further adjustment, equitably to apportion the total value of the milk purchased by any handler, or by all handlers, among producers and associations of producers, on the basis of their marketings of milk, which may be adjusted to reflect sales of such milk by any handler or by all handlers in any use classification or classifications, during a representative period of time which need not be limited to one year. In the event a producer holding a base allocated under this clause (d) shall reduce his marketings, such reduction shall not adversely affect his history of production and marketing for determination of future bases. Allocations to producers under this clause (d) may be transferable under an order on such terms and conditions as may be prescribed if the Secretary of Agriculture determines that transferability will be in the best interest of the public, existing producers, and prospective new producers. Any increase in class one base resulting from enlarged or increased consumption and any producer class one bases forfeited or surrendered shall first be made available to new producers and to the alleviation of hardship and inequity among producers. In the case of any producer who during any accounting period delivers a portion of his milk to persons not fully regulated by the order, provision may be made for reducing the allocation of, or payments to be received by, any such producer under this clause (d) to compensate for any marketings of milk to such other persons for such period or periods as necessary to insure equitable participation in marketings among all producers;

and by adding at the end of said subparagraph (B) the following: "Notwithstanding the provisions of section 8c(12) and the last sentence of section 8c(19) of this Act, order provisions under (d) above shall not become effective in any marketing order unless separately approved by producers in a referendum in which each individual producer shall have one vote and may be terminated separately whenever the Secretary makes a determination with respect to such provisions as is provided for the termination of an order in subparagraph 8c(16) (B). Disapproval or termination of such order provisions shall not be considered disapproval of the order or of other terms of the order."

SEC. 102. Such Act is further amended (a) by adding to subsection 8c(5) the following new paragraph: "(H) Marketing orders applicable to milk and its products may be limited in application to milk used for manufacturing.": and (b) by amending subsection 8c(18) by adding after the words "marketing area" wherever they occur the words "or, in the case of orders applying only to manufacturing milk, the production area".

SEC. 103. The provisions of this title shall not be effective after December 31, 1969.

SEC. 104. The legal status of producer handlers of milk under the provisions of the Agricultural Adjustment Act, as reenacted and amended by the Agricultural Marketing Agreement Act of 1937, as amended, shall be the same subsequent to the adoption of the amendments made by this title as it was prior thereto.

Title II — Wool

SEC. 201. The National Wool Act of 1954, as amended, is amended, as follows:

(1) By deleting from section 703 "March 31, 1966" and inserting in lieu thereof "December 31, 1969".

(2) By changing the period at the end of the third sentence of section 703 to a colon and inserting the following:

"Provided further, That the support price for shorn wool for the 1966 and each subsequent marketing year shall be determined by multiplying 62 cents by the ratio of (i) the average of the parity index (the index of prices paid by farmers, including commodities and services, interest, taxes, and farm wage rates, as defined in section 301 (a) (1) (C) of the Agricultural Adjustment Act of 1938, as amended) for the three calendar years immediately preceding the calendar year in which such price support is determined and announced to (ii) the average parity index for the three calendar years 1958, 1959, and 1960, and rounding the resulting amount to the nearest full cent."

(3) By deleting the fourth sentence of section 703.

Title III — Feed Grains

SEC. 301. Section 105 of the Agricultural Act of 1949, as amended, is amended by adding the following new subsection (e):

"(e) For the 1966 through 1969 crops of feed grains, the Secretary shall require, as a condition of eligibility for price support on the crop of any feed grain which is included in any acreage diversion program formulated under section 16(i) of the Soil Conservation and Domestic Allotment Act, as amended, that the producer shall participate in the diversion program to the extent prescribed by the Secretary, and, if no diversion program is in effect for any crop, he may require as a condition of eligibility for price support on such crop of feed grains that the producer shall not exceed his feed grain base: *Provided,* That the acreage on any farm which is diverted from the production of feed grains pursuant to a contract hereafter entered into under the Cropland Adjustment Program shall be deemed to be acreage diverted from the production of feed grains for purposes of meeting the foregoing requirements for eligibility for price support: *Provided further,* That the Secretary may provide that no producer of malting barley shall be required as a condition of eligibility for price support for barley to participate in the acreage diversion program for feed grains if such producer has previously produced a malting variety of barley, plants barley only of an acceptable malting variety for harvest, does not knowingly devote an acreage on the farm to barley in excess of 110 per centum of the average acreage devoted on the farm to barley in 1959 and 1960, does not knowingly devote an acreage on the farm to corn and grain sorghums in excess of the acreage devoted on the farm to corn and grain sorghums in 1959 and 1960, and does not devote any acreage devoted to the production of oats and rye in 1959 and 1960 to the production of wheat pursuant to the provisions of section 328 of the Food and Agriculture Act of 1962. Such portion of the support price for any feed grain included in the acreage diversion program as the Secretary determines desirable to assure that the benefits of the price-support and diversion programs inure primarily to those producers who cooperate in reducing their acreages of feed grains shall be made available to producers through payments-in-kind. Such payments-in-kind shall be made available on the maximum permitted acreage, or the Secretary may make the same total amount available on a smaller acreage or acreages at a higher rate or rates. The number of bushels of such feed grain on which such payments-in-kind shall be made shall be determined by multiplying that part of the actual acreage of such feed grain planted on the farm for harvest on which the Secretary makes such payments available by the farm projected yield per acre: *Provided,* That for purposes of such payments, the Secretary may permit producers of feed grains to have acreage devoted to soybeans considered as devoted to the production of feed grains to such extent and subject to such terms and conditions as the Secretary determines will not impair the effective operation of the price support program: *Provided further,* That for purposes of such payments, producers on any farm who have planted not less than 90 per centum of the acreage of feed grains permitted to be planted shall be deemed to have planted the entire acreage permitted. Notwithstanding the provisions of subsection (a), that portion of the support price which is made available through loans and purchases for the 1966 through 1969 crops may be reduced below the loan level for the 1965 crop by such amounts and in such stages as may be necessary to promote increased participation in the feed grain program, taking into account increases in yields, but so as not to disrupt the feed grain and livestock economy: *Provided,* That this authority shall not be construed to modify or affect the Secretary's discretion to maintain or increase total price support levels to cooperators. An acreage on the farm which the Secretary finds was not planted to feed grains because of drought, flood, or other natural disaster shall be deemed to be an actual acreage of feed grains planted for harvest for purposes of such payments provided such acreage is not subsequently planted to any other income-producing crop during such year. The Secretary may make not to exceed 50 per centum of any payments hereunder to producers in advance of determination of performance. Payments-in-kind shall be made through the issuance of negotiable certificates which the Commodity Credit Corporation shall redeem for feed grains (such feed grains to be valued by the Secretary at not less than the current support price made available through loans and purchases, plus reasonable carrying charges) in accordance with regulations prescribed by the Secretary and notwithstanding any other provision of law, the Commodity Credit Corporation shall, in accordance with regulations prescribed by the Secretary, assist the producer in the marketing of such certificates. The Secretary shall provide for the sharing of such certificates among producers on the farm on the basis of their respective shares in the feed grain crop produced on the farm, or the proceeds therefrom, except that in any case in which the Secretary determines that such basis would not be fair and equitable, the Secretary shall provide for such sharing on such other basis as he may determine to be fair and equitable. If the operator of the farm elects to participate in the acreage diversion program, price support for feed grains included in the program shall be made available to the producers on such farm only if such producers divert from the production of such feed grains, in accordance with the provisions of such program, an acreage on the farm equal to the number of acres which such operator agrees to divert, and the agreement shall so provide. In any case in which the failure of a producer to comply fully with the terms and conditions of the programs formulated under this subsection (e) and subsection (d) of this section preclude the making of payments-in-kind, the Secretary may, nevertheless, make such payments-in-kind in such amounts as he determines to be equitable in relation to the seriousness of the default.''

SEC. 302. Section 16 of the Soil Conservation and Domestic Allotment Act, as amended, is amended by adding the following new subsection:

(1) For the 1966 through 1969 crops of feed grains, if the Secretary determines that the total supply of feed grains will, in the absence of an acreage diversion program, likely be excessive, taking into account the need for an adequate carryover to maintain reasonable and stable supplies and prices of feed grains and to meet any national emergency, he may formulate and carry out an acreage diversion program for feed grains, without regard to provisions which would be applicable to the regular agricultural conservation program, under which, subject to such terms and conditions as the Secretary determines, conservation payments shall be made to producers who divert acreage from the production of feed grains to an approved conservation use and increase their average acreage of cropland devoted in 1959 and 1960 to designated soil-conserving crops or practices including summer fallow and idle land by an equal amount. Payments shall be made at such rate or rates as the Secretary determines will provide producers with a fair and reasonable return for the acreage diverted, but not in excess of 50 per centum of the estimated basic county support rate, including the lowest rate of payment-in-kind, on the normal production of the acreage diverted from the commodity on the farm based on the farm projected yield per acre. Notwithstanding the foregoing provisions, the Secretary may permit all or any part of such diverted acreage to be devoted to the production of guar, sesame, safflower, sunflower, castor beans, mustard seed, crambe, plantago ovato, and flaxseed, if he determines that such production of the commodity is needed to provide an adequate supply, is not likely to increase the cost of the price support program, and will not adversely affect farm income subject to the condition that payment with respect to diverted acreage devoted to any such crop shall be at a rate determined by the Secretary to be fair and reasonable, taking into consideration the use of such acreage for the production of such crops, but in no event shall the payment exceed one-half the rate which otherwise would be applicable if such acreage were devoted to conservation uses. The term 'feed grains' means corn, grain sorghums, and, if designated by the Secretary, barley, and if for any crop the producer so requests for purposes of having acreage devoted to the production of wheat considered as devoted to the production of feed grains, pursuant to the provisions of section 328 of the Food and Agriculture Act of 1962, the term 'feed grains' shall include oats and rye and barley if not designated by the Secretary as provided above: *Provided,* That acreages of corn, grain sorghums, and, if designated by the Secretary, barley, shall not be planted in lieu of acreages of oats and rye and barley if not designated by the Secretary as provided above: *Provided further,* That the acreage devoted to the production of wheat shall not be considered as an acreage of feed grains for purposes of establishing the feed grain base acreage for the farm for subsequent crops. Such feed grain diversion program shall require the producer to take such measures as the Secretary may deem appropriate to keep such diverted acreage free from erosion, insects, weeds, and rodents. The acreage eligible for participation in the program shall be such acreage (not to exceed 50 per centum of the average acreage on the farm devoted to feed grains in the crop years 1959 and 1960 or twenty-five acres, whichever is greater) as the Secretary determines necessary to achieve the acreage reduction goal for the crop. Payments shall be made in kind. The acreage of wheat produced on the farm during the crop years 1959, 1960 and 1961, pursuant to the exemption provided in section 335(f) of the

Agricultural Adjustment Act of 1938, as amended, prior to its repeal by the Food and Agriculture Act of 1962, in excess of the small farm base acreage for wheat established under section 335 of the Agricultural Adjustment Act of 1938, as amended, may be taken into consideration in establishing the feed grain base acreage for the farm. The Secretary may make such adjustments in acreage as he determines necessary to correct for abnormal factors affecting production, and to give due consideration to tillable acreage, crop-rotation practices, types of soil, soil and water conservation measures, and topography. Notwithstanding any other provision of this subsection (i)(1), the Secretary may, upon unanimous request of the State committee established pursuant to section 8(b) of the Soil Conservation and Domestic Allotment Act, as amended, adjust the feed grain bases for farms within any State or county to the extent he determines such adjustment to be necessary in order to establish fair and equitable feed grain bases for farms within such State or county. The Secretary may make not to exceed 50 per centum of any payments to producers in advance of determination of performance. Notwithstanding any other provision of this subsection, barley shall not be included in the program for a producer of malting barley exempted pursuant to section 105(e) of the Agricultural Act of 1949, who participates only with respect to corn and grain sorghums and does not knowingly devote an acreage on the farm to barley in excess of 110 per centum of the average acreage devoted on the farm to barley in 1959 and 1960.

(2) Notwithstanding any other provision of this subsection, not to exceed 1 per centum of the estimated total feed grain bases for all farms in a State for any year may be reserved from the feed grain bases established for farms in the State for apportionment to farms on which there were no acreages devoted to feed grains in the crop years 1959 and 1960 on the basis of the following factors: Suitability of the land for the production of feed grains, the past experience of the farm operator in the production of feed grains, the extent to which the farm operator is dependent on income from farming for his livelihood, the production of feed grains on other farms owned, operated, or controlled by the farm operator, and such other factors as the Secretary determines should be considered for the purpose of establishing fair and equitable feed grain bases. An acreage equal to the feed grain base so established for each farm shall be deemed to have been devoted to feed grains on the farm in each of the crop years 1959 and 1960 for purposes of this subsection except that producers on such farm shall not be eligible for conservation payments for the first year for which the feed grain base is established.

(3) There are hereby authorized to be appropriated such amounts as may be necessary to enable the Secretary to carry out this section 16(i).

(4) The Secretary shall provide by regulations for the sharing of payments under this subsection among producers on the farm on a fair and equitable basis and in keeping with existing contracts.

(5) Payments in kind shall be made through the issuance of negotiable certificates which the Commodity Credit Corporation shall redeem for feed grains in accordance with regulations prescribed by the Secretary and, notwithstanding any other provision of law, the Commodity Credit Corporation shall, in accordance with regulations prescribed by the Secretary, assist the producer in the marketing of such certificates. Feed grains with which Commodity Credit Corporation redeems certificates pursuant to this paragraph shall be valued at not less than the current

support price made available through loans and purchases, plus reasonable carrying charges.

(6) Notwithstanding any other provision of law, the Secretary may, by mutual agreement with the producer, terminate or modify any agreement previously entered into pursuant to this subsection if he determines such action necessary because of an emergency created by drought or other disaster, or in order to prevent or alleviate a shortage in the supply of feed grains.

SEC. 303. Section 326 of the Food and Agriculture Act of 1962, as amended, is amended by deleting the language beginning with "the requirements" and ending with "Agricultural Act of 1961, and" and substituting therefor "the requirements of any program under which price support is extended or payments are made to farmers, and price support may be extended or".

Title IV — Cotton

SEC. 401. The Agricultural Adjustment Act of 1938, as amended, is amended as follows:

(1) Section 348 of the Act is amended by adding the following new sentences at the end thereof: "The Secretary may extend the period for performance of obligations incurred in connection with payments made for the period ending July 31, 1966, or may make payments on raw cotton in inventory on July 31, 1966, at the rate in effect on such date. No payments shall be made hereunder with respect to 1966 crop cotton."

(2) Section 346 of the Act is amended by adding at the end thereof a new subsection as follows:

"(e) Notwithstanding any other provision of this Act, for the 1966, 1967, 1968, and 1969 crops of upland cotton, if the farm operator elects to forego price support for any such crop of cotton by applying to the county committee of the county in which the farm is located for additional acreage under this subsection, he may plant an acreage not in excess of the farm acreage allotment established under section 344 plus the acreage apportioned to the farm from the national export market acreage reserve, and all cotton of such crop produced on the farm may be marketed for export free of any penalty under this section: *Provided,* That the foregoing shall be applicable only to farms which had upland cotton allotments for 1965 and are operated by the same operator as in 1965 or by his heir.

"For the 1966 crop the national export market acreage reserve shall be 250,000 acres. For each subsequent crop —

If the carryover at the end of the marketing year for the preceding crop is estimated to be less than the carryover at the beginning of such marketing year by —	The National export market acreage reserve shall be —
At least 1,000,000 bales	250,000 acres.
At least 750,000 bales, but not as much as 1,000,000 bales	187,500 acres.
At least 500,000 bales, but as much as 750,000 bales	125,000 acres.
At least 250,000 bales, but not as much as 500,000 bales	62,500 acres.
Less than 250,000 bales	None.

"The national export market acreage reserve shall be apportioned to farms by the Secretary on the basis of the applications therefor. No application shall be accepted for a greater acreage than is available on the farm for the production of upland cotton. After apportionments are thus made to farms, the Secretary shall provide farm operators a reasonable time in which to cancel their applications (and agreements to forego price support) and surrender to the Secretary through the county committee the export market acreage assigned to the farm. Acreage so surrendered shall be available for reassignment by the Secretary to other eligible farms to which export market acreage has been apportioned on the basis of the applications remaining outstanding. The operator of any farm who elects to forego price support for any such crop under this subsection shall not be eligible for price support on cotton of such crop produced on any other farm in which he has a controlling or substantial interest as determined by the Secretary. Acreage planted to cotton in excess of the farm acreage allotment established under section 344 shall not be taken into account in establishing future State, county, and farm acreage allotments. The operator of any farm to which export market acreage is apportioned, or the purchasers of cotton produced on such farm, shall, under regulations issued by the Secretary, furnish a bond or other undertaking prescribed by the Secretary providing for the exportation, without benefit of any Government cotton export subsidy and within such time as the Secretary may specify, of all cotton produced on such farm for such year. The bond or other undertaking given pursuant to this subsection shall provide that, upon failure to comply with the terms and conditions thereof, the person furnishing such bond or other undertaking shall be liable for liquidated damages in an amount which the Secretary determines and specifies in such undertaking will approximate the amount payable on excess cotton under subsection (a). The Secretary may, in lieu of the furnishing of a bond or other undertaking, provide for the payment of an amount equal to that which would be payable as liquidated damages under such bond or other undertaking. If such bond or other undertaking is not furnished, or if payment in lieu thereof is not made as provided herein, at such time and in the manner required by regulations of the Secretary, or if the acreage planted to cotton on the farm exceeds the sum of the farm acreage allotment established under section 344 and the acreage apportioned to the farm from the national export market acreage reserve, the acreage planted to cotton in excess of the farm acreage allotment established under section 344 shall be regarded as excess acreage for purposes of this section and section 345. Amounts collected by the Secretary under this subsection shall be remitted to the Commodity Credit Corporation."

(3) Section 350 of the Act is amended, effective with the 1966 crop, to read as follows:

"SEC. 350. In order to afford producers an opportunity to participate in a program of reduced acreage and higher price support, as provided in section 103 (d) of the Agricultural Act of 1949, as amended, the Secretary shall determine a national domestic allotment for the 1966, 1967, 1968, and 1969 crops of upland cotton equal to the estimated domestic consumption of upland cotton (standard bales of four hundred and eighty pounds net weight) for the marketing year beginning in the year in which the crop is to be produced. The Secretary shall determine a farm domestic acreage allotment percentage for each such year by dividing (1) the national domestic allotment (in net weight pounds) by (2) the total for all States of the product of the State acreage allotment and the projected State yield. The farm domestic acreage allotment shall be established by multiplying the farm acreage allotment established under section 344 by the farm domestic acreage allotment percentage: *Provided,* That no farm domestic acreage allotment shall be less than 65 per centum of such farm acreage allotment. Such national domestic allotment shall be determined not later than October 15 of the calendar year preceding the year in which the crop is to be produced; except that in the case of the 1966 crop, such determination shall be made within 15 days after enactment of the Food and Agriculture Act of 1965.''

SEC. 402. (a) Section 103 of the Agricultural Act of 1949, as amended, is amended by adding the following new subsection at the end thereof:

"(d) (1) Notwithstanding any other provision of this Act, if producers have not disapproved marketing quotas, price support and diversion payments shall be made available for the 1966, 1967, 1968, and 1969 crops of upland cotton as provided in this subsection.

"(2) Price support for each such crop of upland cotton shall be made available to cooperators through loans at such level, not exceeding a level which will reflect for Middling one-inch upland cotton at average location in the United States 90 per centum of the estimated average world market price for Middling one-inch upland cotton for the marketing year for such crop, as the Secretary determines will provide orderly marketing of cotton during the harvest season and will retain an adequate share of the world market for cotton produced in the United States taking into consideration the factors specified in section 401(b) of this Act: *Provided,* That the national average loan rate for the 1966 crop shall reflect 21 cents per pound for Middling one-inch upland cotton.

"(3) The Secretary also shall provide additional price support for each such crop through payments in cash or in kind to cooperators at a rate not less than 9 cents per pound: *Provided,* That the rate shall be such that the amount obtained by —

(i) multiplying the rate by the farm domestic acreage allotment percentage, and

(ii) dividing the product thus obtained by the cooperator percentage established under section 408(b), and

(iii) adding the result thus obtained to the national average loan rate shall not be less than 65 per centum or more than 90 per centum of the parity price for cotton as of the month in which the payment rate provided for by this paragraph is announced. Such payments shall be made on the quantity of cotton determined by multiplying the projected farm yield by the acreage planted to cotton within the farm domestic acreage allotment: *Provided,* That any such farm planting not less than 90 per centum of such domestic acreage allotment shall be deemed to have planted the entire amount of such allotment. An acreage on a farm in any such year which the Secretary finds was not planted to cotton because of drought, flood, or other natural disaster shall be deemed to be planted to cotton for purposes of payments under this subsection if such acreage is not subsequently devoted to any other income-producing crop in such year.

"(4) The Secretary shall make diversion payments in cash or in kind in addition to the price support payments authorized in paragraph (3) to cooperators who reduce their cotton acreage by diverting a portion of their cotton acreage allotment from the production of cotton to approved conservation practices to the extent prescribed by the Secretary: *Provided,* That no reduction below the domestic acreage allotments established under section 350 of the Agricultural Adjustment Act of 1938, as amended, shall be prescribed: *Provided further,* That payment under this paragraph shall be made available for diverting to conserving uses that part of the acreage allotment must be diverted from cotton in order that the producer may qualify as a cooperator. The rate of payment for acreage required to be diverted in order to qualify as a cooperator shall not be less than 25 per centum of the parity price for upland cotton as of the month in which such rate is announced. The rate of payment for additional acreage diverted shall be such rate as the Secretary determines to be fair and reasonable, but shall not exceed 40 per centum of such parity price. Payment at each applicable rate shall be made on the quantity of cotton determined by multiplying the acreage diverted from the production of cotton at such rate by the projected farm yield. In addition to the foregoing payment, if any, payment at the rate applicable for acreage required to be diverted to qualify as a cooperator shall be made to producers on small farms as defined in section 408 (b) who do not exceed their farm acreage allotments on a quantity of cotton determined by multiplying an acreage equal to 35 per centum of such farm acreage allotment by the projected farm yield.

"(5) The Secretary may make not to exceed 50 per centum of the payments under this subsection to producers in advance of determination of performance and the balance of such payments shall be made at such time as the Secretary may prescribe.

"(6) Where the farm operator elects to participate in the diversion program authorized in this subsection and no acreage is planted to cotton on the farm, diversion payments shall be made at the rate established under paragraph (4) for acreage required to be diverted to qualify as a cooperator on the quantity of cotton determined by multiplying that part of the farm acreage allotment required to be diverted to qualify as a cooperator by the projected farm yield, and the remainder of such allotment may be released under the provisions of section 344 (m) (2) of the Agricultural Adjustment Act of 1938, as amended. The acreage on which payment is made under this paragraph shall be regarded as planted to cotton for purposes of establishing future State, county, and farm acreage allotments, and farm bases.

"(7) Payments in kind under this subsection shall be made through the issuance of certificates which the Commodity Credit Corporation shall redeem for cotton under regulations issued by the Secretary at a value per pound equal to not less than the current loan rate therefor. The Corporation may, under regulations prescribed by the Secretary, assist the producers in the marketing of such certificates at such times and in such manner as the Secretary determines will best effectuate the purposes of the program authorized by this subsection.

"(8) Payments under this subsection shall be conditioned on the farm having an acreage of approved conservation uses equal to the sum of (i) the reduction in cotton acreage required to qualify for such payments (hereinafter called "diverted acreage"), and (ii) the average acreage of cropland on the farm devoted to designated soil-conserving crops or practices, including summer fallow and idle land, during a base period prescribed by the Secretary: *Provided,* That the Secretary may permit all or any part of such diverted acreage to be devoted to the production of guar, sesame, safflower, sunflower, castor beans, mustard seed, crambe, plantago ovato, and flaxseed, if he determines that such production is necessary to provide an adequate supply of such commodities, is not likely to increase the cost of the price support program, and will not adversely affect farm income, subject to the condition that payment under paragraph (4) or (6) with respect to diverted acreage devoted to any such crop shall be at a rate determined by the Secretary to be fair and reasonable, taking into consideration the use of such acreage for the production of such crops, but in no event shall the payment exceed one-half the rate which otherwise would be applicable if such acreage were devoted to conservation uses.

"(9) The acreage regarded as planted to cotton on any farm which qualifies for payment under this subsection except under paragraph (6) shall, for purposes of establishing future State, county, and farm acreage allotments and farm bases, be the farm acreage allotment established under section 344 of the Agricultural Adjustment Act of 1938, as amended, excluding adjustments under subsection (m)(2) thereof.

"(10) The Secretary shall provide adequate safeguards to protect the interests of tenants and sharecroppers, including provision for sharing diversion payments on a fair and equitable basis under this subsection. The Secretary shall provide for the sharing of price support payments among producers on the farm on the basis of their respective shares in the cotton crop produced on the farm, or the proceeds therefrom, except that in any case in which the Secretary determines that such basis would not be fair and equitable, the Secretary shall provide for such sharing on such other basis as he may determine to be fair and equitable.

"(11) In any case in which the failure of a producer to comply fully with the terms and conditions of the programs formulated under this Act preclude the making of payments under this section, the Secretary may, nevertheless, make such payments in such amounts as he determines to be equitable in relation to the seriousness of the default.

"(12) Notwithstanding any other provision of this Act, if, as a result of limitations hereafter enacted with respect to price support under this subsection, the Secretary is unable to make available to all cooperators the full amount of price support to which they would otherwise be entitled under paragraphs (2) and (3) of this subsection for any crop of upland cotton, (A) price support to cooperators shall be made available for such crop (if marketing quotas have not been disapproved) through loans or purchases at such level not less than 65 per centum nor more than 90 per centum of the parity price therefor as the Secretary determines appropriate; (B) in order to keep upland cotton to the maximum extent practicable in the normal channels of trade, such price support may be carried out through the simultaneous purchase of cotton at the support price therefor and resale at a lower price or through loans under which the cotton would be redeemable by payment of a price therefor lower than the amount of the loan thereon; and (C) such resale or redemption price shall be such as the Secretary determines will provide orderly marketing of cotton during the harvest season and will retain an adequate share of the world market for cotton produced in the United States.

"(13) The provisions of subsection 8 (g) of the Soil Conservation and Domestic Allotment Act, as amended (relating to assignment of payments), shall also apply to payments under this subsection.

"(14) The Commodity Credit Corporation is authorized to utilize its capital funds and other assets for the purpose of making the payments authorized in this subsection and to pay administrative expenses necessary in carrying out this subsection."

(b) Section 408 (b) of the Agricultural Act of 1949, as amended, is amended, effective only for the 1966 through 1969 crops, by changing the period at the end of the first sentence thereof to a colon and adding the following: "*Provided,* That for upland cotton a cooperator shall be a producer on whose farm the acreage planted to such cotton does not exceed the cooperator percentage, which shall be in the case of the 1966 crop, 87.5 per centum of such farm acreage allotment and, in the case of each of the 1967, 1968, and 1969 crops, such percentage, not less than 87.5 or more than 100 per centum, of such farm acreage allotment as the Secretary may specify for such crop, except that in the case of small farms (i.e. farms on which the acreage allotment is 10 acres or less, or on which the projected farm yield times the acreage allotment is 3,600 pounds or less, and the acreage allotment has not been reduced under section 344 (m)) the acreage of cotton on the farm shall not be required to be reduced below the farm acreage allotment."

SEC. 403. Section 301 of the Agricultural Adjustment Act of 1938, as amended, is amended by adding the following new subparagraphs to paragraph (13) of subsection (b):

"(L) 'Projected national, State, and county yields' for any crop of cotton shall be determined on the basis of the yield per harvested acre of such crop in the United States, the State and the county, respectively, during each of the five calendar years immediately preceding the year in which such projected yield for the United States, the State, and the county, respectively, is determined, adjusted for abnormal weather conditions affecting such yield, for trends in yields, and for any significant changes in production practices.

"(M) 'Projected farm yield' for any crop of cotton shall be determined on the basis of the yield per harvested acre of such crop on the farm during each of the three calendar years immediately preceding the year in which such projected farm yield is determined, adjusted for abnormal weather conditions affecting such yield, for trends in yields, and for any significant changes in production practices, but in no event shall such projected farm yield be less than the normal yield for such farm as provided in subparagraph (I) of this paragraph."

SEC. 404. Section 407 of the Agricultural Act of 1949, as amended, is amended by adding at the end thereof the following: "Notwithstanding any other provision of this section, for the period August 1, 1966, through July 31, 1970, (1) the Commodity Credit Corporation shall sell upland cotton for unrestricted use at the same prices as it sells cotton for export, in no event, however, at less than 110 per centum of the loan rate, and (2) the Commodity Credit Corporation shall sell or make available for unrestricted use at current market prices in each marketing year a quantity of upland cotton equal to the amount by which the production of upland cotton is less than the estimated requirements for domestic use and for export for such marketing year. The Secretary may make such estimates and adjustments therein at such times as he determines will best effectuate the provisions of part (2) of the foregoing sentence and such quantities of cotton as are required to be sold under such sentence shall be offered for sale in an orderly manner and so as not to affect market prices unduly.''

SEC. 405. The Agricultural Adjustment Act of 1938, as amended, is amended by adding after section 344 the following new section:

"SEC. 344a. (a) Notwithstanding any other provision of law, the Secretary, if he determines that it will not impair the effective operation of the program involved, (1) may permit the owner and operator of any farm for which a cotton acreage allotment is established to sell or lease all or any part or the right to all or any part of such allotment (excluding that part of the allotment which the Secretary determines was apportioned to the farm from the national acreage reserve) to any other owner or operator of a farm for transfer to such farm; (2) may permit the owner of a farm to transfer all or any part of such allotment to any other farm owned or controlled by him: *Provided,* That the authority granted under this section may be exercised for the calendar years 1966, 1967, 1968, and 1969, but all transfers hereunder shall be for such period of years as the parties thereto may agree.

"(b) Transfers under this section shall be subject to the following conditions: (i) no allotment shall be transferred to a farm in another State or to a person for use in another State; (ii) no farm allotment may be sold or leased for transfer to a farm in another county unless the producers of cotton in the county from which transfer is being made have voted in a referendum within three years of the date of such transfer, by a two-thirds majority of the producers participating in such referendum, to permit the transfer of allotments to farms outside the county, which referendum, insofar as practicable, shall be held in conjunction with the marketing quota referendum for the commodity; (iii) no transfer of an allotment from a farm subject to a mortgage or other lien shall be permitted unless the transfer is agreed to by the lienholder; (iv) no sale of a farm allotment shall be permitted if any sale of cotton allotment to the same farm has been made within the three immediately preceding crop years; (v) the total cotton allotment for any farm to which allotment is transferred by sale or lease shall not exceed the farm acreage allotment (excluding reapportioned acreage) established for such farm for 1965 by more than one hundred acres; (vi) no cotton in excess of the remaining acreage allotment on the farm shall be planted on any farm from which the allotment (or part of an allotment) is sold for a period of five years following such sale, nor shall any cotton in excess of the remaining acreage allotment on the farm be planted on any farm from which the allotment (or part of an allotment) is leased during the period of such lease, and the producer on such farm shall so agree as a condition precedent to the Secretary's approval of any such sale or lease; and (vii) no transfer of allotment shall be effective until a record thereof is filed with the county committee of the county to which such transfer is made and such committee determines that the transfer complies with the provisions of this section. Such record may be filed with such committee only during the period beginning June 1 and ending December 31.

"(c) The transfer of an allotment shall have the effect of transferring also the acreage history, farm base, and marketing quota attributable to such allotment and if the transfer is made prior to the determination of the allotment for any year the transfer shall include the right of the owner or operator to have an allotment determined for the farm for such year: *Provided,* That in the case of a transfer by lease, the amount of the allotment shall be considered for purposes of determining allotments after the expiration of the lease to have been planted on the farm from which such allotment is transferred.

"(d) The land in the farm from which the entire cotton allotment and acreage history have been transferred shall not be eligible for a new farm cotton allotment during the five years following the year in which such transfer is made.

"(c) The transfer of a portion of a farm allotment which was established under minimum farm allotment provisions for cotton or which operates to bring the farm within the minimum farm allotment provision for cotton shall cause the minimum farm allotment or base to be reduced to an amount equal to the allotment remaining on the farm after such transfer.

"(f) The Secretary shall prescribe regulations for the administration of this section, which shall include provisions for adjusting the size of the allotment transferred if the farm to which the allotment is transferred has a substantially higher yield per acre and such other terms and conditions as he deems necessary.

"(g) If the sale or lease occurs during a period in which the farm is covered by a conservation reserve contract, cropland conversion agreement, cropland adjustment agreement, or other similar land utilization agreement, the rates of payment provided for in the contract or agreement of the farm from which the transfer is made shall be subject to an appropriate adjustment, but no adjustment shall be made in the contract or agreement of the farm to which the allotment is transferred.

"(h) The Secretary shall by regulations authorize the exchange between farms in the same county, or between farms in adjoining counties within a State, of cotton acreage allotment for rice acreage allotment. Any such exchange shall be made on the basis of application filed with the county committee by the owners and operators of the farms, and the transfer of allotment between the farms shall include transfer of the related acreage history for the commodity. The exchange shall be acre for acre or on such other basis as the Secretary determines is fair and reasonable, taking into consideration the comparative productivity of the soil for the farms involved and other relevant factors. No farm from which the entire cotton or rice allotment has been transferred shall be eligible for an allotment of cotton or rice as a new farm within a period of five crop years after the date of such exchange.

"(i) The provisions of this section relating to cotton shall apply only to upland cotton."

Title V — Wheat

SEC. 501. Effective beginning with the crop planted for harvest in the calendar year 1966, the Agricultural Adjustment Act of 1938, as amended, is amended as follows:

(1) Section 332 is amended by changing item (iv) in subsection (b) to read: "will be utilized during such marketing year in the United States as livestock (including poultry) feed, excluding the estimated quantity of wheat which will be utilized for such purpose as a result of the substitution of wheat for feed grains under section 328 of the Food and Agriculture Act of 1962" and by adding the following new subsection:

"(d) Notwithstanding any other provision of this Act, the Secretary shall not proclaim a national marketing quota for the crops of wheat planted for harvest in the calendar years 1966 through 1969, and farm marketing quotas shall not be in effect for such crops of wheat."

(2) Section 333 is amended to read as follows: "The Secretary shall proclaim a national acreage allotment for each crop of wheat. The amount of the national acreage allotment for any crop of wheat shall be the number of acres which the Secretary determines on the basis of the projected national yield and expected underplantings (acreage other than that not harvested because of program incentives) of farm acreage allotments will produce an amount of wheat equal to the national marketing quota for wheat for the marketing year for such crop, or if a national marketing quota was not proclaimed, the quota which would have been determined if one had been proclaimed.

(3) Subsection (a) of section 334 is amended to read as follows:

"(a) The national allotment for wheat, less a reserve of not to exceed 1 per centum thereof for apportionment as provided in this subsection and less the special acreage reserve provided for in this subsection, shall be apportioned by the Secretary among the States on the basis of the preceding year's allotment for each such State, including all amounts allotted to the State and including for 1967 the increased acreage in the State allotted for 1966 under section 335, adjusted to the extent deemed necessary by the Secretary to establish a fair and equitable apportionment base for each State, taking into consideration established crop rotation practices, estimated decrease in farm allotments because of loss of history, and other relevant factors. The reserve acreage set aside herein for apportionment by the Secretary shall be used to make allotments to counties in addition to the county allotments made under subsection (b) of this section, on the basis of the relative needs of counties for additional allotments because of reclamation and other new areas coming into production of wheat. There also shall be made available a special acreage reserve of not in excess of one million acres as determined by the Secretary to be desirable for the purposes hereof which shall be in addition to the national acreage reserve provided for in this subsection. Such special acreage reserve shall be made available to the States to make additional allotments to counties on the basis of the relative needs of counties, as determined by the Secretary, for additional allotments to make adjustments in the allotments on old wheat farms (that is, farms on which wheat has been seeded or regarded as seeded to one or more of the three crops immediately preceding the crop for which the allotment is established) on which the ratio of wheat acreage allotment to cropland on the farm is less than one-half the average ratio of wheat acreage allotment to cropland on old wheat farms in the county. Such adjustments shall not provide an allotment for any farm which would result in an allotment-cropland ratio for the farm in excess of one-half of such county average ratio and the total of such adjustments in any county shall not exceed the acreage made available therefor in the county. Such apportionment from the special acreage reserve shall be made only to counties where wheat is a major income-producing crop, only to farms on which there is limited opportunity for the production of an alternative income-producing crop, and only if an efficient farming operation on the farm requires the allotment of additional acreage from the special acreage reserve. For the purposes of making adjustments hereunder the cropland on the farm shall not include any land developed as cropland subsequent to the 1963 crop year.''

(4) Subsection (b) of section 334 is amended to read as follows:

''(b) The State acreage allotment for wheat, less a reserve of not to exceed 3 per centum thereof for apportionment as provided in subsection (c) of this section, shall be apportioned by the Secretary among the counties in the State, on the basis of the preceding year's wheat allotment in each such county, including for 1967 the increased acreage in the county allotted for 1966 pursuant to section 335, adjusted to the extent deemed necessary by the Secretary in order to establish a fair and equitable apportionment base for each county, taking into consideration established crop rotation practices, estimated decrease in farm allotments because of loss of history, and other relevant factors.''

(5) Subsection (c) of section 334 is amended by adding new paragraphs (3) and (4) to read as follows:

''(3) Notwithstanding the provisions of paragraph (1) of this subsection, the past acreage of wheat for 1967 and any subsequent year shall be the acreage of wheat planted, plus the acreage regarded as planted, for harvest as grain on the farm which is not in excess of the farm acreage allotment.

''(4) Notwithstanding any other provision of this subsection (c), the farm acreage allotment for the 1967 and any subsequent crop of wheat shall be established for each old farm by apportioning the county wheat acreage allotment among arms in the county on which wheat has been planted, or is considered to have been planted, for harvest as grain in any one of the three years immediately preceding the year for which allotments are determined on the basis of past acreage of wheat and the farm acreage allotment for the year immediately preceding the year for which the allotment is being established, adjusted as hereinafter provided. For purposes of this paragraph, the acreage allotment for the immediately preceding year may be adjusted to reflect established crop-rotation practices, may be adjusted downward to reflect a reduction in the tillable acreage on the farm, and may be adjusted upward to reflect such other factors as the Secretary determines should be considered for the purpose of establishing a fair and equitable allotment: *Provided,* That (i) for the purposes of computing the allotment for any year, the acreage allotment for the farm for the immediately preceding year shall be decreased by 7 per centum if for the year immediately preceding the year for which such reduction is made neither a voluntary diversion program nor a voluntary certificate program was in effect and there was noncompliance with the farm acreage allotment for such year; (ii) for purposes of clause (i), any farm on which the entire amount of farm marketing excess is delivered to the Secretary, stored, or adjusted to zero in accordance with applicable regulations to avoid or postpone payment of the penalty when farm marketing quotas are in effect, shall be considered in compliance with the allotment, but if any part of the amount of wheat so stored is later depleted and penalty becomes due by reason of such depletion, the allotment for such farm next computed after determination of such depletion shall be reduced by reducing the allotment for the immediately preceding year by 7 per centum; and (iii) for purposes of clause (i) if the Secretary determines that the reduction in the allotment does not provide fair and equitable treatment to producers on farms following special crop rotation practices, he may modify such reduction in the allotment as he determines to be necessary to provide fair and equitable treatment to such producers.''

(6) Subsection (d) of section 334 is repealed.

(7) Subsection (g) of section 334 is amended by striking out the language "except as prescribed in the provisos to the first sentence of subsections (a) and (b), respectively, of this section" in the first sentence.

(8) Section 335 is amended by adding at the end thereof the following: "This section shall not be applicable to the crops planted for harvest in 1967 and subsequent years."

(9) Section 339 (b) is amended (1) by striking out "1964 and 1965 crops of wheat" and substituting "crops of wheat planted for harvest in the calendar years 1964 through 1969"; and, (2) by striking out of the third sentence "20 per centum of the farm acreage allotment" and "fifteen acres" and substituting "50 per centum of the farm acreage allotment" and "twenty-five acres", respectively.

(10) Section 339(e) is amended to read as follows; "(e) The Secretary may permit all or any part of the diverted acreage to be devoted to the production of guar, sesame, safflower, sunflower, castor beans, mustard seed, crambe, plantago ovato, and flaxseed, if he determines that such production of the commodity is needed to provide an adequate supply, is not likely to increase the cost of the price-support program and will not adversely affect farm income, subject to the condition that payment with respect to diverted acreage devoted to any such crop shall be at a rate determined by the Secretary to be fair and reasonable taking into consideration the use of such acreage for the production of such crops: *Provided,* That in no event shall the payment exceed one-half the rate which otherwise would be applicable if such acreage were devoted to conservation uses."

SEC. 502. Effective only with respect to the crops of wheat planted for harvest in the calendar years 1966 through 1969, and the marketing years for such crops, section 379b is amended to read as follows:

"SEC. 379b. A wheat marketing allocation program as provided in this subtitle shall be in effect for the marketing years for the crops planted for harvest in the calendar years 1966 through 1969. Whenever a wheat marketing allocation program is in effect for any marketing year the Secretary shall determine (1) the wheat marketing allocation for such year which shall be the amount of wheat he estimates will be used during such year for food products for consumption in the United States, but the amount of wheat included in the marketing allocation for food products for consumption in the United States shall not be less than five hundred million bushels, and (2) the national allocation percentage for such year which shall be the percentage which, when applied to the farm as provided in this section, will result in marketing certificates being issued to producers in the amount of the national wheat marketing allocation. The cost of any domestic marketing certificates issued to producers in excess of the number of certificates acquired by processors as a result of the application of the five hundred million bushel minimum or an overestimate of the amount of wheat used during such year for food products for consumption in the United States shall be borne by Commodity Credit Corporation. Each farm shall receive a wheat marketing allocation for such marketing year equal to the number of bushels obtained by multiplying the number of acres in the farm acreage allotment for wheat by the projected farm yield, and multiplying the resulting number of bushels by the national allocation percentage."

SEC. 503. Effective beginning with the 1970 crop, section 379b is amended by striking out "normal yield of wheat for the farm as determined by the Secretary" and substituting "projected farm yield".

SEC. 504. (a) Effective upon the enactment of this Act, section 379d(b) is amended by striking out the third sentence and substituting the following: "The Secretary may exempt from the requirements of this subsection wheat exported for donation abroad and other noncommercial exports of wheat, wheat processed for use on the farm where grown, wheat produced by a State or agency thereof and processed for use by the State or agency thereof, wheat processed for donation, and wheat processed for uses determined by the Secretary to be noncommercial. Such exemptions may be made applicable with respect to any wheat processed or exported beginning July 1, 1964. There shall be exempt from the requirements of this subsection beverage distilled from wheat prior to July 1, 1964. A beverage distilled from wheat after July 1, 1964, shall be deemed to be removed for sale or consumption at the time it is placed in barrels for aging except that upon the giving of a bond as prescribed by the Secretary, the purchase of and payment for such marketing certificates as may be required may be deferred until such beverage is bottled for sale. Wheat shipped to a Canadian port for storage in bond, or storage under a similar arrangement, and subsequent exportation, shall be deemed to have been exported for purposes of this subsection when it is exported from the Canadian port."

(b) Section 379d(d) is amended by inserting after the word "flour" the following: "(excluding flour second clears not used for human consumption as determined by the Secretary)", and by inserting at the end thereof the following: "The Secretary may at his election administer the exemption for wheat processed into flour second clears through refunds either to processors of such wheat or to the users of such clears. For the purpose of such refunds, the wheat equivalent of flour second clears may be determined on the basis of conversion factors authorized by section 379f of the Agricultural Adjustment Act of 1938, even though certificates had been surrendered on the basis of the weight of the wheat."

This subsection shall be effective as to products sold, or removed for sale or consumption on or after sixty days following enactment of this Act, unless the Secretary shall by regulation designate an earlier effective date within such sixty-day period.

(c) Section 379d(b) is amended by adding at the end thereof the following: "Whenever the face value per bushel of domestic marketing certificates for a marketing year is different from the face value of domestic marketing certificates for the preceding marketing year, the Secretary may require marketing certificates issued for the preceding marketing year to be acquired to cover all wheat processed into food products during such preceding marketing year even though the food product may be marketed or removed for sale or consumption after the end of the marketing year."

(d) Section 379g is amended by inserting "(a)" after "SEC. 379g" and adding a new subsection (b) as follows:

"(b) Whenever the face value per bushel of domestic marketing certificates for a marketing year is substantially different from the face value of domestic marketing certificates for the preceding marketing year, the Secretary is authorized to take such action as he determines necessary to facilitate the transition between marketing years. Notwithstanding any other provision of this subtitle, such authority shall include, but shall not be limited to, the authority to sell certificates to persons engaged in the processing of wheat into food products covering such quantities of wheat, at such prices, and under such terms and conditions as the Secretary may by regulation provide. Any such certificate shall be issued by Commodity Credit Corporation."

SEC. 505. The Agricultural Act of 1964 is amended as follows:

(1) Amendment (7) of section 202 is amended by striking out "1964 and 1965" and substituting "the calendar years 1964 through 1969".

(2) Amendment (13) of section 202 is amended by striking out "only with respect to the crop planted for harvest in the calendar year 1965" and substituting "with respect to the crops planted for harvest in the calendar years 1965 through 1969".

(3) Section 204 is amended by striking out "1964 and 1965" and substituting "1964 through 1969".

SEC. 506. Effective only with respect to the 1966 through 1969 crops, section 107 of the Agricultural Act of 1949, as amended (7 U.S.C. 1445a), is amended to read as follows:

"SEC. 107. Notwithstanding the provisions of section 101 of this Act, for any marketing year —

"(1)(a) Price support for wheat accompanied by domestic certificates shall be at 100 per centum of the parity price or as near thereto as the Secretary determines practicable, and (b) price support for wheat not accompanied by marketing certificates shall be at such level, not in excess of the parity price therefor, as the Secretary determines appropriate, taking into consideration competitive world prices of wheat, the feeding value of wheat in relation to feed grains, and the level at which price support is made available for feed grains.

"(2) notwithstanding the provisions of paragraph (1), for the 1966 crop, price support for wheat accompanied by domestic marketing certificates shall be at 100 per centum of the parity price therefor, and price support for wheat not accompanied by marketing certificates shall be not less than $1.25 per bushel. For any crop of wheat planted for harvest during the calendar years 1967 through 1969 for which the diversion factor established pursuant to section 339(a) of the Agricultural Adjustment Act of 1938, as amended, is not less than 10 per centum, the total average rate of return per bushel made available to a cooperator on the estimated production of his allotment based on projected yield through loans, domestic marketing certificates, estimated returns from export marketing certificates, and diversion payments for acreage diverted pursuant to section 339(a) of the Agricultural Adjustment Act of 1938, as amended, shall not be less than the total average rate of return per bushel made available to cooperators through loans and domestic marketing certificates for the 1966 crop.

"(3) Price support shall be made available only to cooperators, and

"(4) A 'cooperator' with respect to any crop of wheat produced on a farm shall be a producer who (i) does not knowingly exceed (A) the farm acreage allotment for wheat on the farm or (B) except as the Secretary may by regulation prescribe, the farm acreage allotment for wheat on any other farm on which the producer shares in the production of wheat, and (ii) complies with the land-use requirements of section 339 of the Agricultural Adjustment Act of 1938, as amended, to the extent prescribed by the Secretary. No producer shall be deemed to have exceeded a farm acreage allotment for wheat if the production on the acreage in excess of the farm acreage allotment is stored pursuant to the provisions of section 379c(b), but the producer shall not be eligible to receive price support on the wheat so stored.''

SEC. 507. Effective beginning with the crop planted for harvest in the calendar year 1967, section 339(a)(1) of the Agricultural Adjustment Act of 1938, as amended, is amended by inserting after the words ''national acreage allotment'', wherever they appear, the following: ''(less an acreage equal to the increased acreage allotted for 1966 pursuant to section 335)''.

SEC. 508. Effective beginning with the crop planted for harvest in the calendar year 1966, section 379c(a) of the Agricultural Adjustment Act of 1938, as amended, is amended by inserting before the period at the end of the third sentence thereof a semicolon and the following: ''except that in any case in which the Secretary determines that such basis would not be fair and equitable, the Secretary shall provide for such sharing on such other basis as he may determine to be fair and equitable.'', and by adding at the end thereof the following: ''An acreage on the farm not planted to wheat because of drought, flood, or other natural disaster shall be deemed to be an actual acreage of wheat planted for harvest for purposes of this subsection provided such acreage is not subsequently planted to any other income-producing crops during such year. Producers on any farm who have planted not less than 90 per centum of the acreage of wheat required to be planted in order to earn the full amount of marketing certificates for which the farm is eligible shall be deemed to have planted the entire acreage required to be planted for that purpose.''

SEC. 509. Section 301(b) of the Agricultural Adjustment Act of 1938, as amended, is amended as follows:

(1) Paragraph (8) is amended by inserting ''(A)'' after ''(8)'' and adding the following new subparagraph:

''(B) 'Projected national yield' as applied to any crop of wheat shall be determined on the basis of the national yield per harvested acre of the commodity during each of the five calendar years immediately preceding the year in which such projected national yield is determined, adjusted for abnormal weather conditions affecting such yield, for trends in yields and for any significant changes in production practices.''

(2) Paragraph (13) is amended by adding the following new subparagraphs:

''(J) 'Projected county yield' for any crop of wheat shall be determined on the basis of the yield per harvested acre of such commodity in the county during each of the five calendar years immediately preceding the year in which such projected county yield is determined, adjusted for abnormal weather conditions affecting such yield, for trends in yields and for any significant changes in production practices.

''(K) 'Projected farm yield' for any crop of wheat shall be determined on the basis of the yield per harvested acre of such commodity on the farm during each of the three calendar years immediately preceding the year in which such projected farm yield is determined, adjusted for abnormal weather conditions affecting such yield, for trends in yields and for any significant changes in production practices, but in no event shall such projected farm yield be less than the normal yield for such farm as provided in subparagraph (E) of this paragraph."

SEC. 510. (a) Section 379c(b) of the Agricultural Adjustment Act of 1938, as amended, is amended, effective beginning with the 1966 crop, by striking out of the fifth sentence the words "normal yield of wheat per acre established for the farm" and substituting therefor the words "projected farm yield".

(b) Section 379i of the Agricultural Adjustment Act of 1938, as amended, is amended, effective as of the effective date of the original enactment of that section, by inserting in subsections (a) and (b) after the word "who", wherever it appears, the word "knowingly".

SEC. 511. (a) Effective beginning with the crop planted for harvest in 1966, paragraph (9) of section 301(b) of the Agricultural Adjustment Act of 1938, as amended, is amended by striking out "cotton" and "wheat" and by adding at the end thereof the following: " 'Normal production' as applied to any number of acres of cotton or wheat means the projected farm yield times such number of acres."

(b) Public Law 74, Seventy-seventh Congress, as amended, is amended by changing the words "normal yield of wheat per acre established for the farm" in paragraph (1) to the words "projected farm yield".

SEC. 512. The national, State, county, and farm acreage allotments for the 1966 crop of wheat shall be established in accordance with the provisions of law in effect prior to the enactment of this Act.

SEC. 513. (a) Section 379d(b) of the Agricultural Adjustment Act of 1938 is amended by striking out the second sentence and substituting the following: "The cost of the export marketing certificates per bushel to the exporter shall be that amount determined by the Secretary on a daily basis which would make United States wheat and wheat flour generally competitive in the world market, avoid disruption of world market prices, and fulfill the international obligations of the United States."

(b) Section 379c(a) of such Act is amended by striking out everything in the next to the last sentence beginning with the words "United States" and substituting the following: "United States. The Secretary shall also provide for the issuance of export marketing certificates to eligible producers at the end of the marketing year on a pro rata basis. For such purposes, the value per bushel of export marketing certificates shall be an average of the total net proceeds from the sale of export marketing certificates during the marketing year after deducting the total amount of wheat export subsidies paid to exporters."

(c) Section 379c(c) of such Act is amended by striking out "and the face value per bushel of export certificates shall be the amount by which the level of price support for wheat accompanied by export certificates exceeds the level of price support for noncertificate wheat".

SEC. 514. Section 328 of the Food and Agriculture Act of 1962 is amended by adding to the end thereof the following: "In establishing terms and conditions for permitting wheat to be planted in lieu of oats and rye, the Secretary may take into account the number of feed units per acre of wheat in relation to the number of feed units per acre of oats and rye."

SEC. 515. Section 379c of the Agricultural Adjustment Act of 1938, as amended, is amended, effective beginning with the crop planted for harvest in the calendar year 1964, by adding the following subsection:

"(e) In any case in which the failure of a producer to comply fully with the terms and conditions of the programs formulated under this Act preclude the issuance of marketing certificates, the Secretary may, nevertheless, issue such certificates in such amounts as he determines to be equitable in relation to the seriousness of the default."

SEC. 516. Section 379e of the Agricultural Adjustment Act of 1938, as amended, is amended by adding at the end thereof the following:

"Notwithstanding any other provision of this Act, Commodity Credit Corporation shall sell marketing certificates for the marketing years for the 1966 through the 1969 wheat crops to persons engaged in the processing of food products at the face value thereof less any amount by which price support for wheat accompanied by domestic certificates exceeds $2 per bushel."

SEC. 517. Subsection (b) of section 379c of the Agricultural Adjustment Act of 1938 is amended by inserting immediately preceding the words "stored" wherever it appears, in the fourth through the sixth sentences, the words "delivered to the Secretary or", and by adding at the end thereof the following: "Any wheat delivered to the Secretary hereunder shall become the property of the United States and shall be disposed of by the Secretary for relief purposes in the United States or in foreign countries or in such other manner as he shall determine will divert it from the normal channels of trade and commerce. Notwithstanding any other provision of this Act, the Secretary may provide that a producer shall not be eligible to receive marketing certificates, or may adjust the amount of marketing certificates to be received by the producer, with respect to any farm for any year in which a variety of wheat is planted on the farm which has been determined by the Secretary, after consultation with State Agricultural Experiment Stations, agronomists, cereal chemists and other qualified technicians, to have undesirable milling or baking qualities and has made public announcement thereof."

Title VI — Cropland Adjustment

SEC. 601. The Soil Bank Act of 1956, as amended, is hereby repealed, except that it shall remain in effect with respect to contracts entered into prior to such repeal.

SEC. 602. (a) Notwithstanding any other provision of law, for the purpose of reducing the costs of farm programs, assisting farmers in turning their land to nonagricultural uses, promoting the development and conservation of the Nation's soil, water, forest, wildlife, and recreational resources, establishing, protecting, and conserving open spaces and natural beauty, the Secretary of Agriculture is authorized to formulate and carry out a program during the calendar years 1965 through 1969 under which agreements would be entered into with producers as hereinafter provided for periods of not less than five nor more than ten years. No agreement shall be entered into under this section concerning land with respect to which the ownership has changed in the three-year period preceding the first year of the agreement period unless the new ownership was acquired by will or succession as a result of the death of the previous owner, or unless the new ownership was acquired prior to January 1, 1965, under other circumstances which the Secretary determines, and specifies by regulation, will give adequate assurance that such land was not acquired for the purpose of placing it in the program: *Provided,* That this provision shall not be construed to prohibit the continuation of an agreement by a new owner after an agreement has once been entered into under this section: *Provided further,* That the Secretary shall not require a person who has operated the land to be covered by an agreement under this section for as long as three years preceding the date of the agreement and who controls the land for the agreement period to own the land as a condition of eligibility for entering into the agreement.''

(b) The producer shall agree (1) to carry out on a specifically designated acreage of land on the farm regularly used in the production of crops (including crops, such as tame hay, alfalfa, and clovers, which do not require annual tillage and which have been planted within five years preceding the date of the agreement), hereinafter called "designated acreage", and maintain for the agreement period practices or uses which will conserve soil, water, or forest resources, or establish or protect or conserve open spaces, natural beauty, wildlife or recreational resources, or prevent air or water pollution, in such manner as the Secretary may prescribe (priority being given to the extent practicable to practices or uses which are most likely to result in permanent retirement to noncrop uses); (2) to maintain in conserving crops or uses or allow to remain idle throughout the agreement period the acreage normally devoted to such crops or uses; (3) not to harvest any crop from or graze the designated acreage during the agreement period, unless the Secretary, after certification by the Governor of the State in which such acreage is situated of the need for grazing or harvesting of such acreage, determines that it is necessary to permit grazing or harvesting in order to alleviate damage, hardship, or suffering caused by severe drought, flood, or other natural disaster, and consents to such grazing or harvesting subject to an appropriate reduction in the rate of payment; and (4) to such additional terms and conditions as the Secretary determines are desirable to effectuate the purposes of the program, including such measures as the Secretary may deem appropriate to keep the designated acreage free from erosion, insects, weeds, and rodents. Agreements entered into under which 1966 is the first year of the agreement period (A) shall require the producer to divert from production all of one or more crops designated by the Secretary; and (B) shall not provide for diversion from the production of upland cotton in any county in which the county committee by resolution determines, and requests of the Secretary, that there should not be such diversion in 1966.

(c) Under such agreements the Secretary shall (1) bear such part of the average cost (including labor) for the county or area in which the farm is situated of establishing and maintaining authorized practices or uses on the designated acreage as the Secretary determines to be necessary to effectuate the purposes of the program, but not to exceed the average rate for comparable practices or uses under the agricultural conservation program, and (2) make an annual adjustment payment to the producer for the period of the agreement at such rate or rates as the Secretary determines to be fair and reasonable in consideration of the obligations undertaken by the producers. The rate or rates of annual adjustment payments as determined hereunder may be increased by an amount determined by the Secretary to be appropriate in relation to the benefit to the general public of the use of the designated acreage if the producer further agrees to permit, without other compensation, access to such acreage by the general public, during the agreement period, for hunting, trapping, fishing, and hiking, subject to applicable State and Federal regulations. The Secretary and the producer may agree that the annual adjustment payments for all years of the agreement period shall be made either upon approval of the agreement or in such installments as they may agree to be desirable: *Provided,* That for each year any annual adjustment payment is made in advance of performance, the annual adjustment payment shall be reduced by 5 per centum. The Secretary may provide for adjusting any payment on account of failure to comply with the terms and conditions of the program.

(d) The Secretary shall, unless he determines that such action will be inconsistent with the effective administration of the program, use an advertising and bid procedure in determining the lands in any area to be covered by agreements. The total acreage placed under contract in any county or local community shall be limited to a percentage of the total eligible acreage in such county or local community which the Secretary determines would not adversely affect the economy of the county or local community. In determining such percentage the Secretary shall give appropriate consideration to the productivity of the acreage being retired as compared to the average productivity of eligible acreage in the county or local community.

(e) The annual adjustment payment shall not exceed 40 per centum of the estimated value, as determined by the Secretary, on the basis of prices in effect at the time the agreement is entered into, of the crops or types of crops which might otherwise be grown. The estimated value may be established by the Secretary on a county, area, or individual farm basis as he deems appropriate.

(f) The Secretary may terminate any agreement with a producer by mutual agreement with the producer if the Secretary determines that such termination would be in the public interest, and may agree to such modification of agreements as he may determine to be desirable to carry out the purposes of the program or facilitate its administration.

(g) Notwithstanding any other provision of law, the Secretary of Agriculture may, to the extent he deems it desirable, provide by appropriate regulations for preservation of cropland, crop acreage, and allotment history applicable to acreage diverted from the production of crops in order to establish or maintain vegetative cover or other approved practices for the purpose of any Federal program under which such history is used as a basis for an allotment or other limitation or for participation in such program. Subsections (b) (3) and (4) and (e) (6) of section 16 of the Soil Conservation and Domestic Allotment Act, as amended, are repealed, except that all rights accruing thereunder to persons who entered into contracts or agreements prior to such repeal shall be preserved.

(h) In carrying out the program, the Secretary shall utilize the services of local, county, and State committees established under section 8 of the Soil Conservation and Domestic Allotment Act, as amended.

(i) For the purpose of obtaining an increase in the permanent retirement of cropland to noncrop uses the Secretary may, notwithstanding any other provision of law, transfer funds available for carrying out the program to any other Federal agency or to States or local government agencies for use in acquiring cropland for the preservation of open spaces, natural beauty, the development of wildlife or recreational facilities, or the prevention of air or water pollution under terms and conditions consistent with and at costs not greater than those under agreements entered into with producers, provided the Secretary determines that the purposes of the program will be accomplished by such action.

(j) The Secretary also is authorized to share the cost with State and local governmental agencies in the establishment of practices or uses which will establish, protect, and conserve open spaces, natural beauty, wildlife or recreational resources, or prevent air or water pollution under terms and conditions and at costs consistent with those under agreements entered into with producers, provided the Secretary determines that the purposes of the program will be accomplished by such action.

(k) In carrying out the program, the Secretary shall not during any of the fiscal years ending June 30, 1966 through June 30, 1968 or during the period June 30, 1968 through December 31, 1969, enter into agreements with producers which would require payments to producers in any calendar year under such agreements in excess of $225,000,000 plus any amount by which agreements entered into in prior fiscal years require payments in amounts less than authorized for such prior fiscal years. For purposes of applying this limitation, the annual adjustment payment shall be chargeable to the year in which performance is rendered regardless of the year in which it is made.

(1) The Secretary is authorized to utilize the facilities, services, authorities, and funds of the Commodity Credit Corporation in discharging his functions and responsibilities under this program, including payment of costs of administration: *Provided,* That after December 31, 1966, the Commodity Credit Corporation shall not make any expenditures for carrying out the purposes of this title unless the Corporation has received funds to cover such expenditures from appropriations made to carry out the purposes of this title. There are hereby authorized to be appropriated such sums as may be necessary to carry out the program, including such amounts as may be required to make payments to the Corporation for its actual costs incurred or to be incurred under this program.

(m) In case any producer who is entitled to any payment or compensation dies, becomes incompetent, or disappears before receiving such payment or compensation, or is succeeded by another who renders or completes the required performance, the payment or compensation shall, without regard to any other provisions of law, be made as the Secretary may determine to be fair and reasonable in all the circumstances and so provide by regulations.

(n) The Secretary shall provide adequate safeguards to protect the interests of tenants and sharecroppers, including provision for sharing, on a fair and equitable basis, in payments or compensation under this program.

(o) The acreage on any farm which is diverted from the production of any commodity pursuant to an agreement hereafter entered into under this title shall be deemed to be acreage diverted from that commodity for the purposes of any commodity program under which diversion is required as a condition of eligibility for price support.

(p) The Secretary may, without regard to the civil service laws, appoint an

Advisory Board on Wildlife to advise and consult on matters relating to his functions under this title as he deems appropriate. The Board shall consist of twelve persons chosen from members of wildlife organizations, farm organizations, State game and fish agencies, and representatives of the general public. Members of such Advisory Board who are not regular full-time employees of the United States shall not be entitled to any compensation or expenses.

(q) The Secretary shall prescribe such regulations as he determines necessary to carry out the provisions of this title.

Title VII — Miscellaneous

SEC. 701. Section 374 (a) of the Agricultural Adjustment Act of 1938, as amended, is amended to read as follows:

"(a) The Secretary shall provide for ascertaining, by measurement or otherwise, the acreage of any agricultural commodity or land use on farms for which the ascertainment of such acreage is necessary to determine compliance under any program administered by the Secretary. Insofar as practicable, the acreage of the commodity and land use shall be ascertained prior to harvest, and, if any acreage so ascertained is not in compliance with the requirements of the program the Secretary, under such terms and conditions as he prescribes, may provide a reasonable time for the adjustment of the acreage of the commodity or land use to the requirements of the program."

SEC. 702. Section 374 (c) of the Agricultural Adjustment Act of 1938, as amended, is amended by deleting the first sentence thereof.

SEC. 703. Subsection (a) of section 316 of the Agricultural Adjustment Act of 1938, as amended, is amended (i) by striking out of the first sentence thereof "1962, 1963, 1964, and 1965," and inserting "1962 through 1969" and (ii) by striking out of the last sentence thereof "1964 or 1965" and inserting "1964 through 1969".

Notwithstanding the provisions of subsection 316(c) and subsection 317(f) relating to lease and transfer of allotments for years subsequent to 1965, of the Agricultural Adjustment Act of 1938, as amended, whenever acreage-poundage quotas are in effect for any kind of tobacco as provided in section 317 of the Act, except in the case of burley tobacco, and other kinds of tobacco not subject to section 316, the lease and transfer shall be on a pound for pound basis and the acreage allotment for the lessee farm shall be increased by an amount determined by dividing the number of pounds leased by the farm yield for the lessee farm, and the acreage allotment for the lessor farm shall be reduced by an amount determined by dividing the number of pounds leased by the farm yield for the lessor farm.

SEC. 704. The last paragraph of the Act entitled "An Act to amend the peanut marketing quota provisions of the Agricultural Adjustment Act of 1938, as amended, and for other purposes", approved August 13, 1957 (7 U.S.C. 1359 note), is amended to read as follows:

"This amendment shall be effective for the 1957 through 1969 crops of peanuts."

SEC. 705. The Secretary of Agriculture shall make a study of the parity income position of farmers, including the development of criteria for measuring parity income of commercial family farmers and the feasibility of adapting such criteria to major types of farms and to selected counties. The Secretary shall report the results of such study to the Congress not later than June 30, 1966.

SEC. 706. Notwithstanding any other provision of law, the Secretary, upon the request of any agency of any State charged with the administration of the public lands of the State, may permit the transfer of acreage allotments or feed grain bases together with relevant production histories which have been determined pursuant to the Agricultural Adjustment Act of 1938, as amended, or section 16 of the Soil Conservation and Domestic Allotment Act, as amended, from any farm composed of public lands to any other farm or farms in the same county composed of public lands: *Provided,* That as a condition for the transfer of any allotment or base an acreage equal to or greater than the allotment or base transferred prior to adjustment, if any, shall be devoted to and maintained in permanent vegetative cover on the farm from which the transfer is made. The Secretary shall prescribe regulations which he deems necessary for the administration of this section, which may provide for adjusting downward the size of the allotment or base transferred if the farm to which the allotment or base is transferred normally has a higher yield per acre for the commodity for which the allotment or base is determined, for reasonable limitations on the size of the resulting allotments and bases on farms to which transfers are made, taking into account the size of the allotments and bases on farms of similar size in the community, and for retransferring allotments or bases and relevant histories if the conditions of the transfer are not fulfilled.

SEC. 707. The Agricultural Adjustment Act of 1938, as amended, is amended by inserting after section 378 the following new section:

"Reconstitution of Farms

"SEC. 379. In any case in which the ownership of a tract of land is transferred from a parent farm, the acreage allotments, history acreages, and base acreages for the farm shall be divided between such tract and the parent farm in the same proportion that the cropland acreage in such tract bears to the cropland acreage in the parent farm, except that the Secretary shall provide by regulation the method to be used in determining the division, if any, of the acreage allotments, histories, and bases in any case in which —

"(1) the tract of land transferred from the parent farm has been or is being transferred to any agency having the right to acquire it by eminent domain;

"(2) the tract of land transferred from the parent farm is to be used for nonagricultural purposes;

"(3) the parent farm resulted from a combination of two or more tracts of land and records are available showing the contribution of each tract to the allotments, histories, and bases of the parent farm;

"(4) the appropriate county committee determines that a division based on cropland proportions would result in allotments and bases not representative of the operations normally carried out on any transferred tract during the base period; or

"(5) the parent farm is divided among heirs in settling an estate.

"(6) neither the tract transferred from the parent farm nor the remaining portion of the parent farm receives allotments in excess of allotments for similar farms in the community having allotments of the commodity or commodities involved and such allotments are consistent with good land uses, but this clause (6) shall not be applicable in the case of burley tobacco.''

SEC. 708. Notwithstanding any other provision of law, in the determination of farm yields the Secretary may use projected yields in lieu of normal yields. In the determination of such yields the Secretary shall take into account the actual yield proved by the producer for the base period used in determining the projected yield, and the projected yield shall not be less than such actual yield proved by the producer.

SEC. 709. The Secretary of Agriculture is hereby authorized to use funds of the Commodity Credit Corporation to purchase sufficient supplies of dairy products at market prices to meet the requirements of any programs for the schools (other than fluid milk in the case of schools), domestic relief distribution, community action, foreign distribution, and such other programs as are authorized by law, when there are insufficient stocks of dairy products in the hands of Commodity Credit Corporation available for these purposes.

Title VIII — Rice

SEC. 801. Section 353 (c) of the Agricultural Adjustment Act of 1938, as amended, is amended by adding the following new paragraph at the end thereof:

''(7) If the national acreage allotment for rice for 1966, 1967, 1968, or 1969 is less than the national acreage allotment for rice for 1965, the Secretary shall formulate and carry out an acreage diversion program for rice for such year designed to support the gross income of rice producers at a level not lower than that for 1965, minus any reduction in production costs resulting from the reduced rice acreage. Under such program conservation payments shall be made to producers who comply with their rice acreage allotments, devote to an approved conservation use an acreage of cropland on the farm equal to the number of acres determined by multiplying the farm acreage allotment by the diversion factor, and comply with such additional terms and conditions as the Secretary may prescribe. The diversion factor shall be determined by dividing the number of acres by which the national acreage allotment is reduced below the national acreage allotment for 1965 by the number of acres in the national acreage allotment. Notwithstanding the foregoing provisions, the Secretary may permit all or any part of such diverted acreage to be devoted to the production of guar, sesame, safflower, sunflower, castor beans, mustard seed, crambe, plantago ovato, and flaxseed, if he determines that such production is not likely to increase the cost of the price-support program and will not adversely affect farm income, subject to the condition that payment with respect to diverted acreage devoted to any such crops shall be at a rate determined by the Secretary to be fair and reasonable, taking into consideration the use of such acreage for the production of such crops; but in no event shall the payment exceed one-half the rate which otherwise would be applicable if such acreage were devoted to conservation uses. Such program shall require the producer to take such measures as the Secretary may deem appropriate to keep such diverted acreage free from erosion, insects, weeds, and rodents. The Secretary may make not to exceed 50 per centum of any payments to producers in advance of determination of performance.

The Secretary shall provide for the sharing of payments under this paragraph among producers on the farm on a fair and equitable basis as determined by the Secretary. The Commodity Credit Corporation is authorized to utilize its capital funds and other assets for the purpose of making the payments authorized in this paragraph and to pay administrative expenses necessary in carrying out this paragraph.''

SEC. 802. Section 403 of the Agricultural Act of 1949, as amended, is amended by inserting at the end thereof the following: "In determining support prices for the 1966 and 1967 crops of rice the Secretary shall, notwithstanding the foregoing or any other provision of law, use head and broken rice value factors for the various varieties which (1) are not lower than those used with respect to the 1965 crop, and (2) do not differ as between any two varieties by a greater amount than the value factors used with respect to the 1965 crop for such two varieties differed.''

Approved November 3, 1965.

Rural Poverty, 1967

From President's National Advisory Commission on Rural Poverty, *The People Left Behind*, (Washington, 1967), pp. ix–xii, 3, 5–9.

Summary

This report is about a problem which many in the United States do not realize exists. The problem is rural poverty. It affects some 14 million Americans. Rural poverty is so widespread, and so acute, as to be a national disgrace, and its consequences have swept into our cities, violently.

The urban riots during 1967 had their roots, in considerable part, in rural poverty. A high proportion of the people crowded into city slums today came there from rural slums. This fact alone makes clear how large a stake the people of this nation have in an attack on rural poverty.

The total number of rural poor would be even larger than 14 million had not so many of them moved to the city. They made the move because they wanted a job and a decent place to live. Some have found them. Many have not. Many merely exchanged life in a rural slum for life in an urban slum, at exorbitant cost to themselves, to the cities, and to rural America as well.

Even so, few migrants have returned to the rural areas they left. They have apparently concluded that bad as conditions are in an urban slum, they are worse in the rural slum they fled from. There is evidence in the pages of this report to support their conclusion.

This Nation has been largely oblivious to these 14 million impoverished people left behind in rural America. Our programs for rural America are woefully out of date.

Some of our rural programs, especially farm and vocational agriculture programs, are relics from an earlier era. They were developed in a period during which the welfare of farm families was equated with the well-being of rural communities and of all rural people. This no longer is so.

They were developed without anticipating the vast changes in technology, and the consequences of this technology to rural people. Instead of combating low incomes of rural people, these programs have helped to create wealthy landowners while largely bypassing the rural poor.

Most rural programs still do not take the speed and consequences of technological change into account. We have not yet adjusted to the fact that in the brief period of 15 years, from 1950 to 1965, new machines and new methods increased farm output in the United States by 45 percent — and reduced farm employment by 45 percent. Nor is there adequate awareness that during the next 15 years the need for farm labor will decline by another 45 percent. Changes like these on the farm are paralleled on a broader front throughout rural America, affecting many activities other than farming and touching many more rural people than those on farms.

In contrast to the urban poor, the rural poor, notably the white, are not well organized, and have few spokesmen for bringing the Nation's attention to their problems. The more vocal and better organized urban poor gain most of the benefits of current antipoverty programs.

Until the past few years, the Nation's major social welfare and labor legislation largely bypassed rural Americans, especially farmers and farmworkers. Farm people were excluded from the Social Security Act until the mid-1950's. Farmers, farmworkers, and workers in agriculturally related occupations are still excluded from other major labor legislation, including the unemployment insurance programs, the Labor-Management Relations Act, the Fair Labor Standards Act, and most State workman's compensation acts.

Because we have been oblivious of the rural poor, we have abetted both rural and urban poverty, for the two are closely linked through migration. The hour is late for taking a close look at rural poverty, gaining an understanding of its consequences, and developing programs for doing something about it. The Commission is unanimous in the conviction that effective programs for solving the problems of rural poverty will contribute to the solution of urban poverty as well.

The facts of rural poverty are given in detail later in this report. They are summarized in the paragraphs that follow.

Rural poverty in the United States has no geographic boundaries. It is acute in the South, but it is present and serious in the East, the West, and the North. Rural poverty is not limited to Negroes. It permeates all races and ethnic groups. Nor is poverty limited to the farm. Our farm population has declined until it is only a small fraction of our total rural population. Most of the rural poor do not live on farms. They live in the open country, in rural villages, and in small towns. Moreover, contrary to a common misconception, whites outnumber nonwhites among the rural poor by a wide margin. It is true, however, that an extremely high proportion of Negroes in the rural South and Indians on reservations are destitute.

Hunger, even among children, does exist among the rural poor, as a group of physicians discovered recently in a visit to the rural South. They found Negro children not getting enough food to sustain life, and so disease ridden as to be beyond cure. Malnutrition is even more widespread. The evidence appears in bad diets and in diseases which often are a product of bad diets.

Disease and premature death are startlingly high among the rural poor. Infant mortality, for instance, is far higher among the rural poor than among the least privileged group in urban areas. Chronic diseases also are common among both young and old. And medical and dental care is conspicuously absent.

Unemployment and underemployment are major problems in rural America. The rate of unemployment nationally is about 4 percent. The rate in rural areas averages about 18 percent. Among farmworkers, a recent study discovered that underemployment runs as high as 37 percent.

The rural poor have gone, and now go, to poor schools. One result is that more than 3 million rural adults are classified as illiterates. In both educational facilities and opportunities, the rural poor have been shortchanged.

Most of the rural poor live in atrocious houses. One in every 13 houses in rural America is officially classified as unfit to live in.

Many of the rural poor live in chronically depressed poverty-stricken rural communities. Most of the rural South is one vast poverty area. Indian reservations contain heavy concentrations of poverty. But there also are impoverished rural communities in the upper Great Lakes region, in New England, in Appalachia, in the Southwest, and in other sections.

The community in rural poverty areas has all but disappeared as an effective institution. In the past the rural community performed the services needed by farmers and other rural people. Technological progress brought sharp declines in the manpower needs of agriculture, forestry, fisheries, and mining. Other industries have not replaced the jobs lost, and they have supplied too few jobs for the young entries in the labor market. Larger towns and cities have taken over many of the economic and social functions of the villages and small towns.

The changes in rural America have rendered obsolete many of the political boundaries to villages and counties. Thus these units operate on too small a scale to be practicable. Their tax base has eroded as their more able-bodied wage earners left for jobs elsewhere. In consequence the public services in the typical poor rural community are grossly inadequate in number, magnitude, and quality. Local government is no longer able to cope with local needs.

As the communities ran downhill, they offered fewer and fewer opportunities for anyone to earn a living. The inadequately equipped young people left in search of better opportunities elsewhere. Those remaining behind have few resources with which to earn incomes adequate for a decent living and for revitalizing their communities.

For all practical purposes, then, most of the 14 million people in our poverty areas are outside our market economy. So far as they are concerned, the dramatic economic growth of the United States might as well never have happened. It has brought them few rewards. They are on the outside looking in, and they need help.

Congress and State legislatures from time to time have enacted many laws and appropriated large sums of money to aid the poverty stricken and to help rural America. Very little of the legislation or the money has helped the rural poor. Major farm legislation directed at commercial farms has been successful in helping farmers adjust supply to demand, but it has not helped farmers whose production is very small. And because the major social welfare and labor legislation has descriminated against rural people, many of the rural poor — farmers and farmworkers particularly — have been denied unemployment insurance, denied the right of collective bargaining, and denied the protection of workman's compensation laws.

This Commission questions the wisdom of massive public efforts to improve the lot of the poor in our central cities without comparable efforts to meet the needs of the poor in rural America. Unfortunately, as public programs improve the lot of the urban poor, without making similar improvements in conditions for the rural poor, they provide fresh incentive for the rural poor to migrate to the central cities. The only solution is a coordinated attack on both urban and rural poverty.

The Commission has endeavored to chart a course to wipe out rural poverty. Emphasis has been placed on the problems of poor rural people, and problems of impoverished rural communities. Changes in existing programs and the development of new programs are considered. Action on the immediate needs of the rural poor is emphasized, as well as action to change the conditions which make them poor. Human development and the physical resources needed for this development are stressed. Improving the operation of the private economy in order to provide rural people with better opportunities for jobs and a decent living is emphasized.

It is the firm conviction of the Commission that the complexity of the problems of rural poverty preclude the success of a single program or approach. Programs addressed to immediate needs will not erase the underlying conditions creating and perpetuating rural poverty. Programs addressed to these conditions will not immediately help the poor. The Commission's recommendations complement and reinforce one another. In total, the recommendations will go far to solve the problems of rural poverty.

The Commission is convinced that the abolition of rural poverty in the United States, perhaps for the first time in any nation, is completely feasible. The nation has the economic resources and the technical means for doing this. What it has lacked, thus far, has been the will. The Commission rejects the view that poverty, in so rich a nation, is inevitable for any large group of its citizens.

Elsewhere in this report there appear the recommendations of the Commission in detail. These recommendations call for action by all branches of government — local, State, and Federal — as well as by private individuals and groups. The major thrust of the recommendations is discussed briefly in the paragraphs that follow.

(1) The Commission recommends that the United States adopt and put into effect immediately a national policy designed to give the residents of rural America equality of opportunity with all other citizens. This must include equal access to jobs, medical care, housing, education, welfare, and all other public services, without regard to race, religion, or place of residence.

(2) The Commission recommends, as a matter of urgency, that the national policy of full employment, inaugurated in 1946, be made effective. The need is even greater in rural areas than in urban areas. The Commission urges that this need be given priority in legislation and appropriations. To the extent that private enterprise does not provide sufficient employment for all those willing and able to work, the Commission believes it is the obligation of government to provide it.

(3) The Commission believes that the United States has the resources and the technical means to assure every person in the United States adequate food, shelter, clothing, medical care, and education and, accordingly, recommends action toward this end. Millions of rural residents today are denied the opportunity of earning a living. The Commission believes it is the obligation of society and of

government, to assure such people enough income to provide a decent living. In order to achieve this, basic changes are recommended in public assistance programs.

In some rural areas of the United States there is not only malnutrition but hunger. Existing public programs for food distribution to those in need have failed to meet the need. The Commission recommends that the food stamp program be expanded nationwide and that eligibility be based upon per capita income. Food stamps should be given to the poorest of the poor without cost.

(4) The Commission recommends a thorough overhauling of our manpower policies and programs, particularly including public employment services, in order to deal effectively with rural unemployment and underemployment. The Commission deplores the fact that the richest, most powerful nation in history compels millions of its citizens to engage in aimless wandering in search of jobs and places to live. The recommendations of the Commission aim at a comprehensive and active manpower program which can be an effective weapon against poverty.

(5) The Commission recommends extensive changes in our rural education system, ranging from preschool programs to adult education. Rural schools must be brought up to par with urban schools. The educational system must reclaim youth and adults who drop out before obtaining sufficient education to cope with the complexities of today's world. An educational extension service is recommended to help teachers and schools meet the needs of all students.

(6) The Commission is deeply concerned at the evidence of disease and the lack of medical care in rural areas. The Commission, therefore, recommends rapid expansion of health manpower — both professional and subprofessional — in rural areas, and the establishment of Community Health Centers which can focus on the health needs of rural people.

(7) The Commission recommends development and expansion of family planning programs for the rural poor. Low income families are burdened with relatively numerous children to feed, clothe, and house. They are prepared psychologically to accept family planning. As a matter of principle, they are entitled to facilities and services to help them plan the number and spacing of their children.

(8) The Commission recommends immediate action to provide housing in rural areas by public agencies and puts special emphasis on a program providing rent supplements for the rural poor. The Commission further recommends that a single unified housing agency be made responsible for housing programs in rural areas and that credit terms be made more responsive to need. The Commission also urges a substantial increase in appropriations for Indian housing.

(9) The Commission believes that the overlapping patchwork of districts, organizations, plans, and programs for development impedes the economic development of lagging and poverty-stricken areas and regions. It, therefore, recommends the creation of multicounty districts, cutting across urban-rural boundaries, to cooperatively plan and coordinate programs for economic development. To finance development, the Commission recommends Federal grants, loans, and industrial development subsidies, as well as State and local tax reform.

(10) The Commission believes that without citizen responsibility, which includes the active involvement and participation of all, antipoverty and economic development programs will flounder. Therefore, the Commission recommends that

increased attention be given to involving the poor in the affairs of the community, on both local and areawide levels. Specific suggestions are made for improving the effectiveness of the antipoverty programs of the Office of Economic Opportunity and the Department of Agriculture.

(11) The Commission recommends that the Federal Government re-examine its commercial farm programs in order to make sure that adjustments in the supply of farm products are not made at the expense of the rural poor. Public programs are recommended to enlarge small farm operations and to retire submarginal land from commercial production, but with safeguards protecting the interest of low income families living on sugmarginal land. The Commission also recommends that the development of additional farmland with public funds cease until the nation's food and fiber needs require this development.

(12) Without effective government at all levels, the recommendations in this report will not result in the eradication of rural poverty. The Commission recommends changes in program development and administration to facilitate and encourage the effective involvement of local, State, and Federal governments.

The Fourteen Million

It is a shocking fact that in the United States today, in what is the richest nation in history, close to 14 million rural Americans are poor, and a high proportion of them are destitute. By their poverty they are deprived of freedom to share in our economic abundance.

We can no longer permit public policy to ignore the rural poor. For if we do, we shall see a continuing movement of rural people to our central cities. As the summer of 1967 illustrated, the slums and ghettos of the city breed hatred and violence, which is no solution to the problems of either city or country.

It is to the problems of the rural poor that this report is addressed. Who are the rural poor? Where are they? How poor are they? What can be done to wipe out their poverty?

It may surprise most Americans to know that there is more poverty in rural America, proportionately, than in our cities. In metropolitan areas, one person in eight is poor, and in the suburbs the ratio is one in 15. But in rural areas one of every four persons is poor (table 1).

Some 30 percent of our total population live in rural areas, but 40 percent of the nation's poor live there. Within this total there are nearly 3 million families, plus a million unattached persons.

Contrary to popular impression, all the rural poor do not live on farms, nor are all of them Negroes. Most live in small towns and villages. Only one in four of these rural families lives on a farm. And, of the 14 million rural poor, 11 million are white.

It is true that a higher proportion of Negroes than of whites are poor — three out of five rural nonwhite families are poor. They are heavily concentrated in some areas. In fact, 90 percent of them are clustered in the poorest counties in America. Low income white people are more widely scattered as well as more numerous.

Where are the Rural Poor?

It has become popular to talk of "pockets of poverty." The truth is there are no such things as pockets of poverty. Poverty refuses to stay in pockets. But there are areas of heavy concentration of rural poor. And there is a continuing exodus to towns and cities.

TABLE 1. — *Persons in poverty, by rural and urban residence, March 1965.*

Item	Persons at all income levels		Poor persons[1]		
	Number (millions)	Percent distribution	Number (millions)	Percent distribution	Percent poor
United States	189.9	100.0	33.7	100.0	17.7
Total rural......................	55.3	29.1	13.8	40.9	25.0
Farm	13.3	7.0	3.9	11.6	29.3
Nonfarm.....................	42.0	22.1	9.9	29.4	23.6
Total urban	134.6	70.9	19.9	59.1	14.8
Small cities	27.1	14.3	6.4	19.0	23.6
Metropolitan areas	107.5	56.6	13.5	40.1	12.6
Central cities	58.6	30.8	10.2	30.3	17.4
Suburbs......................	48.9	25.8	3.3	9.8	6.7

[1]Income data relate to 1964. Poverty statistics presented here are preliminary estimates, based on the Social Security Administration poverty lines for urban and rural nonfarm, but using 85 percent rather than 70 percent as the farm-to-nonfarm ratio. The methods used in deriving this ratio and the above data are discussed in a technical report, to be published. Percentages may not add to 100 because of rounding.

Poor people live everywhere, including cities, but some areas and regions have such heavy concentrations of rural poverty that they stand out. Much of the South has a heavy concentration of rural poverty. Outside of the South, Indian reservations, noticeably in the Southwest and the upper Great Plains, contain distinct concentrations of the rural poor, along with New England and the upper Great Lakes.

Within the South several areas of rural poverty can be distinguished. Appalachia perhaps has become best known in recent years, but there is also the Coastal Plain to the east, the Ozarks to the west, the Black Belt of the Old South, and the Mexican-American concentrations along our southern border. Even within a State, distinct areas with high concentrations of poverty may be identified, as in the Delta and the hill country of Mississippi.

Symptoms of Poverty

Average family incomes are low in poverty areas, but there are many additional symptoms of poverty, as indicated by the factors used to reflect economic status. . . . A low level of formal schooling among adults parallels low income levels. Rural housing is dilapidated and in need of extensive repair or replacement. Relatively high proportions of children, youths, and the aged depend on those of working age. And the working-age population is less likely to be in the labor market, with the result that the burden of workers in supporting nonworkers is heavier than in more prosperous sections of America.

When a family's income is less than $3,000, that family is usually defined as poor.[1] In the poverty areas of rural America, however, an income of $3,000 per family is the exception, not the rule. Of the poor families in these areas, more than 70 percent struggle along on less than $2,000 a year, and one family in every four exists, somehow, on less than $1,000 a year.

Schooling in low income areas is as inadequate as incomes. Rural people generally have poorer schooling than city people, and rural poor people are severely handicapped by lack of education. Few rural poor adults attain the general rural average of 8.8 years of school completed. Male farm laborers between 55 and 64 years of age and earning incomes of less than $1,000 average only 5 years of schooling.

Moreover, low educational levels seem to be self-perpetuating. If the head of a rural poor family has had little schooling, his sons are often handicapped in their efforts to get an education.

It is especially difficult for rural people handicapped educationally to acquire new skills, or get new jobs, or otherwise adjust to a society increasingly urbanized. This is as true on the farm as in urban industry, for modern farming requires skills that the poorly educated lack. The less the schooling, the poorer the job and the lower the income.

Lacking in education, the rural poor either concentrate in low-paying jobs on the farm or elsewhere in rural areas, or swell the ranks of the unemployed and the underemployed.

Negroes, Indians, and Mexican Americans suffer even more than low income whites from unemployment and underemployment. Their schooling, as a rule, is even less than that of whites in the rural poverty areas. Negroes emerging from the sharecropper system often migrate to urban ghettos. Those who remain in rural areas are frequently unemployed, and when they do have jobs, they are found mostly in wage work; few become farm operators. Indians on reservations live in poverty, in the main, with few opportunities for work at well-paying jobs. Off the reservations Indians rarely find it possible to get a better paying job, if they find one at all.

At best, job opportunities in rural areas are scarce, and in many places they are getting scarcer year by year. For rural people living within commuting distance of nonfarm jobs, it is sometimes possible to combine farming with a variety of jobs off the farm, but in isolated areas the need for such opportunities is far greater than the supply. At that, even with every adult member of the family working, many families in rural poverty areas don't make enough for decent living.

In fact, some rural families make so little that their children are not only malnourished but literally starving, as a team of six physicians discovered on a 1967 survey in the rural South. The physicians summed up their findings in these words:

In sum, we saw children who are hungry and who are sick — children for whom hunger is a daily fact of life and sickness, in many forms, an inevitability. We do not want to quibble over words, but "malnutrition" is not quite what we found; the boys and girls we saw were hungry — weak, in pain, sick; their lives are being shortened; they are, in fact, visibly and predictably losing their health, their energy, their spirits. They are suffering from hunger and disease and directly or indirectly they are dying from them — which is exactly what "starvation" means.

. . . It is unbelievable to us that a nation as rich as ours, with all its technological and scientific resources, has to permit thousands and thousands of children to go hungry, go sick, and die grim and premature death.

Population Growth and Migration

Rural low income areas have lost population for a number of years, mainly through the exodus of rural farm people. From 1790 to the present, the nation's population has grown from about 4 million to nearly 200 million persons. In the process, it has switched from about 95 percent to 30 percent rural. As late as 1910 a third of the entire population was on farms, but this figure has dropped to only 6 percent. The more than 6,000 cities contained 125 million persons in 1960, or 70 percent of the total population.

The strictly rural areas, and areas with the lowest incomes, have the heaviest out-migration. Consider, for example, the counties classed as all rural — lacking a city (or place) of 2,500 or more population. By 1960, aside from the natural increase (births minus deaths) these counties had lost almost 2 million people, or 15 percent of their 1950 populations through migration. In contrast, the mainly urban counties (with 70 percent or more of their population in urban centers) gained more than 5 million, or about 6 percent through migration.

The poorest counties, with median family incomes of less than $2,000 in 1959, lost more than 600,000 persons — over a fourth of their 1950 population — through migration. In the Deep South, for example, a mass migration of Negroes, mainly to northern industrial centers, has helped reduce southern rural poverty at the expense of cities. At the same time, high income counties, with median family incomes of $7,500 or more in 1959, increased through migration by about 200,000 people.

Americans are well-known for their geographic and social mobility, and the freedom to be mobile is perhaps one of our most cherished values. Many seek to escape rural poverty by moving from the farm or small town to larger cities and into nonfarm work. But the fact remains that if one's origin is in agriculture, his chances of remaining there are relatively great. Given the low income levels of many farmers and farmworkers, the tendency to inherit one's occupation serves as an obstacle to an escape from poverty. Studies demonstrate that persons entering the labor market at the lowest income levels have the greatest difficulty in rising to better jobs and higher incomes. Many simply do not make the transition. Migration to a city is therefore no guarantee of escaping poverty, as the presence of millions of poverty-ridden exruralites now in cities testifies.

More Children than Income

The size of many low income families makes escape from poverty extremely difficult. The world over, large families have been traditional in rural areas, and the tradition lives on in rural America, especially in poverty areas. The result, of course, is that meager resources have to be stretched beyond the breaking point to feed, house, clothe, and educate the children.

The birth rate has been declining in the nation as a whole since 1957, but average number of births is still high in rural poverty areas. The 1960 statistics revealed that throughout the nation women 40 to 44 years of age had produced an average — statistically speaking — of 2.5 children each. In farm families with incomes of less than $2,000, the average was 3.7 for white mothers and 6.4 for nonwhites.

Persistence in rural America of the tradition favoring large families is understandable. The rural way of life, at one time, dictated the need for large families. Before machines and modern technology came along, the family farm needed children as potential workers. Religious beliefs buttressed the tradition. And society more or less expected and sanctioned large families.

To add to the burden, the households of low income people in rural areas often include several generations. This is partly from necessity, partly cultural inheritance. Rural people cling tenaciously to the custom of caring for the old folks at home. And when the children of friends and neighbors need a place to stay, they are taken in.

Then, when the youths and young adults of these households go to the city in search of jobs, those who are left have more dependents to support. The combination of few workers, low incomes, and more people to support creates a dependency problem that is acute.

The Residual Population

The mass exodus from low income rural areas in recent years has meant that those left behind are often worse off than before. Their chances of escaping from poverty, or avoiding deeper poverty, or even easing their burden have been reduced. Partly this is because the areas have too many old people and children for the working-age population to support. Partly it is because a smaller population, spread too sparsely, cannot support or build a strong, flexible social and economic superstructure in the area. Local governments, schools, and churches are dying from lack of support. And as local facilities and services continue to decline, the chances for redevelopment diminish.

Figures on the age of heads of households in rural poverty areas underline the hopelessness of the situation. In 1965, among low income families in these areas, one of every four heads of household was 65 years of age, or older. Contrast this with rural areas with adequate incomes. There, only about 7 percent of the heads of households were as old as 65. Nor is the picture brighter for heads of households who were younger but living in poverty areas. Of the age group 22 to 54, half were poor.

Measuring Poverty

The Concept and The Reality

"Poverty" is a controversial word. Not everyone agrees on what it means. This applies to experts as well as to laymen. In the opinion of the Commission, poverty is partly inadequate income, but it goes much deeper than that. Poverty afflicts the mind and the spirit as well.

Income is important in escaping from poverty, though not the whole answer. Education and jobs are also essential, and they can lead to higher income. Income is obviously needed to buy the food, clothing, housing, schooling, and health services required by anyone in this money economy if he is to escape from poverty — if he is to preserve some self-esteem.

But poverty is much more:

- It is lack of access to respected positions in society, and lack of power to do anything about it.
- It is insecurity and unstable homes.
- It is a wretched existence that tends to perpertuate itself from one generation to the next.

Low income is widely used as an index of poverty; the number of low income people is taken as the umber of poor, though this may be an oversimplification. The poverty line is the minimum level of income needed to provide the kind of living that our society considers a basic human right.

Opinions as to where the poverty line really is, or should be, have changed as America has become more prosperous and more highly urbanized. Our standard of what is an adequate income for the poor will probably rise. Just as the poverty budgets of the 1920's by today's standards appear grossly inadequate, Americans in the year 1980 may have the same opinion of today's poverty lines.

If Billions Alone Were The Remedy

What would it cost to bring all the poor of the United States above the poverty line, if we merely transferred money to them?

In 1964, for the nation as a whole, it would have cost about $12.5 billion to lift the incomes of the poor above the poverty level. The sum of $12.5 billion is about 2.6 percent of all personal incomes in the United States. It would transfer roughly $1,000 to each of the "poor" households. To close the income gap for white households considered poor, the total needed would be about $9 billion; for nonwhite households, the total needed would be $3.5 billion.

These estimates include both urban and rural poor. To close the income gap for the rural poor alone would require nearly $5 billion.

This does not mean that rural poverty would be eliminated simply by adding $5 billion to the incomes of the rural poor. Poverty cannot be ended that way. Even if the incomes of the rural poor were automatically increased by perpetual transfers of income through relief checks and other welfare payments, many of the poor would remain dependent, lacking in self-esteem, never able to make their own way or to win the respect of their neighbors.

How Income Needs of The Poor Vary

But how much income must a family have to get out of poverty? The answer obviously depends on size of family, the prices they have to pay and, in addition, the changing standards of living which our society regards as essential.

The figure of $3,000 as the poverty line is useful as a rough approximation, though it cannot be applied universally or indiscriminately. For some households an income of $3,000 is more than is needed for a decent level of living. For other households $3,000 is not nearly enough.

While it is possible to use the $3,000 income level as a rough indicator of poverty, more refined measurements are available. Poverty income levels that vary by family size and type, and by farm and nonfarm residence, have been developed by Orshansky in the Social Security Administration of the Department of Health, Education, and Welfare. These levels are so designed that they center around the $3,000 family income level. A rural nonfarm family of four, for example, would need at least $3,200 to be above poverty. A rural nonfarm family of seven would need $5,205.

The comparable income levels for farm families were set at 70 percent of the nonfarm levels — $2,240 for a farm family of four, for example. This means that a farm family needs only 70 percent as much income as a rural nonfarm or urban family to be above poverty. We doubt that this is lating census data, in determining overall trends and characteristics of the nation's poor. For this purpose they have served fairly well, aside from accurate. The procedures and assumptions used in deriving this 70-percent adjustment factor are questionable and should be re-examined.

The Social Security Administration developed its set of poverty income levels to be used in tabulating the shortcomings discussed above. They are a big improvement over the straight $3,000, which completely ignored variations in family needs.

However, their apparent precision has invited misuse. Many Federal, State, and local government agencies have adopted these new poverty income levels, and are using them as eligiblity criteria for welfare and antipoverty programs. The experts who developed the poverty levels are appalled at their being used in this way. They were not intended for this purpose and they are not adequate.

Further analysis is needed to determine the exact income needed to raise a household above the poverty level. Regional variations in the cost of living remain to be taken into account. The fact that rural people often must travel great distances to buy necessities, or to obtain medical service, has yet to be allowed for. We still need indices of poverty that will be both accurate and fair. The Federal Government should take the initiative in developing a standard set of poverty lines. As a start, this Commission has conducted a study to determine the income needed to support a comparable level of living for farm, rural nonfarm, and urban families. Preliminary results indicate that farm families need about 85 percent, rather than 70 percent, as much income as a comparable family in urban areas. Using this ratio, the Commission estimated that the number of rural poor have been undercounted by 700,000 persons, or more than 20 percent.

In interpreting and using poverty income levels, it is necessary to recognize that people whose incomes are a few dollars above the poverty level may nevertheless be in genuine distress and living at a level below an acceptable one. We have to keep in mind that training and educational programs designed to help the poor can help the near-poor, and should be so used.

The urgent goal, of course, must be to help those in greatest need. But an income level of $3,000 ought not to be thought of as an upper limit for today's poor. Rather, it should be considered a threshold over which low income families may pass to higher levels. This Commission firmly believes that antipoverty programs should not only lift people to the poverty line, but help them to rise as much further as their abilities will permit.

We do not know how many people in rural America have lost all hope in a future. It is tragic and shameful that any have.

This Commission believes that by adopting the program of action recommended in this report, we can restore hope to many who are now without it, and we can help the 14 million rural poor climb out of poverty. The nation can do this, that is, if there is the will to do it.

The time for action is now.

Hunger and Food Stamps

From Letter, Senator Joseph S. Clark and others to the President, Apr. 27, 1967, in United States Congress, 90th, 1st. Sess., Senate, Committee on Labor and Public Welfare, *Poverty: Hunger and Federal Food Programs* (Committee Print), pp. 29–30.

April 27, 1967.

The PRESIDENT,
The White House,
Washington, D.C.

DEAR MR. PRESIDENT:

The Subcommittee on Employment, Manpower and Poverty of the Senate Committee on Labor and Public Welfare, as part of its examination of the war on poverty, conducted a public hearing and field inspection trip in Mississippi on April 10 and 11. The Committee heard testimony and observed, first-hand, conditions of malnutrition and wide-spread hunger in the Delta counties of Mississippi that can only be described as shocking, and which we believe constitute an emergency.

The Secretary of Agriculture, at the request of the subcommittee, has since sent a team of departmental representatives, accompanied by a committee staff representative, to make a personal field study of these conditions.

The findings of the subcommittee, which were confirmed by a report by the department inspection team, may be summarized as follows:

(1) There is clear evidence of acute malnutrition and hunger among many families in the Mississippi Delta.

(2) Many families subsist without discernible income and cannot afford to meet the minimum purchase requirements for food stamps.

(3) Many low-income families also have serious difficulty in meeting the purchase requirements for food stamps.

The findings acquire more meaning, perhaps, when just one family which the committee saw and interviewed is used as an example. This family had thirteen children. They told us that they had had grits and molasses for breakfast, no lunch, and would have beans for supper. Some of the children could not go to school because they had no shoes, and had distended stomachs, chronic sores of the upper lip, and were extremely lethargic — all of which are the tragic evidence of serious malnutrition.

In the judgment of the subcommittee, the situation has reached emergency proportions, due to the steeply rising level of unemployment produced by the mechanization of agriculture. This process has been forcing people out of work in the Delta and throughout the South for some years. It has now accelerated sharply due to factors associated with the implementation of the agricultural minimum wage. In the Delta alone, it is estimated that some 40 to 60 thousand people will be either without or almost without cash income by this summer. It is our strong belief that this economic upheaval has reached a level of emergency, as grave as any natural disaster.

Accordingly, the subcommittee recommends the following action be taken immediately in those areas where the food stamp program is in operation.

First, the Secretary of Agriculture should make food stamps available without cost to people who have no cash income. Our study of this law and the regulations convinces us that such action is within the Secretary's authority.

Second, we believe that the coupon purchase requirements for families which have very low cash incomes are in many cases excessive and should be lowered to reflect more realistic standards.

Third, we have been informed that receipients of food stamps have been required to pay more for food stamps than departmental regulations require for families of their income level. We believe such incidents should be investigated immediately and corrected.

Fourth, the Secretary should find that an emergency situation (as defined by the Food Stamp Act) exists so that he may distribute federally owned foods under the authority of other applicable federal laws. In making such distributions the Secretary should use private as well as public agencies.

We also recommend that other appropriate federal agencies be requested to use their authority under applicable federal laws to take immediate action to alleviate this emergency situation wherever it is found, regardless of whether a federal food program is presently in operation. Thus, the following steps should be taken:

First, the Office of Economic Opportunity should utilize its emergency family loan authority to subsidize the purchase of food, whether through the food stamp mechanism or otherwise.

Second, the Department of Health, Education and Welfare should consider invoking its authority to extend supplementary welfare assistance on a demonstration basis, seeking the required matching funds from private non-profit sources.

Third, consideration should be given to invoking such other emergency authority as may be vested by law in the Executive Branch.

While the subcommittee has had an opportunity to observe these conditions only in the State of Mississippi, we have been informed by the Department of Agriculture, the Office of Economic Opportunity and the Civil Rights Commission that similar conditions have been found in other states. We trust, therefore, that whatever action is taken will be addressed to these conditions wherever they exist.

Respectfully submitted.

Subcommitteee on Employment, Manpower, and Poverty: Joseph S. Clark, Chairman; Jennings Randolph, U.S.S.; Claiborne Pell, U.S.S.; Edward M. Kennedy, U.S.S.; Gaylord Nelson, U.S.S.; Robert F. Kennedy, U.S.S.; Winston L. Prouty, U.S.S.; Jacob K. Javits, U.S.S.; George Murphy, U.S.S.

USDA Food Programs

From Letter, Orville L. Freeman, Secretary of Agriculture to Ralph D. Abernathy, May 23, 1968. In Files, Agricultural History Group, Economic Research Service, U.S. Department of Agriculture.

DEAR DR. ABERNATHY:

The Department of Agriculture has devoted much time and careful attention to the requests made when you and your associates in the Poor People's March met with us on April 29.

Some of your requests we can meet. Others are beyond our authority or resources. There are still others which call for difficult judgments where further work and careful consideration are needed.

We, too, are concerned that our food programs do not reach as many people as they should, but today, they are reaching 5.9 million people.

We, too, are concerned that even the 50¢ minimum payment may keep some poor people from participating in the food stamp program, though 200,000 people were benefited when this minimum requirement was reduced from $2 last year.

We, too, would like to broaden the variety and increase the nutritional value of the foods available under the commodity distribution program and we have taken action to add canned chicken, dried eggs, fruit juice, instant hot cereal, and vitamin-enriched instant mashed potatoes to the items already distributed.

And, we, too, worry that there are needy school children who do not have equal access to school lunch or breakfast programs, even though more than 2 million needy children now receive a free or reduced price lunch and over 100,000 participate in the breakfast program.

We are committed to placing food programs into all the hard core poverty counties. We are troubled by the harsh lot of so many farm laborers. We are determined to eliminate discrimination from employment practices within the Department of Agriculture and from the full range of services afforded by this Department.

If our goals were easily reached, they would have been reached long ago. There are real obstacles on the path of their accomplishment.

The programs we administer are framed by laws enacted by the Congress. For each program, the Congress has prescribed certain standards of operation.

In addition to the legal limits, there are resource limitations. We can spend only what the Congress appropriates and authorizes. We cannot expand food stamp programs into additional counties until the start of the next fiscal year, July 1, because we have committed all the money available. Further, we will not have the resources to expand into additional counties after July 1, unless Congress raises or eliminates the $225 million ceiling on funds authorized for the Food Stamp Program, and appropriates additional money.

In closing, I would like to emphasize my belief that it would be a tragic mistake for those who share our hope for a better life for the poor to use farm programs as a scapegoat.

The farm programs are designed to promote a rough balance between what our farmers produce and what the nation and the world can take through regular marketing arrangements and government food programs. If we produce more than can be used, the resulting surpluses force prices down and the narrow margin on which the American farmer operates disappears. When the farmer loses, it is the poor, small farmer who suffers most.

The problem of the hungry poor in America is not a shortage of food. American agriculture is producing all the food that Americans can consume and more. The problem is that the poor lack the purchasing power to buy the food they need. And this is the problem we are trying to meet through our food stamp and commodity distribution programs.

I enclose herewith a detailed document in response to your requests. When you have had an opportunity to review this document I will be more than willing to go over it with you and to explore together what more might be done within the framework of existing law and budgets.

We welcome your advice and counsel and believe that this document will attest to the fact that this Department and this Administration are firmly committed to the objective of eliminating hunger, poverty, and discrimination in this country.

Sincerely yours,
ORVILLE L. FREEMAN
Secretary of Agriculture

Enclosure

President Nixon on Food Needs

From Richard M. Nixon, Remarks to the White House Conference on Food, Nutrition and Health. Dec. 2, 1969.

As all of you are aware, this is an historic conference. It is particularly an historic conference for me because it is the first White House Conference that I have had the opportunity to address as President of the United States. I have addressed others as Vice President. And it is the first that we have had in this administration.

This meeting marks an historic milestone. What it does is to set the seal of urgency on our national commitment to put an end to hunger and malnutrition due to poverty in America.

At the same time, it marks the beginning of a new, more determined, and more concerted drive than ever before, to reduce the malnutrition that derives from ignorance or inadvertence.

I recognize that many of you who are here and who have participated in the panels have been under enormous pressure, because you have had a relatively short time for the vast amount of work that it took to put this conference together and to prepare for it.

However, that pressure reflects the priority of the subject we are here to discuss. It reflects the sense of urgency that we all feel.

Until this moment in our history as a Nation, the central question has been whether we as a Nation would accept the problem of malnourishment as a national responsibility.

That moment is past. On May 6 I asserted to the Congress that "the moment is at hand to put an end to hunger in America itself. For all time."

Speaking for this administration, I not only accept the responsibility — I claim the responsibility.

Malnourishment is a national concern because we are a Nation that cares about its people, how they feel, how they live. We care whether they are well and whether they are happy.

First of all there is a moral imperative: Our national conscience requires it. We must because we can. We are the world's richest nation. We are its best educated nation. We have an agricultural abundance that ranks as a miracle of the modern world. This Nation cannot long continue to live with its conscience if millions of its own people are unable to get an adequate diet.

Even in purely practical terms there are compelling considerations requiring this challenge to be met.

A child ill-fed is dulled in curiosity, lower in stamina, distracted from learning. A worker ill-fed is less productive, more often absent from work. The mounting cost of medical care for diet-related illnesses; remedial education required to overcome diet-related slowness in school; institutionalization and loss of full productive potential; all of these place a heavy economic burden on a society as a whole.

And for many of us, and for me, as I know for many of you, this subject also evokes vivid personal memories. I grew up in the Great Depression. I shall never forget the hopelessness that I saw so starkly etched on so many faces — the silent gratitude of others lucky enough to enjoy three square meals a day, or sometimes even one.

I recall in my native State of California in the '30's, families that I knew, that I went to school with, subsisted on bread and gravy, bread and milk, beans. And later on in the '30's, in North Carolina, families who knew nothing much more than black-eyed peas, turnip greens.

We have come a long way since then, but we still have a long way to go.

The question now is: What will we do about it?

We begin with the troublesome complex of definitions and causes.

Now experts can argue — and they do — and you will — about the magnitude of the problem: how many are hungry, how many malnourished, how severely they are malnourished. Precise statistical data remain elusive and often contradictory. However, Dr. Arnold Schaefer, the man in charge of the National Nutrition Survey, recently made this cautions but very forceful observation. He said:

"We have been alerted by recent studies that our population who are 'malnutrition risks' is beyond anticipated findings, and also that in some of our vulnerable population groups — pre-school children, the aged, teenagers and the poor — malnutrition is indeed a serious medical problem."

We don't know just how many Americans are actually hungry and how many suffer from malnutrition, who eat enough but do not eat the right things. But we do know there are too many Americans in both categories.

We can argue the extent, but hunger exists.

We can argue the severity, but malnutrition exists.

The plain fact is that a great many Americans are not eating well enough to sustain health.

We see, then, that the problem of hunger and malnutrition is, really, two separate problems. One is to ensure that everyone is able to obtain an adequate diet. The second is to ensure that people actually are properly fed, where they have the ability to obtain the adequate diet.

On the one hand, we are dealing with problems of income distribution. On the other hand, with problems of education, habit, taste, behavior, personal preferences — the whole complex of things that lead people to act the way they do, to make the choices they do.

The answers to many of these questions are difficult to come by. The very fact that the same question evokes so many different, conflicting answers is itself testimony as to how fragile is the basis of our knowledge.

Assuming we can agree on definitions, and the causes of malnourishment, how do we eradicate it?

Now some will answer that the magic ingredient is money, and money certainly is one ingredient, and a very important one. The more than $5 billion that I have proposed for new or expanded programs for food and family assistance next year would go a long way toward bringing the problem under control.

And in this connection, I would urge each of you in this great conference to enlist yourself in an effort to win passage of three landmark pieces of legislation I have already recommended to Congress.

One of these is what many observers consider to be the most important piece of domestic legislation proposed in the past 50 years, the establishment of a floor under the income of every American family. [*Applause*]

For the first time — Mr. Moynihan please notice — for the first time, this new family assistance plan would give every American family a basic income, wherever in America that family may live. For the first time, it would put cash into the hands of families because they are poor, rather than because they fit certain categories. When enacted, this measure alone will either supplement the incomes or provide the basis for the incomes of 25 million American men, women, and children.

Our basic policies for improvement of the living conditions of the poor are based on this proposition: that the best judge of each family's priorities is that family itself; that the best way to ameliorate the hardships of poverty is to provide the family with additional income — to be spent as that family sees fit.

Now, some will argue with this proposition. Some argue that the poor cannot be trusted to make their own decisions, and therefore, the Government should dole out food and clothing and medicine, according to a schedule of what the Government thinks is needed.

Well, I disagree. I believe there are no experts present in this great gathering who know more about the realities of hunger and malnutrition than those among you who are here because you have suffered from it, or than those among you who are here who do suffer from it, from great cities, from wornout farms, from barren reservations, from frozen tundra, from tiny islands half a world away.

The task of Government is not to make decisions for you or for anyone. The task of Government is to enable you to make decisions for yourselves. Not to see the truth of that statement is fundamentally to mistake the genius of democracy. We have made too many mistakes of this type — but no more. Our job is to get resources to people in need and then to let them run their own lives.

And now I would stress that all of you who have been so strong and effective in achieving a breakthrough on national awareness on hunger, will become an equally strong citizen lobby for welfare reform. The needs of the poor range far beyond food, though that is often the most visible and heart-rending aspect of poverty. More basically, the poor need money with which they can meet the full range of their needs, from basic shelter, to medicine, to clothes for school, to transportation. And they need these resources in a program framework that builds incentives for self support and family stability.

Let the reform of the bankrupt welfare system in this country be the next great cause of those who come together here today.

Now the second measure that I would especially urge your support for is one that you will be considering in your deliberations. It is the reform and expansion of the food stamp program. I requested this in my May 8 message on hunger. This has been designed to complement the welfare program. While the welfare proposals may be subject to long debate, I hope and I expect that Congress will act quickly on the expanded food stamp plan.

The Nation's food programs have been shot through with inequities, as you will find — notably, the fact that many counties have not participated, and the fact that because food stamps had to be bought with cash many of the neediest were unable to participate.

We are pressing hard to bring every county into one or other of the food distribution programs, and the new food stamp bill would provide stamps free to those most in need — while expanding the program to a level that would reach $2.5 billion a year when fully implemented.

In a related matter, we already are greatly expanding our school lunch programs, with the target of reaching every needy school child with a free or reduced-cost lunch by the end of the current fiscal year.

Now, there is a third measure, a third measure which at first will seem unrelated, but which is directly related to this conference. I ask your support for the Commission on Population Growth and the American Future which I have proposed to Congress and which has been most favorably received, not only in the Congress, but by church and civic organizations throughout the Nation.

America, I believe, has come to see how necessary it is to be responsibly concerned with this subject. In proposing the Commission, I also declared that it would be the goal of this administration to provide "adequate family planning services within the next five years to all those who want them but cannot afford them." And there are some 5 million women in low-income families who are in exactly that situation. I can report that the steps to meet that goal, a goal 5 years away, have already been taken within the administration, and the program is underway.

Now taken together, these three measures would virtually eliminate the problem of poverty as a cause of malnutrition.

Their dollar cost is high, but their practical benefits to the Nation are immense.

I know that your panels have advanced proposals for massive efforts on many fronts. They demonstrate that the goal cannot be won by government alone.

It is for each to ask how he, individually, can respond to the questions being asked here. For example:

— can foods be better labeled, be made more nutritious, and be fortified with available additives?
— can industry, the schools, government, and citizens individually join effectively in a program of public education?
— can school lunch programs feasibly be improved?
— can voluntary programs by citizens and community organizations teach people what to eat, to close the knowledge gap?

The fact that so many groups are represented here today is itself evidence of a new sense of community responsibility, of industry responsibility, of individual responsibility. The fact that so many women are represented here, especially, is evidence of an enormous resource, particularly in the volunteer field, a resource that can do so much to ensure our success. . . .

Ours is the most productive and most generous country the world has ever known. Less than 5 percent of our population — according to Secretary Hardin, Secretary of Agriculture — produces enough food to feed all the American people and to supply the needs of millions in other countries as well. In the years since World War II the United States has provided more than $30 billion in food, in the form of aid, to needy nations and peoples abroad.

I have traveled to most of the nations of the world, in Asia, in Africa, and Latin America. Do you realize that in most of the world today a conference like this would be meaningless because those nations would lack the resources to produce the food to meet the objectives that this conference may decide should be met or lack the resources to purchase the food which they themselves would not be able to produce?

It is precisely because our system has succeeded so well that we are now able to address the goals of this conference and the fact that we are gathered here is an example of one of the greatest strengths of that same system. It has a capacity for self-correction, for self-regeneration; its constant reaching out to identify new or additional needs and to meet those needs, the readiness of its citizens to join in that effort, volunteering their time and their talents, as you are volunteering your time and your talents today.

This Nation has the capacity to provide an adequate diet for every American. The calling of this conference demonstrates that we have the will to achieve this goal. What we need is to find the most effective means for doing so consistent with maintaining the vitality of the system that makes it all possible.

And so I will review your recommendations with great care.

And I will ask you to go about drawing up those recommendations with equally great care.

My fellow Americans, as you begin this conference I commit to your concern the lives of millions of Americans, too young, too old, or too hurt by life to do without your help. I commit to your concern the not less serious task of helping to bring the rest of America to understand what we seek and to join us in adding this new dimension to the concept of American democracy. For at this very moment we are gathered at one of those great historical moments when it becomes possible for all of us to act a little better than we are, and in so doing, to leave this great and good Nation a little better because we were there.

Agricultural Act of 1970

From 84 Statutes at Large 1358.

Title I — Payment Limitation

SEC. 101. Notwithstanding any other provision of law —

(1) The total amount of payments which a person shall be entitled to receive under each of the annual programs established by titles IV, V, and VI of this Act for the 1971, 1972, or 1973 crop of the commodity shall not exceed $55,000.

(2) The term "payments" as used in this section includes price-support payments, set-aside payments, diversion payments, public access payments, and marketing certificates, but does not include loans or purchases.

(3) If the Secretary determines that the total amount of payments which will be earned by any person under the program in effect for any crop will be reduced under this section, the set-aside acreage for the farm or farms on which such person will be sharing in payments earned under such program shall be reduced to such extent and in such manner as the Secretary determines will be fair and reasonable in relation to the amount of the payment reduction.

(4) The Secretary shall issue regulations defining the term "person" and prescribing such rules as he determines necessary to assure a fair and reasonable application of such limitation: *Provided,* That the provisions of this Act which limit payments to any person shall not be applicable to lands owned by States, political subdivisions, or agencies thereof, so long as such lands are farmed primarily in the direct furtherance of a public function, as determined by the Secretary.

Title II — Dairy

Dairy Base Plans

SEC. 201. (a) The Agricultural Adjustment Act, as reenacted and amended by the Agricultural Marketing Agreement Act of 1937, as amended, is further amended by striking in subparagraph (B) of subsection 8c (5) all that part of said subparagraph (B) which follows the comma at the end of clause (c) and inserting in lieu thereof the following: "(d) a further adjustment to encourage seasonal adjustments in the production of milk through equitable apportionment of the total value of the milk purchased by any handler, or by all handlers, among producers on the basis of their marketings of milk during a representative period of time, which need not be limited to one year; (e) a provision providing for the accumulation and disbursement of a fund to encourage seasonal adjustments in the production of milk may be included in an order; and (f) a further adjustment, equitably to apportion the total value of milk purchased by all handlers among producers on the basis of their marketings of milk, which may be adjusted to reflect the utilization of producer milk by all handlers in any use classification or classifications, during a representative period of one to three years, which will be automatically updated each year. In the event a producer holding a base allocated under this clause (f) shall reduce his marketings, such reduction shall not adversely affect his history of production and marketing for the determination of future bases, or future updating of bases, except that an order may provide that, if a producer reduces his marketings below his base allocation in any one or more use classifications designated in the order, the amount of any such reduction shall be taken into account in determining future bases, or future updating of bases. Bases allocated to producers under this clause (f) may be transferable under an order on such terms and conditions, including those which will prevent bases taking on an unreasonable value, as are prescribed in the order by the Secretary of Agriculture. Provisions shall be made in the order for the allocation of bases under this clause (f) —

"(i) for the alleviation of hardship and inequity among producers; and

"(ii) for providing bases for dairy farmers not delivering milk as producers under the order upon becoming producers under the order who did not produce milk during any part of the representative period and these new producers shall within ninety days after the first regular delivery of milk at the price for the lowest use classification specified in such order be allocated a base which the Secretary determines proper after considering supply and demand conditions, the development of orderly and efficient marketing conditions and to the respective interests of producers under the order, all other dairy farmers and the consuming public. Producer bases so allocated shall for a period of not more than three years be reduced by not more than 20 per centum; and

"(iii) dairy farmers not delivering milk as producers under the order upon becoming producers under the order by reason of a plant to which they are making deliveries becoming a pool plant under the order, by amendment or otherwise, shall be provided bases with respect to milk delivered under the order based on their past deliveries of milk on the same basis as other producers under the order; and

"(iv) such order may include such additional provisions as the Secretary deems appropriate in regard to the reentry of producers who have previously discontinued their dairy farm enterprise or transferred bases authorized under this clause (f); and

"(v) notwithstanding any other provision of this Act, dairy farmers not delivering milk as producers under the order, upon becoming producers under the order, shall within ninety days be provided with respect to milk delivered under the order, allocations based on their past deliveries of milk during the representative period from the production facilities from which they are delivering milk under the order on the same basis as producers under the order on the effective date of order provisions authorized under this clause (f): *Provided,* That bases shall be allocated only to a producer marketing milk from the production facilities from which he marketed milk during the representative period, except that in no event shall such allocation of base exceed the amount of milk actually delivered under such order.

The assignment of other source milk to various use classes shall be made without regard to whether an order contains provisions authorized under this clause (f). In the case of any producer who during any accounting period delivers a portion of his milk to persons not fully regulated by the order, provision shall be made for reducing the allocation of, or payment to be received by any such producer under this clause (f) to compensate for any marketings of milk to such other persons for such period or periods as necessary to insure equitable participation in marketings among all producers. Notwithstanding the provisions of section 8c(12) and the last sentence of section 8c(19) of this Act, order provisions under this clause (f) shall not be effective in any marketing order unless separately approved by producers in a referendum in which each individual producer shall have one vote and may be terminated separately whenever the Secretary makes a determination with respect to such provisions as is provided for the termination of an order in subparagraph 8c(16)(B). Disapproval or termination of such order provisions shall not be considered disapproval of the order or of other terms of the order.''

(b) The legal status of producer handlers of milk under the provisions of the Agricultural Adjustment Act, as reenacted and amended by the Agricultural Marketing Agreement Act of 1937, as amended, shall be the same subsequent to the adoption of the amendments made by this Act as it was prior thereto.

(c) Nothing in subsection (a) of this section 201 shall be construed as invalidating any class I base plan provisions of any marketing order previously issued by the Secretary of Agriculture pursuant to authority contained in the Food and Agriculture Act of 1965 (79 Stat. 1187), but such provisions are expressly ratified, legalized, and confirmed and may be extended through and including December 31, 1971.

(d) It is not intended that existing law be in any way altered, rescinded, or amended with respect to section 8c(5)(G) of the Agricultural Adjustment Act, as reenacted and amended by the Agricultural Marketing Agreement Act of 1937, as amended, and such section 8c(5)(G) is fully reaffirmed.

(e) The provisions of this section shall not be effective after December 31, 1973 except with respect to orders providing for Class I base plans issued prior to such date, but in no event shall any order so issued extend or be effective beyond December 31, 1976.

Suspension of Butterfat Support Program

SEC. 202. Effective only with respect to the period beginning April 1, 1971, and ending March 31, 1974 —

(a) The first sentence of section 201 of the Agricultural Act of 1949, as amended (7 U.S.C. 1446), is amended by striking the words ''milk, butterfat, and the products of milk and butterfat'' and inserting in lieu thereof the words ''and milk''.

(b) Paragraph (c) of section 201 of the Agricultural Act of 1949, as amended (7 U.S.C. 1446(c)), is amended to read as follows:

''(c) The price of milk shall be supported at such level not in excess of 90 per centum nor less than 75 per centum of the parity price therefor as the Secretary determines necessary in order to assure an adequate supply. Such price support shall be provided through purchases of milk and the products of milk.''

Transfer of Dairy Products to the Military and to Veterans Hospitals

SEC. 203. Section 202 of the Agricultural Act of 1949, as amended (7 U.S.C. 1446a), is amended by changing "December 31, 1970" to read "December 31, 1973" both places it appears therein.

Dairy Indemnity Program

SEC. 204. (a) Section 3 of the Act of August 13, 1968 (Public Law 90–484; 82 Stat. 750), is amended by striking out the word "June 30, 1970.", and inserting in lieu thereof the word "June 30, 1973.".

(b) The first sentence of section 1 of said Act is amended by inserting, "and manufacturers of dairy products who have been directed since the date of enactment of the Agricultural Act of 1970 to remove their dairy products," after "milk", and the second sentence is revised to read: "Any indemnity payment to any farmer shall continue until he has been reinstated and is again allowed to dispose of his milk on commercial markets.".

Title III — Wool

SEC. 301. The National Wool Act of 1954, as amended, is amended as follows:

(1) Designate the first two sentences of section 703 as subsection "(a)", and, in the second sentence, delete "1970" and substitute "1973".

(2) In the third sentence of section 703, delete the portion beginning with "The support price for shorn wool shall be" and ending with "*Provided further, That the*" and substitute "The", designate the third sentence as subsection "(b)", change the period at the end thereof to a colon and add the following: "*Provided. That* for the three marketing years beginning January 1, 1971, and ending December 31, 1973, the support price for shorn wool shall be 72 cents per pound, grease basis.".

(3) Designate the fourth and fifth sentences of section 703 as subsection "(c)", change the period at the end of the fifth sentence to a colon and add the following: "*Provided, That* for the three marketing years beginning January 1, 1971, and ending December 31, 1973, the support price for mohair shall be 80.2 cents per pound, grease basis.".

(4) Designate the sixth sentence of section 703 as subsection "(d)".

(5) Designate the last sentence of section 703 as subsection "(e)".

Title IV — Wheat

SEC. 401. Effective only with respect to the 1971, 1972, and 1973 crops of wheat, section 107 of the Agricultural Act of 1949, as amended, is further amended to read as follows:

"SEC. 107. Notwithstanding any other provision of law —

"(a) Loans and purchases on each crop of wheat shall be made available at such level as the Secretary determines appropriate, taking into consideration competitive world prices of wheat, the feeding value of wheat in relation to feed grains, and the level at which price support is made available for feed grains: *Provided,* That in no event shall such level be in excess of the parity price for wheat or less than $1.25 per bushel.

"(b) If a set-aside program is in effect for any crop of wheat under section 379b(c) of the Agricultural Adjustment Act of 1938, as amended, certificates, loans and purchases shall be made available on such crop only to producers who comply with the provisions of such program."

SEC. 402. Effective only with respect to the 1971, 1972, and 1973 crops of wheat sections 379b and 379c of the Agricultural Adjustment Act of 1938, as amended, are further amended to read as follows:

"SEC. 379b. (a) The Secretary shall provide for the issuance of wheat marketing certificates for the purpose of enabling producers on any farm for which certificates are issued to receive, in addition to the other proceeds from the sale of wheat, an amount equal to the face value of such certificates. The face value per bushel of domestic marketing certificates for the 1971, 1972, and 1973 crops of wheat shall be in such amount as, together with the national average market price received by farmers during the first five months of the marketing year for such crop, the Secretary determines will be equal to the parity price for wheat as of the beginning of the marketing year for the crop.

"(b) The domestic wheat marketing certificates shall be made available for a farm on the number of bushels determined by multiplying the domestic allotment for the farm for the crop to which such certificates relate by the projected yield established for the farm with such adjustments as the Secretary determines necessary to provide a fair and equitable yield.

"(c)(1) The Secretary shall provide for a set-aside of cropland if he determines that the total supply of wheat or other commodities will, in the absence of such a set-aside, likely be excessive taking into account the need for an adequate carryover to maintain reasonable and stable supplies and prices and to meet a national emergency. If a set-aside of cropland is in effect under this subsection (c), then as a condition of eligibility for loans, purchases, and certificates on wheat, the producers on a farm must set aside and devote to approved conservation uses an acreage of cropland equal to (i) such percentage of the domestic wheat allotment for the farm as may be specified by the Secretary and will be estimated by the Secretary to result in a set-aside not in excess of 13.3 million acres in the case of the 1971 crop, or 15 million acres in the case of the 1972 or 1973 crop, plus (ii) the acreage of cropland on the farm devoted in preceding years to soil-conserving uses, as determined by the Secretary. The Secretary is authorized for the 1971, 1972, and 1973 crops to limit the acreage planted to wheat on the farm to such percentage of the domestic wheat allotment as he determines necessary to provide an orderly transition to the program provided for under this section. Grazing shall not be permitted during any of the five principal months of the normal growing season as determined by the county committee established pursuant to section 8(b) of the Soil Conservation and Domestic Allotment Act, as amended, and subject to this limitation (1) the Secretary shall permit producers to plant and graze on the set-aside acreage sweet sorghum, and (2) the Secretary may permit, subject to such terms and conditions as he may prescribe, all or any of the set-aside acreage to be devoted to grazing or the production of guar, seasame, safflower, sunflower, castor beans, mustard seed, crambe, plantago ovato, flaxseed, or other commodity, if he determines that such production is needed to provide an adequate supply, is not likely to increase the cost of the price-support program, and will not adversely affect farm income.

"(2) To assist in adjusting the acreage of commodities to desirable goals, the Secretary may make land diversion payments, in addition to the certificates authorized in subsection (b), available to producers on a farm who, to the extent prescribed by the Secretary, devote to approved conservation uses an acreage of cropland on the farm in addition to that required to be so devoted under subsection (c)(1). The land diversion payments for a farm shall be at such rate or rates as the Secretary determines to be fair and reasonable taking into consideration the diversion undertaken by the producers and the productivity of the acreage diverted. The Secretary shall limit the total acreage to be diverted under agreements in any county or local community so as not to adversely affect the economy of the county or local community.

"(3) The wheat program formulated under this section shall require the producer to take such measures as the Secretary may deem appropriate to protect the set-aside acreage and the additional diverted acreage from erosion, insects, weeds, and rodents. Such acreage may be devoted to wildlife food plots or wildlife habitat in conformity with standards established by the Secretary in consultation with wildlife agencies. The Secretary may provide for an additional payment on such acreage in an amount determined by the Secretary to be appropriate in relation to the benefit to the general public if the producer agrees to permit, without other compensation, access to all or such portion of the farm as the Secretary may prescribe by the general public, for hunting, trapping, fishing, and hiking, subject to applicable State and Federal regulations.

"(4) If the operator of the farm desires to participate in the program formulated under this subsection (c), he shall file his agreement to do so no later than such date as the Secretary may prescribe. Loans and purchases on wheat, marketing certificates, and payments under this section shall be made available to producers on such farm only if the producers set aside and devote to approved soil conserving uses an acreage on the farm equal to the number of acres which the operator agrees to set aside and devote to approved soil conserving uses, and the agreement shall so provide. The Secretary may, by mutual agreement with the producer, terminate or modify any such agreement entered into pursuant to this subsection (c)(4) if he determines such action necessary because of an emergency created by drought or other disaster, or in order to prevent or alleviate a shortage in the supply of agricultural commodities.

"(d) The Secretary shall provide for the sharing of certificates issued and of payments made under this section for any farm among producers on the farm on a fair and equitable basis.

"(e) In any case in which the failure of a producer to comply fully with the terms and conditions of the program formulated under this section preclude the issuance of certificates and the making of loans, purchases, and payments, the Secretary may, nevertheless, issue such certificates and make such loans, purchases, and payments in such amounts as he determines to be equitable in relation to the seriousness of the default.

"(f) The Secretary shall advance to producers, as soon as practicable after July 1 of the year in which the crop is harvested, an amount equal to 75 per centum of the Secretary's estimate of the face value of certificates to be issued with respect to such crop and such advance shall be repaid through the withholding of certificates for such crop having a face value equal to such advance. If the face value of the certificates as finally determined is less than the advance, the difference shall not be required to be repaid.

"(g) The Secretary is authorized to issue such regulations as he determines necessary to carry out the provisions of this title.

"(h) Marketing certificates issued under this Act and transfers thereof shall be represented by such documents, marketing cards, records, accounts, certifications, or other statements or forms as the Secretary may prescribe.

"(i) The Secretary shall carry out the program authorized by this section through the Commodity Credit Corporation.

"Sec. 379c. (a)(1) The farm domestic allotment for each crop of wheat shall be determined as provided in this section. The Secretary shall proclaim a national domestic allotment for the 1972 and 1973 crops of wheat not later than April 15 of each calendar year for the crop harvested in the next succeeding calendar year. The national domestic allotment for any crop of wheat shall be the number of acres which the Secretary determines on the basis of the estimated national yield will result in marketing certificates being issued to producers participating in the program in an amount equal to the amount of wheat which he estimates will be used for food products for consumption in the United States during the marketing year for the crop (not less than 535 million bushels). The national domestic allotment for any crop of wheat shall be apportioned by the Secretary among the States on the basis of the apportionment to each State of the national domestic allotment for the preceding crop adjusted to the extent deemed necessary by the Secretary to establish a fair and equitable apportionment base for each State, taking into consideration established crop rotation practices, the estimated decrease in farm domestic allotments, and other relevant factors.

"(2) The State domestic acreage allotment for wheat, less a reserve of not to exceed 1 per centum thereof for apportionment as provided in this subsection, shall be apportioned by the Secretary among the counties in the State, on the basis of the apportionment to each such county of the domestic wheat allotment for the preceding crop, adjusted to the extent deemed necessary by the Secretary in order to establish a fair and equitable apportionment base for each county taking into consideration established crop-rotation practices, the estimated decrease in farm domestic allotments, and other relevant factors.

"(3) The farm domestic allotment for each crop of wheat shall be determined by apportioning the county domestic wheat allotment among farms in the county which had a domestic wheat allotment for the preceding crop on the basis of such allotment, adjusted to reflect established crop-rotation practices and such other factors as the Secretary determines should be considered for the purpose of establishing a fair and equitable allotment. The farm domestic allotment for the 1971 crop of wheat shall be determined by multiplying the farm acreage allotment established for the 1971 crop by a national allocation percentage established in the same manner as for the 1970 crop, but which will result in the allotment of a total of not less than 19.7 million acres and will be based on a wheat marketing allocation of not less than 535 million bushels. Notwithstanding any other provision of this subsection, the farm domestic allotment shall be adjusted downward to the extent required by subsection (b).

"(4) Not to exceed 1 per centum of the State domestic allotment for any crop may be apportioned to farms for which there was no domestic allotment for the preceding crop on the basis of the following factors: suitability of the land for production of wheat, the past experience of the farm operator in the production of wheat, the extent to which the farm operator is dependent on income from farming for his livelihood, the production of wheat on other farms owned, operated, or controlled by the farm operator, and such other factors as the Secretary determines should be considered for the purpose of establishing fair and equitable farm domestic allotments. No part of such reserve shall be apportioned to a farm to reflect new cropland brought into production after the date of enactment of the set-aside program for wheat.

"(5) The planting on a farm of wheat of any crop for which no farm domestic allotment was established shall not make the farm eligible for a domestic allotment under subsection (a)(3) nor shall such farm by reason of such planting be considered ineligible for an allotment under subsection (a)(4).

"(6) The Secretary may make such adjustments in acreage under this Act as he determines necessary to correct for abnormal factors affecting production, and to give due consideration to tillable acreage, crop rotation practices, types of soil, soil and water conservation measures, and topography, and in addition, in the case of conserving use acreages and to such other factors as he deems necessary in order to establish a fair and equitable conserving use acreage for the farm.

"(b)(1) If for any crop the total acreage of wheat planted on a farm is less than the farm domestic allotment, the farm domestic allotment used as a base for the succeeding crop shall be reduced by the percentage by which such planted acreage was less than such farm domestic allotment, but such reduction shall not exceed 20 per centum of the farm domestic allotment for the preceding crop. If no acreage has been planted to wheat for three consecutive crop years on any farm which has a domestic allotment, such farm shall lose its domestic allotment. Producers on any farm who have planted to wheat not less than 90 per centum of the domestic allotment for the farm shall be considered to have planted an acreage equal to 100 per centum of such allotment. An acreage on the farm which the Secretary determines was not planted to wheat because of drought, flood, or other natural disaster or a condition beyond the control of the producer shall be considered to be an acreage of wheat planted for harvest. For the purpose of this subsection, the Secretary may permit producers of wheat to have acreage devoted to soybeans or to feed grains for which there is a set-aside program in effect considered as devoted to the production of wheat to such extent and subject to such terms and conditions as the Secretary determines will not impair the effective operation of the program.

"(2) Notwithstanding the provisions of subsection (b)(1), no farm domestic allotment shall be reduced or lost through failure to plant the farm domestic allotment, if the producer elects not to receive certificates for the portion of the farm domestic allotment not planted, to which he would otherwise be entitled under the provisions of this Act."

SEC. 403. Effective only with respect to the marketing years beginning July 1, 1971, July 1, 1972, and July 1, 1973, the Agricultural Adjustment Act of 1938, as amended, is further amended as follows:

(1) by deleting in the first sentence of section 379d(b) the words "During any marketing year for which a wheat marketing allocation program is in effect," and substituting "During each marketing year,";

(2) by adding at the end of section 379d(b) the following: "Notwithstanding the foregoing, the Secretary is authorized, to temporarily suspend the requirement for export marketing certificates for the period beginning July 1, 1971, and ending June 30, 1974.

(3) by adding at the end of section 379e the following: "Notwithstanding any other provisions of this Act, Commodity Credit Corporation shall sell marketing certificates for the marketing years for the 1971, 1972, and 1973 crops of wheat to persons engaged in the processing of food products but in determining the cost to processors the face value shall be 75 cents per bushel."

SEC. 404. Effective only with respect to the 1971, 1972, and 1973 crops, the Agricultural Adjustment Act of 1938, as amended, is further amended as follows:

(1) sections 331, 332, 335, 336, 338, and 339 shall not be applicable to the 1971, 1972, and 1973 crops of wheat;

(2) sections 333 and 334 shall not be applicable to the 1972 and 1973 crops of wheat;

(3) by adding in section 378 a new subsection (e) to read as follows:

"(e) The term 'allotment' as used in this section includes the domestic allotment for wheat."

(4) by adding at the end of section 379 the following sentence: "The term 'acreage allotments' as used in this section includes the domestic allotment for wheat." and

(5) by adding in the first sentence of section 385 after the words "parity payment," the words "payments (including certificates) under the wheat and feed grain set-aside programs,".

SEC. 405. Effective only with respect to the 1971, 1972, and 1973 crops of wheat, section 706, Public Law 89–321 (79 Stat. 1210), is amended as follows:

(1) by adding in the first sentence after the words "the Soil Conservation and Domestic Allotment Act, as amended," the words "or the Agricultural Act of 1949, as amended,"; and

(2) by adding at the end thereof the following sentence: "The term 'acreage allotments' as used in this section includes the domestic allotment for wheat."

SEC. 406. Public Law 74, Seventy-seventh Congress (68 Stat. 905), shall not be applicable to the crops of wheat planted for harvest in the calendar years 1971, 1972, and 1973.

SEC. 407. The amount of any wheat stored by a producer under section 379c(b) of the Agricultural Adjustment Act of 1938, as amended, prior to the 1971 crop of wheat may be reduced by the amount by which the actual total production of the 1971, 1972, or 1973 crop on the farm is less than the number of bushels determined by multiplying three times the domestic allotment for such crop on the farm by the yield established for the farm for the purpose of issuance of domestic marketing certificates. The provisions of such section shall continue to apply to the wheat so stored to the extent not inconsistent therewith.

SEC. 408. Effective only with respect to the 1971, 1972, and 1973 crops of the commodity the Agricultural Act of 1949 as amended is further amended by adding in section 408 a new subsection (k) as follows:

"References to terms made applicable to wheat and feed grains

"(k) References made in sections 402, 403, 406, and 416 to the terms 'support price,' 'level of support,' and 'level of price support' shall be considered to apply as well to the level of loans and purchases for wheat and feed grains under this Act; and references made to the terms 'price support,' 'price support operations,' and 'price support program' in such sections and in section 401(a) shall be considered as applying as well to the loan and purchase operations for wheat and feed grains under this Act.''

Sec. 409. Section 407 of the Agricultural Act of 1949, as amended, is further amended effective only with respect to the marketing years for the 1971, 1972, and 1973 crops of the commodity as follows:

(1) by deleting in the third sentence the language following the third colon and substituting the following: ''*Provided,* That the Corporation shall not sell any of its stocks of wheat, corn, grain sorghum, barley, oats, and rye, respectively, at less than 115 per centum of the current national average loan rate for the commodity, adjusted for such current market differentials reflecting grade, quality, location, and other value factors as the Secretary determines appropriate, plus reasonable carrying charges.''

(2) by deleting in the fifth sentence ''current basic county support rate including the value of any applicable price-support payment in kind (or a comparable price if there is no current basic county support rate)'' and substituting ''current basic county loan rate (or a comparable price if there is no current basic county loan rate)'', and

(3) by deleting in the seventh sentence '', but in no event shall the purchase price exceed the then current support price for such commodities.'' and substituting ''or unduly affecting market prices, but in no event shall the purchase price exceed the Corporation's minimum sales price for such commodities for unrestricted use.

Sec. 410. Notwithstanding any other provision of law, for the 1971, 1972, and 1973 crops of wheat, feed grains and cotton, if in any year at least 55 per centum of the cropland acreage on an established summer fallow farm is devoted to a summer fallow use, no further acreage shall be required to be set aside under the wheat, feed grain and cotton programs for such year.

Title V — Feed Grains

Sec. 501. Effective only with respect to the 1971, 1972, and 1973 crops of feed grains, section 105 of the Agricultural Act of 1949, as amended, is further amended to read as follows:

''Sec. 105. Notwithstanding any other provision of law —

''(a)(1) The Secretary shall make available to producers loans and purchases on each crop of corn at such level, not less than $1.00 per bushel nor in excess of 90 per centum of the parity price therefor, as the Secretary determines will encourage the exportation of feed grains and not result in excessive total stocks of feed grains in the United States.

"(2) The Secretary shall make available to producers loans and purchases on each crop of barley, oats, and rye, respectively, at such level as the Secretary determines is fair and reasonable in relation to the level that loans and purchases are made available for corn, taking into consideration the feeding value of such commodity in relation to corn and the other factors specified in section 401(b), and on each crop of grain sorghums at such level as the Secretary determines is fair and reasonable in relation to the level that loans and purchases are made available for corn, taking into consideration the feeding value and average transportation costs to market of grain sorghums in relation to corn.

"(b)(1) In addition, the Secretary shall make available to producers payments for each crop of corn, grain sorghums, and, if designated by the Secretary, barley. The payment rate for corn shall be at such rate as, together with the national average market price received by farmers for corn during the first five months of the marketing year for the crop, the Secretary determines will not be less than (A) $1.35 per bushel, or (B) 70 per centum of the parity price of corn as of the beginning of the marketing year, whichever is the greater. The payment rate for grain sorghums and, if designated by the Secretary, barley, shall be such rate as the Secretary determines fair and reasonable in relation to the rate at which payments are made available for corn. Notwithstanding the foregoing, the rate of payment for the 1973 crop shall not be such as will result in a total amount of payments which the Secretary estimates will be made pursuant to this subsection with respect to the 1973 crop of feed grains above the total amount of payments made pursuant to this subsection with respect to the 1972 crop of feed grains by reason of the level specified in clause (B) being fixed above 68 per centum of the parity price for corn.

"(2) The payments with respect to a farm shall be made available on 50 per centum of the feed grain base for the farm and shall be computed on the basis of the yield established for the farm for the preceding crop with such adjustments as the Secretary determines necessary to provide a fair and equitable yield.

"(3) If for any crop the total acreage on a farm planted to feed grains included in the program formulated under this subsection is less than the portion of the feed grain base for the farm on which payments are available under this subsection, the feed grain base for the farm for the succeeding crops shall be reduced by the percentage by which the planted acreage is less than such portion of the feed grain base for the farm, but such reduction shall not exceed 20 per centum of the feed grain base. If no acreage has been planted to such feed grains for three consecutive crop years on any farm which has a feed grain base, such farm shall lose its feed grain base: *Provided*, That no farm feed grain base shall be reduced or lost through failure to plant, if the producer elects not to receive payment for such portion of the farm feed grain base not planted, to which he would otherwise be entitled under the provisions of this Act. Any such acres eliminated from any farm shall be assigned to a national pool for the adjustment of feed grain bases as provided for in subsection (e)(2). Producers on any farm who have planted to such feed grains not less than 90 per centum of the portion of the feed grain base on which payments are made available shall be considered to have planted an acreage equal to 100 per centum of such portion. An acreage on the farm which the Secretary determines was not planted to such feed grains because of drought, flood, or other natural disaster or condition beyond the control of the producer shall be considered to be an acreage of feed grains planted for harvest. For the purpose of this paragraph, the Secretary may permit producers of feed grains to have acreage devoted to soybeans or to wheat considered as devoted to the production of such feed grains to such extent and subject to such terms and conditions as the Secretary determines will not impair the effective operation of the feed grain or soybean program.

"(c)(1) The Secretary shall provide for a set-aside of cropland if he determines that the total supply of feed grains or other commodities will, in the absence of such a set-aside, likely be excessive taking into account the need for an adequate carryover to maintain reasonable and stable supplies and prices of feed grains and to meet a national emergency. If a set-aside of cropland is in effect under this subsection (c), then as a condition of eligibility for loans, purchases, and payments on corn, grain sorghums, and, if designated by the Secretary, barley, respectively, the producers on a farm must set aside and devote to approved conservation uses an acreage of cropland equal to (i) such percentage of the feed grain base for the farm as may be specified by the Secretary, plus (ii) the acreage of cropland on the farm devoted in preceding years to soil-conserving uses, as determined by the Secretary. The Secretary is authorized for the 1971, 1972, and 1973 crops to limit the acreage planted to feed grains on the farm to such percentage of the feed grain base as he determines necessary to provide an orderly transition to the program provided for under this section. If for any crop, the producer so requests for purposes of having acreage devoted to the production of wheat considered as devoted to the production of feed grains, pursuant to the provisions of section 328 of the Food and Agriculture Act of 1962, the term 'feed grains' shall include oats and rye, and barley, if not designated by the Secretary as provided above. Such section 328 shall be effective in 1971, 1972, 1973 to the same extent as it would be if a diversion program were in effect for feed grains during each of such years. Grazing shall not be permitted during any of the five principal months of the normal growing season as determined by the county committee established pursuant to section 8(b) of the Soil Conservation and Domestic Allotment Act, as amended, and subject to this limitation (1) the Secretary shall permit producers to plant and graze on the set-aside acreage sweet sorghum, and (2) the Secretary may permit, subject to such terms and conditions as he may prescribe, all or any of the set-aside acreage to be devoted to grazing or the production of guar, sesame, safflower, sunflower, castor beans, mustard seed, crambe, plantago ovato, flaxseed, or other commodity, if he determines that such production is needed to provide an adequate supply, is not likely to increase the cost of the price-support program, and will not adversely affect farm income.

"(2) To assist in adjusting the acreage of commodities to desirable goals, the Secretary may make land diversion payments, in addition to the payments authorized in subsection (b), to producers on a farm who, to the extent prescribed by the Secretary, devote to approved conservation uses an acreage of cropland on the farm in addition to that required to be so devoted under subsection (c)(1). The land diversion payments for a farm shall be at such rate or rates as the Secretary determines to be fair and reasonable taking into consideration the diversion undertaken by the producers and the productivity of the acreage diverted. The Secretary shall limit the total acreage to be diverted under agreements in any county or local community so as not to adversely affect the economy of the county or local community.

"(3) The feed grain program formulated under this section shall require the producer to take such measures as the Secretary may deem appropriate to protect the set-aside acreage and the additional diverted acreage from erosion, insects, weeds, and rodents. Such acreage may be devoted to wildlife food plots or wildlife habitat in comformity with standards established by the Secretary in consultation with wildlife agencies. The Secretary may provide for an additional payment on such acreage in an amount determined by the Secretary to be appropriate in relation to the benefit to the general public if the producer agrees to permit, without other compensation, access to all or such portion of the farm as the Secretary may prescribe by the general public, for hunting, trapping, fishing, and hiking, subject to applicable State and Federal regulations.

"(4) If the operator of the farm desires to participate in the program formulated under this section, he shall file his agreement to do so no later than such date as the Secretary may prescribe. Loans and purchases on feed grains included in the set-aside program and payments under this section shall be made available to producers on such farm only if the producers set aside and devote to approved soil conserving uses an acreage on the farm equal to the number of acres which the operator agrees to set aside and devote to approved soil conserving uses, and the agreement shall so provide. The Secretary may, by mutual agreement with the producer, terminate or modify any such agreement entered into pursuant to this subsection (c)(4) if he determines such action necessary because of an emergency created by drought or other disaster, or in order to prevent or alleviate a shortage in the supply of agricultural commodities.

"(d) The Secretary shall provide for the sharing of payments under this section among producers on the farm on a fair and equitable basis.

"(e)(1) For the purpose of this section, the feed grain base shall be the average acreage devoted on the farm to corn, grain sorghums and, if designated by the Secretary, barley in 1959 and 1960.

"(2) The Secretary may make such adjustments in acreage under this section as he determines necessary to correct for abnormal factors affecting production, and to give due consideration to tillable acreage, crop-rotation practices, types of soil, soil and water conservation measures, and topography, and in addition, in the case of conserving use acreages to such other factors as he deems necessary in order to establish a fair and equitable conserving use acreage for the farm. The Secretary shall, upon the request of a majority of the State committee established pursuant to section 8(b) of the Soil Conservation and Domestic Allotment Act, as amended, adjust the feed grain bases for farms within any State or county in order to establish fair and equitable feed grain bases for farms within such State or county: *Provided,* That except for acreage provided for in subsection (b)(3), adjustments made pursuant to this sentence shall not increase the total State feed grain acreage. The Secretary is authorized to draw upon the acreage pool provided for in subsection (b)(3) in making such adjustments. Notwithstanding any other provision of this subsection, the feed grain base for the farm shall be adjusted downward to the extent required by subsection (b)(3).

"(3) Notwithstanding any other provision of this subsection not to exceed 1 per centum of the estimated total feed grain bases for all farms in a State for any year may be reserved from the feed grain bases established for farms in the State for apportionment to farms on which there were no acreages devoted to feed grains in the crop years 1959 and 1960 on the basis of the following factors: suitability of the land for the production of feed grains, the extent to which the farm operator is dependent on income from farming for his livelihood, the production of feed grains on other farms owned, operated, or controlled by the farm operator, and such other factors as the Secretary determines should be considered for the purpose of establishing fair and equitable feed grain bases. No part of such reserve shall be allocated to a farm to reflect new cropland brought into production after the date of enactment of the set-aside program for feed grains. An acreage equal to the feed grain base so established for each farm shall be deemed to have been devoted to feed grains on the farm in each of the crop years 1959 and 1960 for purposes of this section.

"(f) In any case in which the failure of a producer to comply fully with the terms and conditions of the program formulated under this section precludes the making of loans, purchases, and payments, the Secretary may, nevertheless, make such loans, purchases, and payments in such amounts as he determines to be equitable in relation to the seriousness of the default.

"(g) The Secretary shall make a preliminary payment to producers, as soon as practicable after July 1 of the year in which the crop is harvested, at a rate equal to 32 cents per bushel for corn, with comparable rates for grain sorghums and, if designated by the Secretary, barley, and the payment so made shall not be reduced if the rate as finally determined is less than the rate of the preliminary payment. If the set-aside in effect under subsection (c) is less than 20 per centum of the feed grain base, the preliminary payment rate under this subsection shall be reduced proportionately.

"(h) The Secretary is authorized to issue such regulations as he determines necessary to carry out the provisions of this section.

"(i) The Secretary shall carry out the program authorized by this section through the Commodity Credit Corporation."

Title VI — Cotton

SEC. 601. The Agricultural Adjustment Act of 1938, as amended, is amended effective beginning with the 1971 crop of upland cotton as follows:

(1) Sections 342, 343, 344, 345, 346, and 377 of the Act shall not be applicable to upland cotton of the 1971, 1972, and 1973 crops.

(2) A new section 342a is added to read as follows:

"SEC. 342a. The Secretary shall, not later than November 15, of the calendar years 1970, 1971, and 1972, proclaim a national cotton production goal for the 1971 and subsequent crops of upland cotton. The national cotton production goal for any year shall be the number of bales of upland cotton (standard bales of four hundred and eighty pounds net weight) equal to the estimated domestic consumption and estimated exports for the marketing year beginning in the calendar year 1971.

*　*　*

"(3) If no acreage is planted to cotton for any three consecutive crop years on any farm which had a farm base acreage allotment for such years, such farm shall lose its base acreage allotment.

"(f) Effective for the 1971, 1972, and 1973 crops, any part of any farm base acreage allotment on which upland cotton will not be planted and which is voluntarily surrendered to the county committee shall be deducted from the farm base acreage allotment for such farm and may be reapportioned by the county committee to other farms in the same county receiving farm base acreage allotments in amounts determined by the county committee to be fair and reasonable on the basis of past acreage of upland cotton, land, labor, equipment available for the production of upland cotton, crop rotation practices, and soil and other physical facilities affecting the production of upland cotton. If all of the acreage voluntarily surrendered is not needed in the county, the county committee may surrender the excess acreage to the State committee to be used to make adjustments in farm base acreage allotments for other farms in the State adversely affected by abnormal conditions affecting plantings or to correct inequities or to prevent hardship. Any farm base acreage allotment released under this provision shall be regarded for the purpose of establishing future farm base acreage allotments as having been planted on the farm and in the county where the release was made rather than on the farm and in the county to which the allotment was transferred: *Provided,* That, notwithstanding any other provision of law, any part of any farm base acreage allotment for any crop year may be permanently released in writing to the county committee by the owner and operator of the farm and reapportioned as provided herein. Acreage released under this subsection shall be credited to the State in determining future allotments.

"(g) Any farm receiving any base acreage allotment through release and reapportionment or sale, lease, or transfer shall, as a condition to the right to receive such allotment, comply with the set-aside requirements of section 103(e) (4) of the Agricultural Act of 1949, as amended, applicable to such acreage as determined by the Secretary.

"(h) Notwithstanding any other provision of this Act, if the Secretary determines for any year that because of drought, flood, other natural disaster, or a condition beyond the control of the producer a portion of the farm base acreage allotment in a county cannot be timely planted or replanted in such year, he may authorize for such year the transfer of all or a part of such cotton acreage for any farm in the county so affected to another farm in the county or in an adjoining county on which one or more of the producers on the farm from which the transfer is to be made will be engaged in the production of upland cotton and will share in the proceeds thereof, in accordance with such regulations as the Secretary may prescribe. Any farm base acreage allotment transferred under this subsection shall be regarded as planted to upland cotton on the farm and in the county and State from which transfer is made for purposes of establishing future farm, county and State allotments."

SEC. 602. Effective beginning with the 1971 crop of upland cotton, section 103 of the Agricultural Act of 1949, as amended, is amended by adding at the end thereof a new subsection (e) reading as follows:

"(e) (1) The Secretary shall upon presentation of warehouse receipts reflecting accrued storage charges of not more than 60 days make available for the 1971, 1972, and 1973 crops of upland cotton to cooperators nonrecourse loans for a term of ten months from the first day of the month in which the loan is made at such level as will reflect for Middling one-inch upland cotton (micronaire 3.5 through 4.9) at average location in the United States 90 per centum of the acreage world price for such cotton for the two-year period ending July 31 in the year in which the loan level is announced, except that to prevent the establishment of such a loan level as would adversely affect the competitive position of United States upland cotton, following one or more years of excessively high prices, the Secretary shall make such adjustments as are necessary to keep United States upland cotton competitive and to retain an adequate share of the world market for such cotton. The average world price for such cotton for such preceding two-year period shall be determined by the Secretary annually pursuant to a published regulation which shall specify the procedures and the factors to be used by the Secretary in making the world price determination. The loan level for any crop of upland cotton shall be determined and announced not later than November 1 of the calendar year preceding the marketing year for which such loan is to be effective. Notwithstanding the foregoing, if the carryover of upland cotton as of the beginning of the marketing year for the 1972 or 1973 crop exceeds 7.2 million bales, producers on any farm harvesting cotton of such crop from an acreage in excess of the base acreage allotment for such farm shall be entitled to loans and purchases only on an amount of the cotton of such crop produced on such farm determined by multiplying the yield used in computing payments for such farm by the base acreage allotment for such farm.

"(2) In addition, the Secretary shall make available to cooperators payments on the 1971, 1972, and 1973 crops of upland cotton. The payments shall be at such rate per pound as, together with the national average market price for Middling one-inch upland cotton (micronaire 3.5 through 4.9) in the designated spot markets during the first five months of the marketing year for the crop, the Secretary determines will be equal to the greater of (i) 35 cents, or (ii) 65 per centum of the parity price for upland cotton as of the beginning of the marketing year, except that the rate of payment so determined for the 1972 crop and the 1973 crop, respectively, shall be adjusted by multiplying the amount thereof by the ratio of (i) the national base acreage allotment for the 1971 crop to (ii) the national base acreage allotment for the crop for which the rate is being determined: *Provided,* That the payment rate with respect to any producer who (i) is on a small farm (that is, a farm on which the base acreage allotment is ten acres or less, or on which the yield used in making payments times the farm base acreage allotment is five thousand pounds or less, and for which the base acreage allotment has not been reduced under section 350(f)), (ii) resides on such farm, and (iii) derives his principal income from cotton produced on such farm, shall be increased by 30 per centum; but, notwithstanding paragraph (3), such increase shall be made only with respect to his share of cotton actually harvested on such farm within the quantity specified in paragraph (3). The Secretary shall make a preliminary payment to producers, as soon as practicable after July 1 of the year in which the crop is harvested, at a rate equal to 15 cents per pound, and the payment so made shall not be reduced if the rate as finally determined is less than the rate of the preliminary payment.

"(3) Such payments shall be made available for a farm on the quantity of upland cotton determined by multiplying the acreage planted within the farm base acreage allotment for the farm for the crop by the average yield established for the farm: *Provided,* That payments shall be made on any farm planting not less than 90 per centum of the farm base acreage allotment on the basis of the entire amount of such allotment. For purposes of this paragraph, an acreage on the farm which the Secretary determines was not planted to cotton because of drought, flood, other natural disaster, or a condition beyond the control of the producer shall be considered to be an acreage planted to cotton. The average yield for the farm for any year shall be determined on the basis of the actual yields per harvested acre for the three preceding years, except that the 1970 farm projected yield shall be substituted in lieu of the actual yields for the years 1968 and 1969: *Provided,* That the actual yields shall be adjusted by the Secretary for abnormal yields in any year caused by drought, flood, or other natural disaster: *Provided further,* That the average yield established for the farm for any year shall not be less than the yield used in making payments for the preceding year if the total cotton production on the farm in such preceding year is not less than the yield used in making payments for the farm for such preceding year times the farm base acreage allotment for such preceding year (for the 1970 crop, the farm domestic allotment).

"(4) (A) The Secretary shall provide for a set aside of cropland if he determines that the total supply of agricultural commodities will, in the absence of such a set-aside, likely be excessive taking into account the need for an adequate carryover to maintain reasonable and stable supplies and prices and to meet a national emergency. If a set-aside of cropland is in effect under this paragraph (4), then as a condition of eligibility for loans and payments on upland cotton the producers on a farm must set aside and devote to approved conservation uses an acreage of cropland equal to (i) such percentage of the farm base acreage allotment for the farm as may be specified by the Secretary (not to exceed 28 per centum of the farm base acreage allotment), plus (ii) the acreage of cropland on the farm devoted in preceding years to soil conserving uses, as determined by the Secretary. If the Secretary determines prior to the planting season for such crop that the carryover of upland cotton as of the beginning of the marketing year for the 1972 or 1973 crop will exceed 7.2 million bales, the Secretary is authorized for such crop to limit the acreage planted to upland cotton on the farm in excess of the farm base acreage allotment to such percentage of the farm base acreage allotment as he determines necessary to reduce the total supply to a reasonable level. Grazing shall not be permitted during any of the five principal months of the normal growing season as determined by the county committee established pursuant to section 8(b) of the Soil Conservation and Domestic Allotment Act, as amended, and subject to this limitation (1) the Secretary shall permit producers to plant and graze on the set-aside acreage sweet sorghum, and (2) the Secretary may permit, subject to such terms and conditions as he may prescribe, all or any of the set-aside acreage to be devoted to grazing or the production of guar, sesame, safflower, sunflower, castor beans, mustard seed, crambe, plantago ovato, flaxseed, or other commodity, if he determines that such production is needed to provide an adequate supply, is not likely to increase the cost of the price-support program, and will not adversely affect farm income.

"(B) To assist in adjusting the acreage of commodities to desirable goals, the Secretary may make land diversion payments, in addition to the payments authorized in subsection (e) (2), to producers on a farm who, to the extent prescribed by the Secretary, devote to approved conservation uses an acreage of cropland on the farm in addition to that required to be so devoted under subsection (e) (4) (A). The land diversion payments for a farm shall be at such rate or rates as the Secretary determines to be fair and reasonable taking into consideration the diversion undertaken by the producers and the productivity of the acreage diverted. The

Secretary shall limit the total acreage to be diverted under agreements in any county or local community so as not to adversely affect the economy of the county or local community.

"(5) The upland cotton program formulated under this section shall require the producer to take such measures as the Secretary may deem appropriate to protect the set-aside acreage and the additional diverted acreage from erosion, insects, weeds, and rodents. Such acreage may be devoted to wildlife food plots or wildlife habitat in conformity with standards established by the Secretary in consultation with wildlife agencies. The Secretary may provide for an additional payment on such acreage in an amount determined by the Secretary to be appropriate in relation to the benefit to the general public if the producer agrees to permit, without other compensation, access to all or such portion of the farm as the Secretary may prescribe by the general public, for hunting, trapping, fishing, and hiking, subject to applicable State and Federal regulations.

"(6) If the operator of the farm desires to participate in the program formulated under this section, he shall file his agreement to do so no later than such date as the Secretary may prescribe. Loans and purchases on upland cotton and payments under this section shall be made available to the producers on such farm only if producers set aside and devote to approved soil conserving uses an acreage on the farm equal to the number of acres which the operator agrees to set aside and devote to approved soil conserving uses, and the agreement shall so provide. The Secretary may, by mutual agreement with the producer, terminate or modify any such agreement entered into pursuant to this subsection (e) (6) if he determines such action necessary because of an emergency created by drought or other disaster, or in order to alleviate a shortage in the supply of agricultural commodities.

"(7) The Secretary shall provide adequate safeguards to protect the interests of tenants and sharecroppers, including provision for sharing on a fair and equitable basis, in payments under this section.

"(8) In any case in which the failure of a producer to comply fully with the terms and conditions of the program formulated under this section precludes the making of loans, purchases, and payments, the Secretary may, nevertheless, make such loans, purchases, and payments in such amounts as he determines to be equitable in relation to the seriousness of the default.

"(9) The Secretary is authorized to issue such regulations as he determines necessary to carry out the provisions of this Title.

"(10) The Secretary shall carry out the program authorized by this section through the Commodity Credit Corporation.

"(11) The provisions of subsection 8(g) of the Soil Conservation and Domestic Allotment Act, as amended (relating to assignment of payments), shall apply to payments under this subsection."

SEC. 603. Effective only with respect to the period beginning August 1, 1971, and ending July 31, 1974, the tenth sentence of section 407 of the Agricultural Act of 1949, as amended, is amended by deleting all of that sentence from the beginning to and including the words "110 per centum of the loan rate, and (2)" and inserting in lieu thereof the following: "Notwithstanding any other provision of law, (1) the Commodity Credit Corporation shall sell upland cotton for unrestricted use at the same prices as it sells cotton for export, in no event, however, at less than

110 per centum of the loan rate for Middling one-inch upland cotton (micronaire 3.5 through 4.9) adjusted for such current market differentials reflecting grade, quality, location, and other value factors as the Secretary determines appropriate plus reasonable carrying charges and (2)''.

SEC. 604. Section 408(b) of the Agricultural Act of 1949, as amended, is amended by inserting a colon in lieu of the period at the end of the first sentence and adding the following: *"And provided,* That for the 1971, 1972, and 1973 crops of upland cotton a cooperator shall be a producer on a farm on which a farm base acreage allotment has been established who has set aside the acreage required under section 103(e).''

SEC. 605. Effective only with respect to the 1971, 1972, and 1973 crops the Agricultural Adjustment Act of 1938, as amended, is further amended as follows:

(1) By adding in section 378 a new subsection (d) to read as follows:

''(d) The term 'allotment' as used in this section includes the farm base acreage allotment for upland cotton.''

(2) By adding at the end of section 379 the following sentence: ''The term 'acreage allotments' as used in this section includes the farm base acreage allotments for upland cotton.''

(3) By adding in the first sentence of section 385 after the words ''parity payment,'' the words ''payments under the cotton set-aside program,''.

SEC. 606. Effective only with respect to the 1971, 1972, and 1973 crops, section 706, Public Law 89–321 (79 Stat. 1210) is amended by adding at the end thereof the following sentence: ''The term 'acreage allotments' as used in this section includes the farm base acreage allotments for upland cotton.''

SEC. 607. Effective only with respect to the 1971, 1972, and 1973 crops of the commodity, the Agricultural Act of 1949, as amended, is further amended by adding in section 408 a new subsection (1) as follows:

"Reference to Terms Made Applicable to Upland Cotton

''(1) References made in sections 402, 403, 406, and 416 to the terms 'support price,' 'level of support,' and 'level of price support' shall be considered to apply as well to the level of loans and purchases for upland cotton under this Act; and references made to the terms 'price support,' 'price support operations,' and 'price support program' in such sections and in section 401 (a) shall be considered as applying as well to the loan and purchase operations for upland cotton under this Act.''

SEC. 608. Section 203 of the Agricultural Act of 1949, as amended, shall not be applicable to the 1971, 1972, and 1973 crops.

SEC. 609. The Secretary shall file annually with the President for transmission to the Congress a complete report of the programs carried out under this title. Such report shall include the amount of funds spent, the purposes for which such funds were spent, the basis for participation in such programs in the various States, and an appraisal of the effectiveness of the programs.

SEC. 610. The Commodity Credit Corporation, in furtherance of its powers and duties under subsections (e) and (f) of section 5 of the Commodity Credit Corporation Charter Act, shall, through the Cotton Board established under the

Cotton Research and Promotion Act, and upon approval of the Secretary, enter into agreements with the contracting organization specified pursuant to section 7(g) of that Act for the conduct, in domestic and foreign markets, of market development, research or sales promotion programs and programs to aid in the development of new and additional markets, marketing facilities and uses for cotton and cotton products, including programs to facilitate the utilization and commercial application of research findings. Each year the amount available for such agreements shall be that portion of the funds (not exceeding $10,000,000) authorized to be made available to cooperators under the cotton program for such year but which is not paid to producers because of a statutory limitation on the amounts of such funds payable to any producer. The Secretary is authorized to deduct from funds available for payments to producers under section 103 of the Agricultural Act of 1949, as amended, on each of the 1972 and 1973 crops of upland cotton such additional sums for use as specified above (not exceeding $10,000,000 for each such crop) as he determines desirable; and the final rate of payment provided in section 103 if higher than the rate of the preliminary payment provided in such section shall be reduced to the extent necessary to defray such costs. No funds made available under this section shall be used for the purpose of influencing legislative action or general farm policy with respect to cotton.

Title VII — Extension of Titles I and II of Public Law 480

SEC. 701. Section 409 of the Agricultural Trade Development and Assistance Act of 1954, as amended (Public Law 83–480; 7 U.S.C. 1736c), is amended by striking the words "December 31, 1970." and inserting in lieu thereof the words "December 31, 1973.".

SEC. 702. Section 104 of such Act is amended by inserting before the comma at the end of paragraph (1) of the first proviso following subsection (k) the following: ", and in the case of currencies to be used for the purposes specified in paragraph (2) of subsection (b) the Appropriation Act may specifically authorize the use of such currencies and shall not require the appropriation of dollars for the purchase of such currencies".

Title VIII — General and Miscellaneous

Long-term Land Retirement

SEC. 801. Section 16(e) of the Soil Conservation and Domestic Allotment Act, as amended, is amended —

(1) By inserting "(A)" after "Sec. 16(e) (1)".

(2) By inserting in the first sentence after "For the purpose of promoting the conservation and economic use of land" the following: ", and of assisting farmers who because of advanced age, poor health, or other reasons, desire to retire from farming but wish to continue living on their farms,".

(3) By inserting in the first sentence after "is authorized to enter into agreements," the following: "during the calendar years 1971, 1972, and 1973,".

(4) By striking out the proviso at the end of paragraph (1) and inserting in lieu thereof the following: "*Provided*, That any agreements entered into under this section after July 1, 1970, shall prohibit grazing of such acreage.".

(5) By inserting a new subparagraph (B) at the end of paragraph (1) to read as follows:

"(B) Such acreage may be devoted to approved wildlife food plots or fish and wildlife habitat which are established in conformity with standards developed by the Secretary in consultation with the Secretary of the Interior, and the Secretary may compensate producers for such practices. The Secretary may also provide for payment in an amount determined by the Secretary to be appropriate in relation to the benefit to the general public if the producer agrees to permit access, without other compensation, to all or such portion of the farm as the Secretary may prescribe by the general public, for hunting, trapping, fishing, and hiking, subject to applicable State and Federal regulations. The Secretary after consultation with the Secretary of the Interior shall appoint an Advisory Board consisting of citizens knowledgeable in the fields of agriculture and wildlife with whom he may consult on the wildlife practice phase of programs under this subsection, and the Secretary may compensate members of the Board and reimburse them for per diem and traveling expenses. The Secretary shall invite the several States to participate in wildlife phases of programs under this subsection by assisting the Department of Agriculture in developing guidelines for (a) providing technical assistance for wildlife and habitat improvement practices, (b) reviewing applications of farmers for the public land use option and selecting eligible areas based on desirability of wildlife habitat, (c) determining accessibility, (d) evaluating effects on surrounding areas, (e) considering esthetic values, (f) checking compliance by cooperators, and (g) carrying out programs of wildlife stocking and management on the acreage set aside. The Secretary shall consult with the Secretary of the Interior regarding regulations to govern the administration of those aspects of this subparagraph (B) that pertain to wildlife. Funds are authorized to be appropriated to the Secretary of the Interior for use in assisting the State wildlife agencies to carry out the provisions of this subparagraph and in administering such assistance."

(6) By adding at the end of paragraph (2) the following: "The foregoing provision shall not prevent a producer from placing a farm in the program if the farm was acquired by the producer to replace an eligible farm from which he was displaced because of its acquisition by any Federal, State, or other agency having the right of eminent domain."

(7) By adding at the end of paragraph (4) the following: "Any agreement may be terminated by mutual agreement with the producer if the Secretary determines that such termination would be in the public interest."

(8) By adding at the end of paragraph (5) the following: "The Secretary may if he determines that such action will contribute to the effective and equitable administration of the program use an advertising-and-bid procedure in determining the lands in any area to be covered by agreements. The total acreage placed under agreements in any county or local community shall be limited to a percentage of the total eligible acreage in such county or local community which the Secretary determines would not adversely affect the economy of the county or local community. In determining such percentage the Secretary shall give appropriate consideration to the productivity of the acreage being retired as compared to the average productivity of eligible acreage in the county or local community."

(9) By adding a new paragraph (6) to read as follows:

"(6) For the purpose of obtaining an increase in the permanent retirement of cropland to noncrop uses the Secretary may, notwithstanding any other provision of law, transfer funds available for carrying out the program to any other Federal agency or to States or local government agencies for use in rural areas in acquiring cropland for the preservation of open spaces, natural beauty, the development of wildlife or recreational facilities, or the prevention of air or water pollution under terms and conditions consistent with and at costs not greater than those under agreements entered into with producers, provided the Secretary determines that the purpose of the program will be accomplished by such action. The Secretary also is authorized to share the cost with State and local governmental agencies and other Federal agencies in the establishment of practices or uses which will establish, protect, and conserve open spaces, natural beauty, wildlife or recreational re- sources, or prevent air or water pollution under terms and conditions and at costs consistent with those under agreements entered into with producers, provided the Secretary determines that the purposes of the program will be accomplished by such action. No appropriation shall be made for any agreement under this paragraph (6) involving an estimated total Federal payment in excess of $250,000 unless such agreement has been approved by resolution adopted by the Committee on Agricul- ture of the House of Representatives and the Committee on Agriculture and Forestry of the Senate."

(10) By striking out the last sentence of paragraph (7) and substituting the following: "In carrying out the program, the Secretary shall not during any of the fiscal years ending June 30, 1971, through June 30, 1973, or during the period June 30, 1973, to December 31, 1973, (A) enter into agreements with producers which would require payments to producers in any calendar year under such agreements in excess of $10,000,000 plus any amount by which agreements entered into in prior fiscal years require payments in amounts less than authorized for such years, or (B) enter into agreements with States or local agencies under paragraph (6) which would require payments to such State or local government agencies in any calendar year under such agreements in excess of $10,000,000 plus any amount by which agree- ments entered into in prior fiscal years require payments in amounts less than authorized for such years. For purposes of applying the foregoing limitations, the annual payment shall be chargeable to the year in which performance is rendered regardless of the year in which it is made."

(11) By striking out "June 30, 1963" in paragraph (7) and substituting "June 30, 1972".

(12) By inserting "farming opportunities and" preceding the words "in- terests of tenants and sharecroppers in paragraph (3)".

Marketing Quota Exemption for Boiled Peanuts

SEC. 802. The last paragraph of the Act entitled "An Act to amend the peanut marketing quota provisions of the Agricultural Adjustment Act of 1938, as amended, and for other purposes", approved August 13, 1957 (7 U.S.C. 1359 note), is amended to read as follows: "This amendment shall be effective for the 1957 and subsequent crops of peanuts."

Voluntary Relinquishment of Allotments

SEC. 803. Notwithstanding any other provision of law, the Secretary may provide for the reduction or cancellation of any allotment or base when the owner of the farm states in writing that he has no further use of such allotment or base.

Indemnification for Beekeepers

SEC. 804. (a) The Secretary of Agriculture is authorized to make indemnity payments to beekeepers who through no fault of their own have suffered losses of honey bees after January 1, 1967, as a result of utilization of economic poisons near or adjacent to the property on which the beehives of such beekeepers were located.

(b) The amount of the indemnity payment in the case of any beekeeper shall be determined on the basis of the net loss sustained by such beekeeper as a result of the loss of his honey bees.

(c) Indemnity payments shall be made only in cases in which the loss occurred as a result of the use of economic poisons which had been registered and approved for use by the Federal Government.

(d) There are hereby authorized to be appropriated such sums as may be necessary to carry out the provisions of this Act.

(e) The Secretary is authorized to issue such regulations as he deems necessary to carry out the purposes of this section.

(f) The provisions of this section shall not be in effect after December 31, 1973.

SEC. 805. (a) Notwithstanding any other provision of law, the Secretary shall permit any producer who is participating in the wheat program under title IV of this Act, in the feed grain program under title V of this Act, or in the cotton program under title VI of this Act, in any year in which an acreage diversion or set-aside program is in effect, under any such program in which such producer is participating, subject to the conditions prescribed in subsection (b) of this section, to plant and harvest hay from 25 per centum of the acreage on the farm diverted from production under such programs or twenty-five acres, whichever is greater.

(b) Any producer who elects to plant and harvest hay on diverted or set aside acreage pursuant to this section shall first agree not to use any such hay harvested from such acreage unless authorized to do so by the Secretary.

(c) When any diverted or set aside acreage has been planted and harvested under authority of this section, the hay harvested therefrom shall be baled and stored in sealed storage on the farm in accordance with such regulations as the Secretary may prescribe and shall be available only for use during periods of emergency declared by the Secretary. In order to avoid deterioration of such hay stored on the farm for emergency purposes pursuant to this section, the Secretary may permit such hay to be removed and used or sold from time to time so long as an amount of hay equal to the amount removed is previously placed in storage and sealed.

(d) Any farmer who has hay stored on his farm for emergency purposes pursuant to this section may remove such hay from storage and use it whenever the Secretary has (1) designated as an emergency area the area in which such farm is located, and (2) specifically authorized the use of emergency hay by farmers in the area.

(e) The Secretary of Agriculture is authorized to make or guarantee loans to farmers, both tenants and landowners, to assist such farmers in the construction of storage facilities on the farm for the storage of emergency hay pursuant to the provisions of this section if such farmers are unable to obtain loans from commercial sources at reasonable rates and on reasonable terms and conditions. Loans made by the Secretary under this subsection shall be made at the current rate of interest for periods not exceeding ten years, and on such other terms and conditions as the Secretary may prescribe.

SEC. 806. (a) Section 306 of the Consolidated Farmers Home Administration Act of 1961, as amended (7 U.S.C. 1926), is amended by adding at the end thereof a new subsection as follows:

"(d) Any amounts appropriated under this section shall remain available until expended, and any amounts authorized for any fiscal year under this section but not appropriated may be appropriated for any succeeding fiscal year."

(b) Subtitle A of the Consolidated Farmers Home Administration Act of 1961, as amended (7 U.S.C. 1921–1929), is amended by adding at the end thereof a new section as follows:

"SEC. 310. Funds appropriated for the purpose of making direct real estate loans to farmers and ranchers under this subtitle shall remain available until expended."

Title IX — Rural Development

Commitment of Congress

SEC. 901. (a) The Congress commits itself to a sound balance between rural and urban America. The Congress considers this balance so essential to the peace, prosperity, and welfare of all our citizens that the highest priority must be given to the revitalization and development of rural areas.

Location of Federal Facilities

(b) Congress hereby directs the heads of all executive departments and agencies of the Government to establish and maintain, insofar as practicable, departmental policies and procedures with respect to the location of new offices and other facilities in areas or communities of lower population density in preference to areas or communities of high population densities. The President is hereby requested to submit to the Congress not later than September 1 of each fiscal year a report reflecting the efforts during the immediately preceding fiscal year of all executive departments and agencies in carrying out the provisions of this section, citing the location of all new facilities, and including a statement covering the basic reasons for the selection of all new locations.

Planning Assistance

(c) The Secretary of the Department of Housing and Urban Development and the Secretary of Agriculture shall submit to the Congress a joint progress report as to their efforts during the immediately preceding fiscal year to provide assistance to States planning for the development of rural multicounty areas not included in economically depressed areas under authority of the Housing and Urban Development Act of 1968. The first such annual report shall be submitted not later than December 1, 1970, and shall cover the period beginning August 1, 1968, the date of enactment of the Housing and Urban Development Act of 1968, and ending June 30, 1970.

Information and Technical Assistance

(d) The Secretary of Agriculture shall submit to the Congress a report not later than September 1 of each fiscal year reflecting the efforts of the Department of Agriculture to provide information and technical assistance to small communities and less populated areas in regard to rural development during the immediately preceding fiscal year. The first such annual report shall be submitted not later than December 1, 1970, covering the period beginning July 1, 1969, and ending June 30, 1970. The Secretary shall include in such reports to what extent technical assistance has been provided through land-grant colleges and universities, through the Extension Service, and other programs of the Department of Agriculture.

Government Services

(e) The President shall submit to the Congress a report not later than September 1 of each fiscal year stating the availability of telephone, electrical, water, sewer, medical, educational, and other government or government assisted services to rural areas and outlining efforts of the executive branch to improve these services during the immediately preceding fiscal year. The President is requested to submit the first such annual report, covering the fiscal year ending June 30, 1970, on or before December 1, 1970.

Financial Assistance

(f) The President shall report to Congress on the possible utilization of the Farm Credit Administration and agencies in the Department of Agriculture to fulfill rural financial assistance requirements not filled by other agencies. The President is requested to submit the report requested by this section on or before July 1, 1971, together with such recommendations for legislation as he deems appropriate.

Approved November 30, 1970.

Food Stamp Legislation, 1971

From 84 Statutes at Large 2048.

Be it enacted by the Senate and House of Representatives of the United States of America in Congress assembled, That section 2 of the Food Stamp Act of 1964, as amended, is amended to read as follows:

"SEC. 2. It is hereby declared to be the policy of Congress, in order to promote the general welfare, that the Nation's abundance of food should be utilized cooperatively by the States, the Federal Government, local governmental units, and other agencies to safeguard the health and well-being of the Nations population and raise levels of nutrition among low-income households. The Congress hereby finds that the limited food purchasing power of low-income households contributes to hunger and malnutrition among members of such households. The Congress further finds that increased utilization of food in establishing and maintaining adequate national levels of nutrition will promote the distribution in a beneficial manner of our agricultural abundances and will strengthen our agricultural economy, as well as result in more orderly marketing and distribution of food. To alleviate such hunger and malnutrition, a food stamp program is herein authorized which will permit low-income households to purchase a nutritionally adequate diet through normal channels of trade."

SEC. 2. (a) Section 3 (e) of the Food Stamp Act of 1964, as amended, is amended to read as follows:

"(e) The term 'household' shall mean a group of related individuals (including legally adopted children and legally assigned foster children) or non-related individuals over age 60 who are not residents of an institution or boarding house, but are living as one economic unit sharing common cooking facilities and for whom food is customarily purchased in common. The term 'household' shall also mean (1) a single individual living alone who has cooking facilities and who purchases and prepares food for home consumption, or (2) an elderly person who meets the requirements of section 10 (h) of this Act."

(b) Add the following sentence at the end of subsection 3 (f) of the Food Stamp Act of 1964, as amended: "It shall also mean a political subdivision or a private nonprofit organization that meets the requirements of section 10 (h) of this Act."

(c) Subsection (j) of section 3 of the Food Stamp Act of 1964, as amended, is amended to read as follows:

"(j) The term 'State' means the fifty States and the District of Columbia, Guam, Puerto Rico, and the Virgin Islands of the United States".

(d) Add the following new subsection at the end of section 3 of the Food Stamp Act of 1964, as amended:

"(1) The term 'elderly person' shall mean a person sixty years of age or over who is not a resident of an institution or boarding house, and who is living alone, or with spouse, whether or not he has cooking facilities in his home."

(e) Section 3 of the Food Stamp Act of 1964, as amended, is amended by adding the following new subsection:

"(m) The term 'authorization to purchase card' means any document issued by the State agency to an eligible household which shows the face value of the coupon allotment the household is entitled to be issued on presentment of such document and the amount to be paid by such household for such allotment."

SEC. 3. Subsections (a) and (b) of section 4 of the Food Stamp Act of 1964, as amended, are amended to read as follows:

"(a) The Secretary is authorized to formulate and administer a food stamp program under which, at the request of the State agency, eligible households within the State shall be provided with an opportunity to obtain a nutritionally adequate diet through the issuance to them of a coupon allotment which shall have a greater monetary value than the charge to be paid for such allotment by eligible households. The coupons so received by such households shall be used only to purchase food from retail food stores which have been approved for participation in the food stamp program. Coupons issued and used as provided in this Act shall be redeemable at face value by the Secretary through the facilities of the Treasury of the United States.

"(b) In areas where the food stamp program is in operation, there shall be no distribution of federally donated foods to households under the authority of any other law except that distribution thereunder may be made: (1) during temporary emergency situations when the Secretary determines that commercial channels of food distribution have been disrupted; (2) for such period of time as the Secretary determines necessary, to effect an orderly transition in an area in which the distribution of federally donated foods to households is being replaced by a food stamp program; or (3) on request of the State agency: *Provided*, That the Secretary shall not approve any plan established under this Act which permits any household to simultaneously participate in both the food stamp program and the distribution of federally donated foods under this clause (3).

Sec. 4. Section 5 of the Food Stamp Act of 1964, as amended, is amended to read as follows:

"Sec. 5. (a) Except for the temporary participation of households that are victims of a disaster as provided in subsection (b) of this section, participation in the food stamp program shall be limited to those households whose income and other financial resources are determined to be substantial limiting factors in permitting them to purchase a nutritionally adequate diet.

"(b) The Secretary, in consultation with the Secretary of Health, Education, and Welfare, shall establish uniform national standards of eligibility for participation by households in the food stamp program and no plan of operation submitted by a State agency shall be approved unless the standards of eligibility meet those established by the Secretary. The standards established by the Secretary, at a minimum, shall prescribe the amounts of household income and other financial resources, including both liquid and nonliquid assets, to be used as criteria of eligibility. Any household which includes a member who has reached his eighteenth birthday and who is claimed as a dependent child for Federal income tax purposes by a taxpayer who is not a member of an eligible household, shall be ineligible to participate in any food stamp program established pursuant to this Act during the tax period such dependency is claimed and for a period of one year after expiration of such tax period. The Secretary may also establish temporary emergency standards of eligibility, without regard to income and other financial resources, for households that are victims of a disaster which disrupted commercial channels of food distribution when he determines that such households are in need of temporary food assistance, and that commercial channels of food distribution have again become available to meet the temporary food needs of such households: *Provided*, That the Secretary shall in the case of Puerto Rico, Guam, and the Virgin Islands, establish special standards of eligibility and coupon allotment schedules which reflect the average per capita income and cost of obtaining a nutritionally adequate diet in

Puerto Rico and the respective territories; except that in no event shall the standards of eligibility or coupon allotment schedules so used exceed those in the fifty States.

"(c) Notwithstanding any other provisions of law, the Secretary shall include in the uniform national standards of eligibility to be prescribed under subsection (b) of this section a provision that each State agency shall provide that a household shall not be eligible for assistance under this Act if it includes an able-bodied adult person between the ages of eighteen and sixty-five (except mothers or other members of the household who have the responsibility of care of dependent children or of incapacitated adults, bona fide students in any accredited school or training program, or persons employed and working at least 30 hours per week) who either (a) fails to register for employment at a State or Federal employment office or, when impractical, at such other appropriate State or Federal office designated by the Secretary, or (b) has refused to accept employment or public work at not less than (i) the applicable State minimum wage, (ii) the applicable Federal minimum wage, (iii) the applicable wage established by a valid regulation of the Federal Government authorized by existing law to establish such regulations, or (iv) $1.30 per hour if there is no applicable wage as described in (i), (ii), or (iii) above. Refusal to work at a plant or site subject to a strike or a lockout for the duration of such strike or lockout shall not be deemed to be a refusal to accept employment."

SEC. 5. Subsections (a) and (b) of section 7 of the Food Stamp Act of 1964, as amended, are amended to read as follows:

"(a) The face value of the coupon allotment which State agencies shall be authorized to issue to any households certified as eligible to participate in the food stamp program shall be in such amount as the Secretary determines to be the cost of a nutritionally adequate diet, adjusted annually to reflect changes in the prices of food published by the Bureau of Labor Statistics in the Department of Labor.

"(b) Notwithstanding any other provision of law, households shall be charged for the coupon allotment issued to them, and the amount of such charge shall represent a reasonable investment on the part of the household, but in no event more than 30 per centum of the household's income: *Provided,* That coupon allotments may be issued without charge to households with income of less than $30 per month for a family of four under standards of eligibility prescribed by the Secretary: *Provided further,* That the Secretary shall provide a reasonable opportunity for any eligible household to elect to be issued a coupon allotment having a face value which is less than the face value of the coupon allotment authorized to be issued to them under subsection (a) of this section. The charge to be paid by eligible households electing to exercise the option set forth in this subsection shall be an amount which bears the same ratio to the amount which would have been charged under subsection (b) of this section as the face value of the coupon allotment actually issued to them bears to the face value of the coupon allotment that would have been issued to them under subsection (a) of this section."

SEC. 6. (a) Subsection (c) of section 10 of the Food Stamp Act of 1964, as amended, is amended by inserting immediately preceding the first sentence the following: "Any household which is receiving public assistance and which makes application for the benefits of this Act shall be certified for eligibility solely by execution of an affidavit, in such form as the Secretary may prescribe, by the member of such household making application. Certification of a household as eligible in any political subdivision shall, in the event of removal of such household to another political subdivision in which the food stamp program is operating, remain valid for participation in the food stamp program for a period of sixty days from the date of such removal.''

(b) Subsection (e) of section 10 of the Food Stamp Act of 1964, as amended, is amended to read as follows:

''(e) The State agency of each State desiring to participate in the food stamp program shall submit for approval a plan of operation specifying the manner in which such program will be conducted within the State, the political subdivisions within the State in which the State desires to conduct the program, and the effective dates of participation by each such political subdivision. In addition, such plan of operation shall provide, among such other provisions as may by regulations be required, the following: (1) the specific standards to be used in determining the eligibility of applicant households; (2) that the State agency shall undertake the certification of applicant households in accordance with the general procedures and personnel standards used by them in the certification of applicants for benefits under the federally aided public assistance programs; (3) safeguards which restrict the use or disclosure of information obtained from applicant households to persons directly connected with the administration or enforcement of the provisions of this Act or the regulations issued pursuant to this Act; (4) for the submission of such reports and other information as from time to time may be required; (5) that the State agency shall undertake effective action, including the use of services provided by other federally funded agencies and organizations, to inform low-income households concerning the availability and benefits of the food stamp program and insure the participation of eligible households; and (6) for the granting of a fair hearing and a prompt determination thereafter to any household aggrieved by the action of a State agency under any provision of its plan of operation as it affects the participation of such household in the food stamp program. The State agency shall, notwithstanding any other provision of law, institute procedures under which any household participating in the food stamp program shall be entitled, if it so elects, to have the charges, if any, for its coupon allotment deducted from any grant or payment such household may be entitled to receive under any federally aided public assistance program and have its coupon allotment distributed to it with such grant or payment. In approving the participation of the subdivisions requested by each State in its plan of operation, the Secretary shall provide for an equitable and orderly expansion among the several States in accordance with their relative need and readiness to meet their requested effective dates of participation.''

(c) Add the following new subsection to section 10 of the Food Stamp Act of 1964, as amended:

''(h) Subject to such terms and conditions as may be prescribed by the Secretary in the regulations issued pursuant to this Act, members of an eligible household who are sixty years of age or over or an elderly person and his spouse may use coupons issued to them to purchase meals prepared for and delivered to them by a political subdivision or by a private nonprofit organization which: (1) is not receiving federally donated foods from the United States Department of Agriculture for use in the preparation of such meals; (2) is operated in a manner consistent with the purposes of this Act; and (3) is recognized as a tax exempt organization by the Internal Revenue Service: *Provided,* That household members or elderly persons to whom meals are delivered are housebound, feeble, physically handicapped, or otherwise disabled, to the extent that they are unable to adequately prepare all of their meals. Meals served pursuant to this subsection shall be deemed 'food' for the purposes of this Act.''

SEC. 7(a). Subsections (a) and (b) of section 14 of the Food Stamp Act of 1964, as amended, are amended as follows:

''(a) Notwithstanding any other provisions of this Act, the Secretary may provide for the purchase, issuance or presentment for redemption of coupons to such person or persons, and at such times and in such manner, as he deems necessary or appropriate to protect the interests of the United States or to insure enforcement of the provisions of this Act or the regulations issued pursuant to this Act.

''(b) Whoever knowingly uses, transfers, acquires, alters, or possesses coupons or authorization to purchase cards in any manner not authorized by this Act or the regulations issued pursuant to this Act shall, if such coupons or authorization to purchase cards are of the value of $100 or more, be guilty of a felony and shall, upon conviction thereof, be fined not more than $10,000 or imprisoned for not more than five years or both, or, if such coupons or authorization to purchase cards are of a value of less than $100, shall be guilty of a misdemeanor and shall, upon conviction thereof, be fined not more than $5,000 or imprisoned for not more than one year, or both.''

SEC. 7(b). Section 14 of the Food Stamp Act of 1964, as amended, is amended by adding the following new subsection:

''(e) No person shall be charged with a violation of this or any other Act, or of any regulation issued under this or any other Act, or of any State plan of operation on the basis of any statements or information contained in an affidavit filed pursuant to section 10 (c) of this Act, except for fraud.''

SEC. 8. Subsection (b) of section 15 of the Food Stamp Act of 1964 as amended, is amended to read as follows:

''(b) The Secretary is authorized to pay to each State agency an amount equal to 62½ per centum of the sum of (1) the direct salary, travel, and travel-related cost (including such fringe benefits as are normally paid) of personnel, including the immediate supervisors of such personnel, for such time as they are employed in taking the action required under the provisions of subsection 10 (e) (5) of this Act and in making certification determinations for households other than those which consist solely of recipients of welfare assistance; (2) the direct salary, travel, and travel-related costs (including such fringe benefits as are normally paid) of personnel for such time as they are employed as hearing officials under section 10 (e) of the Act.''

SEC. 9. Section 16 (a) of the Food Stamp Act of 1964, as amended, is amended by striking ''$170,000,000 for the six months ending December 31, 1970'' and inserting in lieu thereof ''$1,750,000,000 for the fiscal year ending June 30, 1971; and for the fiscal years ending June 30, 1972 and June 30, 1973 such sums as the Congress may appropriate''.

Approved January 11, 1971.

Rural Development Act of 1972

From 86 Statutes at Large 657.

Be it enacted by the Senate and House of Representatives of the United States of America in Congress assembled, That this Act may be cited as the "Rural Development Act of 1972".

Title I — Amendments to the Consolidated Farmers Home Administration Act of 1961

SEC. 101. SHORT TITLE. — Section 301(a) of the Consolidated Farmers Home Administration Act of 1961 is amended to read as follows:

"(a) This title may be cited as the 'Consolidated Farm and Rural Development Act'."

SEC. 102. RURAL ENTERPRISE LOANS. — Section 304 of the Consolidated Farmers Home Administration Act of 1961 is amended by —

(1) inserting "(a)" before the first sentence and striking out "(a)" and "(b)" in the first sentence; and

(2) adding at the end of section a new subsection as follows:

"(b) Loans may also be made or insured under this subtitle to residents of rural areas without regard to the requirements of clauses (2) and (3) of section 302 to acquire or establish in rural areas small business enterprises to provide such residents with essential income."

SEC. 103. APPRAISALS. — Section 305 of the Consolidated Farmers Home Administration Act of 1961 is amended by striking out "normal" in the first and second sentences and striking out the last sentence.

SEC. 104. ESSENTIAL RURAL COMMUNITY FACILITIES. — Section 306 (a) (1) of the Consolidated Farmers Home Administration Act of 1961 is amended (1) by inserting after "corporations not operated for profit," the following: "Indian tribes on Federal and State reservations and other federally recognized Indian tribes,"; and (2) by striking out "and recreational developments" and inserting in lieu thereof "recreational developments, and essential community facilities including necessary related equipment".

SEC. 105. GRANTS FOR WATER AND WASTE DISPOSAL SYSTEMS. — Section 306 (a) (2) of the Consolidated Farmers Home Administration Act of 1961 is amended by striking out "$100,000,000" and inserting in lieu thereof "$300,000,000".

SEC. 106. PLANNING REQUIREMENTS. — The first sentence of section 306 (a) (3) of the Consolidated Farmers Home Administration Act of 1961 is amended to read as follows: "No grant shall be made under paragraph (2) of this subsection in connection with any project unless the Secretary determines that the project (i) will serve a rural area which, if such project is carried out, is not likely to decline in population below that for which the project was designed, (ii) is designed and constructed so that adequate capacity will or can be made available to serve the present population of the area to the extent feasible and to serve the reasonably foreseeable growth needs of the area, and (iii) is necessary for an orderly community development consistent with a comprehensive community water, waste disposal, or other development plan of the rural area and not inconsistent with any planned development provided in any State, multijurisdictional, county, or municipal plan approved by competent authority for the area in which the rural community is located, and the Secretary shall require the submission of all applications for financial assistance under this section to the multijurisidictional substate areawide general purpose planning and development agency that has been officially designated as a clearinghouse agency under Office of Management and Budget Circular A–95 and to the county or municipal government having jurisdiction over the area in which the proposed project is to be located for review and comment within a designated period of time not to exceed 30 days concerning among other considerations, the effect of the project upon the areawide goals and plans of such agency or government. No loan under this section shall be made that is inconsistent with any multijurisdictional planning and development district areawide plan of such agency. The Secretary is authorized to reimburse such agency or government for the cost of making the required review.''

SEC. 107. EXTENSION. — In the second sentence of section 306(a) (3) of the Consolidated Farmers Home Administration Act of 1961 strike out ''1971'' and insert ''1973''.

SEC. 108. WATER AND WASTE DISPOSAL PLANNING GRANTS. — Paragraph (6) of section 306 (a) of the Consolidated Farmers Home Administration Act of 1961 is amended by —

(1) striking out ''$15,000,000'' and inserting in lieu thereof ''$30,000,000'';

(2) striking out ''official''; and

(3) striking out ''sewer'' and inserting in lieu thereof ''waste disposal''.

SEC. 109. DEFINITIONS. — Section 306 (a) (7) of the Consolidated Farmers Home Administration Act of 1961 is amended to read as follows:

''(7) As used in this title, the terms 'rural' and 'rural area' shall not include any area in any city or town which has a population in excess of ten thousand inhabitants, except that for purposes of loans and grants for private business enterprises under sections 304 (b), 310B, and 312 (b), (c), and (d) the terms 'rural' and 'rural area' may include all territory of a State, the Commonwealth of Puerto Rico and the Virgin Islands, that is not within the outer boundary of any city having a population of fifty thousand or more and its immediately adjacent urbanized and urbanizing areas with a population density of more than one hundred persons per square mile, as determined by the Secretary of Agriculture according to the latest decennial census of the United States: *Provided,* That special consideration for such loans and grants shall be given to areas other than cities having a population of more than twenty-five thousand.

SEC. 110. REPEAL OF MAXIMUM SIZE LOAN. — Section 306 (a) of the Consolidated Farmers Home Administration Act of 1961 is amended by striking out paragraph (5).

SEC. 111. RURAL DEVELOPMENT PLANNING GRANTS. — Section 306 (a) of the Consolidated Farmers Home Administration Act of 1961 is amended by adding at the end thereof a new paragraph as follows:

"(11) The Secretary may make grants, not to exceed $10,000,000 annually, to public bodies or such other agencies as he may select to prepare comprehensive plans for rural development or such aspects of rural development as he may specify."

SEC. 112. PRIORITY FOR CERTAIN WATER FACILITY AND WASTE DISPOSAL LOANS AND GRANTS. — Section 306 (a) of the Consolidated Farmers Home Administration Act of 1961 is amended by adding at the end thereof the following:

"(12) In the making of loans and grants for community waste disposal and water facilities under paragraphs (1) and (2) of this subsection the Secretary shall accord highest priority to the application of any municipality or other public agency (including an Indian tribe on a Federal or State reservation or other federally recognized Indian tribal group) in a rural community having a population not in excess of five thousand five hundred and which, in the case of water facility loans, has a community water supply system, where the Secretary determines that due to unanticipated diminution or deterioration of its water supply, immediate action is needed, or in the case of waste disposal, has a community waste disposal system, where the Secretary determines that due to unanticipated occurrences the system is not adequate to the needs of the community. The Secretary shall utilize the Soil Conservation Service in rendering technical assistance to applicants under this paragraph to the extent he deems appropriate."

SEC. 113. INTEREST RATES ON RURAL DEVELOPMENT LOANS. — Section 307 (a) of the Consolidated Farmers Home Administration Act of 1961 is amended by inserting before the period at the end of the second sentence thereof the following: "; except that loans (other than loans to public bodies or nonprofit associations (including Indian tribes on Federal and State reservations and other federally recognized Indian tribal groups) for community facilities, or loans of a type authorized by section 306 (a) (1) prior to its amendment by the Rural Development Act of 1972) made or insured under section 304 (b), 306 (a) (1), or 310B shall —

(1) when made other than as guaranteed loans, bear interest at a rate, prescribed by the Secretary, not less than a rate determined by the Secretary of the Treasury taking into consideration the current average market yield on outstanding marketable obligations of the United States comparable to the average maturities of such loans, adjusted in the judgment of the Secretary of the Treasury to provide for a rate comparable to the rates prevailing in the private market for similar loans and considering the Secretary's insurance of the loans, plus an additional charge, prescribed by the Secretary, to cover the Secretary's losses and cost of administration, which charge shall be deposited in the Rural Development Insurance Fund: *Provided,* That the rate so prescribed shall be adjusted to the nearest one-eighth of 1 per centum; and

(2) when made as guaranteed loans, bear interest at such rate as may be agreed upon by the borrower and the lender".

SEC. 114. ESCROW PAYMENTS. — Section 307(a) of the Consolidated Farmers Home Administration Act of 1961 is amended by inserting before the period at the end the following: ", and borrowers under this title shall prepay to the

Secretary as escrow agent such taxes and insurance as he may require, on such terms and conditions as he may prescribe''.

SEC. 115. AGRICULTURAL CREDIT INSURANCE FUND AMENDMENTS. — (a) Section 309 (f) of the Consolidated Farmers Home Administration Act of 1961 is amended by —

(1) changing ''$100,000,000'' to ''$500,000,000'' in paragraph (1);

(2) changing paragraph (2) by —

(A) striking out ''the interest'' and inserting in lieu thereof ''amounts'';

(B) changing ''prepayments'' to ''payments'' in all three places; and

(C) inserting after ''until due'' the following: ''or until the next agreed annual or semiannual remittance date''.

(3) striking out ''section 335(a) in connection with insured loans.'' in paragraph (5) and inserting in lieu thereof ''connection with insured loans, including the difference between interest payable by borrowers and interest to which insured lenders or insured holders are entitled under agreements with the Secretary included in contracts of insurance.''.

(4) inserting in paragraph (5) after ''to pay'' the following: ''for contract services,''.

(b) Section 309 of such Act is amended by adding at the end thereof the following new subsections:

''(g) (1) The assets and liabilities of, and authorizations applicable to, the Farmers Home Administration direct loan account created by section 338 (c) and the Emergency Credit Revolving Fund referred to in section 326 are hereby transferred to the fund, and such account and such revolving fund are hereby abolished. Such assets and their proceeds, including loans made out of the fund pursuant to this section, shall be subject to the provisions of this section, section 308, the last sentence of section 306 (a) (1), and the last sentence of section 307.

''(2) From time to time, and at least at the close of each fiscal year, the Secretary shall pay from the fund into the Treasury as miscellaneous receipts interest on the value as determined by the Secretary, with the approval of the Comptroller General, of the Government's equity transferred to the fund pursuant to the first sentence of this subsection plus the cumulative amount of appropriations made available after enactment of this provision as capital and for administration of the programs financed from the fund, less the average undisbursed cash balance in the fund during the year. The rate of such interest shall be determined by the Secretary of the Treasury, taking into consideration the current average yield on outstanding marketable obligations of the United States with remaining periods to maturity comparable to the average maturities of loans made or insured from the fund, adjusted to the nearest one-eighth of 1 per centum. Interest payments may be deferred with the approval of the Secretary of the Treasury, but any interest payments so deferred shall themselves bear interest. If at any time the Secretary determines that moneys in the fund exceed present and any reasonably prospective future requirements of the fund, such excess may be transferred to the general fund of the Treasury.

''(h) The Secretary may provide financial assistance to borrowers for purposes provided in this title by guaranteeing loans made by any Federal or State chartered bank, savings and loan association, cooperative lending agency, or other legally organized lending agency.''

SEC. 116. RURAL DEVELOPMENT INSURANCE FUND. — The Consolidated Farmers Home Administration Act of 1961 is amended by inserting the following new section after section 309:

"SEC. 309A. (a) There is hereby created the Rural Development Insurance Fund (hereinafter in this section referred to as the 'Insurance Fund') which shall be used by the Secretary as a revolving fund for the discharge of the obligations of the Secretary under contracts guaranteeing or insuring rural development loans. For the purpose of this section 'rural development loans' shall be those provided for by sections 304(b), 306(a) (1), 310B, and 312(b), except loans (other than for water systems and waste disposal facilities) of a type authorized by section 306(a) (1) prior to its amendment by the Rural Development Act of 1972.

"(b) The assets and liabilities of the Agricultural Credit Insurance Fund referred to in section 309(a) applicable to loans for water systems and waste disposal facilities under section 306(a) (1) are hereby transferred to the Insurance Fund. Such assets (including the proceeds thereof) and liabilities and rural development loans guaranteed or insured pursuant to this title shall be subject to the provisions of this section and section 308.

"(c) Moneys in the Insurance Fund not needed for current operations shall be deposited in the Treasury of the United States to the credit of the Insurance Fund or invested in direct obligations of the United States or obligations guaranteed by the United States. The Secretary may purchase with money in the Insurance Fund any notes issued by the Secretary to the Secretary of the Treasury for the purpose of obtaining money for the Insurance Fund.

"(d) The Secretary is authorized to make and issue notes to the Secretary of the Treasury for the purpose of obtaining funds necessary for discharging obligations under this section and for making loans, advances, and authorized expenditures out of the Insurance Fund. Such notes shall be in such form and denominations and have such maturities and be subject to such terms and conditions as may be prescribed by the Secretary with the approval of the Secretary of the Treasury. Such notes shall bear interest at a rate fixed by the Secretary of the Treasury, taking into consideration the current average market yield of outstanding marketable obligations of the United States having maturities comparable to the average maturities of rural development loans made, guaranteed, or insured under this title. The Secretary of the Treasury is authorized and directed to purchase any notes of the Secretary issued hereunder, and, for that purpose, the Secretary of the Treasury is authorized to use as a public debt transaction the proceeds from the sale of any securities issued under the Second Liberty Bond Act, as amended, and the purposes for which such securities may be issued under such Act, as amended, are extended to include the purchase of notes issued by the Secretary hereunder. All redemptions, purchases, and sales by the Secretary of the Treasury of such notes shall be treated as public debt transactions of the United States.

"(e) Notes and security acquired by the Secretary in connection with rural development loans made, guaranteed, or insured under this title or transferred by subsection (b) of this section shall become a part of the Insurance Fund. Notes may be held in the Insurance Fund and collected in accordance with their terms or may be sold by the Secretary with or without agreements for insurance thereof at the balance due thereon, or on such other basis as the Secretary may determine from time to time. All net proceeds from such collections, including sales of notes or property, shall be deposited in and become a part of the Insurance Fund.

"(f) The Secretary shall deposit in the Insurance Fund any charges collected for loan services provided by the Secretary as well as charges assessed for losses and costs of administration in connection with making, guaranteeing, or insuring rural development loans under this title.

"(g) The Secretary may utilize the Insurance Fund —

"(1) to make rural development loans which could be insured under this title whenever he has a reasonable assurance that they can be sold without undue delay, and he may sell and insure such loans;

"(2) to pay amounts to which the holder of insured notes is entitled on loans heretofore or hereafter insured accruing between the date of any payments by the borrower and the date of transmittal of any such payments to the holder. In the discretion of the Secretary, payments other than final payments need not be remitted to the holder until due or until the next agreed annual or semiannual remittance date;

"(3) to pay to the holder of insured notes any defaulted installment, or upon assignment of the note to the Secretary at the Secretary's request, the entire balance due on the loan;

"(4) to purchase notes in accordance with contracts of insurance heretofore or hereafter entered into by the Secretary;

"(5) to make payments in compliance with the Secretary's obligations under contracts of guarantee entered into by him;

"(6) to pay taxes, insurance, prior liens, expenses necessary to make fiscal adjustments in connection with the application and transmittal of collections or necessary to obtain credit reports on applicants or borrowers, expenses for necessary services, including construction inspections, commercial appraisals, loan servicing, consulting business advisory or other commercial and technical services, and other program services, and other expenses and advances authorized in section 335(a) of this title in connection with insured loans. Such items may be paid in connection with guaranteed loans after or in connection with acquisition by the Secretary of such loans or security therefor after default, to an extent determined by the Secretary to be necessary to protect the interest of the Government, or in connection with grants and any other activity authorized in this title;

"(7) to pay the difference between interest payments by borrowers and interest to which holders of insured notes are entitled under contracts of insurance heretofore or hereafter entered into by the Secretary; and

"(8) to pay the Secretary's costs of administration of the rural development loan program, including costs of the Secretary incidental to guaranteeing rural development loans under this title.

"(h) When any loan is sold out of the Insurance Fund as an insured loan, the interest or other income thereon paid to an insured holder shall be included in gross income for purposes of chapter 1 of the Internal Revenue Code of 1954."

SEC. 117 INSURED WATERSHED AND RESOURCE CONSERVATION AND DE-
VELOPMENT LOANS. — Subtitle A of the Consolidated Farmers Home Administration Act of 1961 is amended by adding at the end a new section as follows:

"SEC. 310A. Loans meeting the requirements of the Watershed Protection
and Flood Prevention Act or title III of the Bankhead-Jones Farm Tenant Act may
be insured, or made to be sold and insured, in accordance with and subject to
sections 308 and 309, the last sentence of section 306(a) (1), and the last sentence of
section 307 of this title."

SEC. 118. RURAL INDUSTRIALIZATION ASSISTANCE. — (a) Subtitle A of the
Consolidated Farmers Home Administration Act of 1961 is amended by adding at
the end thereof, after section 310A as added by this Act, a new section as follows:

"SEC. 310B. (a) The Secretary may also make and insure loans to public,
private, or cooperative organizations organized for profit or nonprofit, to Indian
tribes on Federal and State reservations or other federally recognized Indian tribal
groups, or to individuals for the purpose of improving, developing, or financing
business, industry, and employment and improving the economic and environmental climate in rural communities, including pollution abatement and control. Such
loans, when originated, held, and serviced by other lenders, may be guaranteed by
the Secretary under this section without regard to subsections (a) and (c) of section
333.

"(b) The Secretary may make grants, not to exceed $50,000,000 annually,
to eligible applicants under this section for pollution abatement and control projects
in rural areas. No such grant shall exceed 50 per centum of the development cost of
such a project.

"(c) The Secretary may also make grants, not to exceed $50,000,000 annu-
ally, to public bodies for measures designed to facilitate development of private
business enterprises, including the development, construction or acquisition of
land, buildings, plants, equipment, access streets and roads, parking areas, utility
extensions, necessary water supply and waste disposal facilities, refinancing, services and fees.

"(d) The Secretary may participate in joint financing to facilitate development of private business enterprises in rural areas with the Economic Development
Administration, the Small Business Administration, and the Department of Housing
and Urban Development and other Federal and State agencies and with private and
quasi-public financial institutions, through joint loans to applicants eligible under
subsection (a) for the purpose of improving, developing, or financing business,
industry, and employment and improving the economic and environmental climate
in rural areas or through joint grants to applicants eligible under subsection (c) for
such purposes, including in the case of loans or grants the development, construction, or acquisition of land, buildings, plants, equipment, access streets and roads,
parking areas, utility extensions, necessary water supply and waste disposal
facilities, refining, service and fees.

(1) No financial or other assistance shall be extended under any provision of
sections 304 (b), 320B, and 312 (b) that is calculated to or is likely to result in the
transfer from one area to another of any employment or business activity provided
by operations of the applicant, but this limitation shall not be construed to prohibit

assistance for the expansion of an existing business entity through the establishment of a new branch, affiliate, or subsidiary of such entity if the establishment of such branch, affiliate, or subsidiary will not result in an increase in unemployment in the area of original location or in any other area where such entity conducts business operations unless there is reason to believe that such branch, affiliate, or subsidiary is being established with the intention of closing down the operations of the existing business entity in the area of its original location or in any other area where it conducts such operations.

(2) No financial or other assistance shall be extended under any provision of sections 304 (b), 310B, and 312 (b) which is calculated to or likely to result in an increase in the production of goods, materials, or commodities, or the availability of services or facilities in the area, when there is not sufficient demand for such goods, materials, commodities, services, or facilities, to employ the efficient capacity of existing competitive commercial or industrial enterprises, unless such financial or other assistance will not have an adverse effect upon existing competitive enterprises in the area.

(3) No financial or other assistance shall be extended under any provision of sections 304 (b), 310B, and 312 (b) if the Secretary of Labor certifies within 60 days after the matter has been submitted to him by the Secretary of Agriculture that the provisions of paragraph (1) and (2) of this subsection have not been complied with. The Secretary of Labor shall, in cooperation with the Secretary of Agriculture, develop a system of certification which will insure the expeditious processing of requests for assistance under this section.''

(b) Section 333 of the Consolidated Farmers Home Administration Act of 1961 is amended by inserting ''310B,'' in paragraph (b) after ''306,''.

SEC. 119. GUARANTEED RURAL HOUSING LOANS. — Subtitle A of the Consolidated Farmers Home Administration Act of 1961 is amended by adding at the end thereof a new section as follows:

''SEC. 310C. (a) Rural Housing Loans which (1) are guaranteed by the Secretary under section 517(a) (2) of the Housing Act of 1949, (2) are made by other lenders approved by the Secretary to provide dwellings in rural areas for the applicants' own use, and (3) bear interest and other charges at rates not above the maximum rates prescribed by the Secretary of Housing and Urban Development for loans made by private lenders for similar purposes and guaranteed by the Secretary of Housing and Urban Development under the National Housing Act or superseding legislation shall not be subject to sections 501(c) and 502(b) (3) of the Housing Act of 1949.''

''(b) For the purposes of title V of the Housing Act of 1949, as amended, a guarantee of payment given under the color of law by the Department of Hawaiian Home Lands (or its successor in function) shall be found by the Secretary reasonably to assure repayment of any indebtedness so guaranteed.''

ISEC. 120. YOUNG FARMERS' LOANS. — (a) Section 311 of the Consolidated Farmers Home Administration Act of 1961 is amended by —

(1) inserting ''(a)'' before the first word; and

(2) adding at the end of the section a new subsection as follows:

''(b) (1) Loans may also be made under this subtitle without regard to the requirements of clauses (2) and (3) of subsection (a) to youths who are rural residents to enable them to operate enterprises in connection with their participation in 4–H Clubs, Future Farmers of America, and similar organizations and for the purposes specified in section 312.

"(2) A person receiving a loan under this subsection who executes a promissory note therefor shall thereby incur full personal liability for the indebtedness evidenced by such note in accordance with its terms free of any disability of minority.

"(3) For loans under this subsection the Secretary may accept the personal liability of a cosigner of the promissory note in addition to the borrowers' personal liability."

(b) Section 312 of the Consolidated Farmers Home Administration Act of 1961 is amended by inserting "(a)" after "311".

SEC. 121. RURAL ENTERPRISE OPERATING LOANS. — Section 312 of the Consolidated Farmers Home Administration Act of 1961, as amended by this title, is amended by —

    (1) inserting "(a)" before the first word; and

    (2) further amending subsection (a) (as so designated by paragraph (1)) by striking out "and (9) for loan closing costs." and by inserting in lieu thereof the following: "(9) loan closing costs, and (10) for assisting farmers or ranchers in effecting additions to or alterations in the equipment, facilities, or methods of operation of their farms or ranches in order to comply with the applicable standards promulgated pursuant to section 6 of the Occupational Safety and Health Act of 1970 or standards adopted by a State pursuant to a plan approved under section 18 of the Occupational Safety and Health Act of 1970, if the Secretary determines that any such farmer or rancher is likely to suffer substantial economic injury due to such compliance without assistance under this paragraph."

    (3) adding at the end of the section new subsections as follows:

"(b) Loans may also be made under this subtitle to residents of rural areas without regard to the requirements of clauses (2) and (3) of section 311(a) to operate in rural areas small business enterprises to provide such residents with essential income.

"(c) Loans may also be made to eligible applicants under this subtitle for pollution abatement and control projects in rural areas.

"(d) The Secretary may make grants, not to exceed $25,000,000 annually, to eligible applicants under this subtitle for pollution abatement and control projects in rural areas. No such grant shall exceed 50 per centum of the development cost of such a project."

SEC. 122. MAXIMUM SIZE. — Section 313 of the Consolidated Farmers Home Administration Act of 1961 is amended by changing "$35,000" to "$50,000".

SEC. 123. INSURED OPERATING LOANS. — Subtitle B of the Consolidated Farmers Home Administration Act of 1961 is amended by adding at the end thereof a new section as follows:

"SEC. 317. Loans meeting the requirements of this subtitle (except section 312 (b)) may be insured, or made to be sold and insured, in accordance with and subject to sections 308 and 309 and the last sentence of section 307 of this title."

Sec. 124. Amendments to Section 331. — Section 331 of the Consolidated Farmers Home Administration Act of 1961, is amended —

> (1) by inserting before the semicolon, in paragraph (a), the following: ", and until January 1, 1975, make contracts for services incident to making, insuring, collecting, and servicing loans and property as determined by the Secretary to be necessary for carrying out the purposes of this title; (and the Secretary shall prior to June 30, 1974, report to the Congress through the President on the experience in using such contracts, together with recommendations for such legislation as he may see fit)", and

> (2) by changing the period at the end of any lettered paragraph thereof to a semicolon and adding at the end of such section the following additional paragraphs:

"(g) Obtain fidelity bonds protecting the Government against fraud and dishonesty of officers and employees of the Farmers Home Administration in lieu of faithful performance of duties bonds under section 14, title 6, United States Code, and regulations issued pursuant thereto, but otherwise in accordance with the provisions thereof;

"(h) Not require borrowers to pay interest accrued after December 31, 1972, on interest which is not more than 90 days overdue on any loan held or insured by the Farmers Home Administration;

"(i) Consent to the transfer of property securing any loan or financed by any loan or grant made, insured, or held by the Secretary under this title, or the provisions of any other law administered by the Farmers Home Administration, upon such terms as he deems necessary to carry out the purpose of the loan or grant or to protect the financial interest of the Government."

Sec. 125. Credit Elsewhere Determination. — Paragraph (a) of section 333 is amended by inserting after "in writing" the following: ", and the Secretary shall determine,".

Sec. 126. Repeal of County Committee Approval Requirement for Association and District Loans. — Section 333 (b) of the Consolidated Farmers Home Administration Act of 1961 is amended by striking out the words "said sections" and inserting "section 321 (b) (2)".

Sec. 127. Disposition of Real Property. — Section 335 (c) of the Consolidated Farmers Home Administration Act of 1961 is amended by —

> (1) striking out "subtitle A" in the first sentence and inserting in lieu thereof "the provisions of any law administered by the Farmers Home Administration";

> (2) striking out "the provisions of subtitle A" in the second sentence and inserting in lieu thereof "such provisions";

> (3) striking out in the fourth sentence "of at least 20 per centum" and "not more than five annual"; and

> (4) adding at the end of the fourth sentence before the period the following: ", but not in any event at rates and terms more favorable than those legally permissible for eligible borrowers".

Sec. 128. (a) Guarantee of Loans. — Section 343 of the Consolidated Farmers Home Administration Act of 1961 is amended by inserting at the end thereof before the period the following: ", and (4) the word 'insure' as used in this title includes guarantee, which means to guarantee the payment of a loan originated, held, and serviced by a private financial agency or other lender approved by the Secretary, and (5) the term 'contract of insurance' includes a contract of guarantee".

(b) Section 307(b) of the Consolidated Farmers Home Administration Act of 1961 is amended by changing "shall" to "may" in the second sentence.

SEC. 129. ORDER OF PREFERENCE, EXTENT OF GUARANTY. — The Consolidated Farmers Home Administration Act of 1961 is amended by adding at the end thereof the following new section:

"SEC. 344. No loan (other than one to a public body or nonprofit association (including Indian tribes on Federal and State reservations or other federally recognized Indian tribal groups) for community facilities or one of a type authorized by section 306 (a) (1) prior to its amendment by the Rural Development Act of 1972) shall be made by the Secretary either for sale as an insured loan or otherwise under section 304 (b), 306(a) (1), 310B, 312 (b), or 312 (c) unless the Secretary shall have determined that no other lender is willing to make such loan and assume 10 per centum of any loss sustained thereon. No contract guaranteeing any such loan by such other lender shall require the Secretary to participate in more than 90 per centum of any loss sustained thereon."

Title II — Amendments to the Watershed Protection and Flood Prevention Act, as Amended

SEC. 201. AMENDMENTS TO PUBLIC LAW 83–566. — The Watershed Protection and Flood Prevention Act (68 Stat. 666), as amended, is amended as follows:

(a) Section 1 is amended by striking out the words "the purpose of preventing such damages and of furthering the conservation, development, utilization, and disposal of water, and thereby of preserving and protecting the Nation's land and water resources" and substituting therefor the words "the purpose of preventing such damages, of furthering the conservation, development, utilization, and disposal of water, and the conservation and utilization of land and thereby of preserving, protecting, and improving the Nation's land and water resources and the quality of the environment."

(b) Section 2 is amended by substituting a comma for the word "or" after clause (1) and adding after the phrase "(2) the conservation, development, utilization, and disposal of water" a comma and the following: "or

"(3) the conservation and proper utilization of land".

(c) Section 3 is amended by changing the period at the end of paragraph (5) to a semicolon and adding the following:

"(6) to enter into agreements with landowners, operators, and occupiers, individually or collectively, based on conservation plans of such landowners, operators, and occupiers which are developed in cooperation with and approved by the soil and water conservation district in which the land described in the agreement is situated, to be carried out on such land during a period of not to exceed ten years, providing for changes in cropping systems and land uses and for the installation of soil and water conservation practices and measures needed to conserve and develop the soil, water, woodland, wildlife, and recreation resources of lands within the area included in plans for works of improvement, as provided for in such plans, including watershed or subwatershed work plans in connection with the eleven watershed improvement programs authorized by section 13 of the Act of December 22, 1944 (58 Stat. 887), as amended and supplemented. Applications for assistance in developing such conservation plans shall be made in writing to the soil and water conservation district involved, and the proposed agreement shall be reviewed by such district. In return for such agreements by landowners, operators, and occupiers the Secretary shall agree to share the costs of carrying out those practices and measures set forth in the agreement for which he determines that cost sharing is appropriate and in the public interest. The portion of such costs, including labor, to be shared shall be that part which the Secretary determines is appropriate and in the public interest for the carrying out of the practices and measures set forth in the agreement, except that the Federal assistance shall not exceed the rate of assistance for similar practices and measures under existing national programs. The Secretary may terminate any agreement with a landowner, operator, or occupier by mutual agreement if the Secretary determines that such termination would be in the public interest, and may agree to such modifications of agreements, previously entered into hereunder, as he deems desirable to carry out the purposes of this paragraph or to facilitate the practical administration of the agreements provided for herein. Notwithstanding any other provision of law, the Secretary, to the extent he deems it desirable to carry out the purposes of this paragraph, may provide in any agreement hereunder for (1) preservation for a period not to exceed the period covered by the agreement and an equal period thereafter of the cropland, crop acreage, and allotment history applicable to land covered by the agreement for the purpose of any Federal program under which such history is used as a basis for an allotment or other limitation on the production of any crop; or (2) surrender of any such history and allotments.''

(d) Paragraph (1) of section 4 is amended by inserting after ''without cost to the Federal Government'' the words ''from funds appropriated for the purposes of this act''.

(e) Clause A of paragraph (2) of section 4 is amended by striking all words after ''fish and wildlife'' and substituting therefor the words ''development, recreational development, ground water recharge, water quality management, or the conservation and proper utilization of land: *Provided,* That works of improvement for water quality management shall consist primarily of water storage capacity in reservoirs for regulation of streamflow, except that any such storage and water releases shall not be provided as a substitute for adequate treatment or other methods of controlling waste at the source, and shall be consistent with standards and regulations adopted by the Water Resources Council on Federal cost sharing for water quality management, and''.

(f) All that part of clause (B) of paragraph (2) of section 4 which follows the word *''Provided,''* where it first appears therein is amended to read as follows: ''That, in addition to and without limitation on the authority of the Secretary to make loans or advancements under section 8, the Secretary may pay for any storage of water for present or anticipated future demands or needs for municipal or industrial water included in any reservoir structure constructed or modified under the provisions of this Act as hereinafter provided: *Provided further,* That the cost of water storage to meet future demands may not exceed 30 per centum of the total estimated cost of such reservoir structure and the local organization shall give reasonable assurances, and there is evidence, that such demands for the use of such storage will be made within a period of time which will permit repayment within the life of the reservoir structure of the cost of such storage: *Provided further,* That the Secretary shall determined prior to initiation of construction or modification of any reservoir structure including such water supply storage that there are adequate assurances by the local organization or by an agency of the State having authority to give such assurances, that the Secretary will be reimbursed the cost of water supply storage for anticipated future demands, and that the local organization will pay not less than 50 per centum of the cost of storage for present water supply demands: *And provided further,* That the cost to be borne by the local organization for anticipated future demands may be repaid within the life of the reservoir structure but in no event to exceed fifty years after the reservoir structure is first used for the storage of water for anticipated future water supply demands, except that (1) no reimbursement of the cost of such water supply storage for anticipated future demands need be made until such supply is first used, and (2) no interest shall be charged on the cost of such water-supply storage begin for anticipated future demands until such supply is first used, but in no case shall the interest-free period exceed ten years. The interest rate used for purposes of computing the interest on the unpaid balance shall be determined in accordance with the provisions of section 8.''

(g) Subsection (4) of section 5 is amended to read as follows: ''(4) Any plans for works of improvement involving an estimated Federal contribution to construction costs in excess of $250,000 or including any structure having a total capacity in excess of twenty-five hundred acre-feet (a) which includes works of improvement for reclamation or irrigation, or which affects public or other lands or wildlife under the jurisdiction of the Secretary of the Interior, (b) which includes Federal assistance for goodwater detention stuctures, (c) which includes features which may affect the public health, or (d) which includes measures for control or abatement of water pollution, shall be submitted to the Secretary of the Interior, the Secretary of the Army, the Secretary of Health, Education, and Welfare, or the Administrator of the Environmental Protection Agency, respectively, for his views and recommendations at least thirty days prior to transmission of the plan to the Congress through the President. The views and recommendations of the Secretary of the Interior, the Secretary of the Army, the Secretary of Health, Education, and Welfare and the Administrator of the Environmental Protection Agency, if received by the Secretary prior to the expiration of the above thirty-day period, shall accompany the plan transmitted by the Secretary to the Congress through the President.''

Title III — Amendments to the Bankhead-Jones Farm Tenant Act, as Amended

SEC. 301. BANKHEAD-JONES FARM TENANT ACT AMENDMENTS. — Section 32(e) of title III of the Bankhead-Jones Farm Tenant Act, as amended (7 U.S.C. 1011), is amended by adding at the end thereof the following:

"The Secretary shall also be authorized in providing assistance for carrying out plans developed under this title:

"(1) To provide technical and other assistance, and to pay for any storage of water for present or anticipated future demands or needs for rural community water supply included in any reservoir structure constructed or modified pursuant to such plans: *Provided,* That the cost of water storage to meet future demands may not exceed 30 per centum of the total estimated cost of such reservoir structure and the public agency or local nonprofit organization shall give reasonable assurances, and there is evidence, that such demands for the use of such storage will be made within a period of time which will permit repayment of the cost of such water supply storage within the life of the reservoir structure: *Provided further,* That the public agency or local nonprofit organization prior to initiation or construction or modification of any reservoir structure including water supply storage, make provision satisfactory to the Secretary to pay for not less than 50 per centum of the cost of storage for present water supply demands, and all of the cost of storage for anticipated future demands: *And provided further,* That the cost to be borne by the public agency or local nonprofit organization for anticipated future demands may be repaid within the life of the reservoir structure but in no event to exceed fifty years after the reservoir structure is first used for the storage of water for anticipated future water supply demands except that (1) no payment on account of such cost need be made until such supply is first used, and (2) no interest shall be charged on such cost until such supply is first used, but in no case shall the interest-free period exceed ten years. The interest rate used for purposes of computing the interest on the unpaid balance shall be the average rate, as determined by the Secretary of the Treasury, payable by the Treasury upon its marketable public obligations outstanding at the beginning of the fiscal year in which the advancement for such water supply is first made, which are neither due nor callable for redemption for fifteen years from date of issue;

"(2) To provide, for the benefit of rural communities, technical and other assistance and such proportionate share of the costs of installing measures and facilities for water quality management, for the control and abatement of agriculture-related pollution, for the disposal of solid wastes, and for the storage of water in reservoirs, farm ponds, or other impoundments, together with necessary water withdrawal appurtenances, for rural fire protection, as is determined by the Secretary to be equitable in consideration of national needs and assistance authorized for similar purposes under other Federal programs."

SEC. 302. SOIL, WATER AND RELATED RESOURCE DATA. — In recognition of the increasing need for soil, water, and related resource data for land conservation, use, and development, for guidance of community development for a balanced rural-urban growth, for identification of prime agriculture producing areas that should be protected, and for use in protecting the quality of the environment, the Secretary of Agriculture is directed to carry out a land inventory and monitoring program to include, but not be limited to, studies and surveys of erosion and sediment damages, flood plain identification and utilization, land use changes and trends, and degradation of the environment resulting from improper use of soil, water, and related resources. The Secretary shall issue at not less than five-year intervals a land inventory report reflecting soil, water, and related resource conditions.

Title IV — Rural Community Fire Protection

SEC. 401. WILDFIRE PROTECTION ASSISTANCE. — In order to shield human and natural resources, financial investments, and environmental quality from losses due to wildfires in unprotected or poorly protected rural areas there is a need to strengthen and synergize Federal, State, and local efforts to establish an adequate protection capability wherever the lives and property of Americans are endangered by wildfire in rural communities and areas. The Congress hereby finds that inadequate fire protection and the resultant threat of substantial losses of life and property is a significant deterrent to the investment of the labor and capital needed to help revitalize rural America, and that well-organized, equipped, and trained firefighting forces are needed in many rural areas to encourage and safeguard public and private investments in the improvement and development of areas of rural America where organized protection against losses from wildfire is lacking or inadequate. To this end, the Secretary of Agriculture is authorized and directed to provide financial, technical, and other assistance to State foresters or other appropriate officials of the several States in cooperative efforts to organize, train, and equip local forces, including those of Indian tribes on Federal and State reservations or other federally recognized Indian tribal groups to prevent, control, and suppress wildfires threatening human life, livestock, wildlife, crops, pastures, orchards, rangeland, woodland, farmsteads, or other improvements, and other values in rural areas as defined in section 306 (a)(7) of the Consolidated Farm and Rural Development Act.

SEC. 402. MATCHING. — The Secretary shall carry out this title in accordance with cooperative agreements, made with appropriate State officials, which include such terms and conditions as the Secretary deems necessary to achieve the purposes of this title. No such agreement shall provide for financial assistance by the Secretary under this title in any State during any fiscal year in excess of 50 per centum of the total budgeted expenditures or the actual expenditures, whichever is less, of the undertaking of such agreement for such year, including any expenditures of local public and private nonprofit organizations, including Indian tribal groups, participating in the activities covered by the agreement. Payments by the Secretary under any such agreement may be made on the certificate of the appropriate State official that the expenditures provided for under such agreement have been made.

SEC. 403. REPORT. — The Secretary of Agriculture shall submit to the President within two years after the date of enactment of this title a written report detailing the contribution of the rural fire protection program toward achieving the purposes of this title. The Secretary shall also include in such report such recommendations regarding the rural fire protection program as he deems appropriate. The President shall transmit the report to the Congress for review and appropriate action.

SEC. 404. APPROPRIATIONS. — There is authorized to be appropriated to carry out the provisions of this title $7,000,000 for each of the fiscal years ending June 30, 1973, June 30, 1974, and Jun 30, 1975.

Title V — Rural Development and Small Farm Research and Education

SEC. 501. PURPOSES. — The purpose of this title is to encourage and foster a balanced national development that provides opportunities for increased numbers of Americans to work and enjoy a high quality of life dispersed throughout our

Nation by providing the essential knowledge necessary for successful programs of rural development. It is further the purpose of this title —

(a) to provide multistate regional agencies, States, counties, cities, multicounty planning and development of districts, businesses, industries, organizations, Indian tribes on Federal and State reservations or other federally recognized Indian tribal groups, and others involved with public services and investments in rural areas or that provide or may provide employment in these areas the best available scientific, technical, economic, organizational, environmental, and management information and knowledge useful to them, and to assist and encourage them in the interpretation and application of this information to practical problems and needs in rural development;

(b) to provide research and investigations in all fields that have as their purpose the development of useful knowledge and information to assist those planning, carrying out, managing, or investing in facilities, services, businesses, or other enterprises, public and private, that may contribute to rural development;

(c) to enhance the capabilities of colleges and universities to perform the vital public service roles of research, transfer, and practical application of knowledge in support of rural development;

(d) to expand research on innovative approaches to small farm management and technology and extend training and technical assistance to small farmers so that they may fully utilize the best available knowledge on sound economic approaches to small farm operations.

SEC. 502. PROGRAMS AUTHORIZED. — The Secretary of Agriculture (hereafter referred to as the "Secretary") is directed and authorized to conduct in cooperation and in coordination with colleges and universities the following programs to carry out the purposes of this title.

(a) RURAL DEVELOPMENT EXTENSION PROGRAMS. — Rural development extension programs shall consist of the collection, interpretation, and dissemination of useful information and knowledge from research and other sources to units of multistate regional agencies, State, county, municipal, and other units of government, multicounty planning and development districts, organizations of citizens contributing to rural development, business, Indian tribes on Federal or State reservations or other federally recognized Indian tribal groups, or industries that employ or may employ people in rural areas. These programs also shall include technical services and educational activity, including instruction for persons not enrolled as students in colleges or universities, to facilitate and encourage the use and practical application of this information. These programs also may include feasibility studies and planning assistance.

(b) RURAL DEVELOPMENT RESEARCH. — Rural development research shall consist of research, investigations, and basic feasibility studies in any field or discipline which may develop principles, facts, scientific and technical knowledge, new technology, and other information that may be useful to agencies of Federal, State, and local government, industries in rural areas, Indian tribes on Federal and State reservations or other federally recognized Indian tribal groups, and other organizations involved in rural development programs and activities in planning and carrying out such programs and activities or otherwise be practical and useful in achieving increased rural development.

(c) Small Farm Extension, Research, and Development Programs. — Small farm extension and research and development programs shall consist of extension and research programs with respect to new approaches for small farms in management, agricultural production techniques, farm machinery technology, new products, cooperative agricultural marketing, and distribution suitable to the economic development of family size farm operations.

Sec. 503. Appropriation and Allocation of Funds. — (a) There is hereby authorized to be appropriated to carry out the purposes of this title not to exceed $10,000,000 for the fiscal year ending June 30, 1974, not to exceed $15,000,000 for the fiscal year ending June 30, 1975, and not to exceed $20,000,000 for the fiscal year ending June 30, 1976.

(b) Such sums as the Congress shall appropriate to carry out the purposes of this title pursuant to subsection (a) shall be distributed by the Secretary as follows:

(1) 4 per centum to be used by the Secretary for Federal administration, national coordination, and program assistance to the States;

(2) 10 per centum to be allocated by the Secretary to States to finance work serving two or more States in which universities in two or more States cooperate or which is conducted by one university to serve two or more States;

(3) 20 per centum shall be allocated equally among the States;

(4) 66 per centum shall be allocated to each State, as follows: One-half in an amount which bears the same ratio to the total amount to be allotted as the rural population of the States bears to the total rural population of all the States as determined by the last preceding decennial census current at the time each such additional sum is first appropriated; and one-half in an amount which bears the same ratio to the total amount to be allotted as the farm population of the State bears to the total farm population of all the States as determined by the last preceding decennial census current at the time such additional sum is first appropriated.

(c) Funds appropriated under this title may be used to pay salaries and other expenses of personnel employed to carry out the functions authorized by this title, to obtain necessary supplies, equipment, services, and rent, repair, and maintenance of other facilities needed, but may not be used to purchase or construct buildings.

(d) Payment of funds to any State for programs authorized under section 502 (a), (b), and (c) shall be contingent upon the Secretary's approval of an annual plan and budget for programs conducted under each part and compliance with such regulations as the Secretary may issue under this title. Funds shall be available for use by the State in the fiscal year for which appropriated and the next fiscal year following the year for which appropriated. Funds shall be budgeted and accounted for on such forms and at such times as the Secretary shall prescribe.

(e) Funds provided to each State under this title may be used to finance programs through or at private and publicly supported colleges and universities other than the university responsible for administering the programs authorized by this title.

Sec. 504. Cooperating Colleges and Universities. — (a) Each of the programs authorized by this title shall be organized and conducted by one or more colleges or universities in each State so as to provide a coordinated program in each State.

(b) To assure national coordination with programs under the Smith-Lever Act of 1914 and the Hatch Act (as amended, August 11, 1955), administration of each State program shall be a responsibility of the institution or university accepting the benefits of the Morrill Act of 1862 (12 Stat. 503) as amended. Such administration shall be in association with the programs conducted under the Smith-Lever Act and the Hatch Act. The Secretary shall pay funds available to each State to said institution or university.

(c) All private and publicly supported colleges and universities in a State including the land-grant colleges of 1890 (26 Stat. 417) shall be eligible to conduct or participate in conducting programs authorized under this title. Officials at universities or colleges other than those responsible for administering programs authorized by this title who wish to participate in these programs shall submit program proposals to the university officials responsible for administering these programs and they shall be responsible for approval of said proposals.

(d) The university in each State responsible for administering the program authorized by this title shall designate an official who shall be responsible for programs authorized by each part of section 502 and an official who shall be responsible for the overall coordination of said programs.

(e) The chief administrative officer of the university in each State responsible for administering the program authorized by this title shall appoint a State Rural Development Advisory Council, consisting of not more than fifteen members. The administrative head of agriculture of that university shall serve as chairman. The administrative head of a principal school of engineering in the State shall be a member. There shall be at least ten additional members who shall include persons representing farmers, business, labor, banking, local government, multi-county planning and development districts, public and private colleges and Federal and State agencies involved in rural development.

It shall be the function of the Council to review and approve annual program plans conducted under this title and to advise the chief administrative officer of the university on matters pertaining to the program authorized.

SEC. 505. AGREEMENTS AND PLANS. — (a) Programs authorized under this title shall be conducted as mutually agreed upon by the Secretary and the university responsible for administering said programs in a memorandum of understanding which shall provide for the coordination of the programs authorized under this title, coordination of these programs with other rural development programs of Federal, State, and local government, and such other matters as the Secretary shall determine.

(b) Annually said university shall submit to the Secretary an annual program plan for programs authorized under this title which shall include plans for the programs to be conducted by each cooperating and participating university or college and such other information as the Secretary shall prescribe. Each State program must include research and extension activities directed toward identification of programs which are likely to have the greatest impact upon accomplishing the objectives of rural development in both the short and longer term and the use of these studies to support the State's comprehensive program to be supported under this title.

SEC. 506. WITHHOLDING FUNDS. — When the Secretary determines that a State is not eligible to receive part or all of the funds to which it is otherwise entitled because of a failure to satisfy conditions specified in this title, or because of a failure to comply with regulations issued by the Secretary under this title, the facts and reasons therefor shall be reported to the President, and the amount involved shall be kept separate in the Treasury until the expiration of the Congress next succeeding a session of the legislature of the State from which funds have been withheld in order that the State may, if it should so desire, appeal to Congress from the determination of the Secretary. If the next Congress shall not direct such sum to be paid, it shall be covered into the Treasury. If any portion of the moneys received by the designated officers of any State for the support and maintenance of programs authorized by this title shall by any action or contingency be diminished or lost, or be misapplied, it shall be replaced by said State.

SEC. 507. DEFINITIONS. — For the purposes of this title —

(a) "Rural development" means the planning, financing, and development of facilities and services in rural areas that contribute to making these areas desirable places in which to live and make private and business investments; the planning, development, and expansion of business and industry in rural areas to provide increased employment and income; the planning, development, conservation, and use of land, water, and other natural resources of rural areas to maintain or enhance the quality of the environment for people and business in rural areas; and processes and procedures that have said objectives as their major purposes.

(b) The word "State" means the several States and the Commonwealth of Puerto Rico.

SEC. 508. REGULATIONS. — The Secretary is authorized to issue such regulations as may be necessary to carry out the provisions of this title.

Title VI — Miscellaneous

SEC. 601. LOCATION OF OFFICES IN RURAL AREAS. — Section 901(b) of the Act of November 30, 1970 (84 Stat. 1383), is amended to read as follows:

"(b) Congress hereby directs the heads of all executive departments and agencies of the Government to establish and maintain departmental policies and procedures giving first priority to the location of new offices and other facilities in rural areas as defined in the private business enterprise exception in section 306 (a) (7) of the Consolidated Farmers Home Administration Act of 1961, as amended (7 U.S.C. 1926). The President is hereby requested to submit to the Congress not later than September 1 of each fiscal year a report reflecting the efforts during the immediately preceding fiscal year of all executive departments and agencies in carrying out the provisions of this section, citing the location of all new facilities, and including a statement covering the basic reasons for the selection of all new locations."

SEC. 602. DESERTLAND ENTRYMEN. — (a) The first sentence of the Act entitled "An Act to enable the Secretary of Agriculture to extend financial assistance to homestead entrymen, and for other purposes", approved October 19, 1949

(63 Stat. 883; 7 U.S.C. 1006a), is amended by striking out "homestead entry" and inserting in lieu thereof "homestead or desertland entry".

(b) The last sentence of the first section of such Act is amended by striking out "reclamation project" and inserting in lieu thereof "reclamation project or to an entryman under the desertland laws".

SEC. 603. COORDINATION OF RURAL DEVELOPMENT ACTIVITIES. — (a) Section 520 of the Revised Statutes (7 U.S.C. 2201) is amended by —

(1) inserting the words "and rural development" after the words "with agriculture", and;

(2) striking "that word" and inserting in lieu thereof "those terms".

(b) Section 526 of the Revised Statutes (7 U.S.C. 2204) is amended by —

(1) inserting "(a)" before the first sentence;

(2) inserting the words "and rural development" after the words "concerning agriculture";

(3) striking out the period at the end of the section and inserting in lieu thereof the following: "; and he shall advise the President, other members of his Cabinet, and the Congress on policies and programs designed to improve the quality of life for people living in the rural and nonmetropolitan regions of the Nation."; and

(4) adding at the end of the section a new subsection as follows:

"(b) The Secretary of Agriculture is authorized and directed to provide leadership and coordination within the executive branch and shall assume responsibility for coordinating a nationwide rural development program utilizing the services of executive branch departments and agencies and the agencies, bureaus, offices, and services of the Department of Agriculture in coordination with rural development programs of State and local governments. In carrying out this responsibility the Secretary of Agriculture shall establish employment, income, population, housing, and quality of community services and facilities goals for rural development and report annually prior to September 1 to Congress on progress inattaining such goals. The Secretary is authorized to initiate or expand research and development efforts related to solution of problems of rural water supply, rural sewage and solid waste management, rural housing, and rural industrialization."

(c) (1) The Secretary of Agriculture shall utilize to the maximum extent practicable State, regional, district, county, local, or other Department of Agriculture offices to enhance rural development, and shall to the maximum extent practicable provide directly, or, in the case of agencies outside of the Department of Agriculture, through arrangements with the heads of such agencies, for —

(A) the location of all field units of the Federal Government concerned with rural development in the appropriate Department of Agriculture offices covering the geographical areas most similar to those covered by such field units, and

(B) the interchange of personnel and facilities in each such office to the extent necessary or desirable to achieve the most efficient utilization of such personnel and facilities and provide the most effective assistance in the development of rural areas in accordance with State rural development plans.

(2) The Secretary shall include in the report required by this section a report on progress made in carrying out paragraph (1) of this subsection, together with such recommendations as may be appropriate.

SEC. 604. ADDITIONAL ASSISTANT SECRETARY OF AGRICULTURE. — (a) In addition to the Assistant Secretaries of Agriculture now provided for by law, there shall be one additional Assistant Secretary of Agriculture, who shall be appointed by the President, by and with the advice and consent of the Senate.

(b) Section 5315(11) of title 5, United States Code, is amended to read as follows:

"(11) Assistant Secretaries of Agriculture (4)."

SEC. 605. LONG-TERM RURAL ENVIRONMENTAL PROTECTION CONTRACTS. — Subsection (b) of section 8 of the Soil Conservation and Domestic Allotment Act, as amended (49 Stat. 163; 16 U.S.C. 590a), is further amended by adding a new paragraph at the end thereof as follows:

"In carrying out the purposes of subsection (a) of section 7, the Secretary may enter into agreements with agricultural producers for periods not to exceed ten years, on such terms and conditions as the Secretary deems desirable, creating obligations in advance of appropriations not to exceed such amounts as may be specified in annual appropriation Acts. Such agreements (i) shall be based on conservation plans approved by the soil and water conservation district or districts in which the lands described in the agreements are situated, and (ii) may be modified or terminated by mutual consent if the Secretary determines such action would be in the public interest. The Secretary also may terminate agreements if he determines such action to be in the national interest and provides public notice in ample time to give producers a reasonable opportunity to make arrangements for appropriate changes in the use of their land."

SEC. 606. COST SHARING FOR AGRICULTURE-RELATED POLLUTION PREŒ VENTION AND ABATEMENT MEASURES. — The Soil Conservation and Domestic Allotment Act, as amended (49 Stat. 163; 16 U.S.C. 590a), is further amended —

(1) By striking in section 7(a) the word "and" immediately before clause (5), substituting a semicolon for the period at the end of clause (5), and adding the following: "and (6) prevention and abatement of agricultural-related pollution.".

(2) By changing the first sentence of section 8 (b) to read as follows: "The Secretary shall have power to carry out the purposes specified in clauses (1), (2), (3), (4), (5), and (6) of section 7(a) by making payments or grants of other aid to agricultural producers, including tenants and sharecroppers, in amounts determined by the Secretary to be fair and reasonable in connection with the effectuation of such purposes during the year with respect to which such payments or grants are made, and measured by (1) their treatment or use of their land, or a part thereof, for soil restoration, soil conservation, the prevention of erosion, or the prevention or abatement of agriculture-related pollution; (2) changes in the use of their land; (3) their equitable share, as determined by the Secretary, of the normal national production of any commodity or commodities required for domestic consumption; (4) their equitable share, as determined by the Secretary, of the national production of any commodity or commodities required for domestic consumption and exports adjusted to reflect the extent to which their utilization of cropland on the farm conforms to

farming practices which the Secretary determines will best effectuate the purposes specified in section 7(a); or (5) any combination of the above.''

(3) By inserting in the second paragraph of section 8 (b) after the words ''soil-building services'' in the two places where they occur the words ''or pollution prevention or abatement aids'' and after the words ''soil-conserving practices'' the words ''or pollution prevention or abatement practices''.

(4) By striking ''or (5)'' in the first sentence of section 8 (d) and substituting ''(5), or (6)''.

(5) By inserting in the proviso of section 8 (e) after the words ''soil-building or soil-conserving practices'' the words ''or agriculture-related pollution prevention or abatement practices''.

(6) By striking the words ''soil-building practices and soil- and water-conserving practices'' in the penultimate sentence of section 15 and substituting ''soil-building practices, soil- and water-conserving practices, and agriculture-related pollution prevention and abatement practices''.

Approved August 30, 1972.

Agriculture and Consumer Protection Act of 1973

From 87 Statutes at Large 221.

''Title I — Payment Limitation

''SEC. 101. Notwithstanding any other provision of law —

''(1) The total amount of payments which a person shall be entitled to receive under one or more of the annual programs established by titles IV, V, and VI of this Act for the 1974 through 1977 crops of the commodities shall not exceed $20,000.

''(2) The term 'payments' as used in this section shall not include loans or purchases, or any part of any payment which is determined by the Secretary to represent compensation for resource adjustment or public access for recreation.

''(3) If the Secretary determines that the total amount of payments which will be earned by any person under the program in effect for any crop will be reduced under this section, the set-aside acreage for the farm or farms on which such person will be sharing in payments earned under such program shall be reduced to such extent and in such manner as the Secretary determines will be fair and reasonable in relation to the amount of the payment reduction.

''(4) The Secretary shall issue regulations defining the term 'person' and prescribing such rules as he determines necessary to assure a fair and reasonable application of such limitation: *Provided,* That the provisions of this Act which limit payments to any person shall not be applicable to lands owned by States, political subdivisions, or agencies thereof, so long as such lands are farmed primarily in the direct furtherance of a public function, as determined by the Secretary. The rules for determining whether corporations and their stockholders may be considered as separate persons shall be in accordance with the regulations issued by the Secretary on December 18, 1970.''

Dairy Program

Milk Marketing Orders

(2) Section 201 is amended by —

(A) amending section 201(e) by striking out ''1973'' and inserting ''1977'', and by striking out ''1976'' and inserting ''1980'', and

(B) adding at the end thereof the following:

''(f) The Agricultural Adjustment Act as reenacted and amended by the Agricultural Marketing Agreement Act of 1937, as amended, is further amended by:

''(1) striking the period at the end of subsection 8c(17) and adding in lieu thereof the following: ': *Provided further,* That if one-third or more of the producers as defined in a milk order apply in writing for a hearing on a proposed amendment of such order, the Secretary shall call such a hearing if the proposed amendment is one that may legally be made to such order. Subsection (12) of this section shall not be construed to permit any cooperative to act for its members in an application for a hearing under the foregoing proviso and nothing in such proviso shall be construed to preclude the Secretary from calling an amendment hearing as provided in subsection (3) of this section. The Secretary shall not be required to call a hearing on any proposed amendment to an order in response to an application for a hearing on such proposed amendment if the application requesting the hearing is received by the Secretary within ninety days after the date on which the Secretary has announced his decision on a previously proposed amendment to such order and the two proposed amendments are essentially the same.'

''(2) inserting after the phrase 'pure and wholesome milk' in section 8c(18) the phrase 'to meet current needs and further to assure a level of farm income adequate to maintain productive capacity sufficient to meet anticipated future needs'.''

Milk Price Support, Butterfat Price Support Suspension

(3) Section 202 is amended by —

(A) striking the introductory clause which precedes subsection (a);

(B) effective April 1, 1974, inserting in subsection (b) before the period at the end of the first sentence in the quotation the following: ''of pure and wholesome milk to meet current needs, reflect changes in the cost of production, and assure a level of farm income adequate to maintain productive capacity sufficient to meet anticipated future needs''; and

(C) inserting in subsection (b) after the first sentence in the quotation the following: ''Notwithstanding the foregoing, effective for the period beginning with the date of enactment of the Agriculture and Consumer Protection Act of 1973 and ending on March 31, 1975, the price of milk shall be supported at not less than 80 per centum of the parity price therefor.''

Transfer of Dairy Products to the Military and to Veterans Hospitals

(4) Section 203 is amended by striking out "1973" and inserting "1977".

Dairy Indemnity Program

(5) Section 204 is amended by —
    (A) striking out "1973" and inserting "1977"; and
    (B) striking subsection (b) and substituting therefor the following:
"(b) Section 1 of said Act is amended to read as follows:
" 'SECTION 1. The Secretary of Agriculture is authorized to make indemnity payments for milk or cows producing such milk at a fair market value, to dairy farmers who have been directed since January 1, 1964 (but only since the date of enactment of the Agriculture and Consumer Protection Act of 1973 in the case of indemnity payments not authorized prior to such date of enactment), to remove their milk, and to make indemnity payments for dairy products at fair market value to manufacturers of dairy products who have been directed since the date of enactment of the Agricultural Act of 1970 to remove their dairy products from commercial markets because of residues of chemicals registered and approved for use by the Federal Government at the time of such use. Any indemnity payment to any farmer shall continue until he has been reinstated and is again allowed to dispose of his milk on commercial markets.' "

Dairy Import Study

(6) Title II is amended by adding at the end thereof the following:
"SEC. 205. The Secretary of Agriculture is authorized and directed to carry out a comprehensive study to determine the effect upon domestic dairy producers, handlers, and processors and upon consumers of increases in the level of imports, if any, of dairy products and report his findings, together with any recommendations he may have with respect to import quotas or other matters, to the Congress of the United States no later than January 1, 1975. For the purposes of this section dairy products include (1) all forms of milk and dairy products, butterfat, milk solids-not-fat, and any combination or mixture thereof; (2) any article, compound, or mixture containing 5 per centum or more of butterfat, or milk solids-not-fat, or any combinations of the two; and (3) lactose, and other derivatives of milk, butterfat, or milk solids-not-fat, if imported commercially for any food use. Dairy products do not include (1) casein, caseinates, industrial casein, industrial caseinates, or any other industrial products, not to be used in any form for any food use, or an ingredient of food; or (2) articles not normally considered to be dairy products, such as candy, bakery goods, and other similar articles."

"Producer Handlers

SEC. 206. The legal status of producer handlers of milk under the provisions of the Agricultural Adjustment Act, as reenacted and amended by the Agricultural Marketing Agreement Act of 1937, as amended, shall be the same subsequent to the adoption of the amendments made by the Agriculture Act of 1973 as it was prior thereto."

Wool Program

(7) Section 301 is amended by —

(A) striking out "1973" each place it occurs and inserting "1977", and by striking out the word "three" each place it occurs; and

(B) adding at the end thereof the following:

"(6) Strike out the first sentence of section 708 and insert the following: 'The Secretary of Agriculture is authorized to enter into agreements with, or to approve agreements entered into between, marketing cooperatives, trade associations, or others engaged or whose members are engaged in the handling of wool, mohair, sheep, or goats or the products thereof for the purpose of developing and conducting on a national, State, or regional basis advertising and sales promotion programs and programs for the development and dissemination of information on product quality, production management, and marketing improvement, for wool, mohair, sheep, or goats or the products thereof. Advertising and sales promotion programs may be conducted outside of the United States for the purpose of maintaining and expanding foreign markets and uses for mohair or goats or the products thereof produced in the United States.'."

Wheat Program

Wheat Production Incentives

(8) Effective beginning with the 1974 crop section 401 is amended by striking out "1971, 1972, and 1973" and inserting "1971 through 1977" and section 107 of the Agricultural Act of 1949, as it appears therein is amended by —

(A) amending section 107(a) to read as follows:

"(a) Loans and purchases on each crop of wheat shall be made available at such level as the Secretary determines appropriate, taking into consideration competitive world prices of wheat, the feeding value of wheat in relation to feed grains, and the level at which price support is made available for feed grains: *Provided,* That in no event shall such level be in excess of the parity price for wheat or less than $1.37 per bushel."

(B) substituting the word "payments" for the word "certificates" in section 107(b);

(C) striking the quotation mark at the end of section 107(b); and

(D) adding at the end of the section the following:

"(c) Payment shall be made for each crop of wheat to the producers on each farm in an amount determined by multiplying (i) the amount by which the higher of —

"(1) the national weighted average market price received by farmers during the first five months of the marketing year for such crop, as determined by the Secretary, or

"(2) the loan level determined under subsection (a) for such crop is less than the established price of $2.05 per bushel in the case of the 1974 and 1975 crops, $2.05 per bushel adjusted to reflect any change during the calendar year 1975 in the index of prices paid by farmers for production items, interest, taxes, and wage rates in the case of the 1976 crop, and the established price for the 1976 crop adjusted to reflect any change during the calendar year 1976 in such index in the case of the 1977 crop, times in each case (ii) the allotment for the farm for such crop, times (iii) the projected yield established for the farm with such adjustments as the Secretary determines necessary to provide a fair and equitable yield: *Provided,* That any increase that would otherwise be made in the established price to reflect a change in the index of prices paid by farmers shall be adjusted to reflect any change in (i) the national average yield per acre of wheat for the three calendar years preceding the year for which the determination is made, over (ii) the national average yield per acre of wheat for the three calendar years preceding the year previous to the one for which the determination is made. If the Secretary determines that the producers are prevented from planting, any portion of the farm acreage allotment to wheat or other nonconserving crop, because of drought, flood, or other natural disaster or condition beyond the control of the producer, the rate of payment on such portion shall be the larger of (A) the foregoing rate, or (B) one-third of the established price. If the Secretary determines that, because of such a disaster or condition, the total quantity of wheat (or other nonconserving crop planted instead of wheat) which the producers are able to harvest on any farm is less than 66⅔ percent of the farm acreage allotment times the projected yield of wheat (or other nonconserving crop planted instead of wheat) for the farm, the rate of payment for the deficiency in production below 100 percent shall be the larger of (A) the foregoing rate, or (B) one-third of the established price. The Secretary shall provide for the sharing of payments made under this subsection for any farm among the producers on the farm on a fair and equitable basis."

Termination of Wheat Certificate Program, Farm Acreage Allotments

(9) Section 402 is amended by inserting "(a)" after the section designation and adding the following at the end of the section:

"(b)(A) Section 379b of the Agricultural Adjustment Act of 1938 (which provides for a wheat marketing certificate program) shall not be applicable to the 1974 through 1977 crops of wheat, except as provided in paragraphs (B) and (C) of this subsection.

"(B) Section 379b (c) of the Agricultural Adjustment Act of 1938, as amended by subsection (a) of this section (which provides for a set-aside program), shall be effective with respect to the 1974 through 1977 crops of wheat with the following changes:

"(i) The phrase 'payments authorized by section 107 (c) of the Agricultural Act of 1949' shall be substituted for the word 'certificates' and the phrases 'certificates authorized in subsection (b)' and 'marketing certificates' each place they occur.

"(ii) The word 'domestic' shall be stricken each place it occurs.

"(iii) The second sentence of section 379b (c) (1) is amended to read as follows: 'If a set-aside of cropland is in effect under this subsection (c), then as a condition of eligibility for loans, purchases, and payments authorized by section 107(c) of the Agricultural Act of 1949, the producers on a farm must set aside and devote to approved conservation uses an acreage of cropland equal to (i) such percentage of the wheat allotment for the farm as may be specified by the Secretary and will be estimated by the Secretary to result in a set-aside not in excess of thirteen and three-tenths million acres in the case of the 1971 crop; plus, if required by the Secretary, (ii) the acreage of cropland on the farm devoted in preceding years to soil conserving uses, as determined by the Secretary.'

"(iv) The third sentence in 379b (c) (1) is amended to read as follows: 'The Secretary is authorized for the 1974 through 1977 crops to limit the acreage planted to wheat on the farm to a percentage of the acreage allotment.'

"(v) '1971 through 1977' shall be substituted for '1971, 1972, and 1973' each place it occurs other than in the third sentence of section 379b (c) (1).

"(vi) The last sentence of section 379b (c) (1) is amended to read as follows: 'The Secretary shall permit producers to plant and graze on set-aside acreage sweet sorghum, and the Secretary may permit, subject to such terms and conditions as he may prescribe, all or any of the set-aside acreage to be devoted to hay and grazing or the production of guar, sesame, safflower, sunflower, castor beans, mustard seed, crambe, plantago ovato, flaxseed, triticale, oats, rye, or other commodity, if he determines that such production is needed to provide an adequate supply, is not likely to increase the cost of the price-support program, and will not adversely affect farm income.'

"(vii) After the second sentence of section 379b (c) (3) the following shall be inserted: 'The Secretary may, in the case of programs for the 1974 through 1977 crops, pay an appropriate share of the cost of practices designed to carry out the purposes of the foregoing sentences.'

"(C) Sections 379b (d), (e), (g), and (i) of the Agricultural Adjustment Act of 1938, as amended by subsection (a) of this section, shall be effective for the 1974 through 1977 crops amended to read as follows:

" '(d) The Secretary shall provide for the sharing of payments made under this section for any farm among producers on the farm on a fair and equitable basis.

" '(e) In any case in which the failure of a producer to comply fully with the terms and conditions of the program formulated under this section precludes the making of loans, purchases, and payments, the Secretary may, nevertheless, make such loans, purchases, and payments in such amounts as he determines to be equitable in relation to the seriousness of the default.

" '(g) The Secretary is authorized to issue such regulations as he determines necessary to carry out the provisions of this title.

" '(i) The Secretary shall carry out the program authorized by this section through the Commodity Credit Corporation.'

"(D) Section 379c of the Agricultural Adjustment Act of 1938, effective only with respect to the 1974 through 1977 crops of wheat is amended to read as follows:

" 'SEC. 379c. (a) (1) The farm acreage allotment for each crop of wheat shall be determined as provided in this section. The Secretary shall proclaim the national acreage allotment not later than April 15 of each calendar year for the crop harvested in the next succeeding calendar year. Such national allotment shall be the number of acres he determines on the basis of the estimated national average yield for the crop for which the determination is being made will produce the quantity (less imports) that he estimates will be utilized domestically and for export during the marketing year for such crop. If the Secretary determines that carryover stocks are excessive or an increase in stocks is needed to assure a desirable carryover, he may adjust the allotment by the amount he determines will accomplish the desired decrease or increase in carryover stocks. The national acreage allotment for any crop of wheat shall be apportioned by the Secretary among the States on the basis of the apportionment to each State of the national acreage allotment for the preceding crop (1973 national domestic allotment in the case of apportionment of the 1974 national acreage allotment) adjusted to the extent deemed necessary by the Secretary to establish a fair and equitable apportionment base for each State, taking into consideration established crop rotation practices, the estimated decrease in farm acreage allotments, and other relevant factors.

" '(2) The State acreage allotment for wheat, less a reserve of not to exceed 1 per centum thereof for apportionment as provided in this subsection, shall be apportioned by the Secretary among the counties in the State, on the basis of the apportionment to each such county of the wheat allotment for the preceding crop, adjusted to the extent deemed necessary by the Secretary in order to establish a fair and equitable apportionment base for each county taking into consideration established crop-rotation practices, the estimated decrease in farm allotments, and other relevant factors.

" '(3) The farm allotment for each crop of wheat shall be determined by apportioning the county wheat allotment among farms in the county which had a wheat allotment for the preceding crop on the basis of such allotment, adjusted to reflect established crop-rotation practices and such other factors as the Secretary determines should be considered for the purpose of establishing a fair and equitable allotment. Notwithstanding any other provision of this subsection, the farm allotment shall be adjusted downward to the extent required by subsection (b).

" '(4) Not to exceed 1 per centum of the State allotment for any crop may be apportioned to farms for which there was no allotment for the preceding crop on the basis of the following factors: suitability of the land for production of wheat, the past experience of the farm operator in the production of wheat, the extent to which the farm operator is dependent on income from farming for his livelihood, the production of wheat on other farms owned, operated, or controlled by the farm operator, and such other factors as the Secretary determines should be considered for the purpose of establishing fair and equitable farm allotments. No part of such reserve shall be apportioned to a farm to reflect new cropland brought into production after the date of enactment of the set-aside program for wheat.

" '(5) The planting on a farm of wheat of any crop for which no farm allotment was established shall not make the farm eligible for an allotment under subsection (a)(3) nor shall such farm by reason of such planting be considered ineligible for an allotment under subsection (a)(4).

" '(6) The Secretary may make such adjustments in acreage under this Act as he determines necessary to correct for abnormal factors affecting production, and to give due consideration to tillable acreage, crop rotation practices, types of soil, soil and water conservation measures, and topography, and in addition, in the case of conserving use acreages to such other factors as he deems necessary in order to establish a fair and equitable conserving use acreage for the farm.

" '(b) (1) If for any crop the total acreage of wheat planted on a farm is less than the farm allotment, the farm allotment used as a base for the succeeding crop shall be reduced by the percentage by which such planted acreage was less than such farm allotment, but such reduction shall not exceed 20 per centum of the farm allotment for the preceding crop. If no acreage has been planted to wheat for three consecutive crop years on any farm which has an allotment, such farm shall lose its allotment. Producers on any farm who have planted to wheat not less than 90 per centum of the allotment for the farm shall be considered to have planted an acreage equal to 100 per centum of such allotment. An acreage on the farm which the Secretary determines was not planted to wheat because of drought, flood, or other natural disaster or condition beyond the control of the producer shall be considered to be an acreage of wheat planted for harvest. For the purpose of this subsection, the Secretary may permit producers of wheat to have acreage devoted to soybeans, feed grains for which there is a set-aside program in effect, guar, castor beans, cotton, triticale, oats, rye, or such other crops as the Secretary may deem appropriate considered as devoted to the production of wheat to such extent and subject to such terms and conditions as the Secretary determines will not impair the effective operation of the program.

" '(2) Notwithstanding the provisions of subsection (b)(1), no farm allotment shall be reduced or lost through failure to plant the farm allotment, if the producer elects not to receive payments for the portion of the farm allotment not planted, to which he would otherwise be entitled under the provisions of section 107(c) of the Agricultural Act of 1949.' "

Repeal of Processor Certificate Requirement

(10) Section 403 is amended by inserting "(a)" after the section designation and by inserting at the end thereof the following:

"(b) Sections 379d, 379e, 379f, 379g, 379h, 379i, and 379j of the Agricultural Adjustment Act of 1938 (which deal with marketing certificate requirements for processors and exporters) shall not be applicable to wheat processed or exported during the period July 1, 1973 through June 30, 1978; and section 379g is amended by adding the following new subsection (c):

"(c) The Secretary is authorized to take such action as he determines to be necessary to facilitate the transition from the certificate program provided for under section 379d to a program under which no certificates are required. Notwithstanding any other provision of law, such authority shall include, but shall not be limited to the authority to exempt all or a portion of wheat or food products made therefrom in the channels of trade on July 1, 1973, from the marketing restrictions in subsection (b) of section 379d, or to sell certificates to persons owning such wheat or food products made therefrom at such price and under such terms and conditions as the Secretary may determine. Any such certificate shall be issued by the Commodity Credit Corporation. Nothing herein shall authorize the Secretary to require certificates on wheat processed after June 30, 1973."

Suspension of Wheat Marketing Quotas

(11) Section 404 is amended by striking "1971, 1972, and 1973" wherever it appears and inserting "1971 through 1977", and by striking "1972 and 1973" and inserting "1972 through 1977".

State Agency Allotments, Yield Calculations

(12)(a) Section 405 is amended by striking out "1971, 1972, and 1973" and inserting "1971 through 1977"; and by repealing paragraph (2) effective with the 1974 crop; by inserting "(a)" after the section designation; by changing the period and quotation mark at the end of the section to a semicolon; and by adding at the end of the section the following:

"(b) Effective with respect to the 1974 through 1977 crops, section 301(b) (13) (K) of the Agricultural Adjustment Act of 1938 is amended by adding after 'three calendar years' the following: '(five calendar years in the case of wheat)', and section 708 of Public Law 89–321 is amended by inserting in the second sentence after 'determining the projected yield' the following '(except that in the case of wheat, if the yield is abnormally low in any one of the calendar years of the base period because of drought, flood, or other natural disaster, the Secretary shall take into account the actual yield proved by the producer in the other four years of such base period)'."

Suspension of Quota Provisions

(13) Section 406 is amended by striking out "1971, 1972, and 1973" and inserting "1971 through 1977".

Reduction in Wheat Stored to Avoid Penalty

(14) Section 407 of the Agricultural Act of 1970 is amended by adding at the end thereof the following: "Notwithstanding the foregoing, the Secretary may authorize release of wheat stored by a producer under section 379c(b) of the Agricultural Adjustment Act of 1938, as amended, prior to the 1971 crop, whenever he determines such release will not significantly affect market prices for wheat. As a condition of release, the Secretary may require a refund of such portion of the value of certificates received in the crop year the excess wheat was produced as he deems appropriate considering the period of time the excess wheat has been in storage and the need to provide fair and equitable treatment among all wheat program participants.".

Application of the Agricultural Act of 1949

(15) Section 408 is amended by striking out "1971, 1972, and 1973" and inserting "1971 through 1977".

Commodity Credit Corporation Sales Price Restrictions

(16) Section 409 is amended by striking out "1971, 1972, and 1973" and inserting "1971 through 1977".

Set-Aside on Summer Fallow Farms

(17) Section 410 is amended by striking out "1971, 1972, and 1973" and inserting "1971 through 1977".

Feed Grain Program

(18) Effective only with respect to the 1974 through 1977 crops of feed grains, section 501 is amended by —

(A) striking out that portion through the first colon and section 105(a) of the Agriculture Act of 1949, as it appears therein, and inserting the following:

"Sec. 501. (a) Effective only with respect to the 1971 through 1977 crops of feed grains, section 105(a) of the Agricultural Act of 1949, as amended, is further amended to read as follows:

" 'Sec. 105. Notwithstanding any other provision of law —

" '(a)(1) The Secretary shall make available to producers loans and purchases on each crop of corn at such level, not less than $1.10 per bushel nor in excess of 90 per centum of the parity price therefor, as the Secretary determines will encourage the exportation of feed grains and not result in excessive total stocks of feed grains in the United States.

" '(2) The Secretary shall make available to producers loans and purchases on each crop of barley, oats, and rye, respectively, at such level as the Secretary determines is fair and reasonable in relation to the level that loans and purchases are made available for corn, taking into consideration the feeding value of such commodity in relation to corn and other factors specified in section 401(b), and on each crop of grain sorghums at such level as the Secretary determines is fair and reasonable in relation to the level that loans and purchases are made available for corn, taking into consideration the feeding value and average transportation costs to market of grain sorghums in relation to corn.'."

(B) adding at the end thereof the following:

"(b) Effective only with respect to the 1974 through 1977 crops of feed grains, section 105(b) of the Agricultural Act of 1949, as amended, is further amended to read as follows:

" '(b) (1) In addition, the Secretary shall make available to producers payments for each crop of corn, grain sorghums, and, if designated by the Secretary, barley, computed by multiplying (1) the payment rate, times (2) the allotment for the farm for such crop, times (3) the yield established for the farm for the preceding crop with such adjustments as the Secretary determines necessary to provide a fair and equitable yield. The payment rate for corn shall be the amount by which the higher of —

" '(1) the national weighted average market price received by farmers during the first five months of the marketing year for such crop, as determined by the Secretary, or

" '(2) the loan level determined under subsection (a) for such crop is less than the established price of $1.38 per bushel in the case of the 1974 and 1975 crops, $1.38 per bushel adjusted to reflect any change during the calendar year 1975 in the index of prices paid by farmers for production items, interest, taxes, and wage rates in the case of the 1976 crop, and the established price for the 1976 crop adjusted to reflect any change during the calendar year 1976 in such index in the case of the 1977 crop: *Provided,* That any increase that would otherwise be made in the established price to reflect a change in the index of prices paid by farmers shall be adjusted to reflect any change in (i) the national average yield per acre of feed grains for the three calendar years preceding the year for which the determination is made, over (ii) the national average yield per acre of feed grains for the three calendar years preceding the year previous to the one for which the determination is made. The payment rate for grain sorghums and, if designated by the Secretary, barley, shall be such rate as the Secretary determines fair and reasonable in relation to the rate at which payments are made available for corn. If the Secretary determines that the producers on a farm are prevented from planting any portion of the farm acreage allotment to feed grains or other nonconserving crop, because of drought, flood, or other natural disaster or condition beyond the control of the producer, the rate of payment on such portion shall be the larger of (A) the foregoing rate, or (B) one-third of the established price. If the Secretary determines that, because of such a disaster or condition, the total quantity of feed grains (or other nonconserving crop planted instead of feed grains) which the producers are able to harvest on any farm is less than 66⅔ percent of the farm acreage allotment times the yield of feed grains (or other nonconserving crop planted instead of feed grains) established for the farm, the rate of payment for the deficiency in production below 100 percent shall be the larger of (A) the foregoing rate, or (B) one-third of the established price.

    " '(2) The Secretary shall, prior to January 1 of each calendar year, determine and proclaim for the crop produced in such calendar year a national acreage allotment for feed grains, which shall be the number of acres he determines on the basis of the estimated national average yield of the feed grains included in the program for the crop for which the determination is being made will produce the quantity (less imports) of such feed grains that he estimates will be utilized domestically and for export during the marketing year for such crop. If the Secretary determines that carryover stocks of any of the feed grains are excessive or an increase in stocks is needed to assure a desirable carryover, he may adjust the feed grain allotment by the amount he determines will accomplish the desired decrease or increase in carryover stocks. State, county, and farm feed grain allotments shall be established on the basis of the feed grain allotments established for the preceding crop (for 1974 on the basis of the feed grain bases established for 1973), adjusted to the extent deemed necessary to establish a fair and equitable apportionment base for each State, county, and farm. Not to exceed 1 per centum of the State feed grain allotment may be reserved for apportionment to new feed grain farms on the basis of the following factors: suitability of the land for production of feed grains, the extent to which the farm operator is dependent on income from farming for his livelihood, the production of feed grains on other farms owned, operated, or controlled by the farm operator, and such other factors as the Secretary determines should be considered for the purpose of establishing fair and equitable feed grain allotments.

    " '(3) If for any crop the total acreage on a farm planted to feed grains included in the program formulated under this subsection is less than the feed grain allotment for the farm, the feed grain allotment for the farm for the succeeding crops shall be reduced by the percentage by which the planted acreage is less than the feed grain allotment for the farm, but such reduction shall not exceed 20 per centum of the feed grain allotment. If no acreage has been planted to such feed grains for three consecutive crop years on any farm which has a feed grain allotment, such farm shall lose its feed grain allotment: *Provided,* That no farm feed grain allotment shall be reduced or lost through failure to plant, if the producer elects not to receive payment for such portion of the farm feed grain allotment not planted, to which he would otherwise be entitled under the provisions of this Act. Any such acres eliminated from any farm shall be assigned to a national pool for the adjustment of feed grain allotments as provided for in subsection (e)(2). Producers on any farm who have planted to such feed grains not less than 90 per centum of the feed grain allotment shall be considered to have planted an acreage equal to 100 per centum of such allotment. An acreage on the farm which the Secretary determines was not planted to such feed grains because of drought, flood, or other natural disaster or condition beyond the control of the producer shall be considered to be an acreage of feed grains planted for harvest. For the purpose of this paragraph, the Secretary may permit producers of feed grains to have acreage devoted to soybeans, wheat, guar, castor beans, cotton, triticale, oats, rye, or such other crops as the Secretary may deem appropriate, considered as devoted to the production of such feed grains to such extent and subject to such terms and conditions as the Secretary determines will not impair the effective operation of the program.'.'',

(C) amending the last sentence of section 105(c)(1) to read as follows:

"The Secretary shall permit producers to plant and graze on set-aside acreage sweet sorghum, and the Secretary may permit, subject to such terms and conditions as he may prescribe, all or any of the set-aside acreage to be devoted to hay and grazing or the production of guar, sesame, safflower, sunflower, castor beans, mustard seed, crambe, plantago ovato, flaxseed, triticale, oats, rye, or other commodity, if he determines that such production is needed to provide an adequate supply, is not likely to increase the cost of the price-support program, and will not adversely affect farm income."

(C) striking out "1971, 1972, 1973" where it appears in that part which amends section 105(c)(1) of the Agricultural Act of 1949 and inserting "1971 through 1977", and by amending the second sentence of section 105(c)(1) to read as follows: "If a set-aside of cropland is in effect under this subsection (c), then as a condition of eligibility for loans, purchases, and payments on corn, grain sorghums, and, if designated by the Secretary, barley, respectively, the producers on a farm must set aside and devote to approved conservation uses an acreage of cropland equal to (i) such percentage of the feed grain allotment for the farm as may be specified by the Secretary, plus, if required by the Secretary (ii) the acreage of cropland on the farm devoted in preceding years to soil conserving uses, as determined by the Secretary."

(D) amending the third sentence of section 105 (c)(1)to read as follows: "The Secretary is authorized for the 1974 through 1977 crops to limit the acreage planted to feed grains on the farm to a percentage of the farm acreage allotment.",

(E) striking out paragraphs (1) and (3) of subsection (e), changing "bases" to "allotments" wherever it appears in paragraph (2) of subsection (e), and striking out all of subsection (g).

(F) inserting after the second sentence of section 105(c)(3) the following: "The Secretary may, in the case of programs for the 1974 through 1977 crops, pay an appropriate share of the cost of practices designed to carry out the purposes of the foregoing sentences."

Cotton Program

Suspension of Marketing Quotas for Cotton, Minimum Base Acreage Allotments

(19) Section 601 is amended by —

(A) striking out "1971, 1972, and 1973" wherever it appears therein and inserting "1971 through 1977",

(B) striking "1970, 1971, and 1972" from paragraph (2) and inserting "1970 through 1976",

(C) effective beginning with the 1974 crop, striking out the following from section 344a(a) in section 601 "for which a farm base acreage allotment is established (other than pursuant to section 350(e)(1)(A))",

(D) striking "1974" from paragraph (3) (1) and inserting "1978", and by striking "1972 and 1973" from paragraph (4) and inserting "1972 through 1977",

(E) effective beginning with the 1974 crop, adding at the end of section 350(a) in paragraph (4) of section 601 the following: "The national base acreage allotment for the 1974 through 1977 crops shall not be less than eleven million acres.",

(F) effective beginning with the 1974 crop, striking "soybeans, wheat or feed grains" from the last sentence of section 350(e)(2) in paragraph (4) of section 601 and inserting "soybeans, wheat, feed grains, guar, castor beans, triticale, oats, rye or such other crops as the Secretary may deem appropriate",

(G) effective beginning with the 1974 crop, striking the words "an adjoining" in the first sentence of section 350(h) as found in paragraph (4) of section 601, and inserting in lieu thereof "any other nearby".

Cotton Production Incentives

(20) Section 602 is amended by —

(A) striking "1971, 1972, and 1973" wherever it appears therein and inserting "1971 through 1977", by striking "the 1972 or 1973 crop" where it appears in that part amending section 103(e)(1) of the Agricultural Act of 1949 and inserting "any of the 1972 through 1977 crops", and by striking out "acreage world price" in that part amending section 103(e)(1) of the Agricultural Act of 1949, and substituting "average price of American cotton in world markets";

(B) in that part amending section 103(e)(1) of the Agricultural Act of 1949 striking out "two-year period" wherever it appears therein and substituting "three-year period"; and by striking out that part beginning with "except that" in the first sentence and substituting "except that if the loan rate so calculated is higher than the then current level of average world prices for American cotton of such quality, the Secretary is authorized to adjust the current calculated loan rate for cotton to 90 per centum of the then current average world price.";

(C) effective, beginning with the 1974 crop, amending section 103(e)(2) of the Agricultural Act of 1949, as it appears in such section 602 to read as follows:

(2) Payments shall be made for each crop of cotton to the producers on each farm at a rate equal to the amount by which the higher of —

"(1) the average market price received by farmers for upland cotton during the calendar year which includes the first five months of the marketing year for such crop, as determined by the Secretary, or

"(2) the loan level determined under paragraph (1) for such crop is less than the established price of 38 cents per pound in the case of the 1974 and 1975 crops, 38 cents per pound adjusted to reflect any change during the calendar year 1975 in the index of prices paid by farmers for production items, interest, taxes, and wage rates in the case of the 1976 crop, and the established price for the 1976 crop adjusted to reflect any change during the calendar year 1976 in such index in the case of the 1977 crop: *Provided.* That any increase that would otherwise be made in the established price to reflect a change in the index of prices paid by farmers shall be adjusted to reflect any change in (i) the national average yield per acre of cotton for the three calendar years preceding the year for which the determination is made, over (ii) the national average yield per acre of cotton for the three calendar years preceding the year previous to the one for which the determination is made. If the Secretary determines that the producers on a farm are prevented from planting, any portion of the allotment to cotton because of drought, flood, or other natural disaster, or condition beyond the control of the producer, the rate of payment for such portion shall be the larger of (A) the foregoing rate, or (B) one-third of the established price. If the Secretary determines that, because of such a disaster or condition, the total quantity of cotton which the producers are able to harvest on any farm is less than 66⅔ percent of the farm base acreage allotment times the average yield established for the farm, the rate of payment for the deficiency in production below 100 percent shall be the larger of (A) the foregoing rate, or (B) one-third of the established price. The payment rate with respect to any producer who (i) is on a small farm (that is, a farm on which the base acreage allotment is ten acres or less, or on which the yield used in making payments times the farm base acreage allotment is five thousand pounds or less, and for which the base acreage allotment has not been reduced under section 350(f), (ii) resides on such farm, and (iii) derives his principal income from cotton produced on such farm, shall be increased by 30 per centum; but, notwithstanding paragraph (3), such increase shall be made only with respect to his share of cotton actually harvested on such farm within the quantity specified in paragraph (3)."

(D) effective, beginning with the 1974 crop, amending the third sentence of section 103 (e)(4)(A) of the Agricultural Act of 1949, as it appears in such section 602 to read as follows: "The Secretary is authorized for the 1974 through 1977 crops to limit the acreage planted to upland cotton on the farm in excess of the farm base acreage allotment to a percentage of the farm base acreage allotment.".

(E) the second sentence of section 103 (e)(4)(A) is amended to read as follows: "If a set-aside of cropland is in effect under this paragraph (4), then as a condition of eligibility for loans and payments on upland cotton the producers on a farm must set aside and devote to approved conservation uses an acreage of cropland equal to (i) such percentage of the farm base acreage allotment for the farm as may be specified by the Secretary (not to exceed 28 per centum of the farm base acreage allotment), plus, if required by the Secretary, (ii) the acreage of cropland on the farm devoted in preceding years to soil conserving uses, as determined by the Secretary."

(F) the fourth sentence of section 103 (e) (4) (A) of the Agricultural Act of 1949 as found in section 602 is amended to read as follows: "The Secretary shall permit producers to plant and graze on set-aside acreage sweet sorghum, and the Secretary may permit, subject to such terms and conditions as he may prescribe, all or any of the set-aside acreage to be devoted to hay and grazing or the production of guar, seasame, safflower, sunflower, castor beans, mustard seed, crambe, plantago ovato, flaxseed, triticale, oats, rye, or other commodity, if he determines that such production is needed to provide an adequate supply, is not likely to increase the cost of the price-support program, and will not adversely affect farm income."

(G) inserting after the second sentence of section 103(e)(5) of the Agricultural Act of 1949 as it appears in such section 602 the following: "The Secretary may in the case of programs for the 1974 through 1977 crops, pay an appropriate share of the cost of practices designed to carry out the purposes of the foregoing sentences."

Commodity Credit Corporation Sales Price Restrictions for Cotton

(21) Section 603 is amended by striking out "1974" and inserting "1978".

Miscellaneous Cotton Provisions

(22) Sections 604, 605, 606, 607, and 608 are each amended by striking out "1971, 1972, and 1973" and inserting "1971 through 1977".

Cotton Market Development

(23) Section 610 is amended by inserting after the words "shall be" in the second sentence the following words "10 million dollars." and by striking the balance of said sentence, and further by striking out "1972 and 1973" and inserting "1972 through 1977" in the third sentence.

Cotton Insect Eradication

(24) Title VI is amended by adding at the end thereof the following:

"SEC. 611. Section 104 of the Agricultural Act of 1949, as amended, is amended by adding a new subsection (d) as follows:

" '(d) In order to reduce cotton production costs, to prevent the movement of certain cotton plant insects to areas not now infested, and to enhance the quality of the environment, the Secretary is authorized and directed to carry out programs to destroy and eliminate cotton boll weevils in infested areas of the United States as provided herein and to carry out similar programs with respect to pink bollworms or any other major cotton insect if the Secretary determines that methods and systems have been developed to the point that success in eradication of such insects is assured. The Secretary shall carry out the eradication programs authorized by this subsection through the Commodity Credit Corporation. In carrying out insect eradication projects, the Secretary shall utilize the technical and related services of appropriate Federal, State, private agencies, and cotton organizations. Producers and landowners in an eradication zone, established by the Secretary, who are receiving benefits from any program administered by the United States Department of Agriculture, shall, as a condition of receiving or continuing any such benefits, participate in and cooperate with the eradication project, as specified in regulations of the Secretary.

" 'The Secretary may issue such regulations as he deems necessary to enforce the provisions of this subsection with respect to achieving the compliance of producers and landowners who are not receiving benefits from any program administered by the United States Department of Agriculture. Any person who knowingly violates any such regulation promulgated by the Secretary under this subsection may be assessed a civil penalty of not to exceed $5,000 for each offense. No civil penalty shall be assessed unless the person shall have been given notice and opportunity for a hearing on such charge in the county, parish, or incorporated city of the residence of the person charged. In determining the amount of the penalty the Secretary shall consider the appropriateness of such penalty to the size of the business of the person charged, the effect on the person's ability to continue in business, and the gravity of the violation. Where special measures deemed essential to achievement of the eradication objective are taken by the project and result in a loss of production and income to the producer, the Secretary shall provide reasonable and equitable indemnification from funds available for the project, and also provide for appropriate protection of the allotment, acreage history, and average yield for the farm. The cost of the program in each eradication zone shall be determined, and cotton producers in the zone shall be required to pay up to one-half thereof, with the exact share in each zone area to be specified by the Secretary upon his finding that such share is reasonable and equitable based on population levels of the target insect and the degree of control measures normally required. Each producer's pro rata share shall be deducted from his cotton payment under this Act or otherwise collected, as provided in regulations of the Secretary. Insofar as practicable, cotton producers and other persons engaged in cotton production in the eradication zone shall be employed to participate in the work of the project in such zone. Funding of the program shall be terminated at such time as the Secretary determines and reports to the Congress that complete eradication of the insects for which programs are undertaken pursuant to this subsection has been accomplished. Funds in custody of agencies carrying out the program shall, upon termination of such program, be accounted for to the Secretary for appropriate disposition.

" 'The Secretary is authorized to cooperate with the Government of Mexico in carrying out operations or measures in Mexico which he deems necessary and feasible to prevent the movement into the United States from Mexico of any insects eradicated under the provisions of this subsection. The measure and character of cooperation carried out under this subsection on the part of the United States and on the part of the Government of Mexico, including the expenditure or use of funds made available by the Secretary under this subsection, shall be such as may be prescribed by the Secretary. Arrangements for the cooperation authorized by this subsection shall be made through and in consultation with the Secretary of State. The Commodity Credit Corporation shall not make any expenditures for carrying out the purposes of this subsection unless the Corporation has received funds to cover such expenditures from appropriations made to carry out the purposes of this subsection. There are hereby authorized to be appropriated to the Commodity Credit Corporation such sums as the Congress may from time to time determine to be necessary to carry out the purposes of this subsection.'."

Skiprow Practices

(25) Title VI is further amended by adding the following new section:

"SEC. 612. Section 374(a) of the Agricultural Adjustment Act of 1938, as amended, is hereby amended by adding the following new sentence: 'Where cotton is planted in skiprow patterns, the same rules that were in effect for the 1971 through 1973 crops for classifying the acreage planted to cotton and the area skipped shall also apply to the 1974 through 1977 crops.'."

Public Law 480

(26) Section 701 is amended by striking out "1973" and inserting "1977"; and title VII is further amended by adding at the end thereof the following:

Section 103 of such Act is amended by inserting before the semicolon at the end of subsection (o) the following: "and that commercial supplies are available to meet demands developed through programs carried out under this Act."

"SEC. 704. Title IV of such Act is amended by adding at the end thereof the following:

" 'SEC. 411. No agricultural commodities shall be sold under title I or title III or donated under title II of this Act to North Vietnam, unless by an Act of Congress enacted subsequent to July 1, 1973, assistance to North Vietnam is specifically authorized.' "

Miscellaneous Provisions

(27) Title VIII is amended as follows:

Beekeeper Indemnities

(A) Section 804 is amended by striking out "December 31, 1973" and inserting "December 31, 1977".

(B) By adding at the end thereof the following:

FHA Loans

"Sec. 807. The first sentence of section 305 of the Consolidated Farm and Rural Development Act is amended by striking out '$100,000' and inserting '$225,000'; and by striking out 'or (b)' and inserting '(b) the loans under such sections to any one borrower to exceed $100,000, or (c)'.

"Cost of Production Study

"Sec. 808. The Secretary of Agriculture, in cooperation with the land grant colleges, commodity organizations, general farm organizations, and individual farmers, shall conduct a cost of production study of the wheat, feed grain, cotton, and dairy commodities under the various production practices and establish a current national weighted average cost of production. This study shall be updated annually and shall include all typical variable costs, a return on fixed costs equal to the existing interest rates charged by the Federal Land Bank, and return for management comparable to the normal management fees charged by other comparable industries. These studies shall be based upon the size unit that requires one man to farm on a full-time basis.

"Livestock Study

"Sec. 809. (a) The Secretary of Agriculture is authorized and directed to carry out a comprehensive study and investigation to determine the reasons for the extensive loss of livestock sustained each year, through injury and disease, while such livestock is being transported in interstate commerce for commercial purposes. The Secretary is also authorized and directed to conduct, in connection with such study and investigation, an intensive research program for the purpose of developing measures that can be taken to reduce materially the number of animals lost, through injury and disease during transportation for commercial purposes.

"(b) The Secretary of Agriculture shall submit to the Congress not more than four years after the date of enactment of this section a final report on the results of his study and investigation and research together with such recommendations for administrative and legislative action as he deems appropriate. He shall submit such interim reports to the Congress as he deems advisable, but at least one at the end of each twelve month period following the date of enactment of this section.

"(c) There is authorized to be appropriated such sums as may be necessary to carry out the provisions of this section, but not more than $500,000 in any fiscal year.

"Wheat and Feed Grains Research

"Sec. 810. In order to reduce fertilizer and herbicide usage in excess of production needs, to develop wheat and feed grain varieties more susceptible to complete fertilizer utilization, to improve the resistance of wheat and feed grain plants to disease and to enhance their conservation and environmental qualities, the Secretary of Agriculture is authorized and directed to carry out regional and national research programs.

"In carrying out such research, the Secretary shall utilize the technical and related services of the appropriate Federal, State, and private agencies.

"There is authorized to be appropriated such sums as may be necessary to carry out the provisions of this section, but not more than $1,000,000 in any fiscal year.

"Technical Support

"SEC. 811. The Department of Agriculture shall provide technical support to exporters and importers of United States agricultural products when so requested. Such support shall include, but not be limited to, a review of the feasibility of the export proposal, adequacy of sources of supply, compliance with trade regulations of the United States and the importing country and such other information or guidance as may be needed to expand and expedite United States agricultural exports by private trading interests.

"Export Sales Reporting

"SEC. 812. All exporters of wheat and wheat flour, feed grains, oil seeds, cotton and products thereof, and other commodities the Secretary may designate produced in the United States shall report to the Secretary of Agriculture, on a weekly basis, the following information regarding any contract for export sales entered into or subsequently modified in any manner during the reporting period: (a) type, class, and quantity of the commodity sought to be exported, (b) the marketing year of shipment, (c) destination, if known. Individual reports shall remain confidential but shall be compiled by the Secretary and published in compilation form each week following the week of reporting. All exporters of agricultural commodities produced in the United States shall upon request of the Secretary of Agriculture immediately report to the Secretary any information with respect to export sales of agricultural commodities and at such times as he may request. Any person (or corporation) who knowingly fails to report export sales pursuant to the requirements of this section shall be fined not more than $25,000 or imprisoned not more than one year, or both. The Secretary may, with respect to any commodity or type or class thereof during any period in which he determines that there is a domestic supply of such commodity substantially in excess of the quantity needed to meet domestic requirements, and that total supplies of such commodity in the exporting countries are estimated to be in surplus, and that anticipated exports will not result in excessive drain on domestic supplies; and that to require the reports to be made will unduly hamper export sales, provide for such reports by exporters and publishing of such data to be on a monthly basis rather than on a weekly basis."

"Disaster Reserve

"SEC. 813. (a) Notwithstanding any other provision of law, the Secretary of Agriculture shall under the provisions of this Act establish, maintain, and dispose of a separate reserve of inventories of not to exceed 75 million bushels of wheat, feed grains, and soybeans for the purpose of alleviating distress caused by a natural disaster.

"Such reserve inventories shall include such quantities of grain that the Secretary deems needed to provide for the alleviation of distress as the result of a natural disaster.

"(b) The Secretary shall acquire such commodities through the price support program.

"(c) Except when a state of emergency has been proclaimed by the President or by concurrent resolution of Congress declaring that such reserves should be disposed of, the Secretary shall not offer any commodity in the reserve for sale or disposition.

"(d) The Secretary is also authorized to dispose of such commodities only for (1) use in relieving distress (a) in any State, the District of Columbia, Puerto Rico, Guam, or the Virgin Islands and (b) in connection with any major disaster determined by the President to warrant assistance by the Federal Government under Public Law 875, Eighty-first Congress, as amended (42 U.S.C. 1855 et seq.), or (2) for use in connection with a state of civil defense emergency as proclaimed by the President or by concurrent resolution of the Congress in accordance with the provisions of the Federal Civil Defense Act of 1950, as amended (50 U.S.C. App. 2251–2297).

"(e) The Secretary may sell at an equivalent price, allowing for the customary location and grade price differentials, substantially equivalent quantities in different locations or warehouses to the extent needed to properly handle, rotate, distribute, and locate such reserve.

"(f) The Secretary may use the Commodity Credit Corporation to the extent feasible to fulfill the purposes of this section; and to the maximum extent practicable consistent with the fulfillment of the purposes of this section and the effective and efficient administration of this section shall utilize the usual and customary channels, facilities, and arrangements of trade and commerce.

"(g) The Secretary may issue such rules and regulations as may be necessary to carry out the provisions of this section.

"(h) There is hereby authorized to be appropriated such sums as may be necessary to carry out the purposes of this section.

"Imported Commodities

"SEC. 814. Notwithstanding any other provisions of this Act, the Secretary shall encourage the production of any crop of which the United States is a net importer and for which a price support program is not in effect by permitting the planting of such crop on set-aside acreage and with no reduction in the rate of payment for the commodity.

"Emergency Supply of Agricultural Products

"SEC. 815. (a) Notwithstanding any other provision of law, the Secretary of Agriculture shall assist farmers, processors, and distributors in obtaining such prices for agricultural products that an orderly, adequate and steady supply of such products will exist for the consumers of this nation.

"(b) The President shall make appropriate adjustments in the maximum price which may be charged under the provisions of Executive Order 11723 (dated June 13, 1973) or any subsequent Executive Order for any agricultural products (at any point in the distribution chain) as to which the Secretary of Agriculture certifies to the President that the supply of the product will be reduced to unacceptably low levels as a result of any price control or freeze order or regulation and that alternative means for increasing the supply are not available.

"(c) Under this section, the term 'agricultural products' shall include meat, poultry, vegetables, fruits and all other agricultural commodities in raw or processed form, except forestry products or fish or fishery products.

"(d) The Secretary of Agriculture is directed to implement policies under this Act which are designed to encourage American farmers to produce to their full capabilities during periods of short supply to assure American consumers with an adequate supply of food and fiber at fair and reasonable prices.

"Rural Development

"SEC. 816 (a) Section 401 of the Rural Development Act of 1972 (86 Stat. 670) is amended by substituting the words 'fire' and 'fires' for the words 'wildfire' and 'wildfires', respectively, wherever such words appear.

"(b) Section 404 of the Rural Development Act of 1972 (86 Stat. 671) is amended to read as follows:

"SEC. 404. APPROPRIATIONS. — There is authorized to be appropriated to carry out the provisions of this title $7,000,000 for each of three consecutive fiscal years beginning with the fiscal year for which funds are first appropriated and obligated by the Secretary of Agriculture carrying out this title.'

"(c) Section 306(a) of the Consolidated Farm and Rural Development Act is amended by adding at the end thereof the following:

" '(13) (A) The Secretary, under such reasonable rules and conditions as he shall establish, shall make grants to eligible volunteer fire departments for up to 50 per centum of the cost of firefighting equipment needed by such departments but which such departments are unable to purchase through the resources otherwise available to them, and for the cost of the training necessary to enable such departments to use such equipment efficiently.

" '(B) For the purposes of this subsection, the term "eligible volunteer fire department" means any established volunteer fire department in a rural town, village, or unincorporated area where the population is less than two thousand but greater than two hundred, as reasonably determined by the Secretary.'

"SEC. 817. Section 310B(d) of subtitle A of the Consolidated Farm and Rural Development Act is amended by adding at the end thereof the following:

" '(4) No grant or loan authorized to be made under this Act shall require or be subject to the prior approval of any officer, employee, or agency of any State.

" '(5) No loan commitment issued under this section, section 304, or section 312 shall be conditioned upon the applicant investing in excess of 10 per centum in the business or industrial enterprise for which purpose the loan is to be made unless the Secretary determines there are special circumstances which necessitate an equity investment by the applicant greater than 10 per centum.

" '(6) No provision of law shall prohibit issuance by the Secretary of certificates evidencing beneficial ownership in a block of notes insured or guaranteed under this Act or Title V of the Housing Act of 1949; any sale by the Secretary of such certificates shall be treated as a sale of assets for the purposes of the Budget and Accounting Act of 1921. Any security representing beneficial ownership in a block of notes guaranteed or insured under this Act or Title V of the Housing Act of 1949 issued by a private entity shall be exempt from laws administered by the Securities and Exchange Commission, except sections 17, 22, and 24 of the Securities Act of 1933, as amended; however, the Secretary shall require (i) that the issuer place such notes in the custody of an institution chartered by a Federal or State agency to act as trustee and (ii) that the issuer provide such periodic reports of sales as the Secretary deems necessary.'

"Agricultural Census

"SEC. 818. Notwithstanding any other provision of law, the Secretary of Commerce shall conduct a census of agriculture in 1974 as required by section 142 of title 13, United States Code, and shall submit to the Congress, within thirty days after the date of enactment of the Agriculture and Consumer Protection Act of 1973, an estimate of the funds needed to conduct such census."

(28) By adding at the end thereof the following new title X:

"Title X — Rural Environmental Conservation Program

"SEC. 1001. Notwithstanding any other provision of law the Secretary shall carry out the purposes specified in clauses (1), (2), (3), (4), and (6) of section 7(a) of the Soil Conservation and Domestic Allotment Act, as amended, section 16(b) of such Act, and in the Water Bank Act (16 U.S.C. 1301 et seq.) by entering into contracts of three, five, ten, or twenty-five years with, and at the option of, eligible owners and operators of land as determined by the Secretary and having such control as the Secretary determines to be needed on the farms, ranches, wetlands, forests, or other lands covered thereby. In addition, the Secretary is hereby authorized to purchase perpetual easements to promote said purposes of this Title, including the sound use and management of flood plains, shore lands, and aquatic areas of the Nation. Such contracts shall be designed to assist farm, ranch, wetland, and nonindustrial private forest owners and operators, or other owners or operators, to make, in orderly progression over a period of years, such changes, if any, as are needed to effectuate any of the purposes specified in clauses (1), (2), (3), (4), and (6) of section 7(a) of the Soil Conservation and Domestic Allotment Act, as amended; section 16(b) of such Act; the Water Bank Act (16 U.S.C. 1301 et seq.); in enlarging fish and wildlife and recreation sources; in improving the level of management of nonindustrial private forest lands; and in providing long-term wildlife and upland game cover. In carrying out the provisions of this title, due regard shall be given to the maintenance of a continuing and stable supply of agricultural commodities and forest products adequate to meet consumer demand at prices fair to both producers and consumers.

"(1) to effectuate the plan for his farm, ranch, forest, wetland, or other land substantially in accordance with the schedule outlined therein;

"(2) to forfeit all rights to further payments or grants under the contract and refund to the United States all payments or grants received thereunder upon his violation of the contract at any stage during the time he has control of the land if the Secretary, after considering the recommendations of the Soil and Water Conservation District Board, or the State forester or other appropriate official in a contract entered into under the provisions of section 1009 of this title, determines that such violation is of such a nature as to warrant termination of the contract, or to make refunds or accept such payment adjustments as the Secretary may deem appropriate if he determines that the violation by the owner or operator does not warrant termination of the contract;

"(3) upon transfer of his right and interest in the farm, ranch, forest, wetland, or other land during the contract period to forfeit all rights to further payments or grants under the contract and refund to the United States all payments or grants received thereunder unless the transferee of any such land agrees with the Secretary to assume all obligations of the contract;

"(4) not to adopt any practice specified by the Secretary in the contract as a practice which would tend to defeat the purposes of the contract;

"SEC. 1002. Eligible landowners and operators for contracts under this title shall furnish to the Secretary a plan of farming operations or land use which incorporates such practices and principles as may be determined by him to be practicable and which outlines a schedule of proposed changes, if any, in cropping systems or land use and of the conservation measures which are to be carried out on the farm, ranch, wetland, forests, or other land during the contract period to protect the farm, ranch, wetland, forests or other land and surrounding areas, its wildlife, and nearby populace and communities from erosion, deterioration, pollution by natural and manmade causes or to insure an adequate supply of timber and related forest products. Said plans may also, in important migratory waterfowl nesting and breeding areas which are identified in a conservation plan developed in cooperation with a soil and water conservation district in which the lands are located, and under such rules and regulations as the Secretary may provide, include a schedule of proposed changes, if any, to conserve surface waters and preserve and improve habitat for migratory waterfowl and other wildlife resources and improve subsurface moisture, including, subject to the provisions of section 1001 of this title, the reduction of areas of new land coming into production, the enhancement of the natural beauty of the landscape, and the promotion of comprehensive and total water management study.

"SEC. 1003. (a) Approved conservation plans of eligible landowners and operators developed in cooperation with the soil and water conservation district or the State forester or other appropriate State official in which their lands are situated shall from a basis for contracts under this title. Under the contract the landowner or operator shall agree —

"(5) to comply with all applicable Federal, State, or local laws, and regulations, including those governing environmental protection and noxious weed abatement; and

"(6) to such additional provisions as the Secretary determines are desirable and includes in the contract to effectuate the purposes of the program or to facilitate the practical administration of the program: *Provided,* That all contracts entered into to effectuate the purposes of the Water Bank Act for wetlands shall contain the further agreement of the owner or operator that he shall not drain, burn, fill, or otherwise destroy the wetland character of such areas, nor use such areas for agricultural purposes: *And provided further,* That contracts entered into for the protection of wetlands to effectuate the purposes of the Water Bank Act may include wetlands covered by Federal or State government easement which permits agricultural use, together with such adjacent areas as determined desirable by the Secretary.

"(b) In return for such agreement by the landowner or operator the Secretary shall agree to make payments in appropriate circumstances for the use of land maintained for conservation purposes as set forth in this title, and share the cost of carrying out those conservation practices and measures set forth in the contract for which he determines that cost-sharing is appropriate and in the public interest. The portion of such cost (including labor) to be shared shall be that part which the Secretary determines is necessary and appropriate to effectuate the physical installation of the conservation practices and measures under the contract, but, in the case of a contract not entered into under an advertising and bid procedure under the provisions of section 1009(d) of this title, not less than 50 per centum or more than 75 per centum of the actual costs incurred by the owner or operator.

"(c) The Secretary may terminate any contract with a landowner or operator by mutual agreement with the owner or operator if the Secretary determines that such termination would be in the public interest, and may agree to such modification of contracts previously entered into as he may determine to be desirable to carry out the purposes of the program or facilitate the practical administration thereof or to accomplish equitable treatment with respect to other similiar conservation, land use, or commodity programs administered by the Secretary.

"SEC. 1004. The Secretary is authorized to make available to eligible owners and operators conservation materials including seeds, seed inoculants, soil conditioning materials, trees, plants, and, if he determines it is appropriate to the purposes of this title, fertilizer and liming materials.

"SEC. 1005. (a) Notwithstanding the provisions of any other title, the Secretary may establish multiyear set-aside contracts for a period not to extend beyond the 1977 crop. Such contracts may be entered into only as a part of the programs in effect for wheat, feed grains, and cotton for the years 1974 through 1978, and only producers participating in one or more of such programs shall be eligible to contract with the Secretary under this section. Producers agreeing to a multiyear set-aside agreement shall be required to devote this acreage to vegetative cover capable of maintaining itself throughout such period to provide soil protection, water quality enhancement, wildlife production, and natural beauty. Grazing of livestock under this section shall be prohibited. Producers entering into agreements under this section shall also agree to comply with all applicable State and local law and regulation governing noxious weed control.

"(b) The Secretary shall provide cost-sharing incentives to farm operators for such cover establishment, whenever a multiyear contract is entered into on all or a portion of the set-aside acreage.

"SEC. 1006. The Secretary shall issue such regulations as he determines necessary to carry out the provisions of this title. The total acreage placed under agreements which result in their retirement from production in any county or local community shall in addition to the limitations elsewhere in this title be limited to a percentage of the total eligible acreage in such county or local community which the Secretary determines would not adversely affect the economy of the county or local community. In determining such percentage the Secretary shall give appropriate consideration to the productivity of the acreage being retired, if any, as compared to the average productivity of eligible acreage in such county or local community which the Secretary determines would not adversely affect the economy of the county or local community.

"SEC. 1007. (a) The Secretary of Agriculture shall appoint an advisory board in each State to advise the State committee of that State (established under section 8(b) of the Soil Conservation and Domestic Allotment Act) regarding the types of conservation measures that should be approved to effectuate the purposes of this title. The Secretary shall appoint at least six individuals to the advisory board of each State who are especially qualified by reason of education, training, and experience in the fields of agriculture, soil, water, wildlife, fish, and forest management. The advisory board appointed for any State shall meet at least once each calendar year. Said appointed members shall include, but not be limited to, the State soil conservationist, the State forester, the State administrator of the water quality programs, and the State wildlife administrator or their designees: *Provided,* That such board shall limit its advice to the State committees to the types of conservation measures that should be approved affecting the water bank program; the authorization to purchase perpetual easements to promote the purposes of this title, as described in section 1001 of this title; the providing of long-term upland game cover; and the establishment and management of approved practices on multiyear set-aside contracts as provided in section 1005 of this title:

"(b) The Secretary of Agriculture, through the establishment of a national advisory board to be named in consultation with the Secretary of the Interior, shall seek the advice and assistance of the appropriate officials of the several States in developing the programs under this title, especially in developing guidelines for (1) providing technical assistance for wildlife habitat improvement practices, (2) evaluating effects on surrounding areas, (3) considering aesthetic values, (4) checking compliance by cooperators, and (5) carrying out programs of wildlife management authorized under this title: *Provided,* That such board shall limit its advice to subjects which cover the types of conservation measures that should be approved regarding the water bank program; the authorization to purchase perpetual easements to promote the purposes of this Act, as described in section 1001 of this title; the providing of long-term upland game cover; and the establishment and management of approved practices on multiyear set-aside contracts as provided in section 1005 of this title.

"SEC. 1008. In carrying out the programs authorized under sections 1001 through 1006 of this title, the Secretary shall, in addition to appropriate coordination with other interested Federal, State, and local agencies, utilize the services of local, county, and State committees established under section 8 of the Soil Conservation and Domestic Allotment Act, as amended. The Secretary is also authorized to utilize the facilities and services of the Commodity Credit Corporation in discharging his functions and responsibilities under this program. The Secretary shall also utilize the technical services of the Soil Conservation Service, the Forest Service, State forestry organizations, soil and water conservation districts, and other State, and Federal agencies, as appropriate, in development and installation of approved conservation plans under this title.

"SEC. 1009. (a) In furtherance of the purposes of this title, the Secretary of Agriculture is authorized and directed to develop and carry out a forestry incentives program to encourage the development, management, and protection of nonindustrial private forest lands. The purposes of such a program shall be to encourage landowners to apply practices which will provide for the afforestation of suitable open lands and reforestation of cutover and other nonstocked and understocked forest lands and intensive multiple-purpose management and protection of forest resources so as to provide for production of timber and related benefits.

"(b) For the purposes of this section, the term 'non-industrial private forest lands' means lands capable of producing crops of industrial wood and owned by any private individual, group, association, corporation, or other legal entity. Such term does not include private entities which regularly engage in the business of manufacturing forest products or providing public utilities services of any type, or the subsidiaries of such entities.

"(c) The Secretary shall consult with the State forester or other appropriate official of the respective States in the conduct of the forestry incentives program under this section, and Federal assistance shall be extended in accordance with section 1003(b) of this title. The Secretary shall for the purposes of this section distribute funds available for cost sharing among and within the States only after assessing the public benefit incident thereto, and after giving appropriate consideration to the number and acreage of commercial forest lands, number of eligible ownerships in the State, and counties to be served by such cost sharing; the potential productivity of such lands; and the need for reforestation, timber stand improvement, or other forestry investments on such land. No forest incentives contract shall be approved under this section on a tract greater than five hundred acres, unless the Secretary finds that significant public benefit will be incident to such approval.

"(d) The Secretary may, if he determines that such action will contribute to the effective and equitable administration of the program established by this section, use an advertising and bid procedure in determining the lands in any area to be covered by agreements.

"(e) In implementing the program under this section, the Secretary will cause it to be coordinated with other related programs in such a manner as to encourage the utilization of private agencies, firms, and individuals furnishing services and materials needed in the application of practices included in the forestry incentives improvement program. The Secretary shall periodically report to the appropriate congressional committees of the progress and conduct of the program established under this section.

"SEC. 1010. There are hereby authorized to be appropriated annually such sums as may be necessary to carry out the provisions of this title. The programs, contracts, and authority authorized under this title shall be in addition to, and not in substitution for, other programs in such areas authorized by this or any other title or Act, and shall not expire with the termination of any other title or Act: *Provided,* That not more than $25,000,000 annually shall be authorized to be appropriated for the programs authorized under section 1009 of this Act."

Advisory Committee Repeal

SEC. 2. Section 301 of the Act of August 14, 1946 (Public Law 79–733) as amended (7 U.S.C. 1628), is hereby repealed.

Food Stamps

SEC. 3. The Food Stamp Act of 1964, as amended, is amended as follows:

(a) The second sentence of section 3(e) of the Food Stamp Act of 1964 (7 U.S.C. 2012(e)) is amended —

(1) by striking out "or"; and

(2) by inserting before the period at the end thereof the following: ", or (3) any narcotics addict or alcoholic who lives under the supervision of a private nonprofit organization or institution for the purpose of regular participation in a drug or alcoholic treatment and rehabilitation program."

(b) Section 3(e) of the Food Stamp Act of 1964 is amended by striking out the last sentence therein and inserting in lieu thereof the following sentence: "No individual who receives supplemental security income benefits under title XVI of the Social Security Act shall be considered to be a member of a household or an elderly person for any purpose of this Act for any month if such person receives for such month, as part of his supplemental security income benefits or payments described in section 1616(a) of the Social Security Act (if any), an amount equal to the bonus value of food stamps (according to the Food Stamp Schedule effective for July 1973) in addition to the amount of assistance such individual would be entitled to receive for such month under the provisions of the plan of the State approved under title I, X, XIV, or XVI, as appropriate, in effect for December 1973, assuming such plan were in effect for such month and such individual were aged, blind, or disabled, as the case may be, under the provisions of such State plan or under Public Law 92–603 as amended. The Secretary of Health, Education, and Welfare shall issue regulations for the implementation of the foregoing sentence after consultation with the Secretary of Agriculture."

(c) Section 3 of the Food Stamp Act of 1964 (7 U.S.C. 2012) is amended by adding at the end thereof the following new subsection:

"(n) The term 'drug addiction or alcoholic treatment and rehabilitation program' means any drug addiction or alcoholic treatment and rehabilitation program conducted by a private nonprofit organization or institution which is certified by the State agency or agencies designated by the Governor as responsible for the administration of the State's programs for alcoholics and drug addicts pursuant to Public Law 91–616 'Comprehensive Alcohol Abuse and Alcohol Prevention, Treatment, and Rehabilitation Act' and Public Law 92–255 'Drug Abuse Office and Treatment Act of 1972' as providing treatment that can lead to the rehabilitation of drug addicts or alcoholics."

(d) Section 5 of the Food Stamp Act of 1964 (7 U.S.C. 2014) is amended by adding at the end thereof the following new subsection:

"(d) The Secretary shall establish uniform national standards of eligibility for households described in section 3(e)(3) of this Act."

(e) Section 5(c) of the Food Stamp Act of 1964 (7 U.S.C. 2014(c)) is amended by adding at the end thereof the following: "For the purposes of this section, the term 'able-bodied adult person' shall not include any narcotics addict or alcoholic who regularly participates, as a resident or nonresident, in any drug addiction or alcoholic treatment and rehabilitation program."

(f) Section 10 of the Food Stamp Act of 1964 (7 U.S.C. 2019) is amended by inserting at the end thereof the following new subsection:

"(i) Subject to such terms and conditions as may be prescribed by the Secretary in the regulations pursuant to this Act, members of an eligible household who are narcotics addicts or alcoholics and regularly participate in a drug addiction or alcoholic treatment and rehabilitation program may use coupons issued to them to purchase food prepared for or served to them during the course of such program by a private nonprofit organization or institution which meets requirements (1), (2), and (3) of subsection (h) above. Meals served pursuant to this subsection shall be deemed 'food' for the purposes of this Act."

(g) Section 5(b) is amended by inserting the following before the period at the end of the second sentence: ": *Provided*, That such standards shall take into account payments in kind received from an employer by members of a household, if such payments are in lieu of or supplemental to household income: *Provided further*, That such payments in kind shall be limited only to housing provided by such employer to such employee and shall be the actual value of such housing but in no event shall such value be considered to be in excess of the sum of $25.00 per month".

(h) The fourth sentence of section 5(b) is amended to read as follows:

"The Secretary may also establish temporary emergency standards of eligibility for the duration of the emergency, without regard to income and other financial resources, for households that are the victims of a mechanical disaster which disrupts the distribution of coupons, and for households that are victims of a disaster which disrupted commercial channels of food distribution when he determines that such households are in need of temporary food assistance, and that commercial channels of food distribution have again become available to meet the temporary food needs of such households: *Provided*, That the Secretary shall in the case of Puerto Rico, Guam, and the Virgin Islands, establish special standards of eligibility and coupon allotment schedules which reflect the average per capita income and cost of obtaining a nutritionally adequate diet in Puerto Rico and the respective territories; except that in no event shall the standards of eligibility or coupon allotment schedules so used exceed those in the fifty States."

(i) Section 10(e) is amended by striking out "and (6)" and inserting in lieu thereof the following: "(6) issuance of coupon allotments no less often than two times per month; (7) notwithstanding any other provision of law, the institution of procedures under which any household participating in the program shall be entitled, if it so elects, to have the charges, if any, for its coupon allotment deducted from any grant or payment such household may be entitled to receive under title IV of the Social Security Act and have its coupon allotment distributed to it with such grant or payment; and (8)''; and (2) by adding at the end thereof the following: ''The State agency is required to submit, prior to January 1, 1974, for approval, a plan of operation specifying the manner in which such State agency intends to conduct the program in every political subdivision in the State, unless such State agency can demonstrate that for any political subdivision it is impossible or impracticable to extend the program to such subdivision. The Secretary shall make a determination of approval or disapproval of a plan of operation submitted by a State agency in sufficient time to permit institution of such plan by no later than June 30, 1974.''

(j) Section 16(a) is amended by striking out in the first sentence ''June 30, 1972, and June 30, 1973'' and substituting ''June 30, 1972, through June 30, 1977'', and by inserting at the end of the first sentence of subsection (a) the following new sentence: ''Sums appropriated under the provisions of this Act shall, notwithstanding the provisions of any other law, continue to remain available until expended.''

(k) Section 10(h) is amended by adding at the end thereof the following: ''Subject to such terms and conditions as may be prescribed by the Secretary, in the regulations issued pursuant to this Act, members of an eligible household who are sixty years of age or over or elderly persons and their spouses may also use coupons issued to them to purchase meals prepared by senior citizens' centers, apartment buildings occupied primarily by elderly persons, any public or nonprofit private school which prepares meals especially for elderly persons, any public or nonprofit private eating establishment which prepares meals especially for elderly persons during special hours, and any other public or nonprofit private establishment approved for such purpose by the Secretary. When an appropriate State or local agency contracts with a private establishment to offer, at concessional prices, meals prepared especially for elderly persons during regular or special hours, the Secretary shall permit eligible households who are sixty years of age or over or elderly persons and their spouses to use coupons issued to them to purchase such meals.''

(1) Section 3(b) of the Food Stamp Act of 1964 (7 U.S.C. 2012(b)) is amended to read as follows: ''The term 'food' means any food or food product for home consumption except alcoholic beverages and tobacco and shall also include seeds and plants for use in gardens to produce food for the personal consumption of the eligible household.''

(m) Section 7(a) of the Food Stamp Act of 1964 (7 U.S.C. 2016(a)) is amended to read as follows:

''(a) The face value of the coupon allotment which State agencies shall be authorized to issue to any households certified as eligible to participate in the food stamp program shall be in such amount as the Secretary determines to be the cost of a nutritionally adequate diet, adjusted semiannually by the nearest dollar increment that is a multiple of two to reflect changes in the prices of food published by the Bureau of Labor Statistics in the Department of Labor to be implemented commencing with the allotments of January 1, 1974, incorporating the changes in the prices of food through August 31, 1973, but in no event shall such adjustments be made for value of the coupon allotment for such households, as calculated above, is a minimum of $2.00.''

(n) The following new section is added at the end of such Act:

"SEC. 17. Notwithstanding any other provision of this Act, members of eligible households living in the State of Alaska shall be permitted in accordance with such rules and regulations as the Secretary may prescribe, to purchase hunting and fishing equipment for the purpose of procuring food for the household except firearms, ammunition, and other explosives, with coupons issued under this Act if the Secretary determines that (1) such households are located in an area of the State which makes it extremely difficult for members of such households to reach retail food stores, and (2) such households depend to a substantial extent on hunting and fishing for subsistence purposes."

(o) Section 3(f) of the Food Stamp Act of 1964 (7 U.S.C. 2012(f)) is amended by striking the second sentence and inserting in lieu thereof the following new sentence: "It shall also mean a political subdivision or a private nonprofit organization or institution that meets the requirements of section 10(h) or 10(i) of this Act."

(p) Section 3(e) is amended by adding at the end thereof the following new sentence: "Residents of federally subsidized housing for the elderly, built under either section 202 of the Housing Act of 1959 (12 U.S.C. 1701q), or section 236 of the National Housing Act (12 U.S.C. 1715z–1) shall not be considered residents of an institution or boarding house for purposes of eligibility for food stamps under this Act."

Commodity Distribution Program

SEC. 4. (a) Notwithstanding any other provision of law, the Secretary of Agriculture is hereby authorized until July 1, 1974 (1) to use funds available to carry out the provisions of section 32 of Public Law No. 320, Seventy-fourth Congress, as amended (7 U.S.C. 612c), and not expended or needed for such purpose to purchase, without regard to the provisions of existing law governing the expenditure of public funds, agricultural commodities and their products of the types customarily purchased under section 32 for donation to maintain the annually programmed level of assistance for schools, domestic relief distribution, and such other domestic food assistance programs as are authorized by law, and (2) if stocks of the Commodity Credit Corporation are not available, to use the funds of the Corporation to purchase agricultural commodities and the products thereof of the types customarily available under section 416 of the Agricultural Act of 1949 to meet such requirements.

(b) The Secretary is prohibited from furnishing commodities to summer camps as authorized under section 416 of the Agricultural Act of 1949, section 32 of Public Law 74–320, and section 709 of the Food and Agriculture Act of 1965 if the number of adults participating in the activities of such camp is in excess of one for each five children under 18 years of age participating in such activities.

(c) No individual who receives supplemental security income benefits under title XVI of the Social Security Act shall be considered to be a member of a household for any purpose of the Food Distribution Program for families under section 32 of Public Law 74–320, section 416 of the Agricultural Act of 1949, or other law for any month if such person receives for such month, as part of his supplemental security income benefits or payments described in section 1616(a) of the Social Security Act (if any), an amount equal to the bonus value of food stamps (according to the Food Stamp Schedule effective for July 1973) in addition to the amount of assistance such individual would be entitled to receive for such month under the provisions of the plan of the State approved under title I, X, XIV, or XVI, as appropriate, in effect for December 1973, assuming such plan were in effect for such month and such individual were aged, blind, or disabled, as the case may be, under the provisions of such State plan or under Public Law 92–603 as amended. The Secretary of Health, Education, and Welfare shall issue regulations for the implementation of the foregoing sentence after consultation with the Secretary of Agriculture.

Short Title

SEC. 5. This Act may be cited as the ''Agriculture and Consumer Protection Act of 1973''.

Approved August 10, 1973.

World War II

Price Guarantees for Increased Production

From 55 Statutes at Large 498.

Be it enacted by the Senate and House of Representatives of the United States of America in Congress assembled, That section 7 of the Act approved January 31, 1935 (49 Stat. 4), as amended, is hereby amended by deleting from the first sentence thereof the term "June 30, 1941" and inserting in lieu thereof the term "June 30, 1943".

SEC. 2. Section 1 of the Act approved March 8, 1938 (52 Stat. 107), as amended, is hereby amended by deleting from the second sentence thereof the term "on the basis of market prices at the time of appraisal" and inserting in lieu thereof the term "on the basis of the cost, including not more than one year of carrying charges, of such assets to the Corporation, or the average market prices of such assets for a period of twelve months ending with March 31 of each year, whichever is less;".

SEC. 3. Section 4 of the Act approved March 8, 1938 (52 Stat. 108), as amended, is hereby amended by deleting the term "$1,400,000,000" and inserting in lieu thereof the term "$2,650,000,000".

SEC. 4. (a) Whenever during the existing emergency the Secretary of Agriculture finds it necessary to encourage the expansion of production of any non-basic agricultural commodity, he shall make public announcement thereof and he shall so use the funds made available under section 3 of this Act or otherwise made available to him for the disposal of agricultural commodities, through a commodity loan, purchase, or other operation, taking into account the total funds available for such purpose for all commodities, so as to support a price for the producers of any such commodity with respect to which such announcement was made of not less than 85 per centum of the parity or comparable price therefor. The comparable price for any such commodity shall be determined and used by the Secretary for the purposes of this section if the production or consumption of such commodity has so changed in extent or character since the base period as to result in a price out of line with parity prices for basic commodities. Any such commodity loan, purchase, or other operation which is undertaken shall be continued until the Secretary has given sufficient public announcement to permit the producers of such commodity to make a readjustment in the production of the commodity. For the purposes of this section, commodities other than cotton, corn, wheat, tobacco, and rice shall be deemed to be nonbasic commodities.

(b) It is hereby declared to be the policy of the Congress that the lending and purchase operations of the Department of Agriculture (other than those referred to in subsection (a) shall be carried out so as to bring the price and income of the producers of non-basic commodities not covered by any such public announcement to a fair parity relationship with other commodities, to the extent that funds for such operations are available after taking into account the operations with respect to the basic commodities and the commodities listed in any such public announcement and the ability of producers to bring supplies into line with demand.

Approved, July 1, 1941.

Establishing a War Food Program

From Executive Order 9280, Dec. 5, 1942.

DELEGATING AUTHORITY WITH RESPECT TO THE NATION'S FOOD PROGRAM

By virtue of the authority vested in me by the Constitution and the statutes of the United States, as President of the United States and Commander in Chief of the Army and Navy, and in order to assure an adequate supply and efficient distribution of food to meet war and essential civilian needs, it is hereby ordered as follows:

1. The Secretary of Agriculture (hereinafter referred to as the "Secretary") is authorized and directed to assume full responsibility for and control over the Nation's food program. In exercising such authority, he shall:

a. Ascertain and determine the direct and indirect military, other governmental, civilian, and foreign requirements for food, both for human and animal consumption and for industrial uses.

b. Formulate and carry out a program designed to furnish a supply of food adequate to meet such requirements, including the allocation of the agricultural productive resources of the Nation for this purpose.

c. Assign food priorities and make allocations of food for human and animal consumption to governmental agencies and for private account, for direct and indirect military, other governmental, civilian, and foreign needs.

d. Take all appropriate steps to insure the efficient and proper distribution of the available supply of food.

e. Purchase and procure food for such Federal agencies, and to such extent, as he shall determine necessary or desirable, and promulgate policies to govern the purchase and procurement of food by all other Federal agencies: *Provided,* That nothing in this subsection shall limit the authority of the armed forces to purchase or procure food outside the United States or in any theater of war as such purchase and procurement shall be required by military or naval operations, or the authority of any other authorized agency to purchase or procure food outside the United States for rehabilitation or relief purposes abroad. Existing methods for the purchase and procurement of food by other Federal agencies shall continue until otherwise determined by the Secretary pursuant to this Executive Order.

2. The Secretary shall recommend to the Chairman of the War Production Board the amounts and types of non-food materials, supplies, and equipment necessary for carrying out the food program. Following consideration of these recommendations, the Chairman of the War Production Board shall allocate stated amounts of non-food materials, supplies, and equipment to the Secretary for carrying out the food program; and the War Production Board, through its priorities and allocation powers, shall direct the use of such materials, supplies, and equipment for such specific purposes as the Secretary may determine.

3. Whenever the available supply of any food is insufficient to meet both food and industrial needs, the Chairman of the War Production Board and the Secretary shall jointly determine the division to be made of the available supply of such food. In the event of any difference of view between the Chairman of the War Production Board and the Secretary, such difference shall be submitted for final determination to the President or to such agent or agency as the President may designate.

4. The Secretary, after determining the need and the amount of food available for civilian rationing, shall, through the Office of Price Administration, exercise the priorities and allocation powers conferred upon him by this Executive Order for civilian rationing, with respect to (a) the sale, transfer, or other disposition of food by any person who sells at retail to any person, and (b) the sale, transfer, or other disposition of food by any person to an ultimate consumer, as is currently provided for in War Production Board Directive No. 1, dated January 24, 1942, and existing supplements thereto; and with respect to (c) the sale, transfer, or other disposition of food by any person at such other levels of distribution as he may determine; and in the administration or enforcement of any such priorities or allocation authority for civilian rationing, the Office of Price Administration, subject to the provisions of this Executive Order, is hereby authorized to exercise all the functions, duties, powers, authority, or discretion conferred upon the Price Administrator by Section 3 of Executive Order 9125 of April 7, 1942. The Secretary, before determining the time, extent, and other conditions of civilian rationing, shall consult with the Price Administrator.

5. In discharging his responsibility under this Executive Order with respect to the exportation of food, the Secretary shall collaborate with the other agencies concerned with the foreign aspects of the food program in the determination of plans, policies and procedures for the feeding of the peoples in foreign countries and

the production and stockpiling of food for use abroad. With respect to the issuance of the directives for the importation of food heretofore issued to the Board of Economic Warfare by the Chairman of the War Production Board under Executive Order No. 9128 of April 13, 1942, the Secretary shall issue those directives which relate to the importation of food for human and animal consumption, and the Chairman of the War Production Board and the Secretary shall jointly issue those directives which relate to the importation of food for industrial uses. The Chairman of the War Production Board shall continue to issue all other directives which relate to the importation of materials, supplies, and equipment required for the war production program and the civilian economy. Schedules of priorities heretofore prepared and issued by the Chairman of the War Production Board under Executive Order 9054 of February 7, 1942 for the importation by overseas transportation of food for human or animal consumption and for industrial uses shall be similarly issued, and transmitted to the Administrator of War Shipping Administration for his guidance.

6. In discharging his responsibility under this Executive Order, the Secretary shall, in the event of a shortage of domestic transportation service, and after consultation with the War Production Board for the purpose of adjusting the relative demands for the movement of food for human or animal consumption and the movement of commodities for other purposes, prepare schedules of priorities for the domestic movement of food, which the Office of Defense Transportation shall take into consideration in determining traffic movements.

7. (a) To advise and consult with him in carrying out the provisions of this Executive Order, the Secretary shall appoint a committee composed of representatives of the State, War, and Navy Departments, the Office of Lend-Lease Administration, the Board of Economic Warfare, the War Production Board, and such other agencies as the Secretary may determine to be concerned with the food program. The Food Requirements Committee of the War Production Board established by the Chairman of the War Production Board by memorandum dated June 4, 1942 is abolished effective as of the date of appointment of said advisory committee. The Secretary shall receive from the members of such advisory committee estimates of food requirements, and consult with such committee prior to the making of food allocations under Section 1 (c) of this Executive Order. Such committee shall perform such other functions in connection with the food program as the Secretary may determine. The Secretary may, in his discretion, appoint such other advisory committees composed of representatives of governmental or private groups interested in the food program as he deems appropriate.

b. Section 1 of the Executive Order No. 9024, dated January 16, 1942, is amended to provide that the Secretary shall be a member of the War Production Board.

8. The Secretary, in carrying out the responsibilities imposed on him by this Executive Order, may, subject to the provisions of this Executive Order, exercise the following powers in addition to the powers heretofore vested in him.

a. The power conferred upon the Department of Agriculture with respect to contracts by Executive Order No. 9023 of January 14, 1942.

b. The power conferred upon the President by Title III of the Second War Powers Act, 1942, insofar as it relates to priorities and allocations of (1) all food for human or animal consumption or for other use in connection with the food program, but excluding that food which has been determined to be available to the War Production Board for industrial purposes pursuant to Section 3 of this Executive Order; (2) those portions of non-food materials, supplies, and equipment which have been allocated by the War Production Board under Section 2 of this Order for carrying out the food program; (3) any other material or facility, when the Secretary determines that it is necessary, in order to carry out the provisions of this Executive Order, to exercise the priorities or allocation power with respect thereto: *Provided,* That in order to avoid overlapping and conflicting action, prior to taking action pursuant to item (3) hereof, the Secretary shall inform the Chairman of the War Production Board of the action proposed to be taken, and in the event that the Chairman of the War Production Board shall object, the issue shall be determined by the President or such agent or agency as he may designate. Contracts or orders, relating to the materials and facilities specified in this sub-section, made by the Secretary, or by any other officer or agency of the Government at the Secretary's direction, and subcontracts and suborders which the Secretary shall deem necessary or appropriate to the fulfilment of any such contract or order, are hereby declared to be necessary and appropriate to promote the defense of the United States. The Secretary may assign priorities with respect to deliveries under any such contract, order, subcontract or suborder, and he may require acceptance of and performance of any such contract, order, subcontract or suborder, in preference to other contracts or orders for the purpose of assuring such priority. Allocations of materials and facilities under this sub-section may be made by the Secretary in such manner, upon such conditions, and to such extent as he shall seem necessary or appropriate in the public interest, to promote the national defense, and to carry out the provisions of this Executive Order.

c. The powers under the Act of October 10, 1940 (54 Stat. 1090), as amended by the Act of July 2, 1942 (56 Stat. 467), and the Act of October 16, 1941 (55 Stat. 742), as amended by Title VI of the Second War Powers Act, 1942, heretofore vested in the War Production Board by Executive Order No. 8942, of November 19, 1941, Executive Order No. 9024 of January 16, 1942, and Executive Order No. 9040 of January 24, 1942, with respect to the requisitioning of food for human or animal consumption.

d. The powers of acquisition of property under the Act of July 2, 1917 (40 Stat. 241), as amended by Title II of the Second War Powers Act, 1942.

e. The powers of taking over and operating facilities under Section 120 of the National Defense Act of 1916 (39 Stat. 213) and Section 9 of the Selective Training and Service Act of 1940 (54 Stat. 892).

f. The powers with respect to anti-trust prosecutions vested in the Chairman of the War Production Board by Section 12 of the Act of June 11, 1942, Public Law 603, 77th Congress.

g. The power of inspection and audit of the war contractors (including the power of subpoena) under Title XIII of the Second War Powers Act, 1942.

9. The Secretary is authorized to delegate any or all functions, responsibilities, powers (including the power of subpoena, authorities, or discretions conferred upon him by this Executive Order to such person or persons within the Department of Agriculture as he may designate or appoint for that purpose. The

Secretary may, except as otherwise provided herein, delegate to any appropriate Federal, state, or local governmental agency, officer, or employee, in such manner and for such periods of time as he shall deem advisable, the execution of any of the provisions of this Executive Order together with any powers of the Secretary under this Executive Order. To the fullest extent compatible with efficiency the Secretary shall utilize existing facilities and services of other governmental departments and agencies and may accept the services and facilities of any state or local governmental agency in carrying out his responsibilities defined hereunder.

10. As used herein, the term "food" shall mean all commodites and products, simple, mixed, or compound, or complements to such commodities or products that are or may be eaten or drunk by either humans or animals, irrespective of other uses to which such commodities or products may be put, and at all stages of processing from the raw commodity to the product thereof in a vendible form for immediate human or animal consumption, but exclusive of such commodities and products as the Secretary shall determine. For the purposes of this Executive Order, the term "food" shall also include all starches, sugars, vegetable and animal fats and oils, cotton, tobacco, wool, hemp, flax fiber, and such other agricultural commodities and products as the President may designate.

11. In the event of any difference of view arising between the Secretary and any other officer or agency of the Government, in the administration of the provisions of this Executive Order, such difference of view shall be submitted for final decision to the President or such agent or agency as the President may designate.

12. The personnel, property, records, unexpended balances of appropriations, allocations, and other funds of the War Production Board primarily concerned with and available for, as determined by the Director of the Bureau of the Budget, the discharge of any of the functions, responsibilities, powers, authorities, and discretions that are vested in the Secretary by this Executive Order are hereby transferred to the Department of Agriculture. In determining the amounts transferred hereunder, allowance shall be made for the liquidation of obligations previously incurred against such balances of appropriations, allocations, or other funds transferred.

13. To facilitate the effective discharge of the Secretary's responsibility under this Executive Order, the following changes are made within the Department of Agriculture:

a. The Agricultural Conservation and Adjustment Administration (except the Sugar Agency), the Farm Credit Administration, the Farm Security Administration, and their functions, personnel, and property; the functions, personnel, and property of the Division of Farm Management and Costs of the Bureau of Agricultural Economics concerned primarily with the planning of current agricultural production; the functions, personnel, and property of the Office of Agricultural War Relations concerned primarily with the production of food; and the functions, personnel, and property established in or transferred to the Department by this Executive Order that are concerned primarily with the production of food, are consolidated into an agency to be known as the Food Production Administration of the Department of Agriculture. The Food Production Administration shall be under the direction and supervision on of a Director of Food Production appointed by the Secretary.

b. The Agricultural Marketing Administration, the Sugar Agency of the Agricultural Conservation and Adjustment Administration, and their functions, personnel, and property; the functions, personnel, and property of the Bureau of Animal Industry of the Agricultural Research Administration concerned primarily with regulatory activities; the functions, personnel, and the property of the Office of Agricultural War Relations concerned primarily with the distribution of food; and the functions, personnel, and property established in or transferred to the Department of Agriculture by this Executive Order that are concerned primarily with the distribution of food are consolidated into an agency to be known as the Food Distribution Administration of the Department of Agriculture. The Food Distribution Administration shall be under the direction and supervision of a Director of Food Distribution appointed by the Secretary.

c. So much of the unexpended balances of appropriations, allocations, or other funds available (or to be made available) for the use of any agency in the exercise of any function transferred or consolidated by subsections a. and b. of this section or for the use of the head of any agency in the exercise of any function so transferred or consolidated, as the Director of the Bureau of the Budget shall determine, shall be transferred for use in connection with the exercise of the function so transferred or consolidated. In determining the amount to be transferred, the Director of the Bureau of the Budget may include an amount to provide for the liquidation of obligations incurred against such balances of appropriations, allocations, or other funds prior to the transfer.

14. Any provision of any Executive Order or proclamation conflicting with this Executive Order is superseded to the extent of such conflict. All prior directives, rules, regulations, orders, and similar instruments heretofore issued by any Federal agency which affect the subject matter of this Executive Order shall continue in full force and effect unless and until withdrawn or superseded by or under the direction of the Secretary under the authority of this Order. Nothing in this Order shall be construed to limit the powers exercised by the Economic Stabilization Director under Executive Order 9250 dated October 3, 1942, as amended. Nothing in this Order shall be construed to limit the power now exercised by the Price Administrator under the Emergency Price Control Act of 1942, Public Law 421, 77th Congress, as amended, or the Act of October 2, 1942, Public Law 729, 77th Congress.

FRANKLIN D. ROOSEVELT

THE WHITE HOUSE
    December 5, 1942

The War Food Administration

From Executive Order 9322, Mar. 26, 1943. 8 F.R. 3807.

By virtue of the authority vested in me by the Constitution and the statutes of the United States, particularly by the First War Powers Act, 1941, as President of the United States and Commander in Chief of the Army and Navy, and in order to assure an adequate supply and efficient distribution of food to meet war and essential civilian needs, it is hereby ordered as follows:

1. The Food Production Administration (except the Farm Credit Administration), the Food Distribution Administration, the Commodity Credit Corporation, and the Extension Service are hereby consolidated within the Department of Agriculture into an Administration of Food Production and Distribution to be under the direction and supervision of an Administrator. The Administrator shall be appointed by the President and shall be directly responsible to him.

2. All of the powers, functions, and duties conferred upon the Secretary of Agriculture by Executive Order No. 9280 dated December 5, 1942, are transferred to and shall be exercised by the Administrator. The Secretary of Agriculture shall, however, continue as Chairman of the Inter-Departmental Committee set up by section 7 (a) of Executive Order No. 9280 to advise the Administrator, and the Administrator shall become a member of such committee. The Secretary of Agriculture shall continue as a member of the War Production Board as provided in section 7b of Executive Order No. 9280. The Secretary of Agriculture shall continue as the American representative on the Combined Food Board.

3. The personnel, property, and records used primarily in the administration of the functions, powers, and duties transferred and consolidated by this order are transferred to the Administrator. So much of the unexpended balances of appropriations, allocations, and other funds available to the Department of Agriculture for the said purposes as the Director of the Bureau of the Budget shall determine shall be transferred to the Administrator for use in connection with the exercise of the functions, powers, and duties so transferred. The authority heretofore vested in the Secretary of Agriculture over personnel of divisions, bureaus, and agencies transferred to and consolidated under the Administrator is vested in the Administrator. The powers in respect to labor and manpower heretofore vested in the Secretary of Agriculture by the orders of the Economic Stabilization Director or the Chairman of the War Manpower Commission are vested in the Administrator. The authority heretofore vested in the Secretary of Agriculture under Title IV of Executive Order 9250 is vested in the Administrator.

FRANKLIN D. ROOSEVELT

Production During World War II

From U.S. War Food Administration, *Final Report of the War Food Administrator,* 1945 (Washington, 1945), pp. 1–2, 5–13, 27–35.

It is now 2 months since VE-day, and a convenient point at which to assess the United States food program of the last 2 years. The wartime food production record has been one of unbroken advances; it reached a peak in 1944 which was 38 percent above the prewar (1935–39) average. But the victory in Europe has increased rather than decreased the immediate requirements for United States food and emphasized the need for continued full production.

Food, of course, is a weapon of war. As such, it ranks with ships, airplanes, tanks, and guns. Food, particularly American food, has been especially crucial in the present war, because it has been essential to the fighting efficiency of our allies as well as of our own military forces, and has been required to maintain colossal industrial productivity here and in other allied countries. Notably, Great Britain and Russia have depended heavily on United States agriculture. Modern war demands enormous food production, not only for consumption by huge forces on land and sea, but for consumption by the personnel employed in war industries, in transport, and in related occupations. The United States' response to the wartime food demand must be set against the fact that the demand was virtually insatiable.

The War Food Administration's interest in food extends from the production on the farm to the final consumption. Food serves its purpose only when it is eaten; but before it can be eaten, it must be distributed; and before it can be distributed, it must be produced. Hence WFA's responsibility covers all main phases of the food job. Starting with guidance and assistance to farmers in producing food, it carries on through the other links in the chain. For example, in cooperation with other war agencies, WFA has many responsibilities in connection with procurement, processing, storage, transport, and distribution. But the main WFA job is on the farm production front, where it involves assistance to farmers in the determination of desirable crop gokals, efforts to see that farmers have the tools they need, encouragement in the use of improved farm practices, and maintenance of adequate price supports.

High Points in Wartime Food Record

The record of the American farmers in producing food during the war years speaks for itself. Production during each of the last 2 years was an all-time record. With the 1935–39 average taken as equal to 100, the index number for 1943 was 132 and that for 1944 was 138. The most outstanding increases were in meat, poultry and eggs, and oil crops. Following the loss in the Pacific area of the source of half of our fats and oils supply, the United States through tremendous expansion in the production of vegetable oil crops and of livestock products changed from an import to an export basis in fats and oils. Also, it achieved a great increase in dairy production, and in beans and peas, important sources of vegetable proteins.

In achieving this record the farmers had to cope with many difficulties and inconveniences. Labor especially was scarce on the farms. Agriculture obtained its record food production in 1944 with 8 percent fewer workers than it had in the 1935–39 period. Moreover, much of the farm working force consisted of inexperienced workers, of women and children, and of older men. Allowance for the difference in strength and skill would make the effective labor force nearly 15 percent smaller.

Machinery was a relatively scarce item. In 1942 and subsequently farm-machinery production had to be restricted, and the new supply fell much below what farmers needed. Use of fertilizers and lime, though the highest on record, would have been still higher, had more of these materials been available. The War Food Administration kept other war agencies informed as to agriculture's requirements for labor, machinery, and supplies and conducted or aided programs that relieved the shortages.

Among the chief direct encouragements by WFA to food production in the last 2 years were extension of the support-price program to include more commodities, special subsidy programs undertaken for dairy products in order to meet increased labor and feed costs, and removal of all limitations on production except for tobacco. The price-support program in 1944 included 7 livestock products, wool among them; 20 field crops; 15 fruits and vegetables for processing; and 49 seed crops. With limitations abolished on all food-crop production, WFA placed additional emphasis on informing farmers of the kinds and quantities of products most needed. In addition, it facilitated migration of agricultural workers within the United States and, with the cooperation of the State Department, imported agricultural labor from Mexico, the Bahama Islands, Jamaica, and Newfoundland. . . .

Meeting the Food Claims

The distribution of our record food output has involved important WFA tasks, which have concerned allocations, Government procurement, and civilian consumption. In collaboration with the armed forces and with the Combined Food Board, WFA has sought first to make sure that the armed forces would have all the food they needed, at the right times and in the right places. Secondly, it has provided for an adequate diet for American civilians, on a per capita level above that of the prewar years. Thirdly, to the limit of the supplies available, it has answered the calls of the allies and of other contributors to the direct war effort. Part of WFA's job is cooperation with the Army and Navy in food procurements, to coordinate United States food distribution with that of the other United Nations, and to indicate foods that should be rationed. Food industries, cooperating with WFA through Food Industry Committees, have done an outstanding job in maintaining a free flow of food in record volume to civilians, and at the same time in meeting the large Government demand for food, much of which requires specialized processing and packing.

Various types of Government assistance to the food industries became available through the War Food Administration, such as representation of the need for certain priorities, Government financing of necessary new processing facilities, regulation of the use of storage facilities particularly cooler and freezer space, and synchronization of Government shipments with production peaks. WFA and other

Government agencies encouraged and aided the conversion of cooler to freezer space, promoted a more continuous and more complete utilization of all types of storage, and helped to coordinate storage with transport. It was a WFA responsibility to see that various claimants received the supplies that had been promised. The task involved the use of set-aside orders, the restriction by quota of commercial sales of certain commodities, special restrictions on the uses of some foods, and occasionally the prohibition of nonessential uses. These procedures were supplementary to rationing.

Bottlenecks in Distribution

Inevitably, certain difficulties in food distribution developed from time to time. In the dry-storage field, grain presented the greatest problem; this necessitated a series of emergency actions, such as the furnishing of bins for increased storage on the farm and a permit system to control shipments to clogged terminal markets.

Some difficulties with hogs and eggs developed in 1944. Probably hog production could have been maintained at higher levels had enough manpower been available at packing plants to process larger runs so that farmers would not have been forced to continue feeding hogs that were ready for market. Frequently, in 1944, the run of hogs was temporarily above the capacity of many packing plants, and in consequence the hog price supports were not always fully effective at receiving points.

Egg production similarly pressed upon the facilities of the distribution system, and caused wide spreads at times between farm price levels and ceilings. This was partly the result of shortages of storage space, of egg cases, and of labor for grading eggs. It was necessary to convert some eggs into tankage. Occasionally, the production of certain vegetables for canning and for the fresh market pressed heavily on the available processing or distribution facilities, the operators of which had difficulty in getting labor and supplies.

On balance, however, the distribution system worked smoothly, and presented few impediments to the flow of production from the farms.

Price Support and Stabilization

Mention has been made of the extensive price-support system, which encouraged farmers to produce the kinds and quantities of production desired. Main features of it were loan programs; purchases of some commodities direct from farmers; purchases of other commodities from processors and dealers, with the sellers required to pay minimum specified prices to farmers; and special payments to producers, either directly or through processors. Simultaneously, WFA cooperated in the "Hold-the-Line" program for stabilizing prices and preventing inflation. This involved purchase and sales operations, accompanied by the use of subsidies. In line with President Roosevelt's "Hold-the-Line" order of April 8, 1943, WFA cooperated with the Office of Price Administration in extending the ceiling principle to commodities not previously covered, and worked out a program of payments to encourage various types of production with no addition to the cost at retail.

By 1944 WFA was operating or aiding stabilization programs for a considerable number of commodities. It assumed losses, for example, in a program designed to keep feed prices low relative to livestock prices; made payments to dairy producers on their sales of milk and butterfat; conducted a program temporarily which allowed farmers to redeem loan wheat at prices compatible with sale of it in line with ceiling prices on flour; and paid part of the cost of supporting prices of vegetables for canning to farmers and at the same time of holding down the prices of some canned vegetables to consumers. Programs similarly designed to support prices to farmers and yet not raise the cost of living were in effect for dry beans, cheddar cheese, vegetable oils, potatoes, sweetpotatoes, sugar and certain dried fruits. Farmers continued to earn good returns, as may be judged from the fact that total receipts from farm marketings in 1944 were about 20 billion dollars as compared with about 5 billions in the depression year 1932. Net incomes to farm operators in 1944 were nearly three times as high as the annual average for 1935–39.

Requests for Production Facilities

As official claimant for scarce materials required in food production, processing, packaging, and storing, WFA endeavored to keep its requests realistic; in other words, adequate to support the war food program and yet not exaggerated in such a way as to conflict unnecessarily with other essential claims for labor and materials. Later chapters in this report give details of the action taken with regard to labor, machinery, agricultural chemicals, container materials, and other requisites in agricultural production. Here it suffices to note that following WFA representations of urgent farm requirements additional supplies of most things needed actually became available in the two fiscal years covered by this report. For example, final output of machinery in the last 2 years, though behind the authorized schedule, has been large as compared with past production. True, the demand has not been fully met, but the outlook is much improved.

Main Credit Belongs to Farmers

Main credit for the efficient, expanded, and properly balanced wartime food production goes to the farmers. They have applied science, skill, energy, and overtime hours to the job and have been ingenious and successful in making out with scarce facilities. Prepared for cooperative endeavor by prewar experience, they have produced needed crops as nearly as possible in the proper quantities and proportions, through programs adapted and applied to individual farms throughout the country. Undoubtedly, when fully recorded, the farm production phase of the national war effort will rank high among all types of war activity.

SUPPORT PRICES JULY 1943–JUNE 1945

The commodities for which prices have been supported in the last 2 years include most of the principal crops sold by farmers, except fresh fruits and vegetables, and all important livestock products except cattle, calves, sheep, lambs and broilers. Altogether, the commodities for which support prices were in effect accounted for about 70 percent of cash income received by farmers from marketings. The list of commodities has changed from time to time as the need for agricultural products in the war effort changed. For example, price supports on castor-bean seed terminated with the 1943 crop and supports for hemp straw and hempseed ended with the 1944 crop.

The primary purpose in supporting prices of agricultural commodities was to stimulate needed production by assuring the farmers at or before the beginning of the production season that they would receive a definite price when the product was marketed. The commodity loans made primarily for the purpose of supporting prices also helped to stabilize marketing, especially at times when normal marketing facilities were not available or were inadequate. This stabilizing influence of the support prices was important in the case of some of the grains when bumper crops in 1943 and 1944 overloaded storage and transportation facilities.

Some commodities, such as fruits, milk, and livestock feed, are normally utilized in several ways, and one of the functions of support prices for processed fruits, dairy products, and livestock products has been to guide the utilization of these products in accordance with war needs. This can be illustrated by milk, the production of which on farms has been encouraged by direct payments to farmers and the utilization of which has been influenced in part by changes in the prices realized for milk utilized in producing butter, cheese, evaporated milk, dried skim milk, and other end products.

Main Features of Price Supports

The level at which prices have been supported has varied from time to time and from commodity to commodity, partly in response to changes in legislative requirements but mostly because the needs of the war effort dictated different price stimuli for the various commodities. The range in the support prices during this period was from 85 percent of parity for the 1943 crops of corn and wheat to more than 200 percent of parity for 1943 and 1944 crops of dried peaches.

The method of implementing the support prices also has varied; loans, purchases of raw products, purchases of processed or derived products, and direct payments to farmers all being used, sometimes alone and sometimes in combination.

The most outstanding development in price-support operations during this 2-year period was the program of direct production payments to dairy farmers. A program for supplementing market returns for daily products was announced in September 1943 and payments began late that year on sales of milk and butterfat made after October 1. These payments, made through the county offices of the Agricultural Adjustment Agency, have proved to be a very flexible and adaptable instrument for encouraging increased production of milk without changing the very complex system of prices paid by consumers for dairy products.

The rates of payment were set higher during the winter season, when costs for feed are higher than during the flush season. When a severe drought dried up pastures and reduced hay and feed production in several Southeastern States in the summer of 1944, a special drought supplement was added to the previously announced payments in the affected counties and the higher winter rates were made effective earlier than originally planned. With the return of normal weather and feed conditions in the spring of 1945, the drought supplement payments in this area were eliminated. Without this flexible program, the output of milk in the affected area would have been appreciably smaller and some liquidation of dairy stock might have occurred.

The support prices, of course, have not worked alone; support prices and production goals have necessarily worked together. The combination of support prices and production goals, by telling the farmers what was needed and by furnishing assurance of minimum prices for the needed output, led to an expansion of agricultural production during this war which was greater than any increase in production ever before experienced by American agriculture in the same length of time. Year after year the output and the income of American farmers have increased and set new records.

Effect on Production Pattern

Although the production has not always changed from year to year exactly in accordance with announced desires or the needs of the war effort, the general production tendencies have been in the right direction and the over-all result has been a supply of food large enough to supply our own armed forces generously, to furnish huge quantities of very essential foods to our allies, and to permit American civilians to enjoy a diet of higher nutritional value per person than before the war.

One of the incidental results of the support-price experience during this war is a legal provision for price supports during the postwar transition period. This provision is designed to give farmers a reasonable period for readjusting agricultural production to a peacetime basis and has been an important background factor in the wartime support price program, as the farmers have been thereby assured against the hasty withdrawal of support prices at the end of the war.

FARM PRODUCTION

Farmers of the United States set a new all-time production record in each of the war years, up to and including 1944. The Government first requested increased production in 1941, with emphasis on hogs, dairy products, eggs, poultry, and canning vegetables. A production pattern, set forth in production goals, was established for each succeeding year. The farmers' response to these requests for the volume and kinds of food, fiber, and oils needed in the war effort has resulted in production surprisingly close to the goals. As previously mentioned, production for sale or home consumption in 1944 was 38 percent more than the average for the prewar years 1935–39.

The acreage of goal crops planted or grown increased from 348 million as an average for 1935–39 to 354 million in 1944. From the beginning, the crop pattern showed many shifts as well as increases. Yields per acre increased as a result of favorable weather, better farming practices, and a wartime demand that called for maximum effort on the part of farmers. Thus the increase in production exceeded the increase in acreage. Record productions were attained for dry edible beans, dry peas, flaxseed, soybeans, peanuts, corn, wheat, potatoes, and burley tobacco.

Changes in war requirements necessitated changes in emphasis on different crops from time to time, and revisions in goals programs. The first need in the wartime food program was to convert feed reserves into food supplies. Greater emphasis was necessary on the need for direct food crops, particularly dry beans, dry peas, rice, and potatoes. Tremendously increased production of oil-bearing crops was imperative to meet increased needs and to offset reduction in imports from the Far East.

Obstacles That Were Overcome

Limitations in the supplies of labor, machinery, fertilizer, and supplies called for efforts to get the most from the available resources. Labor, materials, transportation, and other facilities needed to be concentrated on the production of most essential crops. This country was not able to produce all the food and fiber desired and it was necessary to emphasize the products that could contribute most to wartime needs. Working out production goals was a problem in the balancing of needs against production facilities.

Getting wide recognition of the need for more production facilities was part of the war food job, as a later chapter of this report will show in more detail. Emphasis on direct war uses for labor and materials tended to divert attention from the agricultural need. Efforts to improve the farm facilities situation brought results. For example, the authorized 1943 manufacture of machinery was doubled in 1944 and was at 80 percent of 1940, and the machinery production order was announced four months earlier than in the preceding year. This facilitated better planning of production, distribution, and rationing.

Price supports and incentive payments for critical war commodities brought increased production of these commodities and helped to get the right balance in production. The dairy feed payment program, for example, was undertaken to compensate for increases in the cost of dairy feeds and was followed by substantial increases in production.

Difficulties developed in marketing the large potato crops and the 122 million pig crop of 1943. Production of potatoes on an acreage 6 percent above the goal was 26 percent greater than that of 1942 and was the largest on record. Domestic disappearance was at the rate of 122 pounds per capita. Large quantities were taken by noncivilian claimants, but the quantity used for feed and losses totaled approximately twice the normal percentage. Slaughtering facilities and storage were the chief limiting factors in handling the volume of hogs.

Changed Feed Situation After 1943

By the end of 1943, the feed situation had changed. The stock pile of feed grain reserves was used up; the United States had a greater number of livestock than could be fed from the feed supply in sight. Greatly increased livestock numbers and abnormally heavy feeding rates made feed supplies in 1944 about 11 percent smaller per grain consuming animal unit than in 1943. A major problem of balancing livestock output with available feed supplies had to be solved.

It was not possible to increase feed crops substantially and still maintain needed acreages of oil crops and direct food crops. Therefore, it became necessary to balance livestock production with the feed supplies that could be produced.

Because wheat was used for feed and in the alcohol program and because large increases in requirements for food uses for military and relief feeding appeared likely, the wheat acreage goal was greatly increased in 1944. WFA recommended that wheat should be grown whenever it would return more feed per acre than other crops.

Before the war direct controls on agricultural production had been in effect. They were gradually relaxed until in 1943 allotments were effective only for cotton and tobacco. Allotments were retained for these crops as a means of checking undue expansion in them at the expense of food and feed crops. By 1944, the only controls remaining were marketing quotas on two types of tobacco, authorized by Congress to encourage greater food production.

In 1944, for the first time in the three war years, production goals were not revised. Special emphasis, however, was placed on achievement of the goals for certain strategic commodities. In a check-up in February 1944, indications were that the goals would not be reached for some strategic commodities unless steps were taken to increase their output above existing plans. The commodities involved were: oil crops, dry beans and peas, potatoes, seeds, feed supplies, milk, poultry, and meat animals.

Specific Aids to Goals Effort

The following specific actions were taken in an attempt to improve the opportunity to meet the goals for these commodities:

1. Support prices were increased for soybeans, peanuts, and Red Kidney beans.

2. Dairy production payment rates were increased.

3. A program was undertaken to stimulate use of nitrogen on pastures and hay crops in order to produce more forage to relieve the feed shortage.

4. Additional emphasis was placed on the use of educational campaigns to encourage attainment of goals for critical commodities.

By the beginning of 1945, the physical job of producing one-third more with 10 percent fewer people on farms was placing farmers under greatly increasing strain. But the time for relaxing had not come. Continued high agricultural production was necessary. Production goals were more selective than in previous years, with some additional recommended shifts in the pattern of production. It was more important than ever to have as nearly as possible the balanced production pattern represented by the goals, so as to avoid serious shortages on the one hand and marketing difficulties on the other.

Hence the 1945 goals called for 364 million acres of cultivated crops and hay, nearly 3 percent more than the 1944 planted acreage. They also called for increased milk production, a larger slaughter of beef cattle, and increased pig farrowings.

Changes in the requirements for various commodities resulted from time to time from the progress of the war. Naturally, these changes necessitated corresponding changes in goals and programs.

For example, in 1943, requirements were high for long-staple cotton and for hemp. Acreage of hemp fiber increased from a prewar base of less than 10,000 acres to 178,000 planted in 1943. Acreage in 1944 was approximately 70,000, with further reductions in prospect for succeeding years. Changing war conditions reduced the need, with the result that in 1944 no goals were established for these commodities.

Among the direct food crops the acreage and production of dry peas showed the greatest percentage increase in response to increased needs. For the years 1942–44 production averaged 350 percent of the prewar years 1935–39.

Marketing difficulties which had developed in handling the large potato crop and pig crop of 1943 were an obstacle in securing maximum production of these commodities in 1944. Surpluses of onions, cabbage, and carrots developed in 1944; also seasonal marketing difficulties in eggs during the peak production. Proportionately, however, the maladjustments were minor.

FARM LABOR

American industry and the Nation's farmers have this distinction in common — they both have set all-time records for production during this war. But there is this difference in their respective achievements: Industry has employed more workers than ever before. Farmers have turned out the vast quantities of food and fiber needed for war with fewer — not more — workers than they had in the prewar years. With 10 percent fewer workers on farms, food production by the end of 1944 had been increased more than one-third above prewar years.

Since 1940 the farm population has decreased more than 5 million, or 17 percent. Migration of more than 5 million farm people to cities, towns, and villages occasioned by the wartime expansion in nonagricultural employment has been by far the most important factor in this unprecedented population decline. About 1,200,000 farm workers — farmers and farm hands — went into the armed services. Added to this number were about 650,000 young men who, prior to entering the services, were living on farms but working at nonagricultural occupations or attending school. In addition, a large number of men and women transferred from farm to industrial occupations, though they continued to live on farms.

There have been some replacements in the farm work force, and these have come largely from within the farm population. According to employment estimates of the Bureau of Agricultural Economics, the average annual farm employment for 1944 was 10,037,000, compared with 10,585,000 for 1940, a reduction of 5 percent. In a breakdown of these estimates, BAE shows that operators and unpaid family workers in 1944 averaged 7,810,000, 3 percent under the 1940 average, while the average of 2,227,000 for hired workers last year was 13 percent below the 1940 average.

Total farm employment each month in the first half of this year has been lower than for the corresponding month of 1944. It has averaged 9,077,000 for the first half of the year, compared with 9,263,000 for the first half of 1944, a drop of 3 percent.

Along with the numerical decline there has been a drastic change in the composition of the farm-labor supply. Male operators and workers who have left agriculture for the armed services or industry have had to be replaced largely by women, youth, and retired men returning to active farm life for the duration of the war. The replacements have not, for the most part, had the stamina and skill of the men whose jobs they were called upon to fill.

Yet the output of our farms has increased, year after year, and in no year since 1940 has there been a significant loss of agricultural production that could be attributed to the labor shortage. How has this been possible?

Ways of Compensating for the Labor Shortage

To compensate for the loss of experienced, able-bodied manpower, the American farmer has worked more hours per day and more days per month, and has overcome the shortage of hired help in many cases through fuller use of family labor. Where a grown son or young hired hand has left the farm, the farmer has replaced him with an elderly man. He has used workers from the towns and cities. He has used foreign workers, prisoners of war, and other unusual types of labor. He has shared labor, machinery, and other facilities with his neighbors to a greater extent than in prewar years and devised ingenious ways of saving labor. Frequently he has let some tasks go, such as repairing fences and buildings, to concentrate on getting essential commodities produced and on their way to market.

Farmers have done much to meet their labor needs from their own resources. However, action needed to be taken — and was taken — to check the drain on farm manpower, mobilize all available workers in the local communities, bring in foreign works, and transport both foreign and United States workers within States and across State lines to areas where local mobilization could not fully meet the need, set up and operate camps, and give the inexperienced recruits as much training as possible to fit them for farm tasks.

Since November 1942, when Congress passed the Tydings Amendment to the Selective Service and Training Act, many skilled men who otherwise might have been lost to the farm work force during the war have been retained in agriculture through occupational deferment. The Tydings Amendment provides that any registrant found by his local Selective Service Board to be necessary to and regularly engaged in an agricultural occupation or endeavor essential to the war effort shall be deferred until a satisfactory replacement can be obtained. Occupational deferment has been granted under this amendment to about 1,600,000 farmers and farm laborers between 18 and 37, inclusive.

Another measure which has helped to check the drain on farm manpower has been the War Manpower Commission regulation No. 7. It requires that before a farm person can transfer to nonfarm employment, except for a temporary period not to exceed 6 weeks, he must be referred to a specific job by the United States Employment Service, or in accordance with an arrangement with the United States Employment Service. This regulation, which went into effect in the fall of 1943, has provided some measure of control over the transfer of workers from agriculture to industry. It is now being relaxed in areas where the manpower problem is no longer acute. Job transfers within agriculture and by persons desiring to leave their nonfarm employment to engage in farming or work on farms have not been restricted.

Farm-Labor Supply Program

The farm labor-supply program, provided for by Congress and jointly administered by the War Food Administration and the State agricultural extension services, is now well into its third year. Under this program, the State extension services and their county agents survey the farm-labor needs within their respective States, receive orders from farmers for workers, and recruit men, women, and youth for temporary, seasonal or year-round agricultural employment. These recruits make up what is known as the U.S. Crop Corps. Affiliated with the Crop Corps are the Victory Farm Volunteers, composed of youths 14 to 17 years of age, and the Women's Land Army, for girls and women 18 years of age and over.

The U.S. Crop Corps has made a substantial contribution to war food and fiber production. The 12,000 local farm-labor placement offices throughout the country placed 3 million different individual workers in some 5½ million temporary, seasonal and year-round farm jobs during 1944. Besides rural people and others with farm backgrounds, these workers included teen-age school youth, college girls, teachers, clerks, stenographers, housewives and businessmen.

For the first 4 months of 1945, the State extension services reported that 640,941 placements had been made. This was an increase of 52 percent over the 422,209 placements made in the same period of 1944. The period of peak demand for farm labor comes during June, July, August, September, and October.

In areas where local and intra-State recruiting campaigns do not provide sufficient labor, workers from other States, foreign workers, or prisoners of war are employed to supplement the local supplies.

The War Food Administration's Office of Labor, established June 21, 1943, has carried on the program initiated by the Department of Agriculture in 1942, of bringing farm workers from foreign countries. This year the Office of Labor is supplying the largest number of these workers to be transported to the United States since the program's inception. By June 30, foreign farm workers in the country under contract with WFA's Office of Labor numbered 95,137. They consisted of 65,633 Mexicans, 22,254 Jamaicans, 6,104 Bahamians, including 85 white Bahamian dairy workers, and 1,146 Newfoundlanders.

The largest number of foreign workers employed on farms at one time in 1944 was 94,649. They consisted of 67,860 Mexicans, 17,437 Jamaicans, 5,653 Barbadians, 908 Barbadians, 1,301 Newfoundlanders, and 1,490 Canadians.

These workers are brought to the United States under agreements between the Governments of this country and of each of the countries concerned. Each worker has a contract with WFA's Office of Labor, and growers or growers' associations contract with the Office of Labor for their employment. They are employed principally on crops requiring large amounts of hand labor and have been an important factor in meeting labor needs in certain critical areas.

Some farm workers of this country also have been transported interstate each year by WFA to relieve shortages in areas where not enough labor has been available locally or within the State to harvest certain crops. Last year the Office of Labor transported 11,322 domestic farm laborers interstate. Responsibility for interstate transportation was shifted this year to the Extension Service, which by the end of the harvest season will have transported 10,000 or more workers interstate.

Housing for Farm Workers

To supplement housing provided by agricultural employers or the State extension services, the Office of Labor last year operated farm-labor supply centers (camps) on 273 sites for 150,000 workers in 29 States. This phase of the labor program is being continued this year on about the same scale. Agricultural workers' health associations, operating with WFA funds, have provided free medical care in the last year to approximately 150,000 foreign workers and domestic farm workers living in farm-labor supply centers or in the vicinity of the centers.

Prisoners are being employed in agriculture this year in increased numbers.

The War Department has announced that a peak total of 85,000 war prisoners will be used in contract work through July, as agricultural laborers. WFA will request an even larger number of prisoners of war for farm work in the peak of the fall harvest season. As of June 7, a total of 74,662 prisoners was reported from the States as available for agricultural work, with 63,753 actually employed. Last year approximately 65,000 POW's worked in agriculture.

The upward trend in farm-wage rates induced by the wartime demand for agricultural workers has continued this year to a new record. On June 1 farm wage rates were about double those paid 3 years ago. For the country as a whole monthly rates on that date averaged $81.30 with board and $93.10 without board. Daily wages were $3.65 with board and $4.16 without board. These were all record highs, except for wages per day with board, which were exceeded slightly in October 1944.

Wage-Stabilization Program

Under WFA's farm wage-stabilization program, administered by the Office of Labor and State WFA Wage Boards, 52 specific wage ceilings have been established to date covering 24 commodities or operations in the States of California, Oregon, Washington, Idaho, Arizona, Delaware, and Florida. The ceilings limit the wage rates paid to approximately 450,000 farm workers in particular areas of these States. Specific ceilings are established only after a majority of growers of a commodity in an area have requested WFA's intervention. In the absence of specific ceilings, an employer may increase wages and salaries of agricultural labor up to $2,400 a year without the War Food Administrator's approval, but the Administrator's advance approval is required to increase the wages or salaries of agricultural labor earning $2,400 a year or more, or to increase an agricultural employee's wage or salary from less than $2,400 to more than $2,400 a year. A number of applications for approval of wage or salary increases has been acted on by the Director of Labor, or by the State WFA Wage Boards, to which this authority has been delegated.

THE "TOOLS" OF FOOD PRODUCTION

The War Food Administration has acted as official claimant for the scarce materials and facilities needed for all food production, processing, packaging, and storing.

A claimant has an important, and difficult, function in the system for apportioning materials and facilities to the various segments of the war economy. As claimant for just one segment of the economy, it is a special pleader. It must, in a sense, compete with the other segments — including the military — and must present its legitimate claims persuasively and successfully. Yet it must recognize that the purpose of the claims — of the whole apportioning procedure — is to expedite the prosecution of the war. It must recognize that the military alone often needs more material than is available for the entire economy. Thus, like any other properly functioning governmental unit, the claimant agency must represent the whole people — the total public welfare — and not merely the interests of its economic segment.

Sound public policy has dictated that the War Food Administration keep its claims realistic at all times, neither too small to support the food program nor exaggerated in such a way as to conflict needlessly with claims of other war-supporting industries or the military services.

It has not been easy to carry out such a policy while kaleidoscopic changes were occurring in both war requirements and supplies of materials.

Producers have needed more equipment and materials either to lighten their work load or, in some cases, to increase their output. Recognizing that more production "tools" — referring to all supplies needed in the food program as tools — would mean more food, the WFA has often found itself in disagreement with final decisions as to the apportionment of supplies. At the same time, the WFA has recognized that public buying power and convenience are interwoven with individual conceptions of "war necessity." Only the long, historical view can show whether more food tools for the production of food should have been made available out of our total war resources.

The fact that military power had to be created rapidly — as is always true in nonaggressor nations such as ours — led to sudden heavy emphasis on direct military supplies and manpower in the preparatory and first active stages of the war. One inevitable result, in the later stages, has been difficulty in shifting the economic gears, reemphasizing war-supporting requirements, remanning the depleted production lines, catching up with essential pent-up demands.

In spite of delays and uncertainties, however, increased supplies of most things needed in the food program have been made available in the two fiscal years covered by this report.

Farm Machinery and Equipment

A case in point is farm machinery and equipment. The carbon steel used in fabricating this equipment, including repair parts, has totaled more than a million tons in each of the last two fiscal years, compared with less than 923,000 tons in 1940 and much less than that in the early stages of the war. Exact comparable figures are not available for the early stages of the war because programming during that time was on neither a fiscal- nor a calendar-year basis.

However, the trends are shown accurately by the following comparisons, by calendar years, of actual sales to U.S. farmers of new machinery (not including repair parts) in terms of manufacturers's 1940 prices:

1940, one of the program base years	$318,400,000
1941, the all-time record and last peacetime year	445,800,000
1942, under the original limitation	$333,300,000
1943, when production was drastically curbed for 3 months, permitted to increase a little for 3 months and then reprogrammed on a fiscal-year basis	218,100,000
1944, including some production authorized but not completed in 1943	410,800,000

This year, 1945, output is likely to exceed that of 1944 by a considerable amount. During the third quarter of the year, manufacturers are being given positive assistance to increase their production at least 30 percent and will be permitted to increase it even more if they can obtain the materials and manpower without

Government assistance. New record output seems to be in sight, although the Government assistance on manpower and components is less than that recommended by the WFA.

The production indicated above, together with greatly increased production of repair parts, has permitted farmers to increase mechanization of their operations during the war. This has been essential because of the smaller and less effective supply of farm labor. Further relief for the farm labor situation has been effected by requiring increases in the production of several labor-saving machines. (This is an important fact in interpreting the preceding over-all figures on farm equipment.)

For example, in 1940 production of corn pickers was 11,436; in the past 2 fiscal years it has amounted to 29,681 and 32,861, respectively. The annual production of large combines has been about tripled since 1940. Production of pick-up hay balers — 2,045 in 1940 — was more than seven times as great in the program year of 1943–44. These are exceptional increases, of course, but many other machines have been produced at replacement levels.

Demand for farm machinery has not been met. Production of machinery has consistently run behind schedule — a matter over which the WFA has had no authority. But authorized programs and final output in the past 2 years have been large in relation to both the past production and to simultaneous military requirements.

The present improved outlook does not necessarily mean the farm machinery problem has been solved. Both needs and buying power will continue to be large while food demands are large, and the materials and manpower needed by farm-machinery plants may not flow to the plants naturally. No chances should be taken so long as the war continues. But assuming reasonable care, the prospects are brighter now than at any time since the war began.

Chemicals and Fertilizers

Most chemicals needed in the food program have been available in relatively large volume during the last 2 fiscal years. There are exceptions in the vast list of needed chemicals — pyrethrum and rotenone insecticides include — but fertilizer materials are not among the exceptions.

Compared with the prewar period of 1935–39, the use of fertilizer materials in the past 2 years has been up greatly — by about 80 percent for nitrogen and phosphoric acid and by more than 90 percent for potash. This has had an extremely important bearing on food production by increasing the efficiency and over-all output of many farms. Fertilizer prices have been low in relation to farm commodity prices, and demand has not been met in all areas.

Increased use of the three principal fertilizer materials is shown by the following tabulation:

Years:	Nitrogen	Tonnage Phosphoric acid	Potash
1935–39 average	368,000	758,000	373,000
1943–44 (fiscal year)	643,000	1,300,000	604,000
1944–45 (estimate for fiscal year)	668,000	1,350,000	718,000

Fertilizer is one of the most important parts of the chemical picture.

Agriculture, directly and indirectly, is probably the biggest single consumer of chemicals. The uses are classed generally in three groups: (1) Fertilizer, (2) protection of crops and livestock, and (3) processing, packaging, and preservation of food.

A separate volume would be required to list all of the chemicals involved and to chart the changing supply situations. Suffice it to say (1) that the increased food output would not have been possible without adequate supplies of chemicals and (2) that supplies would not have been adequate without care, conservation, and cooperation — together with considerable ingenuity — on the part of both industry and Government.

Examples of the means used include:

Insecticides. — Agricultural use of pyrethrum and rotenone has been permitted for only the most essential needs; nicotine, scarce since the end of 1943, is being conserved through cooperation between industry and WFA without the formality of an allocation order; military use of the new material DDT is permitting release of some pyrethrum and rotenone for agricultural uses; substitutes for scarce materials are being used constantly, thus enabling farmers in general to "get by" with minimum crop losses.

Fertilizers. — Rates of application have been limited, first according to essentiality of crop, later according to State experiment station recommendations or normal local rates. The number and content of grades of mixed goods has been limited. Distribution has been kept equitable by putting responsibility on each manufacturer, dealer and agent to supply his regular area. Needs of farmers who buy materials for straight application or home mixing have been safeguarded. On the recommendation of WFA, sulphuric acid production facilities have been ex panded; likewise in response to WFA requests, scarce shipping space has been assigned by War Shipping Administration to imports of Chilean nitrate.

During the early days of the war, serious shortage developed in the supply of chemicals used as supplements in foods and feeds and in food processing — edible acidulants, such as citric, tartaric, and lactic acids, phosphates for production of yeast; vitamins for food and feed enrichment — and among some of the food processing chemicals such as chlorine and benzcyl peroxide for bleaching and aging of flour; acids, salts, alkalies, and synthetic detergents for the sanitation of food processing plants; and refrigeration chemicals.

While a few of these are still in short supply, the needed chemicals have been provided. This was accomplished by locating new sources of supplies of raw materials, providing new production facilities, and wherever possible, providing suitable substitutes.

It is worth noting that needs of Victory gardeners for both fertilizers and insecticides have been met adequately during the period of this report.

One of the most noteworthy footnotes in the story of chemicals and fertilizers is the fact that rationing and other expensive administrative measures have been avoided through close cooperation between the industries and the WFA and other Governmental agencies.

As to the future: The 1945–46 chemicals and fertilizers supply picture is not clearly delineated. While it is certainly brighter than in the past war years, there are elements of uncertainty which will need to be carefully worked out to prevent dislocations and seasonal shortages in chemical materials required to achieve food-production goals.

Meat Problems During World War II

From Grover J. Sims, *Meat and Meat Animals in World War II*, U.S. Department of Agriculture War Record Monograph No. 9 (February, 1951), pp. 9–13, 39, 50–53, 64–66.

Despite large requirements for meat by the armed forces and for export, civilian per capita consumption of meats in the United States during all of the war years was maintained at a higher level than in most of the 1930's. In fact, civilian per capita consumption in 1944 reached 153.5 pounds, the greatest since 1909. It was almost as large during 1946. Demand for meat by civilians exceeded the supply at controlled prices in 1942 and the gap between supplies and demand widened in the following 3 years under price controls as consumer incomes rose. Point rationing of meat became necessary early in 1943. Controls on civilian distribution followed, and meat allocations and set-asides for Government procurement were developed. The principal objectives of these controls were to distribute existing supplies of meat, to assure needed quantities for the armed forces and other Government organizations (Veterans Administration and War Shipping Administration, for example), and to aid procurement for shipment through lend-lease.

During 1940–42, consumption of meat averaged around 140 pounds per person. Although production was stepped up during the war, the increasing needs of our armed forces and our allies kept down supplies for civilian consumption. The 1942 output of 21.9 billion pounds was 2.3 billion pounds higher than that of 1941; half of this increase was in pork. Military takings in 1942 amounted to about 2 billion pounds; other Government purchases totaled 1.6 billion pounds. About 104 million pounds were exported through commercial channels to foreign countries and our territories. Ceiling prices, placed on meats in March 1942, gave rise to many problems in regional distribution. Civilian supplies fell below increased civilian demand early in 1942, when military and lend-lease takings accelerated. Some attempts were made at voluntary restriction of consumption, to offset rising prices and poor distribution of available supplies as well as to increase supplies for war purposes, but in the main these efforts were unsuccessful. A slaughter-restriction order was put into effect October 1, 1942 which limited deliveries of meat by slaughterers to civilians and thereby increased deliveries to the Government. This order, however, was not entirely effective in providing adequate quantities of meat for Government purchase, and an additional order requiring specific percentages of meat produced in federally inspected plants to be set aside for the Government was put into effect a few months later.

Production of meat increased still further in 1943 reaching 24.5 billion pounds. Military takings that year totaled 3.4 billion pounds, of which 1.9 billion were beef and veal. Other Government purchases totaled 2.4 billion pounds. The first set-aside order was announced late in March. Although it was taken off after 2 weeks of operation to avoid interference with the beginning of rationing, it was reinstituted in June. The slaughter quotas, started under the meat restriction order, were in operation until September. They were designed to strengthen the set-asides, and to prevent increased operations by nonfederally inspected slaughterers and a reduction in meat supplies available for the armed forces and our Allies. In the last quarter of 1943, output increased markedly because of the slaughter of the record large spring pig crop.

Meat rationing was instituted March 29, 1943, and contributed materially to more equitable distribution, particularly for areas that depended mainly on federally inspected slaughter. Only meats slaughtered under Federal inspection can enter into interstate commerce. Civilian supplies from these sources were directly affected by Government procurement.

A new record in meat production was reached in 1944. Military takings were the largest for any year, but other Government purchases were materially less than in 1943. Government-owned stocks were cut in half, despite the prospects for a smaller output in 1945 and larger requirements. Consumption of meat averaged 154 pounds per person in 1944, the greatest since 1909. If supplies for civilians had been sufficient for the demand at the established ceiling prices, it appears likely that per capita consumption might have reached 165 to 170 pounds, even though these prices were about 30 percent above those of 1935–39. Civilian supplies were very large during the first 4 months of 1944, and ration points were lowered to permit consumers to make larger purchases. All meats, except beef roasts and steaks, had point values at zero in May and June 1944. Civilian supplies were particularly large during that period because of the large output and the lack of adequate storage space and shipping facilities. In July 1944, the ration points required to buy the better grades and cuts of lamb were increased and in mid-August they were raised for most of the popular pork cuts. Beef was short of demand during most of the year. The large supplies of meat were mainly pork. Hog slaughter established a new record but the armed forces took a smaller proportion of pork than beef. By the fourth quarter, the effect of the considerably reduced 1944 spring pig crop was reflected in smaller supplies of pork. With relaxation of restrictions on civilian consumption, commercial stocks in cold storage were reduced 330 million pounds during the year. Consumption of beef per person averaged about 5 percent greater in 1944 than in 1943. Much more veal was available for civilians in 1944. Relatively higher ceiling prices for veal than for beef and increased marketings of calves apparently accounted for increased production and for larger civilian supplies. Supplies of lamb and mutton continued large.

Until the last quarter of 1945, supplies of meat were a great deal shorter than in 1944, because of the decrease in output of 1.5 billion pounds from the 1944 record of 25.2 billion. Purchases for noncivilian use were smaller. In 1945, on a per capita basis, civilians consumed 144 pounds of meat (wholesale dressed weight) compared with 154 pounds in 1944. Early in 1945 slaughter of hogs dropped off and military procurement took 25 to 30 percent of the inspected supply. An additional 5 to 10 percent of the pork was purchased for shipment to our allies. As military needs were still large, exports were considerably reduced in order to maintain civilian supplies. Even so, civilian supplies during the late spring and summer were so small compared with the potential consumer demand (perhaps a fourth too small) that distribution of available supplies was spotty. To meet the problems of distribution and to assure supplies for war use, several Government actions were taken. Control Order No. 1 was instituted. It set slaughter quotas for nonfederally inspected slaughterers and required distributors to deliver civilian supplies according to the trading-area distribution in the first quarter of 1944. An enforcement campaign was waged against sales of meat above ceiling prices and without surrender of ration points.

Also, the Department of Agriculture set up a certification system for certain nonfederally inspected plants to enable them to ship meat across State lines and to sell the Government.

After the end of the fighting in August 1945, the military procurement program was sharply curtailed. With the seasonal rise in output, civilian supplies increased considerably and increased exports to liberated areas were scheduled. Rationing of meats was liberalized during September and October and was ended November 28, 1945. On September 8, 1945, slaughter quotas administered by the Office of Price Administration and area distribution controls were suspended. Set-asides of beef and veal, hams, and bacon for Government purchase were taken off on August 19, and on September 2 they were taken off all other pork cuts. However, set-asides on lower grades of beef and veal and on all grades of mutton were reinstituted on October 14 to expedite Government buying of meat for shipment to liberated areas.

Consumption of meat by civilians in 1946 was considerably above the 1945 figure. Production in 1946 totaled around 700 million pounds less than in 1945, but noncivilian use was sharply lower. Surplus army stocks of canned meat had been turned over to UNNRA and to the Production and Marketing Administration for export in late 1945 and early 1946. This allowed continued large exports in 1946, but with reduced Government procurement.

Supplies of meat for civilians again became very short in the spring of 1946, when slaughter of livestock was sharply reduced in anticipation of the end of price controls June 30. Lapse of price controls June 30, 1946, was followed by a rush of producers to market livestock. This continued until price control was reimposed on livestock and meats around September 1. After the reinstatement of price controls, slaughter of livestock under Federal inspection reached the lowest level of record. It continued at this low level until the removal of price ceilings on October 14, 1946. Marketings of hogs, cattle, and calves for slaughter were unusually large late in the year.

Termination of price controls on meat October 14, 1946, was accompanied by the ending of consumer subsidies paid to livestock slaughterers and compulsory grading of meat by Federal graders. Export allocations were the principal wartime controls still in operation that affected meat. Slaughter controls ended June 30, 1946. . . .

Price Control

Prices of meat animals and meat were controlled under the provisions of the Emergency Price Control Act of 1942 and subsequent amendments. The Act authorized the establishment of maximum prices which in the discretion of the Price Administrator would be fair and equitable and would in general check "speculative and excessive price rises, price dislocations, and inflationary tendencies." Maximum prices for agricultural commodities could not be set lower than the highest of the following:

> (1) 100 percent of parity (or the "comparable price") for such commodity adjusted for grade, location, and seasonal differentials.

(2) The market price for such commodity on October 1, 1941.

(3) The market price for such commodity on December 15, 1941.

(4) The average price for such commodity during the period July 1, 1919 to June 30, 1929.

Ceiling prices for pork, beef, and veal were established in conformance with these limitations early in 1942. Maximum wholesale prices for lamb were not established until prices of live lambs advanced above the July 1919–June 1929 average late in the summer of 1942.

The Emergency Price Control Act of 1942 was amended October 2, 1942. The amended Act authorized and directed the President to issue a general order stabilizing prices, wages, and salaries affecting the cost of living, on the basis of levels existing September 15, 1942. Maximum prices for agricultural commodities could not be set at a level that would result in a price to producers lower than the higher of the following: (1) The parity price or "comparable price" for such commodity adjusted for grade, location, and seasonal differentials, or (2) the highest price received by a producer for a commodity between January 1, 1942, and September 15, 1942, also adjusted for grade, location, and seasonal differentials. . . .

Black Markets. — Extensive "black-market" operations in meat were evident during all of the war period and they apparently became even greater after the end of the fighting. "Black-market" operations most commonly took the form of selling meat at prices higher than the established ceilings. Another common violation of meat orders was sale of meat by wholesalers and retailers without collecting ration points. Counterfeiting of ration coupons was detected in numerous instances. Short weighing and upgrading of meats were rather common practices. Meat dealers also violated the price orders by so-called "tie-in sales," in which purchasers were required to buy less desirable meats or meat products to obtain a supply of the types they wished.

Black-market sales in meat apparently varied inversely with public support of the rationing and price control programs. While the war was on patriotic motives served to prevent many people from violating the regulations. With the end of actual fighting, these incentives were largely removed. Consumers and dealers alike appeared to hold less regard for Government regulations after the fighting had stopped. However, average prices of meat at wholesale and retail under OPA, even with the overcharges, were much lower than they would have been in a free market.

Ceilings on live animals were as hard to enforce. On May 18, 1945, the Office of War Mobilization and Reconversion directed the Office of Price Administration and the War Food Administration to develop a plan by June 15 whereby the movement of livestock through public stockyards and public sale yards could be traced, to effectuate compliance of the ceiling-price regulations on meat and live animals. It was stated that record-keeping requirements would be announced to aid in checking compliance of the slaughter-control program then in operation and the meat-distribution plan that was to be announced (Control Order 1).

Reporting provisions were provided in Control Order No. 1 for checking compliance under the order, as was done for most of the livestock and meat orders of the Government. But no plan was announced to trace the movement of livestock through public stockyards and public sale yards. This remained an important gap in enforcement of the wartime ceiling-price orders. Such a plan would necessarily have had to be very comprehensive. Although only some 222 public stockyards were posted under the Packers and Stockyards Act, the number of other public sale yards was much larger. It was hardly possible to place a reporting scheme in operation at the leading markets without strict record-keeping at all markets. The livestock price-control regulations already were being circumvented at country points and small markets where it was much easier to cover up above-ceiling sales than at the posted public markets where more comprehensive record-keeping was required. This was one of the causes of marked diversion of livestock from the principal livestock markets.

The large number of livestock not passing through stockyards emphasizes the difficulties of combating sales of live animals at prices above the ceilings. In 1940, in the 14 Corn Belt States, 24 percent of all livestock (exclusive of horses and mules, combined in terms of carlot equivalents) sold by farmers did not pass through a livestock market (3, p. 28). Of all livestock sold, 28 percent went through one or more local markets but not through a terminal market. Outside of the Corn Belt region, livestock are marketed through somewhat similar channels.

Price ceilings brought about many changes in the wholesaling of meats. The price ceilings on meat made an allowance for each stage of processing and marketing. The regulations provided for a mark-up in prices for cutting, processing, packaging, and delivery. These allowances proved to be rather liberal, so that processed products such as canned meat and sausage were good paying operations. Nonprocessing slaughterers of cattle did not have similar outlets, but they were paid special subsidies. Under the price ceilings, slaughterers tended to cut carcasses into wholesale cuts, for, in this way they could take advantage of the higher realizations provided. As a rule, much of the beef sold by slaughterers is in the form of half or quarter carcasses. Veal, lamb, and mutton are more often distributed as whole carcasses.

Control of prices for meat and meat animals in Wolrd War II was much more extensive than in World War I. During World War I, the Food Administration embarked upon a program to support prices of 100 pounds of live hogs at the value of 13 bushels of corn. To carry out its price policy for hogs, the Government not only bought pork products; it controlled receipts at primary markets through a system of embargoes and car allotments and licenses to dealers and packers. To some extent it regulated the profits of packers. The Food Administration of World War I found it difficult to maintain hog prices equivalent to 13 bushels of corn at Chicago, and so it effected changes which lowered the ratio to 11. Control over prices of beef was indirect; it comprised regulation of market supplies and curtailment of consumption. Meatless meals and meatless days were resorted to at various times (6).

Subsidy Programs

During 1943–46, Government subsidy payments were made to livestock slaughterers and to livestock producers to hold down the price of meat to consumers and to maintain or increase returns to producers. A third objective was to prevent losses by slaughterers and meat processors because of Government price controls as required by the Price Control Act. Subsidy payments to livestock slaughteres also were used to implement programs to control prices of live animals (with slaughterers forced to comply with ceiling price regulations to be eligible for payments), and to channel more livestock through federally inspected packing plants to aid Government procurement and obtain better distribution of meat for civilians in deficit meat areas. To accomplish the last objective, subsidy payments to nonfederally inspected slaughterers were limited for a time during 1945 to a percentageof the kill in a previous period, with no limitation of payments to plants operating under Federal inspection. . . .

War Meat Board

The War Meat Board was created May 15, 1943, chiefly to coordinate the meat rationing and Government meat-buying programs from day to day and week to week. The principal responsibility of the Board was to divide weekly supplies of meat among the different claimants. This was done largely by allocation of weekly purchases of meat by the Department of Agriculture and the Army, which bought most of the meat for the Armed Forces. The Board also helped the Government obtain its meat requirements by recommending changes in the set-asides, in the ceiling price regulations, or in meat rationing. The quarterly meat allocations continued to be made by the Meat Requirements Committee in Washington after the War Meat Board was set up.

The War Meat Board operated at Chicago, the slaughter center of the country and the seat of the Quartermaster Corps, Chicago Quartermaster Center, and Chicago Quartermaster Depot. The 12-man board consisted of one representative of the War Food Administration, 1 from the Army, 2 from OPA (1 from the Price Branch and 1 from the Rationing Branch) and 7 members from the meat-packing industry to cover the following divisions of the meat trade: Pork, beef, lamb, veal, and canned meat. The Board usually met once a week to discuss various proposals to improve the meat-management program as: Allocation of weekly purchases between the Army and the Department of Agriculture, packers' processing problems, changes in meat set-asides, or changes in meat rationing, or meat ceiling price regulations.

The permanent secretary of the War Meat Board made current weekly estimates of federally inspected slaughter by regions and meat production estimates for the United States, as the basis for the current division of meat between civilians and other claimants. Weekly estimates were based upon telegraphic reports from a sample of federally inspected slaughterers. The Board also prepared estimates of supply and distribution and checked on compliance under the meat set-asides.

Combined Food Board

Early in the war, as supplies of meat in the United States and in the other allied nations became short of total requirements, it became necessary to develop a system of dividing supplies among the allied nations. International allocation of meat supplies was fostered by agreements of the United Nations to share armaments, food, and raw material resources for the prosecution of the war. The allocation procedure embraced various activities directed toward the division of food among claimants in such a way that the available supplies would be most effectively utilized in the conduct of the war. It involved (1) bringing together information on stocks and anticipated production during the period for which the allocation was to be made, (2) estimating the requirements to be met from the anticipated supplies, and (3) determining the amounts to be made available against the requirements of each claimant.

The Combined Food was charged with the responsibility "to work in collaboration with others of the United Nations toward the best utilization of their food resources, and, in collaboration with the interested nation, or nations, to formulate plans and recommendations for the development, expansion, purchase, or other effective use of their food resources." This Board discussed general allocation problems, passed on specific recommendations, reviewed international documents, and settled questions of mutual interest. International allocations of all foods were determined on the basis of requirements and supplies of each country in the light of shipping conditions or other considerations.

The Board, as first established in June 1942, consisted of the Secretary of Agriculture and the head of the British Food Mission, and a staff of officers. It was also made up of a number of subordinate commodity committees, each of which handled a group of foods. In October 1943, membership of the Board was expanded to include the Canadian Minister of Agriculture and the War Food Administrator. The Secretary of Agriculture remained on the Board as chairman.

Early in the war, the United Kingdom was designated as the sole purchaser of canned meats from South America. Some canned beef from foreign countries was allocated to the United States armed forces, during the war, but most of the exportable supply from South America, Australia, New Zealand, and Canada went to the United Kingdom.

The first international allocation for export supplies of all meat from the Americas and other United Nations was announced by the President on February 6, 1946. The export goal from the United States was set at 1.6 billion pounds (dressed-meat basis) for the year 1946. A large portion of United States export supplies were to be shipped by the United Nations Relief and Rehabilitation Administration to famine relief countries. . . .

Meat Rationing

Civilian supplies of meat became short of the demand at ceiling prices in mid-1942, especially in areas of deficit production. This situation was due principally to the combination of large requirements for meat for the armed forces and for lend-lease shipment, and increased demand for meat by domestic consumers. Regional distribution of meat supplies was particularly uneven because of the imposition of price ceilings. It was the view within the Department that some program of curtailed consumption of meat would have to be inaugurated, if price ceilings were to be maintained in the face of the greatly increased demand for meat and if Government requirements were to be filled. Meatless days or formal ration appeared to be the only alternatives.

As it would take some time to get a program of formal meat rationing into operation, Department of Agriculture officials suggested that a program of meatless days should be started, which perhaps could be terminated during the period of seasonally large slaughter from October to February. It was felt that equitable distribution of the limited supplies of meat would be difficult for the duration of the war and formal consumer rationing appeared to be the only satisfactory alternative.

The Secretary of Agriculture, as Chairman of the War Production Board's Foods Requirements Committee, announced a voluntary plan for meat conservation September 1, 1942, to be followed in due time by rationing. Civilians were asked to consume no more than 2½ pounds of meat per person per week.

Responsibility for determining "the need and the amount of food available for civilian rationing" was transferred to the Secretary of Agriculture by Executive Order 9280, issued December 5, 1942. This authority was limited, however, by provisions in the Executive Order requiring the Secretary to consult with the Price Administrator before making decisions on rationing and by specifying that the rationing programs were to be carried out by the Office of Price Administration.

OPA instituted point rationing of meat, along with butter, cheese, canned milk, canned fish, edible offal products, and fats and oils on March 29, 1943. Consumption of these commodities was controlled with red ration coupons and canned fruits and vegetables were controlled by blue ration coupons. Poultry and fresh fish were not rationed.

Under rationing each consumer was issued a set of ration books. Specified coupons from designated books were needed to buy meat. The coupons became valid at certain dates for use during a monthly period or other time interval. Each coupon was worth a specified number of ration points. The consumer presented his coupons to the butcher who took a certain number of points per pound as prescribed by the OPA which varied according to the kind of meat the consumer bought. The butcher made change in red ration tokens. The quantity of meat a retailer received was based on the number of ration points he was able to take in. The quantity of meat a retailer received from a wholesaler or slaughterer was based upon the number of ration points he had been able to accumulate.

It was not possible to achieve even distribution of civilian meat supplies under point rationing alone. Consumption of meat tended to be relatively greatest in the areas nearest production. Set-asides from the output of federally inspected slaughterers (for Government purchase) restricted the civilian meat supply most in areas that relied heavily on federally inspected supplies. In areas in which nonfederally inspected production of meats was large, the supply for civilians was relatively greater.

Other factors that contributed to the unequal distribution of meat by geographical areas were: (1) Ceiling prices that did not allow for normal geographical price differentials, largely within OPA regional price zones; (2) higher allowable ceilings on meat delivered to hotel supply houses, which resulted in relatively larger supplies available for restaurants than for household consumers; (3) black-market sales at above-ceiling prices and/or without surrender of ration coupons.

In order to reduce the administrative load for the meat-price program of OPA, the United States was divided into several price zones. Retail prices set for meat in all areas of each zone were equal. For example, prices at New York City and Boston were set at the same level under ceilings. Under a free market, prices of meat in Boston tend to be slightly higher than at New York City. Under ceiling prices, meat distributors would tend to send supplies to that part of an OPA price zone where their costs were lowest. However, they were prevented from doing this to some extent because of fear of the loss of peacetime markets and the disuse in some areas of their facilities for distribution.

Meat allocation and rationing programs were closely related. It was the view originally that rationing could be used to control the civilian supply, that by adjusting ration points the supply going to civilian channels could be controlled and stocks of meat built up during periods of peak production and withdrawn during times of light slaughter. It was soon apparent that the cold-storage facilities of the country were inadequate for any great accumulation of meat and that if it were not allowed to flow out of the rationing system into consumption legally, it would do so through black-market channels. It finally became accepted that the rationing system was not strong enough to control the total quantity of meats consumed by civilians, that it would only distribute supplies more equitably.

The meat allocations provided for peak purchases by the armed forces and WFA during periods when production was seasonally large. This would leave civilians with more uniform supplies throughout the year. However, this objective could not always be carried out. A shortage of refrigerator shipping space developed in the late winter and spring of 1944, so that storage facilities for meat became over-taxed and purchases for export had to be reduced. This, combined with record large production and other factors, resulted in the decision to remove most meats from rationing in the second half of 1944. The military also failed to purchase its full allocation during the last quarter of the year. For the year 1944 as a whole, civilians in the United States received the largest quantity of meat per person in 35 years. The relaxation of rationing in 1944 and the reduction in stocks were partly responsible for the strict rationing of meats in 1945. However, the reduction in stocks was small in relation to a decline in production of 1.5 billion pounds from 1944 to 1945. Storage space for holding meat was not adequate to carry over such large supplies and there was little incentive for packers to store meat under price ceilings which provided for no seasonal price changes.

Deliveries of meat to hotel supply houses were controlled by OPA rationing regulations and quotas were set for institutional users and manufacturers of products containing meat. Exports of the Bureau of the Census showed that in 1939, 9 percent of all meat delivered by the wholesale meat-packing industry was delivered to institutional users (1, p. 63). During meat rationing, OPA alloted roughly 20 percent of the meat ration points to institutional users and cafes. The exact use of meat by these users was not known. Consumption of meat in cafes increased greatly during the war because of the many troops and others traveling, the high wartime incomes, and scarcities of meat for households.

It was the view of many that, when rationing of meat became effective, other aids to distribution of the available supply would not be needed. Adjustment of point values would be the only thing needed to obtain even distribution. Point-value adjustments did even out supplies of meat when the gap between supply and demand was small (in 1944 for example). However, when supplies of meat fell far below demand in the summer of 1945, all the aids to distribution — rationing, slaughter controls, quotas for cafes, hotels and similar users, and quotas for institutional users — did not achieve even distribution of the meat supply by areas. A severe shortage existed in cities which depended largely upon federally inspected supplies. There was a shortage of fat back in the South because Chicago restaurants were serving fried fat back in place of unobtainable bacon. City people were buying meat from their relatives in the country. Cold-storage lockers were being filled with point-free meat.

One controversy in the rationing program was whether to ration meats separately from fats and oils and dairy products (cheese, butter, and canned milk), or whether to ration all meats, fats, oils, and dairy products as a group. The latter was done during all of the rationing period. A separation allowing meat to be rationed as one group, and fats, oils, and dairy products as another would have permitted more definite and accurate control over both the meat-ration system and the fats, oils, and dairy-products systems. Rationing fats, oils, and dairy products as a group gave ration-book holders more latitude to distribute purchases and it minimized adjustments in point values. Considering the magnitude of the task, rationing all these foods under the red ration stamp plan actually worked very well, except in the case of butter rationing. Point values were adjusted to limit the demand for each particular item. The setting of high points on butter was necessary, however, in an effort to get good distribution of the butter supply in those areas far from producing centers. The setting of high points tended to create black-market dealing in butter.

The Office of Price Administration resisted pressures to increase meat rations for workers in heavy industries. However, when production of coal lagged behind requirements in 1945, at a time when meat rations were lowest for the war period, miners struck for larger meat rations, which were granted. In many countries, under wartime rationing, special food allotments were given to persons engaged in certain types of work. But in the United States, the average diet was materially better than in many other countries. OPA issued special meat rations to persons who were ill when a doctor certified to the need.

Removal of meats from rationing November 24, 1945, was in large degree responsible for the difficulties in controlling black marketing in meat in the next year, the poor distribution of meat, and the difficulties in meeting the meat-export goal. It contributed in part to the break-down of the whole price-wage stabilization program in 1946. The decision to remove meat from rationing resulted from the cut-back in larger meat supplied with seasonally large marketings, record production of poultry, and prospects for record supplies of eggs. It was thought that curtailed purchases by the Army of canned meats and the seasonal large run of grass-fat cattle would result in prices of lower-grade beef falling below the ceilings.

The meat-supply situation did not ease as much as had been anticipated. On December 20, 1945, the Bureau of Agricultural Economics (11) reported, "Civilian demand for meats is so strong, particularly since the end of rationing on November 24, that procurement to fill Government needs has been difficult." Demand for meat continued exceptionally strong throughout 1946 and the meat supply situation was aggravated by the small slaughter in May and June and again in September and early October.

The even distribution of meat supplies under the rationing program helped to a large degree to control prices of meat. When supplies were poorly distributed black markets flourished. The inability of the OPA to enforce price ceilings on meat, particularly beef, was one of the reasons advanced by Congress for curbing the powers of OPA. The freeing of meat and other foods from price control paved the way for removal of price ceilings from other products and removal of wage controls.

Farm Price Policies

From Walter W. Wilcox, *The Farmer in the Second World War,* Iowa State University Press Ames, Ia., 1947), pp. 243–63.

In a sense, the precedent for the Steagall Amendment grew out of the corn and other commodity loans started in the fall of 1933. These government loans on commodities were administered in conjunction with the AAA programs during the 1930's and were extremely popular with farmers and farm leaders. In most years prices were pegged at the loan level which usually was higher than open market prices would have been. During the same period farmers and the Department of Agriculture also obtained experience with government purchase and distribution programs as a means of supporting prices of farm products.

Secretary Wickard had this background in mind in April, 1941, when he announced that the Department would support hog prices at $9.00 per hundred pounds to encourage increased hog production. This was followed by legislative action during the summer directing the Secretary (1) to support the prices of all products for which he asked production increases (2) at a minimum of 85 per cent of parity (3) for a long enough period to permit farmers to make readjustments back to normal systems of farming.

As a result of this legislation, the Department of Agriculture promised price supports at 85 per cent of parity or higher on a large number of commodities in the fall of 1941 and the spring of 1942.

It is possible that no further price support legislation would have been enacted during the war (except to increase the level to 90 per cent of parity) if farm leaders had not succeeded in setting minimum farm price ceilings at 110 per cent of parity in the original price control act. In the summer of 1942, the President was convinced by his advisers that the price control act should be amended to permit ceilings on farm products at 100 per cent of parity in order to prevent further food price rises. At the same time, the Secretary of Agriculture, concerned that farmers should receive equal treatment with business firms contracting with the military services, proposed that farm income be guaranteed by the government for a reasonable readjustment period after the war. The proposal was discussed informally with congressional committees and with farm organizations. Reactions were favorable. Farm organization leaders recommended that such legislation take the form of government support of prices at a stated percentage of parity. This plan received the approval of the President's advisers, especially Henry Wallace and Harry Hopkins.

The President proposed such legislation at the same time that he asked for a reduction in the minimum permissible price ceilings from 110 to 100 per cent of parity. His statement was as follows:

"As a part of our general program on farm prices, I recommend that Congress in due time give consideration to the advisability of legislation which would place a floor under prices of farm products, in order to maintain stability in the farm market for a reasonable future time. In other words, we should find a practicable method which will not only enable us to place a reasonable ceiling or maximum price upon farm products but which will enable us also to guarantee to the farmer that he would receive a fair minimum price for his products for one year, or even two years — or whatever period is necessary after the end of the war. Every farmer remembers what happened to his prices after the last war. We can, I am sure, if we act promptly and wisely, stabilize the farmer's economy so that the postwar disaster of 1920 will not overtake him again.

"The farmer, instead of looking forward to a new collapse in farm prices at the end of the war, should be able to look forward with assurance to receiving a fair minimum price for one or two years after the war. Such a national policy could be established by legislation."

Two matters of interest regarding this recommendation should be pointed out. The first is that though the Department of Agriculture maintains a highly competent Bureau of Agricultural Economics, there is no evidence that the Bureau was asked for an analysis of the feasibility of such a proposal nor for a statement of the fiscal and other commitments which might be involved in carrying out such a mandate from Congress. The second is the fact that a government official rather than organized farm groups took the initiative in sponsoring the original proposal.

The House of Representatives, acting on the President's recommendation, passed a bill which provided for government price supports for a three-year period beginning January 1 following the official end of the war. The Senate bill failed to specify any definite period, and there is little evidence in the Congressional record indicating that this provision was the subject of controversy. Congressmen were more vitally concerned about the language spelling out minimum ceiling levels for farm products and directives for wage controls than with farm price supports after the war. Thus one of our more significant additions to farm legislation during the war came into existence in a rather casual manner.

The House and the Senate conferees compromised on the two-year price support period. All basic commodities (corn, wheat, cotton, rice, tobacco, and peanuts for nuts) were covered, as well as all commodities which the Department of Agriculture had requested farmers to increase during the war. This compromise was enacted into law without opposition.

Few Price Support Difficulties During War

Only twenty products were covered by legislation (there are fourteen "Steagall" commodities). As a technique of wartime production management, however, price supports were extended to more and more commodities until in 1945 some 166 were included. As USDA officials gained experience, they improved the manner of announcing price supports with respect to timing, grade specifications and geographic differentials, and the mechanics of carrying out support guarantees. Actually, government activities to support prices were not extensive during the war. The wartime demand for all farm products was so great that prices dropped to support levels in only a few exceptional cases and for very short periods. Egg prices dropped to and below support levels in the spring of 1944 and again in the spring of 1945. Poultry dropped to support price levels in the fall and winter of 1945–46. Potato prices dropped to support levels in the summer of 1943, and have required some government loan, purchase or diversion activities each year since that time. Prices of several other vegetable and truck crops fell to support levels for short periods when temporary seasonal gluts occurred. During the winter of 1943–44 the market glut of hogs brought prices down to support levels, and only government action kept them from going lower. With these exceptions the government was not required to make good on its price support guarantees.

At least two major issues have been crystallized as a result of the limited war experience. (1) How far shall the government go in setting up area and local marketing organizations to assure support prices to individual farmers in each locality of the United States? (2) How far shall the government go in supporting prices of inferior-quality products? The administration purchased nearly all the offerings of some commodities such as eggs and potatoes, without regard to quality. It paid some producers for eggs and potatoes so low in quality they could not be used for food. It also developed local marketing programs in some cases which extended government price support to local dealers. The purchase of eggs in ten-case lots from local dealers in the South is an example. For most commodities, however, support price guarantees were limited to specified grades of products at central markets. Since prices of few products fell to support levels, farmer dissatisfaction did not have an opportunity to develop.

During the war the government tried to expand production of most foods as far as possible in every locality. Price supports were designed mainly to stimulate this increase in production on a selective basis in line with annual national goals. Farmers in localities with inadequate marketing facilities insisted that they had done their part in producing the food wanted. It was up to the government to do its part by assuring them prices at promised support levels in each community. The government recognized the validity of this argument in several cases. . . .

Little useful experience was gained during the war in the disposal of products bought by the government to support market prices. Wartime conditions were too different from those that can be expected to prevail in peacetime. We can be sure that once any product passes into the hands of the government, strenuous efforts will be made by all private interests to prevent its use in competition (actual or fancied) with privately owned supplies. During the war, potatoes were diverted into livestock feed and alcohol. A few eggs were used in tankage and fertilizer. In order to avoid later uncertainties, plans for handling and disposing of products acquired by the government in support price activities should be agreed upon and made a part of the support price announcement. To a large extent this would avoid later claims of unfair government action.

Stronger Distribution Controls Needed

The greatest mistake made by Congress in basic legislation and appropriations, and by the Office of Price Administration in its program, was the imposition of price ceilings on thousands of products without adequate provision for keeping the supplies flowing through the established channels. The difficulties arising from the absence of marketing controls were particularly serious in dairy products, poultry, livestock, and meat, and in farm supplies, such as baling wire, milk cans, and vegetable shipping crates. Many more examples could be cited. If it becomes necessary to impose price ceilings again, the public and Congress should be fully informed regarding the necessity of supplementary distribution controls to avoid black markets and to assure accomplishment of desired objectives.

Farm Income More Than Doubled

As a result of both rapidly expanding production and price increases, farm income more than doubled between 1939 and 1943. Only slight further gains were made in 1944 and 1945. Bigger subsidies were more important than further price rises in accounting for the increase in farm income after 1943. When production expenses were deducted, net income to persons on farms from farming increased from 5.3 billion dollars in 1939 to 13.6 billion in 1944, an increase of 156 per cent. . . .

Farm Price Increases Exceeded Wage Increases

When government controls become necessary to accomplish some public purpose, two criteria usually are used evaluate them. The first is whether the control produces the effect desired. The second is whether those individuals affected by the controls are equally treated. Farm organizations believed that the Price Control Act restricted farm prices more than wages would be held in check by the labor boards. The record indicates, however, that farm prices averaged from 106 to 119 per cent of parity for the years 1942 through 1945. The rise in farm prices between the summer of 1939 and the summer of 1945 when the war ended was 131 per cent. This is in contrast to an increase of 61 per cent in hourly earnings of labor during the same period. (Hourly earnings of labor, including overtime payment rates, are more comparable with prices received by farmers than any other statistical series available.) . . . .

Wheat Farmers' Incomes Increase Most

The Bureau of Agricultural Economics has compiled data showing the approximate production, income, and expenses for different kinds of family-operated farms during the war years. These figures indicate the annual net returns to the farm operators producing different crops and livestock.

Wheat farmers in 1938 and 1939 had yields somewhat below normal. In contrast, wheat yields in 1944 and 1945 were substantially above their long-time average. Increases in wheat yields on the family-operated farms amounted to as much as 50 to 75 per cent between 1938–39 and 1944–45. This was an important factor in the phenomenal increases in net income achieved by wheat farmers. Typical family-operated wheat farms in the Southern Plains had net incomes of $558 and $934 in 1938–39. In 1944–45 their net incomes had increased to $6,708 and $8,196 per farm.

Midwest farmers producing hogs and fattening beef cattle ranked second to the wheat farmers in increases in net income during the war. Midwest cash grain farmers had almost as large increases. Corn Belt livestock farmers increased their production more than any other regional group by growing larger acreages of soybeans and corn and feeding up their reserve feed supplies. Net incomes of family-operated farms increased from two to four times.

Were Subsidies Necessary?

Agricultural leaders criticized the "consumer subsidies" adopted during the war years more severely than any other phase of the government's price program. Their objection to these subsidies was an important factor contributing to Congressional opposition to the extension of price control after June 30, 1946. In view of this opposition an analysis of the contribution of food and agricultural subsidies to the wartime price program is in order.

The first attempt to use government payments or subsidies on a large scale in the war agricultural program was defeated in Congress. This was the incentive payment plan proposed early in 1943. It was based on the sound economic principle of offering farmers a special payment for each acre of needed war crops in excess of what they might normally grow. Economists pointed out that the additional production called for by high goals meant higher costs than with the usual levels of production. Through incentive payments the farmer could be induced to expand without the price of the entire crop being raised. In this way costs to the government and to consumers could be minimized.

When the Secretary of Agriculture in early 1943 proposed such incentive payments totaling $100,000,000 to growers of soybeans, flax, peanuts, potatoes, and truck crops, the political reaction against it was prompt and vigorous. The Secretary decided that he had enough funds at his disposal to make incentive payments on increased acreages of potatoes and truck crops anyway. Incentive payments for these two crops totaled $29,000,000 in 1943 but were discontinued in 1944, because sufficient production was expected to meet the goals without additional payments.

In May, 1943, the executive branch of the government decided subsidies were needed to "roll back" meat and butter prices. This time the Administration went ahead, using funds currently available in the Reconstruction Finance Corporation, without asking Congressional approval.

Unfortunately, most discussions of the relative merits of subsidies fail to take into account the most important issues. Whether one agrees or disagrees with the government action, it is important to see clearly the issues faced by the administrators when they decided to pay out subsidies totaling 500 to 700 million dollars a year to reduce retail prices of meat and butter 10 per cent in the middle of 1943.

The index of the cost of living had been rising steadily in spite of price ceilings. Food and meat prices in particular had increased sharply.

Labor leaders were complaining bitterly about rising food and living costs with threats of strikes which would seriously hamper the war effort. The drive for rolling back food prices started early in April. Labor's shift from demands for wage increases to demands for lower food prices came as a surprise and was welcomed by individuals concerned with preventing wartime inflation. On April 2, 1943, the *Washington Post* reported: "Organized labor yesterday reversed its strategy and asked President Roosevelt to lower prices, instead of asking him to raise wages.

"Phillip Murray, president of the C.I.O., after a meeting of the Combined Labor Board with President Roosevelt, said that the committee of the A.F. of L. and C.I.O. leaders had requested President Roosevelt to roll food prices back to September 15, 1942, levels and keep them there with rigid ceilings.

"The joint labor group scheduled the meeting with the President originally with the disclosed intention of asking him to raise the War Labor Board's 'Little Steel' wage ceiling from 15 percent to 23 percent."

The following day Walter Lippman wrote: "Not for a long time has anything so promising happened on the home front as the decision which labor leaders made public after their meeting at the White House Thursday. Mr. Green and Mr. Murray tell us that, instead of a campaign to increase wage rates, they will make a campaign to restore and stabilize food prices. They could not have made a decision which serves better the country as a whole, their own rank and file and the cause of organized labor."

On the same day the *Post* editorialized favorably: "Organized labor is now showing signs of putting national interest above its own group interests. The gesture from Messrs. Murray and Green in seeking price stability in place of wage increases deserves a similar gesture from the farm bloc."

Labor unrest and dissatisfaction reached a climax in May with the threatened strike of the coal miners. Agnes Meyer of the *Washington Post* made a trip through the coal fields in early May and quoted miners as saying, "Tell those folks in Washington to give us enough to eat at the right prices and we'll go along. But if they can't make good, we've got to have more money. And we're not going to wait long for the answer." She reported, "That statement in one form or another was made in every discussion I have had with the miners during the past four days of travel through the bituminous coal regions of Southeastern Pennsylvania."

Administration leaders in the Office of Economic Stabilization, the Office of Price Administration, and the War Labor Board carried on a series of discussions before deciding on the program adopted. Officials of the War Food Administration were also consulted, and in spite of their opposition, were advised of the administrative decision to lower retail meat and butter prices through the use of subsidies.

The Administration had several alternatives. It might grant further wage increases. It might refuse to grant any wage increases and use whatever measures were necessary to prevent work stoppages. At the other extreme it could lower price ceilings and allow the lower ceilings to be reflected in lower returns to producers. Instead, it chose the compromise plan of reducing meat and butter prices 10 per cent but absorbing this reduction by subsidies to processors in order that the price would not be lowered to producers. The decision to introduce subsidies rather than either reduce prices to producers or allow wage increases was largely a political decision.

Some people pointed out that laborers had little ground for their claims for increased wages based on rising living costs. As a matter of fact, the increase in average hourly earnings from prewar levels was about double the increase in the cost of living. Between August, 1939, and April, 1943, average hourly earnings had increased 49 per cent while the cost of living index only increased 25 per cent. In view of this, perhaps the government could and should have taken decisive steps to stabilize both labor earnings and living costs at their current levels instead of introducing subsidies to lower the cost of living index. If it had done so with success, a great deal of later controversy might have been avoided. Whether the administration merely allowed itself to be bluffed by labor or whether it made a wise political decision we can leave to future historians. In any event a new pattern was set by these subsidies; more followed, and once a substantial subsidy was established, there was no serious effort to remove it until after the end of the war.

At the end of the war in the summer of 1945, subsidies were being paid on eighteen different foods and agricultural products, or groups of foods, at the rate of around 1.6 billion dollars a year.

Opa's Defense of Subsidies

Subsidies had become such a political issue in 1944 that the Office of Price Administration issued a special bulletin in their defense. This bulletin pointed out that, "Between September 1942, the month set by Congress in the Stabilization Act as the base for wage and cost-of-living stabilization, and April 1943, the cost of living rose 5.3 percent, the cost of foods 11 percent. A continuation of this same rate of increase would by April 1944 have brought the cost of living 15 percent above the level named in the statute . . . one year after issuance of the hold-the-line order, the cost of living still shows no significant net change . . . after two and a half years of steady increase in the cost of living the line has been held for a solid year."

The program announced April 30, 1943, comprised four main points:

(1) The reduction of retail fruit and vegetable prices . . . back to levels reflecting reasonable distributors' margins and farm returns.

(2) The reduction of retail meat and butter prices by 10 per cent.

(3) The rapid establishment of specific dollar and cents prices, community by community, so that housewife and retailer alike might know exact ceiling prices.

(4) The tightening up of enforcement to eliminate violations . . . (Stores reporting to the Bureau of Labor Statistics voluntarily reported prices averaging 5 per cent above ceiling levels.)

Following the original program ". . . key cost-of-living prices which would have had to rise still further were held stable by the use of subsidies to cover increased costs of production . . .

"Subsidies are, of course, only a single element in the program developed to effectuate the Stabilization Act, but they are an essential element."

If one accepts the literal interpretation of the Stabilization Act of October, 1942, that the cost of living was to be stabilized at the September level, subsidies were the only alternative to reducing prices to producers when retail prices were reduced. In the case of fruits and vegetables, returns to producers were recognized as unnecessarily high, and lower retail prices were reflected in lower farm prices. Farm leaders, the opponents of the subsidies on meat, butter, and subsequent products, never suggested that producer prices be lowered to avoid the necessity of subsidies. They continually demanded price ceiling increases sufficient to eliminate the subsidies.

The crux of the argument for the elimination of subsidies was that consumers, if accustomed to paying higher prices for food during war years, would be more willing to continue the practice in later years. Opinion polls of farmers usually showed divided opinions, with a majority favoring price ceiling increases to eliminate subsidies. Wallace's Farmer in Iowa conducted farmer polls throughout the war, several of which throw light on farmer opinion toward subsidies.

In May, 1943, after Congress had refused to approve $100,000,000 for incentive payments, a poll was conducted to determine whether farmers preferred incentive payments of $15.00 an acre for each acre in excess of 90 per cent of their soybean goal, or an increase in the support price of soybeans from $1.70 to $1.80. Thirty-two per cent favored incentive payments, 57 per cent voted for higher prices, and the rest were undecided.

In August, 1943, after the roll back on butter and meat prices had been in effect several weeks, farmers were polled on two questions relating to the use of food subsidies and inflation. Forty-three per cent voted to "let the consumer pay the full bill — he's making good money." Nineteen per cent voted that "We'll either have subsidies or inflation," while 38 per cent were undecided. When specifically asked if they approved of the roll back subsidy for butter, only 22 per cent approved. But when it was a question of continuing subsidies or taking a chance on lower farm incomes, as might be expected, farmers opposed the dropping of subsidies. This is brought out by questions on hog prices and supports by Wallaces' Farmer in December, 1945. The result of the poll was as follows:

"A. Drop subsidies and let the market set the price — no matter whether that price is $15 or $8 (per 100 pounds). Don't permit government interference—favored by 12 percent.

B. Use federal subsidies to the amount necessary to keep hog returns up to 90 percent of parity ($11 on Iowa farms) — favored by 62 percent.

C. Undecided — 26 percent."

The Wisconsin Agriculturist and Farmer, March 2, 1946, reported a survey in which 53 per cent of those interviewed were in favor of removal of all subsidies with comparable price increases to consumers, while 42 per cent preferred the continuation of direct farmer subsidies. Farm ogranizations, with the exception of the National Farmers Union, opposed subsidies vigorously at every opportunity throughout the war.

Their leaders argued that government payments should be eliminated because the public looked upon them as subsidies to farmers when in reality they were consumer subsidies in lieu of increases in price ceilings. They were afraid that when farmers asked for political considerations in the future the large government payments during the war might be used as an argument for not granting their requests.

Were Increased Returns to Farmers Necessary?

Another way of analyzing the desirability of the subsidies during the war is to examine the evidence indicating whether or not a price increase or government payment was necessary to obtain or continue production at desired levels. This question has been raised with respect to the dairy production payments. The hog-dairy competition reached its climax in 1943 and would have been much less severe after the feed-livestock crisis of that year in any event. The dairy production payments were a substantial addition to dairy farmers' incomes. They no doubt increased dairying a little — but their production effects are generally overestimated.

The decision not to roll back the prices of live hogs and cattle when retail prices were rolled back was based on both political and production considerations.

Political considerations probably were most important. Feed was the limiting factor in livestock production in 1943 and the following years. The OPA price ceilings on corn and livestock established a ratio between corn and livestock prices 15 to 30 per cent more favorable than in peacetime years. Yet we had no difficulty in getting all our available grain converted into livestock products in peacetime. Why was it necessary to widen these ratios during the war? The answer appears to be that we encouraged unusually favorable feeding ratios in the early war years to convert our abnormal grain supplies into edible food. By the time these supplies were gone, we had established a pattern which could not be changed for political reasons. The favorable feeding ratios had an effect opposite to that expected after the abnormally large reserve stocks had been reduced. Many farmers who had more grain than they could feed held it until they could grow the necessary livestock. This was done to make the extra profit from feeding, rather than selling the grain to other feeders and dairymen. Thus national carryovers of grain throughout the war years were above normal in spite of the urgency to convert all available feed into food.

Again in 1945 a series of producer subsidies were introduced to encourage the fattening of cattle and lambs to heavier weights. These subsidies had some production effects, but the most acute feed crisis of the entire war occurred the following year. As it turned out, it would have been far better if no extra feeding had been stimulated in the fall of 1945.

This discussion can be appropriately closed with observation that price policies, in an over-all sense, during the war period were intelligent and successful. In spite of important concessions to meet political pressure, they implemented our wartime goals. In specific cases, the government yielded to pressure groups or mistakingly granted subsidies or price increases to obtain production responses with little demonstrable effects on production.

Probably the policies which resulted in the most serious adverse developments were: (1) continued favorable livestock feeding ratios when reserves of cereals should have been accumulated for direct human consumption in famine areas and (2) failure to remove food subsidies and allow price rises in February, 1946, when wage rates were allowed to rise. This latter decision to continue subsidies on foods rather than permit price rises was made at the insistence of Chester Bowles and the President's advisers on economic stabilization, in spite of vigorous opposition by Secretary of Agriculture Anderson and his staff. In retrospect, this appears to have been a major political error which contributed substantially to the political opposition to the continuation of effective price control beyond June 30, 1946.

World War II Brings Changes in Farming

From Sherman E. Johnson, *"Changes in American Farming,"* U.S. Department of Agriculture Miscellaneous Publication No. 707 (December, 1949), pp. 1, 3–5, 10, 58, 61–62.

Record Farm Output

Farmers in the United States achieved a remarkable production record in the war years. The increase in total farm output from 1935–39 to 1944 was twice as large as during the entire period from 1919–23 to 1935–39. This was accomplished without significant expansion in the acreage of cropland, and despite scarce supplies of labor, machinery, and farm materials. The high level reached during the war has been maintained in the early postwar years, and the 1948 output was an all-time record.

The output of farm products available for human use for the three full war years 1942–44 averaged 128 percent of the prewar years 1935–39. In 1946 the level was 133 percent of prewar. Despite a short corn crop the output in 1947 averaged 129 percent of prewar. If the corn crop had been as large as might have been expected with average weather the total output in 1947 would have been about 132 percent of prewar. With a bumper corn crop in 1948 farm output reached the record total of 140 percent of 1935–39 (fig. 1, p. 2).[1]

This increase in output constitutes an unprecedented break from previous trends. Usually, changes in farming develop very slowly. They are often unnoticed until the record over a period of years is examined. Even such major innovations as the tractor and complementary machines adapted for mechanical power were introduced so gradually that they escaped special attention until their cumulative effects became unusually pronounced.

Sometimes extremely favorable or unfavorable weather brings large year-to-year changes in production. For example, 1934 was a year of catastrophic drought, and farm production was much lower than in the preceding years. In 1942, growing conditions were unusually favorable. In fact, consistently good weather was experienced in the three war years 1942–44 compared with the average of the years 1935–39. But those prewar years reflect weather conditions that were less favorable to farm production than is the expectancy over a period of years. And although weather factors were more favorable in 1942–44 than longer-time expectancy, other forces were responsible for most of the increase in production.

Considering the average of the years 1942–44, it appears that about one-fourth of the total increase in production can be accounted for by weather conditions that were more favorable than in the prewar years 1935–39. This means that with normal weather farm output in 1942–44 would have averaged about 120 percent of 1935–39.

Obviously then, only a rather small part of the wartime increase in production can be explained by favorable weather. And it follows that average weather alone would not bring a return to prewar production levels. Extremely unfavorable weather would reduce output temporarily. But agriculture experienced a production revolution during the war years, and a large part of the change is irreverisble. It will persist under peacetime conditions. To understand what has taken place it is necessary to analyze what happened in the war and early postwar years, to compare this experience with the record in World War I, and to trace the foundation for production increases that was laid in the interwar years.

The War Years

Combination of Forces Back of Higher Output

War and wartime needs for food, and the doubling of the prices received by farmers for their products, furnished the driving force for increased production, but a combination of favorable physical circumstances made the large-scale increase possible. Potential production capacity had been built up over the several years previous to the outbreak of World War II. This increased capacity had its origin in several factors, and each contributed to the higher wartime output. By a fortunate conjuncture of circumstances widespread progress in mechanization, greater use of lime and fertilizer, cover crops, and other conservation practices, use of improved varieties, a better balanced feeding of livestock, and more effective control of insects and disease, had all gathered momentum over the several years preceding World War II. Their current effects were obscured by the drought and depression of the 1930's, but developments had reached a stage where these improvements could be effectively combined and used in an all-out production effort. The result was an unprecedented increase in output.

The joint effects of these technological improvements on the volume of production may be illustrated by comparing them with the effects of the flow of water in its several tributaries on the water level of a large river. If water rises to flood stage in one of the tributaries this will, of course, increase the water level in the main stream, but if the tributary is small the effect may be scarcely noticeable when its flood reaches the main channel. Similarly, the effect of single improvements in farm production, that are important by themselves, are scarcely perceptible in their effect on total production. But if all the tributaries of a large river reach flood stage at the same time, the water in the main channel also rises to flood stage, and the change in the water level does not escape notice. In a sense this is the effect that adoption of the accumulation of technological improvements had on farm production in the years of World War II.

But one might make the comparison somewhat differently, and more correctly, by saying that the production-increasing potentialities of improvements that were made over a decade, and that normally would have been diverted gradually into the production stream, were held back by the drought and depression of the 1930's. It was the breaking of these restraints that caused the flood of production in the war years — in the same way that a simultaneous breaking of dams on several tributaries will cause a river to reach flood stage from water that was accumulated from a normal flow at the source.

Accumulation of Potential Capacity

As this accumulation of potential production capacity had escaped notice, the increase that was achieved was much larger than could have been forecast from past trends. It was much greater than the expansion that took place in World War I, because there was no similar accumulation of potential improvements at that time.

Perhaps none familiar with the South would have been so rash as to forecast, in the fall of 1941, that the acreage of peanuts picked and threshed in 1942 would be 177 percent of 1941, and that production for the years 1942–44 would average 175 percent of 1935–39. Likewise, none from the Corn Belt would have dared to forecast in 1941 that the production of soybeans harvested for beans in the years 1942–44 would be 338 percent of the production in 1935–39. Figure 2 shows the average 1942–44 production compared with prewar for some products in which major changes occurred. An optimistic advance estimate of wartime production probably would have averaged less than half of the increase that actually was achieved.

Mechanization was one of the most influential factors back of the increased output of farm products. The number of tractors on farms had gradually increased from less than 250,000 in 1920 to nearly 2,500,000 in 1945. Use of mechanical power and complementary equipment usually means more total production, but its most important effect is that a much larger share of the product goes to market. As mechanical power is substituted for draft animals, the land formerly used for horse and mule feed becomes available for producing commodities for human use. The shift to mechanical power from 1918 to 1945 made available about 55,000,000 crop acres, or about 15 percent of the available cropland, for the production of marketable commodities. In World War I this large area of cropland and millions of acres of pasture had to be used for producing feed for horses and mules.

Greater use of fertilizer and lime was another influential factor in stepping up farm output. Measured in plant nutrients (N,P_2O_5, K_2O), the total consumption of commercial fertilizer in 1945 was 95 percent above the quantity used in the prewar years, 1935–39. Application of liming materials was more than three times as large as in the prewar years. Based on estimates of additional output from increased use, it appears that the increased production resulting from the additional use of lime and fertilizer in 1945 accounted for about 15 percent of the total increase in output since 1935–39.

Crop improvements were another notable source of increased output. Use of hybrid seed increases the yield expectancy of corn about 20 percent. New varieties of oats adapted for use in the Corn Belt and Lake States, and rust-resistant improved winter varieties for the Southern States, were widely adopted in the later war years. Continued progress was made in shifting to the higher yielding and more nutritious legume hays.

Total land used for intertilled crops increased by about 6,000,000 acres, or 4 percent, from 1935–39 to 1944. Meanwhile, the total cropland used for crops increased about 9,000,000 acres, or 3 percent. This is a rather small change and is therefore a minor factor in increased output.

The building up of both livestock numbers and feed supplies in the years immediately preceding the war, and in 1942, made possible larger marketings of livestock and livestock products, especially in 1943 and 1944. Livestock production was increased also by the feeding of accumulated supplies of wheat, and of some imported wheat and feed grains. But feeding of both the accumulated supplies and the larger imports accounted for only about 10 percent of the total concentrates fed to livestock in the year ended October 1, 1944. Thus by far the largest proportion of the livestock output came from current production of grain, forage, and pasture; and from an increase of more than one-half in oilseed meals for livestock feed.

Fortunately there were no major outbreaks of either plant or animal diseases or of insect damage in the years of World War II. That no livestock diseases reached epidemic proportions despite record-breaking inventories of livestock was not only good fortune; it was an indication of the effectiveness of modern control methods, and of the vigilance of both farmers and technicians in controlling sporadic outbreaks. Insect damage was held to low levels despite shortages of such important insecticides as rotenone and pyrethrum.

With financial and patriotic incentives as encouragement, and with education and persuasion centered on virtually all-out production of strategic products, farmers and their families worked long hours and often utilized, to the best of their knowledge, every possible means of increasing output. Their efforts bore fruit so well that, even though about one-fourth of the food output went to military and other war-emergency uses, there was food enough in 1944 and 1945 to provide our civilians with a per capita food consumption 12 to 14 percent higher than took place in the prewar years, 1935–39. In somewhat different terms, the output of food in 1944 was enough to feed about 50,000,000 more people than were fed by the average quantity produced in 1935–39, assuming the same dietary levels for both periods.

Unfavorable Factors Minimized

That more people could be fed resulted partly from a change in the production pattern — more oil crops, beans, and peas, and less cotton — and from a more complete utilization of the output. But the shifts in production that were necessitated by war needs, made increases in the total volume of production more difficult (fig. 2, p. 4). Production per acre of per animal is usually lowered when a product is grown on land that is less suited for its production, or by growers who have insufficient experience.

The wartime increases in production were achieved with a constantly shrinking labor supply. The total farm population dropped from 30,000,000 in 1940 to 25,000,000 in 1945. In many small farm areas the decrease in farm population represented a correction of under-employment on farms that existed before the war; but in most of the commercial farming areas the result was a labor shortage.

Figure 3, page 6, shows the downward trend in farm employment and the contrasting sharp upward trend in production per worker. In 1944 farmers had a percent fewer workers than in 1935–39. Many of the hired workers who were available did not have the strength and skill that are usually considered necessary for farm work. But farmers and their families worked longer hours and, somehow the job was done. . . .

Higher Production Per Unit of Resources

The shift to mechanical power and the increase in production per acre have made it possible also to increase the number of animal units of productive livestock. Thus the total increase in livestock production is derived both from larger numbers of breeding stock and from the higher output per unit of breeding stock as shown in figure 5. On the other hand, figure 4 shows that increased crop production is largely the result of higher production per acre because changes in the acreage of cropland have been relatively small.

The higher output per acre and per animal, combined with mechanization, made possible the larger output per worker. The three series — production per acre, per animal, and per worker — summarize the startling changes that have taken place in farming since the years of World War I.

During the time that progress in technology has increased output per man so greatly in agriculture, the same phenomenon has occurred in industry. But if data were available for the service industries they probably would show a less rapid climb. Increases have occurred in all sectors, however.

This poses a key question for the postwar years. Will peacetime industry and service occupations expand sufficiently to absorb at satisfactory wage levels (1) the workers currently displaced by technological progress in both agriculture and industry and (2) the net supply of new workers (after allowing replacements for death and retirement) that enter the labor market each year? This is a crucial question. But before it is discussed in relation to peacetime agricultural production it is necessary to examine our wartime and early postwar records more closely. And first of all, it seems desirable to compare changes that took place in World War II with those of World War I, because production responses were so different despite the similarity of incentives to increase farm output. . . .

Postwar Developments

The end of the war relieved some of the scarcities of labor and materials. Farm employment averaged 92 percent of 1935–39 in 1946, 93 percent in 1947, and 92 percent in 1948, compared with 90 percent in 1945. New machinery was not available in sufficient volume to supply all farmers with all the machines they would like to buy until the spring of 1949, when most scarcities disappeared.

Production goals and support-price programs were in effect for the years 1946–48, but the price-ceiling structure lapsed temporarily in July 1946 and, after a short period of reinstatement, was removed from nearly all products in the fall of 1946. Most farm products sold at prices above support levels until the summer of 1948, although potatoes, eggs, and some other commodities required Government support at different times.

Prices received by farmers were 204 percent of their 1935–39 average in June 1946. In October 1946, after most of the price ceilings were removed, they were 255 percent of prewar. In January 1948 they had risen to 287 percent. In January 1949 they were 250 percent of 1935–39, and in April 1949 they were 243 percent.

It is evident that price incentives were even better in the first two postwar years than during the war. On the expense side, however, farm costs have also risen, but not so rapidly as prices received. Prices paid for goods and services used in farm production (not including farm wages) were 150 percent of 1935–39 in June 1946. They had risen to 163 percent in December 1946, and to 199 percent in December 1947. For the entire year of 1948 they averaged 201 percent of prewar, and in April 1949 they were 192 percent. Farm wage rates in the prewar years, 1935–39, were only about two-thirds of the level prevailing in the 1920's. But they rose very rapidly during the war, and in June 1946 they were 321 percent of 1935–39. They averaged 346 percent of prewar in 1947, and 367 percent in 1948.

With cost rates lagging behind the rise in farm prices, and with a much larger volume of output of marketable products, net farm incomes have increased a great deal. Figure 34, page 59, summarizes the gross and net farm-income results to the farmers of the country of their production job during the war and early postwar years. The realized net income of farm operators for the war years 1942–44 averaged 240 percent of the 1935–39 level. In 1946 it was 324 percent of the average for those years; and in 1947 it was 386 percent — nearly four times the net in ome of prewar years. The rise in net incomes from 1946 to 1947 is almost entirely attributable to changes in prices because the volume of production was slightly lower in 1947 than in 1946. In 1948 the net income was somewhat lower because of the decline in prices for farm products and rising rates of costs, but it still averaged 364 percent of 1935–39.

The greatly increased production per farm in recent years has meant relatively lower expenses per unit of product; and with more products to sell the net incomes rose faster than did the prices received for those products. If farmers should encounter several consecutive years of lower prices with cost rates remaining at or near present levels, their margin between expenses and gross income would narrow; and net incomes would be reduced faster than the drop in farm prices unless efficiency could be increased to reduce costs per unit of product and thus to offset the lag in cost rates.

IMPLICATIONS OF RECENT AND PROSPECTIVE CHANGES

The forces that shaped the course of agricultural production in the interwar, the war, and the early postwar years, have been analyzed briefly in these pages. Their effects on production are evident in the record-breaking volume of recent years. Most of these forces still have unexpended power. They will continue to influence production in the years beyond the transition from war to peace. New forces, expected and unexpected, will be set in motion. Always farmers will need to adapt their operations to the rapidly changing conditions.

Prospect Changes

Assuming that a stable peace can be established, and then looking forward beyond the transition years to the time when farming will be adjusted to peacetime conditions, some changes seem fairly certain. They will result from the operation of the forces now under way, and of those that are on the horizon. The changes that seem most likely to occur are summarized as follows:

1. A continuation of the shift to mechanical power until it has largely supplanted animal power is to be expected. The smaller tractors that are more suitable for small farms and rolling land will accelerate this shift in the South, and in other areas that have small farms.

2. Further adaptation of machines for use with mechanical power is certain. Each phase of agricultural production will become more mechanized, and more fully adapted to mechanical-power techniques. Eventually the same type of stability may be achieved with mechanical power as was attained with machinery adapted for animal power, previous to World War I. But this process will require some time for full development.

Haying equipment will be adapted to the special conditions of each producing area. Mechanical cotton pickers and strippers will be adopted, gradually at first, and then more rapidly as changes are made in them for more effective use in areas of rolling land and small farms. Some progress may be expected in mechanizing the production of such traditionally hand-labor crops as sweetpotatoes and even tabacco.

3. Use of lime and commercial fertilizer will rise above the high 1947 levels. How rapidly this increase will come depends partly on the kind of educational and conservation programs that are developed, and partly on the level of farm incomes. But many farmers have now learned the value of lime and fertilizer, and they are not likely to reduce their purchases except under conditions of severe depression.

4. Along with the use of more lime and fetilizers will come more rapid adoption of other conservation practices, such as using winter cover crops, grass and legume crops in the rotations, and following contour farming, strip cropping, and other practices designed to control erosion.

5. Further progress will be made in varietal improvements. For example, Lincoln soybeans and Clinton oats are now being adopted. Suitable corn hybrids are being developed and will be adopted in the Southern States. The effects of improved varieties of grain sorghums will become more pronounced.

6. Progress will be made by farmers in combining the use of improved varieties, lime and fertilizer, and conservation and other practices, in effective crop rotations and systems of farming that will result in much higher production because the combined effects of these improvements will be greater than if they are adopted as single practices. In North Carolina, for example, a number of corn experiments combining high nitrogren fertilization, hybrid seed, and other improved practices, resulted in yields of more than 80 bushels per acre compared with usual yields of 15 to 20 bushels.

7. More efficient methods to control pests and diseases of both plants and animals will be available. The effectiveness of the new materials and improvedtechniques for applications will become more evident within the next few years.

8. Results from animal-breeding experiments will gradually increase the efficiency of livestock production. Work now under way is likely to produce hogs that are more efficient converters of feed into pork of the more desirable cuts. Dairy-herd improvement will be accelerated by more widespread use of artificial insemination.

9. Further improvements will be made in feeding methods. More adequate and better balanced rations will contribute to increased output per animal.

10. Some new land will be brought under cultivation by irrigation, drainage, and clearing, but the total new farm acreage is not likely to be large. If public development work now under way is continued and if all authorized work is carried out, about 4,500,000 acres will be brought under irrigation in the next 10 years. Around 8,000,000 acres might be improved by drainage or clearing during the same period. About half of these developments would take place on existing farms and the rest would involve bringing new areas into production.

11. Supplementary irrigation in humid areas has developed rapidly during the last few years. It is likely to be extended further, especially if the market demand for the products that are irrigated is sustained at fairly high levels.

12. If opportunities for employment are freely open in the cities, many small and unproductive farms will shift from full-time to part-time operation, or even

become rural homes where little or no farming is done. If depression conditions should prevail for any length of time this movement might be reversed, as many unemployed people are likely to try to make at least a part of their living from the land.

13. As good roads, electricity, and other conveniences, become more readily available in rural areas more and more people engaged in nonfarm work will seek to establish rural homes. Thus the number of part-time farms and rural homes will be augmented from two sources: (1) Farm people shifting from full-time to part-time farming and (2) urban people seeking homes on the land.

14. Fewer workers will be needed in full-time farming as mechanization gains momentum in cotton production, and in other enterprises that now require much hand labor.

15. Family farms are likely to become larger and somewhat fewer as the productive capacity of farm workers is increased by the newer techniques. Some increase in the number of large-scale farms should be expected. They are not likely to constitute more than a small percentage of the total number of farms but they may produce a rather large percentage of total output.

16. Commercial farming will become a more complex business as technological advances continue. As family farms grow larger more capital will be needed for equipment and livestock. This means that adequate training and managerial ability of a higher order will be needed for successful operation of commercial farms.

Changes will occur that are now unforeseen. For example, we have no way of foretelling the impact on agriculture of developments in regard to atomic energy. Over the next quarter-century innovations may be even more significant than those that are now on the horizon. But they are likely to be less important in the next few years because a period testing of new developments is usually required, and later adoption by farmers is a gradual process.

Effect of Prospective Changes on Farm Output

Farm Output Likely to Continue at High Levels

Prospective changes that have been outlined are preponderantly those that will tend to push the output of farm products higher and higher, instead of allowing them to recede toward the prewar levels. In their study of peacetime production adjustments, State committees estimated that under favorable economic conditions after the war it would pay farmers to produce at a level about 43 percent above the prewar average.[7] These estimates were based on average weather conditions. They gave consideration to maintenance of soil resources, and included the effects of the adoption of known improvements that would be profitable under conditions of prosperity. Farm output in 1948 was 40 percent above 1935–39, but growing conditions were unusually favorable in that year.

If economic adversity should prevail, the rate of increase in output would be slowed down, but even under unfavorable price conditions, it does not seem likely that the total output would be reduced substantially, unless weather were less favorable than the average. Any reduction that would come from the use of less fertilizer, or from attempts to reduce other variable costs, would probably be partly offset by the effects of the landward pressure of unemployed people.

Severe drought, or other unfavorable growing conditions, could reduce the level of output considerably. In a drought year, like 1934 or 1936, the output might drop about 20 percent. But it would increase again when growing conditions improved. Some of the improved practices — such as using hybrid seed corn and drought-resistant varieties of wheat and grain sorghum, summer fallowing, and contour farming — provide considerable protection against unfavorable weather. But on the other hand, he yield-increasing effects of fertilizer and some other practices would not be realized in case of severe drought. Crop loss from unfavorable weather is one of the major hazards in present-day commercial farming.

Changes will occur that are now unforeseen. For example, we have no way of foretelling the impact on agriculture of developments in regard to atomic energy. Over the next quarter-century innovations may be even more significant than those that are now on the horizon. But they are likely to be less important in the next few years because a period of testing of new developments is usually required, and later adoption by farmers is a gradual process.

Aside from this hazard, most of the changes that have already taken place, as well as those in prospect, seem to point irreversibly in the direction of increased production. When the transition to peacetime market outlets has been completed, food production at high levels may have to face market difficulties, unless high employment and purchasing power are maintained, and the channels of international trade are kept open. Financial and trade barriers may limit exports that would supply unmet food needs in other countries.

But regardless of the market outlook, there is no road back from the agricultural revolution that we have experienced. Attention therefore necessarily centers on mobilization for efficient and profitable peacetime agriculture instead of reconversion to a prewar situation that will never return.

If the belief still lingers that production will recede to prewar levels, under average weather, the steps that would be retraced should be considered. Farmers generally cannot go back to animal power because there are too few horses and mules now on farms. The annual colt crops do not begin to maintain the numbers. The mechanical-power phase of mechanization is here to stay, and it is the cornerstone of high-volume output for the market. Going back to open-pollinated corn, or to low-yielding strains of other crops would be decidedly unprofitable even in a depression. And more effective control of insect pests and diseases is likely to be continued, somewhat regardless of price conditions.

It is possible that less fertilizer and lime would be used in a depression, of course, although it would be poor economy in the long run to reduce yields in this way. It would be contrary to the national interest to fail to apply the fertilizer that is necessary for maintaining stable, soil-saving crop rotations. Similarly, temporary reductions in expenses could be made by not carrying out certain conservation practices, but these savings would be made at the expense of future productivity.

Education and Experimentation

Research in Marketing

From 60 Statutes at Large 1082.

AMENDMENT OF THE BANKHEAD-JONES ACT AND THE AGRICULTURAL MARKETING ACT OF 1946

An act to provide for further research into basic laws and principles relating to agriculture and to improve and facilitate the marketing and distribution of agricultural products

Be it enacted by the Senate and House of Representatives of the United States of America in Congress assembled,

Title II

This title may be cited as the "Agricultural Marketing Act of 1946".

SEC. 202. The Congress hereby declares that a sound, efficient, and privately operated system for distributing and marketing agricultural products is essential to a prosperous agriculture and is indispensable to the maintenance of full employment and to the welfare, prosperity, and health of the Nation. It is further declared to be the policy of Congress to promote through research, study, experimentation, and through cooperation among Federal and State agencies, farm organizations, and private industry a scientific approach to the problems of marketing, transportation, and distribution of agricultural products similiar to the scientific methods which have been utilized so successfully during the past eighty-four years in connection with the production of agricultural products so that such products capable of being produced in abundance may be marketed in an orderly manner and efficiently distributed. In order to attain these objectives, it is the intent of Congress to provide for (1) continuous research to improve the marketing, handling, storage, processing, transportation, and distribution of agricultural products; (2) cooperation among Federal and State agencies, producers, industry organizations, and others in the development and effectuation of research and marketing programs to improve the distribution processes; (3) an integrated administration of all laws enacted by Congress to aid the distribution of agricultural products through research, market aids and services, and regulatory activities, to the end that marketing methods and facilities may be improved, that distribution costs may be reduced and the price spread between the producer and consumer may be narrowed, that dietary and nutritional standards may be improved, that new and wider markets for American agricultural products may be developed, both in the United States and in other countries, with a view to making it possible for the full production of American farms to be disposed of usefully, economically, profitably, and in an orderly manner. In effectuating the purposes of this title, maximum use shall be made of existing research facilities owned or controlled by the Federal Government or by State agricultural experiment stations and of the facilities of the Federal and State extension services. To the maximum extent practicable marketing research work done hereunder in cooperation with the States shall be done in cooperation with the State agricultural experiment stations; marketing educational and demonstrational work done hereunder in cooperation with the States shall be done in cooperation with the State agricultural extension service; market information, inspection, regulatory work and other marketing service done hereunder in cooperation with the State agencies shall be done in cooperation with the State departments of agriculture, and State bureaus and departments of market.

SEC. 203. The Secretary of Agriculture is directed and authorized:

(a) To conduct, assist, and foster research, investigation, and experimentation to determine the best methods of processing, preparation for market, packaging, handling, transporting, storing, distributing, and marketing agricultural products: *Provided,* That the results of such research shall be made available to the public for the purpose of expanding the use of American agricultural products in such manner as the Secretary of Agriculture may determine.

(b) To determine costs of marketing agricultural products in their various forms and through the various channels and to foster and assist in the development and establishment of more efficient marketing methods (including analyses of methods and proposed methods), practices, and facilities, for the purpose of bringing about more efficient and orderly marketing, and reducing the price spread between the producer and the consumer.

(c) To develop and improve standards of quality, condition, quantity, grade, and packaging, and recommend and demonstrate such standards in order to encourage uniformity and consistency in commercial practices.

(d) To conduct, assist, foster, and direct studies and informational programs designed to eliminate artificial barriers to the free movement of agricultural products.

(e) To foster and assist in the development of new or expanded markets (domestic and foreign) and new and expanded uses and in the moving of larger quantities of agricultural products through the private marketing system to consumers in the United States and abroad.

(f) To conduct and cooperate in consumer education for the more effective utilization and greater consumption of agricultural products: *Provided,* That no money appropriated under the authority of this Act shall be used to pay for newspaper or periodical advertising space or radio time in carrying out the purposes of this section and section 203 (e).

(g) To collect and disseminate marketing information, including adequate outlook information on a market-area basis, for the purpose of anticipating and meeting consumer requirements, aiding in the maintenance of farm income, and bringing about a balance between production and utilization of agricultural products.

(h) To inspect, certify, and identify the class, quality, quantity, and condition of agricultural products when shipped or received in interstate commerce, under such rules and regulations as the Secretary of Agriculture may prescribe, including assessment and collection of such fees as will be reasonable and as nearly as may be to cover the cost of the service rendered, to the end that agricultural products may be marketed to the best advantage, that trading may be facilitated, and that consumers may be able to obtain the quality product which they desire, except that no person shall be required to use the service authorized by this subsection. Any official certificate issued under the authority of this subsection shall be received by all officers and all courts of the United States as prima facie evidence of the truth of the statements therein contained.

(i) To determine the needs and develop or assist in the development of plans for efficient facilities and methods of operating such facilities for the proper assembly, processing, transportation, storage, distribution, and handling of agricultural products.

(j) To assist in improving transportation services and facilities and in obtaining equitable and reasonable transportation rates and services and adequate transportation facilities for agricultural products and farm supplies by making complaint or petition to the Interstate Commerce Commission, the Maritime Commission, the Civil Aeronautics Board, or other Federal or State transportation regulatory body with respect to rates, charges, tariffs, practices, and services, or by working directly with individual carriers or groups of carriers.

(k) To collect, tabulate, and disseminate statistics on marketing agricultural products, including, but not restricted to statistics on market supplies, storage stocks, quantity, quality, and condition of such products in various positions in the marketing channel, utilization of such products, shipments and unloads thereof.

(l) To develop and promulgate, for the use and at the request of any Federal agency or State, procurement standards and specifications for agricultural products, and submit such standards and specifications to such agency or State for use or adoption for procurement purposes.

(m) To conduct, assist, encourage, and promote research, investigation, and experimentation to determine the most efficient and practical means, methods, and processes for the handling, storing, preserving, protecting, processing, and distributing of agricultural commodities to the end that such commodities may be marketed in an orderly manner and to the best interest of the producers thereof.

(n) To conduct such other research and services and to perform such other activities as will facilitate the marketing, distribution, processing, and utilization of agricultural products through commercial channels.

SEC. 204. (a) In order to conduct research and service work in connection with the preparation for market, processing, packaging, handling, storing, transporting, distributing, and marketing of agricultural products as authorized by this title, there is hereby authorized to be appropriated the following sums:

(1) $2,500,000 for the fiscal year ending June 30, 1947, and each subsequent fiscal year.

(2) An additional $2,500,000 for the fiscal year ending June 30, 1948, and each subsequent fiscal year.

(3) An additional $5,000,000 for the fiscal year ending June 30, 1949, and each subsequent fiscal year.

(4) An additional $5,000,000 for the fiscal year ending June 30, 1950, and each subsequent fiscal year.

(5) An additional $5,000,000 for the fiscal year ending June 30, 1951, and each subsequent fiscal year.

(6) In addition to the foregoing, such additional funds beginning with the fiscal year ending June 30, 1952, and thereafter as the Congress may deem necessary.

Such sums appropriated in pursuance of this title shall be in addition to, and not in substitution for, sums appropriated or other wise made available to the Department of Agriculture.

(b) The Secretary of Agriculture is authorized to make available from such funds such sums as he may deem appropriate for allotment to State departments of agriculture, State bureaus and departments of markets, State agricultural experiment stations, and other appropriate State agencies for cooperative projects in marketing service and in marketing research to effectuate the purposes of title II of this Act: *Provided,* That no such allotment and no payment under any such allotment shall be made for any fiscal year to any State agency in excess of the amount which such State agency makes available out of its own funds for such research. The funds which State agencies are required to make available in order to qualify for such an allotment shall be in addition to any funds now available to such agencies for marketing services and for marketing research. The allotments authorized under this section shall be made to the agency or agencies best equipped and qualified to conduct the specific project to be undertaken. Such allotments shall be covered by cooperative agreements between the Secretary of Agriculture and the cooperating agency and shall include appropriate provisions for preventing duplication or overlapping of work within the State or States cooperating. Should duplication or overlapping occur subsequent to approval of a cooperative project or allotment of funds, the Secretary of Agriculture is authorized and directed to withhold unexpended balances on such projects notwithstanding the prior approval thereof.

SEC. 205. (a) In carrying out the provisions of title II of this Act, the Secretary of Agriculture may cooperate with other branches of the Government, State agencies, private research organizations, purchasing and consuming organizations, boards of trade, chambers of commerce, other associations of business or trade organizations, transportation and storage agencies and organizations, or other persons or corporations engaged in the production, transportation, storing, processing, marketing, and distribution of agricultural products whether operating in one or more jurisdictions. The Secretary of Agriculture shall have authority to enter into contracts and agreements under the terms of regulations promulgated by him with

States and agencies of States, private firms, institutions, and individuals for the purpose of conducting research and service work, making and compiling reports and surveys, and carrying out other functions relating thereto when in his judgment the services or functions to be performed will be carried out more effectively, more rapidly, or at less cost than if performed by the Department of Agriculture. Contracts hereunder may be made for work to be performed within a period not more than four years from the date of any such contract, and advance, progress, or other payments may be made. The provisions of section 3648 (31 U. S. C., sec. 529) and section 3709 (41 U.S.C., sec. 5) of the Revised Statutes shall not be applicable to contracts or agreements made under the authority of this section. Any unexpended balances of appropriations obligated by contracts as authorized by this section may, notwithstanding the provisions of section 5 of the Act of June 20, 1874, as amended (31 U.S.C., sec 713) remain upon the books of the Treasury for not more than five fiscal years before being carried to the surplus fund and covered into the Treasury. Any contract made pursuant to this section shall contain requirements making the result of such research and investigations available to the public by such means as the Secretary of Agriculture shall determine.

(b) The Secretary of Agriculture shall promulgate such orders, rules, and regulations as he deems necessary to carry out the provisions of this title. In his annual report to Congress, he shall include a complete statement of research work being performed under contracts or cooperative agreements under this title, showing the names of the agencies cooperating and the amounts expended thereon, segregated by Federal and non-Federal funds.

SEC. 206. In order to facilitate administration and to increase the effectiveness of the marketing research, service, and regulatory work of the Department of Agriculture to the fullest extent practicable, the Secretary of Agriculture is authorized, notwithstanding any other provisions of law, to transfer, group, coordinate, and consolidate the functions, powers, duties, and authorities of each and every agency, division, bureau, service, section, or other administrative unit in the Department of Agriculture primarily concerned with research, service, or regulatory activities in connection with the marketing, transportation, storage, processing, distribution of, or service or regulatory activities in connection with, the utilization of, agricultural products, into a single administrative agency. In making such changes as may be necessary to carry out effectively the purposes of this title, the records, property, personnel, and funds of such agencies, divisions, bureaus, services, sections, or other administrative units in the Department of Agriculture affected thereby are authorized to be transferred to and used by such administrative agency to which the transfer may be made, but such unexpended balances of appropriations so transferred shall be used only for the purposes for which such appropriations were made.

SEC. 207. When used in this title, the term "agricultural products" includes agricultural, horticultural, viticultural, and dairy products, livestock and poultry, bees, forest products, fish and shellfish, and any products thereof, including processed and manufactured products, and any and all products raised or produced on farms and any processed or manufactured product thereof.

SEC. 208. The Secretary of Agriculture shall have the power to appoint, remove, and fix, in accordance with existing law, the compensation of such officers and employees, and to make such expenditures as he deems necessary including expenditures for rent outside the District of Columbia, travel, supplies, books, equipment, and such other expenditures as may be necessary to the administration of this title: *Provided,* That the Secretary of Agriculture may appoint and fix the compensation of any technically qualified person, firm, or organization by contract or otherwise on a temporary basis and for a term not to exceed six months in any fiscal year to perform research, inspection, classification, technical, or other special services, without regard to the civil-service laws or the Classification Act of 1923, as amended.

Title III

SEC. 301. In order to aid in implementing the research and service work authorized under titles I and II of this Act, and to assist in obtaining the fullest cooperation among Federal and State agencies, producers, farm organizations, and private industry, in the development of and in effectuating such research and service programs, and in order to secure the greatest benefits from the expenditure of funds, the Secretary of Agriculture shall establish a national advisory committee. The functions of such advisory committee shall be to consult with the Secretary of Agriculture and other appropriate officials of the Department of Agriculture, to make recommendations relative to research and service work authorized by this Act, and to assist in obtaining the cooperation of producers, farm organizations, industry groups, and Federal and State agencies in the furtherance of such research and service programs. The chairman of the committee shall be the Secretary of Agriculture or such other official of the Department of Agriculture as he shall designate. The committee shall consist of eleven members, six of whom shall be representatives of producers or their organizations. The committee shall meet at least once each quarter and at such other times as are deemed necessary. Members of the committee may not appoint alternates to serve in their stead. Committee members other than the chairman shall not be deemed to the employees of the United States and are not entitled to compensation, but the Secretary of Agriculture is authorized to allow their traveling and subsistence expenses necessary in connection with their attendance at meetings called by him for the purposes of this section.

SEC. 302. In the furtherance of the research and service work authorized by this Act, the Secretary of Agriculture may, in addition to the national advisory committee, establish appropriate committees, including representatives of producers, industry, government, and science, to assist in effectuating specific research and service programs.

Approved August 14, 1946 (60 Stat. 1082).

Artificial Breeding

From Ralph W. Phillips, "Artificial Breeding," U.S. Department of Agriculture, *Yearbook,* 1943–1947 (Washington, 1947), pp. 113–21.

A bull can cover 30 to 50 cows a year under average conditions. Each time he spends millions of sperms, any of which could fertilize an egg and beget a calf. To correct such profligacy of nature, careless with the individual however concerned she may be with the species, man has developed a technique called artificial insemination, whereby semen is obtained from the male, diluted considerably, and a part of it placed manually in the cervix or uterus of the female. Thus a bull can impregnate 500 or 1,000 cows a year, or even more in special circumstances. The usefulness of good bulls and other males is multiplied manifold. There is less chance of spreading disease. The semen of valuable males can still be utilized even when they become too big or too old for natural service.

Animal breeders in the United States became actively interested in the technique a decade or so ago, although actually it is much older. The Italian scientist Lazaro Spallanzani in 1780 artificially inseminated a bitch to show that semen alone was sufficient to start normal pregnancy. The Russian Professor Elie Ivanov in 1919, after 20 years of preliminary work, set up the Central Experimental Breeding Station in Moscow to further the method.

At first some failures resulted in the United States from improper handling of semen, mismanagement of bulls, and inadequate financing of associations, but the work was successful generally, and it has become well established. In 1939, six associations of dairy cattle breeders used artificial insemination; they had 646 members who owned 33 bulls and 7,539 cows. In 1946, there were 336 associations, with 73,293 members in 29 States. These members owned 579,477 cows and were using 900 bulls. The leaders were Wisconsin, Pennsylvania, Ohio, New York, and Iowa. Another interesting comparison: In 1946, cooperative bull associations and bull studs in which natural mating is practiced had an average of 11.1 cows to a herd and 38 cows to a bull; artificial-breeding associations had 7.9 cows to a herd and 644 cows to a bull.

Artificial insemination is used mostly among dairy cattle. An example of its use with beef cattle is in the purebred Hereford herd of the Apache tribe of San Carlos, Ariz. The herd comprises about 1,000 cows, which are kept in a pasture of approximately 10,000 acres. Bulls are kept at a central plant near one of two watering places. The plant has a laboratory, four corrals, a feed barn, and breeding and semen collection chutes, built especially to handle range cattle. Cowboys check cows for estrus, and the cows in heat are brought to the central plant, or to a subsidiary set of corrals and breeding chute about 5 miles from the central plant, where they are inseminated.

Horses and sheep also are bred artificially to some extent, primarily to meet the needs of individual breeders or experiment stations. Little use is made of the technique with goats and swine. Poultrymen employ it in experimental crossing and in studies that require controlled conditions of insemination. It is useful where birds are kept in individual laying cages, but commercial breeders find its cost is relatively high compared to the cost of roosters. Breeders of broad-breasted turkeys use it to maintain fertility, because many broad-breasted males are clumsy and unable to mate efficiently. Such use is of doubtful value, however, for breeding stock from flocks developed with the aid of artificial insemination may go to flocks where natural mating is the only economical procedure. Males that cannot give satisfactory service under these conditions are of little value.

Most artificial-breeding associations in the United States started as individual units, each having its own staff and bulls and operating in a small area. More recently, a trend began toward the more efficient federated type of organization, which functions in a larger area, such as a State or a part of a State.

Usually, a number of local organizations combine to form a federated organization, and members of the local groups belong to the central association that owns or leases the barn, laboratory, and all bulls, which are kept at the central barn. Semen is mailed or shipped to the local associations. The local associations usually employ their own technicians, manage local procedures, and elect directors of the central organization. The work is financed by an equitable division of income between the central and local associations. The local associations may be incorporated as affiliates or subsidiaries of the central association. After a central association is formed, local associations can become affiliated with it. . . .

The Place of Artificial Insemination

What economic consequences can we expect from the expanding use of artificial insemination with dairy cattle? One result surely will be a reduction in the number of bulls on farms and correspondingly more cows on the farms where bulls are no longer required. Improved feeding and management practices will come through better keeping of records and contacts with technicians and other farmers. The health and fertility of animals should improve, along with the genetic make-up of herds. Regional specialization in the raising of dairy heifers is likely to be stimulated. There may be a tendency for a larger proportion of producers in deficit feed areas to buy replacements from areas where feed supplies are abundant, and buyers should be able to purchase heifers in carload lots from artificial breeding associations.

The various advantages of artificial insemination over natural mating, mentioned often enough, lead some persons here and abroad to be too enthusiastic about its use. But it cannot be said too often that the primary purpose of the technique is to speed up the rate of livestock improvement. To accomplish this, farmers must use sires that are genetically superior to the females to which they are to be bred.

Another point: These superior bulls must be used in a breeding program adapted to the farmer's locality. That means that adaptability must be considered when the technique is used in areas where the environment imposes limitations on livestock production. Sires well suited for use in New York or Wisconsin, for example, may not be adapted to use in some other areas where climate and feed supplies limit production. We have heard much discussion about possibilities of using artificial insemination to introduce improved stock quickly and on a large scale in countries or areas where the existing animals are relatively unproductive. If the animals are unproductive because of conditions imposed by nature, the widespread introduction of improved stock from more favorable environments may be a hazardous undertaking. Animals resulting from the first cross between improved stock and animals containing somewhat larger proportions of improved blood often perform satisfactorily under these conditions, while higher grade animals do not.

Any large-scale program involving the introduction of new types into areas of rigorous environment, employing either artificial or natural mating, should be based on experimental work designed to determine the amount of improved blood that may be safely introduced and the method of breeding best suited to those conditions.

Research in Nutrition

From Elizabeth Neige Todhunter, "The Story of Nutrition," U.S. Department of Agriculture, *Yearbook*, 1959 (Washington, 1959), pp. 7–22.

This is the story of man's long search for exact knowledge of the food his body needs.

It is a story of laboratories, experiments, failures, successes, and discoveries. It is even more a story of men and women with curiosity, ideas, persistence, and a driving desire to help people live better.

It is a story of a fight against ignorance and supersititions and the strange ideas people always have had — now, too! — about the things they eat.

It is an old story that could begin with the first man and the little he knew beyond the fact that he like to eat.

It is, though, primarily a story of accomplishments in this century — indeed, in the last few years; a story so new that it is far from its end.

Although for centuries people tried to solve some of their problems of what to eat and how much and why, they made little progress until chemistry was well developed and we could analyze foods and know what they are made of. We also had to wait until physiology became a science that could provide understanding of the human body and how it functions. We needed as well the contributions of physics, medicine, agriculture, and biology.

Because it is a "new" science, then, let us begin with the man who has been called "the father of American nutrition" and later go back to the men and ideas that preceded him — for nutrition, like every science and almost every other great development, has been built on things that went before.

Wilbur Olin Atwater was born in 1844 in Johnstown, N.Y. He attended the University of Vermont and Wesleyan University in Middletown, Conn. For his thesis for his doctor's degree at Yale University in 1869 he — for the first time in this country — used modern methods to analyze corn fodder.

He went to Europe in 1869 to study agricultural and physiological chemistry at the Universities of Leipzig and Berlin. When the first experiment station in the United States was established at Middletown in 1875, he became its first director.

He later became director of the Connecticut Agricultural Experiment Station at Storrs when it was organized in 1887.

His studies on the acquisition of atmospheric nitrogen by plants and on the composition of feeds, begun several years earlier, he continued as part of the work at Storrs during the 14 years he was director. These investigations led to his interest in the composition of man's food.

Dr. Atwater made a series of analyses of fish for the United States Fish Commission and of the flesh of domestic animals for the Smithsonian Institution between 1879 and 1883. He conducted studies of the dietaries of people in Massachusetts and Canada.

Dr. Atwater returned to Europe in 1887. He worked in the laboratory in Munich where Carl Voit was doing outstanding work in studies of respiration — the exchange of gases between the blood and the tissues — and calorimetry, the measurement of heat, the first steps toward quantitative knowledge of nutritional requirements.

Another American student who worked in Dr. Voit's laboratory was Graham Lusk, who brought back with him a small model of a calorimeter Voit had made and later built others at Cornell University Medical College in New York City for studies with dogs and children. We shall come back to Dr. Voit later.

Dr. Atwater also returned to this country inspired to do further calorimetry studies at Wesleyan University. With his coworkers be built a calorimeter for studies on man and designed a bomb calorimeter for measurement of caloric value of foods. He made adjustment for the indigestible fraction in food and the incomplete oxidation of protein in the body and gave the values, widely used ever since, of 4, 9, 4 Calories per gram of carbohydrate, fat, and protein in a mixed diet.

The Congress in 1894 appropriated 10 thousand dollars 'To enable the Secretary of Agriculture to investigate and report upon the nutritive value of the various articles and commodities used for human food, with special suggestion of full, wholesome, and edible rations less wasteful and more economical than those in common use.''

This work was assigned to the office of Experiment Stations under Dr. Atwater, who was designated "chief of nutrition investigations."

From that time forward, biochemists, nutritionists, home economists, and investigators in animal and poultry husbandry at agricultural experiment stations throughout the country have steadily and continuously helped build the newer knowledge of nutrition.

Headquarters for the work were established at Middletown, and Dr. Atwater was made chief. He and his colleagues investigated the diets of hundreds of persons of different occupations and compared the results of similar studies in other countries. They made many experiments with men on digestion and carried on special studies of the nutritive value of cereals, meats, vegetables, fruit, and nuts and the effects of cooking and other forms of preparation on nutritive values.

He and his coworkers demonstrated that the amount of heat — energy — a person develops during a given period is the amount that can be derived from the energy liberated in the oxidation of food materials during the period.

Dr. Atwater studied digestibility of food, made numerous dietary studies, and analyzed many foods. He prepared in 1896 the famous Bulletin 28 of the United

States Department of Agriculture. It was the first extensive table of food values ever prepared in this country.

Atwater sought to find what was the best and most economical diet for man. At that time only protein and Calories, as supplied by fat and carbohydrate, were considered of importance, and such foods as green, leafy vegetables and fruit were regarded as expensive purchases or luxuries.

A chapter Dr. Atwater wrote for the 1894 Yearbook of Agriculture has meaning for us today. I quote a few sentences from it:

"Materials for the food of man make up the larger part of our agricultural production and the largest item of our export abroad. Our food production is one-sided. It includes a relative excess of the fat of meat, of starch, and of sugar, the substances that serve the body for fuel to yield heat and muscular power, while the nitrogenous substances, those which make blood and muscle, bone and brain, are relatively deficient. . . . What is needed is more nitrogen in the soil for plant food, more nitrogen in plants to make better food for animals and man, and more nitrogen in the food of man. Better culture of the soil and better manuring will bring not only larger crops, but crops richer in nitrogen. . . .

"The power of a man to do work depends upon his nutrition. A well-fed horse can draw a heavy load. With less food he does less work. A well-fed man has strength of muscle and of brain, while a poorly nourished man has not."

He defined food as "that which, when taken into the body, builds up its tissues and keeps them in repair, or which is consumed in the body to yield energy in the form of heat to keep it warm and create strength for its work. . . ."

"The most healthful food is that which is best fitted to the wants of the user. . . .

"The cheapest food is that which furnishes the most nutriment at the least cost.

"The most economical food is that which is both most healthful and cheapest.

"To make the most out of a man, to bring him up to the desirable level of productive capacity, to enable him to live as a man ought to live, he must be well fed.

"One of the ways in which the worst economy is practiced is in the buying of high-priced foods. For this error, prejudice, the palate, and poor cooking are mainly responsible. There is a prevalent but unfounded idea that costly foods, such as the tenderest meats, the finest fish, the highest priced butter, the choicest flour, and the most delicate vegetables possess some peculiar virtue which is lacking in the less expensive materials. . . . The maxim that 'the best is the cheapest' does not apply to food."

LET US GO BACK now for a glimpse at the beliefs and knowledge on which Atwater and other scientists of the 20th century built. Such a quick survey will help us to understand better the growth of the science of nutrition — and the speed with which it has grown.

Back in the days of the Greeks, before the birth of Christ, man's inquiring mind was asking questions about the world in which he lived. The "science" of that day believed that there were four elements — earth, air, fire, and water; four qualities — dry, cold, hot, and wet; and four humors, or liquids, that comprised the body — blood, phlegm, black bile, and yellow bile.

Hippocrates, the father of medicine, taught the value of diet, but he believed in one universal aliment, an idea that prevailed until the early part of the 19th century.

Galen, a Greek physician who settled in Rome in A.D. 164, wrote many books about anatomy, diet, and health. His word was accepted without question through the centuries that saw the decline of Rome, the Dark Ages, and the first light of the Renaissance, until Andreas Vesalius (1514–1564), a Flemish student of anatomy, overthrew some of Galen's ideas and dared to investigate for himself, rather than follow blindly the master's dicta.

One original thinker in Italy tried to study nutrition. He asked the right questions, but he could not get the answers because he had neither a knowledge of chemistry nor the necessary tools. Santorio Sanctorius (1561–1636) day after day sat on his big balance and weighed himself and the food he ate, but could not find the answer to the difference in weight after he had eaten. He has truly been called the father of experiments in metabolism, but it was some 300 years later before investigators could explain the nutrition problem he had posed.

In the 17th century, "the Golden Age of Science," the experimental method began to take hold. The British William Harvey revolutionized our concept of the human body by demonstrating that blood circulates from the heart throughout the body. The Dutch Anton van Leeuwenhoek developed the microscope and studied the red cells or corpuscles of the blood stream. At meetings of the Royal Society, which received its charter in 1662, scientists discussed their experiments and the curiosities of nature they had found.

The 18th century brought the rise of modern chemistry. Joseph Black, a professor at Glasgow, discovered the gas that to us is carbon dioxide. Wealthy, eccentric Henry Cavendish discovered hydrogen. Daniel Rutherford, a Scottish physician, discovered nitrogen. Joseph Priestly, the English minister who was happiest when he was in his laboratory, was credited with discovering oxygen.

Antoine Lavoisier of France, outstanding in his ability to interpret and integrate the new discoveries, showed that the life process is one of respiration and that as oxygen was consumed by the body, carbon dioxide was exhaled. He measured those gases and calculated the body's heat production. He realized that the working man expended more calories and therefore needed more food than those who were less active.

Interest in physiology grew. René Réaumur (1683–1757), a French naturalist and physicist, fed various foods to birds and then, after short periods of time, retrieved the food and studied the changes that had taken place during digestion.

Lazzaro Spallanzani (1729–1799) in Italy experimented on himself. He swallowed linen bags containing meat and bread and withdrew them later by strings attached to the bags. From the changes he found in the partly disgested food, he realized that some chemical changes were taking place.

A Scottish naval physician, James Lind, conducted a carefully controlled experiment, the first of its kind, and demonstrated how to prevent and cure scurvy, "the scourge of the sea," that killed hundreds of sailors on ships taking long voyages. Dr. Lind in 1747 found that lemon juice could cure or prevent this disease; yet it was more than 50 years later before the British Navy required that lemon juice be provided on all ships. Even then no one seemed to realize the significance of the cure; some 150 years later vitamin C was discovered as the antiscurvy vitamin.

The 19th century was the period of chemical investigation and measurement of respiration and energy use by animals.

Hippocrates had taught that there was one ultimate principle in food, and not till 1834 did this idea change. William Prout, a London physician, published a book, *Chemistry, Meteorology and the Functions of Digestion,* in which he put foward the idea that food contained three staminal principles, which he called saccharine, oily, and albuminous material.

A new era began in 1816 when Francois Magendie, the great French physiologist, discovered that dogs died if given only sugar or oil or butter but would live if given a nitrogen-containing food. Soon Jean Boussingault, a French chemist and experimental farmer, made the first experiment of nitrogen balance with a horse and a cow. Gerrit Jan Mulder, the Dutch physician and chemist, exploring the nitrogen-containing foods, introduced the term "protein" in 1838. He was wrong in what he thought these proteins were, but the name stuck.

The chemistry of the albuminous (protein) substances, as these were first called, began to be understood when some of the "building units" of these complex substances were isolated. The first amino acid, cystine, was discovered in 1810 by the English chemist and physicist William Wollaston when working with kidney stones. He failed to recognize its true chemical nature. The simplest of all the amino acids is glycine. It was first identified by M. H. Braconnot, the French chemist who obtained glycine as a breakdown product from hydrolysis of gelatin.

By the end of the 19th century, 12 of the 22 amino acids now known to be present in proteins of food had been discovered.

The spotlight was on protein. Organic chemistry developed, and Justus von Liebig, the great German chemist, branched out to develop the new agricultural chemistry that was later to lead to biochemistry.

Studies of nitrogen balance were made on dogs and other experimental animals in attempts to determine the amount of protein they needed. Chemists were busy improving methods of food analysis, and the general belief was that through knowledge of chemical composition of foods one would be able to plan an adequate diet.

The French chemist Jean Dumas evolved an accurate method for quantitative measurement of nitrogen. The protein content could be calculated from it. But it was such a long, painstaking process that not many studies could be made. Then the keen mind of Johann Kjeldahl, a Danish chemist, devised a new and relatively easy method of determining nitrogen in organic matter (1883), and the work could push ahead more rapidly. The availability of equipment and suitable chemical methods of analysis have always been an influencing factor in the development of the science of nutrition.

IN AMERICA, physiology and the study of disgestion of food were aided by the work of a backwoods surgeon, William Beaumont. He was on Army duty at Fort Mackinac in Michigan Territory when a gunshot wound of a French Canadian trapper, Alexis St. Martin, gave him an opportunity to show his medical and surgical skill. The trapper's life was saved, but he lived with a hole in his stomach. The hole let Dr. Beaumont have a living organ for the study of digestion. Patiently and accurately, he made his experiments so that the findings presented in his book, *Experiments and Observations on the Gastric Juice and the Physiology of Digestion* (1833), were unsurpassed until the researches of the Russian physiologist, Ivan Petrovich Pavlov.

Dr. Beaumont might have accomplished more, but Alexis did not like being experimented with. He slipped away to Canada and declined to return. Chemistry was not far enough advanced in Beaumont's day to be able to identify what was in the sample of gastric juice that he sent to the leading chemists to analyze. But digestion was clearly recognized now as a chemical process of breaking down food, and men could begin to find out what it involved.

Next came the study of respiration and calorimetry that led to the measurement of man's energy needs — the first steps to quantitative knowledge of nutritional requirements.

Foremost in this work was Carl Voit, who had learned his chemistry from Liebig and later provoked his former teacher by daring to disagree with some of his findings.

Voit, with the help of Max von Pettenkofer, who had been Liebig's assistant, built an apparatus for the study of respiratory exchanges in man and animals. Between 1866 and 1873, these two men published seven long papers on the metabolism of healthy persons during fasting and at work. Dr. Voit showed that, contrary to current belief, nitrogen metabolism is not increased by muscular work.

One of the greatest of all Voit's pupils was Max Rubner, who continued the calorimetry studies begun under his master teacher. He determined caloric values of 4.1, 9.3, and 4.1 per gram of carbohydrate, fat, and protein.

Rubner also established the law of surface area in basal metabolism from his experiments, which showed that heat production of man in the resting state is proportional to the surface area of the body. He showed that the law of conservation of energy — which says that energy must have a source; it cannot come from nothing, nor can it disappear into nothing; it only changes form — holds true for the animal world as for the physical. Rubner also demonstrated that fat and carbohydrate are interchangable in nutrition on the basis of energy value.

An entirely different concept of food values was introduced some 20 years later.

Elmer V. McCollum in 1918 published a book, *The Newer Knowledge of Nutrition* — a title that was used by many workers from then on to describe the change which had taken place in our understanding of nutrition. In that book, Dr. McCollum also introduced a term that has been widely used ever since — "the protective foods." Milk and the leaves of plants, he wrote, are to be regarded as protective foods and should never be omitted from the diet.

The rapid growth of knowledge of nutrition in the 20th century is also illustrated by the book. The first edition in 1918 had 189 pages. It went through five editions, and the latest in 1939 had 684 pages.

The 20th century opened with the general recognition that protein, fats, and carbohydrates as sources of energy and some inorganic salts were the necessary components of the diet.

This, despite the fact that some two centuries earlier, Dr. Lind had shown that because lemon juice would cure scurvy there must be something else in food. Other investigators some 10 to 20 years earlier also had unusual things happen with diets they were using. Christiaan Eijkman, a Dutch army surgeon, discovered that chickens fed polished rice developed a neuritis, like beriberi, which he could cure or prevent by feeding brown rice. He was the first person to produce a dietary deficiency disease experimentally. In Japan, Baron Kanekiro Takaki had found that he could prevent beriberi, which took the lives of many Japanese sailors, by increasing the amount of meat and fish in their diets.

Nicolai Lunin, a young student in a Russian laboratory, found in 1880 that mice thrived on milk, but they died if they were given a mixture of protein, fat, sugar, and ash of milk. These findings could not be explained and attracted little attention in a world that was making rapid progress in chemistry and bacteriology. The time was coming when the limited viewpoint provided by chemical analysis would be replaced by the new biological method.

VITAMINS now are household words, but the term was coined only in 1912 by a Polish chemist who was working at the Lister Institute in London.

Casimir Funk was trying to isolate some substance from rice polishings that would forestall beriberi. He reasoned that if there was something in food that prevented beriberi, scurvy, and pellagra, this something was vital for life.

His laboratory preparation, which was effective in curing beriberi in birds, was an amine compound, and so he coined the name "vitamine." The name caught on.

Support was given to Dr. Funk's suggestion of the existence of vitamines by the work of Frederick G. Hopkins, biochemist in Cambridge University, England. Dr. Hopkins fed rats an artificial diet prepared from constituents of the same nature as those present in milk. He used a diet of casein, starch, cane sugar, lard, and inorganic salts, each constituent as carefully purified as possible. The rats grew for a short time but then drooped and died. A similar group of rats grew normally when they were given as little as 2 cubic centimeters of milk daily in addition to the artificial diet.

Dr. Hopkins showed that it was not a lack of calories that caused the death of the animals, nor was it lack of palatability of the diet — a reason often given then to explain the failure of growth in animals on special diets. He postulated that there were unsuspected dietetic factors, or accessory food substances, that were essential for health.

Louis Pasteur's brilliant researches of the 1870's helped establish the new science of bacteriology and fixed the germ theory of disease firmly in the minds of scientists.

Cleanliness and sanitation in the handling of food were recognized as essential. But the idea that something not present in food, something lacking, could cause disease was indeed difficult to accept. Men's minds must be ready for the acceptance of new ideas and the findings of research; there was much resistance to the vitamin theory for a decade at least.

Some experiments started at the University of Wisconsin in 1907 were to lead, by halting steps at first, to the actual discovery of the first of the many vitamins with which we are familiar. Rations of the same chemical composition, but each from a different single plant, were fed to cows. The corn-fed animals were sleek, trim, healthy looking after a year. Those receiving the ration from the wheat plant had a rough coat and a gaunt appearance. Those fed the oat plant were midway between. The experiment proved that chemical analysis did not give the complete answer about nutritive values.

Elmer V. McCollum was one of the assistants in those early classic experiments with cows. He was a farm boy from Kansas with a thirst for knowledge and a retentive mind, and he had studied under the great Lafayette Benedict Mendel at Yale University.

Dr. McCollum was given the assignment to try to find what was the cause of the difference in the three rations, which were chemically similar, at least according to the analytical methods then available, although they gave different results.

The young McCollum read and pondered. He came to the conclusion that he must experiment with the simplest of rations prepared from purified foodstuffs if he was to find the cause of the difference. Because a large amount of foodstuff would have to be prepared and it would take a long time for results to show up in cows, he decided he must use some small animal. He chose the rat, and so started what was probably the first rat colony and first extensive series of experiments with these widely used test animals.

By 1913 Dr. McCollum had found an artificial diet of protein, lactose, starch, and inorganic salts, that, with butterfat, gave good growth. If he used the same diet, but replaced the butterfat with olive oil or lard, the rats failed in growth and health. Some essential unknown factor was thus shown to be present in butterfat. It was first called fat-soluble A and, later, vitamin A.

Further study of the purified diets then being used disclosed that the lactose was not "pure"; when it was further purified, the rats developed polyneuritis, or beriberi, which could be cured by feeding a water extract of rice germ. Thus water-soluble B — vitamin B — was discovered.

Similar findings were reported almost at the same time by Thomas Burr Osborne and Dr. Mendel at Yale, and so opened up the era of what Mendel has called "the little things" in nutrition.

Back in 1907, two Norwegian investigators — Axel Holst and Theodor Frölich — wanted to study what was "ship beriberi," which was common among Norwegian seamen. They tried to produce beriberi in guinea pigs. Like the Princes of Serendip, they found something other than what they were seeking. The diet used produced scurvy in the guinea pigs, and thus by lucky chance a suitable test animal was found. They were able to feed different foods and find which ones would cure scurvy. Once vitamins A and B were discovered, it was realized that the "unknown" in fruit and vegetables must be another vitamin, and vitamin C was added to the list.

The change in spelling, with the dropping of the final "e", was made in 1920, because it was realized that these unknown substances were not "amines."

The nutritional deficiency diseases scurvy and beriberi thus were known to be curable by proper food. What about rickets, pellagra, and pernicious anemia — would they, too, respond to a vitamin?

A pooling of knowledge gained from the early writers, clinicians, pathologists, experimental nutritionists, and biochemists soon set the investigations of vitamins in high gear.

More young scientists were being attracted by the new science of nutrition and did their study under great teachers at Yale, The Johns Hopkins University, Columbia, and Wisconsin. These young men and women went forth to the colleges, universities, and experiment stations throughout the country to set up laboratories and to continue the search for new nutrients and the study of how they function.

They encountered difficulties. The rats, guinea pigs, chickens, and dogs with which they worked did not all react in the same way, and soon many letters of the alphabet were used up as designations for what were believed to be new factors.

Vitamin D and vitamin E were identified.

By 1926, what had been called vitamin B was found to be at least two separate factors. One was destroyed by heat and was the antiberiberi factor. Another new substance was stable to heat.

Each new discovery made it possible to prepare more highly purified diets and thus lead to more new discoveries, as other deficiency symptoms showed up in animals and the new curative substances were sought — and found.

A young chemist, Charles G. King, at the University of Pittsburgh, in 1932 prepared pure crystals of vitamin C from lemon juice. It was the first of the vitamins to be isolated in pure form. It was later named ascorbic acid.

Soon others were isolated and identified chemically, their functions and food sources studied, and the amount required daily for maintenance of health and vigor was determined. The old terms of "antiberiberi," "antiscorbutic," and so forth were dropped when it became apparent that the vitamins did much more than just prevent disease. They were essential for health and well-being and functioned as part of many systems of the body.

The latest discovery is vitamin B_{12} (1948). It was found to be a preventive factor for pernicious anemia, which had been described by Dr. Thomas Addison about 100 years before.

The vitamin story has developed mainly since the 1920's. Vitamins held the spotlight, but many advances were being made in our knowledge of proteins, trace elements, and other aspects of nutrition.

ONLY PROTEIN received much attention at the beginning of this century.

Dr. Atwater advocated 125 grams daily for a laboring man. Rubner had declared that a large protein intake was the right of civilized man, a view that was shared by many persons in temperate climates who enjoyed meat, cheese, and eggs. Those who preferred a vegetarian or a more limited diet strongly advocated a much lower intake of protein, and controversy raged in the early decades. Later discoveries showed that the kind of protein was a key factor, but we still hear of the early differences of opinion.

Russell H. Chittenden, first university teacher of physiological chemistry in this country, helped lay the foundations of nutrition science through his own investigations at Yale University and his training of many men. He published in 1904 his revolutionary studies of groups of athletes, soldiers, and professional men who were maintained in nitrogen equilibrium on what corresponded to 44 to 53 grams of protein for a man of average weight.

Slowly they learned that protein was not just protein — there are many different proteins in food. Thomas Burr Osborne, a chemist at Yale, was a leader in these studies. He learned that not all proteins are equally efficient in promoting growth or maintaining nitrogen equilibrium.

Karl Thomas, of Germany, introduced in 1909 the term "biological value" of protein and a formula for determining it. Basically, the biological value of a protein means the percentage of nitrogen retained by the body. Comparisons of many proteins were made in this way by feeding experiments with animals and a few similar studies with human beings.

The biological value of a protein was seen to be related to the composition of amino acids in it. Frederick G. Hopkins at Cambridge University was a pioneer in these studies. He and Sidney Cole in 1901 had discovered a new amino acid, tryptophan. Later, when Dr. Hopkins and his coworkers fed mice a diet with casein as the sole nitrogen-containing constituent, the animals flourished. They died when zein, a protein from corn, replaced casein. If tryptophan was added to the zein, however, the mice lived but did not grow.

Dr. Osborne was joined in 1909 by Dr. Mendel at Yale. They were "the most fertile combination of minds ever directed toward studies of nutrition." They studied almost every phase of nutrition, especially protein and amino acids, and conducted feeding experiments with rats that led to the discovery of vitamins A and B. They measured the biologic value of isolated proteins and showed that amino acids were the limiting factors. In history-making experiments in 1915 they showed that gliadin, a protein in wheat, would maintain life but would not promote growth in rats unless lysine was added and that zein must be supplemented with tryptophan and lysine for life and growth.

At this time proteins were described as being "complete" (they were adequate to maintain life and promote growth) and "incomplete" — that is, they lacked certain amino acids. The concept of quality as well as quantity of protein thus was introduced.

More amino acids were discovered. Nineteen were known then to occur in food proteins. The next step was to find whether they were essential in the diet. Some were hard to get in pure form and in amounts sufficient to feed to test animals.

William C. Rose, one of Dr. Mendel's students, by 1930 at the University of Illinois was able to combine the 19 amino acids as the sole source of protein in diets for rats. The animals failed to grow. Something was still lacking. Because casein or gelatin added to the diet gave good growth, he concluded that some other amino acid, rather than a vitamin or mineral, was the missing factor.

A search for the new amino acid began. It turned out that the new compound was closely tied to another amino acid, isoleucine, and so was difficult to separate and identify, but 4 years of patient work on the problem finally yielded the answer. The new amino acid essential for growth of rats was identified in 1934 and was named "threonine" because of its close relationship to the sugar threose. Continuing his protein researches with mixtures of pure amino acids, Dr. Rose was able by 1938 to prove that nine were essential for normal rate of growth in rats. If arginine was omitted, animals grew at about two-thirds the normal rate — an indication that the organism would synthesize this amino acid but not at a rate that would permit normal growth.

Amino acids could then be grouped as essential and nonessential — needed and unneeded. The next step was to find whether people needed these amino acids. With young men as volunteer subjects, Dr. Rose learned that eight of the amino acids are essential to maintain nitrogen equilibrium.

He then set for himself the task of determining exactly how much of each was required each day. These were the first long-continued series of studies in which human beings were maintained on diets of purified nutrients. Patiently and persistently, the work went forward, until by 1955 Dr. Rose presented data for the recommended daily intake of each of the amino acids essential for people.

Investigators in many laboratories have been at work since 1930 on the protein problem, including the nutritive value of individual proteins and the specific function of individual amino acids.

Protein has been found to be the material for building muscle and body tissue, and to be part of the hemoglobin molecule in red blood cells. Enzymes and hormones have been crystallized and found to be derived from proteins. Enzyme systems contain protein. Antibodies present in the blood stream, an aid in resistance to infection, are protein in nature.

We usually discuss pellagra along with the vitamins. A "pellagra-preventive vitamin" was sought in the early 1920's. The search continued until 1937, when Conrad Elvehjem, of the University of Wisconsin, fed nicotinic acid (which had been on the chemists' shelves for a long time) to dogs with blacktongue, a disease comparable to pellagra in humans. Nicontinic acid cured the blacktongue, and soon was found to be effective in treating human pellagra. Nicontinic acid was added to the list of known vitamins. Its name was changed to niacin to avoid confusion in the mind of the public.

But the story of the fight against pellagra belongs with the proteins. Investigations were carried on by Joseph Goldberger throughout the South, where pellagra was serious from early 1900's till the late 1930's. He found that certain protein-rich foods prevented or cured pellagra. The complexities of this relationship were difficult to unravel and illustrate the interrelationship between nutrients. The answer was found not long ago: The amino acid tryptophan can be converted to niacin. Approximately 60 milligrams of tryptophan are equivalent to 1 milligram of niacin.

Problems of metabolism of protein and its requirement are still being investigated.

Attention also has centered on world problems of nutrition — especially on the nutritional disease, kwashiorkor. The first description of this disease of young children was given in 1933, and attempts to identify the cause have gone on ever since. Kwashiorkor is prevalent in the Tropics and in many poor countries were carbohydrate foods form the bulk of the diet and protein-rich foods are unavailable or too costly. "Protein malnutition" often is used as the term for kwashiorkor, but present knowledge indicates that they are not synonymous.

Kwashiorkor may be due to a deficiency in the kind and the amount of protein or of many of the other essential nutrients. The advances since 1900 in our knowledge of proteins and amino acids have centered attention on people the world over who do not get enough protein. We also know we need to study the vegetable proteins further.

Fats and oils have been foods since ancient times, but not until 1814 did a chemist, Michel Eugene Chevreul of France, discover that fats are made of fatty acid and glycerol. He also named margarine.

A century ago heated arguments went on over whether the animal body could change carbohydrates into fat. Experiment was the only way to find an answer. Fat-free diets were fed to pigs, ducks, and geese. Analysis of the carcasses later disclosed the presence of fat in the body; it could have arisen only from the carbohydrate of the diet.

The use of the calorimeter demonstrated that fats have two and one-fourth times the caloric value of carbohydrate and protein. By the beginning of the 20th century, it was accepted that fats and carbohydrates could be used interchangeably in the diet. It was thought therefore that fats were not essential in the diet. Fats were consumed in large amounts because of their flavor and satiety value, but comparatively little nutritive importance was attached to them, except for their energy value. Then in 1915 came the startling discovery that certain fats, such as butter, were sources of the newly discovered vitamin. Soon other fat-soluble vitamins were discovered.

New interest was aroused in 1929 when scientists observed that rats kept on a fat-free but otherwise adequate diet (with vitamins supplied in other preparations) did not maintain health. The animals lost hair from the body and developed a skin disease and necrosis of the tail. This condition could be prevented by feeding fatty acids that were highly unsaturated in structure. Linoleic acid was identified as the essential fatty acid. Linolenic and arachidonic acids serve the same function. This new knowledge made it possible for researchers to prepare experimental diets, which led to the discovery of more of the vitamins. Once again, interest centered on the vitamins in nutrition.

The high content of fatty substances in the thickened artery walls that is often associated with heart ailments has again aroused interest in the possible relation of dietary fat to those conditions. Much work is being done on fats, the amount and chemical nature of the fats, and the fatty acids that should form part of man's daily diet. Perhaps there is yet to be found a pattern of the kind and amount of fatty acids needed in the diet, as was done for amino acids.

Inorganic elements — or mineral constituents, ash, or inorganic salts, as they have been called — were known a century ago to be essential for plantlife. Farm animals did not thrive if common salt was omitted from their diet.

At the beginning of this century, Henry C. Sherman began studies on calcium, phosphorus, sulfur, and iron in human nutrition, first at Wesleyan University under Dr. Atwater and later at Columbia University. These elements were recognized as essential in the diet, and many experiments were conducted to try to determine just how much of each was needed, exactly how they functioned in the body, and how they were affected by food preparation. Some of these questions are not yet satisfactorily answered.

Doubt existed for a time as to the form of these mineral elements, but belief in the special virtues of organic combinations, especially of phosphorus and iron, gradually gave way to the recognition that inorganic combinations were equally well utilized.

By 1930, as newer techniques and apparatus made it possible for chemists to measure minute amounts of certain inorganic substances, the significance of the trace elements in nutrition was recognized.

Iodine had been identified a century earlier. In the 1920's it was identified as an essential nurtient. The thyroid gland at the base of the neck enlarges when it is deprived of iodine.

The condition is known as simple goiter. In the Great Lakes area, where iodine has been leached out of the soil and so is not available in food or drinking water, goiter used to be a common occurrence among children, especially girls.

One of the earliest large-scale controlled human experiments was conducted by David Marine and O. P. Kimball in 1921 with 6 thousand schoolchildren in Akron, Ohio. They showed that children given iodine in drinking water did not develop goiter; a large proportion of those not so treated did develop this condition. A more effective way of providing a readily available and safe supply of iodine for all people was developed later by adding potassium iodide to table salt. Use of this salt has always been on a voluntary basis, but it provides a wise public health measure available to all people.

Investigators in the University of Wisconsin in 1928 found that pure iron salts were ineffective in curing anemia in rats and that small amounts of copper had to be present in the diet before the iron should be utilized.

Manganese, magnesium, and zinc were next added to the list of elements that are needed to maintain growth and health in experimental rats.

Cobalt was found necessary to prevent disease in cattle and sheep (1935). With the discovery of vitamin B_{12} (1948) and the later chemical identification of cobalt as one of its constituents, this element has joined the list of those which are known to be essential for people.

These are the major nutrients that have been identified so far.

The story of nutrition is more than one of discoveries of new compounds needed by the body, however.

The problems of nutrition continue to grow more complex. New discoveries reveal that there is close interrelationship between many of the nutrients. Numerous factors affect the availability of the different nutrients as they exist of food. The biochemical individuality of each person must be kept in focus in providing for man's nutritional needs.

Foods nutrients are converted into body structure. For a long time it was thought that the body material, especially the fat deposits, was more or less stable.

How could one tell? It was possible to analyze and know exactly what was taken in by mouth and what was excreted, but what happened inside the body was pretty much unknown.

This was so until the early 1930's brought the discovery of heavy hydrogen and heavy nitrogen by Harold C. Urey, an Indiana boy who became a professor in Columbia University and in 1934 won the Nobel Prize for chemistry.

His discovery was put to work by biochemist Rudolf Schoenheimer, who incorporated heavy hydrogen into fatty acids and fed them to mice. By sacrificing the animals, he could determine where the heavy hydrogen was deposited. He found that the fatty acids of the stored fats are constantly transported to and from organs. They merge indistinguishably with the fat from the diet and are converted into other fatty acids of both longer and shorter chains. Only the essential unsaturated fatty acids did not take up heavy hydrogen — thus further confirming the earlier finding that the unsaturated fatty acids cannot be synthesized in the body but must be supplied in food.

Another series of experiments was made in a similar way. Heavy nitrogen was used as part of the amino acids fed to mice. As with fats, there was a rapid interchange between dietary amino acids and those of the blood and tissues. The amino acid lysine was the only one that did not take up heavy nitrogen from the "labeled" amino acids. Dr. Schoenheimer demonstrated that the body constituents were in a dynamic state. Another new concept of nutrition was introduced.

Radioactive isotopes of other elements — calcium, phosphorus, iron — are now available, valuable tools for following the pathway of nutrients within the body.

Dietary studies on man have been carried out through the ages, and I mention some examples to show progress by this avenue of study. Most of the nutrition studies have been made on experimental animals. One cannot deliberately deprive man of essential foods, but history and geographical and economic circumstances have provided opportunities for the experimental study of man.

Sanctorius in the 17th century sought an explanation of metabolism as he weighed himself and his food.

The outcome was a book of aphorisms — a happier ending than the one a young physician, William Stark, had in the 18th century. He was a healthy young man of 29, with a desire to find the effect of diet on health. He ate carefully weighed amounts of bread and water, and added various other foods one at a time. He fell ill in a few months and died from what in the light of today's knowledge was probably severe vitamin deficiencies.

James Lind was more fortunate. His classic experiment was the first clinically controlled one and showed that lemon juice cured scurvy.

Toward the end of the 19th century, Max Rubner in Germany, Lyon Playfair in England, and Wilbur O. Atwater in the United States made many studies of diets. They reasoned that groups that were vigorous and healthy surely had adequate diets. By analysis of diets of these groups, they believed they could find what was an adequate intake of calories and protein.

Atwater recommended 3,400 Calories and 125 grams of protein for a man who does moderately active muscular work. He considered fat and carbohydrate to be interchangeable as a source of calories.

The newer knowledge of nutrition was well established by 1926, and adequate human diets could readily be obtained from natural foods.

The inquiring mind of Dr. H. C. Corry Mann, an English physician who was in charge of a boys' home, led him to wonder if he could improve what was considered by all standards of the day to be an adequate diet. One group of his boys remained on the regular diet. Six other groups received, respectively, additions of sugar, butter, margarine, casein, watercress, and milk. All the groups that got the extra items increased more in weight and height at the end of a year than the group on the regular diet. The group that got milk made far greater gains.

Later discoveries of vitamins and further knowledge of nutrients have contributed some of the answers regarding the value of milk as a food. This study again demonstrated the value of the concept introduced early in the century by Dr. McCollum that biological investigation provides information that cannot be obtained by chemical analyses.

Another study was that of Lord John Boyd-Orr and his coworkers in 1931 of the health of two African tribes living in the same area but with different food customs.

Physical and medical examinations, blood analyses, and careful examination of food intakes were made on several thousand tribesmen. The Masai tribe was a pastoral group that lived mainly on milk, meat, and raw blood — a diet relatively high in protein, fat, and calcium. The Akikiyu were agriculturists living on cereals, roots, and fruit — a diet relatively high in carbohydrate and low in calcium. The Akikiyu had a higher incidence of bone deformities, dental caries, anemia, pulmonary conditions, and tropical ulcer. The full-grown Masai males averaged 5 inches taller and 23 pounds heavier and had greater muscular strength than their neighbors.

Once again, the evidence suggests that laboratory findings about nutritive value of foods are borne out by direct studies of human beings.

Further emphasis of the importance of nutrition was given by the studies of Dr. Frederick Tisdall and coworkers in Toronto, who in 1941 found that the physical condition of infants at birth was markedly superior when the mothers had received an adequate diet during pregnancy.

The findings were verified in 1943 by Dr. Harold Stuart and Mrs. Bertha Burke in Boston. They took records of 216 pregnant women whose diets could be classed as good, fair, poor, and very poor. The health of each baby reflected the quality of the mother's diet. Most of the infants born to mothers who had good or excellent diets during pregnancy were in good or excellent physical condition at birth. Infants born to mothers on poor diets were mostly in fair or poor physical condition, stillborn, or prematurely born. The poor diet during pregnancy did not appear to affect the mother's health, but it did affect the health of the infant. The amount of protein in the mother's diet also was correlated with the weight and length of the infant at birth.

Scientists have wondered for a long time whether nutrition affects the length of a person's life.

Luigi Cornaro, a Venetian of the 16th century, was overindulgent in his youth, but after the age of 40 he kept to a strict dietary regimen. The results were fine for Cornaro; he lived to be 100. In his old age he wrote enthusiastically of the joy of living.

Science demands better evidence than that, however.

It is difficult, if not impossible, to study longevity in relation to diet of man under controlled experimental conditions; no one investigator lives long enough to complete such a study. But if results from experimental rats can be applied to man (and there is evidence that such findings are in many cases applicable), then Henry C. Sherman's experiments at Columbia University have provided an answer.

Beginning in 1920, Dr. Sherman started two series of rats on different diets. Diet A, of dried whole milk and ground whole wheat, was adequate for growth and reproduction. Diet B had a higher proportion of milk powder, and so was better. Succeeding generations from the original animals were maintained on the same two diets. By 1949, the 70th generations were still thriving. This is somewhat like taking two families before the time of Julius Caesar and studying their descendants continuously up to the present time.

Diet A was adequate for growth and reproduction through all the generations of rats. On diet B, the better diet, the animals showed differences which were statistically significant: A more rapid and efficient growth, earlier maturity, longer duration of reproductive life, greater success in rearing of young, and increased length of life.

Other studies by Dr. Sherman showed that the increased vitamin A and calcium from the added milk powder in diet B definitely contributed to the improved growth and longevity of these animals.

The depression years provided clinical material for the study of nutritional deficiencies in man. They also aroused nationwide concern that our people be adequately fed.

What is an adequate diet is hard to say. Lord Boyd-Orr has defined health as a "state of well-being such that no improvement can be effected by a change in diet." But what kind of a diet will maintain such a state of health?

Hazel K. Stiebeling, now Director of the Institute of Home Economics in the Department of Agriculture, was one of the scientists who considered the problem of the hungry 1930's and set up a working pattern of amounts of nutrients and food required daily for individuals of different ages, sex, and activities. Dr. Stiebeling guided a nationwide study of food consumption of a representative sampling of the population of the United States in the mid-1930's. The diets were evaluated in terms of adequacy as compared with the standard of requirements. The publication, "Are We Well Fed? A Report on the Diet of Families in the United States," aroused widespread concern and led President Franklin D. Roosevelt to call the National Nutrition Conference for Defense in May 1941. At the same time the National Academy of Sciences-National Research Council appointed a Committee on Food and Nutrition to develop a table of "Recommended Daily Allowances for Specific Nutrients."

War problems provided a further stimulus to the study of nutritional needs of all people. Representatives of 44 nations met at Hot Springs, Va., in 1943 to consider ways and means by which each country might increase the food resources and improve the diets of their people. From this conference came the meeting in 1945 in Quebec when the Food and Agriculture Organization of the United Nations was established. It has done much through the years to study malnutrition, determine nutritional needs, and promote food production and improvement of diets of people all over the world.

Enrichment and fortification of food was another milestone in nutrition progress. Enrichment was made possible in the 1940's by the chemists' ability to prepare pure nutrients in inexpensive forms and was made necessary by the findings that the average American diet of that period was inadequate.

I have mentioned the incidence of goiter and its prevention by the addition of small amounts of iodine. Potassium iodide was added to table salt and made available to the public on the grocery-store shelves in 1924 and the benefits of this public health measure have been demonstrated.

Vitamin A has been added to margarine to make it a good source of vitamin A. Such fortification is mandatory in some States, and margarine with 15 thousand International Units of vitamin A per pound is available in most parts of the country.

The Danes first realized the need for adding vitamin A in this way. During the First World War, practically all the butter of Denmark was exported. Subsequently an eye ailment was observed in young children and was recognized as a vitamin A deficiency. As a preventive measure, vitamin A concentrates were added to margarine. Other countries adopted the practice. The Council on Foods and Nutrition of the American Medical Association approved it in 1939, and it has since been advocated by the food and Nutrition Board.

The discovery of vitamin D as the antirachitic vitamin and the recognition of fish-liver oils as a potent source led to the advice that babies should receive cod-liver oil or some concentrate of vitamin D. Prevention of rickets and development of strong bones in young children depend on an adequate intake of calcium and phosphorus, as well as vitamin D, and therefore fortification of milk with vitamin D was begun in the early 1930's. The Council on Foods and Nutrition of the American Medical Association approved the fortification of milk with 400 International Units of the vitamin per quart.

Considerable evidence had accumulated by 1941 that many American families were consuming diets that were inadequate in thiamine, ribloflavin, niacin, and iron. Because we also were concerned with the problems of war in Europe, the National Nutrition Conference for Defense was called in May of that year. The Government was studying proposals to add some vitamins to flour and bread. A Committee on Food and Nutrition (later called the Food and Nutrition Board) had been established in 1940 to provide direction for the national nutrition program. The committee proposed the use of the term "enriched" and set up minimum and maximum limits for the enrichment of bread and flour with thiamine, riboflavin, niacin, and iron. With the support of the millers, enriched flour became available to the public and was used by the Army and Navy. Riboflavin, however, was not available in adequate amounts to use until the end of 1943.

The bread-and-flour-enrichment program has been a controversial one. Some have maintained that the public should be educated to the use of natural foods that would supply all nutrients, but experience of centuries has shown that people are reluctant to change their food habits and the education regarding food choices is a slow process. More than half the States require the enrichment of flour and bread. South Carolina was the first to do so.

Dietary studies give evidence of the nutritional improvement of the food intake of various groups and clinicians have reported declines in nutritional deficiency symptoms. But there have been improvements in family income and family food expenditures since the enrichment program began and these are contributing factors. Nevertheless, all experimental evidence to date shows that nutritional improvement of diets brings improvement in health. Especially is this so when the article of food is a staple.

From the minds of men have come the ideas and from the laboratories have come the proof (and sometimes disproof) of the ideas on which our knowledge of nutrition is based. Nutrition laboratories are expensive to maintain.

Therefore the story of progress would not be complete without reference to some of the organizations and agencies that have contributed funds for support of research in nutrition and have provided opportunities to know the work of others through professional meetings and publications.

Our account of how the study of nutrition emerged as a science began with Wilbur O. Atwater and his research in the Office of Experiment Stations. Experiment stations in every State now carry on the search for knowledge. Other divisions of the Department of Agriculture are engaged in a wide variety of basic and applied problems related to nutrition. Chief among them is the Institute of Home Economics, which was established in 1923 as the Bureau of Home Economics.

The United States Public Health Service also has made an outstanding contribution. The story of the fight against pellagra and the use of iodine to prevent endemic goiter have been told. Men of the Public Health Service were in the forefront.

Three professional organizations have among their members many men and women who were the students of Mendel, McCollum, and Sherman and who have carried on research and teaching in all phases of nutrition. These organizations are the American Home Economics Association (1909), the American Dietetic Asociation (1917), and the American Institute of Nutrition (1933).

The Food and Nutrition Board of the National Acadcmy of Sciences-National Research Council (1940) has guided the application of the science of nutrition through its recommended dietary allowances. The members of the Board also prepare bulletins summarizing and interpreting current research in nutrition.

Nutrition research workers in the laboratory have been greatly aided by grants from the Williams-Waterman Fund (1940). This fund was named for Robert R. Williams, "the father of enrichment," who devoted to 26 years to the search for thiamine. Robert E. Waterman was Williams' partner in the last 12 years of his search. Together they found the way to make thiamine so cheaply that it can be used for enriching bread, flour, cornmeal, and rice.

Another important source of financial aid to the research works in nutrition is the Nutrition Foundation (1941). Food manufacturers throughout the country support the foundation, and Dr. Charles G. King, who isolated pure viatmin C in 1932, in 1942 became director of its program of aid for research and dissemination of information about nutrition.

Alone and in teams, in private laboratories and the State experiment stations, and in colleges, universities, clinics, medical schools, and industrial firms, men and women in this and many other countries have sought the answers to the intricate problems of man's health and well-being as influenced by his food. Great progress has been made. Much remains to be learned, however, and that is the challenge we have now.

Elizabeth Neige Todhunter *is the Dean of the School of Home Economics, University of Alabama, and a past president, 1957–1958, of the American Dietetic Association. She has done extensive research in nutrition and written widely on the history of nutrition. She is a graduate of the University of New Zealand and of Columbia University, New York.*

Penicillin

From Kenneth B. Raper, "Penicillin," U.S. Department of Agriculture, *Yearbook*, 1943–1947 (Washington, 1947), pp. 699–703.

Penicillin was still a laboratory curiosity in the summer of 1941. It might have remained so had it not been for certain fortuitous events and the urgency of developing new drugs during the war. Today the drug is being manufactured in large quantities. It is the drug of choice for the treatment of many infections and diseases, and it aided immeasurably in reducing the number of war casualties. To produce the drug in the quantities needed in war and peace, it was necessary to develop a new industry with buildings and equipment valued at more than 25 million dollars. New outlets for agricultural products were realized in the development of this industry. The production of lactose, or milk sugar, was almost doubled, and a new and important use was found for corn steep liquor, a byproduct of the wet corn milling industry.

Penicillin was discovered in 1928 at St. Mary's Hospital in London by Alexander Fleming. He noted the presence of a contaminating blue-green *Penicillium* in plate cultures of *Staphylococcus* and observed that adjacent to this mold the colonies of bacteria were apparently being lysed, or dissolved. The phenomenon was investigated. When grown in pure culture, the mold, which was subsequently identified as *Penicillium notatum* Westling, was found to produce a substance that inhibited the growth of *Staphylococcus* and other disease-producing, gram-positive bacteria. Professor Fleming published the results of his investigations in 1929 and to the active substance he applied the name "penicillin," after the generic name of the mold that produced it. He determined that the substance was relatively nontoxic and he pointed out that it might have therapeutic value if it could be produced in quantity.

In the years that followed, penicillin was almost forgotten. It was not until 1940 that real interest in it was revived. Professors Florey, Chain, Heatley, and their collaborators at Oxford University demonstrated that a crude penicillin in the form of a brown powder (now known to have contained only 2 or 3 percent pure penicillin) possessed curative properties when injected into mice previously infected with *Staphylococcus* and other disease-producing bacteria. A year later they presented clinical data on six patients, who showed a favorable clinical response. The toxicity of the substance was found to be very low.

Because of conditions then prevailing in England, it was not feasible to produce there the amount of penicillin needed for further clinical trials. For that reason, aided by the Rockefeller Foundation, Drs. Florey and Heatley came to the United States. Here they were referred to the National Research Council and to Charles Thom, principal mycologist in the Department of Agriculture in Washington. They were advised to come to the Northern Regional Research Laboratory in Peoria, Ill., where members of the staff of the fermentation division had had experience in mold fermentations and a large collection of molds was maintained. Dr. O. E. May, then director of this laboratory, and Dr. R. D. Coghill, head of the Fermentation Division, realized the tremendous possibilities of the drug, and arrangements were made to begin work on the problem at once.

Research on penicillin at the Peoria laboratory was directed primarily along the following lines: To develop, if possible, a culture medium that would favor the production of a greater amount of penicillin; to investigate the possibility of producing penicillin in submerged culture; and to try to develop strains capable of producing increased yields.

The Lactose-Corn Steep Liquor Medium

Dr. Fleming had employed a nutrient broth as a culture medium, and Florey and his associates produced penicillin in a modified Czapek-Dox solution containing yeast extract and glucose. At the Northern Regional Research Laboratory, the nutrient solution was altered in many ways by A. J. Moyer, microbiologist, and many substances, known to promote the growth of micro-organisms, were investigated for their ability to increase penicillin production. Of such substances, corn-steep liquor, commonly referred to as "steep liquor," was found to be outstanding. At levels below those that actually inhibited mold growth, yields of penicillin were found to increase with the addition of increased amounts of this product. It was recognized that the steep liquor constituted the principal source of nitrogen and apparently contributed other important nutrients necessary for the formation of penicillin.

At the same time various sources of carbon were investigated, including glucose, sucrose, lactose, corn dextrin, and corn starch. Of these different carbon sources, lactose, or milk sugar, was found to be slowly assimilable by the mold and most generally favorable for penicillin production.

The Northern Regional Research Laboratory therefore recommended for the production of penicillin a culture medium whose principal ingredients were corn-steep liquor and lactose. Through Dr. A. N. Richards, chairman of the Committee on Medical Research, Office of Scientific Research and Development, these discoveries were made available to all producers of penicillin in the United States and allied countries. With certain modifications in the proportions of the ingredients used, depending upon the particular mold culture employed and the method of production, this medium has remained in general use.

The pioneer work of Professor Fleming had been done with surface or still cultures, as had also the equally important work of Professor Florey and associates. It was natural, therefore, that the same method should have been followed in our early work, and it was from studies with surface cultures that the lactose-steep liquor medium was developed. Experience with other fermentations, however, indicated that penicillin could, in all probability, be produced at a much lower cost, if a satisfactory tank or submerged fermentation could be developed. Attention was early directed toward this goal. Penicillin-producing molds were inoculated into lactose-steep liquor medium and subjected to continuous and vigorous agitation for several days, during which time the broth was assayed daily for penicillin content. When thus agitated, the mold grows submerged, usually assuming the form of small, rounded pellets.

The original Fleming strain and all substrains derived from it were found to produce disappointingly low yields of penicillin when grown submerged. Different molds in our collection that belonged to the *P. notatum-chrysogenum* group were then investigated. Another culture of *P. notatum,* designated NRRL 832, was found to produce promising yields. The details of the work were communicated to other research laboratories and to the producers of penicillin. Strain NRRL 832 was made available to the penicillin industry and for several months in 1943 and 1944 it was responsible for a large proportion of the penicillin production in this country. More productive strains have since supplanted it.

Culture solutions whose principal ingredients are corn-steep liquor and lactose are most favorable for the production of penicillin in both surface and submerged culture. For submerged production, however, the concentration of these nutrients should be approximately one-half that employed for production in surface culture. When increased amounts of steep liquor are employed, the growth of the mold is excessively heavy and the yield of penicillin is markedly reduced. Standard solutions for surface and submerged production were recommended.

Some modifications in the composition of the culture solution for both surface and submerged cultures can be made without seriously affecting penicillin yields, and such alterations are often desirable when new equipment is employed or a new penicillin-producing mold is investigated.

The two methods of penicillin production worked out in the laboratory have their direct counterparts in industry. Penicillin has been made successfully on a commercial scale by both methods.

In the surface-culture method, the mold is grown upon the surface of a quiescent nutrient solution which is dispensed in flasks, bottles, or trays usually to a depth of ½ to ¾ inch. A common practice is to use bottles of approximately 2-quart capacity and to incubate them on their sides to obtain the greatest possible amount of culture surface. This method entails a great deal of hand labor, and manufacturing costs are high. In some industrial plants as many as 30,000 bottles were inoculated each day and the plants were operated on a 6- to 10-day cycle. Maximum penicillin is produced at a temperature of about 24° to 25° C., and large incubating rooms had to be built to accommodate the 200,000 to 300,000 growing cultures.

The surface-culture method has now been supplanted by the submerged process. It was the process first developed on an industrial scale, however, and all the penicillin used in the clinical trials that first established the curative properties of the drug was produced by it.

All penicillin now made in the United States is produced by the submerged, or tank process. Inoculation with the mold may be in the form of spores or growing culture, commonly referred to as preformed inoculum. Fermentation periods vary somewhat, depending upon the mold employed and the equipment used, but commonly range from 2½ to 4 days. Large amounts of sterile air are required and the mold growth must be constantly stirred. The fermentation must be run at a favorable temperature of approximately 24° to 25° C., and measures must be taken to remove or dissipate the heat generated by the vigorously growing mold.

Other methods of producing penicillin have been recommended but have not succeeded in large-scale operations.

Different molds are employed for different methods of production. The strain isolated by Fleming was employed for all of the early studies, and in early tests made at this laboratory it was found to produce higher yields than any other unimproved strain when grown in surface culture. The Fleming strain was observed to be quite unstable in laboratory culture, and substrains possessing different cultural characteristics could be separated from it. Although most of the latter failed to equal the productivity of the parent strain, one of them, designated NRRL 1249.B21, produced yields approximately double those of the parent culture and raised the titre, or penicillin content, from about 75 to 100 units per milliliter to 150 to 200 units per milliliter. It was made available to producers and was thereafter generally employed for the production of penicillin by the surface-culture method.

More spectacular success has been achieved in developing improved cultures for the production of penicillin in submerged culture. As it became apparent that the submerged fermentation was industrially feasible, the need for developing higher-yielding submerged cultures was recognized. Strain NRRL 832, the culture employed for this type of production, was studied intensively. Efforts to obtain from it a natural variant characterized by substantially increased production were unsuccessful. Attention was then directed toward the isolation of new strains from nature. Previous work had shown that almost all members of the *P. notatum-chrysogenum* group produced some penicillin. It seemed probable, therefore, that new strains possessing greater productive capacity than NRRL 832 might be obtained if a large number of isolates were examined. Such a search was undertaken early in 1943.

New cultures were obtained from moldy food products, fruits and vegetables in early stages of spoilage, and from fertile soil collected from various stations in the United States and from many foreign countries.

The most important culture discovered, however, was isolated from a moldy cantaloupe in Peoria. The culture represented a strain of *Penicillium chrysogenum* Thom, a species closely allied to *P. notatum*, and was designated NRRL 1951 in our collection of cultures. When first studied, it produced penicillin in slightly greater yields than NRRL 832, but within a few months a natural variant, which more than doubled the amount, was developed from it. This substrain, designated NRRL 1951.B25, was studied intensively here, and was at the same time made available to the penicillin industry in 1944. It was soon generally adopted for submerged production.   .   .   .

Agricultural Leaders

From Alfred Stefferud, "Men and Milestones," U.S. Department of Agriculture, *Yearbook*, 1962 (Washington, 1962), pp. 21–36.

MANY MEN long ago planted the seeds that produced modern agriculture and the Department of Agriculture. The discoverers, explorers, colonists, and pioneers; yes. After them the farmers, inventors, scientists, administrators. The seeds they sowed were great, but we need not use that labe for them, because to Nature one seed is not greater than another. What counts, in total, is a symbiosis, in which different organisms live, work, and progress in an association that is of advantage to all. The seedbed was well prepared before 1862. An inventive generation produced a cast-iron plow, a plow with interchangeable parts, mowing machines, barbed wire, a steel plow, a refrigerator, and other machines that moved agriculture to the threshold of the machine age. One of the inventors was Cyrus Hall McCormick (1809–1884), who carried forward the project his father had worked on for 20 years. One day in July of 1831 young McCormick tried out on the family farm in Rockbridge County, Virginia, the crude machine that he called a reaper. It worked. It cut 6 acres of oats. He advertised that he would sell the machine for 50 dollars, but he had no sale until 1840. Two years later he sold seven at 100 dollars each. He moved his factory to Chicago in 1847. Farmers of the Middle West welcomed the machine: It helped them settle and work new land; with it they could cut their grain with less work when it was ready. McCormick's use of modern business methods enabled him to eclipse some of his competitors, who also had invented practical reapers.

Of a different type was the contribution of Henry Leavitt Ellsworth (1791–1858), who has been called the founder of the Department of Agriculture. Ellsworth was a lawyer, farmer, leader of an agricultural society, and head of an insurance company in Hartford, Conn., before he became head of the newly established Patent Office in 1836. He received from naval and consular officers overseas certain seeds and plants, which he distributed to farmers, without Government authority or aid. He pleaded forcefully and constantly for Government aid to agriculture, and in 1839 he got an appropriation of a thousand dollars to collect and distribute new and valuable seeds and plants, carry on agricultural investigations, and collect agricultural statistics. He foresaw the importance of crop improvement through selection of outstanding varieties: "If the application of the sciences be yet further made to husbandry, what vast improvements may be anticipated! Mowing and reaping will, it is believed, soon be chiefly performed on smooth land by horse power. Some have regretted that modern improvements make so important changes of employment — but the march of the arts and sciences is onward, and the greatest happiness of the greatest number is the motto of the patriot."

Daniel Lee, M.D., a former editor of the Genesee Farmer and professor of agriculture, was hired in 1849 as a "practical and scientific agriculturist" to supervise agricultural matters in the Patent Office and to prepare separate annual reports on agriculture. The first, dated 1849, was the seed of the Yearbooks of Agriculture. Lee decried the "universal impoverishment" of the soil: "Neither the earnest recommendation of the illustrious farmer of Mount Vernon, nor the prayers of two generations of agriculturists, nor the painful fact that nearly all tilled lands were becoming less and less productive, could induce any Legislature to foster the study of agriculture as a science." He estimated that a farmer lost 175 dollars' worth of soil constituents every time he raised and sold 1 thousand dollars' worth of produce. His reports covered a wide range — tillage, run-off, drainage, insects, fertilizers, the improvement of farm animals, rural science, statistics of weather. Few now are aware of his name, but the principles he stood for — the spirit of scientific inquiry, practical wisdom, intellectual honesty, and forthright advocacy of what he considered necessary for agricultural progress — have been guiding principles of the Department of Agriculture.

The work of the Division of Agriculture of the Patent Office expanded. A chemist, a botanist, and an entomologist joined the staff. Townend Glover (1813–1888), a British entomologist, who was 23 years old when he came to the United States, was hired to collect statistics and other information on seeds, fruit, and insects in the United States. He made a thorough study of insects of the Southern States and gathered an extensive collection of insects, birds, models of fruit, and herbarium plants. In 1865, he represented the Department of Agriculture at an exposition in Paris of insects useful or injurious to crops. In his report he warned: "As European insects are liable at any time to be introduced into this country in roots, bark, wood, grasses, and seeds, their nature and habits cannot be too well studied or understood here. It is well known that several of the insects most destructive to our crops are of European origin, and I would suggest that all foreign seeds and plants imported by this department be subjected to a careful investigation.''

Isaac Newton (1800–1867) grew up in Pennsylvania, where he managed a model dairy farm. He carried on a butter trade with special customers, including the White House in Washington. After the formation of the United States Agricultural Society, he was delegate to many of its meetings, at which he repeatedly introduced resolutions calling on Congress to establish a Department of Agriculture. In 1861 he was appointed Superintendent of the Agricultural Division of the Patent Office. When the Department of Agriculture was organized the next year, President Lincoln, whose friend he had become, made him the first Commissioner of Agriculture. Newton established an agricultural library and a museum. He selected the present grounds of the Department of Agriculture, a 40-acre tract some distance from his office in the old Patent Office Building. One July afternoon in 1866, as a storm was approaching, he remembered that some wheat samples on the experimental tract had been cut but had not been taken in. He rushed over to attend to them. He bustled about in his high silk hat and frock coat until he suffered a sunstroke. He never fully recovered and died the following summer. Lincoln in his Message to Congress in 1864 said: "The Agricultural Department, under the supervision of its present energetic and faithful head, is rapidly commending itself to the great and vital interest it was created to advance. It is peculiarly the people's Department, in which they feel more directly concerned than in any other."

One of Newton's appointments was William Saunders (1822–1900), scion of a family of noted gardeners in Scotland, who was called to Washington in 1862 for consultation about laying out the Department grounds and planning its horticultural work. As botanist and superintendent of the propagating garden, he filled an important place in the Department for 38 years. He laid out many of the parks in Washington. He was instrumental in introducing a number of useful plants from abroad, among them the navel orange. His interest in rural social conditions led him to join with Oliver Hudson Kelley (1826–1913) in organizing the Patrons of Husbandry.

Kelley, a New Englander, had settled on a farm near Itasca, Minn. He went to Washington as a clerk in the Department of Agriculture and was sent through the Southern States to survey agricultural conditions. He was struck by what he called a lack of progressive spirit among the agricultural classes. On the trip he got the idea of organizing the farmers into a fraternal association. In 1867, with six other men, he organized the Patrons of Husbandry, later known as the National Grange. Kelley was elected secretary. A few months later he started for the West, dispensing charters for local granges to pay his expenses. He continued the organization work and emphasized the social, intellectual, and fraternal benefits of the order; others saw in it a way to attack the monopolies that were thought to be oppressing the farmers. The organization flourished and grew, a landmark in cooperative effort and an example of the power of united endeavors.

Agriculture (but not only agriculture) at times has encountered roadblocks to further progress in one or another of its overlapping segments. The actions to remove the hindrances — pests, diseases, economic maladjustments, inadequate experimentation and sharing of knowledge, or whatever — are the milestones of farm progress, especially since the 1880's, when agriculture was becoming more extensive and intensive and problems therefore were building up. Each is worth a book, but there is space here only for brief mention of a few. One example is the work of F. L. Kilborne, Cooper Curtice, Theobald Smith, and Dr. D. E. Salmon, a distinguished veterinarian who headed the new Bureau of Animal Industry, in solving the puzzle of the spread of cattle-tick fever. Another example was the work of Dr. Harvey Washington Wiley (1844–1930), who came to the Department of Agriculture in 1883 as Chief of the Bureau of Chemistry. He often said that he developed the Bureau from a room in a basement, where four scientists and one dishwasher led an isolated life, into 16 practical laboratory divisions. His first work with the Department included chemical studies of sugar and sugar-producing crops, but even more noteworthy was his campaign against misbranded and adulterated food, which led to the passage of the first Food and Drug Act in 1906. Another was Marion Dorset (1872–1935), who entered the Department in 1894 as a biochemist and later became Chief of the Biochemic Division of the Bureau of Animal Industry. His scientific contributions had many applications in the livestock, meat, and dairy industries and in public health. He was known especially for his discovery of the anti-hog-cholera serum. He was one of the first scientists to make chemical analyses of the tubercle bacillus. He organized the system of Federal inspection in establishments licensed by the Government to manufacture serums, viruses, toxins, and related veterinary biological products. He formulated also the laboratory procedures in the administration of the Federal Meat Inspection Act.

The first State agricultural experiment station in the United States was organized largely through the efforts of Wilbur Olin Atwater (1844–1907) in Connecticut in 1875. He was its director for 14 years. The Hatch Act in 1887 provided for the establishment of similar stations in all States and Territories in the Union. The Office of Experiment Stations was formed in the Department of Agriculture as a central agency for the stations. Dr. Atwater was its first director. In his first annual report he wrote: ''In studying the food of animals we have no right to neglect the food of man. The principles involved are essentially the same. The majority of our people and practically all wage-workers spend and must spend at least half the money they earn for food. . . .The need and the wisdom of such studies require no urging.'' When the Congress appropriated funds for investigations of human nutrition, Dr. Atwater returned to the Connecticut station to become chief of the investigations. He prepared our first extensive table of food values, a pioneering and revolutionary work.

Alongside his achievements are those of Seaman Asahel Knapp (1833–1911), a farmer, teacher, and publisher, who urged farmers to produce more stock and abandon the one-crop system. Knapp in 1886 began growing rice in Louisiana and later in other States for a corporation engaged in agricultural development. Secretary of Agriculture James Wilson sent him overseas to seek new varieties of rice. The result was the introduction of Japanese rice and improvements in growing the crop. During his work in the South, he recognized the importance of crop diversification. He began to set up demonstration farms to show what could be done in growing crops other than cotton. When the cotton boll weevil became widespread in 1903, Dr. Knapp and Secretary Wilson visited the infested region.

Dr. Knapp was put in charge of bringing to the farmer on his own farm information that would enable him to grow cotton despite the weevil. In 1906, the first country agent was appointed. Within a few years, Knapp's Farmers Cooperative Demonstration Work had been expanded to include boys' and girls' club work and home demonstration work.

James Wilson (1836–1920) served as Secretary for 16 dynamic years, under Presidents McKinley, Theodore Roosevelt, and Taft. Wilson was born in Scotland and came to this country in 1851. He settled first in Connecticut and then in Tama County, Iowa. He was elected to the House of Representatives, where he became a member of the Committee on Agriculture and began to be called "Tama Jim" to differentiate him from Senator James Falconer Wilson, also of Iowa. As Secretary of Agriculture, Wilson advanced the Department's status as a scientific institution, increased the number of its professional employees, persuaded Congress to appropriate money for new buildings, encouraged farm demonstration and cooperative extension work, started investigations in agricultural economics and farm credit, and, when the National Forests were placed in the Department's custody, put reforestation and conservation in positions of importance. He transformed his burgeoning agency into an outstanding research, regulatory, educational, and custodial institution, all of whose parts and functions he knew so well that he could answer the questions of congressional committees without first consulting a battery of experts.

Gifford Pinchot (1865–1946), the first professional forester in the United States and the first Chief of the Forest Service, began crusading for forestry the very day he was graduated from Yale. He began the first systematic forestry work in the United States when he became forest manager of the George W. Vanderbilt estate in North Carolina. When he became head of the Division of Forestry in 1898, lumber interests were slashing their way through the Nation's forests with little thought of what might be left. He introduced better forestry methods into the operations of owners of timberland by helping them make working plans and by demonstrating good practices on the ground. When the Forest Service was created in 1905 and the National Forests were placed in the custody of the Department, Pinchot developed effective protection and administration for them. He made the conservation of natural resources a national issue. During a controversy between Pinchot and Richard A. Ballinger, then Secretary of the Interior, over the leasing of public coal lands and other issues, President Taft dismissed Pinchot, who later became Governor of Pennsylvania and then professor of forestry at Yale. A year before he died he said, "I am a forester all the time — have been, and shall be, to my dying day." He was. At the time of his death, when he was 81 years old, he was working on a new forest management plan for his estate at Milford, Pa., and crusading for conservation.

Two other men are outstanding for their work in conservation — Hugh Hammond Bennett (1881–1960) and Curtis Fletcher Marbut (1863–1935). Dr. Marbut, a soil scientist who revolutionized the American conception of soil development and influenced world thought in this field, was for many years Chief of the Soil Survey Division. He has been called the father of the modern soil survey as we know it today. During his career, he traveled in practically every county of the United States and many countries to study soils. His great contribution to soil science was the development and application of a consistent, comparable system of soil classification, based entirely on soil characteristics. The citation accompanying an honorary doctor's degree from the University of Missouri in 1916 read: "The one who knows more about the soils of the United States than any other man has ever known."

Hugh Bennett received recognition as the "father of soil conservation." His crusade against soil erosion lasted for more than half a century. The publication of his bulletin, "Soil Erosion, A National Menace," in 1928 was a milestone in his fight to secure recognition of soil erosion as a national problem. The Congress appropriated funds in 1929 for research on the cause and control of soil erosion, and Dr. Bennett was given responsibility for directing the soil erosion investigations, which were carried on as a cooperative project with State agricultural experiment stations. In 1933 he organized and administered the Soil Erosion Service, which was established as an emergency agency of the Department of Interior, and carried on a nationwide program to provide technical assistance for farmers and ranchers in erosion-control projects. Legislation passed in 1935 declared it to be the policy of Congress "to provide permanently for the control and prevention of soil erosion" and established the Soil Conservation Service in the Department of Agriculture to replace the Soil Erosion Service. Dr. Bennett became its first Chief, a position he held until October 1951. His program provided for an integrated attack against erosion. His slogan was "to use each parcel of land according to its capability and treat it according to its needs." Beginning in 1937, the Soil Conservation Service began shifting its emphasis from demonstration projects to providing technical assistance for organized groups of farmers. Twenty-two States passed enabling legislation for the establishment of soil conservation districts in 1937. Other States followed. He retired from active service in 1952, but he continued to work for soil conservation. He advised other countries on land use problems and continued to speak and write. At the time of his death, the Milwaukee Journal editorialized, "Great men usually are memorialized in stone or metal but the earth itself is being carved into a memorial to Hugh Bennett."

The National Farmers Union was born during Tama Jim's tenure. In its history, the name of Charles S. Barrett (1866–1935) is prominent. He was its leader from 1906 to 1928. He was a farmer and teacher in his native Georgia, a leader in progressive movements, and one of the first to join the Farmers Union in Upson County. When the Georgia State Union was organized in 1905, he became president of it. As national president, he was in close touch with representatives of the Government. He was a member of important commissions. He represented farmers at the Paris Peace Conference in 1919. When cotton brought 8 cents a pound in 1908, he started a "plow-up" campaign. During the money crisis of 1907–1908, he attacked the commodity exchanges. A man of conviction, he made his organization one also of conviction.

Edward Asbury O'Neal (1875–1958) was born on a farm in Alabama, and he returned to it when he finished college. He believed always that agriculture was best served when it was in the hands of farmers operating their own farms, working for and managing for themselves. He served in turn as president of his county Farm Bureau and vice president and president of the Alabama Farm Bureau Federation and the American Farm Bureau Federation. Hard work, mental alertness, a friendly interest in people, a genius for cooperation and organization, and an abiding faith in the ability of united farmers to help themselves made him a leader in American agriculture: "Farmers in every part of the country must think and act together through their own organization under leaders of their own choosing. There must be a sound national program for all agriculture." He fought for equality for agriculture as a major aim of the Farm Bureau. He and other farm leaders had a role in securing the enactment of the original Agricultural Adjustment Act and other legislation to secure parity for agriculture.

Louise Stanley (1883–1954) was head of the Home Economics Department of the University of Missouri when she and other home economists were called to Washington by Secretary Henry C. Wallace in 1923 to discuss the organization of a Bureau of Home Economics in the Department of Agriculture, and she became Chief of the new Bureau. She directed the first national survey of farm housing; more than 600 thousand families supplied facts on the physical conditions of farmhouses, and from it came nationwide programs for improving rural conditions. She stressed the application of science to the solution of day-to-day problems of families. She served as chairman of the committee on education for home and family life of the White House Conference on Child Health and Protection in 1930. She was a member of the Food and Nutrition Board, National Research Council, for several years. She was official representative of the Department of Agriculture to the American Standards Association — the first woman to hold such an appointment. During the war she helped our country and others on matters of research, nutrition, and dietary deficiencies of diverse groups of people. To her work she brought the ability and wisdom of a practical homemaker, scientist, and administrator and the thoughtfulness of a kind woman.

Howard Ross Tolley (1889–1958) was a leader in developing agricultural economics as a field of research and in shaping agricultural policy during a period of change. As Chief of the Program Planning Division of the Agricultural Adjustment Administration, he helped develop a long-range, conservation-oriented approach to farm problems that became the basis of the Soil Conservation and Domestic Allotment Act of 1936. Dr. Tolley was given responsibility for translating his ideas into action with his appointment as Administrator of the Agricultural Adjustment Administration in 1936. He became Chief of the Bureau of Agricultural Economics in 1938 and had the task of shifting the emphasis in the Bureau from straight research to long-range policy planning for the Secretary and the Department as a whole. He took on another pioneering job in 1946 as chief economist for the newly established Food and Agriculture Organization of the United Nations. That position as well as a later one, vice president of the Ford Foundation, gave him opportunity to utilize his experience and his creative mind in helping to solve world problems as well as American farm problems. The Washington Post commented editorially at the time of his death in 1958: "Tolley helped to plant and nurture the seeds of agricultural policy that during the last 25 years have grown into programs which are now as familiar a part of the American farm scene as a silo."

John Hollis Bankhead (1872–1946), of Alabama, served in the Senate from 1930 until his death. As a Senate leader for the administration in handling important farm legislation, he had a big role in the fight for farm parity. He sponsored the Bankhead Cotton Control Act of 1934, which established marketing quotas for cotton with a penalty tax on cotton ginned in excess of individual quotas. Later legislation provided for the use of marketing quotas to control the supplies of other major crops marketed. He was instrumental in securing the enactment of legislation providing price-supporting loans for cotton and other crops. The Bankhead-Jones Farm Tenant Act of 1937 provided loans to enable farm laborers, sharecroppers, and tenants to become farmowners, and authorized a continuation of the rehabilitation loan program, which had been carried on for the relief of destitute and low-income farmers. The act directed the Secretary of Agriculture to develop a program of land conservation and utilization, including the retirement of submarginal land. Senator Bankhead also sponsored legislation to increase Federal support for State agricultural experiment stations and extension services. Senator Lister Hill said at the time of Bankhead's death: "He labored long and tirelessly for American agriculture and was recognized throughout the Nation as the valiant champion of the American farmer and agriculture's foremost leader in Congress."

George William Norris (1861–1944), a Nebraskan, served in Congress from 1903 through 1943 and in the early twenties became the symbol and leader of progressive legislation. He was an outspoken advocate of the necessity of relief for agriculture. He worked for conservation of the Nation's natural resources and public ownership of the generation, transmission, and distribution of hydroelectric power. He sponsored the Tennessee Valley Authority Act of 1933, which brought to a successful conclusion his prolonged fight to save valuable Government properties at Muscle Shoals, Ala., from private exploitation. The first large dam built in Tennessee by TVA was named for him.

Charles Linza McNary (1874–1944), the son of a pioneer family of Oregon, grew up on a farm near Salem and later owned and managed a fruit farm. His 27-year career in the Congress was one of prestige and influence. His interests and visions were broad, but his chief concerns were the welfare of agriculture, the advancement of reforestation, irrigation, reclamation, and development of water power. He introduced the McNary-Haugen bill in the Senate in 1924. Its objective was to secure economic equality for agriculture. It passed twice and was vetoed. He sponsored the Clarke-McNary Act, which broadened Federal participation in the better management of forest lands and increased fire protection. The act made possible the purchase of lands on the watershed of navigable streams for timber production. Most of the National Forests east of the Mississippi River have been formed under this act and the Weeks Law. The McSweeney-McNary Law in 1928 set up a 10-year program that included a system of forest and range experiment stations, expanded research in forest products, and a nationwide survey of forest resources and requirements.

George Washington Carver (1864–1943) was a pioneer of agricultural research and chemurgy. He was born of slave parents on a farm in Missouri. After receiving a master's degree in agriculture from Iowa State College, he was placed in charge of the greenhouse. Booker T. Washington invited him to join the faculty at Tuskegee Institute as director of agriculture in 1896. Later Dr. Carver became the director of the Tuskegee Agricultural Research and Experiment Station. By creative research, he developed pigments for paints, wood stains, wallpapers, and ceramic products from the clays of Alabama. He developed more than 118 products from the sweet-potato. He made more than 300 products from peanuts. He produced paving blocks, cordage, paper, fiber for rope, and many other products from cotton. From the soybean he made several types of flour and many other products. His contribution to the field of agricultural chemistry greatly expanded the agricultural economy of the South.

Liberty Hyde Bailey (1858–1954) grew up on a fruit farm in Michigan. After serving as professor of horticulture and landscape gardening at Michigan Agricultural College, he became director of the College of Agriculture of Cornell University in 1888. Theodore Roosevelt made him chairman of his Commission on Country Life in 1908, and he made the most of that opportunity and responsibility to work for the improvement of rural life. He was the editor and author of many volumes on agricultural subjects. He edited three Cyclopedias of Horticulture and Agriculture.

David Fairchild (1869–1954) joined the staff of the Section of Plant Pathology in 1889, when he was 19 years old. He resigned after 4 years to become the first occupant of the Smithsonian Table of Research at Naples Zoological Station. He returned to Washington in 1897 and organized a section of foreign seed and plant introduction. He made many trips as a special agent for the Department of Agriculture. He introduced dates from Egypt and the Persian Gulf; nectarines from Afghanistan; paprika from Spain; rhodesgrass from South Africa; sweet peppers, broccoli, and a seedless raisin grape from Italy; a hardy variety of avocado from Chile; grain sorghums; cotton from Egypt; flowering cherry trees from Japan; tung trees, the beginning of a profitable business; and other plants.

Morris Llewellyn Cooke (1872–1960), a mechanical engineer, embarked upon a career of public service in 1911, when he became Director of Public Works in Philadelphia. His hatred of waste in any form was to form the basis for much of his most outstanding work in later years. When Gifford Pinchot was Governor of Pennsylvania, he made Dr. Cooke director of the Giant Power Survey Board to recommend a policy that would secure for industries, railroads, farms, and homes of the State an abundant and cheap supply of electrical current. He worked with utilities people and farmers to make workable plans for getting electricity to isolated farms. In a report on the Mississippi Valley, made to President Roosevelt, Dr. Cooke recommended a 20-year anti-erosion program; plans for flood control, basin by basin; power installations; independent, self-liquidating projects for rural electrification; and plans for the Forest Service to acquire and protect the forest cover. President Roosevelt issued an Executive Order creating a Rural Electrification Administration in 1935 and appointed Mr. Cooke its administrator.

William A. Jump (1891–1949) served under 11 Secretaries of Agriculture from his appointment in 1907 as a messenger at a salary of 360 dollars a year. His first major staff appointment was as personal secretary to Secretary Henry C. Wallace in 1921. The next year he became budget officer of the Department, a post he held 26 years. To him a budget was a plan of work; the problems of his onerous work he met with tact, honesty, and ability. His ideal was the advancement of public administration. On his retirement, President Truman wrote: "Your example of selfless effort to improve public administration has blazed a wide and clear trail which is already being followed by many of your associates and will be followed by many others for a long time." *(A. S.)*

Evaluating the Agricultural Experiment Stations

From H. C. Knoblauch, E. M. Law, and W. P. Meyer, *State Agricultural Experiment Stations; A History of Research Policy and Procedure,* U.S. Department of Agriculture Misc. Publ. No. 904 (Washington, 1962), pp. 207–15.

The American system of State Experiment Stations, dedicated to encouraging scientific initiative at research centers dispersed throughout the Nation, provides for the American people an enduring example of significant tax-supported research activity. The station administrators in each generation have successfully maintained the separate identity and the localized control of the station establishment. Moreover, they have repeatedly illustrated the soundness of the principle, first formulated in the Hatch Act of 1887, that local responsibility for research, financed in part by Federal authority but never dominated by that authority, economically and efficiently produces scientific dividends in a democratic society. Plurality and decentralization of organization and support of agricultural research have demonstrated their value and effectiveness, just as has our American system of divided and joint Federal and State responsibilities for so many other governmental activities.

The station movement has perennially prized the individual enterprise of its personnel and the autonomy of its member institutions. Simultaneously, however, it has participated prominently in building, with the collaboration of the Federal Department of Agriculture, a unique system of cooperation which has organized State and Federal funds, personnel, institutions, and resources of all types into the most comprehensive structure in the 20th century world for the continuous conduct of scientific research in agriculture. This pattern of cooperative activity, evolving steadily in a process of administrative adjustment to the needs of research, has sought to insure and to stimulate freedom of expression for scientific initiative and, at the same time, to combine with local individualism and responsibility the benefits of centralized coordination.

The nationwide network of State stations has demonstrated a time-tested capacity not only to serve the local and immediate interests of the people of each State but also to provide, via a continuous and systematic concentration on applied and basic research, scientific discoveries universally vital to human health and nutrition. The stations' record of outstanding accomplishments, which span the years from the discovery of the vitamin a half century ago to the discovery in recent years of streptomycin and dicoumarol, would fill the pages of a fascinating book. The American people would appreciate, could they know the story of the long-continued scientific productivity and the brilliant achievements which the illustrations in the present volume can only suggest, the continuing utility implicit in the station system for administering Federal grants to dispersed institutions. They would realize, furthermore, that research in agriculture via the station system has contributed in the past — and will contribute in the years to come — benefits so pervasive in the American way of life that the title "Biological Experiment Stations" would aptly designate the preeminent function and mission of these scientific institutions in the 20th century. Similarly they would recognize the merit of a most important feature of station activity; namely, the specialized training of graduate student-apprentices who assist top-notch scientists on station projects in every State.

The American people should not overlook, as they face decision-making in the troubled years ahead, the values perennially present in the station system for administering scientific research, a system developed patiently and managed carefully for decades before tax-supported research in nonagricultural applications achieved spectacular victories in man's endless attempts to solve the mysteries of his physical environment. American legislatures, both State and Federal, have through the years sought to keep the stations securely financed and thus insured the efficient operation of a scientific enterprise which, pioneered in the 19th century and astutely developed for the public benefit in the 20th century, has demonstrated its permanent usefulness. The American public can view with justifiable pride the carefully built capacity of its nationwide system of agricultural research. If adequately administered in future years, this system should yield a broad and steady penetration into the biological sciences.

Does not the station movement reveal in the present day, furthermore, the instructive experience that governmental policy in other scientific areas could and should allocate Federal funds "to a wide number of [university-connected] institutions in a deliberate attempt to develop a geographically diversified research competence"? With these words President Eric A. Walker of the Pennsylvania State University stressed in November 1960 the current and many-faceted problem of the relation between the Federal Government and American universities in the sponsorship of scientific productivity. "In casting around for models on which to base these arrangements," he noted with perceptive concern, "we have almost completely overlooked the oldest active program of this sort in the country. Yet, ironically, it is probably the most successful of them all. I'm speaking here of the Federal support program for agricultural research."

The champions of the experiment station movement, America's first major experience with the nationwide administration of tax-supported scientific research, have consistently contended from the earliest years that the tax-paying public, the Federal and State legislators, and the professional station personnel must assume a collective responsibility for the steady encouragement of research in agriculture. Always, however, the station leadership has insisted that station men themselves accept the prime obligation for directing the development of their numerous institutions in the public interest. This obligation has expected each director to stimulate scientific enterprise in his station and his State. This obligation has also expected, no less firmly, the encouragement of cooperative endeavor and voluntary joint action among station leaders in the various States in order that American station research, guarding itself against too great a dispersion of its energy, could develop with interstate cohesiveness despite the geographic dispersion of the research institutions.

Stations Face Challenges

The station movement in its century-long history has exhibited the vigor, the resourcefulness, and the independent individuality inherent in its democratic environment. No one in the western world would deny the importance of retaining these indigenous assets. The responsibilities of the coming years, however, require that the station men of the present generation build anew the *esprit de corps* characterizing the earlier years and, in addition, discipline themselves to a greater measure of group and cooperative activity. To achieve a balance between applied and basic research; to attract and recruit the finest talent as a working force; to maintain institutional strength and leadership; to take time, in the midst of daily pressures, to think and to plan: these realistic challenges confront the station directors in the dynamic world of today.

The perceptive wisdom of the Atwater-Johnson-Cook report applies as meaningfully in 1961 as it did in 1887. "The future usefulness of the stations will depend upon what they discover of permanent value," that trio of pioneer directors counseled, "and this must come largely from the most abstract and profound research." This maxim could well stand as the station motto across the land. The administrators and the scientists of today can take pride in the origins of their stations and draw inspiration from the enduring traditions and high standards established by their predecessors in the public service.

As the anniversary year begins, we come to the close of a text that began in modest form in reply to a scientist's question: "How old is ESCOP?" Members of that important policy-making committee themselves couldn't answer. So they took action to gather, assemble, and interpret the facts for the record. Those of us who have been able to observe for some years the integrity and dedication to principle that prevails when ESCOP and the Directors of Experiment Stations meet — differing frequently relative to means, but after careful evaluation and debate always adhering devotedly to decisions reached — have faith in the future of the agricultural experiment stations. We know that great contributions will continue to come from them, as in the past. Even as this chapter ends, ESCOP is actively engaged in evaluating challenges that lie ahead. Progressive and forward looking action was taken during its annual meeting in November 1961. It presages better coordination and planning of cooperative research in the future, and continued close working relations with the Department of Agriculture.

For those youthful scientists embarking on a career in agricultural research and to all others seeking to understand how publicly supported research, under a dual Federal-State system, can be democratically administered in a republic made up of 50 States, the record presented above is worthy of careful study.

The strength of the cooperative State-Federal agricultural research system, built on the framework of free governments as conceived under the Bill of Rights, reflects the brilliance of those who created our political institutions. The great contributions contributed by the State Experiment Stations and the Department of Agriculture to scientific advancement and national progress reflect the highest quality of administrative decision making, intellectual democracy at its best.

Past is Prologue

"What Is Past Is Prologue" are the words inscribed near the Pennsylvania Avenue entrance of the National Archives Building in Washington, D.C. To those engaged in agricultural research, both at the State experiment stations and in USDA, these words have a practical meaning.

Late in 1961 the Department of Agricultural Graduate School presented a Centennial Lecture Series, featuring five distinguished leaders, nationally recognized and each with some past practical experience in land-grant or USDA administration. The chairman of the series was Assistant Secretary of Agriculture Frank J. Welch, himself the former Dean of Agriculture and Director of the Agricultural Experiment Station, University of Kentucky.

Vernon Carstensen, historian and associate dean of the graduate school, University of Wisconsin, traced the modest beginnings of three items of legislation, recommended by Abraham Lincoln in his first annual message to Congress:

There is nothing in this modest, almost tentative proposal to suggest that during the next year Congress would pass three acts of monumental importance to American agriculture. The Department of Agriculture was created, the Homestead Act was finally adopted, and the Morrill Act was passed providing public lands for the establishment of colleges of agriculture. All were adopted during the second year of the Civil War and, except for the Homestead Act, received very little notice. That was true then. It seems to be almost true today thanks to the ardent and aggressive 'celebration' of the centennial of the Civil War. . . .

Many men of George Washington's generation assumed the perfectability of man and society. Equally important was the companion idea that man not only could improve himself but ought to do so. Although much of the eager innocence of a century and a half ago has been dissipated by bitter experience, one has only to consider the assumptions underlying many of our public acts — our technical aid programs, our enormous expenditures for education and research — to realize that we continue to live in that faith.

Concerning the part of the agricultural experiment stations in subsequent administrative developments, Dr. Carstensen said:

The experiment station development with its close and intimate connection with the Department of Agriculture, represents a unique achievement as a national cooperative research establishment supported by State and Federal funds. It was important for the scientific investigations conducted; it was important for demonstrating the fruitfulness of collaborative research so brilliantly revealed in the cattle fever inquires; and it was also important, in a much more subtle way, providin ple of how organized research could be conducted.

Another centennial series lecturer was Jesse W. Tapp, economist and vice president of California's Bank of America. The following are excerpts from what he said:

The Hatch Act in 1887 established an Experiment Station for each Land Grant college and set up funds and guidelines for research designed to make farmers more efficient. In 1914 the Smith-Lever Act established the Federal-State Extension Service, thus completing the three-cornered program of teaching, research and extension by the Land Grant Colleges.

The establishment of the USDA and the Land Grant College system was an attempt to improve the opportunities for rural people. Prior to that time, only the relatively wealthy normally attended universities. The new program meant the opportunity for a college education would be available to just about everyone who wanted it and who was otherwise determined to get it. Furthermore, it elevated the study of agriculture and the mechanical arts to the university level.

Although in actual dollars it doesn't bulk very large, relative to the cost of other factors, the most significant inputs that were made in American agriculture, I believe, are those spent in the establishment of the U.S. Department of Agriculture and Land Grant College System, and their subsequent programs of research and education. In few, if any, other ventures has the marginal productivity of capital been so great.

In the same series Hon. Henry A. Wallace, Secretary of Agriculture from 1932 to 1940, and subsequently Vice President of the United States said:

We cannot turn our backs on science or on world hunger. When I was Secretary many people suggested that we should greatly curtail or halt altogether our scientific research programs because they contributed to the surplus problem. Since I left the Department in 1940, farm workers have been increasing their efficiency at the rate of 4.6 percent a year. One farm worker today can support 26 people. In 1940 one farm worker could support only 11 people. . . .

We should be proud of our ever expanding agricultural technology. Properly used, our technology and our surpluses represent national strength, not weakness. Only in agriculture is it definitely certain that we shall remain superior to the rest of the world for many years to come. Food and our technological skills properly used can help the crowded hungry lands into a position to help themselves.

From among the Land-Grant College Presidents of 1961, President James H. Hilton of Iowa State University, Ames, Iowa, a former director of the North Carolina Experiment Station, voiced the following challenges:

In a world in which great masses of men are still lacking the bare necessities for existence itself, in a world in which a growing population is pressing ever harder on existing resources, the Land-Grant college must continue to carry on research which will increase the world's capacity to produce more food, more clothing, more shelter, more of the things that make life comfortable.

But our research task can no longer end there. The Land-Grant colleges can no longer see their major research function as solely that of discovering the means for more abundant production of either manufactured or agricultural goods. Nor can we assume that our *only* research task today is to make scientific and technological discoveries which will "put us ahead" in the nuclear and space fields as vital as these needs may be in the times in which we live.

Today, the Land-Grant colleges, in their programs of research, must *also* deal with the complex problems of economic and social adjustments, which are so important to men's welfare and survival. Increasingly, the orientation of our research must be more around people and their welfare. . . .

One of the first needs in organizing a research program which deals with economic and social problems will be — as it has been in the physical and biological sciences — to find a fruitful balance between basic and applied research. In all of our research areas — both old and new — we must withstand the pressures to put too large a share of our resources into applied research. We all know that our applied research projects which have produced immediate, concrete rewards, have drawn their information from the well of basic research. We all know that if our applied research is to continue to be productive and rewarding, we cannot allow the well of basic research to run dry. Fortunately, so many of the recent great "useful" and "practical" scientific discoveries, such as atomic energy, have been so directly the result of the basic research of so-called impractical "theorists" that today the value of basic research is being more widely recognized and materially supported.

Second, we must recognize the restrictions which limitations in budget, trained personnel, and research facilities place upon the scope and types of research projects undertaken. Although we must work toward building research organizations which will fill all our new research needs, such a retooling process takes time. In the meantime, we should carefully confine our efforts to only those projects which can be adequately carried through. Our limited research energies should not be dissipated and wasted in diverse and scattered undertakings.

Third, many of the new problems which are troubling Americans today are a combination of socio-political and economic factors. The complex which in real life does not break down neatly into problems which are either scientific, economic, sociological, or political. The difficulties which confront farm and urban families are no respectors of academic disciplines. And their solution will often require the special knowledge and competence of a variety of disciplines. . . .

Fourth, we must recognize that we cannot stop at the State line in our investigations of economic and social problems. Such problems do not recognize state boundaries.

A direct challenge came from Secretary of Agriculture Orville L. Freeman after he had given full credit to the Department and the agricultural experiment stations for their accomplishments, but had also pointed out that all problems confronting agriculture in 1961 must be presented in terms of the scientific and technological revolution that dominates the age. His challenge came in the following excerpts:

The magnitude of the potential effect of this revolution upon our lives and our future is so great that the impact of previous great historical developments, such as the industrial revolution, fade into relative insignificance. . . .

Science has shown us that we can produce more abundantly than we can consume (in both commercial channels and by special programs to provide food where it is needed) but social science has not yet shown us how to engineer this efficient productivity to benefit the producer.

Technological advance had decreed that a constantly dwindling number of farmers, on fewer acres, but with greater investment of such inputs as machinery and fertilizer, can continue to increase total production; but we have not yet determined how to make the best use of those excess acres, nor have we developed programs for maximum benefit of the human beings whose labor is no longer needed by this efficient agriculture.

We can and must find the answers to these questions — and without delay. We can do it by devoting to these problems the same kind of talent, ability, study and research that we have given to problems of increased production.

I submit that this presents a major challenge to our land grant colleges, to our experiment stations, to our Extension Service, and to the Department of Agriculture. It presents a challenge that some would prefer to avoid because it involves controversial matters, because it relates to the formulation of public policy, because it deals with matters that cannot be proved or disproved by chemical analysis or controlled experiments.

But I submit that we cannot avoid this challenge. We cannot avoid it, simply because it deals with the welfare of human beings, with the future of our resources and our children, with principles and ideals relating to human dignity, and with values we regard as vitally important.

Second Century Begins

The historical centennial conference of the American Association of Land-Grant Colleges was held at Kansas City, Mo., November 12 to 16, 1961. In the traditional spirit of the Land-Grant institutions, while full tribute was given to the founders and contributions of the past, the emphasis was on the forward look, the problems, the challenges of the century of land-grantism that lies ahead. A new constitution was adopted and with it a new name, effective January 1, 1962, "Association of State Universities and Land-Grant Colleges."

Probably the most historic contribution of the 75th annual (centennial) convention was the honest soul-searching each division did. A grant from the Carnegie Foundation had enabled some carefully planned self-evaluation as the new century begins — where we are, the problems we face, the direction to be taken in order to advance the basic functions of land-grant leadership — efficacy of learning by the many and advancement of knowledge and search for truth.

The evaluation session in the Division of Agriculture was held under the chairmanship of R. D. Lewis, Director of the Texas Agricultural Experiment Station. The Division of Agriculture heard from its two principal evaluators, J. Earl Coke, Vice President of the Bank of America, a former Assistant Secretary of Agriculture and before that Director of Extension Work in California; and Paul A.

Miller, Provost of Michigan State University and President-designate of the University of West Virginia at the time he presented his paper. While they had received assistance from persons all over the United States in the preparation and documentation of their papers, the two evaluators took full responsibility for the conlusions drawn and the recommendations made.

The papers reflected considerable thought and study. They revealed tremendous accomplishments in the century that has passed. They also recognized great challenges that must be faced if the agricultural colleges, experiment stations, and extension services are to continue influencing national progress as in the past. Mr. Coke underlined the fact that the consumer is the long-run beneficiary of agricultural research. He accepted that the change from rural to urban life has taken place and that the "comfortable past" has been blown to bits by the technological revolution. He recommended revisions in college curricula, with greater emphasis on basic understanding of finance, management, and organization in undergraduate studies plus better communications training in all levels of study. Dr. Miller pointed to the National design of the Land-Grant Colleges in terms of response to a national purpose, the organizational linkage with the people the land-grant institution serves. A problem of first concern seen by Dr. Miller was how to express the technology of agriculture in the organization of the colleges. Although the commodity departments are in the right direction, he reasoned, the colleges may wish to consider two sets of vantage points from which to give leadership, preparation to serve technological needs in agriculture along with preparation to serve society's needs with the fruits of agricultural technology.

Following the two evaluations, each section of the Division — residence instruction, experiment stations, and extension — discussed the evaluations made. Associate Director W. E. Krauss of the Ohio Experiment Station spoke for the Experiment Station Section. Following are excerpts from Dr. Krauss' comments:

Research is the process of critical inquiry or examination in seeking facts or principles. It may be extremely simple, as in a study of existing documents, or extremely complicated as in the case of building an atomic pile based upon complex formulae of mathematics, physics and chemistry. It may be "basic" or "applied" or "developmental," or a combination, as is usually the case; it may be superficial or profound. Agricultural research has all these elements but may be distinctive in that historically some reason for doing it must be apparent. . . .

. . . both depth and breadth of the research effort will vary from year to year and from state to state. We should not be guilty of looking down at applied research, for this must definitely be an important part of a Land-grant institution's research effort if it is to fulfill its obligation to serve the needs of people. Neither do we need to avoid production research that results in greater production efficiency and higher quality in terms of consumer needs and consumer demands. . . .

The flow of research results directly into scientific channels affords a communications problem in itself. The scientific literature has become so voluminous as to defy keeping up to date in one's reading of the literature even in a highly specialized field. Some study is being given to this problem but greater consideration needs to be given to development of improved library services and central storehouses of scientific data from which references and abstracts in any language in any given field may quickly be assembled on request. This is a need of the scientist that will demand the best in communications research to solve. . . .

Successful launching of satellites and the knowledge that this is only the forerunner of an era of almost infinite dimension, practically guarantees support with public funds for research, and development of research personnel, in those areas directly related to defense and war. This is covered under the now familiar phrase "scientists for basic research." While at first emphasis may need to be on those sciences and technological developments that make for destruction it is inevitable that other scientific needs will be met and even ultimately benefit from a "crash research program" in missiles and space travel. It must never be forgotten that the secret of life and the secret of manufacture of food nutrients by plants have not been solved and that since all biological activities are related to these two basic processes there is as much need for encouragement of research in life-building and life-preservation as there is in life-destruction even as a defensive mechanism.

The proceedings for the above Centennial session of the Division of Agriculture on November 14, 1961 merit careful reading. The following *Postscript on the Future,* ending Dr. Miller's presentation before the Division of Agriculture, sums up the challenges facing the agricultural colleges and experiment stations as 1961 comes to a close and as the Centennial year 1962 is about to begin:

Every land-grant college leader must search his heart and mind today as to whether or not the agricultural colleges have received the message of great excitement and adventure which the world community now sends out to them. And he must be asked if he is confident that the colleges are making their way between one world that is dead or dying and another which is as yet unborn. And collectively, are we as sure as we ought to be that the colleges' finest chapters are ahead and are we stoutly free of cringing at the occasional claim that these chapters may be behind us? Are we willing to serve faithfully the states and counties about us but intellectually encircle our hopes with national and international needs? And are we as determined as we ought to be that our choices for the future will be as sufficient as they were in the past?

Attacking Screw-Worms

From Marshall Gall, "The Insect Destroyer — Portrait of a Scientist," U.S. Department of Agriculture, *Yearbook,* 1968 (Washington 1968), pp. 54–57.

Back in the 1930's, when flies had little to fear except flypaper, a young entomologist in the U.S. Department of Agriculture began working out a new theory of insect control — a theory that was to earn him first ridicule, then worldwide acclaim.

At the time, Edward F. Knipling did not consider himself a theorist, really. He was just looking for a better way to destroy insects.

His job at USDA called for controlling screw-worms and other livestock pests on the Nation's cattle ranges.

This was a frustrating assignment. Arsenic, mercury, phenolic dips, and other poisons were available at the time, but these sometimes killed animals as well as insects. Furthermore, insects had on their side the advantage of tremendous reproductive capacity. Consider the ordinary house fly, for example: One pair can produce nearly 200 billion *billion* offspring during the course of a summer.

This capacity for reproduction, it seemed to Knipling, lies at the heart of many major insect control problems. Killing every insect within reach doesn't solve the problem — not if a few insects remain out of reach and continue to multiply. If an insect's reproductive capacity could be sabotaged — if an entire population of insects could be made infertile — the problem of controlling that insect would be solved once and for all.

These musings led to development of the sterility principle of insect control, one of the most original scientific ideas of this century.

Briefly, the sterile-insect principle involves raising insects in captivity, sterilizing them, and releasing them into the environment in overwhelming numbers. Some of the sterilized males mate with wild females. The resulting eggs are infertile, and the insect's population dwindles.

Knipling's early efforts to win support for his scheme were largely unsuccessful. The thought of introducing birth control to the insect world was too far-fetched for most scientists to accept. Still, a few loyal colleagues thought he had something — among them, R. C. Bushland, another USDA entomologist, whose contributions to the sterility principle Knipling is very quick to credit.

The first thing the scientists had to do was figure out a way to sterilize insects. Other scientists had sterilized certain insects with X-rays. Could the feat be duplicated on a large scale? An Army hospital made its X-ray facilities available for the project; Knipling's men spent weekends and holidays at the hospital, exposing insects to the rays and noting the effects. Later, an obsolete cobalt-60 gamma ray source was acquired from the Atomic Energy Commission. This helped, but the work still progressed slowly.

Meanwhile, Knipling's reputation was advancing on the basis of other efforts. In 1938, he demonstrated that treating an animal internally could destroy external parasites. During World War II, he directed a USDA entomology laboratory at Orlando, Fla., where work was being done to furnish the Armed Forces with insect and disease control measures.

From this laboratory came louse powders used by grateful GI's all over the world, as well as insect and disease preventatives that were to be adopted by health agencies throughout the world.

Knipling could have put aside his "crackpot" scheme and settled back to enjoy the fruits of his other successes. But this son of an immigrant Texas farmer was not accustomed to taking the easy way. As a child, he worked in his father's fields, sometimes picking insects off from plants by hand in order to save a crop. In college, he mowed lawns, waited on tables, and studied.

To go with talent and willingness to work, he exhibited a wide stubborn streak; it was this quality that kept the sterile-insect principle alive. As his scientific reputation spread and his authority as a research administrator grew, he was able to channel more and more research effort toward perfecting the sterility technique. In 1953, he was named director of all USDA entomology research. Now he was in a position to put his pet theory to the test.

Screw-worms were to be the first victims of the sterility eradication technique. The screw-worm is the larva of a large fly. The fly lays its eggs in barbed wire cuts or other small wounds of livestock. When the larvae hatch, they burrow into the flesh of the animal. If undeterred, screw-worms can kill a full-grown steer in 10 days.

Screw-worm flies were raised in captivity and sterilized. The first field test took place on Sanibel, a small island off the coast of Florida, in 1953. It was successful, but proof of eradication could not be demonstrated because the island quickly became reinfested by flies from the nearby Florida coast. In 1954, the technique was tried again, this time on the 170-square mile island of Curaçao, which is located far enough out in the Caribbean so that no outside screw-worm flies could possibly reach it. The screw-worm was eradicated from Curaçao within less than 6 weeks.

The next step was a large-scale program in 1957–58 to eradicate the screw-worm from the Southeastern United States, sponsored by USDA, the Florida Livestock Board, and other organizations. During the program, more than 2¾ billion sterile flies were released from airplanes. These flies completed the race-suicide scheme over an 80,000-square mile area within 18 months.

A few years later, similar results were achieved in a screw-worm eradication program in the Southwest.

Knipling's project, 20 years in the making, was a success.

Now in his fifties, the soft-spoken research director has amassed a closetful of scientific awards and citations, including the $10,000 Rockefeller Public Service Award, one of the highest honors accorded Government employees, and the $10,000 Hoblitzelle Award for achievement in agricultural science, shared with collaborator Bushland. In 1966, he was elected to the National Academy of Sciences, a limited-membership group consisting of the top scientists in the country.

But Knipling continues to sprout new ideas upon the subject of insect control.

One of the shortcomings of the sterile-insect technique right now is that insects must be raised in captivity, he points out. And this creates nursery problems.

The screw-worm fly, for instance, normally lays her eggs in open wounds. To get her to lay eggs in captivity, researchers had to duplicate an open wound on a mammoth scale. They did this by heating up a ground meat mixture to the body temperature of livestock.

But the principle of sterility can probably be used against insects in ways other than by releasing sterile males, Knipling believes. For example, a sterilizing agent might be mixed with an insect attractant and broadcast throughout an infested area. Insects would be drawn by the attractant and would be sterilized upon eating or touching the sterilizing agent. Selective attractants that appeal to specific insects would have to be used in order to avoid sterilizing nontarget species.

But why all this bother? If you are going to spread poison, why not spread something that will kill rather than sterilize?

"Look at it this way," Knipling says. "If 90 percent of a population of 1,000 pests in a given area are killed, 100 will remain to reproduce. If 90 percent are sterilized, the 900 which are sterilized cannot reproduce. So far, it's a draw. But remember, the sterilized insects are as sexually active as ever and are competing with the unsterilized individuals for the attentions of the opposite sex. Under such circumstances, we would expect only 10 individuals to reproduce. This brings our efficiency up to 99 percent for the sterility technique."

Another promising variation of the sterility technique may be to use it in combination with pesticides, Knipling says. To illustrate, he cites a fruit fly eradication program carried out by his researchers on the island of Guam. In 1953, the island was struck by a devastating typhoon. Breadfruit trees and other fruit fly breeding places were destroyed, and the fly population fell sharply. Knipling's men immediately began releasing sterile flies. In a short time, and at modest cost, the fruit fly was eradicated from the island.

"We can do the same thing with pesticides," Knipling contends: "Use them to get the population down to a minimum, then release sterile insects to eradicate." Pesticides achieve peak efficiency when they are used against large insect populations, because the same amount of pesticide must be applied to an area whether it contains a thousand insects or a million. The sterility technique, on the other hand, is most efficient against small populations because fewer sterile insects are needed. Thus, by reducing an insect population with pesticides, then releasing sterile insects to eradicate the remaining individuals, entomologists would be making the most efficient use of both techniques.

Whatever the innovations, it appears certain that Knipling's sterility technique is here to stay. Besides making insect eradication or suppression possible, it has other advantages over conventional methods of insect control. It is selective, it leaves no harmful residues to accumulate in the environment, and it solves the problem of immunity — the tendency of insects to build up resistance to pesticides.

Some insects are probably more vulnerable than others, but research thus far indicates that the sterility technique will have broad application. Boll weevils, codling moths, and various fruit flies seem likely candidates for sterility treatment.

The technique has one important limitation, however: Some insects, particularly biting ones, should not be released into the environment because they could do considerable harm themselves before their sterility brought about eradication. In Burma, entomologists used the sterility technique to eradicate a disease-carrying mosquito from one village — but they released only sterile males, and the male of the species does not bite. In contrast, plans to use the sterility technique against tsetse flies in Africa are proceeding with caution; both sexes of this species bite. Scientists will try to lower the population by some other means, then use sterile flies just long enough to finish the eradication job.

Theoretically at least, anything that breeds can be sterilized — and wiped out. Biologists are exploring the sterility principle as a means of eradicating unwanted animals — rats, for example. Furthermore, the principle could be used to manage as well as to eradicate animal populations. Sometimes deer and other desirable wildlife produce more offspring than the available food supply can support. In such cases, induced sterility would be one way of balancing population and food supply.

To many, perpetuation of life is something not to be tampered with, yet population control on this crowded planet seems destined to become commonplace among humans as well as animals if we are to avoid widespread starvation. In the animal world, Knipling asserts, sterilization is infinitely more humane than poisoning, and it is more efficient.

The Negro Land-Grant Colleges

From William Payne, "The Negro Land-Grant Colleges," Civil Rights Digest, 3:12–17. Spring 1970.

FORGOTTEN . . . BUT NOT GONE

Fort Valley . . . Alcorn . . . Prairie View . . . Langston — not exactly household words in the lexicon of higher education. Few people recognize them as the Negro land-grant colleges of Georgia, Mississippi, Texas, and Oklahoma, respectively. There are in fact 16 Negro land-grant colleges in the United States— sad reminders that the day of "separate and unequal" is still very much with us. What has happened and what is happening to these colleges is a story which requires telling and which should be of great concern to all people who believe in equal protection of the laws.

The notion of land-grant colleges began with Justin Smith Morrill, a Whig member of Congress, whose own formal education ended when he was 14. He sponsored legislation, first vetoed in 1859 by President Buchanan but subsequently signed into law in 1862 by President Lincoln, that provided for

. . . the endowment, support, and maintenance of at least one college where the leading object shall be . . . to teach such branches of learning as are related to agriculture and the mechanic arts . . . in order to promote the liberal and practical education of the industrial classes in the several pursuits and professions of life.

By authorizing legislation granting 30,000 acres of Federal land for each State's member in Congress, the proceeds from the sale of which were to be used as a permanent endowment for what were soon to be called the land-grant colleges, the First Morrill Act was the initial step in democratizing higher education in America. Prior to this time, higher education in this country was the exclusive province of the elite, the rich, or the professional classes. The First Morrill Act came at a time when more than 80 percent of the labor force in the country was engaged either in agriculture [59 percent] or industry [24 percent]. It also came at a time when 90 percent of the Negroes in America were slaves.

Almost 30 years later, in 1890, the Second Morrill Act was passed which authorized the establishment of separate land-grant colleges for Negroes. Seventeen Southern and border States chose to do so, either by designating existing private Negro schools as the second land-grant institution in the State; designating existing State-supported Negro institutions; assigning funds to existing private Negro schools and subsequently taking them over as State institutions; or by establishing new land-grant colleges for Negroes under State control. Sixteen of the Negro land-grant colleges established under the 1890 law remain today. West Virginia discontinued the separate Negro land-grant college status of West Virginia State in 1957.

At the outset, the Negro land-grant colleges were little more than secondary schools offering the equivalent of a high school education. Although every one of the 17 States, except Tennessee,* had established a separate Negro land-grant college by 1900, none of the colleges offered college-level courses until 1916. A survey that year revealed that only three predominantly Negro colleges in the United States offered programs of standard collegiate grade and all three were private institutions. In the same year, there were only 64 public high schools for Negroes in the Southern States and only 45 of them offered a full high school curriculum. Enrollment in public Negro high schools was only 8,700. Even as late as 1928 Negro land-grant colleges enrolled more students in sub-college work than in college work. Arkansas AM&N, for example, only became a 4-year college in 1929 and Fort Valley State (Georgia) did not graduate its first 4-year college class until 1941.

Thus it can be seen that today's Negro college student represents possibly only the second, and in some cases the first, generation of college-educated Negroes in the United States. The 1960 census showed, for example, that of Southern Negroes born in 1890, the year the Second Morrill Act was passed, the median school years completed was less than 4 years. Even of those who were born in 1930, the median school years completed varied between 5 and 9 years, depending upon place of residence (rural or urban).

Despite the tremendous handicaps they have faced and are still facing today, the Negro land-grant colleges, which enroll approximately 50,000 students or about 20 percent of all the Negro students in college today, have made significant contributions to higher education in this country. In 1969, the Negro land-grant colleges graduated nearly 8,000 students, Approximately 450 alumni have gone on to obtain Ph.D's. Some of the graduates are leading public figures: Whitney Young, Executive Director of the National Urban League, is a graduate of Kentucky State, for example; Howard E. Lee, Mayor of Chapel Hill, North Carolina, is a graduate of Fort Valley State; Ercell Watson, Superintendent of Schools in Trenton, New Jersey, graduated from Delaware State; The Honorable Damon J. Keith, District Court Judge in the Sixth Circuit, is a graduate of West Virginia State; The Honorable Russell Frye, first Negro to serve in the North Carolina State Legislature since Reconstruction, is a graduate of North Carolina A&T. It might also be added that the Negro land-grant colleges are the primary source for Negro officers in the Armed Services.

Some of the Negro land-grant colleges are among those with top curriculums. Alabama A&M has a 4-year program in computer science and Lincoln University (Missouri) was among the first institutions in the State to install a computer (1960). In addition, four colleges have degree programs in engineering, five have nursing programs, and one has a law school.

Even during the years that the Negro colleges were struggling to achieve collegiate status, they were controlled by white boards of governors. As late as 1940, only three of the Negro land-grant colleges had Negro board members with voting powers. Although legal segregation applied to elementary and secondary schools in the South prior to 1900, ironically it did not apply to colleges and universities. Nonetheless, a pattern of segregation was in fact created in such institutions and this was shortly confirmed by various State legislation. Thus, when

*Tennessee did not establish a separate Negro land-grant college until 1912. All other Negro land-grant colleges were founded in the 19th century, between 1871 and 1897, although their current land-grant status was accorded as early as 1878 and as late as 1958.

one speaks of a predominantly white or Negro institution even today, it must be remembered that they are rooted in a history of segregation.

Segregation, in an informal though not legal sense, exists in the white and Negro land-grant colleges today. A survey by the Department of Health, Education, and Welfare of undergraduate enrollment in public institutions of higher learning in 1968 revealed that none of the predominantly white land-grant institutions have more than a 2 percent Negro undergraduate enrollment. Of approximately 330,000 students enrolled in predominantly white land-grant institutions in States where there is also a Negro land-grant college less than 1.5 percent are Negro. Ten of these institutions have less than 1 percent Negro enrollment.

Negro land-grant colleges have a somewhat larger percentage of white students. Of the more than 50,000 students enrolled at predominantly Negro land-grant institutions, approximately 5 percent are white. Eight of the colleges have more than 99 percent Negro enrollment and two colleges have only Negroes enrolled as undergraduates. With the exception of the Negro land-grant colleges in four border States, Maryland, Delaware, Missouri, and Kentucky, none of the remaining colleges has less than 96 percent enrollment of Negroes. In addition, West Virginia State, which was formerly all-Negro, is now predominantly white, having a Negro undergraduate enrollment of 26.7 percent.

The Second Morrill Act contained a "separate but equal" clause:

No money shall be paid . . . for the support or maintenance of a college where a distinction of race or color is made in the admission of students, but the establishment and maintenance of such colleges for white and colored students shall be held to be a compliance . . . if the funds received in such State or Territory be equitably divided . . .

It is notable that the act called for an *equitable* division of funds but not necessarily an *equal* or *proportionate* division.

Testimony by then Deputy Attorney General Nicholas DeB. Katzenbach, during congressional consideration of the Civil Rights Act of 1964 with respect to Title VI of the act, forbidding discrimination in programs receiving Federal assistance, describes the effects of that title on this portion of the Morrill Act:

In addition, Title VI will override those provisions of existing Federal law which contemplate financial assistance to 'separate but equal' facilities. Assistance to such facilities appears to be contemplated under . . . the Second Morrill Act. . . . Title VI would override all such 'separate but equal' provisions without the need for further litigation, and would give, to the Federal agencies administering laws which contain such provisions, a clear directive to take action to effectuate the provisions of Title VI.

A survey of the distribution of both Federal and State aid to predominantly white and Negro land-grant colleges shows that Negro colleges are discriminated against in terms of a fair share of such funds. A report by the National Science Foundation reveals that in Fiscal Year 1968, the predominantly white land-grant colleges in States where there is also a Negro land-grant college received $200 million from various agencies of the Federal Government — *11 times* the amount of just over $18 million which went to the predominantly Negro land-grant colleges. (Although Federal aid constitutes nearly 20 percent of income for all public institutions of higher learning, it amounts to only 10 percent of the income for predominantly Negro public colleges.) Just to cite a few examples (note chart on page 16): in 1968 the Federal Government gave $5.8 million to Clemson, the predominantly white land-grant institution in South Carolina, but the same year the Federal Government gave only $490,000 to South Carolina State, the predominantly Negro land-grant college in the State. Thus, although Clemson, the smallest of all the predominantly white land-grant institutions, has an enrollment only slightly more than three times that of South Carolina State, it received *almost 12 times* as much Federal money.

Similarly, in the same year the Federal Government gave almost $9 million to Mississippi State but only $650,000 to Alcorn A&M. Thus, although Mississippi State enrolls less than 4½ times as many students as Alcorn A&M, it received *almost 14 times* as much in Federal aid. And so on down the list.

The University of Georgia, with 10 times the enrollment of Fort Valley, received *nearly 24 times* as much Federal aid. The University of Florida, with less than five times the enrollment of Florida A&M, received *24 times* as much in Federal aid. Virginia Polytechnic Institute, with only 1½ times the enrollment of Virginia State, received *five times* as much Federal aid. North Carolina State, with less than 3½ times the enrollment of North Carolina A&T, received *nearly nine times* as much Federal aid.

Federal funds are derived from two sources: so-called "formula" funds and specific grants or aid from individual Federal agencies. The formula funds are administered by the Department of Health, Education, and Welfare (for resident teaching assistance) and the Department of Agriculture (for research and extension). One of the chief sources of the Federal aid imbalance is the Department of Agriculture. In Fiscal Year 1968, it gave nearly $60 million to the predominantly white land-grant colleges — *150 times* the figure of less than $400,000 it gave to the predominantly Negro land-grant colleges in the same States. The complaints of the Negro land-grant colleges against the Department of Agriculture are not new. Historically the most neglected functions of the Negro land-grant colleges have been research and extension and the Department of Agriculture is the chief Federal source for such funding. In 1939 the President's Advisory Committee on Education commented:

The most liberal interpretation that can be made of the situation indicates that the Negro has been discriminated against in the administration of the Smith-Lever Act in the South and that this discrimination has occurred in spite of the fact that there was sufficient basis in the legislation for the Department of Agriculture to have prevented it.

Not only are the Negro land-grant colleges discriminated against in terms of Federal aid, but in terms of State aid as well. (This is especially a critical problem because the predominantly Negro public colleges traditionally have received a greater portion of their income from State aid than from any other source — about 50 percent as compared to only 40 percent for all other public institutions.) A report of the National Association of State Universities and Land-Grant Colleges shows that 16 predominantly white land-grant institutions receive $450 million in State appropriations — *almost nine times* the figure of $52.3 million received by the Negro land-grant colleges in the same States. It must be remembered that enrollment in the predominantly white land-grant institutions is only about 5½ times that of the predominantly Negro land-grant institutions.

Reflecting the above, a few examples include: The Texas State Legislature appropriated $37.2 million for the operation of Texas A&M, the predominantly white land-grant institution in the State. The appropriation for Prairie View A&M was only $4.5 million. Thus, although Texas A&M has an enrollment of only slightly more than three times that of Prairie View A&M, it received *more than eight times* as much in State aid. And so, just as in the case of Federal aid, the list of cases where State aid favors the white institutions continues.

FEDERAL AND STATE AIDS TO PREDOMINANTLY WHITE AND NEGRO LAND-GRANT COLLEGES

INSTITUTIONS	1968 Enrollment	Ratio of White to Negro	Fiscal Year 1968 Federal Aid (thousands)	Ratio of White to Negro	1969–70 State Aid (thousands)	Ratio of White to Negro
Auburn U.	14,422		$ 8,945		$18,161	
Alabama A&M	2,076	6.9:1	851	10.5:1	2,339	7.8:1
U. of Arkansas	11,620		10,804		17,850	
Arkansas AM&N	3,445	3.4:1	1,454	7.4:1	2,690	6.6:1
U. of Delaware	12,810		4,527		11,977	
Delaware State	909	14.1:1	524	8.6:1	1,998	6.0:1
U. of Florida	21,389		21,737		60,708	
Forida A&M	4,508	4.7:1	902	24.1:1	6,693	9.1:1
U. of Georgia	21,182		19,831		41,808	
Ft. Valley State	2,102	10.1:1	830	23.9:1	2,079	20.1:1
U. of Kentucky	24,331		17,922		47,287	
Kentucky State	1,606	15.2:1	390	45.9:1	2,170	21.8:1
Louisiana State U.	31,902		9,374		48,252	
Southern U.	9,978	3.2:1	3,177	2.9:1	9,172	5.3:1
Maryland	*		*		*	
Mississippi State	9,786		8,841		10,501	
Alcorn A&M	2,305	4.4:1	651	13.6:1	1,626	6.5:1
U. of Missouri	44,482		21,933		45,611	
Lincoln U.	2,094	21.2:1	266	82.5:1	2,588	17.6:1
North Carolina State	12,758		13,916		32,183	
North Carolina A&T	3,781	3.4:1	1,569	8:9:1	4,087	7.9:1
Oklahoma State	17,381		9,829		19,004	
Langston U.	1,324	13.1:1	610	16.1:1	849	22.4:1
Clemson U.	6,839		5,759		11,154	
South Carolina State	2,081	3.3:1	490	11.8:1	3,944	2.8:1
U. of Tennessee	30,771		23,616		29,561	
Tennessee A&I	4,536	6.8:1	2,082	11.3:1	4,198	7.0:1
Texas A&M	12,867		14,711		37,189	
Prairie View A&M	4,028	3.2:1	2,860	5.1:1	4,536	8.2:1
VPI	10,289		7,597		18,693	
Virginia State	6,894	1.5:1	1,508	5.0:1	3,348	5.6:1
TOTALS	282,829		$199,342		$449,939	
	51,667	5.5:1	$ 18,164	8.4:1	$ 52,317	8.4
	$ 52,317	10.4:1				

*Separate figures not available.

(Italics indicate predominantly Negro land-grant colleges)

North Carolina State, which has less than 3½ times the enrollment of North Carolina A&T, received *almost eight times* as much State aid. Virginia Polytechnic, with only 1½ times the enrollment of Virginia State, received *more than 5½ times* State aid. The University of Arkansas, with less than 3½ times the enrollment of Arkansas AM&N, received *more than 6½ times* as much State aid. The University of Georgia, with 10 times the enrollment of Fort Valley, received *20 times* as much State aid. Louisiana State University, with slightly more than three times the enrollment of Southern University, received *more than five times* as much State aid. The University of Florida, with less than five times the enrollment of Florida A&M, received more *than nine times* as much State aid.

When totaled, Federal and State aid to the predominantly white land-grant institutions runs approximately $650 million a year. Aid to the predominantly Negro land-grant colleges in the same States is only slightly more than $70 million. Thus, although the predominantly white land-grant colleges enroll only about 5½ times as many students, combined Federal-State aid equals *more than nine times* as much. Federal aid is 11 times as much and State aid is more than 8½ times as much.

Total Federal aid would be considerably more disproportionate if it were not for the grants and contracts of agencies other than those who administer so-called "formula" funds (Morrill-Nelson, Hatch, Smith-Lever, Bankhead-Jones, etc.). Formula funds to white land-grant institutions in Fiscal Year 1967 amounted to $59.3 million as compared to only $1.4 million to the Negro land-grant colleges — a ratio of 43 to 1.

Looked at another way, total Federal-State aid equals almost $2,300 per student in the predominantly white land-grant institutions but less than $1,365 in the predominantly Negro ones — less than 60 percent the per capita aid to students in the white institutions. While shocking enough in these terms, the total dollar gap is one of almost $580 million. By source, the per capita Federal and State aids are $705 and $1,591 respectively for the student in the predominantly white land-grant college but only $352 and $1,013 for the student in the predominantly Negro land-grant college — only 50 and 64 percent, Federal and State respectively, of the per capita in the white schools.

Discriminated against by both Federal and State governments, the Negro land-grant colleges are in deep financial trouble. Their most pressing needs, by the estimation of their presidents, are for student aid ($3.6 million); fellowships for faculty members ($1.3 million); research funds ($1.8 million); new facilities ($84.8 million); renovation of existing buildings ($30.6 million); and increased operating funds ($1.3 million), primarily for upgrading of staff. Especially is the need critical for student aid, faculty, and facilities. The majority of students come from families where the average income is less than $4,000 a year. The average salary for faculty at Negro land-grant colleges is less than 95 percent of that of faculty at white land-grant colleges. Moreover, the lack of sufficient faculty members and adequate facilities accounts for having to deny admittance to many otherwise qualified students. Last year, of nearly 14,800 students who applied, only 6,800 were admitted.

By conservative estimate, it would take approximately $125 million just to "catch up" in the above areas. Even at that, the needs may be understated. Earl J. McGrath, in his book, *The Predominantly Negro Colleges and Universities in Transition* (New York: Columbia University, 1965), states:

. . . anyone who thinks that a significant percentage of [Negro colleges] can be substantially helped by an expenditure of a few million dollars sadly deludes himself. The presently predominantly Negro colleges will need several hundred million dollars in the next five or ten years merely to keep step with the growing needs of their potential student bodies and the unprecedented advancements in higher education. . . . Anything less than such efforts will result in continuing restrictions nearly as demeaning and privational as segregation itself.

In today's world, in which the role of quality education for all men has come to be recognized as the foundation on which our national future lies, the time is at hand for a first hard look at one of the Nation's most neglected resources — its Negro land-grant colleges. In whatever form and on whatever ethnic basis they function in the future, their immense potential for enrichment of the country must be brought to fruition. Understaffed, underfinanced, overlooked for far too long, Negro land-grant colleges must become a national priority among educational and social goals. Their renaissance is a necessity to the country; it must be expedited with every ability at our command.

Changes in Farming and Farm Life

West Virginia Farmers' Markets

From "State Farmers' Markets," in West Virginia Department of Agriculture, *Report*, 1941–42 (Charleston, 1942), pp. 73–77.

For years one of the big problems in West Virginia's agriculture has been that of finding profitable markets for farm products. On the face of things the opportunity is here. West Virginia is a deficit production state for a great many commodities, growing less than it consumes, so that within the state's boundaries the market demand, generally speaking, is larger than the available supply.

Nevertheless, development of modern forms of transportation, especially refrigerated transportation, plus gradual expansion of trunk highway systems have combined to put West Virginia farmers into direct competition with producers from north, east, the deep south and even the far west. Lacking suitable outlets in many areas, West Virginia farmers have been hard put to hold their own.

Officials of the state department of agriculture have long recognized the fact that West Virginia farmers, who are largely "general farmers," face a handicap in competing with production specialists from other areas. West Virginia production as a rule heretofore has been in small units, generally lacking uniformity in packaging and standardization. These factors do not recommend themselves to the average commercial buyer, with a result that a great part of West Virginia farm production must find a market locally. If the local market is flooded, it is almost inevitable that prices will be affected adversely and that some supplies, lacking an outlet, will go to waste.

For a number of years the state department of agriculture has devoted time and effort, and substantial sums of public money, to the development of grading and standardization in farm production, essential in any comprehensive marketing program.

For those not familiar with the commercial application of official grading to farm marketing, an example is given. Standards for farm commodities are uniform throughout the United States. Therefore, if a buyer in New York City telephones an apple grower in West Virginia's eastern panhandle and orders a carload of apples of a certain variety and grade, he knows he will get what he orders. Meanwhile the buyer can, with confidence begin to take orders from his retail customers in advance of actual delivery. The New York buyer doesn't have to see the fruit before he buys. He buys on *grade,* knowing that the product will be inspected for verification by an official federal-state inspector at the shipping point. The example deals with the commercial sale of fruit. It may be applied to any other farm commodity, including livestock.

The grading program in West Virginia had its inception in the commercial apple producing areas of the state where conditions were most suitable for development. Since the present commissioner of agriculture took office this program has been expanded; and during the biennium with which this report deals has taken in the grading of apples, peaches, cherries, strawberries, potatoes, cabbage, and other garden produce, eggs and livestock.

Indicating the extent of this one feature of the state department of agriculture's program, the department's inspection force passed on, for example, 3,747 carlots of apples during the 1940–1941 seasons; in 1941 inspected 50-million pounds of apples at state canneries; and livestock inspectors graded 99,492 lambs at auction markets and co-operative yards during the 1941 season. Over 7,000 cases (30 dozen to a case) of eggs were graded for government buyers alone from April 15, 1942 to the end of the biennial period, June 30.

In West Virginia's marketing program, orchardists were equipped to meet commercial demands since individually they are producers of heavy volumes. The livestock auction markets and the co-operative concentration points serve to permit producers to assemble their lambs and calves for grading and selling in large lots.

In a great many other instances, however, producers of farm commodities were without an assembly point where their products could be graded, put into uniform packs and offered in volume to buyers who are accustomed to pay for quality, or who have profitable outlets for off-grade but still healthful, nourishing and valuable farm produce. It is this situation which prompted the state department of agriculture to launch its program of State Farmers' Markets. Entrance of the United States into the war only served to intensify the need for organized marketing of farm food products.

Organizing A Farmers' Market

In the following paragraphs is described the method followed when a state farmers' market was organized in the Greenbrier Valley for the purpose of creating an outlet for farm produce in that area in the season of 1942 and thereafter.

This same method of organization may not serve in another community where conditions are dissimilar. Generally speaking, however, the approach to the organization of a farmers' market in the Greenbrier area may recommend itself to farmers and businessmen in other parts of the state where markets are not now in operation. The state department of agriculture will be glad to hear from interested persons in such areas, and department representatives will enter into discussions with such interested persons at times mutually convenient with the objective of establishing additional markets at key points where a need for such exists; providing, of course, that the department has funds available and personnel to supply necessary service.

For the purpose of establishing a farmers' market in the Greenbrier Valley, a group of businessmen and farmers of that area met during the winter of 1941–42 with the commissioner of agriculture. As a consequence, the businessmen-farmers group formed what is now known as The Greenbrier Valley Farm Products Marketing Association, a non-profit corporation. This organization entered into an agreement with the commissioner of agriculture under which a farmers' market, open to all farmers of the area, would be conducted at a suitable point in the area taking in Greenbrier, Pocahontas, Monroe, and Summers counties. A site was made available on the State Fairgrounds between Lewisburg and Ronceverte and a market was opened in June, 1942.

Prior to the actual opening of the market, however, a great deal of "field work" was carried out. A representative of the marketing organization visited the farms of scores of producers in the four-county area, in advance of the planting of their summer crops, and discussed with them the plans for the market and the prospects for returns on various types and varieties of produce. Additionally, meetings were held in many communities. Newspapers of the area were of considerable assistance in building up interest among growers.

It is necessary to go beyond the end of the biennial period with which this report deals in order to make a partial report on results obtained at this farmers' market at Lewisburg.

Although in its first season, the Lewisburg market handled and sold a substantial volume of produce, equal to 65½ truck loads of 10,000 pounds each, or 20½ carloads of 32,000 pounds each, as of September 30, 1942. This approximates one truck load of 10,000 pounds sold for every day the market was open for business in its initial season. Principal items handled up to the end of September were potatoes (316,473 pounds); cabbage (153,789 pounds); green beans (50,280 pounds); and tomatoes (20,190 pounds). Other produce handled included apples, sweet corn, cucumbers, kale, pears, peaches, peppers, onions, turnips, and chickens and eggs.

As this was written, plans were being made by the officials of the State Farmers' Market at Lewisburg to sponsor an all-day meeting of interested farmers to discuss production plans for 1943, as well as such vital things as transportation and other problems presented by wartime conditions.

Farm Planning in Colorado

From R. T. Burdick, "More Sugar Beets, Wheat, Barley and Vegetables — Colorado's Postwar Goal," *Colorado Farm Bulletin*, September–October 1945, pp. 2–3, 11–13.

For 4 years Colorado farmers have been concentrating on producing to the utmost. Their record has been outstanding. Now that the war is over the question that many ask is, "What can the future offer to Colorado farmers?"

During the last 3 years I have been chairman of a special Production Capacity Committee made up of representatives of state and federal agencies who are familiar with the problems of Colorado's agriculture.[1] Each year the committee has made confidential reports to the War Food Administration as aids in guiding the national administrators in their farm production program. At all times the objective of the Colorado committee was to formulate a plan for Colorado agriculture which would make the best possible use of the natural farming conditions in the state.

One of the reports which this committee prepared dealt with the future. We prepared an estimate as to what seemed to be a reasonably sound crop and livestock program for the state as a whole. In making this report the committee did not conform to the generally anticipated trend of crop and livestock production for the nation as a whole, but we did attempt to make certain estimates which we believe represented the best use of Colorado's farm resources.

Now that the war is over this particular report takes on increased significance. Many members of our committee feel that the main items in this report should be presented to Colorado farmers for their consideration and criticism.

Before this postwar report was made the War Food Administration supplied us with an estimate of postwar production for the United States as a whole, as presented in table 1.

These are production figures not acreage figures or numbers of livestock. For the United States as a whole this estimate indicates that in the postwar period the entire nation should reduce wheat production, increase sugar beet production, reduce bean and potato production, increase hay and vegetable production. It shows that hogs, sheep and eggs should be decreased in production while all other classes of livestock should be increased.

TABLE 1. — *Recommended Postwar Production for the United States*

Farm product	U.S. postwar as percent of U.S. 1943 production
Wheat (all)	92
Rye harvested for grain	129
Corn (all)	95
Oats	101
Barley	106
Sorghums harvested for grain	90
All tame hay	117
Sugar beets	162
Dry edible beans and peas	54
Processing vegetables (11 crops)	115
Commercial vegetables (25 crops)	120
Potatoes	76
Hogs	96
Cattle and calves	103
Sheep and lambs	91
Chickens and broilers (Colorado 1943 was up ⅓ from "normal")	103
Turkeys	161
Milk	109
Eggs	88

[1] Additional members include Floyd K. Reed, agricultural statistician, Denver, Colo.; T. H. Summers, Colorado Extension Service; C. C. Hicks, Colorado AAA; A. G. Goth, Bureau of Agricultural Economics, USDA; and about 40 others.

Estimate Made in Acres

It would be difficult to make a reliable estimate as to the yield which Colorado farmers can expect in future years. Accordingly our report emphasizes the acreages of crops rather than production. However, for livestock it is possible to make a fairly close estimate as to probable production if the numbers of animals are assumed to be known. The following tables, 2 and 3, show for Colorado crops and livestock the recommended acreages and numbers for the postwar period as compared to actual acreages and numbers in recent years.

TABLE 2. — *Recommended Postwar Acreage of Colorado Crops, (000) Acres Omitted*

Use of farm land	Acreage	1934–43 average	1943	1944	1945	Recommended postwar acreage	Postwar as percent of 1943 acreage
All wheat	Planted	1504	1493	1608	1727	1700	113.86
Winter wheat	Planted	1172	1340	1420	1548	1000	11940
Spring wheat	Planted	332	153	188	179	100	65.36
Rye for grain	Harvested	60	126	69	69	60	47.62
Corn, all	Planted	1231	987	908	790	911	92.3
Oats	Planted	195	209	221	230	155	74.16
Barley	Planted	630	894	831	798	1040	116.33
All sorghum	Planted	804	602	785	715	725	120.43
Sorghum for grain	Harvested	—	134	289	—	162	120.89
All tame hay	Harvested	1018	1021	1046	1025	1066	104.41
Sugar beets	Planted	163	139	136	163	195	140.29
Dry edible beans	Planted	443	595	387	348	350	58.82
Dry edible peas	Planted	—	51	46	46	25	49.02
Processing vegetables (11 crops)	Planted	12	16	17	−18	112.50	
Fresh vegetables (25 crops)	Harvested	44	49	58	—	57	116.33
Potatoes	Planted	92	90	93	102	82	91.11

In comparing these recommendations with the national estimates some of the differences need attention. The U.S. recommendation was for wheat to be cut back to 92 percent of the 1943 production. Our committee recommends (as shown in table 2) that Colorado wheat acreage be increased to 114 percent of the 1943 acreage. This is a result of the acceptance by Colorado farmers of the practice of summer fallowing for winter wheat and the proved adaptation of improved wheat varieties in Colorado. This increase is in winter wheat. The committee advised a reduction in spring wheat acreage. The U.S. figure shows a slight increase in oats. The Colorado committee suggests a reduction in oat production since other grains have shown themselves to be better adapted. We recommended an increase in grain sorghum while the U.S. advised a reduction. For some crops the committee recommended changes in acreage which were in the direction of the U.S. recommendations but not to the same extent.

Possible Yield Changes

One caution should be kept in mind. The committee recommended acreage changes. The U.S. recommended production changes. Colorado in 1943 (as was true generally in the U.S.A.) had better than average crop yields. If future crop yields are more nearly average, then these recommended acreages would actually produce less crops and the recommended level of production would not be reached. For example, the 14 percent increase in wheat acreage might produce less wheat than Colorado's actual 1943 production. Colorado wheat yields were 22.4 bushels per acre in 1943 compared to 13.7 bushels for the 10 years 1933–42. This average yield, if applied to the acreage recommended for the future, would give a total wheat crop about 74 percent of the 1943 crop even with the 14 percent increase in acreage. What the future wheat production of Colorado will be remains to be seen. The use of our land for wheat production remains a sound proposition. Somewhat similar comments might be made about some of the other crops.

TABLE 3. — *Recommended Postwar Production of Colorado Livestock, with Number and Production of Livestock on Colorado Farms. (000) Omitted*

Item	1934–43 average	1943	1944	1945‡	Postwar	Postwar as pct. of 1943
NUMBER ON COLORADO FARMS JANUARY 1						
Horses, mules, colts	256	222	211	200	175	78.8
All cattle and calves	1,535	1,745	1,920	1,882	1,650	94.6
All sheep and lambs	2,810	2,711	2,602	2,475	2,525	93.1
Hens and pullets	3,251	4,421	4,782	3,444	3,853	87.2
Hogs	354	656	774	356	450	68.6
Cows kept for milk	249	249	251	246	250	100.4
Number of pigs raised	475	961	427	—	620	64.5
Number calves raised	571	670	705	—	640	95.5
Number lambs raised	1,283	1,375	1,185	1,254	1,170	85.1
Number cattle on feed	131	160	148	137	150	93.8
Number lambs on feed	1,067	860	825	840	950	110.5
ANNUAL PRODUCTION						
Hogs, pounds produced	81,338	203,234	140,881	—	125,000	61.5
Cattle and calves produced	372,520	483,970	488,440	—	472,000	97.5
Sheep and lambsproduced	107,931	124,131	107,560	—	108,000	87.0
Chickens and broilers raised, number	6,033	8,579	5,576	—	7,000	81.6
Turkeys raised	782	861	861	—	1,000	116.1
Milk, pounds produced	1,009*	1,099*	1,056*	—	1,200*	109.2
Eggs, dozen produced	27,967	40,167	43,417	—	35,000	87.1
Wool shorn, pounds	13,631	15,458	13,259	13,372	13,000	84.1

‡All 1945 data not available.   *(000,000) omitted.

As to livestock, table 3 gives both numbers and estimated production. The chief differences between the committee's recommendations as compared to the U.S. suggestions are these: The Colorado hog production is reduced more as compared to the 1943 output because Colorado in 1943 had an abnormally large hog production. Likewise the committee recommended some reduction in cattle production although the U.S. estimated that an increase was needed. Colorado must keep its cattle and sheep numbers in line with the available grazing and production of roughage. No one can anticipate future conditions exactly, but it would seem to be wise to reduce present cattle numbers.

For both crops and livestock the 1934–43 averages in tables 2 and 3 offer some valuable comparisons as we look to the future.

Sugar Beet Research

From Eubanks Carsner and F. V. Owen, "Saving Our Sugar Beets," U.S. Department of Agriculture, *Yearbook*, 1943–1947 (Washington, 1947), pp. 357–62.

Only 30 years ago curly top of sugar beets seemed an insurmountable barrier to progress of the beet-sugar industry in much of the West. One authority at that time even advised the abandonment of infested and susceptible areas. Had that been necessary, we would not have the sugar and sugar-beet seed now produced in a vast territory in 12 Western States, and their settlement and development would have been retarded.

But now, in retrospect, curly top appears to have been a blessing in disguise. The need to conquer it prompted much research, which led to the development of varieties adapted to American conditions and the establishment of a new industry, growing sugar-beet seed. The two results completed the integration of the American beet-sugar industry and made it independent of Europe.

The violent vicissitudes through which sugar-beet growing and the beet-sugar industry in the Western States passed before curly-top-resistant varieties were produced can be brought out best in the record of a representative region. Farmers in the Burley area of southern Idaho started growing sugar beets in 1912. Average yields were low at first but gradually improved with increasing experience, and the acreage was expanded because of the sugar shortage during the First World War. In 1919 came the first outbreak of curly top. From then until 1935 yields dropped recurringly to disastrous levels — in 1924, 1926, 1931, 1934. Areas in Arizona, California, Colorado, Nevada, New Mexico, Oregon, Texas, Utah, and Washington suffered in much the same way.

The deep dips in the curve of average yields in southern Idaho indicate only a part of the losses that curly top caused in those years. Average yields of 5 to 6 tons an acre meant heavy losses to processors and the growers who carried their beets through harvest. Besides, a big acreage was plowed up. The average yield in 1934 was 4.88 tons an acre from 2,754 acres harvested — but in that season, of 21,389 acres planted to beets, 18,635 were abandoned. Contrast with this the record for 1941, a season in which damage from curly top also caused a conspicuous decline. It would have been a disastrous year if varieties of relatively high resistance had not been used. That year 22,005 acres were planted, 21,418 were harvested, and the average yield was 13.45 tons an acre.

The progress that has been made in the control of curly top through breeding resistant varieties can be indicated by results obtained in 1941 on experimental plots. Under the drastic disease conditions of that season a standard European variety once widely used in this country failed completely; U.S. 1, the first resistant variety to be released to growers, gave 6.31 tons to the acre, and the latest commercial variety, the second release of U.S. 22, yielded 16.61 tons. The test plots were purposely planted late to get more severe exposure to curly top. There was a good deal of curly-top damage that year in the commercial fields and, even with the resistant varieties now in use, curly-top losses of economic importance occur under some conditions. However, it can be stated with assurance that crop failures of sugar beets due to curly top need no longer be feared anywhere. It is not uncommon now to have the resistant varieties yield 25 and 30 tons an acre even when exposed to curly top, under conditions that cut the production of the old susceptible varieties to unprofitable levels.

Mass selection has been used to breed the varieties thus far released for commercial use. But the method involves much more than it did when breeding for curly-top resistance was started 29 years ago. We used to depend on naturally occurring epidemics to differentiate degrees of resistance. Now we regularly induce epidemics artificially in the breeding field regardless of the severity or mildness of the injury in the surrounding territory.

We introduce an abundance of the curly-top virus into the breeding field early in the spring. There are several ways to do it. In the first place, as many viruliferous leafhoppers (carriers of the curly-top virus) as possible are held over winter on hardy food plants, like annual mustards, spinach, and sugar beets, which are planted late in summer next to the field to be used for the sugar-beet plots the following spring. Leafhoppers held over in this way move into the young beets in the spring and inoculate beets here and there.

A second important measure is setting out in the field infected mother beets that have been carefully stored over winter. We usually also introduce virus into the experimental field by releasing viruliferous beet leafhoppers that are reared in insectaries. The newly infected young plants or the transplanted, diseased mother beets serve as reservois of curly-top virus. From these reservoirs the spring-brood leafhoppers invading from natural breeding grounds in the desert obtain a supply of virus which they then pass on to the healthy beets they feed upon. The presence of an adequate source of virus in the experimental field at the time of the spring invasion accelerates the rate of development of the curly-top epidemic in the field because many of the invading leafhoppers carry no virus with them.

Planting the breeding plots late is another way we use to bring about severe epidemics. Beets generally are more susceptible to infection and injury when they are small. The leafhopper vector is more active under warm temperatures. And the curly-top virus multiplies more rapidly under relatively high temperatures when the beets are growing rapidly. Plants that withstand such severe epidemics give rise to highly resistant varieties.

But besides resistance to curly top, extensive areas, especially in California, require sugar beets that do not bolt and that resist downy mildew. Some varieties like that have been bred and are in wide use. Better adapted varieties are needed in several districts, however, and efforts are being directed toward producing them.

New Breeding Methods

Methods of breeding sugar beets, other than mass selection, have been investigated while that method was being used to produce and improve better kinds. The investigations open new vistas of progress.

We discovered lines of self-fertile beets that in their sexual reproduction would not follow the general pattern of cross-fertilization. The usefulness of these highly self-fertile beets for breeding purposes was increased when beets were discovered that produced no pollen themselves and hence needed pollen from other beets for their fertilization. These male-sterile plants can be fertilized by pollen from self-fertile beets, and so produce pedigreed hybrids. With the way thus open to produce self-fertile or inbred lines with characteristics that can be determined, the possibility has arisen that many desirable combinations of characters can be bred in pedigreed hybrids. Inbred lines must be produced and evaluated before desired combinations can be planned and developed.

An indication of the promising possibilities from pedigreed hybrids is afforded by the performance of one such hybrid that has been studied. S.L. 4108 was produced by crossing a vigorous inbred line with a male-sterile beet of fair quality and high resistance to curly top. Under conditions entirely free from curly top, S.L. 4108 yielded 513 pounds more sugar to the acre than the average of seven other leading mass-selected kinds. This excellence was due partly to high vigor and partly to greater resistance to a parasitic disease that affects the petioles and roots. Under very severe exposure to curly top, S.L. 4108 proved as resistant as the most resistant variety now in commercial use.

We have another significant indication of the possibilities of pedigreed breeding. By studying the reaction between certain inbred lines of beets and the different strains of the curly-top virus, it was discovered that some of the inbred lines are immune to some of the virus strains. We hope that the same immunity will be found in hybrids made with these immune inbreds. None of the best commercial varieties now in use has such immunity.

Also possible is the production of varieties that have single-seeded, or unilocular, seedballs and kinds having bilocular seedballs. Inbred lines have been found with a high proportion of bilocular seedballs. These characteristics can be reproduced in pedigreed hybrids. Two-seeded seedballs would be inferior to single ones, but would be a big improvement over the mechanically segmented seed now generally used.

Certain inbred lines have shown a noticeably low bolting tendency. This fact brightens the prospect for breeding for general adaptation to conditions where nonbolting varieites are required, as with early fall and early winter plantings in California. Such plantings are necessary. In the Imperial Valley, for example, the summer heat is so intense that in this extensive, highly productive area sugar beets must be planted in the fall, grown through the winter, and harvested in the spring. The winters are cold enough, however, that varieties very low in bolting tendency are necessary. Varities of higher bolting tendency were extensively planted there by mistake one year and in the spring the fields looked more like plantings for seed than for sugar production.

Greater uniformity in size and shape of beets and consequently better adaptation to harvesting machinery seems a likely possibility through pedigreed breeding.

Another approach to the control of curly top is unique, and perhaps has a point for many other farmers. It is through an ecological study of the vegetation in desert range lands where disturbances of the natural plant cover encourage weedy areas that serve as breeding grounds for the beet leafhopper. A large-scale disturbance of that kind occurred in several regions under the stimulus of high prices for food during the First World War. Later, many of the areas that had been under cultivation were abandoned and they were immediately invaded by annual mustards, Russian thistle, and other hosts of the beet leafhopper. Bad practices prolonged those objectionable early stages of the plant succession.

The factors in the restoration of the natural plant cover, plants like sagebrush and grasses on which the beet leafhopper does not breed, were sought in the investigation. We found that with adequate protection from destructive agencies — temporary farming and abandonment, fire, and excessive grazing — a grass cover will replace the leafhopper weed-hosts in 5 years. Cattle, incidentally, are not the only animals that may overgraze: The persistent, year-round feeding of large numbers of jack rabbits destroys more vegetation than we had realized. Large experimental plots in the desert, portions of old abandoned farms, protected from fire and the grazing of domestic animals, continued to produce crops of mustards and Russian thistle and consequently large numbers of beet leafhoppers — until jack rabbits were excluded. Then the desired change in plant cover began. Rodents sometimes thwart efforts to reseed the ranges with perennial grasses; such failures often are wrongly attributed to too little rain.

Good management of range land and farm land, besides helping to control curly top of sugar beets, by keeping the population of beet leafhoppers below dangerous levels, is highly important to several other commercial crops. Tomatoes and a good many varieties of beans, for example, would be produced in a number of areas if it were not for the frequent heavy invasion of beet leafhoppers and the consequent damage from curly top.

Establishing the Seed Industry

Sexual reproduction in sugar beets depends on two environmental factors of primary importance, prolonged low temperatures that permit only very slow growth, and long days or long daily periods of light exposure. Varieties vary genetically in these reproduction requirements. Only those high in bolting tendency gave good seed yields in the warmer areas first developed. And if they were repeatedly reproduced there, natural selection eliminated those individuals that did not go to seed and the bolting tendency of the resulting varieties increased to a degree unacceptable in fields of beets grown for sugar production.

Research overcame the difficulties. The factor of temperature required most attention. Early planting, proper fertilization, and right irrigation gave large growth of leaves in the fall to shade the soil and keep the beets comparatively cool through the winter. Deterioration of varieties in bolting tendency was avoided by growing the stock seed under climatic conditions of other regions that afforded complete reproduction. Such stock seed is used to produce only a single generation of commercial seed in the warmer areas.

The regions better adapted climatically were also found to reproduce satisfactorily the varieties so low in bolting tendency as to merit the designation "nonbolting varieties."

Thinning or spacing beets, a laborious, expensive operation in producing sugar, is undesirable in seed-growing areas where winter days are often warm. Leaving the plants thick to shade the soil and each other helps reduce the temperature. The process of thermal induction of flowering goes forward slowly under favorable low temperatures, but under high temperatures it is rapidly reversed. Spacing may prove economically practicable in seed districts where daytime winter temperatures are seldom high enough to reverse the reproductive processes. Better light relations for photosynthesis and more economical use of nutrients and water in the soil result if there is not too much crowding.

Disease factors have been encountered in the seed-growing areas, too. Curly top in the interior regions, several fungus diseases, and one bacterial disease in the coastal regions have required attention. Breeding for resistance to all these diseases offers the best control.

The production of seed was firmly established in the United States as a result of the need for multiplying American varieties resistant to curly top. The foundation for the method of growing seed generally used in this country was laid some years before we had varieties that resist curly top. In Europe, the beets are grown one season, dug, stored over winter, and set out in the spring. Our method is much less laborious. The seed is planted in late summer or early fall, the plants allowed to grow slowly over winter in place, usually without thinning, and the seed harvested the following summer. The method permits mechanized operations that eliminate much of the hand labor required in the transplanting method.

Growing beet seed has benefited the agriculture of the areas where the industry has been established. The soil fertility has been improved as a result of research on the soil requirements for sugar-beet seed production and by the residual effect of fertilizers applied for the beet seed crop.

New Wheat Varieties

From B. B. Bayles, "New Varieties of Wheat," U.S. Department of Agriculture, *Yearbook,* 1943–1947 (Washington, 1947), pp. 379–84.

More than 50 improved varieties of wheat have been distributed to American farmers in the past decade. They resist rust, smut, other diseases, drought, insects, or winterkilling, major hazards that threaten crops always in one place or another. They increased our total wheat production by more than 800 million bushels in the years 1942 to 1946.

Most of them were developed at State agricultural experiment stations in breeding and testing work in which the Department of Agriculture cooperated and which is closely coordinated in each of the four main wheat-growing regions — hard spring, hard red winter, soft red winter, and western. All varieties developed in these programs are carefully tested to determine where they are adapted for growing and to insure that the grain quality of those released is satisfactory.

Varieties resistant to stem rust, released for growing in the preceding decade, occupied more than 12 million acres of the 15,700,000 acres of hard red spring wheat grown in 1944. This class of wheat predominates in the northern Great Plains and Prairie States, where stem rust formerly caused losses as high as 100 million bushels in some years. Approximately two-thirds the total acreage was sown to varieties resistant to both stem and leaf rust in 1946. Some of them also resist stinking smut and loose smut and one of them withstands the hessian fly.

Thatcher, the first extensively grown hard red spring wheat that is highly resistant to stem rust, was developed in cooperation with the Minnesota Agricultural Experiment Station and released in 1934. Because of its spectacular performance during the stem rust epidemic of 1935, when other varieties were badly damaged, it increased rapidly. By 1939 it was grown on an estimated 14.5 million acres in the United States and Canada. The acreage continued to increase until it was partly replaced by varieties resistant to both stem and leaf rust. In 1944 the acreage of Thatcher in the United States had decreased to 4.5 million but had increased in Canada to nearly 17 million. Before the distribution of Thatcher, stem rust had caused such heavy losses to Marquis and later to Ceres, the susceptible varieties then grown, that the damage from leaf rust was scarcely apparent. But when the stem-rust-resistant but leaf-rust susceptible Thatcher was grown on large acreages the plants undamaged by stem rust were attacked by leaf rust.

Wheat breeders had foreseen this possibility and had been developing adapted varieties that could also withstand leaf rust. The first of these — Renown, a beardless variety — was developed at Canadian experiment stations and distributed in 1937. Pilot and Rival, two high-yielding bearded varieties, were distributed from the North Dakota Experiment Station in 1939. These are resistant to both stem and leaf rust as well as bunt; Pilot is also resistant to mildew. By 1944 Rival was grown on 4,050,000 acres and Pilot on 1,216,000 acres.

Regent, another beardless variety distributed in Canada in 1939, resists stem rust and bunt, and is fairly resistant to leaf rust. It was grown on about 1,334,000 acres in the United States in 1944.

Four other hard red spring varieties were distributed between 1944 and 1946. All merit special mention. They are Mida, in North Dakota; Newthatch, in Minnesota; Henry, in Wisconsin; and Cadet, in North Dakota. Mida is bearded, medium early, high-yielding, and highly resistant to stem rust, leaf rust, and bunt. It is also somewhat resistant to the hessian fly. It was extensively grown in 1946, but its tendency to shatter, susceptibility to loose smut, and the greater injury suffered by it during the late 1946 spring freeze may retard its increase. Newthatch resembles Thatcher, except that it has more resistance to leaf rust. Henry is resistant to stem rust and is more resistant to leaf rust than other commercial varieties. It is recommended for growing only in Wisconsin, because its milling characteristics differ in some respects from other recently developed, high-quality, hard red spring wheats. Cadet is an excellent beardless type that compares favorably with the other varieties in resistance to both stem and leaf rusts. It performed well in 1946.

Rescue, a still newer variety, was developed by breeders at the Swift Current Station in Saskatchewan to combat losses from the wheat stem sawfly in sections of Canada and Montana. It has shown promise in tests where the sawfly does damage, but it does not resist leaf rust, bunt, or mildew.

The stem rust susceptible Durum varieties, Kubanka and Mindum, are now being replaced by two new varieties, Carleton and Stewart, both highly resistant to stem rust. They have excellent grain quality and were first distributed in North Dakota in 1943.

The Hard Red Winter Region

Hard red winter wheats in 1944 occupied an estimated 30,600,000 acres, about 47 percent of our total wheat acreage. In the central and southern Great Plains, where most of the hard red winter wheats are grown, stem-rust losses have been heavy in some years, and leaf rust, septoria, stinking smut, loose smut, and the hessian fly also have taken a heavy toll. The goal of plant breeders has been to overcome those plagues and to develop sorts that mature early enough to escape drought.

Tenmarq, the first early variety of satisfactory quality, was developed in the coordinated regional program and distributed from the Kansas Agricultural Experiment Station in 1932. In 1944 it was grown more widely in the United States than any other variety of wheat. In then occupied 8,744,000 acres. Tenmarq is 2 or 3 days earlier than Turkey, the variety that had been grown by most farmers in the region for more than half a century. Its weight per bushel is low, but the milling and baking qualities of Tenmarq are excellent.

Cheyenne and Nebred, distributed in Nebraska in 1933 and 1938, have been popular in western Nebraska and the adjacent sections of Kansas and Colorado. Cheyenne is considered a good combine variety because of its stiff straw and erect heads. Nebred is resistant to stinking smut. Both are high-yielding varieties of satisfactory quality, but mature too late to be grown farther south.

Most hard red winter wheat is milled into flour for bread. Bakers want flour having certain characteristics of quality because they must be able to produce a uniform product month after month. Varieties differ markedly in characteristics that determine quality. During the past few years a considerable acreage of varieties that produce inferior flour for bread has been grown in Kansas, Oklahoma, and Texas. These varieties, Chiefkan, Red Chief, and Early Blackhull, have some desirable characteristics from the farmer's standpoint; their test weights are 1 to 2 pounds heavier, and that often means a higher grade on the market. Bakers, however, have difficulty making satisfactory bread from flour that contains a high percentage of those varieties.

Four new varieties of satisfactory grain quality, Pawnee, Comanche, Wichita, and Westar, released to growers in 1943 and 1944, give promise of replacing the varieties of inferior quality. They are earlier and have higher test weights and stiffer straw than the popular Tenmarq, which is a parent of the first three varieties. Pawnee, Comanche, and Westar are about 3 days and Wichita 6 days earlier than Tenmarq. Pawnee is somewhat resistant to leaf and stem rust, loose smut, and hessian fly. Comanche resists stinking smut. Westar withstands leaf rust. Wichita often escapes damage from the rusts as well as drought because of its early maturity. Comanche was selected from an Oro × Tenmarq cross, Pawnee from a Kawvale × Tenmarq cross, and Wichita from an Early Blackhull × Tenmarq cross. While none of these varieties was grown on more than a few acres in 1943, it is estimated that Pawnee was grown on 1,500,000 acres, Comanche on 1,000,000 acres, Wichita on 200,000 acres, and Westar on 3,000 acres for the 1946 crop.

The Soft Winter Regions

Wheat is not a major crop in the East, although soft red winter varieties are grown there on some 12 million acres and soft white varieties on a million acres annually. Wheat is needed in the rotation and it serves as a cash crcrop. Wheat of these classes is used for making cake, pastry, cracker, biscuit, and similar flours, and prepared breakfast cereals, and the desired quality characteristics are entirely different from those for the hard wheats. The major production hazards have been the leaf rust, loose smut, septoria, scab diseases, the hessian fly, and winterkilling. Resistance to lodging and short straw are important because much of the wheat is sown as a companion crop with seedings of legumes and grasses.

Thorne, the leading soft red winter variety, was grown on more than a million and a half acres in 1944, about three-fourths of it in Ohio. Thorne was developed by the Ohio Agricultural Experiment Station and was distributed in 1937. Its high yields, short, stiff straw, and resistance to loose smut make it popular with farmers, even though its weight per bushel is low.

Fairfield, distributed in Indiana in 1942, is winter hardy, resistant to loose smut and lodging, and is moderately resistant to leaf rust. It has soft grain of good quality. Prairie, distributed in Illinois in 1943, is a bearded winter-hardy variety with moderate resistance to leaf rust. It promises to become an important variety in central Illinois, where soft wheat varieties previously available have been subject to winterkilling. Blackhawk, distributed in Wisconsin in 1944, is one of the most winter-hardy soft wheat varieties adapted for commercial growing. It is resistant to stem rust, leaf rust, and stinking smut, but is probably too late in maturity for growing except in Wisconsin and northern Illinois.

Hardired and Sanford, distributed in South Carolina and Georgia, respectively, in 1940, are moderately resistant to leaf rust. Both are becoming popular varieties in the South, where they are replacing Purplestraw, a leading variety for more than a century. The development of leaf-rust-resistant varieties adapted to the Southeast should aid in the shift from soil-depleting row crops, such as cotton and corn, to the soil-protecting legumes, grasses, and small grains.

Austin, which resists stem and leaf rust and loose smut, was released in Texas in 1943 and was grown on an estimated million acres for the 1946 crop. Plant breeders are watching with interest to see whether growing this variety in central and south Texas will have an effect on the development of rust epidemics in wheat-growing areas to the north. We expect that the use of resistant varieties in Texas will eliminate a source of overwintering rust spores that start the northward movement of rust in the spring and, if weather conditions are right, build up into the major epidemics farther north.

Yorkwin, a variety of white winter wheat distributed in New York in 1936, is now the leader in its class in New York and Michigan. The acreage of Cornell 595, a still newer variety of this class, is increasing rapidly. Both varieties are high yielding with stiff straw and resistance to loose smut.

The Western Region

The extremely diverse climatic conditions in the Pacific Northwest permit all classes of wheat except durum to be grown there successfully.

The principal varieties are white, and of both winter and spring habit. A considerable acreage of hard red winter varieties is also grown. Stinking smut, or bunt, was one of the most serious hazards to wheat production in the region as recently as the early 1930's. The development and distribution of resistant varieties reduced the percentage of cars grading smutty at the Pacific Northwest markets from 36.7 percent in 1931 down to 2.8 percent in 1942. A more virulent type of stinking smut, referred to as "dwarf bunt", formerly caused extremely heavy losses in the valleys of Utah, Idaho, and western Montana. In 1935, 39.8 percent of the cars received at the Utah markets graded smutty. However, the introduction of adapted varieties resistant to that type of smut caused the percentage of cars grading smutty to drop to 9 percent in 1943. The figures are on market grade and do not reflect the losses in yield on the farm from smut.

The hard red winter varieties Rdit, Oro, and Rio, and the white club variety Albit, were among the first smut-resistant varieties distributed to growers in the Columbia Basin. They have been largely replaced by even better strains. Rex, a bunt-resistant, high-yielding white winter wheat with medium short stiff straw, was distributed in Oregon in 1933. Its milling qualities are not considered equal to those of the better varieties by the trade. Reduced losses in recent years have made growers indifferent to the smut problems. This fact, together with the poor quality of Rex, has caused the acreage of resistant varieties to decrease in the Columbia Basin during the past few years. This has increased the percentage of cars grading smutty to 8.3 percent in 1945. Hymar, a smut-resistant white club wheat distributed from the Washington station in 1935, has yielded well in the sections of higher rainfall.

Orfed, the newest bunt-resistant variety for the Columbia Basin, was distributed from the Washington station in 1944. This high-yielding, smut-resistant variety has soft white grain of good quality and has stiff straw that will stand for combining. It can be grown from either fall or spring seeding, although it is not so winter-hardy as are some of the strictly winter varieties. It should not be seeded early in the fall.

Alicel and Elgin, two prooductive club wheats with soft white grain and very short stiff straw, are grown to some extent in Oregon, Washington, and Idaho. They are susceptible to most races of bunt and should always be treated before seeding.

Relief was the first resistant wheat released in the area where the dwarf bunt was causing almost complete losses in some fields. It is a hard red winter variety distributed in Utah in 1934. It is being replaced with Wasatch, a bearded variety, and Cache, a beardless variety in Utah and southern Idaho. These two hard red winter wheats also are replacing the other hard red winter varieties in the Gallatin and Kalispell Valleys of Montana, where dwarf bunt has caused heavy losses. These three varieties, all developed in Utah, are susceptible to some races of tall or ordinary bunt, but they have enabled farmers in areas infested with dwarf bunt to continue wheat production. Dwarf smut cannot be controlled by seed treatment or cultural practices, while ordinary bunt can be largely controlled by these measures. Relaxation in seed treatment programs, increase in races of smut that attack varieties resistant to races formerly present, and the continued growing of completely susceptible varieties are resulting in an increase in the percentage of wheat grading smutty at Utah markets.

Growers on irrigated lands needed a spring variety with short stiff straw for use with new clover seedings. Lemhi, which has soft white grain of excellent pastry quality, was developed for them.

Losses caused by stem rust have been practically eliminated from the wheat fields of California through the distribution of Baart 38 and White Federation 38, which are resistant to stem rust and to bunt. Released by the California Agricultural

Experiment Station in 1939, they are grown on more than two-thirds of the acreage in that State. Big Club 43, which resists the hessian fly, a cause of heavy losses in some sections of California, was distributed in 1944. Bunt and stem rust do it little harm.

Hybrid Corn in the South

From Merle T. Jenkins, "Corn Hybrids for the South," U.S. Department of Agriculture, *Yearbook,* 1943–1947 (Washington, 1947), pp. 389–94.

Progressive farmers in all parts of the South want to know what is being done to develop corn hybrids suited to their soil and climate and whether adapted hybrids can duplicate in their fields the outstanding performance of those in the Corn Belt. Encouraging answers can be given them.

The Department of Agriculture is conducting corn-improvement programs in cooperation with 12 State agricultural experiment stations. Five are in the South — North Carolina, Tennessee, Mississippi, Louisiana, and Georgia. Informal cooperation is maintained with all other southern stations that have corn-improvement experiments.

Because corn hybrids are produced by crossing inbred lines, the general quality of a group of hybrids depends upon the characteristics of the parent lines. Outstanding, or elite, inbred lines are isolated only infrequently, and the numbers and relative superiority of elite lines isolated depends largely upon the total number of lines examined and tested.

The early inbreeding programs in the South, like those in the Corn Belt, were small. The elite lines that founded the present hybrids in the Corn Belt were developed as a result of the greatly expanded inbreeding programs organized in the early 1920's. Similar expansion of the southern corn-breeding programs occurred in the late 1930's and early 1940's, but was relatively less extensive than that in the Midwest. The group of elite lines that is beginning to emerge from the expanded programs promises a marked improvement in hybrids for the South in the next few years.

Another prime factor in developing outstanding Corn Belt corn hybrids was the exchange of breeding materials among the cooperating experiment stations. The Purnell Corn Improvement Conference, which functioned from 1926 to 1932, and its successor, the Corn Improvement Conference of the North Central Region, organized in 1937, promoted the exchange. In 1933 a series of uniform tests of hybrids involving a group of elite lines contributed by the different cooperating experiment stations was organized to promote further the wide use of the best of the available breeding material. U.S. Hybrid 13, a direct result of the first of these uniform tests, is the most widely grown hybrid in the country. Many other Corn Belt hybrids involve a relatively small group of elite lines; the uniform tests aided materially in identifying them.

The Southern Corn Improvement Conference was organized in New Orleans, in November 1939, at the instigation of Fred H. Hull of the Florida Agricultural Experiment Station. Uniform tests of crosses among lines grown in the South were organized in 1941 to further the ready interchange of breeding materials; the first tests were made in 1942.

The uniform tests bring to light and permit the selection of parent lines whose hybrids perform satisfactorily over a wide range of growing conditions. Numerous advantages derive from this procedure. Uniform tests in different States give an opportunity to find out how the new kinds perform in different kinds of soil and climate in the same season. We thus get in one season results that are somewhat comparable to those from tests in each of several seasons at a single location. Hybrids involving parent inbred lines whose crosses perform satisfactorily under a wide range of conditions are not likely to perform badly under some peculiar or unusual set of conditions. The identification of these widely adapted parent lines permits simplification of the hybrid corn program as a few widely adapted hybrids can be made to serve a whole region.

Many of the promising new experimental hybrids of the South involve this new crop of elite lines. Outstanding white lines among those of suitable maturity for the area in which Neal Paymaster is adapted are T61 and T13 from Tennessee, and NC34, NC37, and NC45 from North Carolina. T61 probably has more yield factors than any other southern inbred line, but it is subject to root lodging. Outstanding yellow inbred lines of suitable maturity for the same general area are CI.21 and CI.7, developed by the Department, Ky35–7 from Kentucky, NC7 and NC13, developed in North Carolina, and Kys, developed in Kansas.

Experience has amply demonstrated that crosses among lines of widely diverse origin usually have the most vigor. The outstanding hybrids of the Corn Belt usually involve lines originating from more than one State program. In all probability, the same will be found to hold true in the South. The promotion of free interchange of breeding materials sponsored by the Southern Corn Improvement Conference stands directly to benefit every southern corn grower by providing him with better hybrids than he would have otherwise.

Available Hybrids

The first general survey of hybrid corn acreage in the Southern States, made in 1941, gave us the estimate that 1,029,000 acres were planted to hybrids in the South that year; in 1946 the acreage was 5,469,000.

Kentucky, Virginia, Texas, Arkansas, and Oklahoma have been able to utilize some of the later Corn Belt inbred lines and hybrids. But the Southeastern States have not been able to use them; except in a limited way, in the mountains or to grow early feed for livestock. The expansion of hybrid corn in the Southeast, therefore, depends on development of suitable local hybrids. The expanding acreages of hybrid corn in these States are evidence that suitable hybrids are becoming available rapidly.

Among the hybrids adapted to the Southeast, the Tennessee hybrids developed by the Tennessee Agricultural Experiment Station and the Department have had the largest commercial expansion. These hybrids, of which Tennessee Hybrids 10 and 15 are most popular, are combinations among inbred lines out of Neal Paymaster. They resemble Neal Paymaster in general characteristics and fit into the general territory in which that variety has been grown in the past. In 34 comparisons conducted in Tennessee between 1939 and 1945, their average yield exceeded that of Neal Paymaster and Jellicorse by 8 percent, or 5 bushels an acre. Tennessee Hybrids 10 and 15 have performed satisfactorily in most of Tennessee, much of northern Alabama and Mississippi, and in the Piedmont area from North Carolina to Georgia. Their greatest weakness is their tendency to lodge; they are not much better than Neal Paymaster in that respect. A new yellow hybrid that has done well in two seasons of trials was produced commercially on a limited scale in 1946. The estimated 1945 production of certified hybrid seed corn in Tennessee was 87,098 bushels, or enough to plant about 600,000 acres in 1946.

An estimated 47,000 bushels of seed of North Carolina corn hybrids were produced there in 1946, enough for approximately 325,000 acres in 1947. Somewhat more than 90 percent of that production was of the four yellow hybrids, North Carolina 26, T11, 27, and 1032, developed cooperatively by the North Carolina Agricultural Experiment Station and the Department. North Carolina Hybrid 1032 has extremely strong roots and stalks; in eight tests in the Piedmont area of North Carolina in 1943 and 1945 it outyielded the standard varieties by 21.5 percent. It also exceeded the standard varieties in yield by 18.5 percent in 10 tests in the coastal plain area of that State in 1942, 1943, and 1944. The yield record of North Carolina Hybrid 26 has surpassed that of 1032. North Carolina T11, a top cross, is one of the older North Carolina hybrids and it probably will be replaced soon with a double cross. North Carolina 27 is a relatively new combination of much promise. It is slightly later in maturing than the other three yellow hybrids.

A limited amount of seed of two white hybrids, North Carolina 1111 and T20, also was produced in 1946. They have excellent records in yield, but they probably will not be widely used because they do not stand appreciably better than the open-pollinated varieties. A group of experimental hybrids already tested 2 or 3 years promises to be materially better than those now in commercial production.

Seed of six hybrids developed in cooperation with the Louisiana Agricultural Experiment Station sufficient for planting about 85,000 acres in 1947 was produced in 1946. Two of them, Louisiana Hybrids 468 and 518 are white dent; one, Louisiana Hybrid 731, is a yellow dent; one, Louisiana Hybrid 2909, is a yellow flint similar to Creole Yellow Flint; and two, Louisiana Hybrids 1030 and 1031, have mixed yellow and white kernels. The Louisiana hybrids in commercial production have exceeded the standard Louisiana open-pollinated varieties in yield by about 30 percent. The white dent hybrids have performed satisfactorily in tests in Mississippi and Georgia, as well as in Louisiana. Louisiana Hybrid 2909 is particularly suited to the sugarcane areas of both Louisiana and Florida. The yellow dent hybrid, 731, is a new combination that should be well suited to the central portion of the State. Louisiana Hybrid 1030, the better of the two hybrids with mixed kernel color, has the best record for lodging resistance of any of the Louisiana hybrids and promises to become very popular for that reason. It also has an enviable record for resistance to the corn earworm and to weevils.

Florida Hybrid W–1, a white, prolific hybrid developed by the Florida Agricultural Experiment Station, has established a good record of performance in Florida and the southern coastal plain of Georgia. It has been produced commercially on a limited scale and seed production is gradually expanding. On fertile soils, Florida W–1 is tall, high-eared, and tends to lodge rather badly because of weak roots.

Some of the experimental hybrids developed in cooperation with the Mississippi Agricultural Experiment Station appear promising. One of these made an outstanding record in 1945 and limited quantities of seed of it were produced in 1946. If it continues to perform satisfactorily it probably will enter commercial production within the next few years.

Future of Hybrid Corn in the South

The corn hybrids now available for planting in the South represent only a preliminary effort in the breeding of special types for the area. They are the product of only a fraction of the time, energy, and funds that have been devoted to the development of corn hybrids for the Corn Belt. It is not surprising, therefore, that they answer the requirements of their region less precisely than do the hybrids now available for the Corn Belt. One should remember that the greater hazards of corn production in the South necessarily increase the attributes required in desirable hybrids and, naturally, multiply the difficulties involved in breeding them.

The great numbers of disease and insect pests in the South will require the concentration of many desirable characters in order to obtain the desired levels of resistance. Encouraging progress is being made, evidence of resistance to many insects and diseases is at hand, and definite sources of resistance have been identified in many cases. But much more time will be needed for breeding the generations necessary to transfer, combine, concentrate, purify, and fix the desired characters in the inbred lines that are to become the parents of the outstanding hybrids of the future. Full-season hybrids for most of the South require long, tight-fitting husks to protect them from weevil damage from the time the ears ripen until they are harvested. Many of the Corn Belt hybrids yield well when grown in the South, but they lack the needed husk protection to prevent the grain from being damaged or entirely destroyed in the field before harvest.

The job before us is not easy or quick, but it is worth our best effort, time, and money. Think of the phenomenal expansion and success of corn hybrids in the Corn Belt. From a small beginning in 1933, confined almost entirely to Iowa and Illinois, hybrid corn expanded by leaps and bounds. In 1946 it occupied more than 62 million acres or 67.5 percent of the national corn acreage. This includes 99 percent or more of the acreage in Iowa, Illinois, and Indiana, 90 percent or more of the acreage in Ohio, Minnesota, Wisconsin, and Missouri, and at least 80 percent of the acreage in Nebraska, Michigan, and New Jersey. In 1942, 1943, 1944, and 1945 the national corn production has exceeded 3 billion bushels and the estimated corn production for 1946 also was above 3 billion bushels. These yields are from national acreages appreciably below normal. The greater standability of the hybrids also has resulted in increased economies of production by decreasing the cost of harvesting and thus has resulted in greater profits to growers.

During the three war years of 1917, 1918, and 1919, we produced 8 billion bushels of corn on a total of 311 million acres. During the three war years of 1942, 1943, and 1944, we produced 9⅓ billion bushels on 281 million acres — 1,366,201,000 more bushels than in the earlier period, on 30,522,000 fewer acres. This is equivalent to 5 billion pounds more meat a year — 38 pounds more per person a year. When you look back to the fact that there were times during the last war when meat rationing got down to as low as 115 pounds a person a year, you can appreciate the importance of this extra production.

The research we are conducting will be a good business investment for Southern States, relatively as good, we hope, as the research of the past. Federal expenditures on corn improvement since the organization of the Department probably total between 4 and 5 million dollars. The increased yield of corn resulting from the planting of hybrid corn in 1945 probably amounted to about 700 million bushels. At a dollar a bushel, the increased income to farmers amounted to 700 million dollars. If only the normal tax of 3 percent were paid back into the United States Treasury on only one-third of this increased income, the extra income tax collected would amount to about 7 million dollars, which exceeds the total Federal expenditures for corn improvement since the Department was organized. These computations omit the extra taxes paid by the producers of hybrid seed corn, a new industry, that amounted to about 70 million dollars in 1945.

Controlling Cotton Insects

From C. F. Rainwater, "Progress in Research on Cotton Insects," U. S. Department of Agriculture, *Yearbook*, 1952 (Washington, 1952), pp. 497–500.

Cotton is a plant that nature seems to have designed specifically to attract insects. It has green, succulent leaves, many large, open flowers, nectaries on every leaf and flower, and a vast amount of fruit. All seem made to order for insects, some beneficial to man and some — the boll weevil, bollworm, pink bollworm, cotton leafworm, cotton aphid, cotton fleahopper, tarnished plant bug, rapid plant bug, conchuela, southern green stink bug, spider mites, grasshoppers, and thrips — notoriously obnoxious.

The cotton leafworm was the first insect of major importance to deprive the early cotton grower of a substantial part of his crop. Records dating from the eighteenth century show that in some years it destroyed 25 to 90 percent of the cotton. Many early planters were keen observers of insects and accurately recorded descriptions of them, the type and amount of damage they caused, the time they appeared in various localities, data on life history, and the effect of predacious insects on them.

The bollworm became notorious early in the nineteenth century. It and the cotton leafworm often destroyed the crop completely in some localities. Many early writers and researchers could not differentiate between the bollworm and the cotton leafworm, and the estimates of damage by the two insects no doubt were often wrong.

Research by individual cotton planters was the chief source of information concerning cotton insects during the first half of the nineteenth century. The information was disseminated largely through individual correspondence and newspapers. The significance of some of the research and its accuracy is shown by the fact that it was a planter who first reported that the bollworm of cotton and the corn earworm are the same insect.

As the country grew and as cotton production increased, other insect pests appeared to plague growers. Stink bugs and aphids were known in 1855 to be serious pests of cotton. Planters often found it unprofitable to grow cotton because of insects. It became evident that the Government must take a hand in the study and control of the insects. Consequently the Congress ordered a special investigation of cotton insects in 1878.

The early studies were directed very largely at determining the life history and habits of the species that were then causing damage, the effects of their natural enemies, and cultural methods of control. The investigations provided much of the background for later control efforts.

The first successful control measures were cultural methods. Even today they are recognized as of fundamental importance. The early planting of early fruiting varieties of cotton, frequent cultivation, clean culture, cleaning up debris and fence rows around fields, and fall and winter plowing were early recognized as valuable aids in the control of the insects that attack cotton.

Artificial methods of control also received the attention of early research workers, both professional and laymen. They tried different kinds of attractants and repellents, poisoned baits, fires in the fields at night to attract insects, mechanical devices for dislodging and collecting the insects from the plants, and hand picking of the insects from the plants.

Plant breeders contributed a great deal to the research during the early 1900's. They undertook studies to develop varieties of cotton that could better withstand insect attack, varieties that were fast growing and early maturing so that the crop could be produced and matured before insects had time to build up their maximum numbers, and more prolific varieties that could produce additional fruit after part of it had been destroyed. Indeed, plant breeding still has a vital part in research on the control of cotton insects.

Research on the chemical control of cotton insects really began in earnest in the early 1900's. Various chemicals were applied as sprays in the hope of finding effective controls. As early as 1905 paris green was recommended as a spray to combat some of the insects. London purple and arsenate of lead also came into general use then. The methods of application were crude; that probably accounted largely for the failure to get effective control. One method, for example, was to stir the chemical in water and sprinkle it over the tops of the plants with a cedar bough. Another method was to drive small holes into wooden buckets or kegs and allow the solution to trickle through them on the plants. Nevertheless, sprays came into fairly general use during the period.

The part of the agricultural engineer was first realized fully during the early 1900's. The development of machines for applying sprays is one example of their early work. Various attachments were constructed and fastened onto the plow to knock the insects and the infested squares from the plant and collect them in some sort of container whereby they could be buried, burned, or otherwise destroyed. One widely recommended device was a chain drag, which pulled infested squares from under the plant and deposited them in the middle of the row so they would be exposed to the sun and the larvae in them would be killed.

The first arsenate of lead ever used in dust form for insect control was in 1908. From then until 1916, hundreds of experiments were conducted with dusts of lead arsenate, paris green, and london purple. Against the cotton leafworm and certain other insects, the dusts were highly effective, but they never proved entirely satisfactory against the boll weevil or the bollworm. Emphasis continued to be placed on cultural methods of control for most cotton pests.

OF GREAT IMPORTANCE was the discovery in 1916 that calcium arsenate dust was highly effective against some cotton insects. For the next three decades, however, research on the control of cotton insects was largely devoted to developing dusts and dust mixtures and methods of applying them. It was demonstrated during this period that insect pests of cotton could be economically controlled and that cotton production could be made profitable even under conditions of heavy attack.

Meanwhile, another serious insect menace appeared. The pink bollworm, the most serious insect pest of cotton known in many parts of the world, was discovered in Texas in 1917. Many people realized that our cotton industry might be doomed if it were allowed to spread as the boll weevil had done. Research efforts were doubled therefore as to the biology, ecology, and control of the pink bollworm. The research provided the basis for the successful fight to prevent its spread to the principal cotton-producing areas through quarantine regulations and control efforts.

During the 1920's research on cotton insects reached its peak. The boll weevil had completed its spread eastward and northward until it had invaded the Cotton Belt from Texas to Virginia. Every State in the Cotton Belt was searching feverishly for more effective controls against cotton insects. A shortage of cotton after the First World War sent prices up, and prosperity was in the grasp of any farmer if he could produce cotton despite the insects. Intensive cultivation created new insect problems — insects that had previously been confined largely to other plants were being forced onto cotton as new land was being brought into cultivation and as the intensity of cultivation increased. The cotton fleahopper, plant bugs, thrips, aphids, spider mites, and stink bugs all were recognized as serious pests of cotton. The primary emphasis of research was on control. Calcium arsenate was then a proved insecticide against the boll weevil, bollworm, and cotton leafworm. Methods of applying it by ground machines and airplanes were perfected. Millions of pounds were being used annually. Nicotine controlled the cotton aphid. The first combination insecticide, calcium arsenate and nicotine, simultaneously controlled the boll weevil-bollworm-cotton aphid. Sulfur was found to be effective against the cotton fleahopper and other plant bugs, as well as against spider mites. So, despite the increased complexity of the insect problems, research demonstrated that insects could be effectively and economically controlled and that cotton could be profitably produced despite the insects.

From 1930 until 1945 the primary emphasis was on developing new methods or improving existing methods of control. The different methods were thoroughly tested under various climatic conditions. Plant bugs were causing serious losses in the irrigated localities of the Southwest. A mixture of 7.5 percent paris green and 92.5 percent sulfur was developed to fight them.

THUS THROUGH A HALF CENTURY control measures had been developed for all of the principal insect pests of cotton. The threat that the cotton industry in the United States might be doomed because of insects no longer existed. The insects had not been eradicated; in fact, they were far more numerous at the end of this period than they were at the beginning, but we had learned how to cope with them. Our success in controlling them only made conditions more favorable for their rapid increase when control was relaxed. It was inevitable that the fight against cotton insects would have to be continued. The cotton planter had become resigned to the fact that insect control was just as important a part of his normal farming operations as the selection of good seed, proper fertilization, or proper cultivation.

In 1945 a new era in the research began. The development of the new and more powerful organic insecticides opened up new avenues. But it likewise created new research problems.

The first experiments with the new organic insecticides proved that they were not cure-alls. DDT was the first to be tested extensively, followed by benzene hexachloride, toxaphene, and chlordane. These were found to be highly effective against certain insect pests of cotton and were adopted in the control recommendations of many States. But not one of these individually controlled all the major pests. Certain combinations were developed, such as 3 percent gamma isomer of benzene hexachloride-5 percent DDT-40 percent sulfur, 20 percent toxaphene-40 percent sulfur, and 10 percent chlordane-5 percent DDT.

The synthesis of new organic compounds was greatly accelerated, and thousands were tested for insecticidal efficacy during the late 1940's and early 1950's. Aldrin, dieldrin, parathion, and tetraethyl pyrophosphate were included in the official recommendations of some States. Others, notably heptachlor, EPN (O-ethyl O-p-nitrophenyl benzenethiophosphonate), methyl ester parathion and a sterio isomer of dieldrin, showed considerable promise in later tests. Again, however, none satisfied the requirements for an all-purpose cotton insecticide. The most effective combinations have to be worked out for each State or area.

Certain organic insecticides can kill insects developing inside of plant tissue as well as those that feed on the exterior parts. Heptachlor, chlordane, aldrin, dieldrin, and (to a lesser extent) benzene hexachloride are known to kill boll weevils developing inside of punctured squares when applied to cotton under field conditions. This property may prove to be extremely important in fixing the ultimate value of the poisons used against cotton insects and may have far-reaching effects in developing better controls.

The organic insecticides in general lend themselves readily to incorporation into emulsifiable concentrates through the use of proper solvents and emulsifiers. Properly formulated, they can then be diluted with water and applied as low-gallonage, low-pressure sprays. The trend in the use of insecticides for cotton insect control now is toward such sprays. In 1950 and 1951 millions of gallons of sprays were applied to cotton. Recent experiments have shown that as little as 1 gallon per acre of a concentrated spray containing the required amounts of the insecticide, or insecticides, may be enough. Since sprays can be applied under conditions that would render dusts ineffective, this research represents a distinct achievement. Many farmers apply concentrated sprays to cotton at the time they cultivate the crop, and thereby reduce the cost of application. Combination sprays have been developed for the simultaneous control of most cotton insects. They may be applied effectively by ground equipment and airplanes.

The development of proper schedules for applying insecticides to cotton has done much to lower the costs. Early season control programs that have been developed for many areas have been so successful as to make unnecessary additional applications later. Considerably smaller amounts of the insecticide per application are needed in the early applications. Killing off many insects of minor importance helps the plants to grow faster, so that the crop is usually matured earlier and the farmer has a better chance to get it properly harvested. Both dusts and sprays have been successfully used in early season control, but sprays appear to be preferable to dusts largely because they can be applied directly onto the small plants by the use of proper spray equipment, whereas with dusts there is some unavoidable wastage. Ground machines are also preferable to airplanes for applying sprays to cotton in the early season for the same reason.

The need for research stems from the fact that the value of the cotton destroyed by insects has averaged more than 100 million dollars annually since 1929, climaxed by an all-time-high loss of more than 900 million dollars in 1950. The value of the research is shown by the thousands of farmers who have followed recommendations and have increased their yields three, four, and five times over comparable areas in which no control was used. Net profits due entirely to insect control of 150 to 175 dollars an acre and net returns of from 20 to 28 dollars for every dollar spent for insecticides have fequently been obtained by cotton farmers who followed research findings and recommendations. The difference between a profit and a loss on any given acre of cotton often depends entirely on whether the insects are controlled.

Grasshoppers

From J. R. Parker, "Grasshoppers," U.S. Department of Agriculture, *Yearbook,* 1952 (Washington, 1952), pp. 595–604.

Grasshoppers have caused concern among men since the beginning of recorded history. They have brought fear and famine at one time or another to every continent. A description of their ravages is given in Joel 2: 3 — "The land is as the Garden of Eden before them, and behind them a desolate wilderness, yea, and nothing shall escape them."

Grasshoppers are recorded as having injured crops in New England in 1797. In 1818 hordes of them destroyed the crops of early settlers in the Red River Valley in Minnesota. During 1874 to 1877 the Rocky Mountain grasshopper, or locust, as it was then called, increased to such numbers that its depredations were considered a national calamity. Great swarms originating in the plains east of the Rocky Mountains in Montana, Wyoming, and Colorado migrated to the Mississippi Valley and Texas, devouring crops wherever they paused in their flights. Damage to crops amounted to 200 million dollars. Congress recognized the seriousness of the outbreak and on March 3, 1877, created the United States Entomological Commission and authorized it to investigate the grasshopper problem.

Grasshoppers still destroy crops somewhere every year and during outbreaks cause losses totaling millions of dollars. Overgrazing by grasshoppers is one of the fundamental reasons for loss of productive grasslands in many States. Grasshoppers contribute to soil erosion and dust-bowl conditions, particularly when drought and mismanagement of the land also occur.

Grasshoppers are found all over the United States, but serious outbreaks seldom develop in the East. Local outbreaks have occurred in New England, New York, Virginia, Georgia, Florida, Alabama, and Mississippi, and grasshoppers are numerous enough to cause some damage in most Eastern States every year. Outbreaks are mostly in the western two-thirds of the United States. They occur most frequently in the Northern Great Plains, including eastern Montana, North Dakota, South Dakota, Nebraska, and Kansas.

Every State within the region subject to outbreaks has more than 100 kinds of grasshoppers. Some are rare and others fairly common. Only a few ever become abundant enough to injure crops seriously. At least 90 percent of all grasshopper damage to crops is caused by five species, the lesser migratory grasshopper, the differential grasshopper, the two-striped grasshopper, the red-legged grasshopper, and the clear-winged grasshopper.

The lesser migratory grasshopper, the two-striped grasshopper, and the red-legged grasshopper are found throughout the grasshopper country. The differential grasshopper seldom moves farther north than the southern borders of North Dakota and Minnesota. The clear-winged grasshopper is confined largely to States bordering the Canadian boundary from Michigan to Washington, but in the mountainous West it extends south to New Mexico, Arizona, and Southern California.

The lesser migratory hopper normally selects well-drained, light soil and sparse vegetation. The differential, two-striped, and red-legged grasshoppers prefer moist, heavy soil and lush vegetation. The clear-winged grasshopper adapts itself to many conditions but is most common in mountain meadows, grassy openings in timbered land, and well-sodded, closely grazed pastures on the open plains. Under outbreak conditions all five species spread far from favored habitats and feed on a variety of crops and vegetation.

Of the five species, the lesser migratory grasshopper is the most widely distributed and most destructive. It is a strong flier. Adults sometimes gather in great swarms, which migrate hundreds of miles and destroy crops and range plants wherever they pause in their flight. In most respects it resembles the Rocky Mountain locust, or grasshopper, which ravaged Western States years ago. The latter has longer wings and stronger power of flight, characteristics that several species are known to develop during periods of great abundance. It was called a locust because its habits were similar to those of Old World locusts.

In most parts of the world the word "locust," or its equivalent, designates grasshoppers that migrate in swarms — the same species may be a grasshopper during its periods of small numbers and a locust when it becomes extremely abundant. Everyone understands the term "grasshopper" as commonly used in the United States. It is less confusing to use the term than to change to locust when the same grasshoppers fly in swarms. The periodical cicada and its relatives are popularly known as locusts. They are entirely different from grasshoppers in appearance and habits.

Of the 142 species collected on range plants in the Western States, only a few are known well enough to have common names. Considerable training in taxonomy is needed to identify the adults correctly. Often it is impossible to recognize the immature stages. On the basis of surveys and observations made in range districts since 1936, the most abundant species in Montana, North Dakota, South

Dakota, Nebraska, and Wyoming have been *Melanoplus mexicanus, Ageneotettix deorum, Amphitornus coloradus, Phoetaliotes nebrascensis, M. angustipennis, Phlibostroma quadrimaculatum, Opeia obscura, Trachyrhachis kiowa, M. infantilis, Aulocara elliotti, M. gladstoni, Mermiria maculipennis, Cordillacris occipitalis, Melanoplus femur-rubrum, Encoptolophus sordidus, Metator pardalinus,* and *Drepanopterna femoratum.*

Mention also should be made of the long-winged plains grasshopper and *Melanoplus rugglesi,* both of which are migratory and highly destructive during outbreaks. The adults fly in swarms and oviposit in well-defined egg beds. The young hoppers march in bands. Outbreaks of the long-winged plains grasshopper have occurred in Colorado, New Mexico, Oklahoma, Texas, and western Kansas. Outbreaks of *M. rugglesi* have occurred in Nevada, southeastern Oregon, and northeastern California. The Mormon cricket, a long-horned grasshopper or katydid, should also be listed as a pest in the Rocky Mountain and Plateau States. It is normally confined to range vegetation in foothills or mountains, but large bands sometimes migrate long distances and attack crops.

Within the regions where conditions are most favorable for grasshoppers are the principal wheat, barley, and flax areas in the United States. In them also are extensive acreages of corn, oats, rye, and alfalfa. Grasshoppers relish all those crops.

Damage even in average years is more serious than most of us realize. The grasshoppers may eat only a small part of the host plants, but they attack them at vulnerable points. They bite off grain heads and lgaeeolls and may injure the rest of the plant only slightly. They go for corn silks; if the silks are eaten in the early stage, pollination is prevented and the ears do not fill. Grasshoppers prefer the flowers of alfalfa and sweetclover to the foliage, and heavy losses consequently befall beekeepers and seed growers. Small numbers of hoppers can greatly reduce cotton yields by cutting the seedlings and later the bolls.

Damage in outbreak years has varied from partial to complete destruction of crops over large areas. Estimates by entomologists and county agents in 23 States put the total of losses at $789,374,140 in the 25 years between 1925 and 1949.

The Forest Service reported that in 1934 grasshopper damage to range vegetation in Colorado, Montana, Nebraska, North Dakota, South Dakota, and Wyoming amounted to $2,455,000. Similar damage continued in 1935. In 1936 the Wyoming State entomologist estimated grasshopper damage to forage in Wyoming at $1,480,351. The figures cover only the normal annual value of the forage and do not include such indirect losses as the forced sale of unfattened animals and breeding livestock. As I said before, overeating of grasslands by grasshoppers, particularly in drought years, hastens soil erosion. Reseeding is prevented, vegetative cover often is completely removed, and the soil is exposed to washing and blowing. Areas so affected for several seasons may remain depleted for years.

The division of cereal and forage insect investigations is responsible for grasshopper research conducted by the Bureau of Entomology and Plant Quarantine. Most of the work is centered in its field station at Bozeman, Mont. Staff members of the station study grasshoppers in many States, but most of their work is done in Montana, North Dakota, South Dakota, and Wyoming, where grasshoppers are a serious problem nearly every year.

Research on grasshoppers also is carried on at other field stations of the Bureau. Stations at Manhattan, Kans., Sacramento, Calif., and Forest Grove, Oreg., have included grasshopper investigations in their work programs. In 1950 work on grasshoppers was done at Tempe, Ariz., and Tifton, Ga. Staff members of the Tempe station test new insecticides and carry on field research during the long period of grasshopper activity that prevails in Arizona, March to December.

The research has two main aspects. One has to do with the recognition, distribution, seasonal development, and habits of grasshoppers, and with ecological studies — the effects of meteorological factors and natural enemics upon their abundance. The second division pertains to the immediate control of grasshoppers by insecticides, cultural methods, or other means. These are termed control investigations. No clear-cut distinction actually exists between the two aspects. The objectives are the same, and one depends on the other.

Permanent study areas were established in Arizona, California, Kansas, Minnesota, Montana, North Dakota, and South Dakota, beginning in 1936. Each area included at least 8 square miles of typical farm land. All had histories of grasshopper outbreaks. Maps were made to show the locations of crops, idle land, and native vegetation. Air and soil temperatures and precipitation records were kept. Annual adult, egg, and nymphal surveys were made on each quarter section for 10 years.

The studies produced data on the seasonal development, preferred habitats, food preference, egg-laying habits, and population records of grasshoppers. Information on the effects of parasites, predators, disease, and meteorological factors also was obtained. I cite some of the findings.

Ten year averages were established for egg hatching, nymphal, adult, and egg-laying periods of the main economic species. On such information is based the timing of control operations and autumn egg surveys. If control begins before the hatching of the major species is completed, it may have to be repeated. If it is continued after egg laying is well under way, it has little effect on preventing grasshopper damage the following year. If the fall egg surveys are made before peak egg laying is completed, a false picture of the next year's potential infestation is obtained. O. L. Barnes used the data from study areas in Arizona in making recommendations for the timing of grasshopper surveys in that State.

In Montana and North Dakota, where the lesser migratory and two-striped grasshoppers are the dominant economic species, eggs were found most heavily concentrated in roadsides, fence rows, idle land, and small grains. Few were found in row crops or fallow land. Knowledgbmmxotre eggs are laid is indispensible in making egg surveys. Weedy roadsides and fence rows harbored more grasshoppers and contained more than twice as many eggs as similar places that were covered with solid stands of grass. E. G. Davis used that information as the basis for recommending the regrassing of weedy roadsides and fence rows to reduce grasshopper damage in nearby crops.

One of the study areas in Montana was in the Centennial Valley in Beaverhead County. The clear-winged grasshopper, the dominant species there, in some years completely destroyed the hay crop. The studies disclosed that this species concentrated its eggs in the roots and crowns of white bunchgrass associations (Poa and Puccinellia), which occur in well-defined patches throughout the native hay lands, constitute only a small fraction of the total hay acreage, and are easily recognized by their light color. Landowners were asked to bait the white bunchgrass whenever they saw grasshoppers in more than ordinary numbers. No outbreaks have occurred since.

Data from Montana and North Dakota provide estimates of what happens to the yearly potential grasshopper population. Females of the more important species lay approximately 200 eggs. Males and females are about equal in numbers. If the same level of population from one year to another is maintained, 198 (99 percent) of the eggs, young grasshoppers, or adults must perish sometime between the completion of egg laying and the beginning of egg deposition the following year. During the 10-year period, approximately 20 percent of the eggs were destroyed by predators, 60 percent of the young grasshoppers died during or shortly after the hatching period, and disease and parasites killed 5 percent of the older nymphs and adults.

Weather conditions during and following the hatching period may start or end outbreaks. If it is warm and dry, the death rate may decline below the 60-percent average and allow grasshoppers to develop in outbreak numbers. If it is cold and wet, mortality may increase to such an extent that few survive.

Our knowledge of grasshoppers on crops has been greatly furthered by seasonal studies in typical agricultural areas. R. L. Shotwell and I have described the 1931 outbreak of the two-striped and differential grasshoppers in South Dakota and northeastern Nebraska, which destroyed 75 percent of the crops on 17,000 square miles and 25 percent on an additional 13,000 square miles. Shotwell has published a bulletin on the histories and habits of grasshoppers that attack crops in the Northern Great Plains. C. C. Wilson reported his observations on the devastating grasshopper, an important economic species in California.

Surveys of numbers of adults and eggs have been conducted by State and Federal entomologists for many years and are of importance in planning control operations. Surveys have evolved from reconnaissance (which merely delineated areas of greatest abundance) to the present standardized type, in which infestations are classified according to the number of adults per square yard and the number of egg pods per square foot of soil.

One of the problems in connection with annual grasshopper egg surveys on the permanent study areas, as well as in State surveys, was the number of samples needed to rate accurately the fields and field margins and the number of stops needed per section, county, or other area unit. Special surveys designed to answer these questions were conducted in Montana in 1939 and 1940 and in South Dakota in 1942. The results of the studies were published by Davis and F. M. Wadley. They concluded that five 1-square-foot samples in each field and two similar samples in its margin should be taken and that no fewer than 10 field stops should be made in a county or group of counties.

Range grasshopper studies have been conducted as a major project since 1936. They include yearly observations at 10 permanent range stations in Montana, 3 in Wyoming, and 2 in South Dakota; adult and egg surveys of the western range region extending from Montana and western North Dakota to Wyoming and western Nebraska; and seasonal observations in places where significant range grasshopper activities are in progress.

State and county distribution of 142 species of grasshoppers found on the western range has been mapped. Adult and egg surveys conducted since 1941 have recorded over-all population trends and the dominant species for each year. Egg-laying records, including the number of pods laid and the number of eggs per pod, have been made for 29 species. Egg pods, nymphs, and adults of the more common species have been photographed or described.

Studies of seasonal development in Montana and Wyoming have shown wide differences among the complex of species found in any locality. Some are early; others are intermediate; and the rest are late in hatching, reaching the adult stage, and egg laying. Differences of 4 to 5 weeks have been found between early- and late-developing species. Knowledge of the seasonal development of the dominant range species is essential to the proper timing of control operations and surveys.

We divide range grasshoppers into two groups on the basis of food preferences — those that feed on grass and those that feed on forbs (which are range herbs other than grass). Of 40 species under study for three seasons in southeastern Montana, half were grass feeders and half were forb feeders. Those that prefer grasses will starve if restricted to forbs, which they refuse to eat in quantity. Forb feeders starve on grass unless it is tender and succulent. Several grass-feeding species would not eat bran bait. *Trachyrhachis kiowa and Opeia obscura* ate no bait. *Phlibostroma quadrimaculatum, Amphitornus coloradus,* and *Metator pardalinus* ate it sparingly. When those species predominate, baiting is ineffective.

Egg predators and parasites of nymphal and adult range grasshoppers have been investigated. Two species of nemestrinid flies, *Trichopsidea (Parasymmictus) clausa and Neorhynchocephalus sackenii,* not previously reported as common parasites of grasshoppers in the United States, were discovered in southeastern Montana in 1940. Females lay their eggs in cracks in wooden fence posts and trees and do it fast. One female laid 1,000 eggs on a single post in 15 minutes. Another confined in a pill box laid 4,700 eggs in 7 hours. The eggs hatch in 8 to 10 days. The tiny maggots are scattered by the wind. When a maggot finds a grasshopper, it bores into the abdomen and lives on its contents. Eventually it kills the grasshopper. Nemestrinid maggots differ from the better known sarcophagid parasites in having long breathing tubes, which they attach to the grasshopper's air circulating system to get their own fresh air. Nemestrinid flies are particularly destructive to the important range species *Metator pardalinus;* 80 percent of the adults of this species were found parasitized in some localities in 1950. The remarkable number of eggs laid by nemestrinid females and the ease of obtaining them suggests the possibility of gathering large quantities for distribution in grasshopper areas where parasites are not abundant.

Many observations have been made to determine the damage done to range vegetation by known numbers of grasshoppers. During drought years, infestations of 20 to 50 per square yard frequently have destroyed 75 to 100 percent of available forage by mid-summer. From outdoor cage experiments conducted in range areas for several years we learned that an adult grasshopper of the larger range species ate 30 milligrams of vegetation (dry weight) a day. In earlier laboratory experiments we found that the relatively small, lesser migratory grasshopper ate 24 milligrams a day. A cow requires 20 pounds of vegetation (dry weight) a day. From these data we calculated that 301,395 adult range grasshoppers and a cow would eat equivalent quantities of forage a day. This number of grasshoppers distributed over 1 acre would average 62 per square yard, or 31 per square yard over 2 acres. The fact that such populations are common during outbreaks shows the stiff competition between grasshoppers and livestock for range vegetation. The same data show that infestations of only 7 grasshoppers per square yard on an acre will eat one-tenth as much forage as a cow. Control measures are seldom employed against such numbers of grasshoppers even though they lower the livestock-carrying capacity of the range.

Many long-time residents in western range districts have commented that range grasshopper outbreaks in their neighborhood always started in certain relatively small places and then spread to surrounding land. Fifteen potential outbreak localities in eastern Wyoming were selected for study. They have been under observation since 1941. Yearly population records have been made for each area and for the range adjacent to it.

Those studies showed that trends during low years were not necessarily uniform; that is, some areas were slowly declining while others held their own, and still others built up slightly and declined again. Build-ups tended to accompany an expansion of the infested area involved, while declines accompanied a contraction of infested areas. During 1946 and 1947, gradual increases occurred at about the same, rate both within hold-over areas and outside them, but independently of each other. The increases continued in 1948 and 1949, and the hold-over areas with their greater populations were the first to reach damaging levels. When they did, there was a tendency for local migrations and light flights to take place — some of them to the outside. Drought tended to stimulate both migrations and flights. It was evident, however, that with a continuation of favorable years, outside populations could, and in some cases did, reach damaging levels without contributions from the hold-over areas. Over-all populations built up through slight to moderate increases of most major species rather than by large increases of a few species.

The results of the studies are disappointing to those who hoped that widespread outbreaks of range grasshoppers could be prevented by prompt use of control methods on a few small areas whenever numbers approached outbreak proportions. They do show that prompt control in hold-over areas is highly desirable, but they also indicate that similar action may be needed in many other places when conditions become unusually favorable for grasshoppers.

Poison bran bait was the most commonly recommended method of controlling grasshoppers in the United States for more than half a century. State and Federal entomologists have devoted many years in experimentation to improve the effectiveness of the bran, arsenic, sugar, and water mixture first used by D. W. Coquillet in California in 1885. Molasses, citrus fruits, lemon and vanilla extracts, apple flavoring, beer, vinegar, saccharin, salt, calcium chloride, amyl acetate, geraniol, soap, and other materials have been used to attract grasshoppers to poisoned bran and induce them to eat it more readily. It is generally conceded now that those materials add little to the attractiveness and palatability of bran and are not worth their cost.

Extensive tests have also been conducted to find substitutes or diluents for bran in grasshopper baits. Materials tested included sawdust, cottonseed hulls, rolled wheat, ground wheat screenings, citrus meal, chopped and ground alfalfa, ground flax fiber, ground peanut shells, bagasse, pear and apple pomace, peat moss, ground beet pulp, ground corncobs, chopped cornstalks, cornmeal, soybean meal, pea bran, oat hulls, and low-grade wheat flour. Of all the materials tested none was eaten more readily by grasshoppers than coarse wheat bran; most were decidedly less palatable.

Substitutes most closely approaching the palatability of bran were rolled wheat, apple and pear pomace, citrus meal, and chopped alfalfa. Sawdust, ground or chopped cornstalks, and cottonseed hulls were effective bran diluents. Mixtures of low-grade flour and sawdust and mill-run bran and sawdust were nearly as effective as coarse bran and sawdust in wet baits.

Arsenic in some form was the toxic agent in grasshopper baits until 1943, when it was replaced by sodium fluosilicate. By 1950 sodium fluosilicate had been largely superseded by chlordane, toxaphene, and aldrin.

The Bureau of Entomology and Plant Quarantine and State research staffs have given attention to the improvement of grasshopper baits. From 1921 to 1938, particular attention was given to testing the value of attractants, bransubstitutes and diluents, and to determining the temperatures and time of day most favorable for bait spreading. More recent accomplishments were the replacement of arsenic by sodium fluosilicate, and later by chlorinated hydrocarbons, as bait toxicants and the development of dry bran baits.

Research on the effectiveness of sodium fluosilicate was conducted in Arizona, California, Colorado, Minnesota, Montana, North Dakota, Oklahoma, and South Dakota from 1931 to 1942. It was found that sodium fluosilicate-bran baits under most conditions killed as many grasshoppers as arsenic baits and killed them faster. In experiments conducted by the veterinary science departments of the University of Nevada and Montana State College in 1939, 1940 and 1941, it was demonstrated that grasshopper baits containing sodium arsenite were approximately eight times more toxic to sheep than baits containing sodium fluosilicate. The experiments also indicated that sodium fluosilicate bait is extremely distasteful to sheep, horses, cows, and rabbits, and is not readily eaten by chickens, ducks, quail, or pheasants. In no instance was enough eaten voluntarily to cause ill effects.

In nearly all cases, sodium fluosilicate bait has been superior to sodium arsenite bait for grasshopper control on range grass and in most dry-land crops. Some failures have occurred in green crops such as alfalfa, but that was also true with sodium arsenite baits.

Tests to determine the effectiveness of chlordane, toxaphene, and aldrin were started in 1946 and continued through 1950. Baits containing them were found to kill grasshoppers faster and for longer periods than sodium fluosilicate. Chlordane at ½ pound, toxaphene at 1 pound, and aldrin at 2 ounces consistently gave as good or better kills than 6 pounds of sodium fluosilicate per 100 pounds of bran. The chlorinated hydrocarbons are soluble in kerosene and, when dissolved, are easily applied to the bran as a spray. Because of their higher, quicker, and longer killing action, small bulk and ease of mixing, chlordane and toxaphene in 1949 and aldrin in 1951 were recommended as bait toxicants. They now have largely replaced sodium fluosilicate in wet baits and are used exclusively in dry baits.

Before 1932, all grasshopper bran baits in general use contained water. Such wet baits have several limitations. To get best results, one has to apply them just before or during the period of the most active feeding, which is limited usually to a few hours each day. Wet bran flakes become hard and curled after drying and are then less palatable to grasshoppers than flakes that have never been wet. Sawdust or other diluent must be included to prevent lumping during mixing and spreading operations. Wet bait molds and cakes if stored for more than a few days. Water in baits doubles their weight.

Research to eliminate these disadvantages was begun in 1932. The first step was to leave out the water, molasses, and sawdust then commonly used in wet baits. Bran was thoroughly mixed with dry sodium arsenite or sodium fluosilicate. Two gallons of lubricating oil per 100 pounds of bran were then added to stick the poison onto the bran. Oil baits with sodium fluosilicate as the toxicant were found to be as effective as wet baits and have been widely used, particularly to control Mormon crickets. Oil baits containing arsenic were usually less effective than wet baits made with the same poison. Dry bran bait came into its own after the appearance of chlordane, toxaphene, and aldrin. Bran can be thoroughly impregnated by spraying it with low-volume kerosene solutions of any of these insecticides without materially affecting the palatability of the bran or the toxicity of the insecticide.

After 2 years of tests with ground equipment on small plots, 6,850 acres of heavily infested range in Montana and Wyoming were treated in 1948 with chlordane- or toxaphene-impregnated bran applied by airplane. The results were so good that similar bait was used almost exclusively in the large-scale campaigns conducted in Montana and Wyoming in 1949 and 1950.

Dry bait can be spread without regard to feeding periods of grasshoppers. In good weather the bran flakes remain effective for days. Those that are not eaten one day may kill grasshoppers the next. It is easier to mix and can be stored for months. It does away with the purchase and transportation of sawdust. It scatters more evenly from an airplane and weighs only half as much as wet bait.

Some insecticide dusts are excellent grasshopper killers, but in general the same insecticide is more economical and more effective when it is used as a spray. From 25 to 50 percent more insecticide per acre is needed with dust, and the cost of the diluent is an added expense. Anyone who has seen airplane dusting knows why higher acre dosages are needed. Dusts are lighter than sprays and more of the poison floats away in the breeze. Dusts are more easily removed from vegetation by wind and rain and therefore, kill for a shorter period. Dusts are more likely to kill bees and other beneficial insects.

Paris green and sodium arsenite sprays were used against grasshoppers years ago but were given up because the poisoned vegetation endangered livestock. The recent development of insecticides that can be used at very low dosages and yet are highly toxic to grasshoppers and easily formulated as sprays aroused new interest in this method of control. The results have been so good that it now looks as though poisoned bait, the standard method of control for half a century, will be superseded by sprays.

Success with the best baits depends on the habits of the grasshoppers. If they do not eat the bait they are not killed. In sparse vegetation during dry weather kills sometimes reach 90 to 95 percent. In succulent vegetation like irrigated alfalfa they seldom exceed 75 percent and are generally lower. Certain range species gorge themselves with bait. Others hardly touch it. Some refuse it entirely. When bait-feeding species predominate, kills on the range may reach 90 or 95 percent. If many nonbait feeders are present, kills are much lower. Kills of 75 to 95 percent prevent serious damage to most crops and range, but they frequently allow grasshoppers to survive in such numbers that control must be repeated the next year. In seed alfalfa and flax almost perfect control is needed to prevent injury to blooms, seed pods, and bolls, which can be severe when only a few grasshoppers are present.

Grasshoppers have little chance of surviving the new sprays, which kill both by contact and as internal poisons. Even if they escape being hit by the spray the first meal of treated vegetation will be their last. Kills with the best sprays usually reach 90 percent in 3 days and continue for 1 or 2 weeks. Populations of 25 to 100 per square yard have been reduced to less than 1 grasshopper in 10 square yards. Such kills give complete protection to crops and range. If spraying is done early enough to prevent egg laying no further control will be needed for several years unless grasshoppers move in from untreated land.

Sprays have other advantages over baits. Standard acre dosages applied as sprays have controlled infestations regardless of the number of grasshoppers per square yard. Bait application must be varied according to numbers present, which can be determined only by time-consuming surveys of the area to be treated. Use of too much bait is wasteful and expensive; too little is still more expensive if re-treatment becomes necessary. Spray materials are more stable in price than bran and cost less to transport and store. Bran for bait is in direct competition with bran for livestock and frequently soars to high prices when large quantities are needed for grasshopper control. Loading planes with sprays takes less time than with bait. A plane loaded with spray can cover more acres than the same plane loaded with bait. The overall cost of spraying is less than baiting.

Of the various new insecticides tested against grasshoppers as sprays, chlorinated hydrocarbons have given the best results and are lowest in cost on a per-acre basis. Chlordane spray was first used in grasshopper control programs in 1947, toxaphene in 1948, and aldrin in 1950. Acre dosages are: Toxaphene, 1 to 1½ pounds; chlordane, ½ to 1 pound; and aldrin, 1 to 2 ounces.

Almost complete destruction of grasshoppers by spraying half a gallon of kerosene containing 2 ounces of poison over an acre seems almost incredible but that is what aldrin does.

Before new insecticides are recommended for general use in grasshopper control they are subjected to extensive tests. Preliminary screening is done in winter with laboratory-reared grasshoppers. The first step is to administer carefully measured quantities of the new insecticide to individual grasshoppers and compare the results with those of a standard chemical for which effective individual and acre dosages have been established. Materials that show slight killing action are discarded. Those that show promise are used in laboratory dusting and spraying experiments. Contact action is tested by treating the grasshoppers and holding them on untreated green plants; stomach action is determined by placing untreated grasshoppers on sprayed or dusted plants. Baits are tested by exposing measured quantities to grasshoppers in screen cages. Laboratory results sometimes agree closely with those obtained later in the field but not always. How the insecticide performs outdoors is most important but laboratory tests are of great value as indicators of the most promising dosage levels for initial field trials.

Field tests, using ground equipment, are made on small plots (1.5 to 5 acres) under a wide variety of conditions. Insecticides outstanding in small plot tests are next applied by ground equipment and airplanes on 10- to 40-acre plots and finally on large tracts.

When the Bureau of Entomology and Plant Quarantine is convinced that an insecticide it has tested is worth recommending for general use, its findings are reported to the State Leaders' Advisory Committee on Grasshopper Control at its annual meeting in Denver, Colo. Data available from State and commercial organizations are also considered. If agreement is reached on formulations and acre dosages, the insecticide is recommended for general use the following year.

Thereafter the insecticide is given farm-scale testing. That is done to compare it with insecticides previously recommended and to test it under the special conditions in the various representative agricultural districts. Blocks of grasshopper-infested farms growing the typical crops of the district are used. The intensity of infestation is determined by surveys of eggs and young grasshoppers in the spring before control is started and by surveys of eggs and adults in the fall after control is completed. Control measures are applied to all economic infestations within the block, regardless of their location. Records are kept of quantities of insecticides used, cost of application, kills obtained, and crop damage. The areas are rechecked to find out if control one year prevents damage the following year.

Such tests have been conducted in corn and small grains in South Dakota, in seed alfalfa in South Dakota and Nebraska, and in flax and small grains in North Dakota. Results proved that crop protection is attainable at reasonable cost by correctly timed applications of new insecticides: One year's effort in treating all economic infestations within a block of farms will eliminate or greatly reduce the need for grasshopper control for several years thereafter. Farmers have shown keen interest in these tests, have commented favorably on them, and have been quick to adopt the control measure.

J. R. Parker is in charge of research on grasshoppers and Mormon crickets at the Bozeman, Mont., field station of the Bureau of Entomology and Plant Quarantine. Dr. Parker represented the United States at the International Conference on Locusts and Their Control in Cairo, Egypt, in 1936.

Changes in Mississippi Cotton Plantations

From: Harald A. Pederson and Arthur F. Raper, The Cotton Plantation in Transition, Mississippi Agricultural Experiment Station Bulletin 508, January, 1954, pp. 3–4, 6, 8–9, 11, 14–18, 20, 22, 24, 26.

The casual observer driving through the Yazoo-Mississippi Delta will be impressed with the fact that though the old ways of life still obtained new ways are becoming increasingly apparent. The mid-summer tourist traveling along US 61 from Memphis to Vicksburg or on US 82 from Greenwood to Greenville may well see four or five self-propelled combines moving through a field or grain on the right and a hundred or more field hands with hoes, seemingly stationary by comparison, in the cotton field to the left. In late summer and fall the mechanical cotton pickers replace the combines and the cotton sacks replace the hoe, but men and machines still work side by side.

These are the outward and visible signs of transition in the Yazoo-Mississippi Delta. Less obvious, but nonetheless real, is the change in the attitudes in plantation operators and plantation workers. The value system which has characterized the culture of the area for generations is being changed. The planter's wife complains that there are no new recruits among the plantation labor families to take over the jobs of the aging domestics. The domestic in the big house no longer enjoys the prestige of yesterday among his fellow workers. The tractor driver has failed to attain prestige in the occupational hierarchy of the plantation labor force. Planter after planter complains that though the drivers are paid well there is no rush for the jobs.

Yes, the Delta is in transition. This is in evidence when looking at the new machines and the old tenant houses, when listening to the plantation owner talk about his operations today and his hopes for tomorrow and when listening to the conversation of the plantation folk around the store and filling station or on the street corner.

The old has not yet gone and the new has not fully arrived. The mixture of the old and the new is the thing. This mixture bids fair to remain prevalent until some sure method other than hand labor is developed for the control of weeds and grass in growing cotton.

There is still considerable hesitancy in the matter of using machines. The mechanical picker can operate well only when the ground is dry, when weeds and grass are under control, when the cotton is defoliated and when the fields are large and regular enough. The planter is torn between conflicting objectives and irreconcilable operating alternatives. Time and again planters have remarked, "If the kind of labor we had twenty years ago were available today they could keep all their machinery."

The plantation is a social institution which is characterized by primary or "face-to-face" relations. The "good" worker, good both in terms of production and in terms of his relations to the boss and to his fellow workers, is rewarded with better land to work and more off-season employment around the plantation. He also is assured of a house to live in and odd jobs around the place when he is too old or otherwise unable to work in the fields. The plantation is an institution in which traditional controls are dominant.

The plantation is also an economic institution which is dependent on a highly competitive commodity for its existence. It must produce cotton at a cost that can compete with the cost of production on the world market if it is to survive. The economic and social objectives are not always in harmony and cannot necessarily be attained through the same operating policies.

The increasing scarcity of labor in the area has raised the labor cost from a dollar a day less than fifteen years ago to four dollars and more. True, the latter is an inflated dollar compared to the former but the rate of inflation is not 400 percent. Even at this higher rate the planter frequently finds himself unable to obtain labor enough to perform the essential operations during the peak work-demand periods.

The alternatives available to the planter are to reduce the acreage in cotton or increase the labor efficiency of his operation through higher capitalization in the form of mechanization. The second alternative is limited in its application by the level of technology. Weed control remains as a primary operation in cotton production for which successful technological substitutes for hand labor have not been developed. This continuing need for hoe hands limits the substitution of machines for manpower on the plantation.

The purpose of the present analysis is to describe the process of adjustment which is taking place on individual plantations in response to the challenge of mechanization and the problem of labor scarcity. The study is concerned primarily with the distribution of people on the land. This then is the story of two plantations and their people.

Case Study Plantations

The plantations selected for study represent fairly typical modes of adjustment to the changing operating situation in the Delta. The one plantation, Tractor Plantation, is relatively advanced in mechanization. The other plantation, Mule Plantation, is relatively unmechanized.

The plantations are not extreme types. There are plantations in the Delta that have progressed farther in the substitution of machines for human and animal labor than has Tractor Plantation. There are plantations that more nearly follow the practices of a quarter of a century ago than does Mule Plantation. There are plantations where practically all the cotton is picked with machines, where mules are never seen in the cotton fields. This is not the case on Tractor Plantation. There are plantations where all the cotton is harvested with hand labor and mechanical pickers have never been seriously considered, where a cropper family with the help of a mule "make" the cotton crop. This is not the case on Mule Plantation.

Though the two plantations are not extreme types, cotton production on Tractor Plantation is tractor oriented whereas on Mule Plantation it remains mule oriented.

Both plantations were established around the turn of the century. Mule Plantation was cut out of the swamp by the father of the present owner. The large block of land surrounding the plantation headquarters of well-drained silt loam soil, good cotton land which was seldom been planted to other crops, was acquired first. Subsequently, additional "forties" were added to the east, west, and north. Some detached tracts not shown on the map complete the holding — 3160 acres in all, 2700 in the home place. The track was completed prior to World War I and no land has been bought or sold since.

The sprawling profile of the unit atests to the characteristics of the planter himself. The story is told that the wife of the planter frequently sought to prevail on her husband to fill in the gaps and square out the plantation. The planter's pet response was "What would I do with the land? It's no good for cotton. Let others pay the tax on it."

Mule Plantation was and is a cotton factory and little attention is given to anything else. Livestock feed, except for scant winter grazing, was bought by the car load lot and usually the entire supply was secured in one shipment. This was a bit of bravado permitted himself by the normally conservative planter and, of course, livestock feed is cheaper by the carload lot.

Another concession, this one to sentiment, is that the track just west of the big house on the town side of headquarters has never been planted to cotton. "We don't like to see cotton growing right up to the front door."

Nevertheless, management on Mule Plantation is essentially conservative. "We don't need to try all these new ideas. We have a laboratory all around us. Let others spend their money on experiments.'' The previous manager took considerable kidding from the neighbors about the conservatism of his operations. His stock response when pushed too far, ''Well, we can still pay our bills.'' The implication is obvious and frequently justified.

Management on Tractor Plantation is more aggressive, more daring, definitely not conservative. After the disastrous White River flood in Arkansas around 1880, the grandfather of the present owner crossed the river to the Mississippi side and bought two small plantations. There are three or four major cotton areas on the plantation which represent the production nucleus of the original small plantations absorbed in the operation.

Management on Tractor Plantation expanded the area by absorbing plantations rather than by buying cotton land as did the owner of Mule Plantation. This is largely a function of the stage in settlement of the two areas in which the plantations are located. Tractor Plantation lies on the river and has access to water transportation, which though not important today means that the area was settled earlier. Mule Plantation lies 15–20 miles inland from the river and settlement had to await the coming of railroads and other forms of transportation. The owner of Mule Plantation **could not** have developed his holdings as he did if he had settled in the area where Tractor Plantation is located. On the other hand the successive owners of Tractor Plantation **would not** have developed the holdings after the pattern of Mule Plantation had they settled in the latter area.

The present owner of Tractor Plantation gave this thumbnail sketch of the development of the holdings. ''Grandfather bought up around 2500 acres. My father added another 1500, but I've managed to add only 240 acres to the plantation.'' There was an adjoining plantation that was bought in the early thirties and sold back a year or two later. Even today there are several farms or small plantations which seem desirable additions when and if they became available. Today the plantation contains approximately 500 acres but the plantation area is by no means fixed and stable. The cropper supervisor remarked about a finger of land stabbing into the heart of the plantation and not owned by them ''When we could buy it, **we** couldn't; and now that **we** can buy it, we can't.''

The philosophy of management on Tractor Plantation is that if there is a better way to grow cotton or a more profitable crop they want to know about it, and if it looks good they will try it. Power take-off combines, self-propelled combines, mechanical cotton pickers, flame cultivators, chemical weed control are all in use or have been tried on the plantation. The owner laughingly admits that lack of sales resistance rather than sound management may have resulted in some experimentation with innovations. On the other hand, ''If we don't try it we won't know if it will work for us. You have to gamble, take a calculated risk occasionally, to make progress.''

Housing The Plantation Workers

The history of mechanization in the cotton fields is beclouded by the conflict between the need for efficiency and the adherence to the traditional paternalism characteristic of the plantation. The people of the nation's number one problem area of a decade and a half ago, at least from the standpoint of the attention given to the area, have become acutely aware of the human element involved in the transition to mechanized operations. Illustrating this awareness, the Rust brothers withheld their patents for a mechanical picker for several years and endowed a training school for field hands with proceeds from royalties to facilitate the readjustment of the workers. Even today nearly 20 years later, planter after planter and other persons involved in management feel impelled to reiterate and reaffirm the defense which became the byword of the area in the late 30's: "Not one family, not one person has been displaced by machines on this plantation."

The years from 1935 to the present have seen a greatly augmented migration stream move out of the Delta to urban and industrial centers of the South, the North Central Region, and the West. The orientation of management currently is toward ways and means of retaining labor rather than toward ways and means for disposing of or replacing labor. The maintenance of favorable landlord-tenant or employer-employee relations has become and continues to be a dominant function of management. The successful operation of the cotton plantation depends upon the ability of management to maintain an adequate supply of labor to perform the operations which cannot yet be performed successfully by machines.

Traditionally, cotton production has been a hand labor operation, and therefore the plantation has been dependent upon an abundant supply of hand labor at a low cost. The arrangements by which the plantation operator assured himself of the continuing availability of labor range from the slave labor of the antebellum era to the seasonal migratory worker of the current period. The constant in all arrangements is the availability of housing on the plantation for the labor families.

Even a casual inspection of the number and location of houses on the two plantations reveals a basic difference in the underlying assumptions with which the managements approach the operation of the plantation. On Mule Plantation the assumption seems to be that though machines may take over eventually, men and mules will still be an important element in cotton production tomorrow. There are too many partly solved and unsolved links in the process for mechanized cotton production to be an immediate and real alternative. On Tractor Plantation the assumption is that machines — planters, flame cultivators, chemicals, mechanical pickers — will do the work tomorrow, but for the present much hand labor will be needed. Effective chemical and mechanical control of weeds and grass is possible even under field conditions in "normal" years. Next year may not be normal; therefore, hand laborers must be retained and hence employed even in normal years.

The story of housing on Mule Plantation is the story of growth and decline. In 1905 there were 92 houses for plantation workers. This represents the maximum number on the plantation and the houses were maintained until 1930. The owner allows that "We haven't built any new cropper houses since 1910, except to replace those that burned and since 1930 we haven't even replaced those that burned." The number of houses decreased by 7 percent in the decade 1930–40 and by 10 percent in the following decade. The loss from 90 houses in 1930 to 74 in 1951 represents the normal attrition resulting from fire and disuse. "It probably isn't good management," the owner remarked "but we haven't torn any houses down or attempted to salvage the lumber for other uses."

When the comparison is made in terms of occupied houses a better evaluation of the labor force is obtained. In 1951 only 56 of the 74 houses were occupied, leaving nearly 25 percent on the houses empty (Table 1). On Mule Plantation this represents a loss of only 7 percent since 1940. The sharpest decline in the number of occupied houses, 31 percent, came in the depression decade from 1930–40, (Table 2). Prior to that, in the judgment of the owner, there never were more than one, two or at the most three empty houses in any crop year. Before 1930 management frequently found it necessary to turn workers away, except during the relatively short period of labor shortage in 1928–29 and during World War I.

As noted above, no new houses have been built since 1920 and there has been no attempt to relocate the houses. The houses that are less accessible have been allowed to fall down or have not been replaced. The summary figures show a net loss of 37% in the number of occupied houses from 1920–1951.

The unoccupied houses on the plantation are, with few exceptions, located on the back ''forties'' away from roads and inaccessible to the plantation headquarters. The adjoining fields, it will be noted are no longer in cotton. When the plantation manager rode out on a horse it was still possible to supervise work on the back forties but now that he rides around in a car, supervision becomes difficult and furthermore most croppers today want access to a road. For all practical purposes the houses on the back forties have been abondoned.

A second reason for the abandonment of these houses is the dominant soil type in the area. This is a heavy clay soil, locally known as ''buckshot,'' which has poor internal drainage and hence is difficult to work in wet years. During the 1920 decade with the depletion of the lighter soils, cotton was planted on these heavy soils with reasonable success. However, with the promotion in the 1930 decade and following of extensive use of commercial fertilizers these heavier soils were again taken out of cotton because they did not respond as well to fertilizers as the lighter soils.

TABLE 1. *Number of cropper and labor houses on the case Study Plantation, Bolivar County Survey, 1951.*

	Tractor		Mule	
	No.	%	No.	%
Total houses	107	100.0	74	100.0
Occupied	90	84.1	56	75.7
Unoccupuied	17	15.9	18	24.3

The unoccupied houses that are located along the roads are not in use for various immediate reasons. In one case the cropper farming the tract lives in town. In another the family skipped out during the night and if the survey had been made a week earlier the house would have been occupied. Another had been rented, but the cropper failed to move in when he was supposed to and then it was too late to get another family.

The houses on Tractor Plantation are assembled along two main roads and around the plantation headquarters. There are 107 tenant and labor houses on the plantation, but only 90 of them are occupied (Table 1). The few houses still standing in the fields will be moved or torn down as soon as there is time. The houses that have been moved have been repaired and electricity has been installed. It is significant that the houses have not been enlarged or otherwise improved. It is apparent that even though management has gone to the expense of relocating the houses the possibility of eventual abandonment is real and not too distant. This practice of relocation may represent an intermediate step in the transition to full mechanization. Eventually, as the labor force becomes stabilized and the need for field hands sharply reduced, it is possible that even some of the relocated houses will be torn down and further improvements will be made on the remaining houses. This, at least, has been observed on one or two plantations, where the labor force consists of the tractor drivers and mechanics necessary to maintain and operate the equipment.

In 1920 there were 136 houses on the land which now comprises Tractor Plantation. By 1951 the total number of houses as noted above had decreased to 107 with only 90 occupied. This represents a net loss of 34% as compared to 37% on Mule Plantation. The lower proportionate loss on Tractor Plantation can be ascribed in part to the higher yields and in part to the higher proportion of lighter soils on the plantation. Management on Tractor Plantation was able to expand cotton acreage following the removal of controls without taking in much of the heavier soil area on the plantation. Mule Plantation, in contrast, would have to expand into the heavy "buckshot" soil which were abandoned when controls were introduced.

The sharpest decline in the number of houses occurred in the decade 1930–40. If we assume that all houses on the plantation were occupied in 1940 and earlier, then there is a more marked decline in the number of occupied houses in the decade 1940–50 (Table 2). This assumption is not entirely justified since defense production with an expanding labor demand in industry had already begun by 1940. The number of houses indicates that there has been a consistent but increasing reduction in labor on the plantation since 1930.

The relocation of housing presents an even more marked transition than does the reduction in number (Figure 4). In 1930 the 136 houses were scattered over the plantation but in 1951 they had been assembled. By relocation of housing and turn rows the fields have been opened up to accommodate the new 4-row equipment which was adopted on the plantation in 1946.

The comparative figures for the two plantations present strong evidence in support of the contention that factors other than machines have been instrumental in bringing about the reduction in labor force. Production controls, no doubt, contributed to dissatisfaction and a high level of mobility among cropper

TABLE 2. *Number of occupied houses for selected years on the Case Study Plantations, Bolivar County Survey, 1951.*

	Tractor		Mule	
	No.	% change	No.	% change
1905.........................	117	—	90	—
1920.........................	136	16.2	89	— 1.1
1930.........................	133	— 2.2	87	— 2.2
1940.........................	114	— 14.3	60	— 31.0
1951.........................	90	— 21.1	56	— 6.7

families in the first decade of the period. For the nation as a whole the acreage planted to cotton declined 38 percent from the 1931–33 average to the 1940–42 average which roughly coincides with the two earlier periods for which housing data were obtained.

The data for Bolivar County, in which these two plantations are located, is equally revealing. The acreage planted to cotton in 1932 before the imposition of acreage controls was 266,000 acres. In 1934 after the imposition of controls, only 179,000 acres were planted to cotton. This represents a reduction of 87,000 acres or 33 percent of the 1932 acreage. The acreage removed from cotton was at first planted to corn and hay — later to oats, hay, soybeans and pasture — all of which are less labor intensive crops than cotton. After 1934 both the acreage planted to cotton and the yield per acre increased, so that in the late thirties the labor surplus created by the initial reduction in acreage had been partially absorbed. Nevertheless, if a constant ratio of acres per worker were maintained, the plantations could expect to lose nearly a third of their workers during the decade. Since the late 1930's the high level of business activity and industrial employment brought on by the onset of the war in 1939 and our entry in December 1941 opened up alternative opportunities for the plantation labor force and spurred large numbers into migrating from the area.

Plantation Management

The operation of a plantation is a big business which involves the establishment of personal relations between two and three hundred people on each of the two plantations studied. The business becomes more complex as the operation becomes more mechanized largely because the mechanized operation requires a higher capitalization. The increasing complexity of the operation is reflected in the management hierachy on each of the two plantations.

The organizational structure on Mule Plantation is relatively simple. The owner of the plantation is in direct communication with every tenant and worker on the placem At "furnish" and settlement time the owner sits behind the counter in the office and deals directly with each of the tenants as they come before him. The tenants are greeted by their first names and the good work of the past year is commended or the slovenly work is condemned. The tenants, furthermore, come directly to the owner with their special problems, such as sickness, trouble with the law, etc., whenever and wherever the occasion arises.

When the commissary was in operation the store manager was directly responsible to the owner and frequently the owner might help out in the store, at least to the extent of recording the advances to each of the tenants as they came in for provisions. The blacksmith and the mule hostlers, likewise, are directly responsible to the owner in the performance of their duties.

There is, however, a plantation foreman who in some instances serves as the intermediary between the plantation tenants and the owner. The foreman's primary function is to see to it that the crop is put in and taken care of. He is the legman in the management hierarchy. He makes the rounds to check on the tenants during the working season. He is the plantation rider. This doesn't mean that the owner himself doesn't make the rounds of the plantation. He does this several times a week or even a day — sometimes with the manager and sometimes alone.

The manager in addition is responsible for the "day crop" on the plantation and for the supplementary crops other than cotton. Working the supplementary crops, however, is incidental to his primary function as overseer for the tenants. He has little or no responsibility for, or contact with, the allied functions of the plantation such as the store, gin, the mule barns, and the blacksmith, except at the direction of the owner.

As mechanization and diversification of an operation increase the management structure becomes more complex. The organization chart for Tractor Plantation still shows the direct line of communication from the owner through the tenant supervisor to the sharecroppers.

However, the organization chart reveals that this phase of management has become a subsidiary phase on Tractor Plantation. The owner has acquired an overall manager and his primary responsibility is for the performance of machine operations on the plantation. He is in essence the supervisor for the "day crop." When it comes to the utilization of labor the division of responsibility between the tenant supervisor and the plantation manager becomes a little cloudy. There are some operations in which he must deal with the tenant supervisor but the manager is solely responsible for the supervision of the tractor work. The supervision is delegated to a tractor foreman and a foreman in charge of heavy equipment. The tractor foreman has supervision over the maintenance and operation of all the row-crop equipment. The heavy equipment foreman is responsible for the crawler type tractors and for the maintenance and operation of the gin.

On Tractor Plantation the line of communication from the individual worker to the plantation owner has been broken. The worker deals almost solely with the tenant supervisor or with the plantation manager. Some few workers of long standing might conceivably find their way to the plantation owner but throughout the period of the study which covered about three months during which several conferences were held with the owner, none of the workers did seek access to him.

This is in sharp contrast to the situation observed on Mule Plantation, where each interview with the owner was interrupted by at least one plantation worker seeking the counsel of the owner.

On Tractor Plantation there are essentially two operating units. The one is the mechanized operation and the other is the hand labor operation. The two merge at some points but in essence an independent structure has been developed for the mechanized operation. The hand labor operation survives much as it was prior to the introduction of mechanized equipment.

Tenure Arrangements

Throughout the Delta considerable thought has been given through the years to the ways and means for securing and retaining labor for the plantation. The basic tenure arrangement is the half and half share-cropper agreement. Under this arrangement the tenant supplies all labor required for the production of the crop. The distribution of other costs of production such as poisoning, fertilizer, and other items has been worked out in each area. The presence or absence of a commissary, the kind and amount of "furnish," all enter into the labor recruitment situation. As tractors are introduced to the operation some of the labor normally performed by the tenant is performed with tractor equipment. The cost of the operation is charged against the tenant's crop.

The half and half arrangement continues to be the customary basis for bargaining between landlord and tenant. On Mule Plantation there are two tenants on the home place who farm on the one-third and one-fourth rental agreement and who supply some of the capital requirement for the operation. The plantation also has two wage hands. The remaining 52 labor families are sharecropper families.

On Mule Plantation tractors are used primarily at the discretion of the cropper with the exception that where experience has taught the plantation manager that a family consistently gets behind in its work he will insist that the particular tract is machine planted so that it can be cultivated with a multiple row cultivator, otherwise the probability is very great that a crop will not be harvested on that field. The charges assessed against the sharecropper for tractor work on Mule Plantation are minimum charges, apparently based on current operating expenses with little overhead included in the cost.

The tenant has the privilege of applying the seed to the ginning cost or of collecting the seed money and paying a fixed charge of sixty cents per 100 pounds for ginning plus $3.50 for packing and ties for each bale. In the latter case the cost of ginning is deferred until settlement time.

The commissary on Mule Plantation has been closed for nearly a decade. In the early 20's the commissary was closed for the first time and cash furnish was given to the sharecroppers. This was necessary to meet the competition for labor from other planters who at that time had begun to pay a cash "furnish." During the early 20's the workers wanted cash for automobiles and other luxury items. However, about 1930 the commissary was reopened and "furnish" was advanced in the form of coupons which could be used only in the commissary. The commissary remained in operation until the advent of rationing at which time management again closed the commissary because it was too much trouble to keep up with the ration coupons.

The plantation owner repreatedly commented that they were not in the merchandising business and had no interest in becoming established in it. The primary business of the plantation is cotton production. If it is necessary to run a commissary to maintain labor they will run a commissary, but if they can do without it they have no intention of operating a grocery and dry goods store.

Currently on Mule Plantation a cash "furnish" is made to the plantation labor force every four weeks beginning the first of March and continuing through July. The last "furnish" is given either in the last week in July or in the first week in August. The "furnish" for the four-week period ranges from $10 to $14 for single individuals and from $50 to $75 for larger families. At present there are some families that are able to finance themselves.

The tenant can arrange for settlement any time after he has two bales to his credit. Settlement day is Thursday on Mule Plantation and usually begins the third Thursday in October. Traditionally, if a tenant does not make a profit on the crop some adjustment is made. Usually about half of the indebtedness is written off and half of it carried forward on account for the next year. The owner commented that if the debt was too large the tenant would skip out and he would lose his labor; therefore, it has become customary to write off some of the indebtedness.

On Tractor Plantation the prevailing arrangement currently is that of wage labor though the tenure pattern is much more complex than on Mule Plantation. In 1940 only 400 of the 1450 acres in cotton were cultivated with day labor. In 1951, the relationship had been reversed with 1200 acres cultivated by day laborers and only 450 acres by tenants or sharecroppers.

Currently the plantation has one renter and one sharecropper who do all the work with mules. These are exceptions. There are 29 sharecropper families on the plantation and 37 families which though ostensibly share-croppers represent an innovation in labor relations on the plantation. The male heads of these 37 families are day laborers on the plantation. As an added incentive to stay on the plantation the wife is given a cropper tract of three acres in which she has a share in the crop and on which she is expected to perform the labor. The plantation also has 16 full-time wage hands. These plus the 37 wage hands whose wives have a crop make 53 wage laborers. The tractor drivers and mechanics are included in the 53 regular wage hands.

Beginning as early as 1905 breaking and planting on Tractor Plantation was done by the landlord. Up to 1945 the tenant continued to be responsible for cultivation, chopping and picking, the first operations being performed with mule equipment. In 1945 four-row equipment was acquired and cultivation was added to the operations performed with machines, leaving for the tenants only the hand labor operations of hoeing and picking. The transition to four-row equipment and tractor cultivating was completed in two years with less than a third of the tenants using mules to cultivate their crops in 1946. By 1947 the mule inventory on the plantation was reduced to 12 mules and all field operations were performed with tractors.

By making these adjustments management on Tractor Plantation has made available a plantation labor force which can work on the day crop after they have finished the work on their own tracts. On Tractor Plantation it is unnecessary for management to hire off-the-plantation labor for weed control except during extremely wet periods. The sharecropper labor force is organized into labor gangs and there are four or five labor foremen who are responsible for these when they work in other fields on the plantation.

By giving tenant families first chance at day-labor work, management has reduced the need for continuing advances through the growing season. The tenant families normally draw more in wage labor than the operating charges against their cropper tracts. The wages on the day crop are paid in cash on a weekly basis and the charges against the crop are carried until settlement time. Management, therefore, has been able to do away almost entirely with a weekly or monthly "furnish."

Skilled Workers

One of the major problems confronting management on a plantation that is being mechanized is the recruiting and training of tractor drivers and operators of the heavy equipment being introduced into the farming operation. Neither of the plantations studied has developed a very definite policy with respect to this problem.

On Mule Plantation in 1951 there were 10 tractor drivers and the manager of the plantation observed that he never went out to look for tractor drivers. There are always applicants for the jobs. Most of the tractor drivers grew up on the plantation or were kinsmen of tenant families on the plantation or they have married into the plantation families. Furthermore, all the drivers on Mule Plantation have a regular crop and drive tractors only when the work on their own crop is caught up.

For 1951 the payroll account on Mule Plantation lists 10 regular tractor drivers with an average of 7 years experience as drivers. Seven are men who have lived on the plantation for 20 years or more, including six who were born on the plantation. Two men have lived there for 10–15 years and one for less than 10 years. The 10 drivers include 3 who have driven for 10 years or more, 4 for 5–9 years, and 3 for less than 5 years. The entire period as drivers for some of the workers has not been on Mule Plantation.

Another measure of the stability of tractor drivers on Mule Plantation may be obtained by comparing the roster of drivers for an earlier year with the current roster. Data were obtained for the year 1944, which was 7 years earlier. At that time there were 5 drivers on the plantation. Of the 5, only two were driving tractors in 1951 on Mule Plantation. Of the remaining 3 one had migrated North, one had left the plantation but was still in the county, and one had been committed to the Federal Penitentiary on a liquor charge.

The comparative data indicate a relatively high mobility of the skilled worker. Only 2 of the current group have been driving tractors on the plantation for as much as 10 years. They have lived on the plantation most of their lives and learned to drive tractors in the more recent years. They are replacements for earlier tractor drivers. It is unlikely that more than one or two of the 7 drivers with less than 10 years experience will remain on the plantation for ten years or more.

The story for Tractor Plantation is not much different. In August 1945 there were only 13 tractor drivers on the plantation payroll. Of these, only 4 still remain as tractor drivers on the plantation, five have moved North, two have been killed, one has been committed to the penitentiary, and one has moved to another plantation.

In 1951 the plantation had 22 tractor drivers. Six of these were Displaced Persons who had been brought to the plantation about two years earlier. The remaining 16 were Negro workers. Nine of the Negro drivers were brought up on the plantation and 3 others have lived on the plantation for 10 years or more. The average length of time that the drivers have been driving tractors is about 6 years. Only 8 were sufficiently skilled to be entrusted with the operation of either the mechanical cotton picker or the self-propelled combine.

In the judgment of the tractor supervisor only about 40 percent of the drivers trained by the plantation remain on the plantation. Of those that leave, nearly 40 percent migrate to northern industrial centers and about 20 percent find employment as bull-dozer operators and drivers of other types of dirt-moving and road-maintaining equipment in the Delta. The tractor supervisor remarked that they were planning to initiate a tractor school to train some of their own personnel to operate the equipment.

In terms of both sets of comparative data Tractor Plantation has experienced a higher loss of drivers than Mule Plantation. This may be, in part, a derivative of the differences in tenure arrangements observed on the two plantations. As noted earlier the drivers on Mule Plantation are croppers first and drivers second, thus having an interest in the crop and tenure rights in the land. The drivers on Tractor Plantation are drivers only and have no interest in the crop or tenure rights in the land, except that management has found it expedient in some instances to award a crop to the wife of the driver on the assumption that this would tend to hold the driver on the plantation.

Machines vs. Mules

Neither of the plantations studied are solely dependent on either tractors or mules in the performance of field operations. The one, Tractor Plantation, depends more on tractors and the other more on mules to supply the work power in the field. The difference between the two is a difference in emphasis, a difference in degree of mechanization.

In 1923 the workstock inventory was at its maximum on Mule Plantation with 98 head. The mule book for the plantation was begun around 1920 and the record of sales, deaths and purchases is available for each year. The mule inventory fluctuates around 85 for most of the period up to 1945. It drops below 80 in the period 1928–34 and again in 1945 when the inventory is 76 head. The year 1945 is the beginning of the period of reduction and the number of mules is 48 in 1951.

The first tractor, a Clete, was acquired in 1920. The second was purchased in 1929 and sold two years later. In 1935 the tractor inventory is two. Tractors continue to be incidental until 1948 when the inventory rises to 7. In 1951 the plantation has 9 tractors but only 5 of them, including two 4-row cultivators, are equipped with cultivator attachments.

On Mule Plantation tractors are used primarily on the land not planted to cotton. As neighboring planters began to use tractors on cotton land Mule Plantation secured tractors that were made available to the individual tenant on request. This continues to be the policy of management. Whether or not tractor work is performed on a given field is determined between the landlord and the tenant usually when they bargain for a crop in the spring. Even stalk cutting, breaking, and discing operations are not performed "through and through" on Mule Plantation. There are some croppers who perform these operations with mules.

Management insists that the spring work be done with tractors when dealing with some croppers because "Experience has taught us," in the words of the landlord, "that these particular croppers make a habit of getting behind and if we are going to make a crop on their land we have to be able to go in there with tractors during the cultivating season. You can't cultivate a field with a 2-row or 4-row cultivator uless it has been planted with a 2-row or 4-row planter."

The charge fortractor work is figured on a cost basis. The figures quoted for work done on specific plots range from $1.60 an acre for stalk cutting, breaking, and discing to $4.40 per acre on a tract where the tractor operations were carried through to two cultivations. These are the actual charges recorded in the plantation record book for two specific tracts.

Spraying and dusting are performed at the sole discretion of management and for the entire acreage. The cost is charged against the cropper tract on a prorata basis. The tenant is charged for all the labor costs on these operations and normally the cost of materials are shared 50–50 between landlord and tenant.

The equipment inventory on Mule Plantation does not include a mechanical cotton picker nor has any of the cotton been harvested with machines. Machine harvesting would entail expensive modernization of the gin which is not necessary as long as the tenants can continue to harvest their own cotton.

On Tractor Plantation the mule records are not as detailed as are the records on Mule Plantation. The maximum number of mules recorded is 105 head in 1935.

The mule inventory remained at about 100 head until 1945 when half of them were disposed of at a mule sale. The following year another sale was held and the inventory was brought down to 12 head which has been maintained since that time.

There are two transition years on Tractor Plantation, 1935 and 1945. Prior to 1935 there were three heavy-duty steel-wheeled tractors on the place. In 1935 one of these was replaced with two row-crop tractors and another row-crop tractor was added the following year. The transition was completed in 1937 when the inventory consisted of 7 row-crop tractors all equipped with 2-row cultivator attachments. The inventory increased to 12 by 1942 and remained at that number through the war period.

In 1945, though the tractors found little use in the 1945 crop season, the transition to 4-row equipment was begun and the 1946 crop year finds the inventory at 18 four-row tractors. One crawler or caterpillar was added to do the heavy work in the spring. In 1951 the inventory stands at 21 four-row tractors and 2 crawlers.

Mechanical cotton pickers were introduced on the place in 1948 with 4 one-row units. The following year 2 additional one-row units were added and in 1950 two 2-row pickers were added, making a total inventory of 8 mechanical pickers in 1950 and 1951. The 12-foot self-propelled combines complete the inventory of major equipment for 1951.

On Tractor Plantation the cropper's responsibility for the cotton begins when the plants "show green in the row." He supplies the hand labor necessary to grow cotton on the acreage assigned him and must harvest his own crop. When that is done he can work on the "day crop" for cash wages, if there is a need for day labor. The field operations from planting to harvesting is a "through and through" operation.

The present owner may not fare so well in comparison with his two predecessors if expansion is measured in terms of acres added to the plantation. The transition in operating method though is revolutionary. It is a transformation that is equalled or exceeded on few plantations in the area.

Land Use

Prior to 1933 and the advent of government regulation and controlled production, there are few data on acres planted on either plantation. The cropper tracts, as one owner remarked, more or less grew up as the plantation was cleared and the houses were built. These tracts haven't changed much through the years. The number of acres in each wasn't important. The tract was measured rather in terms of its ability to produce cotton.

The philosophy credited earlier to the owner of Mule Plantation, "Let the other fellow pay the taxes on the poor land" was not an idle boast. This is revealed by the high ratio of the land used for crops, namely, 83 percent and nearly 88 percent if the improved pasture is included. The Plantation, however, is no longer as distinctively a cotton factory as was true before the crop control program was enacted. Cotton acreages which currently range around a thousand acres approached 2000 prior to 1933. The highest measured acreage planted since then was 1466.5 in 1937. The year of the plow-up approximately 1300 measured acres were harvested. Since 25 percent of the planted acres were plowed under, an estimated 1750 acres were planted in cotton in that year. In its heyday as a cotton factory, cotton was harvested from more than 60 percent of the land in the plantation annually.

Aside from the stream beds and adjoining woodland areas there is very little land on Mule Plantation that has never been planted to cotton (Figure 6). The block of land south and west of the plantation headquarters is cotton land and, except for the meadow west of the house, has been used as such every year since the plantation was organized. The tracts of land farther away from headquarters and from the road have been planted to cotton when and if tenants could be secured for them. In periods of labor abundance, families could be secured for the back "forties." Characteristically, these families received little supervision and seldom 'paid off." In periods of labor scarcity the back "forties" remained idle.

Another factor contributing to the distribution of cotton acreage on the plantation is the distribution of soil types. The soil survey for the farm reveals that about ten percent of the area falls in the Class I soil group. This is a high proportion for that section of the county. Class I soils are the light sandy loam and silt loam soils which have made the Delta famous as a cotton producing area. The soils on about 25 percent of the area are Class II soils which also are high producing soils but which require more careful management if yields are to be maintained. Soils in the remaining areas of the plantation are Class III or poorer soils. These can be used effectively for cotton production only under the most favorable weather conditions and then only if adequate surface drainage can be provided. The latter soils predominate on the back "forties" of the plantation. The nature of the soils, no doubt, is a strong contributing factor to the inability of management to maintain labor on these tracts and helps to explain why the back "forties" seldom paid off.

On Tractor Plantation 56 percent of the land is currently used for crops. An additional 17 percent is in improved pasture, which brings the total improved land up to 73 percent of the total acreage or 3000 acres. Thirty-six percent of the total or 50 percent of the improved land is currently planted to cotton. The acreage in cotton has ranged from around 1300 to 2000 acres. Prior to 1933 the acreage planted to cotton seldom fell below 50 percent of the acreage in the plantation.

Aside from the segments of waste and forest land on the plantation most of the land has been used for cotton at some time or other. Around a third of the acreage has been planted to cotton every year since the tract was added to the plantation. Another fourth of the land has been used dominantly for cotton and then there is some additional land that has been planted to cotton only in exceptional years.

The soil survey for Tractor Plantation shows that with only minor exceptions, all the land always or predominantly in cotton falls in the Class I or Class II soil groups. These soils predominate on approximately half of the plantation area. In years of production controls, when acreage allotments are in effect, some of these soils must be diverted to other crops. Even in years of expanding acreages management still has a backlog of fair cotton land that can be brought into production, if labor is available and the price seems to justify it.

The historical land use patterns for the two plantations show that in the pre-depression era nearly 2000 acres on the two units were planted in cotton annually. Both units curtailed the acreage planted when production controls were initiated in 1934. The acreage planted in cotton fluctuates around 1200 acres from 1935—1939 on each plantation. In the next five year period 1940–1944 the acreage on Mule Plantation is reduced to around 1000 acres; whereas, on Tractor Plantation the acreage planted is increased to 1400 acres. In the post-war era from 1945–1949, the opposing trends continue and the acreage on Mule Plantation ranges around 800, whereas on Tractor Plantation the acreage varies around 1600 acres.

The diverging trends in acreage and the difference in the productive capacity of the land on the two plantations have resulted in a lower total production on Mule Plantation. Since 1940 production on Mule Plantation has not been over 1000 bales in any year, whereas on Tractor Plantation production has never fallen below 1000 bales in any year. The range on the former is from 482 to 961 bales and on the latter from 1105 to 2136 bales. Neither the high records nor the low records fall in the same year on the two plantations. The variation in production reflects the vicissitudes of controls, weather, and labor supply and the responses of the plantation managements and the plantation soils to these variables.

The more intensive cultivation and the retirement of the poorer soils from cotton production on Mule Plantation are accompanied by a slight net increase in yields per acre. For the five year period 1935–1939 the average yield of lint per acre is just over 350 pounds, as compared to just under 400 pounds for the period 1945–1949. In contrast, Tractor Plantation has expanded its cotton acreage and substituted tractor power for mule power and hand labor. During this period the 5-year average yield has dropped from nearly 600 pounds on the restricted acreage in 1940–1944 to below 500 pounds on the expanded acreage in 1945–1949.

At the present level of operation Mule Plantation averages approximately 15 acres of cotton per occupied house. Based on the 5-year average yields this results in a net production of 11 bales of lint per occupied house. The more extensive operation on Tractor Plantation only averages 18 acres in cotton per occupied house but when combined with the higher yields obtained, the plantation shows a net production of 16 bales of lint per occupied house. The higher capitalization has enabled the latter plantation to absorb a 15 percent net loss in average yields and still produce nearly 50 percent more cotton per unit of labor than was produced on the unmechanized plantation.

Summary and Conclusions

The preceding analysis is concerned primarily with the distribution of people on the land, the factors which are associated with the observed historical changes in the distribution, and the resulting differences in distribution between the two plantations. The observations are indicative of the effects which differing management policies will have and should be viewed as tentative hypothesis subject to further verification.

The two plantations were selected because the managements have adopted divergent methods to cope with the problem of labor scarcity. Mule Plantation is a tenant operation and continues to use mules as the primary source of work power, but has a few tractors which are available to the tenants on request. Tractor Plantation is primarily a "day crop" operation and is extensively mechanized with tractors used for all operations at the convenience of the manager. The few tenants remaining are responsible for hand labor — hoeing and picking — one the acreage assigned to them. The "day crop" is machine harvested.

The cropper tract is the unit of operation on Mule Plantation. Housing is associated with the tract and dispersed on the plantation. If a house is empty, the field adjoining it is idle. If a house stands empty for more than one season, the field adjoining will in all probability be diverted to crops other than cotton. The field is the unit of operation on Tractor Plantation. The houses are no longer associated with specific tracts and have been moved out of the fields to locations on three main roads. The fields are prepared and planted by the tractor crew and at hoeing time a number of rows are assigned to the cropper. The acreage thus assigned accounts for less than a fourth of the total acreage planted.

The decline in occupied houses has been greater on Mule Plantation (37 percent) than on Tractor Plantation (34 percent). The availability of tenants, willing to bargain for specific tracts is the primary determinant of cotton acreage in any given year on Mule Plantation. Historically management has found it difficult in periods of labor scarcity to secure tenants for the heavier, poorly drained soils and most of this land has been taken out of cotton.

Soil type, price, and the availability of labor substitutes — tractors, chemicals and mechanical pickers — are the primary determinants of cotton acreage in any given year on Tractor Plantation. The acreage is determined and labor (resident or non-resident) or labor substitutes necessary to do the job are secured.

Tenure rights in the land are recognized as an important factor in recruiting and retaining labor on both plantations. All workers are tenants on Mule Plantation. The cropper arrangement predominates, but there are some renters. All workers are potential "day hands" on Tractor Plantation, Tenure rights to a crop are assigned to a worker, or to his wife, if this is necessary to secure his services as a hoe hand, tractor driver or mechanic.

The phenomenon which distinguishes the management on Tractor Plantation from Mule Plantation is the new management hierarchy which is being established to operate and maintain the tractor equipment. There are in essence two operating units on Tractor Plantation. One unit is operated under the traditional-sharecropper system and in 1951 accounted for less than one-third of the cotton acreage on the plantation. The remaining two-thirds of the crop is in management or day cotton. All hand labor for the operation is hired on the day-wage basis and as much of the work as possible is done with tractor equipment. When possible the day hands who work on the operator cotton are secured from the tenant families on the plantation and paid a fixed daily wage which is determined at the time the families bargain for the current crop.

Mechanization on Mule Plantation is nominal and includes only preplanting operations and some cultivation. Most of the cultivating on Mule Plantation is done with mules. In contrast mechanization on Tractor Plantation is extensive, including even some weed control operations, such as flame-cultivation and chemical weed control. Nearly 70 percent of the cotton crop on Tractor Plantation has been harvested with machines each year for the past 4 or 5 years.

Neither plantation has embarked upon a clearly defined program for selecting and training operators of the mechanized equipment on the farm. Literally, if a man wants to drive a tractor and he can keep the tractor in the row he can become a tractor driver. Tractor Plantation did inaugurate in the fall of 1951 a training school for tractor drivers which was designed to acquaint the potential drivers with the operation and maintenance of the equipment. It is too early to assess the effect of this program on the skill and efficiency of the drivers on the plantation.

Looking to the future the development of the fully mechanized operation will result in the elaboration and specialization of the mechanized wing of the management structure, and in the deletion of the tenant wing of the structure. It is unlikely that this will be attained, however, until such time as management can see itself no longer dependent upon a relatively large hand labor force. Currently management on Tractor Plantation is willing to pay the additional cost of the sharecropper program in order to retain the labor force for work when needed on the operator cotton. The decision to retain a sharecropper arrangement on a portion of the plantation is made not so much in terms of the economics of the operation as it is in terms of the availability of labor. The operator of a mechanized plantation who does not have an accessible labor force must depend upon the availability of sufficient workers in nearby towns and villages. When he competes for this non-resident labor the cost of weed control becomes higher on a per-day basis, but the critical problem is that he is never completely sure on any given day or in any given week that he will be able to obtain the 100 or 200 workers which he needs if he is to get through the fields in the time available.

Western Irrigation

From Elco L. Greenshields, "Water for Irrigation," U.S. Department of Agriculture, *Yearbook*, 1955 (Washington, 1955), pp. 247–51.

The total area of irrigated land in the 17 Western States was about 27.5 million acres in 1953. That is only 3.5 percent of the total land in farms in those States, but its significance to agriculture is much greater than the figure indicates. Above 12 percent of all cropland harvested was irrigated. More than 21 percent of all farms had some irrigated fields. The value of the crops harvested from irrigated land was about 35 percent of the value of all crops harvested.

Despite higher and higher costs of installing irrigation works and tighter limitations on the use of the available water, irrigation agriculture continues to expand. In the 10 years to 1950, 7 million acres were added to the irrigated land area of the 17 States. In each of the 5 years to 1950, an average of more than a million acres was brought under irrigation.

A great deal of new irrigation has been done since 1950, but the annual rate of increase appears to have been only about half the 1945 - 1950 rate. Expansion at the rate of a million acres a year could not be expected to continue indefinitely. During the Second World War, the Government and individuals had been kept from installing new irrigation facilities. With the release of material after the war, they were able to go ahead with their plans. High costs and lower prices for farm products caused some farmers to curtail the expansion of new irrigation. Another factor is that in most of the West easily developed water supplies are already utilized for irrigation. In places where water is still plentiful, topgrade land generally now can be reached only by costly pumping lifts or diversions.

Our estimate of irrigation acreage is based on sparse data for most States. Since the Census of 1950, which recorded 24,270,000 acres under irrigation in the West, the extent of irrigation has been surveyed only for a small part of the West.

That census, in April 1950, showed 1,138,000 acres irrigated in Utah in 1949. A sample census by the Bureau of the Census in October of 1953 in Utah indicated a total of 1,356,000, not including irrigated land not harvested and not pastured. About half of the increase, 90,000 acres, was irrigated pasture land.

The Nebraska State-Federal Division of Agriculture Statistics, which has made annual reports on irrigation in Nebraska, gave a total of 1,218,385 acres irrigated in 1953, an increase of more than 25 percent in 5 years. Land irrigated from wells gained 50 percent, to a total of 588,000 acres. By the end of 1953, Nebraska farmers were pumping 9,718 wells for irrigation. An estimated 1,000 additional wells were drilled in 1954.

The rapid development of well irrigation in Nebraska has been possible because of the comparative abundance of relatively good ground water in generally shallow water-bearing materials, which are available to recharge from precipitation and streamflow. The danger of an overdevelopment in Nebraska appears to exist only in some small areas where recharge is restricted; the ground-water reservoirs are said to be large enough to hold reserves for the drier periods when depletion is likely to be greater than recharge. One factor in the expansion of well irrigation in Nebraska has been the use of gas engines for pumping. This cheap fuel has made deep-well irrigation practical for farmers.

An interagency committee survey of irrigation in the basins of the Arkansas, White, and Red Rivers in 1954 showed 1,648,000 acres under irrigation in Oklahoma and the parts of Colorado, Kansas, New Mexico, and Texas that are in those basins. That was 500,000 acres more than in 1949. The largest part of the increase was in the High Plains of Texas. Oklahoma in 1954 had 108,000 irrigated acres — more than twice the acreage in 1949. Irrigation in the Arkansas River Valley of Kansas has increased markedly.

The Texas Agricultural Experiment Station reported 4,680,000 acres irrigated in 1954 — 1.5 million more than in 1949. Since 1944, Texas farmlands put under irrigation have expanded by 3.3 million acres — a growth that put Texas close to California in total amount of irrigation. The 1950 Census reported 6.5 million acres irrigated in California. Irrigated acreage in California in 1945 totaled nearly 5 million acres, compared to 1.3 million acres in Texas.

More than half of the irrigated land in Texas is in the High Plains, where irrigation depends entirely on ground water, and annual rainfall varies from about 6 to 40 inches. More than half of the irrigation in the High Plains has been developed since 1950, but irrigation activity appears to have about reached a peak, and there has been some speculation as to whether ground-water supplies could support the 1955 level of development on a stable basis.

The lower Rio Grande Valley, the second largest general area of irrigation in Texas, has the most concentrated irrigation in that State. It is densely settled and intensively farmed. The climate is semitropical, and mainly vegetable crops and citrus fruits are irrigated. Of 718,000 acres equipped for irrigation, 680,000 acres were irrigated in 1954. Most of the water comes from the Rio Grande River. The low flow of the river in 1952 and 1953 led to a rapid expansion in the use of ground water. In 1951, 23,000 acres were irrigated by ground water. Some 160,000 acres were equipped for ground-water irrigation in 1954.

Some of the water from the lower Rio Grande is pumped twice or more before it reaches the fields. The completion in October 1953 of the Falcon Dam by the International Boundary and Water Commission was expected to make water supplies for the Lower Valley more dependable.

The Bureau of Reclamation has contributed greatly to the development of irrigation in the West. In 1953, 69 Reclamation projects provided a full or partial supply of water to 7,147,000 acres. Between 1950 and 1954, Reclamation projects added 282,000 acres in new-land irrigation and provided supplemental water to an additional 995,000 acres, most of it in the Big Thompson project in Colorado. Projects under construction and authorized as of January 1, 1955 by the Congress included about 6.5 million acres of new irrigation in the West and provided for supplemental water for nearly 4 million acres.

Several programs of the Department of Agriculture have encouraged the growth of irrigation. Through the water facilities loan program, administered by the Farmers Home Administration, credit assistance is given to individual farmers or groups of farmers in the Western States for a number of irrigation purposes. The basic law was amended in August 1954 to extend the use of water-facility loans to all States. Between 1949 and 1955, 4,002 initial water-facility loans were made for irrigation works on 6,585 farms. More than 450,000 acres will be irrigated by the facilities built through those initial and subsequent loans to the same borrowers. A total of 1,247 loans were made for drilling wells to irrigate 138,000 acres. Sixty loans were made for small dams to store water to irrigate 41,000 acres. Loans to construct canals and ditches to irrigate 83,000 acres were made to 210 borrowers. Two hundred borrowers obtained loans to purchase stream pumps to irrigate 15,000 acres. More than 1,000 loans were made to level 52,000 acres.

Through the agricultural conservation program of the Commodity Stabilization Service, aid has been given since 1941 for a number of irrigation practices, chiefly in the Western States. Farmers have used the help to construct nearly 14 million rods of ditches, dikes, and laterals, to build 11,400 dams to store or divert irrigation water, and to level more than 6 million acres of land. Other aids have included lining 675,000 rods of distribution ditches, building more than 400,000 drops, chutes, weirs, checks, and similar structures, and installing 3.5 million rods of flumes, siphons, pipelines, and culverts.

Another program of the Department, administered by the Soil Conservation Service, provides engineering and technical guidance to farmers for land and water conservation practices.

Farmers in the West sought this assistance in connection with more than 5 million acres of land leveling in 1949 — 53, and got technical guidance in applying water on more than 12 million acres.

No one measure of importance of irrigation in the total agricultural picture in the West can be devised. Half the land of the West is used for grazing. Only a small part of it is irrigated. Of the Nation's total nonforested pasture and rangeland, 85 percent, or more than 700 million acres, is in the Western States. Something like two-fifths of the cattle and calves and one-half of the sheep and lambs are produced on western ranches and farms. Irrigation has a part in this livestock output mostly through the production of feed grain and roughage.

Without irrigation, several million acres of western croplands would produce little or nothing. In appraising the value of irrigation, however, one has to consider that much western irrigable land could produce grazing for livestock or dry-farming crops without irrigation. The contribution of irrigation ranges from an increase in production of 100 percent on some lands down to an increase of 15 or 20 percent in the more humid sections. A reasonable overall estimate seems to be that irrigation means a 25- to 50-percent increase in yields over that obtainable without irrigation.

Irrigation also has increased hay and feed crops and so has made possible a larger and a more stable livestock industry.

Irrigation has brought a new agriculture to the valleys of the West — a greater variety of crops, many specialty crops, diversity in farming enterprises, longer seasons, a larger measure of stability.

The part of irrigation in western crop production would seem relatively larger if it were not for the vast wheat-producing capacity of the region under dry-farming methods. The 17 Western States account for three-fourths of the Nation's wheat output. Nearly four-fifths of the aggregate of four food grains — wheat, rice, rye, and buckwheat — are produced in the Western States.

Of the acreage of wheat in the West, ranging from 50 million to 62 million acres in the 5 years to 1953, 2 million to 3.7 million acres have been irrigated. With the higher yields obtained, wheat produced with irrigation ranged from about 7 to 15 percent of the West's total production of wheat. Because wheat can be grown successfully by proper water conservation and dry-farming practices with annual rainfall as low as 12 to 15 inches, irrigation is unlikely to be extended greatly to wheat. Relatively higher potential gains through irrigation can be obtained on other crops.

Nearly all the rice, sugar beets, and citrus fruits in the West depend on irrigation. Two-fifths of the West's hay and forage production comes from irrigated land. Irrigation accounts for about one-tenth of the feed grains, two-fifths of the feed crops, a third of the cotton, and nearly four-fifths of all vegetables and fruits. While the crops that farmers irrigate shift from year to year in response to price fluctuations and other factors, the general tendency in recent years has been to irrigate the crops producing the highest values per acre.

About a fifth of the Nation's cotton in 1939 came from irrigated acres in the cotton-producing States of the West — Oklahoma, Texas, New Mexico, Arizona, and California. In 1954, the five States produced half our total cotton crop. One-third of the cotton of the West was grown by irrigation in 1949. By 1950, half of the cotton of the West came from irrigated land — by 1953, more than three-fifths.

The one-eighth of the Nation's crops that comes from irrigated land requires the use of only one-sixteenth of the Nation's harvested cropland. One acre of irrigated land thus has twice the capacity of nonirrigated land on the average. But in the Western States, 12 percent of the harvested cropland with irrigation produces 35 percent of the total crops other than pasture and forestry. Thus, in the West, an acre of irrigated cropland on the average approaches the equivalent of 3 acres of dry-farmed land.

The extent of irrigation in the West varies with the amount of rainfall and the type of farming. In the three Pacific Coast States, 70 percent of the crops, as measured by value, is grown under irrigation. In California about 85 percent of all crops is irrigated, in Oregon about 35 percent, and in Washington about 45 percent. In the eight Mountain States, about 60 percent of the total crop production is from irrigated land and in Arizona and Nevada nearly all crops are irrigated. In Utah and Wyoming, irrigation ranges between 75 and 85 percent of the total. In the North Dakota-Texas tier of States, about 5 percent of the crop production comes from irrigated land. In Texas roughly 15 percent of all crops comes from irrigated acres. In Nebraska better than 10 percent of crops are now produced under irrigation.

A continued expansion of irrigation may be expected in the West, although at a slower rate than in 1945–1954. Much additional feasible development of surface water for irrigation will be carried out. Individual farmers will continue to expand the use of ground water for irrigation. Competition for unutilized water supplies, however, will grow keener and in general the cost of bringing in new land is likely to rise.

The surveys of the Arkansas-White-Red River Basins Inter-Agency Committee indicate an ultimate total potential of 3,040,000 acres for the part of the Basin that is in the Western States. The realization of this potential would put an additional 1,400,000 acres under irrigation. A need for providing supplemental water supplies to 525,000 acres irrigated in 1954 is also shown by the Committee report. The Committee pointed out that this indicated physical potential would require the maximum practicable utilization of available water supplies within the limits of available lands. Many possible projects are included that would not meet currently acceptable standards of economic feasibility.

The Bureau of Reclamation estimated that water supplies in the West were sufficient to irrigate a total of 42,243,000 crop acres. That would mean the irrigation of 6 out of every 100 acres of land in farms in the West. On the basis of this projection and my 1953 estimate of the extent of irrigation, there remains roughly 15 million acres of possible further development. The Bureau of Reclamation estimated that about 7.5 million irrigated acres do not get a full season's supply of water.

In the Missouri Basin, data available in June 1952 show a total area of 5.5 million acres developed for irrigation. An additional area of 6 million acres is physically susceptible of future development with a full water supply. The Missouri Basin Project is expected to bring in about 500,000 acres of new land and provide supplemental water to about the same acreage before 1962. In the Columbia River Basin, the area developed for irrigation is around 4,400,000 acres, and ultimate development could exceed 8 million acres. In the Central Valley of California, 5,600,000 acres are irrigated, with future prospects of an added 3,400,000 acres.

The Bureau of Reclamation in 1954 set forth a 7-year schedule of new development to supply a full water supply to 1 million acres and a supplemental supply to about 1.5 million acres. The fulfillment of the projected development would add 144,558 acres of new irrigation and supply additional needed water to 210,150 acres each year through 1960.

It should be pointed out that these Bureau of Reclamation projections of potentials are based primarily on physical — not economic — factors, principally on the factors of further conservation and storage of runoff. They consider that with present technical knowledge and facilities about a third of the water runoff can be put to use. Only about one-fifth of the average annual stream runoff of Western States is now being utilized. Further utilization of ground water for irrigation was not taken into account in the projections.

Present knowledge of supplies of ground water and recharge rates is insufficient for estimating the practical limits of well irrigation. Overexpansion of ground water may very well occur in many areas before the safe withdrawal rate is known. Overdraft by pumped irrigation wells may have occurred in some localities. Water-level measurements in observation wells in a six-county area of the High Plains of Texas show declines ranging up to 12 feet for 1 year, January 1953 to January 1954. Water authorities in the area say that the water table is dropping and that the economically recoverable water can be exhausted. But for the West as a whole, the full potential of underground water use has not been reached.

As greater reliance is placed on the use of the underground water storage, care must be taken to avoid depletion of these supplies beyond the average annual natural recharge. The possibility of the adoption of measures to speed up the recharge of underground water by various conservation practices should be explored thoroughly. Through research work now underway we may find practical means of adding water to underground reservoirs.

The future sound development of further irrigation in the West will require not only the harnessing of new water supplies but the better management of existing water supplies. The West will need to make more efficient use of its available water. Distribution losses in irrigation water supplies can and undoubtedly will be reduced.

Elco L. Greenshields *is in charge of water utilization research work in the Production Economics Research Branch, Agricultural Research Service. He joined the Department of Agriculture in 1934. He has two degrees from Oklahoma Agricultural and Mechanical College. Recent assignments include work with the Departmental Task Force on Water Policy and Consultant to the Staff of the Cabinet Committee on Water Resources Policy.*

Dryland Farming

From: F. L. Duley and J. J. Coyle, "Farming Where Rainfall Is 8–20 Inches a Year," U.S. Department of Agriculture, *Yearbook*, 1955 (Washington, 1955), pp. 407–15.

Dryland farming no longer means simply farming in a region of low rainfall. Rather, it has come to refer to a fairly well established system of managing crops and soils that is adapted to semiarid or dry climates.

Such a climate exists in various parts of the world, including parts of all the Western States, notably the Great Plains, the Great Basin, the Pacific Northwest, and the Central Valley in California.

The total precipitation in the dry-farming areas generally is low, about 20 inches down to 8 inches annually.

Scant rainfall, though, is only one aspect. The average temperature in the Northern States is much lower than in the Southwestern States. A given amount of precipitation therefore is much more effective in the North than in the South. The distribution of the precipitation through the year also is important. The limited precipitation in parts of the Pacific Northwest comes mainly in winter, when evaporation is low. So the rain penetrates deeper into the soil and subsoil than does the much higher rainfall of the Central Plains, where the moisture comes chiefly in summer. A rain of one-half inch on a hot, dry day may lose so much of the water by evaporation that only a small fraction is available to the plant. During cool weather a rain of one-half inch may penetrate the soil to the extent that much of it may be used eventually by a crop.

Wind erosion of the soil is common in most dry-farming regions, particularly in sandy areas. In many places an occasional torrential rain or a sudden heavy shower may cause considerable erosion.

Great progress has been made toward producing a great share of the Nation's food in the West, a part of which the early explorers called the Great American Desert. Livestock and small grains are the food products that can be grown to best advantage. Research has had a great effect on the progress of all limited-rainfall regions. The mechanization of farm operations has altered labor requirements and has changed the cost of production in regions where an extensive agriculture is practiced.

As the Great Plains were settled, largely during the last quarter of the 19th century, farmers drove their covered wagons westward from the humid areas of the Eastern States to those low-rainfall regions. They brought with them the methods of a humid agriculture. They also brought the seed for crops that had been found suitable for humid conditions. They soon learned that the types and varieties of crops they had used back east would not withstand the climate of the Plains: Corn was not successful in most years. The soft wheats of the East would not produce satisfactory yields in the Plains.

New methods were developed only with the coming of certain Europeans, like the German-Russians, who settled in central and western Kansas. They brought from the regions around the Black Sea varieties of hard red winter wheats that had been grown under conditions like those of the Great Plains. Since then great improvement has been made in varieties and in the methods of managing soils and crops, and greater agricultural stability has come to all dry-farming localities.

The improvement in methods came from two main directions: The hard-earned experience of farmers in the new and demanding environment and the work of experiment stations.

The experiment stations for studying dryland problems were authorized by the Congress in 1905. Within the next decade about 25 stations were established in the dry-farming areas.

Some stations gave attention to livestock. Some studied horticulture, landscape gardening, and forestry so as to improve living conditions on the Plains. But their work was devoted mainly to problems of soils and crops — testing and comparing methods of production, conserving soil moisture, and, much later, conserving the soil itself.

Failure to recognize the capability of the land brought about a great number of failures in the dryland areas.

Many of the critical problems there arose because of plowing up grassland that is unsuited for cropping in places of limited rainfall. Particularly in the southern part are the soils hazardous — very sandy or shallow. An estimated 7 to 8 million acres of that kind were cultivated in the Southern Great Plains in 1954. Even moderately sandy and moderately deep soils in the southern dryland regions are hard to protect against wind damage if they are placed under cultivation. It is advisable to cultivate them only occasionally. Grass should cover the land at least half the time.

Steepness of slope adds to the complexity of the erosion problem. Cultivated lands on 2-percent to 5-percent slopes in the 17-inch rainfall belt of the Southern Plains tend to be damaged 2½ times as fast as similar land that is nearly level. When rain totals 20 inches, the rate of erosion becomes about 16 times faster.

The slope of a piece of land should therefore be given full consideration in deciding whether it is suitable for longtime cultivation.

Livestock men were the first settlers in the Plains and other dryland areas of the United States. Up to that time the Indians had obtained much of their food from the great herds of buffalo. Cattle replaced the buffalo, and the cattlemen virtually took over the Plains as a grazing region.

As settlements increased and towns grew, the demand for farmland increased. The cattlemen were thus gradually pushed back until all the land that could be plowed easily had been broken. The open range disappeared and barbed wire enclosed the plowed fields and pastures. Mostly only rough land was left for grazing, which farmers used for small herds, which got some feed from crops grown on the plowed land.

This livestock system has come to be one of the stabilizing types of dryland farming. The man who lives on the land and farms on a year-round basis usually gets along better and is more sure of a good living if he has some livestock.

He can then work out his cropping system so as to make use of land for grazing and also produce grain and rough feed for winter. His main precaution is to adjust the number of livestock to the feed and pasture he will probably have in unfavorable years. He then will be able to build up some reserve supply of feed for the poor years, or he may have some for sale in good years.

The crops grown for feeding vary in different sections of the dry-farming area. Grain sorghums, sudan grass, or some type of sorghum for hay may be used in the southern part of the Plains to supplement native pasture. Some legumes, like cowpeas for feed, and pinto beans may be grown if climate is favorable. In many places wheat may be used for pasture at certain times if overgrazing and pasturing too late are avoided.

In the central and northern parts, some other crops may be used to supplement the pasture. Some corn may be produced, but sorhums are less well adapted than farther south. Barley and oats also are feed crops. Rye may be used for pasture and in some localities vetch may be seeded with it.

Throughout the dryland country, cattle seem to be the type of livestock best adapted to the climate and the type of feed available. They make good use of native grasses and can be wintered on rough feed and native grass hay.

In extensive areas in many parts of the Plains cattle raising is still the main industry. Rangelands may be concentrated in a large block of country with only limited areas of farmland. What farmland there is may be mostly irrigated. Examples of these extensive range areas are in the Sandhills of Nebraska and the short-grass county in eastern Wyoming, Montana, and several other Western States.

In some areas sheep have been grazed in mountains and foothills. Texas, Wyoming, Montana, California, New Mexico, Utah, and Idaho have produced thousands of sheep as range animals. It is a type of livestock production for low-rainfall regions, but is not classed as typical dryland farming, since in these areas it is chiefly a range type of livestock production and involves a minimum of crop production to support it.

Soil erosion by wind and water has come to be a big problem in nearly all dry-farming areas. Special precautions need to be taken against erosion wherever the sod has been broken and cultivated crops grown. On steep slopes an occasional heavy shower or the water from melting snow may cause severe erosion if the land is in a condition to wash.

On level land, as well as on rolling or hilly land, wind erosion does extensive damage to crops and soils. In practically all dry-farming regions the control of wind erosion is one of the most important points in any system of farming. Wind erosion may not be severe every year, but it is always a threat and can occur almost any year if the principles of control have been neglected.

Sandy soils are more subject to wind erosion, and on them it is harder to control. Fine-textured soils may also suffer from wind erosion, and during long droughts they may suffer from soil drifting.

Some effective yet simple methods have been developed to hold down wind erosion. Some of the more important principles of control are:

Keep the soil covered with a growing crop as much of the time as possible.

When land is not in a growing crop, keep the residue from the previous crop on it by the use of stubble mulch, in which the land is tilled with an implement that pulverizes the soil without inverting it or buying the residue.

Use strip cropping — alternate strips of growing crop and stubble or stubble-mulch fallow.

Make use of cloddy fallow.

Use tree shelterbelts or strips of tall growing crops to protect adjoining land.

Use emergency methods of tillage when soil starts to drift.

The equipment needed for use against wind erosion is discussed under methods of preparing the seedbed for wheat.

Steps to avoid wind erosion should be taken at least a year before the time that erosion is most likely to occur. If an attempt is made to control the erosion by shelterbelts, the trees may have to be planted several years before they can be expected to have much effect.

Highly effective in many areas is the stubble-mulch method. It involves the use of stubble, straw, stalks, or other form of residue to reduce the velocity of the wind at ground level and thus reduce its ability to move soil. A common form of stubble mulch is wheat stubble and straw left after the combine. It must be left on the surface during the preparation of the seedbed for the next crop. Row crops that leave a dense stubble may also offer effective protection.

Sudan or sorghum, even though much of the plant is removed for hay or feed, may still leave a dense stubble in the row. If it is cut 6 to 12 inches high, depending on the density, the field may be reasonably well protected. Such stubble should be left upright until the next crop is planted, if possible. Sometimes it is feasible to drill small grain or grass mixtures in the stubble without previous cultivation if there are no weeds. If that can be done, the old stubble may afford effective protection against wind erosion while the new grass crop is getting started. Cornstalks or sparse stubble usually do not give good protection.

A third method, that of using strip crops to control wind erosion, has been widely used in some sections. Alternating strips of wheat and fallow may be 5 to 10 rods wide or even wider. Sometimes they are at right angles to the most destructive winds. Sometimes the strips are on the contour to get the greatest protection against runoff and erosion during a heavy rain. If the fallow strip is handled by the stubble-mulch method, almost complete protection against wind erosion usually can be achieved.

In this system one strip would be in growing wheat, which was seeded on mulched land for protection against soil blowing. The adjoining strips would be receiving the fallow treatment, in which the land is subtilled with equipment that leaves the residue on the surface. After the wheat is harvested, the stubble and straw protect that strip, and the fallowed strip is seeded to wheat. All the land is thus protected at all times.

Cloddy fallow may be used with any type of fallowing; if the surface is left largely covered with clods that cannot be moved by the wind they will protect the fine material from blowing. Fine-textured soils form rather stable clods that protect the soil. Sandy soils do not form stable clods; even if the soil is worked when moist, the clods weather down quickly. The effectiveness of the method therefore depends on the kind of soil.

The use of tree shelterbelts received a great stimulus during the decade 1933–1942. Millions of trees were planted in the Great Plains with the idea that they would greatly affect wind movements and do much toward controlling wind erosion. Narrow belts have been placed at intervals of 20 to 40 rods in some sandy areas.

After the trees reach considerable height under such conditions, they are quite effective in reducing wind damage to the soil or crops.

The use of shelterbelts seems to have about reached its peak, for several reasons: They take considerable space away from the cultivated acreage on the farm; their esthetic value is great, but their economic value may be questionable; we have agronomic methods for reducing wind erosion.

The use of emergency tillage methods is usually brought into use when more effective methods have been neglected. If a cultivated field has no growing crop or residue on it, wind erosion may start. Roughening the surface or a part of it may then stop soil movement over the entire area. Any shovel-type tillage implement, like a plow, lister, or shovel cultivator, will throw up clods or chunks of soil, which will tend to stop soil movement. One or two lister furrows spaced 2 or 3 rods apart across the field may hold the soil or a wheat field from drifting for a while.

It may be necessary to run more furrows between the first ones if drifting starts again. Disk tools may be used to stop wind erosion on tilled land temporarily, but since disk implements tend to pulverize the soil and do not throw up clods, they are less effective than shovel-type tools.

If land is kept covered with stubble mulch, the emergency methods will seldom be needed. Emergency methods are sometimes necessary on a large scale if widespread drought has reduced the amount of mulch protection that can be provided. Some States have laws requiring farmers to use emergency methods when needed.

Water erosion is a more serious problem in the dryland farming area than is generally thought. In the eastern part, a rainfall intensity of 3 inches an hour for 30 minutes can be expected to occur about once in 5 years. The comparable figure farther west is about 1 inch. Only permeable soils or soils protected with residue can absorb rains of that intensity.

The resulting runoff creates a water erosion problem on the more sloping land and on nearly level land if the slopes are long, because the water accumulates on the lower part of the slopes. A stubble mulch effectively controls water erosion, as well as wind erosion. The litter maintained on or in the surface breaks the force of the falling raindrop, reduces the speed with which water moves across the land, and maintains a favorable condition for intake of water at the soil surface. If slopes are so long or steep that residues will not control erosion, mechanical measures, such as terraces and contouring, are needed.

Terraces generally are considered applicable on slopes steeper than about 1 percent, on which even small concentrations of flowing water attain erosive velocities. Terraces intercept the runoff before it reaches damaging proportions.

On long slopes of less than 1 percent, one or more diversions may be needed to reduce the length to one on which erosion can be controlled by vegetative measures.

The diversions may be several hundred feet apart. Even on the gentle slopes some farmers prefer a regular terrace system with closer spacing because they help conserve water. Planting and cultivating row crops on the contour has noticeable benefits in some years and is especially important on terraced land. Contour drilling of wheat is especially beneficial if deep-furrow drills are used.

The term "crop rotation" is less aptly applied in dry-farming areas than elsewhere: There are fewer crops from which to choose and few legumes that can be generally used to maintain the nitrogen supply in the soil. It is therefore not so important that any particular sequence of crops be followed. One of the main considerations is to arrange the sequence with a view to the possibility of a moisture supply for the oncoming crop. For example, corn (in areas where it is adapted) usually leaves the soil with a better supply of moisture than does small grain. Wheat usually exhausts the available soil moisture almost entirely by harvest-time. Consequently some time should elapse before another crop is seeded. Early preparation of the seedbed after wheat is essential if another seeding of wheat is to follow.

Wheat may often be seeded on cornland from which the crop is removed for fodder or silage. Or it may be drilled between wide-spaced corn rows.

Another reason for not using the term "rotation" so much is the possibility of crop failure. Because of the wide fluctuations in annual rainfall, nearly all dryland areas experience some crop failures or near failures, which may break the sequence of a rotation. Then the farmer has to put in the crop that has the best chance for success under the conditions of soil moisture and weather at the time.

Some examples of types of cropping systems that might be adapted in different parts of the dryland farming areas of the United States are: Corn, wheat, wheat; corn, wheat, fallow, wheat; corn in wide rows, wheat, wheat on early worked land; wheat, fallow; wheat, sorghum, fallow; corn removed for silage, wheat; corn, barley, fallow, wheat; wheat, peas for canning; wheat, grass several years, sorghum, small grain; kafir, cowpeas, milo (Southern Plains).

The type of cropping system used on a given farm has evolved on the basis of the type of farming a man wanted to carry out. Several rather distinct types of dryland farms exist.

The first is the general farm that has considerable livestock. This type usually occurs in localities in which a good supply of range or pastureland is available to supply summer grazing. Enough grain and roughage should be produced to carry the livestock through the winter. Practically all crops produced are fed on the farm. Nearly all the income is obtained from the sale of livestock and livestock products. Some livestock and a limited acreage for feed crops may mean a more stable system and a more steady income than a one-crop wheat system. In many areas the total longtime income may be higher with a wheat system, but that, it must be admitted, will mean some total failures.

The farmer must decide whether he can stand the financial strain in order to realize more income in the long run.

Another type of mixed farming is the cash-grain farm, in which the returns are from the sale of grain, seed, or hay.

The wheat farm derives practically all its income from the sale of wheat. The farmer lives on the land and devotes his time chiefly to this one enterprise.

The "suitcase" farmer is the absentee wheat grower. He may have a profession or business in a city and occasionally visit the farm or employ someone to do the farm work. He does not become part of the farm community. He may not see the wind erosion in the spring; maybe he does nothing to help control erosion during that season.

Some farmers try to adjust their plantings on the basis of the moisture present in the soil at seeding time. The practice returns a higher total income over a period, although there may be considerable variability from year to year.

Suppose a man started out on the basis of a wheat-fallow system. If good rains should follow harvest, he might get moisture into the soil to a depth of 2 feet or more. Then he might decide not to fallow the land the following year but to put it back to wheat for another year. Likewise, if he held wheatland over with the idea of fallowing for another wheat crop, but found the soil well filled with moisture by spring, he would have the choice of several crops. He could hold it over for wheat, but would produce no crop that year. Instead he might plant the land to corn, sorghum, potatoes, or some other crop and thus make use of the soil moisture as soon as possible after it had been stored.

This idea of farming according to the moisture supply offers a basic principle for the dryland farmer. If he would plant a crop in season every time he has an adequate supply of soil moisture and leave the seed in the bag when he does not have the moisture, he would put his farming on a more realistic basis. He would be taking less of a chance with the possibility of rain after the crop is planted. If the idea were adopted, a tile spade or a soil auger should become standard equipment on a dryland farm. Either of those tools permits a farmer to determine quickly the depth to which the moisture has been stored in the soil.

Available soil moisture is one of the main concerns in dryland farming. The rainfall during the time a crop is on the land seldom is enough to produce a good crop. It is necessary therefore to have some reserve moisture stored in the soil before the crop is planted.

Research workers of the Kansas Agricultural Experiment Station at Hays found that when wheat was seeded in dry soil with no available moisture stored in the subsoil the average yield of wheat was 4.9 bushels an acre; when the soil was wet 1 foot deep at seeding time, 8.7 bushels; wet 2 feet deep, 15.2 bushels; and when wet 3 feet deep or more, 26.5 bushels an acre. The uneven distribution of rainfall and the frequent occurrence of extended dry periods has led to the practice of fallowing. This means keeping the land free of a crop or weeds for a period of time so that moisture and nitrates may be accumulated in the soil for use by the next crop.

A year of wheat followed by a year of fallow has come to be a common practice in the wheat territory. A wheat crop is harvested in the central Great Plains in July. Unless the field becomes weedy the land is allowed to lie without treatment until the following spring, when tillage operations for fallow begin. The land to be fallowed would be one-wayed or plowed about the first of May or about the time weeds or volunteer wheat start. The land is then worked often enough to keep down weeds. Many men work the land oftener than necessary to keep down weeds, but do it to break the crust on the surface of plowed land, to reduce runoff during the next rain, and to avoid wind erosion on smooth, crusted soil.

Work at numerous dryland experiment stations has shown that deep working of the soil has not perceptibly mitigated the effect of drought. It has not increased yields of crops enough to be profitable, no matter what method has been used to deepen the cultivated layer of soil. Despite the proof furnished by 60 years of experiments, which have failed to show any consistent profit from deep tillage or tilling into the subsoil, interest in the practice waxes and wanes periodically. Perhaps deeper tillage may be of some value in connection with the deeper placement of fertilizers, but that point has had little study in regions of limited rainfall.

Fertilizers have been used very little in most of our dry-farming areas, as those soils are reasonably well supplied with the mineral elements plants need. In some places the addition of phosphorus has given favorable results. Enough nitrogen usually is present to allow crops to make use of the available moisture — especially if a crop follows fallow.

Fallowing not only allows the soil to store water, but it accumulates nitrates at the same time. The use of nitrogen fertilizer on fallowed land has given little return in most places and usually has been considered impractical. On some soils, particularly the sandier types, good results from nitrogen fertilizers have been obtained, even on fallowed land. Increases in yield of grain, straw, or protein content have been obtained under many conditions.

As to the failure: As the fertility of dryland soils is gradually reduced through cropping, greater returns from the use of fertilizers can be expected. After a half century of farming, nitrogen fertilizers may begin to show greater returns on many dryland soils. If one crop follows another without an intervening fallow, added nitrogen in the form of fertilizer may offset somewhat the effect of no fallow, especially if the moisture is reasonably adequate. Chemical analyses of soils in various parts of the dryland region have shown that they have lost 25 to 40 percent of their total nitrogen since the land was put under cultivation.

Since many of the soils have been farmed for only 30 to 50 years, the loss can be considered serious. The use of nitrogen fertilizer would appear to be only a matter of time. The need for phosphorus or other mineral elements will be ascertained for various localities as the land continues to be farmed.

The use of barnyard manure has given only slight returns. Likewise green manure has not been very effective in improving the growth of the following crop. The benefits from these treatments may increase after the land has been farmed for a longer time, and further experiments determine the most effective methods of using them.

Some farmers burn straw and stubble before preparing the seedbed for the next crop. Often they have found that the yields were as high as from land where the straw was not burned. Since tillage was easier after burning, they have asked whether the practice is sound. The explanation of the good yields following the burning of stubble involves several points. In the first place, burning all the trash on the field makes possible a good, smooth job of plowing.

The rate of nitrate accumulation may be increased for a time after the straw is burned. The soil micro-organisms which cause straw to decay use some nitrate present in the soil for their own growth; consequently in the burned area this reaction does not take place and more nitrate may be stored for the immediate use of the wheat crop. If the straw is burned every year for a few years, however, the advantage in improved yields at the start gradually disappears. The land to which straw was returned may then give the higher yields.

The great advantages in returning straw, instead of burning it, is that the straw increases the capacity of the soil to absorb water and protects it against wind erosion. The nitrogen returned with straw amounts to about 10 pounds a ton of straw.

The equipment for dryland farming used by the early settlers was what they took along with them. The tough grass sod was first broken with a sod plow, or prairie breaker, which had a long moldboard, or steel bar, for inverting the furrow slice.

In later years came the stubble plow, which had a much shorter moldboard. It turned the furrow slice and did much pulverizing of the soil.

Much of the early research on the dryland experimental farms was concerned with the time and depth of moldboard plowing for various crops. Plowing was a good way to start preparation of a seed bed, but later people realized that it had some shortcomings. It permitted much erosion during heavy rains and exposed the soil to severe wind erosion.

Other types of tillage tools have been introduced since. One of the most widely used is the one-way diskplow. It stirs the soil, gives a minimum of trouble in operation, and land can be covered rapidly with it. The principal objections are that, being a disk implement, it tends to pulverize the soil too finely and tends to bury the crop residue too completely. It may be used for the first operation to kill weeds and volunteer plants, but if used a second time or more it may bury most of the residue and lead to wind erosion.

A more appropriate implement for the second and later operations is the subtiller, usually a V-sweep-type machine that has come into use for stubble-mulch farming. By the careful use of subtillers, enough residue may be preserved from one crop to hold the soil until the next crop is started to control wind and water erosion. With this stubble-mulch system, of course, other useful methods should be used — practical cropping systems, stripcropping, cloddy fallow, and sometimes terracing.

The use of power machinery has helped the dryland farmer immeasurably. Tractors and large equipment enable him to do his tillage, seeding, and harvesting operations in less time and at the most advantageous time. Timely operations may be of importance not only for the crop but also in the control of insects and diseases.

Reseeding dry-farming land to grass has been suggested as a way to treat the drylands that are not well adapted to cultivation.

A considerable amount of reseeding is done by farmers who need additional pastureland to support their livestock program. But many farmers feel that they will realize a higher return from the land if it is in cultivated crops. Another reason why reseeding to grass is not done more widely is that it is hard to establish grass on cultivated land. Very dry weather may follow seeding, so that germination will be low and the chance for survival of the seedlings greatly reduced. Only about one-third as much land is seeded to grass in the 17 Western States as is seeded in the rest of the country.

The types of grass used in different parts of the dry-farming area vary with climatic conditions. The methods of seeding also vary widely. In order to conserve moisture and obtain protection against soil blowing, much of the grass seeding is being done through some sort of residue cover. In the Northern Plains it is common practice to drill grass seed into wheat stubble in late fall with no previous seedbed preparation. The seed is then in the ground ready to germinate and start growth with the first warm days of spring, when the soil very likely is moist enough.

In the Southern Plains some tillage of the seedbed may be given, but the seeding is best done with drills that have depth gages, so the seed will be planted deep enough to get moisture but not so deep that the seedlings cannot come through to produce a good stand. Seeding with some protective residue cover aids in holding moisture for germination and prevents the young plants from being blown out or from being cut off by blowing soil or sand particles.

The seeding program in dryland areas depends on a number of circumstances. The wheat acreage allotments may induce many men to put idle acres to grass. A change in the relative demand for wheat and cattle also may affect it. Any general trend toward mixed farming would encourage the seeding of more land to grass. Eventually we may have a better adjustment of cultivated crops to those lands well suited to their use. The rough lands, or those for other reasons not so well suited to cultivation, may gradually be put to the grasses best adapted to the locality.

F. L. Duley is project supervisor of research for the Soil and Water Conservation Research Branch, Western Section, Department of Agriculture, in cooperation with the University of Nebraska. He obtained his college training at the University of Missouri and University of Wisconsin. At the Missouri Agricultural Experiment Station he collaborated in some of the first research conducted for determining the effect of cultivated crops on runoff and erosion.

J. J. Coyle is agricultural engineering specialist, Engineering Division, Soil Conservation Service, Washington, D. C. He was formerly Soil Conservation Service Regional Engineer, Western Gulf Region, Fort Worth, serving Oklahoma, Arkansas, Louisiana, and Texas.

The Matanuska Colony, 1935–1948

From Hugh A. Johnson and Keith L. Stanton, *Matanuska Valley Memoir*, Alaska Agricultural Experiment Station, Bulletin 18, July, 1955, pp. 48–63, 89–94.

Low-hanging leaden skies pressed about the colonist-loaded *St. Mihiel* as it steamed slowly up Resurrection Bay and docked at Seward. The first contingent of Matanuska Colonists from Minnesota set foot on Alaskan soil May 6, 1935. They were a weary lot. Tired anxious mothers, fretful children and worried fathers began facing realities of their Alaskan adventure.

For weeks they had been in the public eye. They had participated in parades, feted by dignitaries, met by bands, and even convoyed by battleships of the U.S. Navy. Now they were anchored in a small bay in remote Alaska. Cold winds whipped the icy rain across decks and against the portholes. Through the scud could be seen towering, snowcovered, mountain peaks.

A hearty welcome by Sewardites partially offset the knowledge that five children aboard had measles — and their future homes were not ready. The inexplicable wisdom of the planners had routed temporary tent housing, supplies and camp laborers to Alaska on the *North Star* to dock at approximately the same time as the *St. Mihiel* arrived with the Colonist families. The families stayed on the *St. Mihiel* another two days while the laborers proceeded to the Matanuska Valley and set up temporary camp.

Early on May 9, the Alaska Railroad backed a train to the dock and the families were on their way again. For a half day they were treated to some of the world's most beautiful scenery along the route between Seward and Anchorage. At Anchorage they received their last big public "feed" and welcome by a city. After the dinner they returned to the train for the last lap of their long journey. At Palmer they were assigned tents to await further developments.

Colonists from Wisconsin and Michigan arrived about two weeks later and were crowded into the temporary tents with them. Many disappointments, disillusionments, and discouragements were to follow before the hardy families became self-supporting. Many families failed. A few stayed, made good and became leaders in the brave new experiment.

Reams of words have been written about the Matanuska Colony and about the Colonists. Impressions vary from glowing to glowering — from claims of eminent success and golden opportunities realized to those of socialism and sedition — depending upon the writer, his "angle" and the persons providing his information. Kirk H. Stone probably has made the fairest, most realistic analysis of the Matanuska Colony during its early years (1935–48). He wrote in his summary:

> The Matanuska Colony was an experiment worked out in an emergency . . . (It) has been an effective and generally successful experiment to increase permanent population in the Territory. In 1934 the Valley was a partly broken and isolated wilderness . . . In 13 years the eastern half of the Valley has become a widely broken and accessible forested area. In addition, the Valley has a population of 2500–3000 people who are participating in a growing farming economy and who work at various non-agricultural occupations. These changes have been made in an area of diversity that borders the northern limits of the inhabitable Western world and they show that additional settlement is feasible there.
>
> It is the methods by which the changes were made that can be improved greatly. Weaknesses in the methods used in the Colony have been disclosed by geographical and financial analyses. In most cases, ineffective action had its origin in the speed required in the planning phase.

The Colony Concept

The concept of the Matanuska Colony came into being in 1934. In the fall of that year, President Franklin D. Roosevelt instructed the administrator of the FERA, Harry Hopkins, to add Alaska to the program of organizing Rural Rehabilitation Corporations in the United States. The Matanuska Valley was picked for the proposed colony. This choice was based on general data which indicated that The Valley had qualities that were favorable for farming and for trade with nearby Anchorage and the Alaska Railroad Belt. The Alaska Railroad had encouraged settlement and trade in The Valley between 1929 and 1933.

The Colony's first administrative agency was the California Emergency Relief Administration (CERA). It was necessary to have some agency control the initial funds granted for settlement before the ARRC was formed. The CERA was selected, it has been reported, because that agency was the only west-coast ERA not engaged in legal disputes early in 1935. The first grant of colonization funds was made to the CERA to expedite purchase of supplies, equipment, and food for the project. This purchasing function may have overloaded the CERA. At any rate, the result was confusion in the early administration of the Colony. Administrators in Palmer did not know what materials had been ordered or what might be expected to arrive at any time. Attempts to have duplicates of the purchase orders, invoices, or shipping lists sent to Palmer ahead of or with shipments were unsuccessful. This administrative arrangement was responsible for the uncoordinated and unexpected arrival of materials and food in Palmer — an ill-timing which was criticized long and loud by nearly every person in The Colony.

In addition to the CERA, the board incorporating the Alaska Rural Rehabilitation Corporation in Juneau and the FERA officials in Washington, D.C. participated in the overall administration of the Colony early in 1935. Each issued orders, occasionally contradictory, to the man in charge in Palmer; the result was an intolerable situation. Direction of the Colony was to be the function of the ARRC, better known as the Corporation. The ARRC was incorporated on April 12, 1935 under the Alaskan laws relating to charitable agencies. It was to be a non-profit corporation, given broad powers to operate anywhere in Alaska for no longer than fifty years. The Articles of Incorporation were drawn up from a standard form used for the incorporation of Rural Rehabilitation Corporation in the United States. The primary purpose for which the Corporation was formed is stated to be "To rehabilitate individuals and families as self-sustaining human beings by enabling them to secure subsistence and gainful employment from the soil, from coordinate and affiliated industries and enterprises or otherwise, in accordance with economic and social standards of good citizenship".

Eleven other objects and purposes in the Articles defined specific powers by which the corporation was to accomplish its primary objectives. Express provision was made that the statements shall not be considered to restrict the Corporation's power in any manner.

The Matanuska Colony was established for three purposes: (1) to take people off, or to keep them off, relief as a result of depression in the United States; (2) to demonstrate whether or not Alaska provided a settlement frontier that could absorb excess population; and (3) to add greater support of the Alaskan economy by production of more locally produced food which would lessen dependence on costly and vulnerable waterborne transportation. It was a spur of the moment idea, carried out in the urgency of the times. Its implementation was hampered by the serious absence of all but the most rudimentary knowledge of natural conditions in the settlement area. Advice of administrators on the job often was ignored by the Washington administrators planning and expediting the program.

The Land

It is not generally known that homesteaders had owned most of the better lands in the Matanuska Valley for 20 years before the Colony was founded. Persons familiar with the Valley during that period reported that 117 families were living here in 1934. Their holdings amounted to 23,000 acres of which about 1,000 had been cleared and cropped. Most of this cleared land lay west of the Seward Meridian, but some of it lay in or adjoining the present site of Palmer.

The ARRC optioned more than 7,500 acres during the spring of 1935. Attempts were made to buy all homesteaded lands in the withdrawn area for Colony purposes. Tracts having land already cleared were highly desirable. But some homesteaders were unwilling to sell for the prices offered. Actually, outside the land along Palmer siding, utilized for the original camp and later for the community center, only about 175 acres of cropland were available to the colonists. (It was really the crop year of 1937 before any appreciable acreage was to be available for cropping.)

Between 1935 and 1938 the Corporation bought 7,780 acres from private owners for $48,814. Prices ranged from a minimum of $1.24 for unimproved tracts to a maximum of $36.42 per acre where cleared fields and buildings were involved.

Land even was purchased from the Federal government. A deed and Patent No. 1120981 were issued on May 27, 1946 for 5,083 acres. This land cost the Corporation $12,248 or a range of $1.25 to $4.00 per acre. Purchase was made to acquire title to tracts allotted colonists from government-owned land under Executive Order 7416.

The Corporation received no free land. Privately owned lands (7,940 acres) and public domain (5,083 acres) totalling 13,023 acres cost $67,063 or about $5.15 per acre.

Settler Selection

About 75 percent of the selected colonists were disadvantaged families from the Cutover Region of the Lake States. Not all settlers for the project were on relief, although the relief load was extremely high in this region during the depression. The planners theorized that the climate and farming conditions of this area were not too different from those of the Matanuska Valley. Thus the relief load could be reduced in the States by transferring families to a similar area in Alaska.

The remaining 25 percent of the colonists came from areas adjoining the Cutover section of Minnesota, Wisconsin and Michigan. One family from Oklahoma was the only exception in the first selection.

Everyone agreed that the Matanuska Colony was to be an agricultural community. Plans called for an agriculturalist to select suitable families for the experiment. Don L. Irwin, the Agronomist in charge of the Matanuska Experimental Farm for the University of Alaska, was selected for the job and during the winter of 1934–35 he began setting up standards he would use. This process was too slow for the program and eventually qualifications for settlers were established in Washington, D.C. during March, 1935. Orders were cut in Washington directing relief and social workers in the county offices to recruit families for Alaska. Colonist selection was made during the following five or six weeks. This time-urgency coupled with the relief aspects of the program and the lack of knowledge concerning Alaskan conditions caused some of the poor selections. A list of specifications was supplied to case workers, but it was so general that much leeway remained with the selectors. Possibly the greatest problem lay in finding families suitable to conditions neither they nor the social worker knew much about. A poor job of screening applicants during the initial stages of the program caused many later difficulties.

Between March and June 1935, 202 families including 903 persons were selected, processed, and shipped on their way. Bands played, speeches were made, parades were held. Some colonists gained the impression that their worries were all over. They learned differently during the weeks and months ahead.

Heads of families were supposed to have had farm experience. Other trades and crafts were to be considered in the selections, but these were extra dividends. When the smoke had cleared and the selections were analyzed, 10 percent of the original colonists had no farming experience; 26 percent had none or less than 6 years and about 40 percent had none or less than 10 years of life on a farm. Some of them had not had farming experience for 10 years or more prior to 1935.

Michigan selectors made the poorest choices with respect to farming experience. Minnesota selectors made the best. Minnesota had the highest and Michigan the lowest percentage of original colonists still living in The Valley after 15 years of the program.

Fitness for colonization was difficult to judge. Because the selection was hurried the results varied from good to bad. The first list of possible colonists was made from county relief rolls but the final selections included some families who were not receiving financial aid from the government. Probably less than 10 families had assets worth $800–1,000 more than their debts. Every family was considered by a case worker with respect to emotional, mental, educational, economic, and physical backgrounds. In Minnesota, at least, families were rejected for: fear of severance of family ties, chronic illness, evidence of emotional instability, the husband and wife having less than eighth-grade educations, signs of being "drifters" or "excitement eaters," being poor economic managers, and for lacking a strong desire to resettle in Alaska. Each family had to pass medical tests. However, mistakes were made. A man with a wooden leg was approved because he had a son who could help farm, three tubercular men were accepted, and some persons lacking adaptability or with chronic illnesses were selected. In general, it appears that the measurement of the fitness of the colonists was weak.

Home Is a Castle

The Colonists lived in tents at Palmer siding for about two months after arrival in the Valley. By late July 1935 most families had been moved to outlying tent camps in the general location of their allotted settlement tracts. Some of them lived in these camps until their homes were available for occupancy before the coldest part of the winter. The interiors of many homes were not completed until mid-summmer of 1936.

Colonists were allowed to chose their homes from a selection of five sketched out tentative sets of plans drafted in Washington, D.C. These sketches were adopted without further study. These "suggested" plans were a source of embarassment to the architect and an irritant to the Colonists who were not allowed to combine desirable features of two or more designs. They could not have full basements or a full foundation on the ground. Although many colonists were experienced carpenters, masons, plumbers or other artisans, they could not work on their homes. Transient relief workers were brought in from California to do that work.

Construction of the barns lagged. Only one plan was available. Each was 32 feet square, 32 feet high and had a "hip" roof. The walls were logs to 10 feet above the ground and then siding to the roof. All were built on small pilings of native spruce which soon rotted away. The colonists complained from the start that the barns were too small, inefficiently partitioned, drafty and poorly built. The criticisms were apparently justified. Dairymen going into Grade A production had to spend large sums to make their barns usable. Some families sold their outbuildings. Many others have abandoned their barns and have allowed them to rot away — a complete loss and temporary monuments to regimentation.

Well drilling lagged also. Reasons for this lay in the emphasis placed on building the Community Center in 1935 and 1936 and also in the difficulty of finding water.

The entire building program was poorly planned and poorly executed. Costs mounted to over double the original estimates. Inefficiency, waste and discouragement were common and served to discourage many families. By July 1936, 67 familes of the original colonists had been sent back to the States soured on Alaska and on the Project.

Settlement Experience

Conditions of colonization were set forth in the *Settlement Agreement* between the Colonist and the Corporation. The agreement provided free transportation to Alaska for the family, food and clothing during the orientation period, at least 40 acres with a set of farm buildings, and funds for further improvements. Interest rates were not to be over three percent and interest payments would begin in September 1938 — three years after settlement. Payment of installments on the principal real estate loan would start in September 1940.

Some of the colonists began planning to leave immediately upon their arrival in the Valley. Confusion reigned. By July 1935, after less than two months of living in The Colony, the departures began. By March 1939, 537 persons in 124 families (61%) had left; but half as many arrivals and more births than deaths kept the total population over 700 colonists. The reasons given for leaving to some extent reflect weaknesses in the selective process. At least 26 families left because of ill health, 24 because they were not suited or were asked to leave, and 47 because they were dissatisfied. These figures show that no less than a fourth of the original colonists were unsuited physically or mentally for colonization.

All of the original colonists who left The Valley were encouraged to return to their homes in the States. Some did this but a few located in the Pacific Northwest. More than half of the families were living in places unknown to persons still in The Valley or to the personnel of Alaskan post offices in 1948. At least 37 families remained in the Territory and 31 went to the Anchorage area from The Valley.

All of the replacement colonists were *selected* until about 1940. Approximately 80 families were chosen in these six years. Selection was by the ARRC administrators after persons desiring to join The Colony had filled in a form. Personal and financial references were interrogated, often personally, and selection was then made. Emphasis was placed on the applicants' farming experience, financial responsibility, and cooperative attitude. About 35 percent of the replacements lived in Alaska at the time of application and about 25 percent were in the three West Coast states and Montana. The rest were in 11 other states west of Ohio.

About 43 percent of the selected replacements, or 34 families, were still in The Valley in 1948. The remainder were as difficult to locate as the original colonists who left The Colony although 14 selected replacements are known to have gone to other places in the Territory.

In general, the selection of replacements was better than that of original colonists. The selectors of replacements were not hurried, they had Alaskan and colonization experience, and they personally interviewed a third of the people accepted; a large proportion of the replacements had funds with which to get started; and some of the confusion in starting the Colony had been eliminated by the time replacements came to The Valley.

At the end of 1948, 63 families, about a third, of the original colonists still lived in The Valley. While the average farming experience of these families in 1935 was 15½ years and 35 have remained on their original tracts, only about 12 families had made all or most of their living from farming. Husbands and wives who were less than 25 years old in 1935 made up the lowest percentages, by age groups, of those in The Valley in 1948. In original family size those of two persons in 1935, the younger colonists, also represented a low percentage; otherwise, original family size up to 10 persons had about the same percentage relationships to total families in 1948 as in 1935.

Farm Development Problems

Plans were developed for locating 208 families on tracts throughout the reservation. These were divided into 144 units of 40 acres each (69%), 52 of 80 acres (25% and the remaining 12 (6½) were held for possible later use. Most of these 12 were on the northern edges of settlement in rough country and still are unused.

Problems of farm organization became apparent even before all tracts were occupied. Administration of the "cooperative rural community" was inconsistent with physical conditions in Alaska and with American tradition of initiative and enterprise.

Forty acres of tillable land may be ample for fruit, vegetable or poultry farms. This size often is suitable for part-time or retirement farms if ample opportunity exists for non-farm income. None of these conditions existed in the Matanuska Valley at the time of colonization. Few of the 40 acre tracts were completely tillable.

No competent detailed soil survey was available as Colony tracts were being laid out. Many of them, consequently, contained less than 50 percent tillable land. Many others contained land that must be left wooded to protect open fields from erosion by winter winds. Possibly the saddest development of all occurred when colonists discovered that their best hope for success lay in development of commercial dairy farms. The Corporation began combining tracts even before all housing units had been established. By 1941, 37 tracts had been enlarged by addition of parts or all of adjoining tracts. The process of combination has continued and is one of the major problems facing farmers who want to expand their holdings to economic size.

In areas where tracts were clustered together, forming solid blocks, it is practically impossible to enlarge farm units. The situation is particularly acute south of Palmer and in the Butte area.

Farming started late and progressed slowly in The Colony. Only about 175 acres of homesteaded land were ready for cultivation in 1935. The start on an active land clearing program was held up in 1935 and 1936 in favor of the construction program. Once clearing was under way in 1937, it proceeded slowly in spite of three programs to stimulate the work and the cost was more than originally anticipated by the planners.

Farm budgets prepared for The Colony indicated that families were to work half an acre in a community garden the first year. They were to slash the timber and have cleared for them a total of 8½ acres in 1936, 11½ in 1937, 15½ in 1938, and 19½ in 1939. By November 1936, there was an average of 4.8 acres cleared and 1.0 acre slashed on 167 developed tracts. This average was only about half the progress that had been hoped for. A series of Supplementary Land Clearing programs then was instituted. The goal of 15 acres cleared per farm was raised to 30 acres and substantial incentives were offered settlers for work at slashing and clearing land.

By March 1940, even after three land clearing programs, only 3,926 acres were tillable. This amounted to an average of 23.5 acres for each of the 169 developed tracts. Only about 400 more acres were bulldozed by August 1941.

The Colonists became increasingly indifferent to farming. An administrator reported in July 1939: "Development of tracts is practically at a standstill . . . I can see no reason for this lack of interest in farming and development of tracts except the desire to work on the numerous jobs furnished by the Corporation . . . Farming in The Colony has developed to the point where it is second consideration with the Colonists."

On the other hand, study of individual family accounts and records on file in the archives of the Corporation disclose that the situation must have been desperate and almost hopeless for many conscientious people about 1940 and 1941. Cropland had not been made ready in proportion to livestock numbers, work for cash was insufficient to meet needs, markets were poor, debts were mounting. Records of livestock inventories show that several families lost ground yearly with their livestock. Each year their inventories were less than for the previous year. Many of them became discouraged after three or four years and finally left The Colony or were forced out by management.

The Corporation has had six general managers during its 20 years of existence. Don L. Irwin, the first manager in 1935, served again in 1945–47. Ross L. Sheeley also served at two separate times. These two men together with James J. Hurley, the present manager, are the only ones who had previous Alaska experience.

Rapid changes in management, directives often contradictory, inexperienced administrators and discontented colonists made for many strained situations. Relief officials in Washington were loath to allow the Board of the ARRC to set policies for administration of affairs locally. Personality clashes occurred frequently. Many of these could have been prevented if certain managers had been students of human nature.

A "get tough policy" was adopted after 1940 just when several potentially good farmers most needed leniency and understanding. Two types of examples are:

One family had purchased young livestock and raised it to where it would be producing an income within a few months. Their work record was good, their farm plan was in order so far as the family could make it. Their cash income was insufficient for them to stay current on interest installments. They needed a little more feed and a few more months before they could begin to make payments. They asked for an extension of time and for a small additional loan to carry them until their livestock would be producing an income. They were rebuffed. The second family had a few hens and had the opportunity to buy a good flock of pullets at bargain prices. They indicated that the supplemental flock would enable them to make substantial payments — if they were helped to finance the purchase. They already had part of their feed.

Both colonists received a form letter as follows:

In regard to your request for another loan from the Corporation, we are willing to give your request full consideration, but such consideration must be upon the following basis: (1) overdue payments on the 1941 loans must be paid in full; (2) the loan must be covered by adequate security; (3) an agreement must be executed that you will make regular periodical payments to repay this loan as promptly as possible, and to pay upon other debts due the Corporation.

Neither colonist received an additional loan and both left The Colony during the next few months. However, in spite of such unfortunate examples, most of the managers made sincere attempts to help the colonists progress and The Colony grew.

By 1941, many of the colonists were becoming worried about making their first payment. Some felt the need for expensive barn improvements to qualify for Grade A milk rating. The inevitability of World War II was felt strongly throughout the Territory; the feeling of insecurity that arose was demoralizing to thoughts about new clearing.

Aerial photographs showed that about 5,500 acres were cleared in The Valley in 1941, of which perhaps 4,500 acres were in colonists' tracts. During the war many of the farms in The Colony were operated by women while the men were elsewhere, either doing military service or working at military bases for high wages. After the war, from 1945 through 1947, the Corporation made a strong effort to complete its obligations under Supplementary Land Clearing Contracts. This work was nearly finished in the summer of 1948. By that time, there were an estimated 8,500 cleared acres in The Valley. In addition to the corporation three private operators did land clearing work in the area. The major concentration of cleared land was on the flat lands north and south of Palmer and around Bodenburg Butte. A minor cencentration was on the flat and gently sloping lands about two miles northwest of Matanuska Junction. The additional land cleared was primarily an expansion on colonists' tracts that were developed in 1941.

The development of cropping was predicated on having cleared land available. However, farming lagged even after land was available for cropping and in spite of the repeated reminders by Colony administrators that colonists must eventually depend on the soil for their livelihood. The lag occurred because many colonists were inexperienced farmers. They welcomed opportunities to work for good wages in the construction boom that accompanied the preparedness effort in the Anchorage area. Many of them could see no way to meet the high indebtedness charged against their holdings unless they worked away from home. Many preferred other occupations to farming.

In view of the colonization history, step by step, it is significant that few people of The Valley were full-time farmers after nearly 15 years of effort — even though the area included the largest area of cropped and cleared land in Alaska.

The growth of farming after colonization was marked by two agricultural changes. These were the developments from nearly subsistence agriculture to a commercial type and from general farming to specialization in dairying and truck crops. The homesteaders' farming was primarily the subsistence type, based on garden crops for use at home, hay and grain for the support of cattle and horses, and potatoes for his own use and for sale. The colonists also were subsistence farmers at first. However, as cleared land became available the tracts were turned quickly into sources of subsistence and cash income. The tendency towards commercial farming continued with the rapid increase of the civilian and military populations in Anchorage. However, the wages for construction made necessary by these increases of population lured colonists from The Valley and slowed down the agricultural development.

It was not expected that the colonists would become specialized commercial farmers. They were to be self-sufficient general farmers. The 40 and 80 acre tracts were to be the basis for specializing in truck crops or dairying by the end of 1939. The results of a survey made in 1940, by employees of the Corporation, show that general farming was predominant and that specialization was starting. The 118 tracts being farmed in 1940 were classified as follows: 83 general farms, 9 dairy farms, 6 truck farms, 2 poultry farms, 1 sheep farm, and 17 unclassified farms. From 1940, dairying continued to grow in importance until by 1948 there were 38 Grade A dairy farms. Truck farming had increased slowly to prevent seriously glutting the market at time of harvest. However, commercial farming was beyond the hopes of The Colony's original planners. It has been estimated that perhaps 50 farmers, mostly dairymen, were full-time operators by 1948. The remainder derived part of their income by working for Federal or Territorial agencies and as individual contractors.

Marketing

Estimates of the potential market for farm products were based on shipments to Alaska. They were an unrealistic basis for a permanent economy. Anchorage, the only "urban" area that could be considered a market had a population of about 2,000 in 1935. It had grown to 3,500 by October 1, 1939. If the original plans for development had materialized, serious overproduction inevitably would have developed.

The colonists had little surplus produce for sale before 1943. Gross sales from the Valley in 1941 were $304,000, in 1942 $219,000 and $370,000 in 1943. Farm products sold in 1948 amounted to $1,120,500. Continued growth of Anchorage and the military bases provided a ready market for all surplus from The Valley.

An Expensive Experiment

The settlement experiment was expensive. Financing was complex, costly and inefficient. Over $5,400,000 of grants were charged against The Colony. This and similar figures have been widely quoted as representing a "gift" to the Colonists of the Matanuska Valley. Little consideration is given that the $5 millions plus includes such items as $648,466 to the Alaska Road Commission for roads and bridges and $716,907 to the California ERA for relief laborers who were sent to Alaska to do work the Colonists should have done. The cows and horses purchased by Montana and Wyoming relief agencies for over $34,000 were high priced. Much of the outfitting expense incurred in Michigan, Minnesota and Wisconsin was spent on poorly suited supplies. A fire and poor record keeping combined accounted for another $313,000.

The construction and land clearing programs lagged and added to the non-productive expenses. Several families were poor managers and went into debt for goods they did not need. Others contracted development expenses on the assumption that cropland would be tillable on time. When the cropland was not available as promised, these families were forced to change their plans. This often resulted in costly adjustments and usually in frustration.

The colonists were told their debt to the Corporation would be $3,500 or less. Within two years their debts approximated $10,000 with many running higher. Dissatisfaction and discouragement at this situation was so strong that a debt readjustment program was instituted in late 1937.

The formula for debt adjustment was complicated. Charges were made that the adjustment program penalized persons who had been paying on debts or had held indebtedness low. Those persons with the highest debts received the largest adjustments to allow a reduction of all accounts to less than $8,000. Over $1,137,000 of colony costs appear to be chargeable to the debt reduction program.

In January 1941 the colonists requested postponement of payments on realty contracts until November 15, 1942 to allow them time to become current on short-term loans. This was granted to all colonists who were making payments and allowed them to liquidate overdue indebtedness for seed loans, special notes and chattels.

Payments were begun on time in 1942, but adjustments on methods of repayment often were necessary during the next several years. Several families borrowed additional funds in 1941 and 1942 for remodelling barns to qualify them for Grade A milk production. These barns had been constructed less than 10 years at the time and were still another irritation to families trying to live with the Project. The poor design of these buildings cost $30,000 in mortgage notes to the few dairymen involved during those two years alone. Expensive remodelling ultimately was necessary on nearly every barn in the project that was used for practical farming.

In spite of a slow start and the innumerable growing pains within the Colony, by 1948 from 70 to 75 percent of realty payments were current or not more than one payment behind schedule.

Old Settlers Loans

In 1934 and 1935, as plans were being formulated for The Colony, several Valley homesteaders hoped they would be able to borrow funds or join in the benefits of the government program. However, no consideration was given them in the organization. This neglect caused hard feelings and a definite rift between the "old settlers" and the newcomers.

Several oldtimers brought pressure through channels and in 1936 approval was granted for the Corporation to divert $25,000 for non-colony loans. Definite discrimination continued. The funds were dispersed on only 20 loans of less than $2,500 each between September 1936 and February 1937. No credit was extended at the Trading Post and settler loans were repayable in 10 years compared to 30 for the colonists.

The repayment history on Old Settler loans was good. Well over 90 percent of them were paid back when due. It is interesting to speculate whether agricultural development of The Valley would have been more rapid, less controversial and less expensive if the colonization program had been keyed to assisting residents and volunteers rather than the program that was followed.

In Retrospect

The Matanuska Colony was developed during an emergency period and under bizarre circumstances. A national emergency relief program obviously was not the best vehicle for a settlement experiment. The experiment was conducted with nearly all the ingredients as unknowns. It was complicated by some administrative decisions and actions obstructive to smooth development. It may not have been a case of the blind leading the blind — although many times it seemed so.

Kirk Stone says of the period:

Some of the early management of the Colony was inefficient. It was necessarily so. Lack of information plagued administrators trying to correct the plans during settlement. Administration in Washington was organized somewhat loosely. Formation of the Alaska Rural Rehabilitation Corporation was tardy. The administration was too paternalistic. Few of the administrators had enough Alaskan experience and training in the administration of cooperative agricultural colonization. The initial results were confusion and higher costs of administration than had been anticipated . . .

Several persons in the National Administration exercised strong control over many phases of colonization. Colonists complained that they were given no chance to express individuality or "to go on their own" but rather were herded through various phases of colonization as a group incapable of thinking.

Surely, many mistakes were made! Money was spent unwisely! Settler selection was hurried and fumbling! Government controls and the pioneer spirit make strange bed-fellows. But, adversity was unable to defeat the program.

Nearly 200 Colonist and replacement families stayed in Alaska. A very fair proportion of them remained on the land and gained a part of their living from agriculture and allied industries. This nucleus was the catalytic agent that drew additional families into the Valley.

About 7,500 acres were cleared for cropping under the impetus of the program. Probably at least 6,000 of it was being cropped in 1947–48. Residences and outbuildings were available for families that needed them. A marketing organization was available and a market was being developed. The highway system had been improved and expanded to bridge the Matanuska and Knik Rivers and people could move about. The nucleus for a trade, business and social center at Palmer had been established.

Agricultural products sold increased in value from less than $100,000 in 1940 to $1,120,500 in 1948. Production from this experiment amounted to over half the Alaskan agricultural products sold in 1948. The Matanuska Valley forged ahead during a very trying period in Alaska.

Perhaps the most valuable contributions from the experiment were: the hard-earned knowledge of agricultural conditions in Alaska, the experience in administering the movement of people and taming the land and a focussing of the limelight upon the production potential of sub-Arctic Alaska.

Colonist experience to 1955

A student of planned settlements would have difficulty locating boundaries of original colony tracts in 1955. Most of the original houses and barns still stand although many of them have been drastically modified. Originally, 208 tracts were numbered. Seven of these never were occupied. Of the 201 occupied tracts, only 47 are unchanged in size.[23] The 40 acre tracts generally are utilized as rural residences or as residences and part-time farms for production of potatoes, vegetables or poultry. The 201 tracts have been absorbed into units as follows:

Acreage	Number	Acreage	Number
40	29	200	7
60	1	240	1
80	36	280	1
120	37	400	1
160	19		

Colony tracts would have averaged 51 acres if all had gone according to original plan. Within less than 20 years, settlers had upset this program and had extended the average holding to 105 acres. Still further combinations would have occurred had contiguous lands been available. The landholding pattern established by the Matanuska Colony has been a major hindrance to development of economic-size units.

This problem was recognized by the Managers before 1940. They began combining tracts wherever it was possible. Tracts relinquished by colonists or repossessed by the Corporation were redistributed to enlarge adjoining farms. But almost irreparable damage had been done in areas of better soils. Smallest tracts were laid out in these areas under the assumption that they would be adequate to support a family at a subsistence level. Unfortunately for the plan, many families were not satisfied to live that way. Some sold their cropland to adjoining dairymen, took off-farm employment and used their buildings as rural residences. Others purchased additional tracts, from the Corporation or from owners who had received warranty deeds after payment of their indebtedness, as the basis for commercial farms. The process continues, and will continue, until a realistic ownership pattern compatible with modern economic conditions is evolved. Many years and perhaps several generations will pass before desirable adjustments are completed. In this respect the Matanuska Valley compares with older, established communities in the States where the small farm is giving way slowly to mechanized modern farming.

Analysis of the methods and the chronology followed in making tract combinations is well nigh impossible. Transfers often are not recorded with the U.S.

Commissioners. Several tracts have changed hands as much as a dozen times since the original drawings in 1935.

Part of this instability is traceable to the colony's early history. Tracts on the margins of settlement were relatively isolated and were improved slowly. Some obviously contained large proportions of poor soils or were heavily timbered. Settlers early realized that farm development would be slow and expensive.

Analysis of the 1955 situation on Colony tracts shows that the original 201 units have shrunk to 132. Almost every conceivable kind of size combination is represented on the next page.

Colony tracts only	Number of operating units	Number of colony tracts represented
40 acres as original	29	29
40 combined with second colony 40	13	26
40 combined with two colony 40's	12	36
40 combined with three colony 40's	1	4
40 combined with part of colony 40 (20)	1	1.5
80 acres as original	18	18
80 combined with colony 40	12	24
80 combined with colony 80	4	8
80 combined with colony 80 & 40	1	3
	91	149.5
Colony tracts and others		
Colony 40 and non-colony 40	5	5
Colony 40 and non-colony 80	2	2
Colony 40 and non-colony 120	2	2
Colony 40 and non-colony 160 or more	6	6
Colony 40, colony 40 and non-colony 40	5	10
Colony 40, colony 40 and non-colony 80	6	12
Part of colony 40 and non-colony 80	1	0.5
Colony 80 and non-colony 40	5	5
Colony 80 and non-colony 80	6	6
Colony 80 and non-colony 160	1	1
Colony 80 and non-colony 200	1	1
Colony 80 and non-colony 320	1	1
	41	51.5
Abandoned and undeveloped	—	7
Total units in 1955	132	208

Thirty-four original or replacement Colonist families still were on tracts they had acquired between the original drawing in 1935 and 1940 when the formal replacement program was dropped. Twenty-three of these located in 1935, three in 1936, three in 1937, two in 1938 and three in 1939. Several are among the better-situated full-time farmers today. All of them depending upon agriculture for their livelihood have increased their original holdings.

The Soil Conservation Service has mapped all areas including colony tracts. Their data shows that the original 208 tracts contained 79 percent classes II or III land, 8 percent class IV and 13 percent classes VI, VII or VIII. Averages based on tracts held by the 34 settlers who have stayed on their land 15 to 20 years are almost identical with averages for all tracts. Consequently, little basis exists for believing that *soil quality* was a factor forcing settlers from their tracts.

Classifying farms by major enterprise also provides no basic condition that would make one family become a rural resident or another become a full-time dairy farmer. Among the 12 rural residents, for example, 79 percent of their land was in classes II or III. Six had small amounts of waste land. Six did not. Four owned only class II land — the best in Alaska. Some are located on the edge of Palmer, some are on the far edge of the Colonization area. Only the three families classified as "subsistence" have a relatively high percentage of untillable land. In each of these cases, conditions other than soils determined the enterprise. Soils and distance from the Community Center were not factors determining the use made of the holdings.

Half of the 34 families are part-time farmers or rural residents because they never were farmers. They were mechanics, tradesmen or craftsmen who returned to their preferred occupations as soon as they could. Perhaps they were more tenacious, or were less individualistic, than other families who left the Matanuska Colony. That cannot be proven. The fact remains: they stayed and they are self-supporting today.

The full-time dairymen and potato-dairymen apparently intended to make a career of farming. They bought more land, remodeled their barns, cleared additional fields and bought necessary modern machinery. They might have succeeded as well back in the states of their origin during the past 20 years. The Matanuska Colony provided an opportunity for them to get a start. Growth of the Anchorage-military market provided a chance for them to keep going.

These 34 families have held their land and have adjusted their operations according to their wishes. Other families had illness or other problems making it logical for them to move — regardless of conditions within the Colony or within the Matanuska Valley. Increasing age, failing health and death are rapidly taking their toll of families still connected with the settlement program of the Matanuska Colony.

Analysis of an old list containing names of 185 Colonist families provides an interesting sidelight. After nearly 20 years, 49 couples still are living in the Valley although not all still live on Colony land. Others were accounted for in March 1955 as follows:

Couple still in the Valley	49
Couple left Alaska	77
Couple left Valley, still in Alaska	27
Couple separated, one still in Alaska	6
Couple separated, both still in Alaska	4
Couple separated, both left Alaska	1
Male deceased, female in Alaska	10
Male deceased, female left Alaska	7
Female deceased, male in Alaska	2
Both deceased	2
	185

A list of original Colonists still in Alaska was prepared for the Colony Day Celebration in 1953. It contains 130 names of men and women to allow for couples broken by death, divorce or separation. Occupations listed were:

47 housewife	3 office worker
25 farmer	3 heavy equipment operator
11 laborer	2 miner
10 carpenter	2 domestic
5 retail clerk	13 miscellaneous*
4 store manager	5 occupation unknown

Recent homesteading experience

Many homesteaders who settled on tracts made available to veterans of World War II picked poor land. Many realized early that they never could hope to develop prosperous farms. Others tired of frontier life and left after a year or so of residence.

A check of 110 such homestead entries made between 1945 and 1950[25] shows that 11 are full-time farmers, 20 are part-time farmers combining farming with off-farm employment, 22 depend on businesses other than farming and the remaining 57 are unknown or were reported to have left the Valley. Study of the conditions surrounding their settlement brings out several distinct situations.

Most of the families who left their homesteads were located on poor land and on the outer edge of settlement. Most of the full-time farmers are located on tracts containing large proportions of tillable land and also are within developing areas. Several part-time farmers are working for high wages which are being used to support their families and develop farm capital in buildings, machinery, land clearing and livestock. Many of the homesteaders who left almost immediately were single men.

The factor of speculative land values, although hard to evaluate, must be considered in recent alienations of public lands. Activities of the Anchorage Chamber of Commerce and others relative to a causeway across Knik Arm, the Susitna birch stand, Susitna power sites and similar potential developments have been responsible for land claims under homesteading laws although the claimants have no apparent intentions of farming. Recent changes in the law making cultivation of land again a requirement of homesteading will largely remove this subterfuge as an instrument for gaining title to land. Activity by oil and gas companies in the Cook Inlet area has encouraged many persons to tie up surface rights in anticipation of windfall profits.

---

*one each of blacksmith, cafe operator, contractor, postmaster, bus driver, bricklayer, trapper, trucker, sawmill operator, plumber, telephone operator, bartender and retired.

Farming In Alaska

From Hugh A. Johnson, "Seward's Folly Can Be a Great Land," U.S. Department of Agriculture, *Yearbook*, 1958 (Washington, 1958), pp. 424–39.

When we bought Alaska from Imperial Russia in 1867, the acquisition was praised by western expansionist interests and opposed by the eastern conservative bloc. Severe criticism was heaped upon Secretary of State Seward for his "folly" in buying "Seward's Icebox," "Icebergia," or "Walrussia."

Actually, the conflict between Great Britain and Russia in the Crimea provided the opportunity for the United States to buy out Russia's interest in North America for a few cents an acre and by the same stroke to limit further British activity in the area and capture a prolific source of furs, fish, and trade. Opposition in the Congress was strong, however, and no legislation for administration of the new possession was enacted until 1884.

Former Governor Ernest Gruening, a longtime student of Alaskan history, said of this admittedly stopgap legislation: "The act was . . . specific in its limitations and prohibitions, indefinite and equivocal in its grants. No legislature, no delegate, no general land laws. . . ." It extended the current Oregon Code to Alaska "as it applied" and as it was "not in conflict with this act or laws of the United States."

A measure of self-government and Territorial status came only with passage of the Second Organic Act of 1912. Since that date many Alaskans have been working for statehood in order to obtain greater control in the management of their own affairs.

The Organic Act of 1912 grants to the Territory specific powers comparable to those of the State legislatures, although the Congress has reserved to itself certain functions, such as responsibility for fish and game. It has prohibited Alaska from establishing a judicial system and has also prohibited the creation of counties without congressional consent.

The Department of the Interior administers most of the laws passed by the Congress for the management and development of Alaska's publicly owned resources outside the national forests.

Alaska's location is a handicap to development. It is far removed from established trade routes and is separated from the United States by the Canadian wilderness and the rough waters of the North Pacific. These and other factors, combined with the abundance of resources nearer populated areas, have kept Alaska in the hinterland of national development.

The presence of extensive natural resources has created durable myths as to their worth in the minds of some Alaskans. Advocates of local development often fail to realize that some resources cannot be developed profitably under present economic and technological conditions. That hope for the use of at least a part of these resources need not be deferred much longer, however, is demonstrated by the modern pulp plant at Ketchikan, the interest in several large ore deposits, the oil and gas explorations, and the recurring industrial interests in potential hydropower sites.

Vilhjalmur Stefansson wrote in *Climate and Man,* the 1941 Yearbook of Agriculture: "If you are willing to be an old-fashioned pioneer — a Lincoln of

Illinois, a Nordic of a Swedish inland valley, or a Mongol of Central Finland — you can make their type of living in the Alaska of today. But there are few places where it is more difficult than in Alaska to be a successful "economic man." The Finns and the Swedes colonized their northern lands when they were subsistence hunters, subsistence fishers, and subsistence farmers. . . . Alaska is a northern land which is at least open for development under our present culture — if a district can be called open that is fenced off by so many economic, sociological, and psychological barbed-wire fences."

The years and events that have occurred since Stefansson's observation have widened the economic gap. The old-fashioned pioneer is rarely found. Bulldozers and chain saws have replaced horses and axes. Airplanes have superseded dogsleds. Scintillometers explore terrain faster and more accurately than wandering prospectors.

Fortuitous participation in the Klondike and later gold rushes of men who were vocal and their bombardment of Congressmen with facts about Alaska and pleas for better government brought about the first serious appraisal of Alaska's resources by the Federal Government. Preliminary explorations were authorized to study the geology of the country, to determine its potentialities, and to discover whether agriculture was feasible.

Three Federal agricultural experiment stations — Sitka, Kodiak, and Kenai — were authorized by the Congress in 1898. Later reservations were made for experiment stations at Rampart (1900), Copper Center (1903), Fairbanks (1906), and Matanuska (1915). A fur experimental station was established at Petersburg in 1938. Only the Fairbanks, Matanuska, and Petersburg stations remained in 1958.

An opening wedge for agricultural settlement was forged in the Homestead Act of 1898. It limited land grants to 80 acres and required homesteaders to pay the expenses of surveying. No baselines for surveys existed, and no provision was made for surveys. No settler to my knowledge acquired title under this act. The law was amended in 1903 to permit entry on 320 acres of surveyed or unsurveyed land. Several good farms were developed from tracts entered under this law. The maximum size of a homestead was reduced to 160 acres in 1916 and has remained so.

Leasing for fur farming was first authorized in 1926. Grazing leases were authorized in 1927. Other widely separated acts over the years have regulated entry and use of land for mining, industrial and commercial purposes, homesite and headquarter sites, small tracts for recreational and residential uses, leases for oil and gas exploration, and for other special purposes. Tongass and Chugach National Forests, Glacier and Katmai National Monuments, and McKinley National Park were established by Presidential proclamation in the early era of conservation.

The depression-born Matanuska Valley Colonization Project established in 1935 generated interest in agriculture as 30 years of homesteading had not done. Wartime and postwar defense programs drew attention to Alaska as a place to live and work.

Alaska covers 586,400 square miles and more than 365 million acres of actual land area. Its great size and its variable climate create problems of land utilization. Each region has unique resources and problems. From east to west, Alaska extends through four time zones and about 38 degrees of longitude. In a north-south direction, it extends over more than 15 degrees of latitude. The distance from Barrow to Ketchikan is comparable with that from Boston to Baton Rouge or from Washington, D. C., to Denver.

Nearest the United States lies a long, narrow strip of mainland and islands, called Southeastern Alaska. It has a marine climate similar to that of the Olympic Peninsula in Washington. Rainfall is heavy, and there is much cloudy weather. Primeval forests cover the lower island and mainland slopes and reach up the mountainsides to about 3 thousand feet. Small areas of fairly fertile soils occur in narrow glacial valleys and on some estuaries. Sporadic interest in homesteading has kept a few of these tracts in the public eye, but history shows that farming is submarginal on all except the tracts that are most favorably situated. Agriculture in this region is limited to a few intensive poultry, dairy, and vegetable farms. Only three fur farms remained in 1957. Southeastern Alaska is better adapted to commercial forestry, fishing, mining, and recreation enterprises.

Nearly all of the area outside townsite eliminations, the national monuments, and the public-domain area around Haines lies within the 16-million-acre Tongass National Forest. Preliminary Forest Service estimates show 84 billion feet of timber on about 6 million acres of merchantable forest. Three-fourths of the commercial timber grows within 2.5 miles of tidewater. Although the region has considerable potential for sawtimber, the immediate interest and need lie in pulp operations.

By early 1957, four large, long-term sales had been made by the Forest Service to private corporations that agreed to harvest forest growth on a sustained-yield basis. Included in these sales were the Ketchikan unit of 8.25 billion board-feet, the Wrangell of 3 billion, the Juneau of 7.5 billion, and the Sitka of 5.25 billion — a total of 24 billion board-feet.

A large, modern pulpmill at Ketchikan and small sawmills at Wrangell, Juneau, and Ketchikan were operating in 1957. A plyboard plant at Juneau had suspended operations temporarily after several years of operation. A large pulp plant was under construction at Sitka. Additional plants and expanded operations are to be introduced for the remaining forested areas when more investment capital has been mobilized and more is known about the economics of plant operations.

Northward lies south-central Alaska, which reaches from the Gulf of Alaska to the Alaska Range and extends westward to the base of the Alaska Peninsula. It includes the 5-million-acre Chugach National Forest, the 2-million-acre (both public and nonpublic lands) Kenai Moose Reserve, the 2.7-million-acre Katmai National Monument, the Anchorage metropolitan area, several large military reservations, and the Matanuska Valley and Kenai Peninsula agricultural areas. The climate and vegetation of this region are affected by its position between the North Pacific marine influences from the south and the shelter of the Alaska Range on the north and west. Spruce, birch, and aspen grow to sawtimber size in commercial quantities. Native grasses and other forage grow luxuriantly on suitable sites. Dairy farmers of the Matanuska Valley have grazing leases for 39 thousand acres of the Matanuska-Susitna area. Areas of fertile soils are sufficient to support several hundred farm families in production of food for local civilian and military markets. Irrigation of crops in spring and early summer is increasingly important to commercial vegetable growers and dairymen.

Central Alaska lies between the Alaska Range on the south and the Brooks Range on the north and includes the 1.9-million-acre Mount McKinley National

Park. It includes the drainages of the Upper Yukon, the Tanana, the Koyukuk, and the Upper Kuskokwim. It has a continental climate with long, cold winters and short, mild summers. Summer temperatures of 100° or more have been recorded, but such days are rare. Precipitation ranges from 8 to 16 inches.

Commercial agriculture is practiced near Fairbanks, and family gardens grow well on suitable sites throughout the region. Irrigation of crops often pays in spring and early summer. Although the Fairbanks area in the Tanana Valley is currently desirable for settlement because it lies near a market, unclaimed potential agricultural soils in other areas are fairly abundant. Climate and soils are suitable for agricultural production in several valleys of the Yukon and Kuskokwim. With limited demand for farm products in these areas, however, there is no pressure for agricultural development.

Both the south-central and the central regions contain forested tracts, although much of the forest is not of a commercial size or concentration. Spruce, birch, and aspen occur on the well-drained ridges and benches. The Bureau of Land Management estimated that there were 40 million acres of commercial forest containing 180 billion board-feet and producing 1.5 billion board-feet annually in these regions in 1956. Another 85 million acres classed as woodland (unsuited to sawmill operations) contain about 170 billion board-feet. Only a little of the commercial-class forest is harvested. Small sawmills process low-grade rough lumber as the needs warrant.

Southwestern Alaska includes Kodiak and nearby islands, the Alaska Peninsula, and the Aleutian Islands. Climate is generally moderated by its marine position. Rainy, foggy weather encourages growth of plant species suitable for grazing. Most of the region is treeless, although some trees grow in protected spots. Several bird and wildlife sanctuaries are on the islands, and Katmai National Monument is at the base of the peninsula.

Its rolling and mountainous grasslands and its relatively mild winters encourage some people to consider possibilities of range cattle and sheep production. As of June 30, 1956, the Department of Interior had in effect 26 grazing leases on 767 thousand acres in southwestern Alaska. Seven ranches on Kodiak Island had 990 head of cattle in 1956. Beeves are butchered and sold locally as 3-year-olds. In the early 1950's, the lessee on Chirikof Island began to butcher bulls descended from the original American stock. He shipped the meat to Anchorage by air. This herd included about 300 head in 1957. About 300 sheep had been added to the operation. The largest and oldest managed spreads are on Umnak and Unalaska Islands. These operators had about 50 cattle, 8,500 sheep, and small herds of horses in 1956. Livestock were butchered for local use, but the major sales were of wool shipped to Seattle by air. The limited supplies of winter feed and distance from market are obstacles to expansion of livestock enterprises.

The climate of western Alaska — or, more precisely, of Bristol Bay and the lower parts of Kuskokwim and Yukon drainages — is moderated by the Bering Sea. Except where hills or other topographic features provide a good drainage, this is a vast, flat area of tundra interspersed with thousands of small lakes and meandering streams. I have seen good family gardens growing on sites protected from cold sea winds at Unalakleet, Akiak, Bethel, Platinum, Aleknagik, Dillingham, and Naknek. Physical opportunities for farming communities exist in a few localities of this region, but markets currently are small and strictly local.

The Seward Peninsula and the Arctic Slope generally have summers too short and cool for crops and for livestock production other than reindeer. Except for isolated stands of protected spruce and cottonwoods along the southern fringes, the region is a tundra wilderness.

A. E. Porsild, speaking before the Second Alaska Science Conference in September 1951, stated of this region: "Plant life, everywhere in the Arctic, is too sparse, dwarfed, and poorly developed to make any considerable contribution to the food supply of man. Only a few Arctic plants produce edible and nourishing roots or stems, and only near the southern fringe of the barren grounds are there some that in favorable seasons produce appreciable quantities of small edible fruits. . . . The most promising and economically practical approach to the problem of utilization of the vast Arctic and subarctic tundra and taiga appears to be the wise and careful administration of the remaining wildlife resources."

Explorations for oil and gas, coal, and minerals may discover exploitable physical resources to form a basis for further settlement. But present knowledge and experience in Alaska and other northern areas of America, Europe, and Asia indicate that extensive food production is not economically feasible in these areas.

Soil characteristics and cool climate are restrictive factors in present and potential crop production. Soils in Alaska are relatively young geologically.

Charles E. Kellogg and I. J. Nygard made a reconnaissance of Alaskan soils for the Department of Agriculture during the summer of 1946 as part of a task-force assignment to study agricultural problems of Alaska. A. H. Mick, of the Alaska Agricultural Experiment Station, later summarized their observations and his own knowledge of Alaskan soils in an article he and I prepared for the Arctic Institute of North America. These men stated that Alaska's mature soils include only the Podzol and Tundra great soil groups.

Tundra is Alaska's most widely distributed zonal great soil group. Vegetal cover subsists at very low levels of activity, and decomposition of organic materials by micro-organisms is still slower. The resultant carpet of tough, fibrous, peaty material increases in thickness year by year, unless it is disturbed by fire, drainage, or some other mechanical change. The high insulating properties of this layer prevent summer warmth from penetrating mineral substrata, which remain frozen for long periods. Most Tundra soils are underlain to varying depths by permanently frozen ground. The frozen subsurface, plus the spongy organic surface materials, usually results in a waterlogged surface condition during summer.

Intrazonal Alpine Meadow, Mountain Tundra, and Mountain-Half Bog soils occur at higher altitudes. These soils have little potential agricultural value, except for extensive reindeer grazing or possibly as summer pasture to supplement other sites capable of producing winter feed for livestock.

Podzols usually are found in well-drained sandy sites. Where very fine sands and silts were deposited, podzolization is feeble and is transitional to the intrazonal subarctic Brown Forest soils.

Most crop production occurs on the well-drained phases of these subarctic Brown Forest soils. These soils are high in potash but deficient in organic matter, nitrogen, and usually in available phosphates. The surface layers are usually acid. Subsoils are well supplied with calcium and magnesium, although free carbonates generally are absent.

New settlers often are disturbed by the extreme acidity of newly cleared soils. Some buy limestone to neutralize this condition. Specialists at the Alaska Agricultural Experiment Station caution that many fields gradually become neutral or slightly alkaline under cultivation. This process is associated with the breakdown of organic matter and a narrowing of carbon-nitrogen ratios. It occurs on any reasonably well-drained soil in Alaska wherever tillage is carried on. The alkaline reaction of older fields is of concern to farmers in the Matanuska and Tanana Valleys who find their potato crops increasingly afflicted with scab.

I saw an extreme example of this change in pH in a small garden at Bethel on the lower Kuskokwim. The garden was on a small hillock in the Tundra where formerly moss, dwarf shrubs, and berries flourished. The strongly acid virgin soil had become almost neutral after only 3 years of cultivation.

Permafrost is of concern in central Alaska north of the Alaska Range. It takes two forms. The most widespread is a poorly drained situation, caused by insulating materials on the soil surface, which prevents thawing and internal drainage. Removal of trees, brush, and moss permits thawing to a depth sufficient for cultivation. Several settlers in the Tanana Valley have developed excellent cropland from these mechanically wet soils. Local frost pockets, however, sometimes limit the crops that can be grown. Vast areas now classed as muskeg probably can be dried out and made physically suitable for crop production, but microclimatic conditions still would be unfavorable on many sites. Extensive drainage of these wet lands eventually might affect ground-water supplies adversely and create serious erosion problems on associated light podzolic soils.

The second condition in permafrost is the occurrence of large blocks, or lenses, of solid ice under the soil surface. Disturbing the insulating materials permits heat to penetrate; the ice melts, leaving holes of various sizes. Sometimes the thermal action causes no particular loss, but it can be so extreme that the fields become untillable. Parts of older fields at the Fairbanks Agricultural Experiment Station are now too rough to be used even as pasture, and a few new fields on homesteads have become too rough for tillage.

The United States Geological Survey conducts studies designed to aid in locating areas where these conditions occur. Their investigations in 1948 helped to show that the Dunbar area, which was under consideration for a group settlement area, was submarginal because of frequent occurrence of these ice lenses.

Frozen ground is of concern also as it affects availability of potable water and sewage disposal. Farmers in the Tanana Valley sometimes cannot develop livestock farms because of the high cost of developing adequate water supplies.

More than 99.9 percent of Alaska's land is owned by the Government.

Vacant, unreserved public lands estimated at 270 million acres, reserved lands at 28 million acres, and 185 thousand acres of unperfected homestead entries are controlled by the Bureau of Land Management. The Bureau and the Navy jointly manage 23 million acres of oil and gas reserve. Another 18 million acres are under the control and management of the National Park Service, the Fish and Wildlife Service, the Bureau of Indian Affairs, and the Bureau of Reclamation. The Forest Service has nearly 21 million acres in two national forests, and the Department of Defense has nearly 4 million acres in military reservations. Land withdrawals of all kinds amounted to 92.3 million acres in 1956.

The Department of the Interior is responsible for 93 percent of the Federal lands, the Department of Agriculture for 5 percent, the Department of Defense for about 1.5 percent, and other agencies for a small percentage.

About 450 thousand acres had been patented by June 30, 1956. Homesteads account for a major part of this acreage, but trade and manufacturing sites, homesites, and similar nonagricultural uses account for about 25 thousand acres of privately owned lands. Alaska has no real-estate taxes, except in school districts and municipalities, and there is no convenient way of ascertaining the proportion of patented lands that are currently used. We do know that absentee ownership and land abandonment are serious problems in the major settlement areas. The revised land registration act of 1957 may help to make absentee-owned lands available to farmers.

Before June 1954, veterans of the Second World War who had had 19 months or more of military service could acquire 160-acre homesteads after 7 months of residence and construction of habitable dwellings. They were not required to cultivate any land. Hundreds of veterans entered tracts under these regulations, but many of them abandoned their entries before patent, and nearly as many more abandoned their holdings after patent was acquired.

The obvious need for nonfarm holdings and for enabling legislation other than the homestead laws have been recognized by the Congress and the administrative departments. Townsites, small tracts, industrial and commercial tracts, and recreation and public-purpose sites are authorized under special legislation, and their development is promoted within the Department of the Interior.

In 1954, I studied 110 predominantly veteran homestead entries made in the Matanuska Valley between 1945 and 1950. Eleven entrymen were full-time farmers, 20 were part-time farmers who combined farming with off-farm work, 22 were in businesses other than farming, and 57 had left the valley. Most of those who had left had applied for entry at the Land Office but had not established residence on their tracts.

The Alaska Agricultural Experiment Station, cooperating with the Bureau of Land Management, in 1955 made a detailed study of agricultural settlement on the Kenai Peninsula. Homesteading had been going on in the Homer area for 40 years. Yet we found that 59 percent of all entered or patented land on the Peninsula was unoccupied and abandoned in July 1955. Another 31 percent was used solely for rural residences by persons who had no intention of farming. This left only 10 percent of the homesteaded land occupied by persons who were farming or planning to farm. Only 1.3 percent of the occupied land was cropland — and nearly half of this had been cleared since 1950, when we made a study here. Only 14 percent of all income reported by homesteaders in 1955 came from sales of farm products.

Detailed study of the Homer community showed that 60 percent of all homestead entries from 1915 to 1945 had been canceled, relinquished, or closed by decision. Abandonment, in the sense that the entryman failed to carry through to patent status, increased from 44 percent of all entries before 1930 to 72 percent for the entries made in the 5 years ending in 1945. Activity picked up between 1946 and 1950, when 172 entries were made, 84 patents were granted, and 95 homestead entries were relinquished.

An additional 237 entries were made between 1950 and 1955. Three-fourths of these were relinquished, canceled, or terminated otherwise than by granting patent before June 1956. Several tracts had a long record of entry and abandonment — one had been entered and abandoned 9 times before it was patented to an institution that still had not occupied it by 1956.

The Kenai Peninsula story is repeated with variations in the Matanuska and Tanana Valleys. The question logically follows, "What happens to change homesteaders' minds?"

Unsatisfactory subsistence from the land and lagging development of markets provided a low level of living in the 1930's. Wartime and postwar defense activities drained active potential farmers from their undeveloped homesteads in the early 1940's.

Publicity about new opportunities to be found after the war brought hundreds of veterans and nonveterans alike to Alaska. Many combat veterans seemed to have had a psychological need to get away from the pressures of modern urban society. Many were deeply interested in farming. Some were lured by stories of possible new Government-aided settlement programs akin to the Matanuska Colonization Project. Many of those who came — veterans and nonveterans alike — lacked fundamental knowledge of modern agricultural methods, and most had overlooked the difficulties of clearing land and getting into production. Very few were financially equipped for the task, and costs proved to be prohibitive. Too many learned from hard experience that productive land is not free, that the raw homestead is not the finished farm. Between the two lies a heavy investment in labor, money, management, and time.

Speculation was another strong influence. With no tax on real estate, hunger for landownership and a rural way of life, publicity about development programs, activity in oil and gas explorations, no land-clearing requirement, and only a 7-month residence requirement, it looked as though relatively unsettled veterans had much to gain and little to lose. Some thought they could live off the land by hunting and fishing.

Both the Department of the Interior and the Department of Agriculture spent considerable effort, thought, and money to help veterans choose the best available lands after the war. Areas known to contain the best soils were surveyed and mapped by technicians of the Soil Conservation Service. The Department of the Interior built roads into settlement areas and attempted by available means under existing limited authority to guide homesteading activity to tracts known to contain areas of tillable soils and away from noncultivable lands.

Early scientists in Alaska estimated its agricultural potential at 200 million to 300 million acres based on what could be observed from boats or rails and gleaned from hearsay. Their reports were too optimistic. We now say that probably 2 million to 3 million acres are physically suitable for cropping. Another 3 million to 5 million acres would be usable for summer pasture in conjunction with cropland; 2 million or 3 million acres more of grassy islands are suitable for year-round use as rangeland, although preservation of forage as silage for winter use and some feeding of concentrates would be desirable on most of them.

Employees of the Departments of Interior and Agriculture work together closely on problems of land settlement and utilization. Absence of legal authority to classify lands according to indicated best use is a handicap in administration of public land-development programs. The Bureau of Land Management through reconnaissance delimits areas that are obviously unsuitable for settlement and locates others that appear to have possibilities.

Specialists in the Department of Agriculture make detailed studies of soils, cover, terrain, and other features. Priorities for work are established, and tasks often are integrated. Delineations of potential agricultural land by the Bureau of Land Management tend to be high, as they are usually of a preliminary reconnaissance nature. The more detailed surveys made by the Soil Conservation Service show the physical limitations of soils. Their estimates of potential agricultural land might be interpreted as low, if productive soils were in short supply. We know that lands considered to be unsuited to agriculture under present conditions might be made to produce under different economic circumstances.

Surveys to date cover the known best lands in or near present settlement areas. They have helped to guide potential farmers away from such marginal areas as the Dunbar area near Fairbanks and the Fritz Creek withdrawal area on the Kenai Peninsula. Their efforts, however, did not prevent entry for nonfarm purposes in the Fritz Creek area under veterans' rights provisions of the homestead laws. The Soil Conservation Service has mapped other withdrawn areas where enough tillable lands exist to support farm enterprises. The Bureau of Land Management used these reports as guides when developing areas for settlement. The Alaska Road Commission used the combined recommendations in planning its expanded road system.

Of more than 2 million acres mapped by field parties, roughly 35 percent is in class II or III and about 10 percent is class IV land. Slightly less than half of the area mapped thus is physically suited to some type of cultivation. No judgment is passed on the economics of the situation in this type of analytical study. Some of this land lies in small blocks that cannot be developed economically. More can be utilized only in carefully balanced conjunction with other resources on areas much greater than the present 160-acre homestead.

The first farms were developed by disenchanted miners during the gold-rush era. They found growing grain and hay for freighters' horses and food for roadhouse tables easier and more profitable than searching for gold. Much of the acreage developed during this heyday later was abandoned and reverted to brush. Its extent was not to be duplicated in Alaska until after the Second World War.

During his visit to Alaska in 1914, H. H. Bennett estimated that a minimum of 1 thousand acres had been cleared for cultivation in the Matanuska Valley. M. D. Snodgrass, a former superintendent of the Matanuska Agricultural Experiment Station, reported about the same acreage (though on other farms) about 1934. Acreages in the Tanana Valley reached a peak of around 1,760 acres on 107 farms in the early 1920's and then declined steadily until after the war. Surveys in 1948 and 1950 found only about 30 full-time and part-time farmers remaining. Farming in the Homer area was largely fur, livestock, and subsistence. Little cropland had been developed. Stagnation in mining, railroad construction, and general activity caused stagnation in agriculture. Small farming areas that had been developed in the Chilkat Valley, at Gustavus, at Point Agassiz near Petersburg, in the McCarthy area, and elsewhere, disappeared from the scene. Fur farming has almost disappeared from the islands and the mainland.

The only significant land clearing from 1935 to 1941 was done in the Matanuska Valley Colonization Project. About 4,300 acres were cleared, although part of the land was used for nonfarm purposes. Only 3,926 acres within the colony were tillable in March 1940. Much of this was idle because many men were working on defense projects. A strong effort was made to fulfill commitments to the remaining colonists after the end of the war, and by 1948 an estimated 8,500 acres had been cleared. More than 12 thousand acres in the valley had been cleared by 1957.

Land clearing and breaking cost 150 to 200 dollars an acre — and much hard work. Money was scarce, and individuals could not afford to expand their farms. Efforts were made therefore to find sources of public funds for farm development.

Legal limitations and administrative policies never intended for homestead development have prevented the Farmers Home Administration and the Farm Credit Administration from meeting Alaskans' needs for credit. These lending agencies will not advance funds because most applicants do not have title to their land and do not get more than half of their income from agriculture. Until recently, banks as a rule loaned available funds for nonfarm activities only.

Payments for land clearing became authorized practices under the Agricultural Conservation Program, beginning in 1945. An average of 587 acres a year was cleared under this arrangement between 1945 and 1954. Allotments were divided roughly in proportion to the agriculture in each area. Inadequate controls during the early years of this program permitted some diversion of cleared land immediately into nonfarm uses.

The Alaska Legislature in 1953 passed an agricultural loan bill with a million dollars authorized and 200 thousand dollars appropriated. In 1955 and 1957, respectively, 150 thousand dollars and 125 thousand dollars were appropriated. These funds are administered by the Commissioner of Agriculture and a five-man board for both development and production loans. The Board of the Alaska Rural Rehabilitation Corporation authorized 50 thousand dollars for land-clearing loans in early 1955. All were allocated by May 1955.

Favorable repayment experience on farm loans held by these agencies encouraged liberalized local bank policies on short-term agricultural loans, and a slight easing of funds resulted. More and more settlers were able to clear enough land for efficient farm units. Progress was particularly notable in the Tanana Valley during the mid-1950's. In the Matanuska Valley, new farms entered commercial production and older units were expanded. Activities in the Kenai Peninsula still lagged.

The 1940 census of agriculture showed 7,305 acres harvested in Alaska during 1939. The 1950 census showed only 6,450 acres harvested, 3,586 acres idle or without a crop, and 2,449 acres of cropland pastured in 1949. Nearly half of the statistical decline in harvested cropland between enumerations was accounted for by a decrease in the reported acreage of wild hay. It occurred despite the 2,637 acres cleared in 1945–1949.

Statistics on agricultural production have been compiled cooperatively by the experiment station and the Territorial department of agriculture since 1953. This annual series shows 8,123 acres harvested in 1953 and 15,743 acres in 1957. Land-clearing activity under the Agricultural Conservation Program was at about the same average tempo, but other funds were used also. Less than half of the clearing in 1955 was supported by the Agricultural Conservation Program. More than 1 thousand acres a year were cleared in 1953 and 1954; 1,710 acres were cleared in 1955 and 2,292 acres in 1957. Estimates of the total acreage of cropland have increased from an optimistic 12,385 acres (because of a questionable figure of 2,449 acres listed as "cropland pasture") in 1949 to 14,764 in 1955 and 20,000 in 1957.

Idle cropland and acres on which crops failed have continued at about 2 thousand acres a year, much of it in raw cleared status and on nonfarm tracts. This figure has declined in significance from 28 percent of cropland reported by the 1949 census to 14 percent of that reported in 1955 and 10 percent in 1956.

About 350 commercial farmers were concentrating on dairy, potato, poultry, and vegetable types of farming in 1957. A few beef and sheep enterprises were on the islands.

Another 500 to 700 part-time and "nominal" operators (of underdeveloped homesteads) were in varying stages of farm development. This net estimate recognizes that roughly half of the present homestead entrymen will not acquire patent and that others will become absentee owners of undeveloped land. It compares favorably with the breakdown of 525 farms into 217 commercial, 14 grazing or fur, 58 part-time, 52 residential, 5 abnormal, and 179 nominal farms from the 1949 census tabulations in "Agricultural Land Use in Alaska," by Robert J. Coffman and Hugh A. Johnson.

The rapid increase in numbers of commercial farms during this 5-year period reflects the vigor instilled into the agricultural scene by a new generation of farmers, a new program of basic agricultural research and extension, a modern marketing program, liberalized credit, and a strong market.

The gross value of farm products sold increased from 1.6 million dollars in 1949 to 2.7 million dollars in 1955 and 3.3 million dollars in 1957. Production of milk accounted for 49 percent of farm sales in 1957, followed by potatoes, 25 percent; eggs and poultry, 11 percent; other livestock products, 8 percent; and vegetables, 7 percent. The Matanuska Valley-Anchorage area supplied 67 percent of this production; the Tanana Valley, 16 percent; Southeastern Alaska, 9 percent; the Kenai Peninsula, 4 percent; and Kodiak and the Aleutians, the remaining 4 percent.

Types of farming in Alaska vary by regions and within regions according to degree of farm development.

We must first rule out an undetermined number of entrymen whose tenure is too new to show what they will do finally — 367 homestead entries, for example, were made at Anchorage and Fairbanks Land Offices in fiscal 1956.

The Tanana Valley probably will develop into a region that is largely self-sufficient in milk, eggs, feed grains, forage, and acclimated truck crops. It may sell feed grains to the Matanuska Valley and Kenai Peninsula. In the 1950's, however, its roughly 100 established homesteaders and farmers were far from this goal. About 30 families depended on potatoes for farm income. About a dozen grew potatoes and small patches of vegetables, a half dozen were full-time general truck-crop farmers, 3 were dairymen, and 2 or 3 specialized in poultry. The rest were part-time farmers, who depended on nonfarm income while they cleared land and grew small acreages of potatoes or other truck crops.

The pattern in the Matanuska Valley appears to be fairly well established. Dairying predominates and is probably the climax type of farming. It is followed in importance by potato, poultry, vegetable, and mixed or general small farms. Farm ownership and occupancy were changing rapidly in the mid-1950's as families adjusted to the Alaskan situation. New farmers, rather than those with long experience, are the rule. Only a few farms were retained by the second generation of a single family. These rapid changes hinder overall, long-range planning on farms and detract from the group decisions so necessary in an agricultural economy.

Richard A. Andrews, of the Alaska Agricultural Experiment Station, determined from a study of farm-management records in the Matanuska Valley that it took an average full-time dairyman in the valley 13 years to develop a dairy farm of adequate size from wilderness. Methods of financing and stocking varied. Most had started with small acreages of vegetables, shifted to potatoes as they cleared more land, and finally dropped the potato enterprise as their acreages and livestock numbers became sufficient to support their families. Shifts to dairying from other enterprises were made in 4 to 7 years. Increases in cropland cleared or rented generally paralleled livestock increases at a rate of 5 acres per animal unit.

An efficient, family-sized dairy farm, therefore, requires about 150 acres of cropland and a tract of 300 acres or more if the soils are distributed in average proportions. Potato, vegetable, or poultry farms require smaller acreages, although the better producers find that grains and grasses must be included in the rotation to insure proper tilth.

Agricultural development on the Kenai Peninsula is in its early formative stage, although parts of this area were occupied almost as early as were the Matanuska and Tanana Valleys. Half of its full-time farms in 1955, nearly all of which were in the Homer sector, were primarily livestock operations. None of the beef or dairy farms was sufficiently developed to provide a satisfactory family living. The largest number had beef enterprises, followed in order by poultry and dairy. Greenhouse, potato, and truck farms were found, particularly among the part-time group.

Climate, soils, and competition probably will encourage farmers in the Homer area to specialize in dairy, beef, poultry, possibly wool, and a few vegetable and greenhouse enterprises. Farther up the coast in the Kenai-Kasilof sector, potatoes, vegetables, dairy, poultry, and some general farming may develop. The climate and marketing conditions will encourage development of grassland farming in the Homer area and probably of truck farms in the Kenai area. They will prevent extensive culture of small grains on the Kenai Peninsula.

Beef and sheep enterprises based on use of native forages are practically exclusive on Kodiak and the islands to the westward. This situation probably will continue. A few dairy and poultry farms may develop from time to time to fill local needs. Limited local markets and expensive transportation to other markets are major limiting factors in this region.

Types of farming in Southeastern Alaska historically have involved dairy, fur, poultry, beef, potatoes, and mixed truck crops. Markets are local, and the success of enterprises apparently depends on the operators' resourcefulness and energy. Relatively little land exists for extensive use as cropland.

Tenure in a frontier area differs from the tenure pattern of established communities. Most farms are operated by their owners, and most owners have debts. Raw land is available. Few families are willing to rent. Few farms are large enough to warrant paid managers. Various arrangements for renting fields are common in the Matanuska Valley and to a lesser extent in the Tanana Valley. This tends to affect "part-owner" status by the census definitions.

The census of 1950 showed 85 percent of farm operators were full owners; 10 percent, part owners; and the rest, managers or tenants. No later tabulation has been made. I estimate that the proportion of tenants has increased in relation to that of managers and that the proportions of part owners and full owners have remained about the same from 1949 to 1957.

The average mortgage of 3,655 dollars per farm on 22 percent of all farms shown in the census of 1950 provides no guide to the present debt load. Most of the mortgages were on colony farms in the Matanuska Valley and possibly on some of the large island operations. The proportion of mortgaged farms may have declined, but the proportion of farmers having developmental debts of other kinds has increased because of the kind of loan funds available and because many loans are made on a man's character and reputation rather than on the tangible assets in his balance sheet.

The capital value of land and buildings, equipment, and livestock in Alaska increased after the war, particularly after 1953. No total estimates are available. Farm management studies begun by the Department of Agriculture in 1948 and continued by economists at the experiment station disclosed that farms are in all stages of development. The average investment in buildings and equipment on 27 potato farms in the Tanana Valley in 1953 was 8,400 dollars. Their average of 37 acres of cropland and 194 acres of other land was worth another 8 thousand dollars to 9 thousand dollars. Few of these farms would support a family as yet.

Thirty-six dairy farmers in the Matanuska Valley had an average investment of 13,500 dollars in buildings and equipment and another 7,900 dollars in livestock. They had about 20 thousand dollars in an average of 288 acres, of which 104 acres were cropland. Most of these farms still were not fully developed but largely supported their operators.

Sample farm budgets prepared by the experiment station and the Bureau of Land Management agree that the equivalent of 40 thousand to 60 thousand dollars must be invested before a family has an efficient 20-cow dairy farm. Almost as much is needed for a commercial potato or truck farm. A beef or sheep ranch that can support a family usually requires a greater investment.

Emerging problems of landownership and control in an area so huge and with problems so diverse mean that the limited capital resources must be husbanded and efforts must be concentrated.

No useful purpose can be served by unwarranted hopes that the great balance of unreserved public lands in Alaska will enter private ownership within the foreseeable future. Most of this land has no known economic use in private hands. The best allocation attainable will occur under intelligent, prompt, and equitable administration when economically feasible enterprises appear — as true under statehood as under Federal control.

Alaska's population is clustered in widely separated areas and communities. Any frontier or sparsely settled area has basic requirements for an economic-social "infrastructure" — a minimum set of facilities required for living and for production.

Harold Jorgensen, of the Bureau of Land Management, summarized the situation thus: "Experience has shown that it is only when effective land and mineral laws, efficient public land administration, and a basic economic-social infrastructure are provided that orderly, economical, and permanent settlement and development occur on America's northern public lands in which private initiative plays its full part, and then only if all are carefully knit into a suitable pattern of area development."

The social costs of isolated settlement have received too little attention.

Alaska has the soils and the climate to permit production of large quantities of grains, forage, cool-weather vegetables, and certain fruits. Under the present economics of trade and transportation, however, products from its farms and interior forests must be consumed locally. Its market, therefore, is limited by the numbers of civilians, military dependents, and military personnel within its trade areas. Only certain crops and livestock products can be produced in competition with goods shipped to Alaska from the United States and other countries. The varied diet of our modern society requires importation of many foods from other producing areas just as in any State. Alaskans can hope to meet about half the total amount of food required by a modern population from the products they can produce.

Analysis of the production and consumption potential in 1949 by Wendell Calhoun and me showed that between 3 thousand and 4 thousand acres of cropland would supply all local farm products needed for each 10 thousand effective consumers at current yields. These estimates were generally verified by independent studies by the Bureau of Land Management. This relationship has not changed basically. Thus, a future consuming population of 200 thousand persons would utilize the products from 60 thousand to 80 thousand acres. Alaska now has between 15 thousand and 19 thousand acres prepared for production and a large unfilled market for certain items. It has several hundred underdeveloped farms and homesteads in private resident or nonresident ownership. Sudden development to full-time farm status on half of these farms and homesteads would create serious surpluses of farm products.

Emphasis on technical, financial, and marketing assistance is needed for the farm families that are already partly in production. No economic need appears to exist for new or additional homesteading lands in the next few years. It would seem wiser to consolidate present gains before additional areas are opened to settlement.

An almost untapped market exists both in Alaska and in the States for specialty products such as low-bush cranberries (similar to European lingenberries), blueberries, smoked and dried salmon, sheefish, ling cod, shellfish, reindeer meat, artifacts, and other local products.

One enterprising firm at Homer has processed local berries successfully and developed a national luxury market for its products. A homesteader on Iliamna Lake hired Indian women to gather cranberries to be shipped by air to Anchorage and Seattle. Similar enterprises offer hope of cash income in currently distressed areas.

Problems inherent in this type of enterprise are almost insurmountable for persons without capital and contacts. Assistance from public and private agencies in establishing necessary production standards, perfecting transportation schedules, and developing market outlets and loans for development would open the way for a possible multimillion-dollar industry based on harvesting and processing the products of natural resources.

Stateside experience in the West under the homestead acts demonstrated that individuals, unless prevented by law, will settle and try to farm land unsuited to agriculture. The western provinces of Canada had this problem, which was aggravated by the scattered population. The foresighted Canadians closed to settlement their public domain that was not in well-defined blocks. Public services thus could be concentrated within prescribed areas.

The experience with homesteading in Alaska demonstrates anew the need for guided and controlled settlement. New legislation is needed to permit classification of land for efficient and economical administration of future settlement and development. Only through this process will it be possible to keep costs of governmental services within bounds.

A tax on real property would aid development of concentrated areas. Nonresident owners currently can hold good undeveloped land, and there is no way to make them bear a share in community expenses. This problem is particularly cirtical on the Kenai Peninsula, although it exists wherever title has passed to absentee owners. Scattered families have great difficulty in developing stable communities. The intervening vacant and idle tracts often contain land that is better than average and should be developed and used before the margins of settlement are extended. The new land registration law may help to alleviate this problem.

Despite the impression in some quarters that policies of the Bureau of Land Management and past slowness in some of its operations have retarded use of resources, the facts show that the Bureau has been generous in its administration of public lands. The principle behind the Homestead Act was to encourage the development of productive farms from the public domain. Pressure to open more lands to entry is constantly brought to bear. Data show that farms develop from about 10 percent of the tracts homesteaded. Of 49 grazing leases in effect on June 30, 1956, covering almost a million acres, most were stocked below the lease requirements. Many were stocked at less than 50 percent of the number scheduled in the leases, and several had no livestock, although the leases had been in effect for at least a year.

The major problem is not to get more land under private control but rather to get into development and use the lands already appropriated or patented. Too many people are trying to develop farms and ranches without adequate financing or knowledge of farming.

Problems of financing have been made less acute in recent years through the half-million dollars of Territorial and Alaska Rural Rehabilitation Corporation revolving funds made available for production, expansion, and development loans. Some local banks are venturing into short-term agricultural loans. Federal lending agencies still lag in their Alaskan programs. Some additional funds are needed to speed worthy operators of underdeveloped farms toward full-time, efficient farming status.

Alaskan consumers are cosmopolitan in their tastes and sophisticated in their requirements. They demand and will pay for high-quality products only. Market development and improved marketing techniques must occur simultaneously with increasing production.

Through the agricultural research program, which was revitalized in 1948, outstanding gains have been made in solving problems of physical production in adapted crops and in dairying. The marketing and consumer-preference problems have been described. Future emphasis focused on storage conditions, packaging, and processing probably would be desirable. The extension program needs strengthening in its technical aids to farmers and expansion of its information service to retailers and housewives. The marketing, grading, and information programs of the Territorial department of agriculture have been expanded in recent years. However, the department has a key role in the future of agriculture and needs further expansion and strengthening in conjunction with a vital extension program.

Relations between the public and its officials in charge of land settlement and development programs may be strained at times, because neither fully understands the problems faced by the other. Greater use of advisory committees and consultation on economic development programs would be mutually advantageous.

In conclusion: Resident Alaskans want action. They want the opportunity to develop agriculture, trade, and industry. They live among potential resources that they believe could form the foundation for growing and prosperous communities. They want to make Alaska a settled, integral part of the United States. They become impatient at restrictions that appear to them to limit the growth of population and, therefore, of trade and business opportunities.

The frontier attitude toward land and resources still thrives in Alaska, where soils await farmers while foodstuffs are shipped in from other places. The forests, the minerals, the waterpower of Alaska are potentials still to be developed. To Alaskans, any prospect of eventual economic overproduction seems far in the future. They believe that resources should be developed now to meet present needs and in anticipation of continued growth.

It should be evident from the record briefly developed here that no simple solution exists for land problems in Alaska. The Federal Government has seemed to move slowly and not always in the direction desired by many Alaskans. But real progress has been made in many fields. Extension of the mining and homestead laws and specific legislation enabling entry and use of land for homesites, recreation, commercial and industrial development, oil and gas exploration, and other purposes has made land resources available for use.

I have tried to demonstrate or illustrate the hard economic facts with which land users in Alaska have been faced. More than laws are required to convert wilderness into prosperous farms. Local markets for farm products are necessary to economically successful farm development.

A majority of the homesteaders who have failed did so because they lacked the necessary capital to develop farms from raw land, the requisite technical knowledge of agriculture, and the tenacity and singleness of purpose required to overcome hardships common on any frontier. Getting additional land into private ownership does not guarantee that food production will follow.

Farm families who have overcome their problems and developed commercial farms within transportation distance of urban areas have a market for nearly anything they can produce. More recent settlers are finding loan funds a little less tight, much more information available about technical production problems, a much larger market, and a market more favorably inclined toward local products.

The potential market for farm products is not unlimited. The problem is to encourage farm development to the point within the available market at which the greatest number of farm families are making satisfactory incomes from their efficient methods.

In this light, one can better understand the current conflicts of interest in landownership and use. Alaska can be a great land. Common understanding, mutual good will, responsible planning based on careful research, and recognition of economic facts are necessary for sound development of its land resources in the best interests of all the people.

Farming in Hawaii

From Perry F. Philipp, "Hawaii's Problems and Many Assets," U.S. Department of Agriculture, *Yearbook*, 1958 (Washington, 1958), pp. 440–48.

The use and ownership of land in Hawaii and in the continental United States differ from each other in many ways because of differences in location, climate, and history.

The eight major islands of Hawaii lie entirely in the Tropics. Honolulu, the largest city, is 2,100 nautical miles from San Francisco, the nearest Mainland harbor. The people of Hawaii refer to the continental United States as the Mainland.

The Islands are of volcanic origin. Large parts of the interior of all of them consist of rugged, mountainous terrain. The two highest peaks are close to 14 thousand feet above sea level. Plateaus, coastal plains, and the lower mountain slopes, although they comprise a small part of the total area, are the most important lands.

The climate is mild. Temperatures change little between summer and winter in most of the inhabited parts. The average annual rainfall in agricultural areas varies from 200 inches to less than 20 inches within a few miles, mostly because of topographic influences. The range from the tropical to the desert and from sea level to high altitudes permits the production of a great variety of agricultural products.

The land area of the Hawaiian Islands is 4.1 million acres, or 0.2 percent of the land area of the Mainland. Less than 8 percent of the total land area is used for crops, about 25 percent is grazed, and 29 percent is forest or woodland. (All figures I give are for 1956, unless otherwise stated.)

The remaining land, more than a third of the total land area, is used for purposes other than agriculture and forests. It includes special-use areas such as cities and towns, roads, parks, and military areas and wasteland, such as bare lava flows and gulches.

When Captain James Cook discovered the Hawaiian Islands in 1778, he found a primitive, self-sufficient economy based mainly on fishing and small farms held under feudal tenure. Hawaii today has a highly developed trading economy, heavily dependent on the Mainland. Its agricultural exports amount to more than a quarter of a billion dollars.

The oldest and largest agricultural industry in the Islands is growing and processing sugarcane. Sugarcane was indigenous to Hawaii at the time of its discovery, but production had reached only 2 tons a year in 1837. The value of 1,100,000 tons of raw sugar, together with molasses and other by-products, amounted to 148 million dollars in 1956. About 221 thousand acres were in cane.

Most of the land in sugarcane consists of what used to be forested areas, semiarid pasturelands, or useless arid areas. The sugarcane acreage is in low-land tracts. Attempts to grow cane at levels above 2,500 feet are seldom made. Some land has been planted to cane almost continuously for more than a century, yet with heavy fertilization and good soil management, these lands are at least as fertile today as when sugar culture began.

It takes about a ton of water to produce a pound of sugar. Slightly more than half of the cane area is irrigated; it produces a little less than two-thirds of the total sugar. The rest of the sugarcane is grown on the wet windward sides of the Islands and depends on rainfall.

The unit of organization in the sugar industry is the plantation, which grows the cane and manufactures it into raw sugar. A steady decline in the number of plantations has been offset by a corresponding increase in their size.

Twenty-seven plantations were in operation in 1957; the average area planted to sugarcane per plantation was 8,200 acres. The largest plantation had 27,700 acres in cane. The smallest had 600 acres. Plantation operations were geared to year-round employment for the 17 thousand employees in the industry.

A plantation consists of the land controlled by the company, the sugar mill, shops and central offices, a road system, and the plantation town and housing areas for plantation employees. About 70 percent of the plantation employees and their families lived in plantation-owned homes in 1957. The plantation town often is a self-contained community. It usually has a business district with stores, a school, churches, a theater, a recreation field and gymnasium, a hospital, and public services and utilities.

Besides the land used for growing sugarcane, many sugar companies hold considerable acreages of nonarable land, which is used mainly for water conservation or grazing.

Approximately 1,300 small growers raise sugarcane on about 9 percent of the total sugarcane acreage. A majority of these operate independently and sell their sugarcane under government-approved contracts to the plantations.

Pineapple production, primarily for canned fruit and juice, is the Islands' second major agricultural industry. The annual output of processed products is valued at 117 million dollars. The acreage in pineapples increased from 5 thousand acres in 1909 to 77 thousand in 1956. The fruit is grown at altitudes ranging from near sea level to about 2 thousand feet.

The most productive pineapple lands have a rainfall of 25 to 60 inches of rain a year. Areas with less rain are usually too arid unless irrigation water is applied. More rain may adversely affect yield and quality. Pineapple production makes it possible to use many areas too dry for most other crops.

The pineapple industry, like the sugar industry, has developed in the direction of large-scale, integrated plantations. Nine pineapple companies operate 13 plantations and 9 canneries. A minor part of the crop is raised on about 120 small, nonplantation farms, most of which have contracts with canneries. The pineapple industry provides employment for about 22 thousand persons during the peak summer canning season and year-round employment for more than 9 thousand.

Crops other than sugar and pineapple, called diversified crops in Hawaii, occupy 16 thousand acres — 5 percent of the total cropland in the Islands. Their wholesale value, however, is high — about 13 million dollars.

Coffee, the largest of the diversified crops, is grown on nearly 6 thousand acres. About 1 thousand small farmers operate groves, which usually are 5 to 10 acres in size. They are mainly in the Kona district of the Island of Hawaii. The coffee is grown at elevations of 800 to 2,200 feet on steep, rocky, and stony slopes. The soil is productive. The climate is excellent for coffee. The yield is high. Kona coffee is highly regarded and is shipped chiefly to the Mainland.

The area planted to macadamia nuts, which are confectionery nuts of excellent quality, has almost tripled since the war. It amounted to about 2,800 acres in 1956. The nuts are planted mostly in tracts previously used for grazing or forest. Hawaii is apparently the only place where macadamia nuts are grown commercially on a sizable scale.

For Island consumption, Hawaiian farmers grow many western vegetables, such as cabbage, tomatoes, and cucumbers, and such Oriental vegetables as burdock, daikon, and watercress. The limited size of the Hawaiian market means that most production is on small fields. This, together with many insects and diseases and high requirements of fertilizer and irrigation, make production costs high.

Papayas, bananas, and passion fruit are the most important of the commercially grown fruits. The rest are mainly avocados, citrus fruits, mangos, guavas, and lychee. Most vegetable and fruit farms are family operated. Only a few are larger than family size. The area in commercially grown fruits and vegetables is about 6 thousand acres.

Taro is the plant from which poi, the Hawaiians' staff of life, is made. The area in taro is about 600 acres, only a fraction of the taro acreage at the time Hawaii was discovered. A decline in the number of Hawaiians and the competition of cheaper starchy foods caused this drop.

Rice, once second in importance and area only to sugar, occupies 200 acres or less. Development of the large-scale mechanized rice industry in California doomed the Hawaiian industry, the mechanization of which is limited by the small size of the paddies.

The growth of air transportation in the postwar period helped Island growers to develop a million-dollar export of floral products, primarily tropical foliage, orchids, and anthuriums. They also produce commercially many other floral products, mainly for the flower-loving Islands. Farmers use an estimated 600 acres for flowers.

Many other crops — cotton, wheat, tobacco, rubber, silk, and sisal — have been tried commercially in Hawaii but have proved economically unsound.

Livestock products are valued at 27 million dollars annually. Most of Hawaii's grasslands are used for cattle and a few sheep.

At least three-fourths of all beef cattle, numbering about 160 thousand head, are raised on large ranches, many of which extend from dry lowland to wet upland zones. The best pastures in the zones of moderate rainfall are set aside for grass fattening. The less productive areas and the wetter rangelands are used mainly for breeding animals and young stock. Most of the small ranches are in areas of moderate rainfall in which there is year-round grazing.

Keeping plant pests from overruning pastures is a major job of the ranchers. To control brush and weeds, they use some of the largest bulldozers known, which pull big anchor chains or disks. Herbicides also are used.

Locally produced milk amounts to 47 million quarts annually, compared to 2 million quarts in 1900. It is mainly consumed as fluid milk. Most cows on the 89 dairies of the Islands are in large herds. Twenty-seven dairymen keep more than 150 cows each and eight keep more than 300 cows. Corporations own several large dairies.

Most of the dairymen operate on the Island of Oahu (on which Honolulu lies) to supply the city market. They usually keep their cows in feedlots and use their limited arable lands for growing soilage crops. They prefer Napier-grass for this purpose, because it yields 100 to 150 tons of green feed an acre. Some dairymen on the Islands other than Oahu pasture their milking cows, but few on Oahu can afford to use their small holdings so extensively. Except for molasses and pineapple bran and pulp, almost all concentrate feeds have to be brought from the Mainland.

Swine producers sell 70 thousand hogs a year for slaughter. They raise their animals in concrete or wooden pens. They feed them garbage, imported grain, and rations compounded of local feedstuffs.

Poultry farmers raise about 1 million chickens mainly on feed imported from the Mainland and usually keep them in wire-floored houses off the ground. Typical Hawaiian poultry and swine farms are small in land area and operated by the farm family.

Hawaiian farmers expect to expand their output only slowly from now on. Sugar exports to the Mainland — Hawaii's main export market — are limited by Federal law. Sugar planters expect no substantial increases in the near future. The production and export of pineapples will depend on the competition of other domestic fruits and juices and of foreign and Puerto Rican pineapple producers.

Exports of other agricultural products are small, although exports of tropical fruit and nut products have a large growth potential. Farmers have increased their production for Island use in the postwar period at the average rate of about 1.5 million dollars a year. They may increase production further if Hawaii's population continues to grow and if they can compete with the prices and quality of Mainland food imports.

Large-scale farms are more important in Hawaii than on the Mainland. According to the 1950 United States Census, farms with annual sales of 25 thousand dollars or more each made 91 percent of all farm sales in Hawaii but only 26 percent of all farm sales on the Mainland.

Many large farms in Hawaii are highly mechanized and efficient. Labor shortages during the Second World War and unionization of workers in the processing plants and in the fields brought much higher wages and shorter hours. Average daily earnings for nonsupervisory sugarworkers on plantations increased from 1.70 dollars in 1935 to 11.20 dollars in 1957. These are cash wages; the 1935 figure does not include substantial perquisites, such as free housing, medical care, fuel, light, and water.

Operators of plantations and other large farms have been trying to offset higher labor costs by more mechanization, laborsaving practices, and higher yields per acre. In the sugar industry, for example, the labor force was cut more than two-thirds, but output per worker more than tripled since 1932. The sugar tonnage per acre increased 50 percent at the same time.

Farmers selling from 2,500 to 25 thousand dollars' worth of agricultural products a year made only 7 percent of all farm sales in Hawaii, compared to 62 percent on the Mainland. These farmers nevertheless are important in Hawaii; they are the backbone of most of the diversified agricultural industries. Their productivity has increased greatly since the war.

Two-thirds of all Hawaiian farmers, 3,750 in number, sold only 2 percent of all agricultural products. Some of them are marginal full-time farmers; their number has been declining. Most farmers in this group are part-time or residential farmers, who derive most of their income from occupations other than farming. Their number increased several times between 1940 and 1950.

In view of the shortening workweek and the increasing urbanization in Hawaii, this trend toward part-time and residential farms probably is a healthy one. It can help to reduce the tendency toward overcrowding into thickly populated areas and offers the family a healthy outdoor life and some economic return.

Managers are the most important type of farm operator in Hawaii. They run the plantations and many large ranches and other large agricultural enterprises. According to the 1950 census, there were only 109 managers, or fewer than 2 percent of all farm operators, but they controlled 78 percent of Hawaii's agricultural land and an even larger share of all the cropland.

Full and part owners amounted to 40 percent of all operators. They used 20 percent of the agricultural land. About 58 percent of the operators were tenants, but they used less than 2 percent of the agricultural land.

Farmers in Hawaii are highly specialized, and many produce only one type of product, such as sugarcane or milk or pork. They become so efficient in producing their specialties that it often does not even pay them to raise their own food for home use.

The numerical importance and status in agriculture of the several races represented in Hawaii vary greatly — depending largely on the time of their arrival in the Islands, their experience, and their traditions in their countries of origin.

The Filipinos were the latest racial group to come to Hawaii. They constitute the largest part of the hired labor force in agriculture and are beginning to establish themselves as tenant farmers, especially as coffee farmers.

The Japanese, second to the last to arrive, are the second largest racial group among plantation workers. Most of the small farmers are of Japanese ancestry.

The Chinese were the earliest immigrants of Oriental origin. They once constituted a large group of plantation workers and farmers, particularly rice growers, but most of them have left agriculture.

Caucasians own or manage many of the large agricultural enterprises. Hawaiians and part-Hawaiians operate some ranches or work on them. They also produce some crops, and a few come close to subsistence farming.

Island farmers, like Mainland farmers, operate within an extensive system of laws and regulations. Regulating authorities include Federal, Territorial, and county agencies.

Public and private agricultural experiment stations do extensive research. The University of Hawaii and the public schools offer courses and training in agriculture.

Commercial banks furnish credit for large-scale agricultural enterprises and small sugarcane producers. Other small farmers, however, obtain most of their capital from the Farmers Home Administration or from their families and friends. Dealers also sometimes carry their accounts for feed, fertilizer, and other supplies.

Farmers owning land, like all other private landowners, pay a Territorial tax on real property. The tax is based on the assessed value of the land and its improvements. A part of the assessed value of an owned home is tax exempt to encourage homeownership. Agricultural land bears the same tax rate as urban property.

Irrigation has long been important in Hawaiian agriculture. The old Hawaiians used efficient methods of irrigation. They brought water through ditches to their taro fields from streams that often were far away. Sugar planters built large-scale irrigation systems. The East Maui ditch system, for example, has a capacity of more than 500 cubic feet a second. Subterranean water resources have been developed by large-scale pumping.

Development of irrigation water in Hawaii has been made almost entirely with private capital. In 1953 the Territorial Legislature created an agency now called the Hawaii Water Authority and provided it with public funds for the further development of the water resources of the Islands.

In 1950, 117 thousand acres were irrigated according to the United States Census. By far the largest part of it was in sugarcane. Most of the rest was in diversified crops. An increasing acreage of pineapple fields and pastures is irrigated in the drier sections.

Soil erosion is a serious problem in Hawaii because of steep slopes and heavy rainfall on some of the farmlands. Conservation of water is vital in many areas.

Farmers and ranchers, assisted by Federal and local agencies, have given soil and water conservation increasing attention. The Territorial Legislature adopted an enabling act in 1947 for the creation of soil conservation districts. Such districts had been established in many areas by 1958.

Territorial forest and water reserve zones cover about 30 percent of the total area of the Islands, or 1.2 million acres. More than two-thirds of the reserve zones are public land. The rest is privately owned. Their primary purpose is to provide plant cover that will prevent rapid runoff and erosion.

A growing trend is to put forest and water reserve zones to such multiple uses as game management, public hunting, hiking, and other recreational purposes. Large areas are used for military training.

Many species of commercial timber can be grown successfully in Hawaii, but the timber industry is still in its infancy. The value of all forest products sold in 1949 was less than 50 thousand dollars. Both the Government and private landowners are interested in the better utilization of forest timber resources, and timber research has been initiated.

About 250 thousand acres have been set aside for recreational use. The Hawaii National Park contains 231 thousand acres. Its larger section, on the Island of Hawaii, includes the active volcanoes Mauna Loa and Kilauea and surrounding areas. Its smaller section, on the Island of Maui, covers mainly the vast crater of Haleakala, an extinct volcano. All major islands have a number of Territorial and city and county parks and playgrounds. Beaches, which are public to the high watermark, are another important recreational asset of Hawaii.

The only mineral resources used commercially at present are rock, limestone, and sand. The possibility of economical development of other mineral deposits, primarily bauxite, is being investigated.

Surveys and classifications of land resources of the Territory have been made for various purposes. A detailed soil survey of the Territory was published in 1955. The Soil Conservation Service has classified the capabilities of land for agricultural uses in many areas. A comprehensive economic classification and study program of Hawaii's lands at the University of Hawaii was initiated by the Territorial Legislature in 1957.

The pattern of land tenure in Hawaii is largely the result of the land division in the 1840's and 1850's (called the Great Mahele), the development of large-scale agricultural enterprises, and the largely unsuccessful policy of homesteading a part of the public domain. In Old Hawaii, all land belonged to the king, who distributed it to his principal chiefs on a feudal basis. They in turn allotted the land to lesser chiefs, who subdivided it among the common people.

The landholding system changed during the Great Mahele. The king divided the land among the chiefs, the Government, and common people, and kept some for himself. The king's own property, or crown land, amounted to somewhat less than 1 million acres; the Government land, about 1.5 million acres; the chiefs', a little more than 1.5 million acres; and the people's, a little less than 30 thousand acres. The farms given to the common people, however, consisted primarily of irrigated taro lands, which were regarded as the most valuable lands at that time.

Much of the land soon passed into the hands of non-Hawaiians (particularly sugar planters and cattle ranchers) by sale, lease, or marriage. Fifty-seven percent of the taxable land belonged to them by 1896. Title to all Government and crown land was conveyed to the United States by the act of annexation in 1898. Agencies of the Territorial Government have continued to manage most of the public lands, however.

Public land amounted to about 42 percent and private land to 58 percent of all land in the Islands in 1956. Of the Government-owned land, 1,250 thousand acres were Territorial; 10 thousand acres were county lands; 170 thousand acres belonged to the Hawaiian Homes Commission; and 320 thousand acres were Federal land.

The Territorial Department of the Tax Commissioner set the market value of all lands in the Territory at 1.4 billion dollars in 1956. Private landholders owned 70 percent of it, and public land accounted for 30 percent.

The most valuable part of the public land was held by the Armed Forces.

Much of the Territorial public land is poor. More than 800 thousand acres are in forest and water reserve zones. Most of the rest is leased out for agricultural purposes, mainly for grazing.

The Hawaiian Homes Commission land was set aside by an act of the Congress in 1920. The act provides for granting land to persons of not less than half Han blood for homesteads, farms, or pastures under 99-year leases at the nominal rent of 1 dollar a year. Hawaiian Homes Commission land includes areas in or near the major cities, some valuable agricultural land, and some poor land. Most of the residents of Hawaiian Homes Commission settlements are city oriented, rather than the men of the soil apparently contemplated by the framers of the act.

A few trusts, corporations, and individuals hold most of the private lands.

The 11 largest landowners in 1956 owned 50 percent of all private lands in the Islands, and the 60 largest owned 80 percent.

About half of the agricultural land is owned by the farmers and plantations who use it, and one-half is leased by them. The ratio between owned and leased land, however, varies from industry to industry. For example, sugar plantations own about 60 percent of the cane land, ranchers about half of the pastures, and coffee growers about a fourth of the orchards, which they operate.

In view of the large amount of leased land, good leasing practices are essential. Farmland usually is rented for cash. Only about 10 percent of all rental agreements are on a share basis.

Public leases are for up to 15 years for cropland and up to 21 years for pastureland that cannot be irrigated. Private grazing, sugar, and pineapple leases for large areas often run for 20 years — some for more than 40 years. Small farmers in diversified agriculture often have to be content with shorter leases and sometimes with only oral leases of a year or less.

Lessees of both private and public agricultural lands ordinarily do not get any credit for improvements they make on the leased property. Removal of these improvements, while not allowed in most old rental agreements, may be permitted in new ones at the expiration of the lease.

The laws governing water rights in Hawaii with respect to surface waters appear to be unique in the United States. In general, the owner of land has the right to the surface water that originates on his land, subject to rights that may be vested in others by ancient usage or deed.

The law is vague on ground water except for artesian waters — that is, subterranean waters confined under pressure. According to one court decision, all owners of land over an artesian basin have a common right to the reasonable use of the artesian water.

Title to surface water is held by both private owners and by the Government. Like land, the control of water resources is highly concentrated. On the larger Islands, except for a few public departments, irrigation water is controlled largely by sugar and pineapple plantations or private water companies closely connected with the sugar-growing interests.

Two methods of land registration exist in Hawaii, the regular system and the land court system.

Under the regular system, the owner has a merchantable, fee-simple, recorded title.

A land court title is considered better than a regular title, because the title-holder is insured with the Territory against losses resulting from a faulty title. About 40 percent of all lands on Oahu and about 8 percent of all lands on other Islands have such titles.

The metes and bounds system is the principal means of measuring land in Hawaii. A land court title to any subdivided piece of land is always conveyed by block and lot number.

The population of the Islands, including military personnel, has grown from 368 thousand in 1930 to more than 600 thousand in 1958.

The importance of agriculture as a source of employment has declined greatly. About one in three gainfully employed persons worked on farms in 1939; in 1955, only about one in nine. Most people not employed in agriculture moved to the cities, mainly Honolulu, to work for the Armed Forces, or in the tourist industry, nonagricultural industries, trades and services.

The population of the "city" of Honolulu — the urbanized area on the leeward side of Oahu — rose from some 20 thousand in 1890 to 138 thousand in 1930 and 302 thousand in January 1958. Express highways were built to bring all parts of Oahu within commuting distance of the center of Honolulu. The population of Oahu outside the "city" of Honolulu increased by 32 percent between January 1955 and January 1958.

Oahu, with 9 percent of the total land area, had 76 percent of the civilian population of the Territory in January 1958. With 735 persons to the square mile, its population density exceeded that of Japan.

A major military base is maintained because of the Islands' strategic location. Almost all of the defense installations are on Oahu.

The military area amounts to almost 15 percent of the land area of Oahu.

The major problem of land use on Oahu is to develop additional residential and industrial areas but to retain enough land for agricultural production and for military and recreational purposes.

About 43 percent of Oahu in 1956 was forest and water reserve zones or was unimproved; 31 percent was agricultural land; and 10 percent was in urban use. At the 1957 rate of population growth, additional urban development would require about 1.7 square miles more land each year. At that rate, by 1980, the urban area would amount to 17 percent of the land area of the Island.

Most of the urban expansion can be expected to take place on the rather flat lands, which have been used for crops. Accordingly, nearly half of Oahu's lands with slopes of less than 10 percent may be urban by 1980.

In the development of additional residential and industrial areas, the scenic beauty of the Island should not be sacrificed. Tourism is Hawaii's fastest growing industry, and Oahu is its center. More than 160 thousand visitors came to the Islands in 1957. Oahu's appeal to tourists may decline greatly unless foresight is used in land development.

Land available for fee-simple purchase in the Islands is scarce — particularly fee-simple land on Oahu that is suitable for urban use. Major reasons for this short supply are the policy of many large landholders not to sell their holdings and the unwillingness of agricultural users to release land for urban use. High land prices have been the result. In suburban areas up to 12 miles from the center of Honolulu, fee-simple homesites sold from 75 cents to 1.25 dollars a square foot in 1957. Many homes, commercial buildings, and industrial installations therefore have been built on leased land.

Urban leasing practices have been improving. Leases for homesites, which formerly ran mostly for 30 years, now are often made for 50 years or more and permit the removal of improvements at the expiration of the lease.

In contrast to the expanding population on Oahu, the number of people living on the other Islands was smaller in 1958 than in 1930. The decline was caused primarily by the mechanization of plantation operations, which forced some residents to seek employment elsewhere.

Land on these other Islands is used mainly for agriculture and forest and water reserves. Cities are generally small, and urban development has been slow compared to Oahu. Hilo, the largest city on the outside Islands, had about 25 thousand inhabitants in 1958.

The location of more industry on Islands other than Oahu might well be encouraged. Such a policy would retard the rate of urban development on Oahu and at the same time strengthen the economy of the outlying Islands. On Oahu, it would tend to reduce the upward pressure on land prices, permit the retention of more valuable agriculture, and allow the use of more land for recreational purposes and scenic reserves. Relocation of some military establishments from Oahu to the other Islands would have similar effects.

Land-use plans existed for several areas in the Islands in 1957. Some private landowners had prepared such plans for both the agricultural and urban development of their lands.

The City Planning Commission of Honolulu had adopted a master plan for future land use, including the location of proposed schools, parks, and other community facilities and major thoroughfares. Plans for several other urban areas, on Oahu and the other Islands, had been made or were under study.

The Armed Forces and the National Park Service had prepared plans for the areas under their jurisdiction, but no comprehensive plan had been made for the best use of public land administered by the Territorial Government.

There existed no basic land policy or land utilization guide for the Territory as a whole in 1957, although modern communication and transportation had brought the several Islands closer together. Practically all interisland travel and transportation of some commodities is by air. An air trip between Honolulu and the most distant airport on the outlying Islands now takes little more than an hour.

The territorial legislature in 1957 created the Territorial Planning Office, headed by a director of territorial planning. He was given the task of preparing a long-range, comprehensive plan to serve as a guide for the future physical and economic development of the Territory. The plan is to include a statement of development objectives dealing with land use and such topics as population density, transportation, and public facilities.

The director was instructed by law to consider the following projects: The reclamation of submerged reefs by creating offshore islands; the return of certain military lands to civilian use; the need for and location of industrial sites and public buildings; the economic feasibility of establishing water sources and systems for underdeveloped or arid areas; and the economics of a further development of land, air, and water transportation between and across the various islands of the Territory.

The director was instructed also — in cooperation with Government agencies on all levels — to plan a comprehensive system of parks and recreational facilities throughout Hawaii.

The director is to guide and integrate the planning work of Territorial agencies and may assist in similar work of local bodies. The Governor of Hawaii is primarily responsible for coordinating the activities of the several agencies of the Territory within the framework of the general plan.

The director is required to prepare the general plan of the Territory in sections, one for each county. A county plan (or amendments to it) is to become effective only when enacted by a county ordinance. The director does not have the power to zone or control subdivision development. Those responsibilities belong to the counties.

Farming in Puerto Rico

From Julio A. Morales, "Puerto Rico: Change and Progress," U.S. Department of Agriculture, *Yearbook*, 1958 (Washington, 1958), pp. 449–57.

Puerto Rico is the smallest of the four major islands of the West Indian chain. It is a little more than 100 miles long and 35 miles wide, and 2,264,000 persons live in this small area.

Natural resources are limited. There are no mineral resources suitable for the development of heavy industry. Water is impounded in reservoirs for the production of electric power, but steam plants generate more than two-thirds of the electricity.

Land is the principal resource. Its use for agriculture is a predominant factor in the welfare of Puerto Ricans. Sugar, rum, molasses, cigars, coffee, and other agricultural products contribute to the economic structure.

An east-west range of mountains, reaching almost 4,400 feet above sea level, is the main topographic feature.

The relief south of the mountains is more craggy, and the coastal plain is narrower than to the north. The northern slope is less rough, and the grades change gradually to the coast. Most of the rivers begin high in the mountains and flow northward into the Atlantic. The rivers that flow down the southern slope are smaller and usually are dry a part of the year. The rivers are not navigable.

Trade winds that blow from the northeast make a mild climate throughout the year. The mean monthly temperature for the island is 73°F. in January and 79° in July. The highest recorded temperature is 103° in the lowlands; the lowest is 39° in the mountains.

Marked fluctuations in rainfall result mainly from the wide diversity of topography. The annual average is 60 inches in the north, 35 inches in the south, and almost 200 inches in the Luquillo Mountains. The mountains that divide the country cool the winds from the northeast and cause a higher precipitation on the northern side of the island. The dry periods usually extend from February to May in the north and from December to May in the south. The heaviest rains usually are in September to November.

A total of 115 soil series and 352 soil types and soil phases has been recorded. Such a large number of soil types result from the variations in climate, relief, vegetation, age, and parent material.

Physical factors restrict the use of land for crops more than they do for pastures. Climate, topography, soil differences, and personal choice — as influenced by economic, social, and related forces - determine the pattern of land use.

The few Indians who originally inhabited the Territory lived from farming, hunting, and fishing. The cultivated small plots of cassava, cotton, tobacco, and a few other plants.

When the Spanish colonists first settled in Puerto Rico, much of its land was fertile and forested. Their original interest was gold, and they paid little attention at first to agriculture. Toward the end of the 16th century, when the gold deposits had become exhausted, they turned to farming. They initially cultivated plantains, bananas, coconuts, ginger, and a few other tropical plants, and raised cattle, hogs, and some other animals. This start led to the gradual accumulation of knowledge of what agricultural uses are more adapted to the resources of the island.

The land resources of Puerto Rico have been grouped into 14 regions according to their agricultural adaptability. They epitomize centuries of experience with the interplay of physical social, and economic factors.

Topography and temperature are dominant factors in the classification of land in the lowlands, foothills, and mountains. Within the broad categories of foothills and lowlands, rainfall is taken into account by dividing each into the northern and southern sections.

The mountain and northern foothills and lowlands categories are each subdivided into two sections, reflecting variations in rainfall and soils. The social and economic factors interacting with these physical limitations gave rise to present patterns of use and ownership of land.

The physical environment has been brought through the centuries into productive use by farmers, operating as a basic part of society. Many of the adjustments and changes they have made through time in the use and ownership of land are essentially reactions to changes in relationships within society.

Drastic changes occurred when Puerto Rico became a Territory of the United States in 1898. Spanish relations with Puerto Rico had favored the cultivation of coffee; relations with the United States favored an expansion of the sugar industry.

The efforts of the United States to apply modern techniques of health, education, and public administration in the new Territory led to a rapid growth in population, and the island became one of the most densely populated areas of the world. A tremendous pressure of population on the land has had deep influences on the patterns of land use and ownership in Puerto Rico.

The early decades of this century brought a fast expansion of agriculture. Export crops, primarily sugarcane and tobacco, accounted for a major share of the expansion. Coffee dropped rapidly from the position of principal export crop to a level that barely covered local requirements.

The process of economic development since 1945 has been characterized by an expansion in the industrial, construction, and service sectors of the economy, and agriculture has remained almost the same.

The earlier period of agricultural expansion brought a pronounced displacement of population from the highlands, where coffee is grown, to the lowlands, where sugarcane is produced. It brought also the corporation as an important instrument of ownership and use of land.

The period of industrial and service expansion, which is still unfolding, has resulted in a fast growth of urban populations, particularly in the San Juan, Caguas, and Ponce metropolitan areas. Investors have been much less interested in land for agricultural uses than in sites for industrial and urban housing developments.

Agricultural enterprises are under heavy pressure to improve the efficiency of their operations in order to hold their labor and other resources in competition with the other sectors of the economy. The patterns of the use and ownership of land that are evolving or may evolve will be largely the result of the relative success achieved by operating units in meeting this competition.

The pressure of population on the land and the establishment of corporate control of large tracts brought the issue of landownership and control to the foreground of the political campaign of 1940. A broad program involving legislative and administrative measures designed to spread ownership and control of land among a larger number of people and to increase the shares of farm laborers in the value of agricultural production was put into effect. The measures had great impact.

Technological improvements also have influenced land use. The sugarcane, pineapple, and dairy enterprises have applied on a broad basis a larger number of significant technological improvements than have the tobacco, coffee, and food crops enterprises.

Easy and free trade with the mainland United States market has led to the development of a land-use pattern that stresses the importation of many food items and the exportation of a few cash crops. That trend has continued through the period of industrial expansion, after a slowdown during the war years, when emphasis was placed on local production of food to compensate for limited imports.

Another factor, essentially a part of the trade relations with the Mainland, is the production-control measures for sugarcane and tobacco, that were established as a part of a national program. The control program for tobacco is a responsibility of the Commonwealth Government. The production allotments and policies of administering the programs have tended to influence the trends in the use and ownership of land since the war.

These factors — density of population, the process of development, technology, political movements and trade, and the physical aspects — form the background and the future of Puerto Rico's land use and ownership.

The total area of the island and the adjacent islands of Vieques, Culebra, and Mona is 2,254 thousand cuerdas. (A cuerda is 0.9712 acre, and for most purposes the measures can be regarded as equal.) Only 13 percent of the total area is in nonagricultural uses. The 300 thousand cuerdas of nonagricultural land are taken up by urban areas, military reservations, highways, parks, cemeteries, airports, and miscellaneous uses.

The number of farm units has fluctuated from 41,078 farms in 1920, 55,519 in 1940, and 53,515 in 1950. Changes in the definition of a farm from census to census account for part of this variation in the number of farms.

A total of 1,841 thousand cuerdas was in farms in 1950.

The area in farms has declined 9 percent since 1930, reflecting the change from cropland and pasture to urban uses, particularly in the metropolitan area of San Juan, and the impact of activities pertaining to road building, military installations, hydroelectric power, and other public developments. The 1950 census recorded 53 thousand cuerdas in rural holdings too small to be classified as farms.

Of the 1,980 thousand cuerdas in farms in 1955, 910 thousand cuerdas were in cropland, 727 thousand were in pasture, and 204 thousand were in forest and brush. Other uses accounted for the balance of 139 thousand cuerdas. Besides the land in farms, 112,800 cuerdas were in forest reservations, of which 77,800 belonged to the Commonwealth of Puerto Rico and 35 thousand to the Federal Government.

Shifts among the major agricultural uses of land since 1920 have been negligible. But as population has continued to increase and the total of land in farms has dropped, the amount of land per capita in the various uses has declined. Thus a greater demand for food could be met only by more imports or higher production per acre, or both.

Greater production may involve higher yields from the same crops or shifts toward more intensive crops. A higher level of imports, however, seems to have been a major factor in closing the gap between increased consumption requirements and local production.

As plants grow the year round and land is so scarce in Puerto Rico, intercropping and double cropping are used extensively in many types of farming. Complex systems of intercropping and double-cropping arrangements are used for coffee, tobacco, and minor crops.

Often the systems are difficult to unscramble, even by men experienced in farm management and land use. Smaller farms, which depend to a large extent on human labor for raising crops, tend to use these practices more than larger, more highly mechanized farms. Intercropping and double cropping may increase cropland used relative to net land in crops by as much as 75 percent in some special situations.

The six geographic regions that include the lowlands and valleys account for one-third of the total area. These regions have a somewhat higher proportion of the area in cropland and a lower proportion in pasture and forest.

Other uses take up a relatively high proportion of the acreage because urban uses, roads, military installations, and swamps tend to be concentrated in these areas.

A high proportion of the southern foothills is in pasture. Pasture and cropland are balanced in the northern foothills. In the east-central mountains, pasture covers a larger area than crops. The opposite is true in the west-central mountains. Forests tend to be concentrated in the foothills and mountains.

The three main crops — sugarcane, coffee and tobacco — are grown on almost two-thirds of the cropland. The other third is devoted to forage, starchy vegetables, fruits, cereals, and other food crops. A part of the cropland is in fallow, but much of it probably is used regularly to pasture animals.

The land devoted to sugarcane, the main cash crop, has almost tripled since 1917. It occupies about two-fifths of the cultivated land. It was grown initially in the coastal plains, but it has tended to displace coffee, pasture and food crops in some sections of the foothills and mountain regions. The harvested area of sugarcane has increased by almost 150 thousand cuerdas since 1940.

Coffee occupies 22 percent of the cropland. It is grown mainly in the deep, reddish upland soils of the west-central mountains. The acreage in coffee has been reduced gradually since 1920 from 194 thousand cuerdas to 176 thousand in 1956. Oranges, bananas, and other food crops are grown as part of the coffee plantings, and the coffee area is a major source of them.

Tobacco uses about 4 percent of the cropland and is planted mainly in the east-central mountain region and a section of the west-central mountains. It is a cigar-filler type. A limited acreage of chewing tobacco is produced in the western coastal lowlands. The area planted to tobacco has shown an irregularly declining trend since 1930. Production, however, has shown less reduction because the yields have increased.

Starchy vegetables, fruits, cereals, and legumes are grown on about one-fifth of the cropland, mostly on small tracts in the foothills and mountain regions. Bananas, plantains, and oranges are intercropped with coffee. Some of these crops are planted as double crops in the tobacco area. The small farms and the plots around rural nonfarm dwellings produce sizable amounts of them.

Nearly one-third of the total area in farms is in pastures. Among the improved pasture grasses are guinea-grass in the south, molassesgrass in the northern foothills and mountains, and pangola and paragrasses in humid lowlands. Merker is the number one cut grass and tropical kudzu is used for forage.

About 40,500 cuerdas have been improved under the pasture improvement program of the Commonwealth Department of Agriculture and Commerce. An extensive area has been improved as a part of the Federal soil conservation program and by independent farmers. The major portion of the pasture acreage, however, is still unimproved, particularly in the foothills and mountain regions. Farmers in the milksheds of San Juan, Ponce, and Mayaǧuez have been the leaders in improvement of pastures.

The land with rougher topography, particularly in places where food crops and tobacco are grown, are tilled more frequently and intensively than the lowland areas.

The type of farming that has been practiced presents a conflict in this respect with recommended practices for soil conservation and improvement.

Nearly three-fourths of the land area is hilly. The Soil Conservation Service has estimated that 48 percent of the total area showed severe erosion and 23 percent showed moderate erosion. The extent of this deterioration is partly confirmed by the rapid rate of silting of water reservoirs.

If one adds together this situation, the tremendous pressure of population on the land, the rapid growth of population, the limited possibilities of land reclamation and development, and the apparent lack of widespread soil-building practices, he can see the seriousness of the problem. Shifts of people to nonagricultural employment may ease the pressure on the land, but more direct measures are also required.

Efforts to reclaim and develop land have centered mostly on irrigation. The Spanish Crown made several concessions before 1898 to permit the use of water for irrigation. Most of the grants facilitated irrigation of the level lands in the southern watershed. Today there are 18 public reservoirs in Puerto Rico. Five supply water for irrigation. Eight are used both for hydroelectric power and irrigation. Together they supply three irrigation systems - the south coast irrigation district, Isabela irrigation service, and the southwestern irrigation project There are several privately controlled systems. The three public irrigation systems, when fully developed, will irrigate 64 thousand cuerdas. The land under both private and public irrigation is close to 100 thousand cuerdas, or about one-tenth of the cropland.

Puerto Rico is divided into 17 soil conservation districts. Considerable progress has been made since 1940 in the adoption of more effective practices of soil conservation, but the problems of soil erosion and maintaining soil fertility were acute in 1958.

About 220 thousand tons of fertilizer are applied each year — about one-fourth ton per acre of cropland. Most of it is applied to the acreage in sugarcane. Tobacco, pineapples, and food crops take most of the rest. The use of fertilizer for pasture and coffee, although increasing, is still limited. Not much lime and other soil amendments are used. Manuring, crop rotation, and other practices designed to maintain or improve land resources have been applied to a limited extent.

The sugarcane, coffee, and livestock farms, when properly managed, have achieved a relatively good balance in maintenance of fertility. Tobacco, minor crops, and some pasturelands seem to be still in need of an adequate land-management system. The overall situation would probably show a net loss, even after reclamation, irrigation, and other land improvements are considered.

The framework of landownership and control was set during the Spanish rule. The system of "encomiendas" — grants of large tracts to a few chosen people — was applied here, as in most of the other Spanish colonies of the New World. By the time Puerto Rico became a part of the United States, the island presented a pattern of landownership that combined plantation, subsistence, and commercial familysize farms.

During the first 30 years as a Territory, the major change in the ownership and control of land was the development of the corporation as an instrument of landownership. The enactment of a joint resolution of the Congress in May 1900 to restrict the ownership and control of land by one corporation to 500 acres was not enforced until 1941.

Fifty-nine operating units, or fewer than 1 percent of sugarcane farms, controlled 58 percent of the area planted and produced 67 percent of the tons of sugarcane by 1935. The 1940 census reported that farms of 260 cuerdas or more represented 2 percent of all farms and covered 42 percent of the land in farms.

The legislature in April 1941 approved the Land Law of Puerto Rico, which was designed to promote a broader distribution of land and of the economic proceeds of its cultivation among those who tilled it. The law created an administrative body, the Land Authority of Puerto Rico, to develop the new policy directive. This organization acquired 100 thousand cuerdas of land by purchase or expropriation.

Two-thirds of this land was placed in proportional-profit farms, and most of the balance was parceled in small lots for resettling farm laborers. The proportional-profit farms are operated on a rental basis, and the manager and the workers share in the profits.

The law also provided for assistance in the settlement of family-type farms and for the establishment of rural communities with certain public services. A total of 28 thousand cuerdas have been distributed by the Social Program Administration for the resettlement of laborer and sharecropper families in rural communities. This area has been divided among 41,600 families in 246 communities. In addition, 12,702 cuerdas have been distributed in 778 family-size farms. Similar efforts, conducted under the Homestead Act, from 1920–1940 had led to the establishment of 2,400 farms covering 26 thousand cuerdas. The Puerto Rico Reconstruction Administration distributed land in small lots to 10,350 families during the period 1935–1943. The Farm Security Administration, which later became the Farmers Home Administration, has helped in the establishment of family-size farms since 1938.

Sharecroppers were included in the census figures as tenants before 1940 but not in 1950.

The percentage of owner-operated farms has varied from 80 to 94 percent since 1910. The proportion of the land in owner-operated farms has varied from 52 to 75 percent. These figures have shown considerable variation from census to census, particularly in the owner- and manager-operator groups. Manager-operated farms covered 17 percent of the area in farms in 1920, 37 percent in 1935, and 18 percent in 1950.

The number of tenant-operated farms represented 20 percent of all farms in 1940, but was down to 5 percent in 1950. The area covered by tenant-operated farms was 11 percent in 1910, 7 percent in 1930, 13 percent in 1940, and 7 percent in 1950. Changes in the definition of a farm and in other census enumeration procedures, particularly in the latest census, accounted for some of the differences.

Land takes on the average about 70 percent of the total farm investment, and buildings 10 to 15 percent, depending on the size and type of farm. Livestock, supplies on hand, and miscellaneous assets account for the balance. These figures reflect the importance of land relative to buildings, machinery, and other farm resources. They also reflect the pressure of population on land resources.

Of the total cost of producing coffee, tobacco, and sugarcane, labor absorbs 40 to 60 percent and the use of the land takes about 12 percent, except for tobacco. Use of the land accounts for only 3 percent of the cost of producing tobacco which is in the ground only a few months.

The net income of all industries of the island was 232 million dollars in 1939–1940 and 1,004 million 1955–1956.

Agriculture contributed 70 million dollars to the 1939–1940 figure and 162 million to the 1955–1956 net income. Agricultural raw materials accounted for about half of the value added by manufacture and processing — including sugar mills and refineries, distilling and bottling of spiritous liquors, miscellaneous food products, and tobacco products. Agricultural activity also provided an important share of the volume of business of finance, trade, and other service industries.

Land values are high relative to those on the Mainland and in other less densely populated countries. Land values near the three principal metropolitan centers have gone up about 1,000 percent since 1940, but the price of farmland that has not been affected by demand for other uses has increased 300 to 500 percent.

Credit is concentrated in short-term production credit and store credit. The equity of farmers generallly is high. The net worth of 347 sugarcane farmers in 1939 - 1940 represented 80 percent of the assets; mortgages accounted for 10 percent and short-term credit for an additional 10 percent. As 70 percent of their assets were in real estate, one can realize the proportion that mortgage credit represented of their total investment in real estate.

A similar situation, although not so pronounced, prevailed among tobacco farmers. The credit available annually for agriculture was estimated in 1956 to total 95 million dollars; that included 8 million dollars for intermediate and long-term credit. Federal agencies, mostly the land bank, provided the major part of the long-term loans. Commercial banks and other private agencies were the principal sources of short-term credit.

The nature of the market for farmland and the system of transferring land from generation to generation influence (and in turn are influenced by) the long-term credit situation. The agricultural land market in Puerto Rico apparently is considerably less active than in most agricultural areas of the Mainland.

The system of taxation of agricultural land is similar to the system on the Mainland, but collection and allocation of tax proceeds is centralized in the Commonwealth Government. The proceeds from real-estate taxes represent a small percentage of the total government income.

If the trend of development of the Puerto Rican economy toward more industry and services continues, the fast rate of change toward urban living and employment will undoubtedly continue to ease the pressure of population on agricultural land.

Part-time farming, which has become a significant aspect, may develop to be an important farming procedure. It may be found, as in Switzerland, that some industrial activities can become an integral part of farming and rural living.

This shift in emphasis toward industrial and service activities presents an opportunity to promote necessary adjustments in the use, ownership, and control of land. In regions where tobacco and minor crops are grown, a basis has not been built for adequate use and development of land. This basic maladjustment may force an intensified search for solutions within the next decade. Probably livestock, orchards and some forest uses, with a reduction in the clean-cultivated acreage, may bring about the necessary balance.

Farmers will face keen competition for labor, management, and capital from other sectors of the economy. A wider use of technological improvements will be necessary to meet such competition.

These changes may lead to more intensive uses for areas of better soils, with higher capital inputs for equipment, supplies, better livestock, and so on, and to less intensive uses for the poorer soils. A lower premium will be attached to land; alert management and capital will be in high demand. A more dynamic type of farming, ready to adopt scientific advances, will be necessary. Farms having an active, direct management will have the best chance.

Government policies and programs designed to promote a well-informed, active management and improve the credit and marketing channels for agriculture should foster this necessary change. Research, extension, and vocational education would emphasize the development of new farm management practices and leadership among farmers. More effective systems of farming, rather than the improvement of isolated practices, would be the desired end result.

As the technical evolution of agriculture tends to increase sharply its demand for capital, more diversified and ample credit will have to be secured. Special efforts should also be made to assure that improved efficiency on farms is matched by a parallel improvement in grading and processing and other phases of marketing farm products.

Agribusiness

From Earl L. Butz, "Agribusiness in the Machine Age," U.S. Department of Agriculture, *Yearbook*, 1960 (Washington, 1960), pp. 380–84.

MODERN AGRICULTURE is much broader than the narrow dictionary definition — "the art or science of cultivating the ground." It is the whole business of supplying food and fiber for a growing population at home and abroad.

The art or science of cultivating the ground is but one link in the long chain of feeding and clothing people. The chain begins many jobs before we reach the farm and continues several processes after our newly produced food and fiber leave the farm gate. For this whole complex of agricultural production and distribution functions some persons use the term "agribusiness."

The United States has shifted in the past century from a predominantly agricultural economy to an industrial and commercial economy. The industrial sector is now beginning to give way, at least relatively, to a growing variety of personal services. That is possible primarily because we have been able to specialize in our production and processing of food and fiber by the increased use of science, technology, and mechanization and an increasing output per worker in farming and in agribusiness. We have transferred many farm jobs off the farm, such as the shift of farm power from horses and oats to tractors and gasoline, but we do the entire job with much less manpower than formerly.

AGRICULTURE is now in the middle of its third great revolution. Agricultural engineers have had a big part in all three revolutions.

The first revolution came in the middle of the 19th century, when we began to substitute animal energy for human energy. The invention of the reaper is the best known event associated with it. This and other developments called for considerable retooling in agriculture. They increased output per worker on farms and started us on the path of feeding our growing Nation with a constantly shrinking proportion of our total population in the field. Agriculture began to take on some characteristics of a commercial enterprise, although sometimes the change was almost imperceptible.

The second great revolution began in the 1920's, with the substitution of mechanical energy for animal energy. It likewise increased the commercialization of agriculture, shifted a number of production functions off the farm, increased output per worker substantially, and resulted in a further reduction in the proportion of our total working population on farms.

The third revolution is the undergirding of agricultural production and marketing with vast amounts of science, thechnology, and business management, This revolution has been in progress for a decade or two, but at an accelerated pace during the past few years. This revolution is transferring still additional production and marketing functions off the farm and continues to underscore the importance of specialization at all levels of the agribusiness complex.

Agricultural historians a generation hence may characterize the decade of the 1950's as the decade of the scientific breakthrough. In this decade we experienced an unprecedented number of discoveries, which have changed agriculture from stem to stern.

The decade of the 1960's opens with the march of agricultural science in full stride. Agriculture is changing from a way of living to a way of making a living. It is changing from a business of arts and crafts to a business undergirded with large amounts of science and technology.

IT IS WRONG to think of agriculture as a declining industry.

American agriculture is an expanding industry in every important respect except one — the number of people required to run our farms. Our agricultural plant each year uses more capital, more science and technology, more managerial capacity, more purchased production inputs, more specialized marketing facilities, and more research than the year before.

We do not think of air transportation as a declining industry just because a pilot in a jet airliner can now take 100 passengers from coast to coast in half a day, compared with 20 passengers in a day and half two decades ago. This, like agriculture, is a strong and growing industry.

Although a smaller share of our total population is engaged directly in farming, the agricultural industry is big, broad, and basic. Of 68 million persons employed in America in 1960, about 26 million worked somewhere in agriculture — 8 million worked on farms, 7 million produced goods and services purchased by farmers, and 11 million processed and distributed farm products. Hence, almost two-fifths of all our employed people are engaged in work related to agriculture.

The declining trend in farm population is itself a sign of a strong agriculture. Brainpower has replaced horsepower as the essential ingredient on our farms. The total United States agricultural output increased by two-thirds in the past two decades, while the number of farmworkers declined some 3 million. This means that production per worker on our farms has doubled in the past 20 years. This remarkable increase in production efficiency can be matched by no other major sector of the American economy.

Progress of this kind can be continued only if we have capable and well-informed men on our farms. We will need fewer farmers in the future, but they must be better. They will be operating on a fast track, and the race will go to the swift.

WE MUST broaden our thinking about agriculture to include the businesses that supply our farmers with items used in production, as well as the processing and distributing concerns that handle the food and fiber produced on farms.

When the total agribusiness is taken into consideration, approximately one-third of the workers are on farms and two-thirds are off farms. Approximately two-thirds of the capital is on farms and one-third off. Approximately one-sixth of the value added is on farms and roughly five-sixths off the farm.

The farm plant in America purchases each year apporximately 17 billion dollars worth of goods and services used in farm production. To this it adds a value of about 17 billion dollars on farms, which means that the total farm produce leaves the farm gates at about 34 billion dollars. Processing and distribution add another 45 billion dollars to this, which makes a total value of output in agribusiness of approximately 80 billion dollars in 1960.

These figures point out the growing importance of agriculture as a market. Industry depends on agriculture as a customer to a greater extent than most persons realize.

A generation ago, farmers were producing most of their own fuel, power, and fertilizer, but now industry is furnishing farmers each year:

6.5 million tons of finished steel — more than is used for a year's output for passenger cars;

45 million tons of chemical materials — about 5 times the amount they used in 1935;

18 billion gallons of crude petroleum — more than is used by any other industry;

285 million pounds of raw rubber — enough to make tires for 6 million automobiles;

22 billion kilowatt hours of electricity — more than enough to serve the cities of Chicago, Detroit, Baltimore, and Houston for a year.

We could go on citing other evidences of the tremendous importance of agriculture in our national life, but the point has been made. Whatever happens to agriculture has a direct and major impact upon industry. And industry, by the same token, has a very great interest in the welfare of agriculture.

The agricultural world and the industrial world are not two separate communities with merely a buyer-seller relationship. They are so bound together and so interrelated that we must think of them jointly if we are to reach sound conclusions about either one.

The modern commerical farm resembles a manufacturing plant in many respects. The large amount of equipment in use on the farm represents a substitution of capital and machinery for labor.

Many family commercial farms today have total capital investment exceeding 100 thousand dollars. It is not uncommon to have capital investment approaching or exceeding 200 thousand dollars on family commercial farms in the Corn Belt. Many Midwest farms have total capital investment per worker in excess of 50 thousand dollars. This is three times the average investment per worker in American industry.

The modern farm operator is much less self-sufficient than his father was. He buys many goods and services needed in his production that father produced on the farm. In a very real sense, he assembles "packages of technology" that have been put together by others on a custom basis. For example, he buys his tractors and petroleum, whereas his father produced horses and oats. Think for a moment of the technology that goes into the modern feedbag, with its careful blending of proteins, antibiotics, minerals, and hormones, as contrasted with the ear corn and a little tankage put out for the hogs in his grandfather's day.

This development obviously calls for a high level of managerial capacity. It is more difficult to manage the modern commercial farm successfully than it is to manage the family-sized manufacturing concern, grocery store, or foundry shop in the city.

The manager of the modern commercial family farm must make more managerial decisions each week covering a much wider range of subject matter than does his conterpart in the city. He has more capital invested, takes greater risks, faces stiffer competition, and has more opportunity for reward if he does a good job.

This kind of "manufacturing operation" means rather narrow operating margins for farmers. In recent years farmers, as a group, have spent some 65 cents of every dollar they take in for operating expense. That is the average. Specialized commercial farmers spend a higher ratio than that for operating expense. They operate on a much narrower margin than their fathers did, but make greater net incomes because of increased volume. A large share of their operating expenses goes for items that their grandfathers produced on the farm himself, but that modern farmers "hire" someone else to produce for them.

Today's farm production is a synthesis of several scientific disciplines.

The earning capacity of the average farmer used to be limited primarily by his physical strength and the amount of work he could do. He substituted some animal muscle for human muscle, but not a great deal. He substituted very little mechanical energy for muscle power. Agriculture was primarily a means of converting muscle energy into farm produce.

Human energy is much less important in today's farm operation. Energy can be purchased so much more cheaply than it can be provided by man. Today's farm operator is a combination manager-applicator of the life sciences, the physical sciences, and the social sciences. The research undergirding modern agriculture ranges all the way from physics to physiology, from biology to business. It is just as complex and just as far on the periphery of knowledge as is the research done in the laboratories of the nuclear scientist, for example.

The first claim of any society upon its total production resources is to get enough food to keep the population alive and well. This is true in primitive societies, in semi-developed societies and in highly developed societies. We do this so efficiently in this country that almost nine-tenths of our population is available to produce the wide variety of goods and services that make up the American standard of living.

A tremendous amount of research lies behind the production and distribution of those 17 billion dollars' worth of production items farmers bought in 1960. That research must be carefully integrated into the farm operation itself. Indeed, it must go beyond that, to the processing and distribution of the farm product after it leaves the farmers' gates. Increasingly, this kind of research calls for a research team representing various disciplines, and requires careful coordination through the entire process of production, processing, and distribution.

The technological revolution in the processing and distribution of food and fiber has been perhaps even more spectacular than the technological revolution on the farm. Countless steps in the processing of food and fiber that once were done on the farm have long since moved to the city.

The textile industry was one of the leaders in this field. In the early 1800's, when the mechanical production of textiles began, weaving in the home first declined and then disappeared. A little later, as the migration of population to industrial centers got under way, it was necessary to move food from the farm to urban areas. Inasmuch as the typical food production cycle is annual, and the human hunger cycle is daily, it became necessary to devise means of preserving and storing an annual food supply to meet daily food needs in locations far removed from areas of production. The result was the development of a commercial food processing and distributing industry which today feeds our vast urban population much better than their farmer ancestors fared. The national diet has improved materially in terms of quality and variety.

The interdependence of the various segments of the agribusiness chain is obvious. When these functions were mostly performed on the farm, there was a high degree of integration among them. The individual farm family saw to this, for failure to do so would mean loss of income and perhaps hunger.

In recent times, especially in some kinds of commodities, there has been a pronounced tendency to integrate the various functions of production and marketing through contractual arrangments of one kind or another.

This process has come to be known as vertical integration. Although contractual integration arrangements are controversial and are viewed with suspicion by some people, they are a manifest effort on the part of the industry to seek such economies as can be attained by careful coordination of the entire chain of production, processing, and marketing.

Vertical integration is essentially an attempt to combine the advantages of specialization in modern society with the good features of a system in which all the steps were fully coordinated, as they had to be on grandfather's farm. A certain amount of vertical integration is inevitable — and beneficial — in the kind of agribusiness we have today.

Capital requirements per farm and per worker have increased to the extent that it is becoming increasingly difficult for an individual, during his productive years, to accumulate a sufficient amount to finance an economically sized operating unit. This will be still more ture in the decades ahead. Moreover, in view of the inheritance tax structure, it is becoming increasingly difficult for a parent to transfer such a unit to his son without substantial operating or financial disruption. This means, perforce, that an increasing share of total farm capital will be supplied by nonoperators. Part of this will be accomplished through some form of vertical integration.

With such large amounts of capital and technology involved, management has become the key factor in successful farm operation. This is in sharp contrast to a generation or two ago, when the farm unit was much more self-sufficient than now, with much less capital involved, with much less science applied, and with many fewer critical managerial decisions to be made.

The movement of population off the farms will continue. They will not necessarily leave the rural community, particularly if urban employment is available within commuting distance. Many of them will find gainful employment in some phase of agribusiness in the city, and will therefore really remain in agriculture.

The question of whether every farm-reared youngster should remain on the farm is no longer a sociological problem. That the opportunity for gainful employment on the farm is not present for all farm-reared boys is simply an arithmetic fact. Fortunately, agribusiness offers a challenging opportunity.

Surveys have shown that in many typical rural areas in the Corn Belt approximately one farm per township per year will become available for new operators in the next generation. In these same townships, the number of farm youth ready for new employment each year ranges from four to eight. Obviously, if they all try to remain on the farm, operating units will necessarily be so small as seriously to limit income opportunities.

The process of "rurbanization" is altering community life in vast areas of our country. Rural and urban cultures are intermingling in countless communities within commuting distance of industrial centers. City folk are moving to the country, and farm families have one or more members commuting to work in the city.

The city limit sign at the edge of your county seat town does not mean the same thing it did just a generation ago. It is now just a tax boundary. It is no longer a cultural boundary, an educational boundary, a social boundary, a recreational boundary, or an economic boundary. The same kind of people live on both sides of that city limit sign. They have the same communications, the same transportation, the same electricity, the same educational opportunities, the same recreational outlets, the same church facilities, the same modernized kitchens, and the same standards of living.

More than half of our farm families have one or more members of the family doing either part-time or full-time work off the farm. On approximately 1.5 million farm units in the United States in 1958, the farm operator either worked off the farm 100 days or more for wages, or his nonfarm income exceeded his farm income. This is one means whereby operators of less than economic-sized units increase their volume and achieve acceptable incomes. There are relatively few farm families who do not live within commuting distance of a nonfarm job.

When this tendency of farm people to get either part-time or full-time work off the farm is put alongside the tendency of growing numbers of urban people to move to a country home, the pattern of our newly rurbanized communities becomes clear. As the farmer himself becomes a well-capitalized, highly specialized producer, a new community culture will emerge in which the farmer will tend to lose his vocational identity, just as the lawyer, the doctor, or the machinist now loses his in his own community.

The very cornerstone of our high standard of life is our ever-increasing efficiency in the production and marketing of food and fiber, made possible by the specialized functions that characterize agribusiness. Increased efficiency in production and distribution of food and fiber and the subsequent release of manpower for other work are the first prerequisites for an industrialized society. The first claim of any organized society on its total production resources is food. The cry for food has echoed through the ages. Food remains man's first physical need.

The Tractor

From E. M. Dieffenbach and R. B. Gray, "The Development of the Tractor," U.S. Department of Agriculture, *Yearbook,* 1960, pp. 25–45. (Washington, 1960) pp. 24–45.

A farmer in 1910 needed 135 hours to produce 100 bushels of corn, 106 hours for 100 bushels of wheat, and 276 for a bale of cotton.

The average for the United States in 1960 was about 23 man-hours to produce 100 bushels of corn, 17 for 100 bushels of wheat, and 77 for a bale of cotton.

A reason for this big drop in the American farmer's labor requirement was the development of the tractor.

Tractors were perfected because of the need for mechanical power for the new machines that were being invented and produced for farmers.

Cyrus McCormick invented his reaper in 1831. It soon created a demand for belt power with which to thresh the mechanically harvested grain crops. By 1860 more than 50 shops from Maine to California were building threshers under license from the Pitts Brothers, American inventors who patented a thresher in 1837.

Steel plows, mowers, shellers, fodder cutters, and other machines were offered to the farmer soon thereafter.

The reaper and the thresher made obsolete the flail, which had been in common use for centuries in all parts of the world for beating out the grain from the heads. First it was a whip, sometimes with two or more lashes. The later versions consisted of a wood handle with a shorter stick hung at the end so as to swing freely.

Work animals also became obsolete, in a manner of speaking, in time. Used with sweeps and treadmills, they provided some power, but not enough for operating the threshers and other belt-driven machines. Manufacturers of threshers and other machines undertook therefore the production of movable steam engines.

The early steam engines furnished belt power, but they had to be pulled from place to place by horses or oxen. One of the first to be produced in the United States was the Forty-Niner. It was built in Philadelphia in 1849 by A. L. Archambault in 4-, 10-, and 30- horsepower sizes. The smallest of these weighed 2 tons, or a thousand pounds per horsepower.

The Baker and Hamilton Co. marketed a movable threshing engine in 1880. The boiler had a jacket of 2-inch staves, held in place by brass bands, and could burn wood, coal, or straw. It had an Ames engine and Laufenburg boiler and was built by the Ames Iron Works of Oswego, N.Y. Henry Ames was one of the early builders and advocates of steampower on the farm, and he founded a factory to make movable engines in 1854.

The next step in the evolution of farm power was the conversion of the portable steam engine into a self-propelled steam traction engine.

The first ones were developed primarily for plowing. Obed Hussey of Baltimore invented and put into operation a "steam plow" in 1855. J. S. Fawkes of Christiana, Pa., produced a more successful steam plowing outfit in 1858. Its frame was of iron, 8 feet wide and 12 feet long, and rested on the axle of a roller (driver) 6 feet in diameter and 6 feet wide.

President Abraham Lincoln, in an address before the Wisconsin State Agricultural Society at Milwaukee, in 1859, said:

"The successful application of steam-power to farm work is a desideratum — especially a steam plow. It is not enough that a machine operated by steam will really plow. To be successful, it must, all things considered, plow better than can be done by animal power. It must do all the work as well, and cheaper, or more rapidly, so as to get through more perfectly in season; or in some way afford an advantage over plowing with animals, else it is no success."

Philander Standish built the Standish steam rotary plow, the Mayflower, at Pacheco, Calif., in 1868. It was offered for sale in several sizes, ranging from 10 to 60 horsepower. Operating speed was 1.7 to 3.4 miles an hour, and the plowing rate was up to 5 acres an hour.

Also in 1868 Owen Redmond of Rochester, N.Y., patented a steam plow. A report of the Commissioner of Agriculture in 1870 announced that "a gang of six plows, designed to go with the engine, has since been constructed, intended to be operated by one man, who also might be the fireman."

While the main efforts in providing self-propulsion systems for steam tractors seemed to center largely around the use of wheel propulsion, many inventors were at work devising methods for providing better traction through the application of tracks and other devices. They worked out many unusual ideas.

Gideon Morgan of Calhoun, Tenn., received a patent for a wheel substitute in 1850. The language of his patent was for an improvement in track-type tractor design; the development of the crawler-type tractor in the United States therefore must have begun before 1850.

R. J. Nunn of Savannah, Ga., patented an "improvement in land conveyance" in 1867. It was essentially two or more bands running over a series of grooved rollers that were mounted in a frame and driven through a larger roller powered by a steam engine.

Thomas S. Minnis of Meadville, Pa., in 1867 patented a locomotive for plowing and in 1870 a steam tractor mounted on three tracks — two in the rear and one in front. Each rear track was driven by a steam engine, attached at the rear, through pinion and drive gear.

According to Hal Higgins, an authority on power farming, "Iowa's first 'dirt farming tractor' was this Minnis Crawler from Pennsylvania that came out to the raw prairie within sight of the new Iowa State Agricultural College as the first students started attending classes within sight of its smoke."

Robert C. Parvin of Illinois in 1873 built a steam tractor propelled by an endless chain of steel plates to which "feet," shod with 2-inch plank, were attached. It pulled six plows.

Charles H. Stratton, Moscow, Pa., in 1893 produced a steam-powered traction engine designed especially "to travel readily over plowed ground, for cross plowing, and other work." The front end was supported by wheels on a pivoted axle and the rear by a pair of compactly arranged tracks actuated through gears and pinions from the horizontal engine. Besides driving the tracks, the engine could be used to drive a shaft that could be used to drive threshers or other machines — a so-called power takeoff.

One of the first attempts to manufacture track-type tractors commercially was made by Alvin O. Lombard of Waterville, Me., in the early 1890's. He patented one of the first practical track-type tractors in 1901. Lombard adopted the ball tread idea of John B. Linn of Cleveland.

Lombard substituted rollers for the balls. He built a workable tractor and sold a number of machines. The unit was "designed specially for transporting lumber and logs over the rough roads and even cross country in the Maine woods." It embodied half-track construction. The front was supported by runners in winter and wheels in the summer. Two power-driven tracks were in the rear.

Another track tractor was the Centiped Log Hauler manufactured by the Phoenix Manufacturing Co., Eau Claire, Wis. It resembled the Lombard machine, but it used a vertical instead of horizontal engine.

Other early inventors tried to solve the problems of traction by making the driving wheels wider and wider.

Daniel Best sold his first steamer, a three-wheeler with vertical boiler, in 1889. One big-wheel outfit which was made by the Best Manufacturing Co. in 1900 for the Middle River Farming Co., Stockton, Calif., had two wood-covered drive wheels 15 feet wide and 9 feet in diameter. The outfit weighed 41 tons.

The Stockton Wheel Co. (later the Holt Manufacturing Co.) built its first steam traction engine (of a track type) in 1890. Topography, soil, and their large acreages led farmers on the Pacific Coast to accept this type of tractor more readily than farmers in other sections.

Benjamin Holt successfully demonstrated his first track-type tractor near Stockton in 1904 after considerable experimentation, in which he devised a pair of rough wooden tracks that he installed on a steam engine from which the wheels had been removed.

He made use of three clutches — the master clutch, for connecting the power source, and the track clutches. When the track clutch was released on one side, the power applied through the track clutch on the other side caused the tractor to pivot around the declutched track. Application of brakes on the declutched side increased the speed of turning. This method of transmission continues to be used by the Caterpillar Tractor Co. and has been adopted by most other manufacturers of tracklaying tractors.

Only eight of the track-type Holt steamers were built. He had already made experiments to replace steam-power by gasoline, and one model tractor of the track type, which burned gasoline, was produced in 1907.

Inventors between 1870 and 1880 devised a suitable gearing for the rear wheels of portable steam engines of the wheel type and also a chain or belt drive from the engine flywheel to a countershaft of this gearing to provide self-propulsion.

The bevel gear and inclined shaft developed by C. and G. Cooper of Mt. Vernon, Ohio, was also a popular method of drive. It enabled the farmer to convert his portable steam engine into a traction engine in the field.

A United States patent was issued in 1880 for a steering device, although English tractors were fitted with steering gears as early as 1863. There followed the introduction of a clutch and gear train between the engine and rear wheels.

The steering gears on these early steamers were not at first considered reliable by some manufacturers, and operators were cautioned about their use on public highways.

The suggestion was made that it might be safer to guide the machine with a team of horses. Some said horses were not frightened when they met a traction engine preceded by a steering team. Others felt that the additional horsepower provided by the team was advantageous — some of the reasons why horse steering remained for a while.

Many farmers started buying self-propelled steam engines in the late 1870's. About 3 thousand steam tractors and almost that many steam threshers were built in 1890. Several plow manufacturers advertised multiple-bottom steam tractor plows or gangs in 1894. By 1900 more than 30 firms were manufacturing 5 thousand large steam traction engines a year.

These tractors were improvements over earlier models. The gearing, shafting, and other wearing parts were built to withstand the immense strains imposed upon them in pulling large threshers and plowing many furrows at one time. Big wheat farms and ranches in the Dakotas, Colorado, Montana, Nebraska, Kansas, California, and western Canada were using steam traction engines.

About this time the Geiser and Friede companies, both of Waynesboro, Pa., offered steam lifts for engine gangs. This development indicated, even this early, that thought was being given to cutting down labor requirements in plowing and to lightening the burden of manually lifting the plows by levers, which always were giving trouble.

Before the abandonment of the steamer and the acceptance of the gasoline tractor, many improvements had been made, and the performance of the huge self-propelled powerplants was the pride of the traction-engine engineers who pioneered in the ultimate placing of power in the hands of the 6 million farmers in this country.

As a matter of fact, the interest is still so great that orgainizations, such as the National Thresher Reunion in Ohio, Rough and Tumble Engineers Association in Pennsylvania, Midwest Old Settlers and Threshers Association in Iowa, and others, composed largely of oldtimer steam buffs, hold annual picnics for their many members.

For these reunions they doll up old traction engines and use them to drive threshers or pull plows. Some of the machines run idle; some are driven by the kids under supervision. The enthusiasts swap yarns of the harrowing experiences when one man's outfit broke through a wooden bridge, another got mired down while crossing a sand creek, and another broke a piston rod so that the piston crashed.

At least one periodical, the Iron-Men Album Magazine, Enola, Pa., is devoted almost entirely to these steam-engine men of a half century ago.

The steam traction engines, pioneers in mechanization, often weighed more than 45 thousand pounds and developed more than 120 horsepower. They operated with a steam pressure of 150 to 200 pounds per square inch.

Both the horizontal-tube boiler (the more popular) and the vertical-tube boiler were used in these early vehicles. The two types were different in form but had many operative points in common.

The horizontal-type boiler was constructed mainly with direct flue, with return flue, or with firebox return flue.

The direct-flue boiler was known as the locomotive firebox, straight-flue boiler. The flues passed horizontally from the firebox at the rear to the smokebox in front.

The products of combustion in the return-flue boiler traveled first through the main flue to the combustion chamber in the front end of the boiler and then back through the many small flues to the smokebox in the rear.

Little space was provided under the grates of all three types to catch ashes and cinders. Grates were always in danger of burning out. This danger was overcome in the firebox return-flue boiler, in which water surrounded the heated surfaces, the grate area was larger, and the boiler had a larger heating surface.

Boilers of the vertical type had a cylindrical shell with a firebox at the lower end. Fire flues extended vertically from the flue sheet above the fire to the top of the boiler or horizontal water tubes placed in courses, so that each course was at right angles to the course next below and next above. These tubes and circulation plates maintained constant circulation.

Of the two main approaches in constructing the steam traction engine, one was to make the boiler the central structure and attach all other parts — engine, drive gears, steering gear, main truck — to it. The other was to provide a separate framework on which to mount the boiler and attach all the parts.

To spare the engine from damage from heavy shocks and jars on rough roads, heavy coil springs were placed between the boiler and front and rear axles. Springs in the steering gear helped prevent breakage when the front wheels hit an obstruction.

The early engine usually was mounted on the boiler, called top-mounted, and the boiler was mounted on the truck. Sometimes the engines in the locomotive type were mounted under the boiler.

One common method of mounting the boilers, known as side mounting, was to attach stub axles of the drivers to brackets placed at about the middle of the sides of the firebox. In another type, known as rear mounting, one continuous axle was located back of the firebox. A continuous axle was often mounted ahead of the firebox on return-flue boilers. It was known as under mounting.

The power of the steam traction engine was transmitted usually to the traction wheels by a simple train of spur gears made of cast iron. A driving pinion attached to the friction clutch engaged an intermediate gear, which in turn engaged a large compensating gear on the countershaft. Pinions on either end of the countershaft drove large master gears, which were fastened in the drive wheels by rigid or spring connections.

Traction engines first were geared with one forward speed to make 2 or 3 miles an hour on the road. Later some — especially on those used in hilly country — were geared with two forward speeds, one slow and one fast.

The front or steering wheels often were of steel, with the outer ends of the spokes riveted to a flange inside the rim, and the inner ends riveted to arms on the hub. A flange, or collar, around the middle of the outside of the front wheels tended to prevent lateral slippage. Steering was done by guiding the front wheels with a chain, winding shaft (roller), worm gear, and hand wheel. Sometimes power from the engine helped in steering.

The rear traction, or drive, wheels usually had steel tires, round or flat spokes, and a cast-iron hub. Cleats of steel or iron were mounted diagonally on the outside of the rims to increase traction. On rims that were cast, the cleats were part of the cast.

Early attempts to develop gasoline tractors were sparked by the need to reduce the size of the threshing crews.

Such crews included two men to operate the steam engine, two to haul coal and water, two to operate the thresher, a waterboy, and several men to haul bundles to the thresher and the grain away by horses and wagons.

Not the least of the problems was to feed them. Days, maybe weeks, before the threshing crew was due at a farm, the farmer's wife started to plan and prepare the gargantuan meals she was going to serve them — hams, a side of beef, chickens, fried potatoes, gallons of milk, at least three kinds of pie, maybe homemade ice cream. Her reputation as a cook was at stake, she knew, and the feasts she fixed were something to be proud of and marvel at. Still in our language are terms that recall her and them — "a meal fit for a threshing crew" and "eat like a bunch of threshers."

Most of the first attempts to develop liquid-fuel tractors consisted of mounting a stationary gasoline engine on a chassis patterned after that of the steam traction engine. This combination became the self-propelled gas engine.

Experimenters even built a gasoline tractor that looked like a steam traction engine with the rather strange idea that thereby they would not scare the horses so much. Also with horses in mind (why, we do not know), some put a whistle on the rig.

Before a tractor could be fully realized, there had to be a promising internal-combustion engine. The early experimenters used gunpowder, turpentine, and natural and artificial gas for fuel.

The discovery of petroleum fuel in quantity speeded the development of the gasoline engine. In 1859, at Titusville, Pa., Edwin L. Drake drilled his first oil well and got the petroleum product that paved the way for the creation of a great industry. The internal-combustion engine made rapid strides when petroleum fuel was available.

About the first internal-combustion engine on record was the one credited to Abbe Hautefeuille, a French physicist, who in 1678 conceived the idea of burning a small amount of gunpowder in a chamber. While he continued experimenting, other French, Dutch, English, and American engineers developed many and various ideas for producing power.

Finally Nicholas Otto, a German, devised a practical power unit of the internal-combustion type. It had one cylinder. Counting the movement of the piston in one direction as one stroke, his engine made four piston strokes per explosion in the same manner as the four-cycle ("Otto cycle") engines used today in all American-made automobiles. Those in the cars have more cylinders, but they are four cycle.

This development did not begin to assume importance until 1876, when it reached a reasonably satisfactory stage. The patents of the Otto cycle engine, however, were so basic in character that not until they expired in 1890 did other companies start to work on similar engines.

One hundred firms in the United States were making internal-combustion engines by 1899.

Another early and important development was the compression-ignition engine. It was the work of Rudolph Diesel, a German scientist, who patented his first engine in 1892. Before inventing the engine that bears his name, he had considerable experience with air compressors and with internal-combustion engines with spark ignition. He used coal dust, a useless byproduct in mining, which was blown into the cylinder with compressed air. He found out that it was not feasible to use coal dust as a fuel.

Before long Diesel came out with an oil-burning, compression-ignition engine that proved successful. His idea was adopted quickly as a source of power. In the diesel engine, the fuel is injected after compression is practically completed, and is ignited by the heat of compression of the air supplied for combustion.

Probably the first gasoline tractor that was an operating success was the one built in 1892 by John Froelich. A good businessman, he ran a grain elevator, a well-drilling outfit, and a threshing outfit powered with a steam traction engine. He wanted to build a smaller tractor — one that would run on gasoline.

He mounted a single-cylinder, vertical-type gasoline engine, made by the Van Duzen Gas and Gasoline Engine Co. of Cincinnati, on a Robinson running gear equipped with a traction arrangement of his own manufacture. It completed a 50-day threshing run belted to a Case 40 × 58 thresher, pulled the thresher over rough ground, and operated in temperatures of −3° to 100° F. The Froelich was the forerunner of the John Deere tractors.

Some of the other tractors of this period were the Patterson, 1892; the Hockett (Sterling), 1893; the Van Duzen, the Otto, and the Lambert, in 1894; the Huber, 1898; and the Morton in 1899. The Patterson became the foundation for the Case line of tractors, and Morton became the fore-runner of the International Harvester line.

C. W. Hart and C. H. Parr built their first tractor model in 1902. Their second model a year later was considerably improved. Their 30–60 "Old Reliable" appeared in 1907; in 1909 came the Hart-Parr 15–30, a tricycle type. Even their early models were designed for pulling (drawbar work) rather than for belt work — they made their transmissions rugged to withstand the heavy strains of plowing.

Hart and Parr formed a company that was to become a part of the Oliver Corp. They established in 1905 the first business in the United States devoted exclusively to making tractors.

Other tractors were the Electric Wheel, 1904; the Dissinger, 1904; the Eason-Wysong Auto-Tractor, 1905; and the Ohio, 1905.

The Ohio Manufacturing Co. later bought the patent rights for the Morton and in 1905 built a few tractors for the International Harvester Co., which in 1907 built its first tractor. Like the Ohio tractor, it was friction drive for both forward and reverse.

Other models were the Waterous in 1906, the Transit and the Ford in 1907, and the Russell, Olds, Joy-McVicker, and the Geiser in 1909. The Ford tractor of 1907, an experimental machine made by the Ford Motor Co. of Detroit, used parts of a Ford car and a binder. The front wheels and axle and steering were from the car. The rear wheels were binder bullwheels.

The origin of the word "tractor" was originally credited to the Hart-Parr Co. in 1906 to replace the longer expression "gasoline traction engine," which W. H. Williams, the company's sales manager, who wrote the advertisements, considered too cumbersome. The word actually was coined previously and was used in 1890 in patent No. 425,600, issued on a tractor invented by George H. Edwards of Chicago.

Although tractors powered with internal-combustion engines had been manufactured for about 20 years, people generally had no chance to compare field operations of steam and gasoline tractors until the first Winnipeg trial in 1908, conducted under the auspices of the Winnipeg Industrial Exhibition in Canada. In that and in tests in 1909–1912, representatives of many countries witnessed the competition of gasoline tractors plowing in the same fields with steam tractors.

The first Winnipeg trials were mainly contests of hauling and plowing for comparison of such factors as the thousand foot-pounds hauled per pint of fuel and the pints of fuel used per acre. The trials became more comprehensive with the years, until in 1912 the score sheet included an economy brake test, maximum brake test, plowing test, and a rating on design and construction. The contests showed, even at that early stage, the possibilities of the gasoline tractor. The interest created by the trials encouraged experimenters and manufacturers to continue their pioneer efforts.

Most of the gasoline tractors before 1910 had automatic intake valves, hit-and-miss governors, and make-and-break ignition systems. Electric current for ignition usually was supplied by dry batteries for starting and low-voltage, direct-current magneto or generator (auto sparker) for furnishing current thereafter. In a few, a low-voltage oscillating magneto furnished the spark for starting and running.

The frames of the wheel tractors were built up of channel iron, to which the engine and other parts were bolted. Most large drive gears were of cast iron, exposed to the dust and dirt, and wore rapidly. The built-up drive-wheels, often 6 feet and sometimes 8 feet in diameter, turned on a one-piece "dead," or floating, axle. Selective-type transmission, where there were any gears to select (many had only one speed forward), was common, although friction drive and planetary-gear transmissions were not uncommon. Clutches varied.

Makers of steam tractors and makers of gasoline tractors competed strongly during 1910–1920, when the number of tractor manufacturing companies increased from 15 to more than 160 and existing companies began to present more than one model. The president of a gasoline tractor company said that when he first went into business the manufacturers of steam tractors refused to load their machines on the same freight cars with gasoline tractors.

The International Harvester Co. in 1910 produced its 45-horsepower Mogul, which had a two-cylinder horizontal opposed engine, with gear drive forward and friction reverse; in 1911, the 45-horsepower Titan, with a two-cylinder twin horizontal engine, with gear drive forward and reverse; in 1912, the 15–30 single-cylinder Mogul; in 1914, the 10–20 Titan with a twin horizontal-cylinder engine, and the 8–16 Mogul with a one-cylinder horizontal engine and planetary-gear drive forward and reverse; and in 1915, the 15–30 Titan, with four-cylinder horizontal engine. The 8–16 International, with a four-cylinder vertical engine, the first to bear the company's name, appeared in 1918. It was one of the early attempts to design a machine suitable for smaller farms.

The International Harvester Co. introduced a practical power takeoff for its tractors in 1918. It permitted direct transmission power from the engine to such equipment as mowers, small combines, and sprayers. That was an important development. Most tractor manufacturers soon had their tractors so equipped, and they started to fit many of their field machines for power takeoff drive.

Deere & Co. brought out the Waterloo Boy in 1916 and a twin horizontal-cylinder kerosene-burning engine and 180-degree crankshaft, and so inaugurated a basic engine design that is to be found in most of its current models. The machine performed well at the National Tractor Demonstration in 1918 at Wichita, Kans.

The Bear, produced by the Wallis Tractor Co. in 1912, proved to be the advance guard of the Massey-Harris line. It had one front steering wheel, a directional vane, and two rear driving wheels.

The Wallis Cub appeared in 1913. It also was a three-wheeler, but it had a more compact design and introduced a revolutionary development — a frameless-type construction. The one-piece, U-shaped crankcase and transmission housing of boiler-plate steel was the backbone of the machine. The industry liked it, and soon designs by various manufacturers were introduced.

The Ford Motor Co., after considerable experimentation, in 1917 started production of the Fordson. It also was of unit-frame construction but of cast iron instead of boiler-plate steel. The tractor was light for its power and relatively low in price. This unit-frame type was practicable. Most manufacturers soon adopted the idea.

This Fordson development came at an opportune time — the year the United States became involved in the First World War. Boatloads of horses were being shipped abroad. Labor was becoming scarce. Materials were restricted. Power became more vital than ever. The manufacture of more than 34 thousand Fordsons in 1918 and 100 thousand by 1925 (25 and 75 percent, respectively, of the tractors produced by all companies) helped greatly to meet difficulties caused by the war. After 1925, with returning normalcy and the increasing interest in the general-purpose tractor, production of the Fordson dropped, and its manufacture was discontinued in this country in 1928.

The J. I. Case Co., which had built its first machine in 1892, resumed building tractors in 1911, when the Case 30–60 appeared. It produced in 1912 the Case 20–40, which performed exceedingly well at the Winnipeg Trials that year. Case built its first tractor with a four-cylinder vertical engine in 1915. It had three wheels — a single front steering wheel, the right rear a driver, and the left rear an idler. Case produced the 9–18 model in 1918 and in 1919 the 15–27, both of one-piece frame, or unit, construction.

The Allis-Chalmers Co. built its first tractor in 1914. It had three wheels and 10–18 horsepower. In 1916 Allis-Chalmers introduced a cultivating tractor of 6–12 horsepower, which also could pull a plow. The company soon became an active contender in the business.

A significant development in 1913 was the introduction of the Bull tractor by the Bull Tractor Co. of Minneapolis. It was powered by a small engine of 12 horsepower. It started a trend toward smaller units, which practically all manufacturers followed. Several hundred machines were sold in its first year; within a year Bull ranked first among all tractor manufacturers in the number produced. Its relative position declined from year to year, though, and in 1918 it ceased production. This tractor had one drive wheel, making a differential unnecessary, and an idler wheel mounted on a crank axle on the left side for leveling.

The Minneapolis Steel & Machinery Co. and the Minneapolis Threshing Machine Co. started producing tractors in 1911. In 1914 the Moline Plow Co. started production of the Moline-Universal, which was one of the earliest practical approaches to a general-purpose tractor. A later edition of the Moline-Universal, the Model D in 1917, probably was the first tractor to make use of a storage battery for ignition, starting, and lighting. The three companies merged in 1929 into the Minneapolis-Moline Power Implement Co., which later became the Minneapolis-Moline Co.

The large tractor, seemingly the predominant type in 1910–1920, could not accomplish the many tasks necessary to mechanize the farm — it could only plow, drive threshers, and pull large headers. Much thought had been given to the problem. Manufacturers began experimenting with light tractors suitable only for cultivating, and some eight or ten companies produced them.

Light tractors did not fill the need, however, for two tractors thus were necessary on the farm, and that was beyond the farmer's needs and pocketbook.

A machine was needed that would plow and thresh and with proper attachments would also cultivate, sow, and perform other field operations — an all-purpose tractor.

Experimentation continued meanwhile on track-type tractors. Various models appeared: The Bullock Creeping Grip (1910) by the Bullock Tractor Co. of Chicago; the Yuba (1912) by the Yuba Manufacturing Co., Marysville, Calif., with the tracks mounted on "balls that rolled in a race"; an improved model (1912) by Holt; the Killen-Strait (1914) by the Killen-Strait Manufacturing Co., Appleton, Wis., with two track drivers in the rear and one front steering track; the Bates Steel Mule C (1916) by the Bates Machinery and Tractor Co., Joliet, Ill., with a single track in the rear for driving and two widely spaced front steering wheels; the Trundaar (1916) by the Buckeye Manufacturing Co., Anderson, Ind.; the Leader (1917) by the Dayton-Dowd Co.; the Bear (1918) by the Bear Tractor Co., N.Y.; the Cleveland H (1918), later to be made by the Oliver Corp.; the Monarch (1918) by the Monarch Tractor Co., Watertown, Wis., later to merge with the Allis-Chalmers Manufacturing Co.; and the Best (1913) by the C. L. Best Gas Traction Co., San Leandro, Calif., which in 1925 combined with the Holt Manufacturing Co. to form the Caterpillar Tractor Co.

It is of interest that during the First World War the Holt Caterpillar tractor was important as an artillery and supply tractor and also was the inspiration of Gen. E. D. Swinton, a Briton, who invented the tank, which worked havoc among enemy troops and installations. This tank consisted of two large motor-driven tracks, one on each side, between which was mounted an armor-plated housing, which protected the crew, turret, and guns.

Tractors in 1920, considered collectively, embodied fundamental principles of engineering and design that exist, perhaps in more refined form, in today's tractors.

The one-piece cast-iron frame, replaceable wearing parts, force-feed and pressure-gun lubrication, enclosed transmission, carburetor manifolding, air cleaner, electric lighting and starting, high-tension magneto ignition with impulse starter, enclosed cooling system, antifriction bearings, alloy and heat-treated steels, and the power take-off had all been introduced. Some experiments had been made with rubber tires. The light-weight, low price tractor had been designed and widely accepted. Several fairly successful motor cultivator-type units were on the market.

The advantages of the tractor as a farm power unit had been well established. More than 160 companies produced 200 thousand units. (Fifteen companies made 4 thousand tractors in 1910. The number of manufacturers reached a peak of 186 in 1921.)

Many makes and types of tractors were on the market. Many turned out to be impracticable, and often the farmers were the scapegoats — many fence corners harbored so-called tractors, abandoned as useless, often even before they were fully paid for.

The farm equipment industry and others began to work for a standardized rating of tractors. Nebraska in 1919 passed a bill that in effect required that all makes and models of tractors to be sold in Nebraska pass certain tests.

The Nebraska Tractor Law specifies: " . . . Each and every tractor presented for testing, shall be a stock model and shall not be equipped with any special appliance or apparatus not regularly supplied to the trade. . .

"Such tests shall consist of endurance, official rating of horsepower for continuous load, and consumption of fuel per hour or per acre of farm operations. The results of such tests shall be open at all times to public inspection. . . ."

The tests began in 1920. With modifications, they have continued since, except during the war. The test codes used in Nebraska were developed by engineers in the University of Nebraska, the Society of Automotive Engineers, and the American Society of Agricultural Engineers.

The tests, which have been used all over this country and in many other countries, have provided standards for rating tractors, have speeded up improvements on many of them, and have eliminated many that were inferior in design and performance.

A drop in production of tractors occurred during the postwar depression. Manufacturers, instead of just marking time, took this chance to incorporate new features. In the keen competition that followed, the tractor was improved steadily, although a number of companies had to discontinue business.

The depression brought a big drop in prices: Fordson tractors sold for 395 dollars in 1932 — a 35-percent drop from the price in 1921. The Moline tractor, which sold for 1,325 dollars in 1920, was reduced to 650 dollars. One result was that many farmers who otherwise would not have been able to take advantage of power farming got good equipment.

Attention had to be given to air cleaners used on the engines. Dust that enters the engine from the intake can damage the working parts — particularly the pistons, rings, and cylinders.

Many makes and types of air cleaners appeared. They differed in ability to remove dust, the degree to which their use imposed vacuum or choking on the carburetor intake, and their effect on the maximum power to be obtained from the engine.

To determine the dust separation efficiency, vacuum imposition, and effect on power, tests were made at the University of California at Davis. The dust-separating efficiency of the 26 cleaners tested in 1922 varied between 42.7 percent and 99.8 percent. Fifteen cleaners had more than 95 percent efficiency.

The International Harvester Co. in 1924 produced the Farmall, probably the first successful attempt to build a resl all-purpose tractor. It could plow (two-plow size), cultivate four rows, and, as attachments were developed, do other jobs. It probably did more than any other to broaden the usefulness of the tractor and thus to further mechanization on the farm.

The Farmall had high rear-axle clearance; small, closely spaced front wheels to run between rows for cultivation; and a hitch for attaching a cultivator or other equipment. Industry accepted it readily. Soon similar machines appeared, designated as General-Purpose, Universal, All-Around, Row-Crop, Ro-Trac, Do-All, and so on.

Deere & Co. in 1923 offered the rugged Model D tractor, which became one of the company's standbys. It produced in 1928 its first general-purpose tractor, the 10–20, with arched front axle and high-clearance rear axle and three-row planting and cultivating equipment. Deere in 1929 put on the market its GP tricycle tractor, equipped with a mechanical power lift for lifting integrally mounted implements. It was the first tractor so equipped.

Several companies developed refinements: The Oliver tricycle row-crop tractor, with tiptoe wheels; the Massey-Harris FWD (four-wheel drive); the Allis-Chalmers all-crop, and the Case.

Mechanical power farming slowed down in 1931, but even in that depression year several more companies offered row-crop machines, among them Huber, Caterpillar (a high-clearance, track-type machine), and Sears, Roebuck and Co.

Another advance in 1931 was Caterpillar's Diesel 65, the first diesel-powered tractor in the United States to be put on the market. It was an important step, and several companies, after experiments, put out diesel-powered tractors in 1934. Most of the tractor companies now have diesel-powered tractors in their lines.

The wheel tractor was rough to ride. A farmer, after a day on one, was well shaken up; he had had it.

Relief came in pneumatic tires, which made riding easier and reduced vibration. They also meant less wear on tractor parts, permitted higher speeds in the fields and on roads, and reduced rolling resistance — all in all, more efficient operation.

Citrus growers in Florida, having noted that the tractors damaged the roots of the trees, in 1928 or so started putting discarded casings (without inner tubes) on steel wheels. That seemed to help.

Tiremakers watched this development, and in 1931 the B. F. Goodrich Co. developed a zero-pressure tire. It consisted of a rubber arch built on a perforated steel base for attachment to standard steel tire drive wheels. The tire was not under air pressure and so was not subject to puncture.

A few companies experimented with pneumatic rubber tires. The Firestone Tire and Rubber Co. fitted an Allis-Chalmers tractor with pneumatic tires. Their advantages were evident, and rubber tires soon were accepted. Fourteen percent of the wheel tractors were mounted on rubber by 1935; by 1940, 85 percent; and by 1950, nearly 100 percent.

The advantage of using water in tires to add weight for better traction became clear. The water could replace the iron weights on the wheels, which often caused trouble, especially under high road speeds. An antifreezing solution had to be provided when tractors were used during freezing weather. Commercial calcium chloride added to the water made an economical and satisfactory solution.

Case tractors were equipped in 1935 with a motor lift for lifting or lowering implements. Pressure on a trip button would cause the implement to be lowered. Tripping the button again raised the implement. The lift was driven by engine power through an enclosed worm and gear operated by a starter button near the driver's heel.

Among the tools developed for use with the motor lift were two- and four-row corn and cotton cultivators, two-row potato cultivators, ten-row truck crop seeders and cultivators, six-row beet planters and cultivators, four-row corn and cotton planters, three-row middlebusters, two-row listers, and 7-foot mower attachments.

Allis-Chalmers in 1938 made a one-plow, general-purpose tractor, Model B, that weighed less than 2 thousand pounds. It sold for 495 dollars at the factory — the first small farm tractor, mounted on rubber, to sell for less than 500 dollars.

Another development that improved the usefulness of tractors was the three-point hydraulic hitch developed by Harry Ferguson in Ireland and brought to this country in 1939 after many tests. It was a revolution in implement control. It strongly influenced the whole trend of design of tractors and equipment.

After a demonstration before Henry Ford, a working agreement was established between Mr. Ford and Mr. Ferguson for mass production of a tractor incorporating the Ferguson system.

Hydraulic systems have become standard or optional equipment on practically all models of tractors. The hydraulic system includes an oil receptacle, pump, valves, and a control lever within reach of the driver, connected by means of high-pressure hose to a power cylinder (a piston within a cylinder), which can be located on any part of the tractor or trailed implement where a control is desired. The hydraulic systems can control mounted and drawn implements, govern the depth of tillage implements, operate loaders, and activate power steering. Sometimes they can be used to increase the traction of the rear wheels by transferring a part of the weight of the implement to the rear wheels of the tractor.

The Minneapolis-Moline Co. in 1941 introduced the first standard tractor fitted at the factory for burning another type of fuel for tractors — LP (liquefied petroleum) gas. Some companies previously had offered kits for converting the tractors in the field from gasoline or kerosene to LP gas.

This LP gas, a light end of the crude oil, had been largely a waste product until means had been developed to liquefy it by compression. When the cost of the two fuels is similar per unit of work, LP gas has advantages in that it burns cleaner and causes less oil dilution. Gasoline is usually more readily available, and the engine is easier to start with it on cold days.

All major manufacturers of wheel tractors produced one or more LP gas-burning models in 1960.

Experimental work on tractors was again curtailed during the Second World War. Few new models appeared. Many tractor plants were converted to make war materials. Tractor production increased rapidly after the war; 793,497 tractors were made for farm use in 1951.

A marked improvement in the extremely improtant power takeoff, which we mentioned, was offered by the Cockshutt Plow Co., Brantford, Ontario, in 1947.

It was a continuous-running power takeoff (direct engine-driven power takeoff), which continued to operate even when the clutch was released. Heretofore, machinery operated by the regular power takeoff, such as sprayers, drawn cornpickers, and combines, would stop when the clutch was released. The continuous-running power takeoff allows one to stop the travel of the tractor without stopping the power takeoff. The same can be done with the independent power take-off, which was developed later.

All major manufacturers of farm tractors now furnish one or more models of their tractors with either continuous-running or independent power takeoff.

Another use of hydraulic control came in 1947, when Allis-Chalmers offered its Model WD tractor, fitted with a device for power adjusting the rear wheel tread. It permitted the operator to use the engine power for changing the spacing of the rear wheels while sitting on the tractor seat. He was spared the strenuous and time-costly job of making tread alterations by the hand-and-jack method.

All but one of the major American manufacturers of tractors offered models with power-adjusted rear wheel tread as standard or optional equipment in 1959.

The International Harvester Co. in 1954 announced a new source of farm electrical power, the Electrall, that can be mounted on its tractors. It is an electric generator driven by the tractor engine. Besides supplying electric power for tractor-drawn machinery, such as hay balers, and for farming operations where the utility companies' wires did not reach, it can also serve as a standby unit in case of failure of electric service.

It is provided with outlets that supply three types of current: 220-volt, three-phase 60-cycle alternating current, mainly for driving electric motors; 120-volt, single-phase current to attach to house wiring circuits; and 220-volt single-phase current for such heavy requirements as the electric range.

Later a trailing model of the Electrall was announced, mounted on a two-wheeled trailer and driven from the power takeoff of the tractor.

Among the major improvements in the transmission systems since 1954 are those that permit "on-the-go" shifts, a greater range of travel speeds, and automatic adjustment of speed to draft requirements.

International Harvester put a new torque amplifier on the Farmall Super M-TA. A lever near the driver allows the operator instantly to reduce the travel speed 33 percent when the going gets difficult and at the same time increase the drawbar pull in any selected gear without stopping, or declutching, or shifting and without touching the governor control or throttle setting.

Another example of a new power transmission is the one announced in 1958 by the J. I. Case Co. A direct-drive clutch, a torque converter, and a master clutch give the tractor operator the option of the hydraulic torque converter or mechanical direct drive.

Still another example of new transmission is the "Select-O-Speed" announced by Ford in 1959. The transmission is a 10-speed, fully selective power shift unit. It is controlled by one small hand lever. There is no clutch pedal, and yet shifting can be made with the tractor in motion with almost no interruption.

We feel we should mention self-propelled machines although they are not tractors — they take the place of tractors where they are used. Their propelling power unit is an integral part of the implement.

The self-propelled combine — harvester-thresher — appeared in commercial production in 1944. About one-fifth of the million combines on farms in the United States were of this type in 1958.

The Massey-Harris Co. received special authority in 1944 from Government war agencies to make and distribute 500 self-propelled combines to experienced operators. This Harvest Brigade began operations early in May in Texas and California and worked north. By the end of the season they had harvested more than a million acres, or an average of more than 2 thousand acres for each combine.

Self-propelled units are easier to operate and have faster working speeds than trailed machines. They lose less time in opening fields and moving between jobs. Because they cost more, single-purpose self-propelled machines must have a relatively larger annual use to be comparable to the trailed units in cost.

Self-propelled machines, sprayers, cornpickers, hay balers, windrowers, and forage harvesters also were made in 1960.

Another machine is the self-propelled chassis, on which various harvesting units can be mounted interchangeably.

The Minneapolis-Moline Co. in 1945 presented details for the Uni-Farmor system, which provided a chassis or Uni-Tractor equipped with a power unit upon which several types of machines could be mounted. The company had four separate and interchangeable harvesting machines ready in 1954 for use with the Uni-Tractor: A combine, cornpicker, cornpickersheller, and forage harvester. Several other manufacturers started to make units that could be used with the Uni-Tractor, including forage harvesters, a sugar beet harvester, and an applicator of anhydrous ammonia.

Attachments of several types have been developed to make the operation of the tractor more automatic.

One kind of tractor guide uses the last plow furrow of the previous round as a guide to steer the tractor. The guides are most successful in large, level fields.

A Department of Agriculture engineer in the Texas High Plains reported: "Some farmers in the Amarillo and Lubbock area use guides for flat breaking and planting. For flat breaking, the operator makes the first few rounds driving the tractor. Then he plows 24 hours a day, and comes back to the field only to refuel. This is accomplished with disks mounted ahead of the front wheels and running in the furrow. If the guide or tractor gets out of the furrow, the ignition is automatically cut off. For planting, the disks are mounted in front of the front wheels of the row-crop tractor and stay in the lister furrow. The operator watches his cotton boxes while going down the row and gets back on the tractor seat to turn it around at the end of the row."

Tractor guides of the furrow type have been commercially available from manufacturers of tractor accessories for many years. Five were listed in a 1959 directory of farm machinery manufacturers.

The International Harvester Co. in 1931 equipped one of their Farmall 30 tractors so that it could be controlled by radio. The tractor was demonstrated to thousands of people at the Century of Progress exposition in Chicago in 1933.

A member of the staff of the Department of Agricultural Engineering in the University of Nebraska in 1958 equipped a farm tractor with radio controls, by means of which the tractor could be started, stopped, and steered and its gears shifted. The operator was some distance away.

Another development for guiding tractors is an automatic pilot. It is actuated by lightweight feelers that can sense the position of the crop row to be cultivated, the windrow to be baled, or the distance to any other row to be followed. This pilot was not intended to replace the operator but to be an aid to make his work better and easier.

Two research engineers who had worked independently announced in 1958 that they had developed an automatic tractor pilot — L. A. Liljedahl, of the Department of Agriculture, and C. B. Richey, of the Ford Motor Co.

The Ford Motor Co. demonstrated a self-steering tractor at its testing center at Birmingham, Mich., in 1958. The sensing antenna for the steering controls is between the front wheels of the tractor and picks up its signals from a small wire buried under the test track. A second antenna receives start and stop signals over the same wire to control the clutch and brake.

Engineers of the University of Reading, England, in 1959 demonstrated a tractor controlled by a wire laid along the ground or just under the surface. Controls were available for steering, starting and stopping, operating the clutch, power takeoff, horn, and other mechanisms.

These and similar controls, which depend on a wire for guidance, may be useful on a test track or for performing certain operations that are repeated frequently in the barnyard or other fixed course. We question their value for work in the fields.

The effieciency of tractors has been improved greatly over the years. One measure of that is the amount of fuel used.

Tests at the University of Nebraska showed that in 1920 the average wheel-type tractor tested delivered 5 drawbar horsepower-hours per gallon of gasoline or distillate. The average wheel tractor tested in 1959 delivered 10 horsepower-hours to the gallon. The average wheel-type tractor with diesel engine delievered 10 drawbar horsepower-hours per gallon of fuel in 1935 and 13.3 horsepower-hours per gallon in 1959.

A reason for the greater efficiency has been the use of higher compression ratios in many of the gasoline-burning engines and the increased use of diesel engines. (The compression ratio is the relation of the volume within the cylinder when the piston is at its bottom dead center to the volume when at the top.)

The compression ratios of spark-ignition engines in 1941 varied from about 4 to 6; in 1959 the compression ratios of spark-ignition engines varied from about 4 to 8.5. Compression ratios of current diesel tractor engines vary from about 15.5 to about 22. (American automobile engines in 1960 had compression ratios from about 8 to 10.5.)

Many other improvements have been made in tractors.

Valves have been improved by the use of better alloys, and their life has been lengthened by the use of rotators and valve seat inserts.

Valve guides and spark plugs have been improved.

Bearings are precision manufactured to carry greater loads with less susceptibility to fatigue and greater resistance to corrosion.

Better oils and methods of lubrication have been provided, as have improved ignition and cooling systems.

Such improvements give the farmer more power from his tractor with little or no increase in cost or weight.

The electric starter, rubber tires, motor lift, hydraulic controls, and easily attached hitches are among the pieces of equipment that have made operation easier.

Many improvements contribute to the operator's comfort. Deere & Co. came out in 1946 with a Powr-Trol unit to be attached to trailing implements so that they could be lifted and lowered by hydraulic power from the tractor. Hydraulic remote controls were common enough by 1949 so that standards on them were adopted by the American Society of Agricultural Engineers and the Society of Automotive Engineers.

Power steering in automobiles inspired power steering in tractors. Allis-Chalmers put power steering attachments on the WD-45 (wheel type) tractor in 1956. All major American manufacturers offered at least one model with power steering as standard or optional equipment in 1960.

Seats on tractors used to be simple things of steel which soon became quite uncomfortable to the driver. Now they are of foam rubber or are equipped with springs, some of which are adjustable to the operator's weight. Some tractors are equipped with umbrellas, windshields, air-conditioned cabs, and radios. They are a matter not only of comfort, although that is improtant when days are from sunup to sundown, the thermometer stays at 100°, and clouds of dust fill eyes, nose, and mouth. They increase efficiency and safety and are a matter of common sense, for a valuable crop, expensive machinery, and a man's life may be involved.

Safety is more important than comfort. In a great number of farm accidents, tractors have been a factor. The National Safety Council, professional engineering societies, manufacturers, and individuals have worked constantly for greater safety. . . .

The usual channel of distribution of farm tractors and repair parts involves manufacturer, branch, dealer, and farmer.

The manufacturer owns the branch. It is in an important regional center and carries a large stock of the equipment and repair parts that may be needed in the territory.

The local dealer, selected or approved by the manufacturer, usually sells and services the full line of farm machinery of the manufacturer for which there is a demand in his community. He is an important link in the distribution of tractors and other farm machines. He must be a good merchant and he must also know the functions of each implement he sells and the size and type of equipment required. He has to be able to furnish good service to keep them running. His repair shop is much more than the old type of blacksmith shop. It is equipped to service and repair gasoline and diesel engines, combines, and others of the more complicated, precision-built implements that have become commonplace in farm operation.

Prompt service is so important in connection with tractors and other important farm machinery that many successful dealers have service shops at their retail stores and provide specially equipped trucks whose drivers can make repairs and adjustments in the field. In emergency, repair parts are delivered by air from the factory or branch.

All of the large manufacturers of tractors have grown to their present stature by developing new and improved types of tractors and other farm equipment and by acquiring other companies engaged in the manufacture of items which they wished to add to their lines. Expansion enabled them to increase their volume and provide complete lines to offer to distributors and dealers.

One 1960 directory of American manufacturers of farm machinery listed 13 manufacturers of crawler tractors and 35 builders of wheel-type tractors. Nine full-line companies made a large percentage of the machines. We give a few details about each of them.

The International Harvester Co., Chicago, the largest manufacturer of agricultural machinery in the United States in 1960, was incorporated originally in 1902 and began producing tractors in 1906. Several large firms were merged to form it. The company maintains a dozen or more factories in this country and several in Canada and other countries. Tractors are manufactured at plants in Chicago, Louisville, and Rock Island.

Deere & Co., Moline, Ill., the largest manufacturer of steel plows and our second largest manufacturer of agricultural machinery, bought the Waterloo Gasoline Engine Co. in 1918 and began to build tractors. The name of the gasoline engine company was changed to John Deere Tractor Co. in 1926 and later to Deere & Co. Back of this tractor company was an organization originally established by John Deere in 1837.

The J. I. Case Co., Racine, Wis., the third largest, was incorporated in 1880 as the J. I. Case Threshing Machine Co. The business was originally established by Jerome I. Case in 1842. The J. I. Case Threshing Machine Co. was actively engaged in the building of steam tractors in the 1890's and was among the first to turn to the gasoline tractor. The plant at Racine was enlarged in 1912 to permit the production of tractors. Engines were bought from the Davis Motor Co., Milwaukee. In 1913 they started building their own engines. In 1919 it merged with the Grand Detour Plow Co. It purchased the implement plant of the Emerson-Brantingham Corp. at Rockford, Ill., in 1928, when the J. I. Case Plow Co. of Racine was taken over by the Massey-Harris Co. of Toronto. The J. I. Case Plow Co. sold the rights to use of the name "Case" and "J. I. Case" to the J. I. Case Threshing Machine Co. of Racine. Thus an end came to years of confusion caused to these two concerns that had the same name but were not connected with each other.

The Massey-Harris Co., an amalgamation in 1891 of the Massey and Harris companies, Canadian manufacturers of agricultural machinery and tractors, extended its holdings in this country through the purchase of the J. I. Case Plow Co. at Racine in 1928. The J. I. Case Plow Co., incorporated in 1919, was a consolidation of the J. I. Case Plow Works Co. and the Wallis Tractor Co., both of Racine. The plow company, established in 1876, engaged primarily in the manufacture of plows and tillage equipment. The Wallis Tractor Co. was organized in 1912 to manufacture farm tractors. Harry Ferguson, Inc., merged with the Massey-Harris Co. in 1953, and the resulting company became Massey-Harris-Ferguson, Inc. "Harris" was dropped from the name in 1958, and the firm became Massey-Ferguson, Inc., with United States headquarters in Racine.

The Oliver Farm Equipment Co., incorporated in 1929, acquired the business and property of six manufacturers to become a full-line agricultural implement company. Chief among these were the Oliver Chilled Plow Works of South Bend, Ind., the Nichols and Shepard Co. of Battle Creek, Mich., the Hart-Parr Co. of Charles City, Iowa, and the American Seeding Machine Co. of Springfield, Ohio. When this consolidation was effected, efforts were concentrated on the well-known Hart-Parr tractor, and the Nichols and Shepard factory was converted into one, building harvesting and threshing machines. The tractors were produced under the name of Oliver Hart-Parr. The Cleveland Tractor Co., which had been making a tracklaying tractor under the name of "Cletrac," in 1944 combined with the Oliver Farm Equipment Co. to form the Oliver Corp., and all of the equipment and tractors are produced under the name of Oliver.

Formation of the Minneapolis-Moline Power Implement Co., incorporated in 1929, was the result of a merger of the Minneapolis Steel and Machinery Co., the Minneapolis Threshing Co., the Moline Implement Co. The Minneapolis Steel and Machinery Co., organized in 1902, had been building Twin City tractors since 1908, and at the time of merger was engaged in the manufacture of threshing machines and tractors. The principal products of the other two companies included tillage implements, which, combined with the tractor and threshing machine companies, gave another full-line agricultural implement company.

The Allis-Chalmers Manufacturing Co. was incorporated in 1913. Its expansion through the acquisition of eight manufacturing concerns widened its scope to embrace a diversified line of power machinery. It began to manufacture farm tractors shortly after the beginning of the First World War. In 1928 it took over the Monarch Tractor Co. (incorporated in 1918) and has since manufactured tracklaying tractors under the name Allis-Chalmers. The Advance-Rumely Co., makers of threshing machines and farm tractors, was acquired in 1931.

The Caterpillar Tractor Co., Peoria, Ill., was formed by a merger of the C. L. Best Tractor Co. of San Leandro, Calif., and the Holt Manufacturing Co., which had plants at Stockton and Peoria. The latter firm was the originator and holder of the Caterpillar trademark. The Best Co. was organized in 1910 and the Holt Co. in 1892, a successor to earlier Holt firms dating from 1869. Benjamin Holt built the first practical crawler tractor in 1904 at Stockton. The Holt Manufacturing Co. purchased the interests of Daniel Best in 1908, and the latter retired from business. C. L. Best, a son of Daniel Best, formed his company in 1910 and in 1913 started producing tracklayers in his father's old plant at San Leandro. Stiff competition ensued between the two interests until the merger. In 1928 the Caterpillar Tractor Co. acquired the Russell Grader Manufacturing Co. of Minneapolis, a manufacturer of roadbuilding machines for more than 20 years. The products of the Caterpillar Tractor Co. then included tracklaying tractors, combined harvesters, stationary engines, and a varied line of roadbuilding equipment.

The Ford Motor Co., Tractor and Implement Division, Birmingham, Mich., was one of the major producers of wheel-type farm tractors in 1960. The Ford Motor Co. produced its first tractor for the trade in 1917 under the name Fordson. The name Ford could not then be used because it had already been given to a tractor manufactured by a group that included a young man by the name of Ford. The production of Fordson tractors increased rapidly to a yearly peak in 1925. Thereafter production declined, and the production of Fordsons in the United States ceased in 1928.

The Ford Motor Co. again started the mass production of tractors in 1939. Henry Ford made a working agreement with Harry Ferguson of Ireland, whereby Ford tractors were made which used the Ferguson system of a combined linkage and hydraulic control. The oral agreement between Mr. Ford and Mr. Ferguson was terminated late in 1946. Thereafter Ford continued to manufacture tractors, making use of the three-point suspension and hydraulic system. Harry Ferguson, Inc., also continued to manufacture tractors with a three-point suspension and hydraulic system, making use of engines from another manufacturer.

Never before has such a wide selection of sizes and types of tractors been available to the American farmer as in 1960.

Among the wheel tractors are sizes that pull a 12-inch plow and sizes that can pull eight 16-inch plows. Speeds of only 1 mile an hour are available for special jobs.

Most of the wheel tractors made in this country use gasoline or distillate as fuel, but each major manufacturer makes at least one model with a diesel engine and at least one model that burns liquid petroleum. Nearly all of the track-type tractors use diesel engines, but one manufacturer, the Oliver Corp., makes three models in the smaller sizes that burn gasoline.

Every major line includes all-purpose tractors — those to which cultivators, planters, and other field equipment can be attached readily. These models are designated in various ways by the manufacturers with such names as General Purpose, Farmall, and Universal. All-purpose tractors usually have three wheels, the front wheels of the others are adjustable as to tread. Other models are available that have higher crop clearance than usual and are sometimes listed under such designations as Hi-Crop.

Small four-wheel tractors of the riding type usually are of less than one 12-inch plow capacity. Many have appeared on the market since the war, and are popular with part-time farmers and others who have occasional need for a small tractor. Most of them have a single-cylinder, air-cooled engine.

Power is usually transmitted from the engine to the drive wheels by combinations of belt, chain, and gears, although some have gear and worm transmission. Many attachments are available — plows, rotary tillers, harrows, seeders, cultivators, sprayers, sickle bars, rotary mowers, and snow-plows.

A variety of garden tractors and motor tillers also are available. They are of the walking type. They usually have one or two wheels, but motor tillers may have no wheels that touch the ground.

Many farmers use garden tractors for odd jobs for which larger tractors are too cumbersome and uneconomical. Commercial vegetable growers also use garden tractors, but most are bought by surburban homeowners.

Nearly 40 thousand garden tractors of the walking type were shipped by American manufacturers in 1958. Nearly 3 thousand had 2 horsepower or less, and more than 37 thousand had more than 2 horsepower. Of the 174 thousand motor tillers shipped by the manufacturers in 1958, more than 152 thousand had more than 2 horsepower.

All of these garden tractors have a single-cylinder, air-cooled engine, which usually is started by a rope. Most of those with an engine of up to 2 or 3 horsepower do not have a clutch for releasing the engine; instead, the engine is released from the drive wheels by loosening the belt, either by means of an idler pulley or by tilting the engine. Many attachments are available for garden tractors — rotary tiller, harrow, cultivator, seeder, mower, hayrake, cart, grader, fertilizer spreader, and snowplow.

Ordinarily it would be advisable to select a make that is available locally. Then one could see and maybe operate the machine before purchasing it. A 1-to 2-horsepower engine will be large enough for light work, such as cultivation, but for plowing with a conventional plow and extensive land preparation, a tractor with an engine of at least 3 to 4 horsepower will be required.

As to the future, we expect more widespread adoption of many of the improvements now limited to particular models.

The trend in automobiles leads us to expect the development of fuels and engines that will use higher octane gasoline.

There may be radical changes in engine design. Ford, for example, began work in 1954 on a free-piston engine that uses heated gases to drive a turbine and does not require many of the parts of a conventional engine. It shows promise of fuel economy, and it is adaptable to a wide range of fuels.

Nuclear power is an intriguing possibility. A small unit suitable for powering tractors may be in the offing using the principles in use in large installations. With nuclear power, it may be necessary to refuel only once a year.

Also possible is a reversible tractor, on which the seat and controls can be easily and quickly reversed. Reversing a tractor and the attached equipment would save turning at the row ends and give a more unrestricted view for cultivation. The operator would have certain implements in full view.

Another possibility is a tractor with hydraulic drive, which would be driven by two hydraulic motors, one in each drive wheel. The National Institute of Agricultural Engineering in England has developed an experimental model of such a tractor.

Perhaps the self-propelled chassis, with its own power unit, will become more competitive with the conventional tractors of today.

Electric tractors are mentioned sometimes. Storage batteries for power have not been satisfactory, nor has electricity from powerlines through cables. Future development of an electric tractor will probably depend on efficient transmission of current without wires or the development of an efficient long-life battery much superior to those now available.

Tractors of the future will be easier to use. More of them will have power steering, scientifically designed seating, and an automatic pilot to guide the tractor along the crop or other row to be followed.

Mechanized Harvesting

From Herbert F Miller, Jr., "Swift, Untiring Harvest Help," U. S. Department of Agriculture, *Yearbook*, 1960 (Washington 1960), pp. 164–83.

The progress men have made during the past century in methods of harvesting crops is the progress from flail to feeedom.

The flail, which was little more than a stick or whip, was all men had for centuries for separating grain from the straw. The sickle, a simple curved blade, was an improvement for cutting grain. It dates from 3000 B.C. or earlier. Otherwise, about the only significant advances during the next 4,800 years were the scythe and the cradle.

Then came the reaper in the 1830's to open the way to complete mechanization of the harvest — to savings in hours and money and food; to a previously unknown freedom from uncertainty in harvesting.

The grain reaper of the 1830's was a one-horse machine made mostly of wood. Its few metal parts included a ground wheel used to drive gears, which transmitted power to a sickle-type cuttings mechanism. The grain was cut near the ground. A revolving reel gently pushed the grain to the rear onto a small platform, where it was raked off onto the ground in small bundles, which were later bound with pieces of straw. The bundles were picked up and placed in shocks in the field for drying before threshing.

The reaper cut in half the labor required to harvest grain and permitted a more timely harvest.

Inventors soon saw ways to improve it. Progress continued step by step and almost year by year, until the first patent was issued on the self-binder in 1850. Both the wire and twine self-tying binders were common by the middle 1870's, but before long the wire binders, self-rake reapers, and the combination reapers and mowers were obsolete.

Farmers almost everywhere were excited over the twine binders and many bought them. They were improved greatly through the years and were the first equipment to be adapted — in 1919 — to power takeoff from tractors. An estimated 1,250,000 binders were in use in the United States in 1938. That year the actual production of another machine, the combine, overtook production of the binder and within a decade replaced it completely.

During the days of the reaper and binder there was still another operation in the harvesting of grain — threshing. The grain had to be separated from the straw. The flail was used for separating the grain from the heads. Sometimes the grain was tread out by the feet of oxen or by sleds and wheels run over the grain on a flat floor or ground. Then the grain was winnowed — the grain was separated from the chaff. A man with a flail could thresh 7 or 8 bushels of wheat in a 10-hour day.

Early stationary threshing machines, known as groundhogs, were operated by tread or sweep horsepower. Some were turned by hand.

A patent was issued in 1837 on a machine known as the combination thresher that used the idea of the groundhog thresher and the ordinary fanning mill.

This portable machine was operated at first by animal power and later by steam engines or gasoline tractors. Models made in 1850 could thresh several bushels of wheat an hour with a four-man crew and six to eight horses on the sweep power —that is, horses hitched to a pivoted pole walked in a circle to furnish power. A larger model 10 years later was operated by eight horses and had a capacity of 300 bushels a day.

A major improvement was a device that vibrated and shook the grain from the straw. Others included steel teeth, elevators, stackers, grain weighers, self-feeders, bandcutters, wind stackers, and all-steel construction.

Steam engines soon replaced the horse and other types of power. The early steam engines, which developed 6 to 8 horsepower, were transported by animal power. Later the horsepower was increased, and the steam tractor furnished belt-power to the thresher.

The gasoline engine began replacing the steam engine not long after 1900, and the steam-powered thresher soon became a curiosity. The thresher itself is rarely seen today. Only a few threshers, but more than 50 thousand combines, were manufactured in 1959. Thus ended a symbol of the earlier days of farm mechanization — the threshing crew. The thresher was put on wheels and coupled with the cutting mechanism of the binder to form the combine.

The story of the grain combine is almost as old as the story of the reaper. The first successful grain combine, it is said, was built in Michigan in 1836, 10 years before the reaper went into commercial production.

It is supposedly the result of a dream of the wife of one of its inventors. The machine had all the major features of the present-day combine, but the idea was almost a century ahead of the technological progress that was necessary to make the machine a success. The machine was used for 10 years and would cut and thresh up to 25 acres a day, but its inventors gave up. The lack of a suitable power unit, such as is used on self-propelled combines today, and excessive moisture, which caused spoilage of the threshed grain, were two of the major difficulties they encountered. It is said that California took up where Michigan left off.

The Michigan combine was shipped around Cape Horn to San Francisco and harvested several hundred acres during the 1854 season. A more favorable climate, larger acreages, and Californians' love for big machinery started this type of harvester on its way to general use. California-made versions of the combine began to appear in a few years. As many as 40 horses were used to pull the large 15-ton machines, which cut swaths up to 35 feet. Factory production began in California about 1880, when the twine binder was coming into general use in the Midwest.

The first hillside combine was built in the late 1880's and the first self-leveling model about 10 years later. Steam engines then were being mounted on the combine to supply a more constant power than could be provided from the ground wheels. Steam tractors began to replace horses as the propelling unit for the entire machine.

The gasoline engine began to replace steam for pulling the combine and operating its mechanism about 1912. Big combines were coming into their own during the 1920's and 1930's.

The design was being improved. Makers adopted the steel frame and body, antifriction bearings, V-belt drives, and rubber tires, and made the machines lighter.

Another major advancement before 1949 helped to reduce manpower requirements: Bulk handling of threshed grain eliminated the sack sewer and sack jigger. For the hillside combines, several ingenious automatic leveling-control devices were developed so that a two-man crew could take the place of the original five-man crew.

A milestone in 1935 was the development of the one-man combine powered by a two-plow tractor. More than a million grain combines were in use on American farms in 1956, and 1.5 million grain binders that had been in use in 1930–1940 virtually had disappeared.

The pull-type combines, generally in sizes of 6 to 12 feet, have gained wide popularity, particularly for the family-sized farms. They have power takeoffs, or power is furnished by an auxiliary engine mounted on the combine.

Self-propelled grain combines have appeared on American farms in increasing numbers since 1938. About 20 percent of the combines in 1960 were self-propelled, and the trend to them seemed to be increasing.

The self-propelled combines are more maneuverable, they save more grain in opening up fields, and the driver has better visibility and control of his machine.

Self-propelled combines were produced in 1960 with cutterbars up to 18 feet wide, lifetime lubricating bearings, improved V-belt and pulley drives, and mechanisms for easy adjustments or change in speed. Windrow pickup attachments for combining grain and other crops from the windrow were available.

Several companies offered attachments for combines that make it a dual machine for harvesting either grain or corn — a development that has increased the utility of the self-propelled combine so that it may replace many of the present cornharvesting machines.

Air-conditioned cabs are available for self-propelled combines. The compressor for cooling is belt driven from the combine engine. Full-view windows of safety glass give greater visibility and comfort to the operator.

Several makes of hillside combines were available in 1954, but the first hillside combine, with factory-installed automatic leveling controls, was introduced that year.

Hillside combines differ from conventional combines in that the separator body is kept level regardless of the ground slope. The separator body is kept level in the lateral direction.

In some combines a part of the separator (or all of it) is kept level to some degree in the longitudinal direction.

The two main types of sensing devices for automatic controls have the force of gravity acting either on a solid mass or on a liquid. The first uses a pendulum, which controls hydraulic valves directly and also controls electric switches, which energize hydraulic-valve solenoids. The second uses the force of gravity acting upon a liquid similar to a mercury-type switch.

Safety precautions are particularly important when using hillside combines. They have a wide wheelbase, so that the center of gravity falls well within the wheelbase in extremely hilly areas. Each individual wheel has its own brake and power steering. Automatic controls make it impossible for the operator to level in the wrong way.

Almost all combines used for grain employ the direct-cut method on the standing grain. In fields badly infested with weeds and crops that do not ripen uniformly, however, the crop may be cut and laid in a windrow and harvested with the combine using a pickup attachment.

Windrower machines are generally made in sizes from 9 to 16 feet and may be either a pull-type unit for attaching behind a tractor or self-propelled. Self-propelled windrowers can cut and windrow 75 acres a day. They are generally powered by small gasoline engines of 20 to 25 horsepower.

Besides wheat, oats, and barley, combines are used for harvesting soybeans, grain sorghums, rye, oats, flax, peas, dry beans, rice, clovers, alfalfa, lespedeza, timothy, millet, lupines, and safflower.

More details about combine adjustments for harvesting such crops are given in Farmers' Bulletin No. 1761, "Harvesting with Combines," by R. B. Gray. Copies can be had by writing to the Office of Information, U.S. Department of Agriculture, Washington 25, D.C.

Equipment for harvesting beans and peas is used on 1.5 million acres each year, mostly in Michigan, California, Idaho, Nebraska, New York, and Wyoming.

The older method of cutting, windrowing, stacking or baling, and stationary threshing of beans is giving way to the use of threshing machines that have been converted to a combine harvester-thresher (either pull-type or self-propelled) fitted with a special pickup device.

A pickup combine, which works from windrows, has come into common use with navy beans in Michigan. Some growers have special bean combines with two cylinders designed especially for the crop, but the trend in harvesting edible beans has been to use the grain combine.

Attachments for harvesting edible beans with a grain combine include cylinder speed reduction drives and screens. Some machines have rubbercovered bars that replace grain threshing bars on the cylinder and special bean grates that can be placed under or back of the cylinder.

A torsion spring-tooth cylinder and concaves for combines help eliminate cracking of beans and reduce the time one must wait for the heavy bean roots to dry before being combined. This spring-tooth equipment is less effective in threshing small grain than regular types of cylinders and concaves.

A common machine used to push dry beans from the soil and form them into windrows is known as a blade-type bean harvesting cultivator. It is fitted with vine turners, row dividers, and windrowing rods.

A rotary crop cutter has been successfully used in harvesting tests. It consists of hydraulic, motor-driven, notched disks horizontally rotating toward each other so that each, in cutting a row, forms a windrow from two rows.

Farmers would prefer to combine beans directly in order to avoid the possible loss in the windrowing due to inclement weather. Scientists therefore have been working on a new variety of navy bean that grows as an upright plant rather than a vine.

In direct combining, a power-driven, six-batt, finger-type reel is used with an eccentric mechanism to vary the pitch of the tines (fingers) during reel rotation.

This reel is more efficient than the standard batt-type reel because the tines can be adjusted to lift the bean plant toward the cutterbar, thereby saving many pods from being cut by the sickle. The shatter loss at the cutterbar is reduced as much as 50 percent.

When a grain combine is used for cutting beans, the cylinder speed should be reduced to about one-half to one-third that required for threshing wheat. For best results, defoliation of the crop (when the beans are harvested standing) is necessary to help reduce the moisture content of the bean.

Harvesting efficiency depends largely upon correct combine adjustment. Many machines are not designed so that these adjustments can be made easily and in a reasonable time. Improvement in the design of combines is needed to rectify this deficiency.

To harvest our large acreage of corn (of the total annual production of 3.5 million bushels, 70 to 80 percent comes from the 12 North Central States) about 750 thousand cornpickers were used in 1960, an increase of about 42 percent since 1950. More than half of the pickers were in the Corn Belt, but their use has increased rapidly in the South, Northeast, and West.

The first machines for harvesting corn were known as row-crop binders and were used on farms around 1893. They cut the entire stalk, bound them with twine or wire, and placed the bundles in neat rows on the ground as the machine traveled through the field. The bundles were generally shocked or put in small stacks in the fields — a sight familiar to many of us today only in pictures in books that show the pumpkins at the foot of corn shocks in the field about Thanksgiving-time.

Row-crop binders also cut the corn and sorghum that was harvested for silage, not for grain. In 1942 there were 609 thousand row-crop binders on farms; by 1952, one-half of them had disappeared. Today row-crop binders have been replaced almost entirely by field-type mechanical corn-pickers, which came into general use soon after the First World War. Farmers had about 10 thousand corn-pickers in 1920; by 1952 the number of pickers increased to 588 thousand.

Cornpickers are of two types.

A snapper-type corn harvester is much the same as a picker-husker, but the snapper does not remove the husks. Snapped ears are removed directly into a wagon or a trailer. The snapping rolls, which operate at about 500 to 600 feet per minute peripheral speed, are made of cast iron or cast steel with spiral ribs or lugs on their surfaces.

On a picker-husker, the husking rolls may be on a separate bed, incorporated in the snapping roll elevator, or may be a direct extension of the snapping rolls. Most husking units have at least one roll of each set made of rubber. Other rolls may be made of steel, wood, rubber, or cast iron.

Field losses with these machines generally range from 5 to 10 percent. Proper adjusting of the machine, careful driving, and avoidance of high speeds generally will keep field losses to a minimum. The speed of the machine, under most operating conditions, should not exceed 3.5 miles an hour.

Cornpickers started out as one-row units, but two-row pickers have become more popular. That is not the end of the story, though. As with most other farm machines, further advances were to be made. One was the picker-sheller.

Picker-sheller corn harvesters are of the same general design as the pickerhuskers. Manufacturers have added the shelling unit and a bin or elevator for conveying the shelled corn into a trailer.

Picker-shellers were introduced in the middle 1930's, but field shelling of corn made slow progress until 1954, when corn header attachments for the grain combines were produced commercially. A further advancement was made in 1958, when sheller attachments for the standard cornpicker were first put into production.

The corn header attachments for grain combines first proved most successful in California, possibly because the drier climate made high moisture in grain less of a problem and because of a fast increase in corn acreage in an area where the combine was already in use on most farms.

When picker-shellers first appeared, commercial drying facilities were too costly and inconvenient for most farmers. About 1949, however, portable driers appeared with capacities to match that of the field machine, and commercial drying became increasingly available. Harvesting corn with field picker-shellers and combine attachments was an established method of harvesting corn in 1960.

Slightly more than 5 thousand picker-sheller units and 9 thousand grain combine header attachments were in use for picking and field shelling of corn in 1957. The use of field shelling equipment no doubt is destined to increase fast, and someday may replace entirely the cornpickers. Corn is now being grown and harvested mechanically in some areas with fewer than 4 man-hours an acre. This is less time than it takes for one man to hand-husk an acre of corn.

Safety is important. Since most of the accidents with cornpickers are due to carelessness, operators must be trained properly.

The Farm Division of the National Safety Council has listed rules for normal and safe operation of cornpickers. They include safety suggestions: Keep all shields in place. Stop the machine when you oil and adjust it. When the mechanism becomes clogged, disconnect the power before cleaning. Keep hands, feet, and clothing away from power-driven parts. Wear tight-fitting gloves and clothing. Keep other persons off.

For 5 thousand years or so forage for hay was cut with a sickle or scythe. Harvesting hay generally remained a hand operation until the middle of the past century. It has progressed from the various hand- and horse-powered methods to the tractor-powered mower, side-delivery rake, and field baler. Perhaps next will come a machine that forms hay into wafers or pellets in the field.

Haying used to be a hot and heavy job. It consists generally of three operations — mowing, raking, and stacking or storing.

More than 100 million tons of hay are produced each year in the United States. Hay accounts for about 20 percent of all harvested crop acreage.

About 25 percent of all hay was baled at the time of the Second World War. More than 75 percent of the crop was put up in bales in 1960. Primarily responsible for the change is the automatic-tie, pickup balers. Baled hay needs less storage space and is easier to handle than loose hay. Less than 20 percent of the total crop now is loose hay, and the percentage of chopped hay for curing and dehydration increased from about 2 to 10 since the war.

Much progress has been made in improving equipment for mechanizing the harvest, although hay generally has a relatively low cash value per acre.

Early cutting devices parralleled those used on reapers and binders for cutting grain. Cutterbars were rigid at first. Then came two-wheeled mowers with flexible or hinged bars. These changes occurred about 1860. It was reported that by 1865 nearly all hay in this country was cut mechanically except on the roughest ground. Tractor-drawn mowers gradually replaced horse-drawn ones after the turn of the century. Today the 5-foot cutterbar on two-wheeled, horse-drawn mowers is a thing of the past.

Cutterbars on tractor mowers usually are 6 or 7 feet long. Modern tractor mowers may cut as much as 30 or more acres a day.

An advertisement of such mowers might very well read as follows: "Featuring a slip-clutch-protected roller-chain drive assembly, fully enclosed and running in an oil bath; tapered roller bearings; a heavy-duty 28-pound flywheel to provide smooth practically vibrationless operation; a safety release spring, which permits the cutterbar to swing back should it hit an obstruction; high, easy lift of the cutterbar; full vision cutting; excellent maneuverability; and ease of handling in the field and on roadside work."

Tractor mowers may be of several types, such as trail-behind, with either traction or power takeoff drive; direct-connected, trail-behind; integral rear-mounted mowers; and integral side or central-mounted mowers. Almost all mowers by 1958 were power-driven instead of having a ground drive.

Newer developments in mower design consist of high-speed operation, with a reduced stroke length and a dynamically counter-balanced reciprocating blade so designed that its operation is not affected by the raising and lowering of the bar. Many are also equipped with special antifriction bearings throughout.

The number of hay crushers, a machine long established but little used, increased from a few hundred to several thousand during the decade before 1960. "Hay in a day" is often promised with the use of hay crushers along with the mowing operation. Consisting of a pair of steel rollers held together under pressure by adjustable springs, the crusher is driven by the tractor power takeoff. The rollers may be attached directly to a mower, or a pickup may lift the hay from the swath and feed it between the rolls. The crushed hay is dropped back onto the stubble, where later it may be further conditioned with a tedder or raked into a windrow.

Many reports indicate that crushed hay generally dries to a moisture content safe for storage in one-third to two-thirds of the time required for uncrushed hay. The drying time is seldom reduced enough to allow cutting and storing in the same day. Crushing, however, often allows the hay to be picked up on the second day in some climates when normally it would take 3 or 4 days for it to reach a safe moisture content. Some crushers have smooth rolls. Others are equipped with fluted rolls, which tend to crimp the hay.

Hay tedders sometimes are used by farmers to turn and fluff up windrows or swaths of hay that become wet to help speed drying. Although this machine has never really been used to any great extent, the tedding process may often be helpful in connection with hay crushing and the general need to dry hay as quickly as possible.

Spring-tooth sulky rakes were used for many years for windrowing or bunching hay. They have been replaced largely by side-delivery rakes, known as cylindrical reel, oblique reel-head, or finger wheel rakes.

The development of side-delivery rakes made the old hay tedder much too slow and tedious.

Side-delivery rakes move hay in a gentle yet rapid pace into a well-formed, fluffy windrow. If the windrow becomes wet on the bottom or needs to be turned, the side-delivery rake can be used to move the windrow over a few more feet, thus aerating and further helping to dry the hay. Early models of such rakes were used soon after 1900, but not until 1940 did the tractor-operated, power takeoff, side-delivery rake appear.

Many stages have come and gone in hay handling. The familiar pitch fork and the portable hay stacker which reached the market about 1882 are examples. The stacker and similar types of equipment were powered first by horses and later by tractors. Now we have mechanical hay balers.

The field pickup baler, which began to attract attention about 1932, was a spectacular development. Baling machines saved at least two handlings of the crop — in itself an important contribution. Self-tying balers came along in 1940. Self propelled machines came in 1958.

The number of automatic pickup balers increased more than threefold between 1950 and 1960. An outstanding change was the use of twine for tying. Of approximately 600 thousand baling machines in the United States in 1958, about 80 percent used twine.

There has been a noticeable trend toward the use of smaller bales, which are easier to handle. With a baler equipped with the bale ejector, one man can operate his machine and unload his hay into the mow with a barn bale conveyor.

The two main types of balers are the plunger-type, which makes a rectangular bale, and the roll-type, which turns out a round bale. Rectangular bales are more popular, although some say the round bales absorb less water when rained on in the field.

Twine used for baling hay, somewhat heavier than binder twine, has a tensile strength of about 275 pounds. The normal rectangular bales use slightly more than 3 pounds of twine per ton. Round bales require slightly more than 2.5 pounds.

Automatic twine tying devices have been refined and improved until they give little trouble. Important features on modern balers include safety clutches or shear pins to prevent overloading in various places — between the flywheel and the plunger; in the needle drive, should it strike an obstruction; in the drive ahead of the baler flywheel on balers driven by power takeoff; in the pickup and conveying drive; in the drive to the tying mechanism; and in the feed mechanism drive.

The development of the field forage harvester marked another milestone in harvesting silage crops. Forage used for silage was cut in the field with row-crop binders during the early days of mechanization and was chopped with ensilage cutters before being placed into a silo. Direct-cutter attachments later enabled these machines to cut and chop silage in a single operation. Special attachments were developed to handle corn and other row crops. Simplified rotary or flail-type forage harvesters became popular in the 1950's, primarily among farmers who chopped forage for immediate drylot feeding.

The number of field forage harvesters on farms increased from about 80 thousand in 1950 to 240 thousand in 1957. They took the place of the row-crop binder. They are of two major types; their cutting knives are placed in a flywheel or in a cylindrical arrangement. A third, the so-called flail-type forage harvester, developed out of the swinging blade stalk cutter-shredders, has gained in importance.

In the flywheel, or cylinder-type, forage harvesters, a separate blower (or blades) is attached to the flywheel for blowing the chopped material into the wagon. The flail-type machine uses the air movement from the swinging blades to carry the material into the wagon. The flail-type machine, of simple design, has relatively few working parts. It can be utilized to harvest ensilage, chop hay and straw, shred stalks, cut weeds, and top beets, among others.

Perhaps machines for pelleting or wafering hay in the field may come into general use someday for harvesting forage. The cost of handling from field to storage and from storage to feeding would be greatly reduced with hay in pellets. Experimental field machines for making wafers or pellets have the capacity of about one-half that of a conventional baler and make wafers best from hay that has a moisture content of 12 to 16 percent.

No doubt ingenious inventors and engineers will continue to improve such machines until they will be satisfactory and perhaps will replace or at least compete with the now popular, powerful, and efficient hay baler.

Mechanical cotton harvesters available in 1960 were of two basic types — strippers and pickers.

Stripper-type harvesters strip the entire plant of both open and unopened bolls and many leaves and stems.

Picking machines remove the seed cotton from open bolls and leave the burs on the plant.

Mechanical picking of cotton has been a great challenge to the imagination of cottongrowers and agricultural scientists and engineers. A cotton-picking device was patented in 1850.

A stripper-type harvester was patented in 1871.

Such problems as uneven opening of the bolls and keeping the cotton lint free of leaves and trash remain. On few farm machines has as much money been invested in engineering development as cotton harvester.

Several hundred patents have been issued on cotton harvesting machines since 1850. Many of those machines no doubt would have done the job just as well as some that are now in use if they had been put into production.

Many factors hindered the early acceptance and use of machines before the Second World War, however. One was that the gins were not equipped with devices to handle and clean the machine-harvested cotton with all the extraneous material it contained. Farmers in general had an ample supply of relatively cheap labor. They wanted machines that would harvest cotton comparable in cleanliness to that of hand-harvested cotton and leave little cotton in the field. The farmer was satisfied with hand-harvesting his crop and was not particularly ready for any great change.

The scarcity and high cost of labor during and after the war and new developments in harvesting and ginning equipment were primarily responsible for changing the cotton farmers' viewpoint about harvesting cotton with machines.

Great strides have been made in mechanizing the cotton crop in places in the Cotton Belt. Reducing costs through mechanization has helped to keep cotton on a more competitive basis with foreign competition and synthetic fibers. The costs were still too high in 1960, however, and considerable effort was still being placed on mechanization of all phases of production and harvesting. In fact, many disciplines of science and engineering have been involved in this overall mechanization endeavor — plant breeding, to produce varieties adaptable to machine picking;

chemistry, to develop defoliants to take the leaves off before picking and chemicals for weed control; soil science, to determine the best method of land preparation and irrigation practices; and engineering, to furnish the right kind of machine for each operation.

Mechanization has reduced the labor to grow an acre of cotton from 150 hours with one-row, horse-drawn equipment to about 30 hours with tractor equipment and machine picking. In the Texas High Plains, where stripper-type harvesting is practiced, labor requirements are as low as 6.5 man-hours an acre for all the work of production and harvesting.

Stripper harvesting, simpler than picking, was first referred to as sledding. Homemade horse-drawn sleds were used in Texas as early as 1914. A few tractor-mounted strippers were built in 1930, but there was little interest in them then.

Stripping machines pull entire bolls from the plant as in hand stripping, which has been done in West Texas and Oklahoma. Gins were improved for handling this type of cotton in the early 1940's. About 30 thousand stripper-type machines were used on farms in 1959 to harvest approximately 14 percent of the United States crop.

Stripper harvesters were used first on low-yielding dryland cotton. They are now used in High Plains irrigated cotton yielding up to a bale or more and in central Texas, Oklahoma, and New Mexico. Stripper use is limited primarily to cotton of a stormproof nature and work most satisfactorily after frost has killed the green leaves and vegetative growth.

The two-row, tractor-mounted stripper will harvest a bale of cotton in about 30 minutes when operating in cotton yielding three-fourths of a bale an acre — one man stripping cotton by hand does that in a 10-hour day.

Cotton-stripping machines include single-steel roller, double-steel roller, and finger types.

The inclined rollers first approach the cotton plant at the base of the stalk. As the harvester moves forward, the bolls and many of the leaves and stems are stripped from the central stalk. The cotton falls into a conveyor on either side of the roller and is conveyed to the rear of the tractor and into a trailer.

The conveying systems for taking the cotton from the stripping rolls to the trailer are mostly of three types — finger-beater, auger, and air. Generally an auxiliary air blower on the loading elevator assists in uniform loading of the trailer.

The best type of plant for mechanical stripping has relatively short-noded fruiting branches 8 to 10 inches long and is less than 3 feet high. Closely spaced plants in the row have shorter limbs, and the main stalk is smaller in diameter. Plant populations of 30 to 50 thousand per acre in 40-inch rows are commonly recommended for stripper harvesting.

In cultivation, sweeps are set flat, so that little or no soil is thrown around the base of the plant. Therefore more clearance is left between the ground at the base of the plants and the lowest limb or boll of cotton, so that the fingers of the stripper can slide easily under the open cotton bolls and strip the plant.

Double-brush nylon rollers used in place of steel rollers gave good efficiency for gathering most varieties of cotton (including open-boll types), but they allowed too much soil and trash to be mixed with the lint. Many trials were made of rubber paddles in place of stripping rolls, but neither they nor the brush rollers had come into wide use in 1960.

A development in the stripper-type harvester is the use of long, brush-type stripping rolls with a combination stick and bur remover. Mechanical conveyors are used between the stripping unit and the basket. The long brush rollers permit the harvesting of taller, higher-yielding cotton of the open-boll type. The combination stick and bur remover takes most of the bur and sticks out of the cotton before putting the partly cleaned seed cotton into the basket.

Further improvements may make this type of harvester economically feasible if the quality of the lint can be maintained. No doubt it can be used successfully for the second picking in many cases. Its obvious advantage is that it deposits the burs and most of the trash in the field rather than carrying them to the gin.

We expect that the stripper-type machines of conventional or improved models will be used more and more as cotton is further mechanized, primarily because of their low cost and the speed at which they can operate, as compared with picking machines.

Approximately 24 thousand picker-type harvesters were used to harvest 22 percent of the crop in the United States in 1959. That and the 14 percent harvested by strippers meant that about one-third or more of the total United States crop was machine harvested.

Less than 5 percent of the cotton in the Southeast is harvested by machine. More than 80 percent of the irrigated crop in the West is mechanically harvested.

Cotton production has been moving west. We think it will continue to do so because of the larger fields, higher yields, fewer insect problems, and more uniform and better weather conditions during the harvesting period.

Picking machines are used primarily in the large fields that often yield as much as 3 bales an acre under irrigation in the West.

Mechanical cottonpickers are of two general types because of their spindles — tapered-tooth and straight-smooth. Pickers are single-row machines, which may be tractor-mounted, or two-row machines, which generally are self-propelled.

The tapered-tooth pickers generally have what is known as a spindle drum arrangement. The spindles are mounted on vertical bars arranged in a cylindrical manner somewhat like a drum set on its end. The spindles are mounted 1.5 inches apart on the bars, which are connected to a crank arm at the top.

The spindle drums are operated with one on each side of the row, but are not directly opposite. As the slightly offset drums of spindles rotate with the forward movement of the picker, the spindles enter the slightly compressed cotton plant on either side. The rotating spindles remove the lint from the burs.

After the revolving spindles and rotating drum reach a position just opposite that of the cotton stalk, the cotton is doffed off the spindle by a rotating mechanism turning in the same direction as the spindles but somewhat faster. This action unwinds the cotton from the spindle. The seed cotton is then picked up by means of air suction and blown or mechanically conveyed into the large picker basket.

The tapered-tooth spindle pickers are available in a low-drum size (14 spindles high) or high-drum (20 spindles high). The low-drum pickers are somewhat less expensive and work satisfactorily in cotton up to 3 feet high. The low drum is also offered as an attachment to tractors, and no major conversion of the tractor is necessary. The small pickers replace 25 men or more and can be considered economically feasible on as few as 40 acres of cotton.

The straight-smooth spindle-type machine may have the spindles slightly roughened, or they may have light knurled surfaces. Such pickers are generally referred to as having the chain-belt arrangement, since the spindle bars are attached to an endless chain belt. The belt has 80 spindle bars or slats, each of which has 16 spindles, or a total of 1,280. The spindles project into the row of plants from one side only. On some models, however, it is possible to place a belt on each side of the row similar to the drums of the tapered-tooth spindle picker. The straight spindle is friction driven. The tapered-tooth spindle-type pickers use gear drives for each spindle.

Both types of spindle pickers have moistened pads, over which the spindles pass during each revolution of the drum or belt. The moisture helps the lint adhere to the spindles and keeps them clean of plant juices and other sticky material. Wetting agents are sometimes used to reduce the amount of water necessary and still do an acceptable job of picking.

Cottonpicking machines perform best when the cotton plants are of medium size and the lowest limbs are at least 4 inches above the ground. The machines require a well-opened boll, locks that are fluffy, and fiber that is long enough to afford good contact with the spindles but set deeply enough into the burs to provide reasonable storm resistance. Fairly thich and uniformly spaced plants (20 thousand to 30 thousand plants per acre) aid in the performance of mechanical cotton pickers. Picker performance depends almost entirely on proper adjustment and operation. A well-trained and careful operator is essential.

A 500-pound bale of lint cotton requires approximately 1,400 pounds of clean hand- or machine-picked seed cotton. The price for handpicking cotton varies from 1.50 to 4.00 dollars a hundredweight. When this cost reaches 2.50 dollars or more, it is generally considered profitable to use machine pickers. That shows how easily the availability of labor and wages for handpicking determine when machine harvesters are used.

Root Crops are grown on about 5 million acres in this country. They include potatoes, peanuts, sugar beets, sweetpotatoes, onions, carrots, and radishes.

The harvesting of sugar beets has been mechanized completely. Some edible crops, such as sweetpotatoes, are dug by machines, but the entire crop is picked up by hand.

The first potato harvesters, used in the 1940's, had attachments for putting the potatoes in sacks. Most of the machines have been converted to load directly into a truck with bulk body. Conveying or dumping attachments on the truck are used for unloading at the storage or processing warehouse. Nearly all the harvesters built after 1950 used the direct-loading method. Approximately 5 thousand potato harvesters were used on farms in 1958.

Production areas with good soil suitable for mechanical harvesting, such as Idaho, the Pacific Northwest, and the Red River Valley in North Dakota and Minnesota, were the first to make good use of mechanical harvesting methods. Modern equipment was used first in Florida in 1953.

Stones in the soil in Maine have limited the use of harvesters there. However, in 1955 many growers started using them as fast as they could adapt their farming operations to the bulk handling methods. Mechanization of potato production in the San Joaquin Valley in California has been deterred primarily because of the difficulty of clod separation.

The two main types of potato harvesters are diggers and the combination digger-pickers — often referred to as a potato combine.

The diggers handle one or two rows and generally are power operated from the tractor power takeoff. Several types of blades or shovels are used for digging or scooping up the potatoes and surrounding soil. One-row diggers are usually equipped with pointed blades. Two-row diggers may have a pointed blade for each row or a continuous straight blade across both rows.

The digger blade delivers potatoes and some soil onto a rod-chain type of elevating conveyor. Oval-shaped idler sprockets support the elevator chain and give it an up-and-down motion to aid in sifting out the soil. Most diggers have adjustments to control the speed of the elevator and sprocket for the different operating conditions. Higher speeds give a better cleaning action, but the potatoes are more apt to be bruised. The potatoes are deposited back onto the ground behind the digger, where they are picked up by hand or by a combine-type machine.

A potato combine may be operated in one of two ways — as a once-over harvester or as an indirect harvester by picking the potatoes off the ground following a digger. The combine may be a one- or two-row machine. An auxiliary motor or power takeoff operates the conveying chains and the separating and loading devices. Potatoes pass from the elevating chain to a sorting conveyor.

Workers stand on a platform near the sorting conveyor and assist in removing vines, stones, clods, and other foreign material that is not separated mechanically. The potatoes are then discharged from the sorting conveyor into an elevator, which carries them into the truck. The number of handpickers required depends on the amount of foreign material to be removed and the forward speed of the machine.

The free-fall distance between conveyors or from the conveyors into the containers should not be more than 6 inches. Rubber-covered links are used on elevator chains to lessen damage to the tubers. The floor and sides of trucks for bulk handling usually are padded.

Sweetpotatoes are harder to harvest mechanically than white potatoes because they bruise more easily. Several types of plows or digging blades may be used to lift them from the ground, but the digging is followed by handpicking. The lack of a completely successful mechanical harvester is one reason for a drop in sweetpotato acreage in the United States. An average of 600 thousand acres were grown in the 1945–1947 period, compared with approximately 300 thousand acres in 1957–1959.

Harvesting of peanuts is becoming increasingly mechanized.

Harvesting involves digging and shaking to remove nuts from the soil, windrowing or stacking, and picking to remove the peanuts from the vines.

The roots are cut just below the nut zone with a half sweep or blade, which also lifts them from the ground. Side-delivery rakes or shaker-windrowers then place the peanuts in windrows, where they can dry somewhat before harvesting.

Before combines were used, the nuts were shaken by hand and stacked in the field, where they were allowed to dry before picking with stationary threshers.

Mechanization of harvesting the Spanish-type peanuts grown in the Southwest was practically complete in 1960. One reason was that weather is apt to be good during the harvest period. After 5 or 6 days, windrowed peanuts in the Southwest often are dry enough to be picked up and threshed. Converted peanut threshers or modified grain combines generally are used.

About one-half of the peanut crop in Alabama, Georgia, and Florida was harvested by machines in 1959.

Machines using the carding principle have been most popular. It has seemed, however, that a combination cylinder and carding principle may be used successfully on the same machine to increase capacity and efficiency. Both the Spanish and the larger runner or bunch varieties of peanuts are grown in the Southeast. Combination equipment, which incorporated tractor-mounted digger-blades and a pull-behind, shaker-windrower, was developed before 1958. This equipment began to replace the side-delivery rakes.

The old method of hand stacking and picking peanuts with stationary threshers were used altogether in the Virginia-Carolina area up until 1957.

The Virginia-type peanuts grown there are the large nuts like those sold in the hull at baseball and football games. Mechanical harvesting was begun by several growers before 1959. The development of special digger-shaker-windrowers, improvements in combines for the larger peanuts, and better techniques for artificial drying may make complete mechanization possible in Virginia-Carolina.

The windrow harvesting methods mean that peanut growers would not have to keep a large labor force for peak harvest seasons. Only one-sixth the man-hours of labor per acre is needed with the windrow method, as compared with the stack-pole method of harvesting. This saving in labor costs alone can justify the cost of equipment needed for the windrow method if more than 30 acres of peanuts are grown.

Although techniques for mechanical drying of combined peanuts have been worked out in general for the Virginia-North Carolina area, increased mechanical harvesting will depend on the speed with which suitable drying equipment can be provided.

Mechanical harvesters for sugar beets were used somewhat in the 1930's. The shortage of workers after the war brought about the extensive use of machines. About 4 thousand harvesters were used in 1947 for 30 percent of the United States crop. Twenty thousand harvesters gathered 100 percent of the crop in 1958.

Modern harvesters do the work of topping, gaging, cutting, lifting, and loading sugar beets into trailers.

Two common harvesting principles have been in use.

One is in-place topping, followed by two rotating converging wheels that loosen the beets and lift them from the ground. Kicker wheels are used for cleaning, and a rod-chain type elevator carries the beets to the trailing container.

In the other, a spiked wheel lifts the untopped beets from the ground. Inclined steel stripper bars raise the beets off the spikes far enough to permit topping at the proper level with a pair of rotating disks. The beets are then deposited in the trailer.

Harvesters for carrots, beets, turnips, radishes, and onions were in various stages of development in 1960 and were used for harvesting vegetables grown primarily for commercial processing and canning. Bruising and cutting is not nearly so serious when vegetables are to be processed as when they go to the fresh market.

Root-crop harvesting machines dig, top, and load in one operation. Special plow points lift the ground around the carrots or beets as guide rods lift the plant, which is firmly held by the leafy portion between two rubber belts. A device removes the tops, which fall to the ground. Then the vegetables are conveyed into a side-delivery elevator and into a truck or trailer. Not many of the harvesters have been sold. Generally they are manufactured by smaller companies that may specialize in this type of equipment.

Small one-row, as well as three- and five-row harvesters, were manufactured and used in several areas for harvesting radishes in 1957–1959. Multiple-row harvesters, at a speed of about 3 miles an hour, can pull and top 10 acres of radishes in a 10-hour day. They are adjusted to harvest 5 rows planted 9 inches apart, but they can be adjusted to several different bed widths and numbers of rows per bed.

Radishes are pulled from the soil by the tops between pairs of inclined moving V-belts and are carried to revolving knives for topping. Conveyors take them to a trailer or truck, which moves beside the harvester. Small, one-row harvesters are available for use in small fields. The operator walks behind the machine. A small gasoline motor powers the unit. A platform is built on the machine for boxes or crates to receive the harvested radishes.

Coby Lorenzen, of the California Agricultural Experiment Station, in 1950 developed an experimental mechanical onion harvester that could dig, lift, top, and sack onions in one operation. It handled about 2 acres of onions in a 10-hour day under normal field operations. This development stimulated further work by manufacturers, who have since developed onion harvesters.

Onions are harvested by cutting underneath the bulbs with a blade or knife, so that the tops will dry. The harvester picks the onions up later. A fan blows the tops up while a cutterbar clips them from the bulbs. An airblast blows the cut tops onto the field while the bulbs are conveyed into a box. Hand labor for harvesting onions often accounts for as much as 50 percent of the total production cost. We believe developments in harvesting equipment will make it possible to harvest a large percentage of the commercial crop in a few years.

Many people have seen how fruit and nuts are gathered by hand from trees. Migrant workers start on the harvesting in the South and work northward with the harvest season. They hurry to get the fruit out of the orchards so they can return to the South before cold weather comes.

The scarcity and high cost of labor and management problems have caused growers to consider what might be done to mechanize the harvest.

Various mechanical shaking methods to remove fruit and nuts have been tested and put into use. Sometimes the product is allowed to fall onto the ground, where it is picked up by machines or by hand. Catching frames sometimes are provided for receiving the product and conveying it into some type of box or container.

The harvest of walnuts is more completely mechanized than is that of other tree nuts. Mechanical shakers remove the nuts from the trees. Tractor-mounted machines, which have closely spaced steel fingers that act as a brush, windrow and pick up the walnuts and rake and throw them onto a drag-type elevator, which dumps the nuts into a screen conveyor. Soil falls through the screen. Leaves and trash are blown out by a fan. The nuts are dumped into a trailer behind the harvester.

Management of the orchard is doubly important when harvesting is mechanical. Trees must be planted suitable distances apart and properly trimmed and pruned. The ground under and between the trees must be kept fairly level. The surface has to be smoothed before the harvest. Operators of mechanical shaking equipment must not damage the limbs when trees are shaken. Workers must be trained to do a particular job efficiently.

Mechanical shaking of pecans has increased. Various devices have been developed to catch the nuts as they are shaken off the trees, but none has proved to be entirely satisfactory. Most of the pecan crop was still picked up by hand in 1960.

About 35 percent of the filbert crop was harvested with mechanical equipment in 1959. Filberts are allowed to fall to the ground when ripe, and so they are left free of the husks. They are swept or brushed with a rake into piles and scooped into a cleaning or sacking machine, which is pulled through the orchard.

Fifty percent of the almond crop in 1959 was gathered with harvesters like those used for picking up walnuts. Mechanical shakers have not been used widely for almonds because they do not clean the tree without additional poling or knocking by hand.

Engineers of the California Agricultural Experiment Station developed an experimental machine for harvesting grapes. It reduces hand labor and approaches handpicking in efficiency. To use the machine, the vines must be trained so that the clusters of grapes hang uniformly under the wires holding them.

Mounted on a four-wheeled tractor, the machine clips the bunches of grapes with a moving knife and loads them into a trailer pulled by another tractor between adjoining grape rows. Because of the difficulty of training the vines just right, it is expected that several years may elapse before vineyards can be grown with properly trained vines.

Prunes also have long been harvested by hand. Some varieties are picked from the trees. Others are left to fall on the ground and be picked and marketed mostly as dried fruit.

Paul A. Adrian and R. B. Fridley, agricultural engineers of the Department of Agriculture and the California Agricultural Experiment Station, respectively, developed a machine in 1958 that picks prunes from the ground.

The prune pickup machine is 20 inches wide and is self-propelled. It is operated by one man walking behind. It can pick up 1 thousand pounds of prunes an hour. Two rollers rotate to pass fruit between them as the machine moves over the ground. The fruit is pulled into the space between the two rollers and passed up between two conveyer belts, which carry the prunes to a box mounted on the rear of the machine. The ground must be level and free of stones, broken branches, and other debris for efficient operation. Commercial manufacturers made several machines based on this principle in 1959.

Picking figs from the ground with the same type of machine as I described for prunes may be possible. Different adaptations and adjustments may be necessary for figs and other crops.

A self-propelled catching conveyor was developed in 1958 for harvesting such small-tree fruit as plums and apricots. It was an improvement over frames previously used. Three men can operate a pair of the catcher-conveyors. With a tractor-mounted tree shaker, the fruit of 30 to 40 trees can be harvested in an hour.

Each catcher-conveyor is about 13 feet long. A conveyor belt, 6 feet wide, runs the length of the machine. On one side of the conveyor is a 4-foot flexible flap, tilted upward. On the other side is a flap, 1.5 feet wide, tilted upward and split in the center so as to fit around a tree trunk. Two catcher-conveyors, with the short tree-side flaps adjusted so as to lap over each other and around the trunk, form a complete seal. As the fruit is shaken from the tree and falls on the conveyor, the belt carries it to the rear of the machine, where it is dumped into bulk boxes.

Engineers at the California Agricultural Experiment Station studied the feasibility of shaking peaches and Bartlett pears onto a catching frame. More than 75 percent of the peaches shaken onto the frame and an average of 68 percent of the mechanically harvested pears were free from visible injury. More fruit was damaged in the fall through the tree than was injured in falling onto and over the catching-handling device. The taller the trees, the more injury is to be expected.

Mechanical lift machines for use in orchards may be of considerable help also in harvesting fruit. One, developed about 1955, enables one man to do about twice as much of the work that used to require ladders. The machines have air-cooled gasoline engines, which also operate an air compressor for pneumatic tools. A hydraulic cylinder raises and lowers a platform on which a man can stand. The operator runs the machine by foot-operated controls, and both hands are free to perform work.

Similar machines have been used more and more for pruning and thinning work but have not been used to any large extent for picking fruit. The cost of such a machine has been too high for the use of one person in a picking operation. Also, it is hard to maneuver such machines in orchards where props are used to hold up the limbs.

J. H. Levin and S. L. Hedden, of the Department of Agriculture, and H. P. Gaston, of the Michigan Agricultural Experiment Station, have studied many aspects of fruit harvesting. They investigated mobile ladders, mobile platforms, hydraulic booms, picking tubes, and other picking aids. They concluded that complete mechanization of apple picking is not promising for the near future. Apples can be picked faster by hand, however, when equipment is used to carry the weight of the harvested fruit.

It is hard to visualize a picking device that can select apples among the leaves and limbs and twist them quickly from the tree faster than a man can with his hands.

The investigators found that bulk boxes can be used for handling apples, peaches, and pears with no more bruising during filling than when field crates are used.

The amount of fruit for processing — harvested directly in bulk boxes and transported to packing or storage houses — has increased from practically none in 1953 to several million bushels in 1960. Each year there was a big increase in the use of bulk bins.

Bulk boxes have been used in increasing numbers since 1957 for bulk harvesting and handling of apples in the Pacific Northwest for the fresh-fruit market. The development of hydraulic lifts and loaders on farm tractors and the change to bulk boxes have saved money over operations that use the smaller boxes. The size of box, details of fabrication, and materials of construction are subjects of continuing study by public and private researchers.

A ventilated picking lug for strawberries was developed in 1957. It is used for picking and transporting the fruit to the processing plant. It is referred to as "ventilated" because the sides, slightly lower than the ends, permit free movement of air through the stacks of lugs after they have been placed on the transport vehicle. The container has an easily removed metal handle.

Also developed was a detachable lug carrier for havesting raspberries, like the one for strawberries. It has a metal frame made from one-fourth-inch iron rod that will hold the lug approximately 10 inches off the ground and provides a means of carrying it.

Further progress has been made in harvesting blueberries by the development of a catching frame and a specially designed shaking device.

The shaker consists of an electric drill motor. It has a rubber-finger attachment used in place of the drill bit. The berries fall onto the catching frame before being further delivered into the boxes. This development is possibly only a transition between hand harvesting and a completely self-propelled harvesting machine. The researchers envision a machine that will travel through the field, straddling a row of blueberries, and harvest and place them in containers as it travels along.

Mechanizing the harvest of vegetable crops has become more and more necessary because of the high cost of hand harvesting and the lack of workers when they are needed. Vegetable growers find it difficult to pay high wages for harvesting such crops as asparagus, celery, and cauliflower. Two to eight times more man-hours are required for hand harvesting them than for all other growing operations.

The generally small acreages per farm of vegetable crops, compared with field crops, does not encourage large manufacturers to develop expensive harvesting equipment for vegetables. Further the number of machines needed is too small for mass production. As the demand for such equipment grows, however, work on harvesting equipment is started in one way or another. Individual growers, manufacturers of small equipment, and research workers tackle the problems. Several breakthroughs were made in the decade before 1960.

Spinach and green peas for commercial processing were among the first major vegetable crops to be mechanized successfully. Machines cut the entire plants near the ground with a sickle-bar cutting device and load them into trailers or trucks pulled behind or beside the harvesters. The crop is hauled to a processing or shelling plant.

Machines for harvesting green beans baffled engineers for many years. It was not until plant scientists produced a bean which would lend itself to mechanical harvesting that the problem began to be solved. Present varieties used for mechanical harvesting mature a large percentage of the beans at one time so that the harvesting may be accomplished in one complete operation. Several hundred mechanical snap bean harvesters were in use by 1960. The two-row machines grasp the leaves and stems between rollers, pull the beans from the plant, and drop the refuse on the ground.

Since snap beans can be harvested by machine only once, some growers pick their beans first by hand and then follow with machines for the second and final harvest.

Plant breeders are continuing to work on varieties of beans that will be even better adapted for machine harvesting. The Stage of maturity, shapes of the plant, and other factors make a difference in the efficiency of machine harvest. Growers often sacrifice total yield in favor of low harvesting cost when it is economical for them to do so, or the lack of available labor dictates that this method of harvest must be used.

Mechanical harvesting of sweet corn for processing came into widespread use during the 1950's. Two-row, tractor-mounted harvesters strip the ears from the stalks and convey them into trucks or trailers. The harvesters reduce the cost about 60 percent. Each replaces 10 to 15 handpickers.

A type of harvester has been developed for such crops as celery, cabbage, and lettuce. It usually is mounted on a large trailer or tractor chassis. It moves slowly through the field as the vegetables are cut by hand and placed onto conveyor belts. The belts extend out on either side of the machine to bring the hand-cut vegetables to a central location. There they are either loaded in bulk on trailers and trucks or fed into a packing line. If the packing lines are on the machine, several workers handle the vegetables through their various cleaning and sorting stages and place them in boxes ready for shipment.

Several attempts have been made to develop a mechanical harvester for celery. None has been used a great extent, primarily because of the difficulty of gaging properly the cutting device for removing the roots from the stalk.

The same difficulty has been encountered with experimental machines for harvesting lettuce and cabbage. If precision planting and cultivating equipment is developed for these crops, perhaps they will be grown with such uniformity in the row that a machine can be made to do a satisfactory job of cutting them at the proper position.

Growers of asparagus have watched with interest the engineering developments made by Robert Kepner, of the California Agricultural Experiment Station, on a machine that may some day be used successfully in harvesting asparagus. Several prototypes of the machine have been made, each one better than the previous model.

The Kepner machine has a bandsaw type of blade, which cuts the asparagus spears just below the ground surface immediately after they have been caught by a gripping unit. The spears grow in level beds 30 to 36 inches wide. Only one bandsaw covers the entire bed, but several of the gripping units operate across the width of the bed. They look like small wheels placed close together rolling down the row. They are made so the gripping units open up while rolling over the asparagus. They close at the ground level, gripping the spears about 3.5 inches above the ground.

The machine cuts all spears regardless of their length. Many of the spears therefore are not long enough to be saved. In tests in 1957, the machine-harvested yield was considered to be 55 percent of the hand-cut, because of the loss of the short spears.

Under certain assumed conditions and estimated costs, mechanical harvesting and hand cutting would yield about the same net return on a per acre basis if the machine-harvested yields were 65 percent of the hand-cut yield. Thus, by further modification of management and cultural practices, it may be possible to increase the percentage of harvested yield so that this method of harvesting asparagus will be practicable. It may also be possible to develop new varieties that would fit into this pattern of harvesting more successfully.

The harvesting of cucumbers was speeded up by machines that had platforms, on which pickers were carried. Conveyor belts also increased picking speed by taking cucumbers from the hand to containers at a central place.

Mechanical cucumber harvesters by 1957 were capable of harvesting 1 to 1.5 acres an hour. One machine did the work of 40 harvest hands. The machine gathers the cucumbers from the vine and leaves the vine practically undamaged. Certain varieties are harvested more easily than others. Care must be taken in planting and cultivating the crop so that the vines are in a condition to be harvested with machines.

The mechanical harvesting of tomatoes can be expedited through the use of self-propelled field conveyors, which speed up the harvest as much as 100 percent. During the decade before 1960, there were reports of partial success in the development of mechanical tomato harvesters. A successful harvester depends largely on the existence of a variety that is adaptable to mechanical separation of the fruit from the vine; the fruit must ripen rather uniformly so that a once-over harvest method may be used.

For other crops, such as melons, broccoli, and cauliflower, field conveyors and mechanical aids make for more efficient harvest. Many of these conveyors have belts as long as 70 feet, which bring the fruit from hand cutters to a central location for loading or packing. It can be expected that this type of equipment will continue to assist in the harvesting of many vegetable crops until satisfactory mechanical harvesters can be developed.

Sugarcane has its share of harvesting problems. Present methods of harvest in Louisiana are mechanized, although harvesting is not accomplished in a once-over cutting and loading operation. The harvesters cut the cane at the ground, remove the tops, and lay the cane back on the ground in windrows. After burning the dry leaves from the cane, it is picked up by tractor-mounted grab forks and loaded on trailers for delivery to the mill or a central loading point.

Experimental machines for gathering, cutting, topping, stripping, and loading the straight variety of cane grown in Louisiana work fairly well. Remaining problems are those of gathering the cane when it is blown down by strong winds and increasing the efficiency and economy of the stripping device.

Sugarcane in Florida is burned while still standing, cut by hand, and placed in windrows. Pickup machines load it into wagons or trucks and transport it to the mill.

The scarcity of labor in Puerto Rico has heightened the interest of commercial and public research workers in harvesting equipment for use there. Problems are even greater there than in Louisiana because of the higher yield, difference in growing characteristics, and irregular terrain. Most of the cane in Puerto Rico is cut by hand and hand loaded into various types of trailers and trucks for transport to the mill.

Machinery for harvesting the high-yielding sugarcane in Hawaii consists primarily of bulldozers. The mass of tangled cane is pushed up in bunches and loaded with grab forks. The mass of cane, leaves, and soil is carried to a mill, where it is washed.

The harvesting of tobacco appears to be yielding to mechanized methods.

Approximately 1 million acres of flue-cured tobacco are grown in the United States. Mechanical aids for harvesting vary from small to large machines that carry several workers. Tobacco is primed — harvested — by workers who ride on the lower platform of such machines. The leaves are elevated by endless conveyors to the upper part of the carrier, where they are tied and placed in racks until unloaded at the end of the row.

In tobacco, as with many other crops, the small acreage on each farm precludes the introduction and use of costly machines. The use of a machine is based on its weekly capacity in acres, as each acre of tobacco must be harvested weekly for up to 6 weeks. A machine capable of harvesting 3 acres a day therefore could handle approximately 18 acres a year. Most growers do not have as much as 18 acres of tobacco, but perhaps a machine of this capacity could be used cooperatively by several.

W. A. Splinter, of the University of North Carolina, has developed a mechanical tobacco harvester for removing the leaves from the stalk. High original cost, bruising of leaves, and accurate selection of mature leaves are some of the problems still being studied.

Some of the common problems in harvesting all crops includes usually fragile or unstable type of material, limitations and uncertainties of the weather, and large tonnages, which need to be handled in a short time.

These and economic problems relating to the size of farm and the need of heavy-duty equipment for some jobs confront the engineer in his attempts to develop machines for completely mechanizing harvesting.

It appears there will be an ever increasing and almost unending demand for modification and improvement of present harvesting machines to perform more efficiently at less cost. Likewise, new machines for crops not yet mechanized will continue to demand more attention, depending on the economic necessity.

Aircraft in Agriculture

From David A. Isler, "Aircraft in Agriculture," U.S. Department of Agricultue, *Yearbook,* 1960 (Washington, 1960), pp. 157–63.

Aircraft were first used in agriculture more than 40 years ago. Military planes of the First World War were used to patrol for forest fire detection in 1919 and for air photography and reconnaissance.

An important new use was opened in 1921 when lead arsenate dust was applied from a wartime Curtis JN6H trainer on a catalpa grove near Dayton, Ohio, to control the larvae of the catalpa sphinx, which were defoliating the trees.

The Department of Agriculture at the Delta Laboratory, Tallulah, La., at the same time was developing ground equipment for applying calcium arsenate to combat the cotton boll weevil. After the work in Ohio, B. R. Coad, an entomologist who was in charge of the laboratory, became interested in the use of planes for dusting cotton. He arranged for the beginning of test and development work at

Tallulah in 1922. Planes and pilots were provided through cooperation of the Air Service of the War Department.

The first dust hopper used in Ohio was constructed to hang over the right-hand side of the plane so that it could be operated by handcrank from the observer's cockpit. The hoppers built at Tallulah were mounted inside the planes. The first model occupied the front half of the rear cockpit and required an operator to stand behind it and turn the feeder crank. Dust discharge was arranged through the bottom of the fuselage. Flow of air across the bottom of the discharge tube interfered with dust delivery. Then a funnel was made and attached to direct air into a slot cut in the front side of the discharge tube. This was the first attempt to use the venturi, or spreader, principle for breaking up the dust and mixing it with air to improve distribution.

Many ideas such as air suction, ram air, and conducting the engine exhaust across the dust outlet for better dispersal of dust from the hopper were tried and discarded.

Improvements made then, and still in use, included wind-driven mechanical agitators to prevent bridging of dust in the hopper; full fuselage-width feed gates; and funnels or spreaders beneath the fuselage to mix the dust with air and improve uniformity of distribution of the materials. These developments at the Tallulah laboratory established the practicability of applying materials from the air.

The first planes designed especially for dusting operations were produced in 1924 by the Huff-Daland Co., of Ogdensburg, N.Y. They were used in the Mississippi Delta in the first cotton dusting under contract on a commercial basis. This company, which later joined Keystone Aircraft Corp., Ogdensburg, N.Y., and Bristol, Pa., about 1925 built a fleet of 14 cotton-dusting planes, which were operated by Huff-Daland Dusters, Inc., of Monroe, La. They carried about 800 pounds of dust, had a cruising speed of 90 miles an hour, and were nicknamed "Puffers."

The present Delta Air Lines, Agricultural Division, Monroe, La., acquired the Huff-Daland planes and continued to build and use them for a quarter of a century.

Aerial dusting to control insect pests in cotton became an established practice during the late 1920's. That, more than any other use, established the airplane as a tool of agriculture.

Trial flights were being made at the same time to test the effectiveness of applications of insecticides to control mosquitoes, crop and orchard insects, and forest insects.

The airplane seemed particularly suited to applying materials to forests because of the difficulty of getting ground equipment into them. Officials in charge of gypsy moth control set up some trials as early as 1922. An airship was tried in a dusting experiment in New Hampshire in 1923. Heavy applications of as much as 40 to 50 pounds of lead arsenate to the acre were used. Because the dust did not adhere well to the foliage and rain washed it off, retreatments were necessary.

Other early uses of aircraft in agriculture included flights to spread grasshopper bait and to seed and fertilize rice. An airplane was first used to distribute wet bran mash grasshopper bait in 1930. The material was fed into the airstream by hand from sacks.

The first liquid larvicides were applied for mosquito control in New Jersey and California and oils were sprayed on orchards about 1930.

The autogiro was used against the gypsy moth in 1936. Special equipment permitted applying thick spray mixtures from rotating disks or screens. Another method released liquids, such as water or adhesives, separately but simultaneously with the dust materials. The spinner disks were adapted later for use on fixed-wing aircraft in the application of thick slurries of cryolite to control the gypsy moth.

Despite all the various uses developed for aircraft in agriculture, only about 200 planes in this country were equipped for application of materials by 1939. Probably the low prices for crops during the depression years caused a general lack of interest in pest control. Aerial application of insecticides was not always economical, partly because chemicals then in use had to be applied in heavy dosages.

Several developments during the Second World War accelerated the use of aircraft in agriculture.

Most important was the discovery of DDT and its effectiveness in protecting people from disease vectors and insect pests. At the request of the War Department, workers at the Orlando Laboratory of the Department of Agriculture developed equipment by spraying DDT from military planes.

Many military planes were declared surplus at the close of the war. Among them were the N3N's and the Stearmans. Both were biplane trainers with 220- to 235-horsepower engines and were converted easily for dusting or spraying. Many pilots and mechanics released by the Armed Forces were anxious to continue in aviation. The per acre value of crops was higher than prewar values.

The effectiveness of DDT was considered to be so spectacular that it was tested against a great number of insects of economic importance as soon as it was available generally in 1944 and 1945. DDT was so potent that only a small amount per acre was required to control most species of pests. Aerial applications once considered uneconomical became practical.

Soon other new, effective insecticides were discovered. They could be used efficiently in the form of concentrated sprays. One planeload of the new compounds would cover up to 10 times as much acreage as a load of the older prewar materials. The use by civilians of such concentrated materials, however, required carefully controlled applications to insure economical and safe distribution over the area being treated.

Efforts to develop more efficient equipment and operational procedures were expanded about 1945 by the Department of Agriculture primarily at the Forest Insect Laboratory of the Forest Service at Beltsville, Md., and at Agricultural Research Service laboratories at Toledo (now at Wooster), Ohio; Forest Grove, Oreg.; and Stoneville, Miss.

The aerial application phases of the gypsy moth, grasshopper, and other plant pest control programs of the Agricultural Research Service were consolidated into the Aircraft and Special Equipment Center in 1951. State experiment stations or agricultural colleges with agricultural aviation research programs included Ohio, Texas, and California. Nebraska and Mississippi later initiated studies of aerial application equipment. Commercial concerns engaged in the manufacture and sale of aerial application equipment have made many valuable contributions toward simplifying and improving such equipment.

Dual spray apparatus — two complete spray systems on one plane — was developed to aid research on forest insect control at the Beltsville laboratory. It permits the release of spray simultaneously from both systems.

The result is that the effect on distribution of spray of any two degrees of automization, and different nozzle arrangements, spray formulations, et cetera, can be compared under identical meteorological conditions. The use of different dyes in the spray liquid of the two systems makes it possible to determine the quantity of spray deposited from each system at any point in the spray swath. A spectrophotometer, which measures the intensity of each color separately in samples of the spray, is used.

The boom and nozzle type of spray release is more commonly used for general-purpose spraying than other types, such as small venturi tubes, or rotating disks, brushes, or screens.

Standard commercial nozzles are comparatively low in price and permit easy variation in flow rate by varying the number of nozzles used. Atomization can also be changed by using different types and sizes of nozzles as well as by changing the direction of the nozzle orifice in relation to the thrust line of the plane.

The efficiency of aerial spray equipment has been improved by the use of corrosion-resistant materials, such as Fiberglas reinforced plastics in tanks. Pumps have been improved by making them of aluminum to reduce weight and providing better seals and bearings. Spray pumps are mounted in some planes inside the fuselage to reduce external resistance. They may be driven by hydraulic motors, which permit fine adjustments in pump speeds.

The equipment for dispersing dry materials was not changed very much in the earlier years, but many improvements have been made since the war. For example, the design of combination dust and spray equipment permitted changing from dust to spray application, or vice versa, with only minor alterations in the apparatus. Feed gates also were improved to provide easier operation and more positive shutoff. A sawtooth baffle just above the hopper gate provided for fine adjustment in feed rates for small seeds and granular materials. Fluted rolls driven by a hydraulic motor also have been devised for metering out granular materials.

Spreaders have been widened or flared out toward the exit end and provided with vanes curved outward to provide lateral thrust for wider and more uniform distribution of the material. These spreaders are about 6 feet wide for such planes as the 450-horsepower Stearman. The Forest Grove laboratory designed and used experimentally a streamlined distributor that is only 1 inch thick at the rear end but is 14 feet, 8 inches wide.

The process of dust fluidization, or forcing air through dry material until it becomes like a liquid, has been experimentally developed for metering, conveying, and distributing pesticides from a small, high-wing monoplane. This work was done at the Toledo laboratory. Further study of this principle will be necessary, however, before it can be applied generally to agricultural aircraft.

The most important commercial use for aircraft in agriculture is aerial application of materials. Aerial applicator aircraft in use in 1957 totaled 5,100, compared to only about 200 in 1939. These aircraft treated more than 61 million acres in 1957. About 75 percent of the acreage was treated for insect control; 12 percent for weed and brush control; 5 percent for fertilization; 3.5 for defoliation; 2.5 for seeding;

and 2 percent for control of plant diseases. The acreage treated in 1957 represents an increase of 63 percent from the 37.5 million acres treated in 1952.

There was a decline in the use of dry materials and an increase in use of liquid materials from 1952 to 1957 for the control of insects, plant diseases, weeds, and brush and for defoliation (removal of foliage to hasten drying or maturity).

The tonnage of dry fertilizer, however, increased more than 50 percent during this period and liquid fertilizer 10 times as much.

The amount of seed sown from the air has varied considerably from year to year, but no significant trend has been apparent.

The fire control program of the Forest Service used aircraft for patrol work in the early 1920's. The dropping of water or chemical bombs to extinguish fires was tried in 1936 and again in 1946 and 1947.

The bombing idea was discarded because of the danger to persons on the ground. The idea of discharging a tankful of water over the fire was tried in 1953. This developed into the use of aerial tankers for spreading fire-retardant chemicals. Agricultural spray planes with extra large discharge gates on the bottom of the tank are used. The Forest Service in 1959 spread 3.4 million gallons of fire retardants from the air. They also carried 908 thousand pounds of freight and dropped 390 thousand pounds of cargo in fire control work.

Aircraft, including helicopters, were used by the Forest Service in 1959 for a total of 32,700 hours of flight time for fire control activities. This includes reconnaissance, smoke jumping, and transportation of firefighting personnel. Nearly 85 percent of the total flying was by private planes under contract or charter.

Numerous State forestry departments and timber companies also operated aircraft for an unknown number of hours.

The use of aircraft by public and private forestry agencies for spotting and appraising insect infestations has increased materially in the past few years. Both visual and photographic methods are used.

Direct seeding of forest areas by aircraft is increasing rapidly since the discovery of repellents to prevent birds and rodents from eating the seeds. More than 108 thousand acres were direct seeded in 1959, as compared to 4.7 thousand in 1955. The ability to cover a large area in one season is the big advantage over tree planting.

Most commonly used for application of materials to crops are biplane trainers, such as the Stearman and N3N, and small monoplanes, such as the Piper and Aeronca.

Large planes are replacing the smaller ones for application of materials to large areas, such as forests and range, and also for forest fire control work. Among the large planes there are probably more Grumman Avenger TBM dive bombers in use than any other make. They haul about 700 gallons. Other large planes that have been used include the C-47 and B-18, B-17 Superfortress, C-97 Stratocruiser, the Trimotor Ford, and C-82 Packet. The Fords carry 400 gallons, and the others 1 thousand to 3 thousand gallons. A number of other surplus military planes have been used.

Helicopters have been used to apply liquids and solids to field crops, orchards, and forests. They can operate from small landing fields close to the area being treated. They can work small areas easily because of their manueuverability and slow speed. Materials can be distributed from a helicopter as uniformly as from a fixed-wing aircraft, and some tests have shown more uniform spray distribution from the helicopter. Operation at slow speeds creates maximum downdraft to carry the material down through vegetation.

The initial cost of helicopters has been high, compared to that of the war-surplus biplane trainers and small high-wing monoplanes. Costs of operation and small payload also make it difficult for helicopters to compete with fixed-wing aircraft in large-scale contract spraying operations.

New aircraft are being designed specifically for aerial application of materials. The Ag-1 low-wing monoplane, designed in 1950 under the direction of Fred Weick, then of the Texas Agricultural and Mechanical College, stimulated the design and construction of the Ag-2 by Transland Aircraft, Torrance, Calif. This all-metal, low-wing monoplane has a 600-horsepower engine and a payload of 2 thousand pounds. Then Mr. Weick designed the Ag-3, a low-wing monoplane with a 135-horsepower engine and a payload of 800 pounds. It was the forerunner of the new Piper Pawnee PA-25, with practically the same performance as their PA-18A agricultural model.

Grumman Aircraft, Bethpage, N.Y., placed the Ag-cat on the market in 1959. It is a biplane with 220-horse-power engine and a payload of 1.2 thousand pounds. Other special agricultural airplanes available commercially are the Fletcher "Utility," the Callair 150 A-5 and 180 A-6, the Snow, and the Rawdon. Kellett Aircraft Corp., Willow Grove, Pa., revived production of their KD-1A autogiro.

Commercial applicators do practically all of the aerial application work. Very little is done by individual farmers. According to a survey by National Aviation Trades Association, the average applicator in 1956 had a capital investment of 48 thousand dollars. The companies used an average of four or five planes. The list prices of small monoplanes equipped for spraying and dusting were 7,500 to 10,500 dollars in 1960. The biplanes and helicopters cost more. Most of the farmer-owned aircraft, used almost entirely for private transportation, listed at 5,000 dollars or more in 1960.

One of the advantages of aerial over ground applications is that large areas can be covered quickly to insure prompt application at the proper time. Aerial operations are also advantageous when mechanical damage to the crop by wheeled machines cannot be tolerated or when soil conditions would not permit heavy machines to pass over it. Application of materials is feasible only from the air in some circumstances — the treatment of large, inaccessible forest areas, for example, and crops, such as rice, under flooded soil conditions.

Aerial applications may not be most efficient when the area to be treated is small. Because of drift, aerial applications afford more chance for damage to adjacent crops than ground applications. Material released from an airplane cannot be placed on the target as precisely as material released from a ground machine. It is also harder to cover the lower side of leaves by air application than by ground machine application.

Not all problems have been solved. Even with all of the recent developments and increase in use of agricultural aircraft, many improvements remained to be made in 1960.

It is characteristic for spray and dust deposits to be heaviest near the flight line of the plane and gradually become lighter toward the edges of a swath. The overall application rate undoubtedly could be reduced if the material could be more uniformly distributed.

The controllable factors that affect distribution include performance of the dispersal equipment, physical characteristics of the material, and operation of the aircraft.

The uncontrollable factors, which affect the material from the time of its discharge from the plane until its deposition on the target, include the aerodynamic forces created by the aircraft and the meteorological conditions. Maximum advantage should be taken of all these factors, and more efficient distribution equipment should be developed.

Faster, more accurate methods for determining the uniformity of distribution of materials would speed up the work on improvement of equipment. Methods for assessing the quantity of spray deposited at various points across the swath and measurement of spray atomization have been developed for oil sprays. Further simplification of these methods is under way at the Beltsville Forest Insect Laboratory.

There is a definite need for the development of procedures for assessing water sprays and dry materials. Accurate methods for use in research and rapid methods for field use are necessary. Research must determine the most effective degree of spray atomization for pesticide applications.

The lines of flight can be marked for the pilot when he is applying materials to farm crops but not when he is treating large inaccessible forest areas. There is urgent need for development of a satisfactory pilot guidance system to insure more uniform swath spacing. Several electronic systems have been suggested and evaluated but had not proved to be practical in 1960.

The future for agricultural aviation will be closely allied with the development and formulation of pesticide materials, fertilizers, chemicals to control forest fires, and so on.

Effective disease control requires fairly complete coverage of plant surfaces, and aerial applications generally are not so satisfactory as ground applications. Development of more efficient air craft dispersal equipment or more effective fungicides could open another field of work for aircraft.

It may turn out that virus materials will be effective for control of several forest insect defoliators. Water suspensions of virus have been effectively used for controlling some sawfly infestations. Experimental applications have also been made for control of the Great Basin tent caterpillar. Aerial applications have not been effective in control of bark beetles in forests because it has not been possible to apply insecticides to the trunks of trees by this method.

If a control method (such as through the use of systemics — an insecticide that would be absorbed and translocated to various parts of the host in amounts lethal to certain insects) could be developed, the destructiveness of these insects over large areas might be halted.

The application of fertilizers is another use of aircraft in forestry that may be expected to develop in the future.

It is certain that we will see increased use of aircraft in the agriculture of the future not only for application of materials but for personal transport. On many ranches in the Western States, small planes have replaced the horse and saddle for inspecting fence lines, pastures, and water supply and for checking livestock.

The legal aspects of aerial application work should be checked with the Federal Aviation Agency and State Aeronautics Commissions. Information on the use of various pest control materials may be obtained from local county agents, State experiment stations and agricultural colleges, and the United States Department of Agriculture, Washington 25, D.C.

New Breeds and Types of Livestock

From Everett J. Warwick, "New Breeds and Types," U.S. Department of Agriculture, *Yearbook*, 1962 (Washington, 1962) pp. 276–80.

Livestock on American farms a century ago were mostly the descendents of nonpedigree types brought from Europe by settlers, who usually were too busy subduing a new land to put much effort into improvement of animals. By 1862, though, the Spanish Merino was well established in the United States and had been extensively modified by breeders here. Trial importations of several European breeds of sheep and other species had been made. Development was well along on native strains, which would emerge shortly as the American breeds of swine. The establishment of these breeds and the extensive importation of purebred cattle and sheep from Europe were well along by 1900. Imported breeds today dominate many sectors of our livestock production, but efforts of our scientists and the genius of American breeders have brought about the development of new breeds at perhaps a more rapid pace than at any time in history. Some of them have a commanding place in an industry. Some fit special niches or overcome specific conditions to which no existing breed was adapted.

The traditional American breeds of swine — Duroc, Poland China, Spotted (or Spotted Poland China), Chester White, and others less numerous — can be considered new, because none was established firmly a century ago, All were developed by private American breeders from foundation stocks based on crosses and the intermingling of older types imported from many parts of the world. The Hampshire usually is included in this group, although its origin is obscure. It may have descended entirely from an English breed of a similar color pattern. In any event, it has been greatly modified by American breeders. Intense selection in all these breeds for meat-type — that is, a high proportion of lean cuts and a minimum of fat — has resulted in a great modification, as compared to the older lard-type, which was favored when lard was a more valuable product.

The Department of Agriculture and the Iowa Agricultural Experiment Station in 1934 imported a number of Danish Landrace hogs, a breed developed in

Denmark with intense selection for both performance and the production of high-quality bacon carcasses. Crosses of American breeds with the Landrace and subsequent intermating of the cross-progeny gave rise to several new, mildly inbred lines, several of which can be termed breeds. These include (with the foundation breeds and developing institution in parentheses): The Minnesota No. 1 (Landrace-Tamworth; Minnesota Agricultural Experiment Station); Beltsville No. 1 (Landrace-Poland China; the Department of Agriculture); Montana No. 1 (Landrace-Hampshire; the Department of Agriculture and Montana Agricultural Experiment Station); Palouse (Landrace-Chester White; Washington Agricultural Experiment Station); and Maryland No. 1 (Landrace-Berkshire; Maryland Agricultural Experiment Station and the Department of Agriculture). Other lines developed with none or only a little Landrace blood include the Minnesota No. 2 (Yorkshire-Poland China; Minnesota Agricultural Experiment Station); and Beltsville No. 2 (principally Yorkshire and Hampshire with a little Duroc and Landrace; the Department of Agriculture). These new strains have been used commercially and are recommended principally for crossing with other lines or breeds in systematic programs. Under terms of the original Landrace importation, pure Landrace swine could not be released for general use in the United States. This provision was later modified, and private breeders have established the American Landrace on the basis of purebred animals of the original importation and animals carrying a small proportion (one-sixteenth to one sixty-fourth) of Poland China blood. Subsequent importations of Landrace swine from Norway and Sweden also have been incorporated into the breed, which has become the third ranking breed in terms of numbers registered.

The Western sheep industry had a problem. The Rambouillet and Merino are fine-wool breeds that are vigorous and hardy, flock well, and produce wool of fine quality. They tend, however, to be deficient in size and in quality of meat. British medium- and long-wool breeds are excellent in meat qualities, but they tend to be deficient in characteristics in which the fine-wool breeds excel. Recognizing these problems, scientists in the Department of Agriculture in 1912 made initial crosses between a long-wool mutton breed, the Lincoln, and fine-wood Rambouillets to investigate the feasibility of combining the good qualities of both in a new breed. Subsequent intermating and selection within the crossbreds led to a new breed, the Columbia, which has had a large influence on the western sheep industry directly and through the stimulation of the production of this type of sheep by breeders. The Targhee is another new breed developed by the Department on a foundation similar to that of the Columbia; it has a higher proportion of Rambouillet inheritance. Private breeders in the United States have utilized the Corridale, a breed developed in New Zealand in the 19th century from crosses of the fine-wool Merino and the Lincoln and Leicester long-wool breeds. Private breeders also have been active in the development of breeds and have produced the Panama, Romeldale, Debouillet, and Montadale — all based on crossbred foundations — and a few other strains that have had only limited distribution.

The breeds of beef cattle that were imported from the British Isles dominate the industry in most parts of the country. More than 95 percent of total registrations are of these breeds. They did not prove satisfactory to many cattlemen in the South, however, apparently because they lacked resistance to heat and insects, and fared poorly on coarse, tropical-type forages. Zebu-type cattle introduced from Indian tolerate heat and insects better, but they did not meet requirements as to carcass and were deficient in reproduction and rate of growth in many places in the South. The American Brahman was created by breeders in this country from an amalgamation of several Indian Zebu breeds. In a sense, it is itself a new creation. Observations on crossbreds of British and Zebu breeds indicated that for many areas they met needs better than purebreds of either type. Decisions therefore were made to interbreed the crossbreds with the purpose of founding new breeds. The first such attempt was by the King Ranch of Texas, where crossing fo the Brahman and Shorthorn breeds culminated in the development of the Santa Gertrudis, which has become popular in many parts of the United States and in several other countries.

After observing results of crossing the Angus and Brahman breeds by the Department of Agriculture and the Louisiana Agricultural Experiment Station at Jeanerette, La., Frank Buttram and Raymond Pope of Oklahoma undertook the development of a new breed, the Brangus, based on such a crossbred foundation. Other breeds or strains developed on similar foundations include the Beefmaster, which was developed on a Brahman-Shorthorn-Hereford foundation by the Lasater Ranch in Texas and Colorado, and the Charbray, developed from crosses of the Brahman and the Charolais, a French breed. The development of polled types within existing breeds, Hereford and Shorthorn, since 1900 has been an outstanding achievement of private American breeders with both the Hereford and Shorthorn breeds. About one-third of all Herefords and Shorthorns now are of the polled type. (*Everett J. Warwick*)

The Changing Rural Population

From Conrad Taeuber, "Rural Americans and the Rest of Us," U.S. Department of Agriculture, *Yearbook,* 1963 (Washington, 1963), pp. 13–18.

One-third of us live in rural areas. The Nation was largely rural in the early days, but as population grew the cities and their suburbs received the greater share of the increase. The census of 1910 was the last to show a majority of the population rural; 70 percent of the population was urban and 30 percent rural in 1960.

Less than one-third of the 54 million rural residents live on farms and get at least part of their livelihood from agriculture. Some live in towns and villages of fewer than 2,500 inhabitants.

Nearly 44 million live in the open country, in the small, unincorporated places, along the highways or stream valleys in settlements that resemble the line villages of some other countries, or in scattered dwellings. But the pull of the city is not lost on them. Nearly one-fourth of the total live close enough to a city of 50 thousand or more to be included within the standard metropolitan statistical area of such a city. Some of them are farmers, but most of them look to the economy of the city and its suburbs for their livelihood.

The words "rural" and "farm" often are used as though they are identical. At one time they were. As recently as 1910, approximately two of every three rural residents lived on farms, and, although this proportion declined, it was still more than one-half in 1940. The decline of the farm population since the midthirties has been rapid; in 1960, only about one-fourth of the rural population was living on farms.

Many rural residents no longer are engaged directly in agriculture. Some supply goods, services, machinery, feed, fuel, fertilizer, or labor to farmers. Some provide financing, marketing services, or primary processing of agricultural products and perform the many activities that are related closely to farming but no longer are done generally on farms or by persons living on farms, such as hatching chicks, dusting and spraying, custom harvesting, packing vegetables and fruit, making butter and cheese and slaughtering meat animals and poultry. Moreover, the growing specialization of agricultural production has caused a decline in barnyard flocks, kitchen gardens, and the use of woodlots. The consequence is that many farmers buy supplies that once were part of the subsistence provided by every farm.

The growth of business related to agriculture has meant a division of labor between those who produce the primary product and others who contribute to its production as well as to its ultimate disposition. This development and increases in the productivity of agricultural workers have led to a reduction in the number of farmers.

The people of the United States are not distributed evenly over the country's 3.6 million square miles. A map of the distribution of population shows large clusters in the metropolitan areas. There also are large spaces with a relatively low density of settlement; many of them have been declining in population. They make up a large part of that half of the counties that lost population during the fifties.

North Dakota, 65 percent of whose population is rural, led in the proportion of the rural population. Mississippi, Alaska, West Virginia, Vermont, South Dakota, and North Carolina were not far behind; each reported more than 60 percent rural. One-half of the population of South Carolina, Arkansas, Kentucky, and Idaho lived in rural areas.

The South, 41.5 percent of whose population is rural, is the most rural region. It includes 42 percent of the rural population of the United States, but only about 30 percent of the total population.

As a result of a substantial movement of Negroes from the rural areas of the South to the cities of the North, West, and South, the proportion of Negroes living in rural areas is now less than that of the white population. The highest proportion of rural residents for any major racial group is that for the Indians; three of every four Indians live in rural areas.

During the fifties, when the population of the Nation as a whole was increasing rapidly, the rural population registered a small decline. It failed to share in the national growth, and it gave up population to the urban areas.

This in part was the result of the growth of cities into rural territory, because cities often take over rural area and rural population as they expand their boundaries. As urban settlement spreads, it takes over areas that formerly were rural. Land generally is reclassified from rural to urban when it is taken into subdivisions.

A substantial migration of people from rural to urban areas has been going on throughout our history. It is a moot point whether the opportunity to move to the cities or the opportunity to move West offered the biggest safety valve for the population pressure that developed in the older settled areas. The movement to cities early became the more important one in terms of numbers of people affected.

The movement to the West in recent times has been largely a movement to western cities.

Birth rates in rural areas tend to be higher than those in cities. A conservative estimate is that the rural population would have increased by about 11 million persons during the fifties if there had not been a migration to cities and if the cities had not spread into what was formerly rural territory. Instead, the rural population gave up this potential growth of about 11 million persons and even registered a small net decline.

These figures are in terms of the areas in which people live. Another rural contribution to the urban segment is the growth in the number of people who commute to cities to work and thus in a sense become a part of the urban population. Fifteen percent of workers who live in rural places work outside the country in which they live; many of them no doubt work in nearby cities. In addition, many rural workers commute to a city in the same county in which they live.

An outstanding change within the rural population has been the change in the farm population.

Thirty-two million persons lived on farms in 1910. That number had dropped to 30.4 million by 1930. It declined to 25.1 million by 1950. It was about 15 million in 1962.

During the depression years, when the normal migration from farms to cities was slowed down and there was some back-to-the-land movement, our farm population increased temporarily, but the growing demands for manpower in industry and the service occupations changed that. The rapid growth in agricultural productivity freed manpower for other sectors of the economy, and there was a large shift from agriculture to other activities.

The net migration from farms amounted to 8.9 million between 1940 and 1950, and between 1950 and 1960 it was only slightly less, 8.6 million persons. The net migration from farms during those 20 years was greater than the net immigration from overseas into this country during the peak years, 1896–1915. Many of our problems of rural and urban adjustment in recent years result from these shifts in the population.

One consequence of the relatively high birth rates among farmers is that the rural population has a larger proportion of children under 15, who accounted for 33.4 percent of the rural population but only 30.1 percent of the urban population.

Rural areas also exceed the urban in the proportion of persons 15 to 19 years old. In other words, a larger proportion of their people is in the school and preschool ages. In the later years, however, the effects of the migration from rural areas become apparent, and there is a relative shortage in each of the age groups between 20 and 64. The shortage is especially large in the age groups that are most mobile — the persons who were 20–44 years old in 1960. Young adults contribute most heavily to the migration, as is shown again in these figures.

The percentage of persons 65 years old and over in rural areas is only slightly higher than that of the urban areas. The large proportion of children brings the average age of the rural population down to about 3 years less than that of the urban population.

Towns of a population between 1,000 and 2,500 constitute about one-eighth of the rural population. Some striking differences exist between the people who live in small towns and most of those who live in cities.

The small towns have a relative shortage of children under 10 and of adults under 55. They have a relative excess of older persons, and this excess is particularly marked for persons 65 and over. The small towns in many sections continue to provide a place to which older persons move from the open country when they retire. In the small towns, one person in every eight is 65 or over. Some midwestern small towns have taken on an even more pronounced retirement function; in Iowa, Missouri, and Nebraska, nearly one-fifth of the residents of the small towns are at retirement age.

The nonwhite farm population has a median age of only 17.4, which is about 10 years below that for the rural population as a whole. This group has a relatively high proportion of children and teenagers and a relative shortage in all other age groups.

Much the same is true of the non-white population in rural areas but not on farms, although for this group the relative excess of children is somewhat less than in the farm population, and the average age is 20 years.

With lower-than-average incomes, rural people have a disproportionately large number of children to be educated. As the children reach adulthood, furthermore, the probability is strong that they will move away from the rural areas in which they were reared. The better trained persons are likely to find greater opportunities in cities, and they constitute therefore a smaller proportion of the rural than of the urban population. This is particularly true of the farm population, which has only about a fourth of its share of the college graduates.

Nevertheless, rural people have high regard for education. One indicator is the proportion of 16 and 17-year-olds who are still in school. For the farm population, the percentage was 81.8 in 1960, practically the same as that for the urban population, and for the rural nonfarm population it was nearly as large.

Advanced education, however, normally means going from country to city. The return migration is much less frequent. The traditional view that country people need less education than others was so widespread at one time that many of the older rural people had little opportunity to attend school beyond the eighth grade.

The rapid growth of high schools in rural areas came in the main after the First World War. The average number of years of school completed by persons 25 years old and over is 10.6 years for the Nation as a whole, but for rural areas it is 9.2. The people on farms have a lower average than those living elsewhere in rural areas.

White rural residents have an average of 9.6 years of schooling, but non-white persons have only 6.2 years — less than eighth-grade graduation. The averages are especially low for the rural farm population — 8.9 years for white persons and 5.7 years for non-white persons. These averages have been rising and can be expected to continue to rise as the older generation with its lower educational levels is replaced by a younger generation, which has had greater opportunities to continue its education through the high school.

About a third of rural residents live on farms, but this refers to their place of residence rather than to their occupational attachment. Sixty-nine percent of the men in the labor force who live on farms and 26 percent of the rural farm women in the labor force reported that their major line of work was in agriculture. Thus nearly one-third of the men and three-fourths of the women in the labor force who live on farms are not engaged primarily in agriculture. Some farm operators and about one-half of the hired farmworkers do not live on farms. The number of farm residents who work at nonagricultural jobs greatly exceeds the number of nonfarm residents who work at agricultural jobs.

The volume of migration from farms to nonfarm areas and from rural to urban areas is largely a matter of the ability of the urban sector to provide employment for the young people now growing up in rural areas. Nearly twice as many young farm people will reach their 20th birthday in the sixties as there are older persons who will die or reach age 65 during the decade. With the declining needs for manpower in agriculture, many of these young people will be looking for jobs in cities.

The growing specialization of agricultural production and the continued trend toward larger units in agriculture are closely related to the large outmigration that has occurred. I see no indication that these trends will not continue and have reason to expect that a substantial number of persons now living on farms will seek opportunities elsewhere in the national economy.

The most productive one-fourth of the farms in 1959 contributed about three-fourths of the total product that reached the market. Many of the other units represent uneconomic operations whose total contribution to agricultural production could readily be had with a much smaller number of units and of manpower.

There were 1.6 million farms that had a gross value of sales of less than 2,500 dollars in 1959. About one-fourth of them were units on which the operator was 65 years old and over. They represent a form of partial retirement. Their contribution to total sales was only about 1 percent. Their significance lies in the opportunities for useful work, housing, and subsistence that they provide to their elderly operators, most of whom are receiving other forms of income as well.

The operators of more than 1 million of these farms with gross sales of less than 2,500 dollars receive most of their income from nonfarm sources, but carry on enough agricultural operations to qualify their places as farms. Their total contribution to the market was less than 3 percent. Like the part-retirement farms, the part-time farms often are carried on as supplements to other sources of income. Whether they are continued depends largely on the possibility of finding jobs with enough income to enable operators to make the part-time farming operations less attractive.

The operators of 349 thousand farms were under 65 years of age and had gross sales of less than 2,500 dollars. Farm production was their major source of income. Agricultural production would be hardly affected if they could be employed in nonagricultural activities, but retraining and relocation would present major challenges. Setting the dividing line at gross sales of 2,500 dollars is arbitrary — many farmers with a larger volume of sales would welcome alternative employment opportunities.

One indication of things to come is the age of farm operators. Farming has lost much of the attraction it once had for young men, many of whom lack the large investment required for a productive farm of adequate size. Unless a significant change comes about, the number of farm operators will decline as men now in farming die or retire.

The average age of farm operators in 1962 was about 50 years, and there were more operators between the ages of 45 and 54 than in any other 10-year age group. Not enough younger men have come forward to replace older farmers, and this has been responsible for a part of the decline in the number of farmers. The indications are that there will be a further decline in the number of farmers as older men retire or die.

Farmers on the less productive farms tend to be older than those on the more productive farms; the operators on farms with gross sales of 2,500 to 5 thousand dollars average nearly 4.8 years older than those on farms with gross sales of 20 thousand to 40 thousand dollars.

Many of the smaller farms give the present occupants an opportunity to use their labor and resources for subsistence or provide a base for substantial off-farm work. As farms, however, they make little contribution to total agricultural production, and many of them are likely to drop out of the farm inventory when the present operator can no longer continue farming.

Three of every 10 farmers in 1959 reported that they worked off the farm 100 days or more. They include young men who are trying to accumulate enough capital so they can take over a full-time farm, business and professional men who carry on highly productive farming as a sideline, industrial workers who commute from a farm which they and their families operate after normal working hours and on weekends, farm laborers who live in the country and produce barely enough products for sale to qualify their places as farms, and more like them.

The larger commercial farms are essentially full-time operations. Only about 10 percent of the operators of farms with sales in excess of 10 thousand dollars reported as much as 100 days of work off the farm. But one of every four operators in the group that had sales of 2,500 to 5 thousand dollars had this much work off the farm. A little more than one-half of the farmers with sales of less than 2,500 dollars reported work off the farm to at least this extent.

The possibilities of combining the operation of a commercial farm with work off the farm vary considerably by type of farming. On fruit and nut farms, poultry farms, and livestock ranches, about one-fourth of the operators report at least 100 days of work off the farm. Cotton or tabacco farms, dairy farms, and general farms are much less well adapted to the combination of farm and nonfarm work.

Income from sources other than the farm include not only the earnings of the operator who also worked off the farm. They include also any other income the operator may have, such as pensions, compensation for disability, or returns from other investments, as well as the earnings and other income received by other members of the family.

Among the larger commercial farms, those with sales of 20 thousand dollars and over, only 6 of 100 operators reported in 1959 that the family income from other sources exceeded the value of sales. For the smaller commercial farms, those with sales of 2,500 to 5 thousand dollars, 27 percent reported that the family income from other sources exceeded the value of sales from the farm.

Altogether, about four-fifths of all farm operators and their families obtain some income from sources other than the farm. This applies to about seven-tenths of the commercial farms and nearly all of the other farms.

Seven percent of the farmers are not living on the farms they operate, and a substantial proportion of seasonal farm laborers do not live on farms. Most of these nonresident agricultural workers live in rural areas.

The proportion of nonresident farm operators is highest on the commercial farms with the largest gross value of sales, and is lowest for the commercial farms with low values of sales. The type of farm is a major element in such arrangements; one-fifth of the livestock ranches and one-sixth of the fruit and nut farms, but only one-fortieth of the dairy farms have a nonresident farm operator.

A small proportion of those who combine agricultural and nonagricultural work do so on a scale that provides relatively high incomes from each source. For the majority, however, the combination is one of relatively low income from agriculture with relatively low income from other sources. The prevalence of low incomes for families in rural areas, particularly for those who live on the farms, has often been observed.

Even when allowance is made for housing and home-produced food and fuel, the total incomes are still low. Insofar as values can be assigned to nonmoney incomes, the amounts tend to be lower for the smaller than for the larger farms.

Money income is not the only (and often not the major) element in determining whether a person stays on a small farm or moves from it. For some persons, the freedom that comes from being self-employed in an acitivity that does not require full-time effort the whole year is an important perquisite that offsets some disadvantages that come from lower money income. Some gain satisfaction from working with the soil or with growing things. Others value the relative isolation from neighbors and the absence of the crowding that is usually associated with living in cities. Security from the hazards of periodic unemployment often is cited as one of the values that hold people on small farms.

The population of the United States is now growing by about 3 million persons a year. The needs of the economy and the preferences of individuals appear to be calling for increasing concentration in metropolitan areas. Even the movement of industry into open country tends to develop urban settlements in the immediate vicinity and thus to increase the urban share of the population. Nevertheless, the rural population continues to be a large part of the total.

Agriculture in the National Economy

From Vernon W. Ruttan, "Agriculture in the National Economy," U.S. Department of Agriculture, *Yearbook*, 1963 (Washington, 1963), pp. 135–38.

Our rapid growth of agricultural productivity has strengthened the favorable terms on which we and the world have had access to agricultural raw materials and has made available an increasing share of the national labor force for nonagricultural employment. In turn, the expanding industrial and urban economy has exerted a strong force on agriculture through the markets for agricultural products, the new technologies embodied in the products of the farm supply industry, an expansion of employment opportunities for workers released from agriculture, and on rural life through a rise in standards of consumption.

The net effect has been to modify the place of agriculture in the national economy and to set the stage for further modifications.

The position of agriculture in the economy has undergone three shifts since 1870.

Between then and 1900, an annual increase in gross inputs of 2 percent a year combined with an increase in productivity of 1.1 percent a year to produce an annual increase in farm output of 3.2 percent. Only a minor increase occurred in the price of agricultural raw materials relative to the wholesale price index, although the additional inputs in the form of land, labor, and capital equipment were substantial.

The rise in output was fast enough to permit sizable exports of farm products to meet the Nation's need for foreign exchange. Agricultural products accounted for 77 percent of the value of American exports in 1870 and still accounted for 65 percent in 1900. A modest rise in farm employment and a rapid rise in nonfarm employment occurred.

The relative contribution of agriculture to national economic growth was less dramatic between 1900 and 1925.

A slow rate of growth in inputs of resources and a failure to achieve measurable increases in output per unit of total input in agriculture reduced the rate of growth of farm output to an average of less than 1 percent a year.

This lag in expansion of production and a continuation of rising domestic and export demand for farm products brought the longest sustained increase in agricultural prices relative to the general price level since 1870. The lag reflected the changing importance of land and the other resources, brought about by the closing of the land frontier. New lands no longer were readily available, and laborsaving technological changes of 1850–1900 had to be supplemented with land-saving technological changes. Rising food prices made clear to many people the meaning of lagging productivity growth in agriculture during the first quarter of this century. Public concern was manifest in increased emphasis on resource development and conservation, and in increased allocation of public funds for research and education designed to increase the rate of productivity.

Agriculture again resumed its historic role during the 1920's as a major contributor to our national economic growth. The replacement of horses and mules by tractors and the release of land formerly used to produce feed for horses and mules for the production of food and fiber proceeded rapidly even during the Great Depression. By the beginning of the Second World War, agriculture was in a position to release a substantial flow of labor to the non-farm sector and to achieve rapid increases in farm output.

The rate of productivity growth has continued to accelerate. Between 1950 and 1961, farm employment declined by more than one-third, while total inputs used in agricultural production remained unchanged and farm output expanded at 2 percent a year — the highest rate since the turn of the century — despite efforts to control the rate of increase in farm output.

The rate of productivity growth has continued to accelerate. Between 1950 and 1961, farm employment declined by more than one-third, while total inputs used in agricultural production remained unchanged and farm output expanded at 2 percent a year — the highest rate since the turn of the century — despite efforts to control the rate of increase in farm output.

During the 1950's, close to 40 percent of the growth in the nonagricultural labor force was accounted for by shifts of labor out of agriculture and declining farm product prices exerted an important restraining force on the rising retail price index.

The effect of urban and industrial development on American agriculture also has changed sharply in a century.

As the agricultural frontier was pushed across the country, the growth of the farm production provided an impetus for the growth of local non-agricultural employment in transportation, processing, and commerce.

Differences in rates of growth in out-put among areas and regions made for local and regional differences in nonfarm growth.

As the accumulation of capital and the growth of population have continued, however, the influence of local and regional variations in resource endowments has become more difficult to distinguish. Research at Vanderbilt University by William H. Nicholls and Anthony M. Tang indicates that in the Southern Piedmont and the Tennessee Valley the impact of "original" differences in resource endowments on differences in agricultural productivity and income among counties had largely disappeared by the turn of the century.

By 1950 there was ample evidence that the level of local industrial and urban development exerts a significant positive impact on the level of income achieved by farm families in most regions. The major exceptions to this generalization are in the West, where the resource base continues to represent an important factor in the location of economic activity.

The economic interactions between the farm and nonfarm parts of the local economy that give rise to these changing relationships have occurred primarily through three sets of market relationships: The product market — the markets for the products produced by agriculture; the input market — the market for the manufactured inputs and capital used in agricultural production; and the labor market — through which labor is allocated between the agricultural and nonagricultural parts of the economy and among firms.

The product market has been regarded as the dominant channel through which the impact of national fluctuations in nonfarm income and local variations in nonfarm demand have been channeled into the agricultural sector. The declining response of consumption of food and fiber to increases in nonfarm income and the development of farm commodity programs, however, have dampened the commodity market effects of economic fluctuations in the nonfarm sector. The regional specialization in production stimulated by technological and organizational changes in processing, transportation, and distribution have reduced the impact of local urban-industrial development on the demand for locally produced farm products. Milk remains a major exception.

The markets for manufactured goods and capital equipment have become increasingly important in transmitting the effect of changes in the nonfarm economy to agriculture. Much of the new technology utilized by agriculture is incorporated in the form of new capital equipment or more efficient fertilizer, insecticides, and other items that raise operating expenses, for which in 1870 the charges amounted to less than 3 percent of the value of farm production. By 1900 nonfarm inputs still amounted to only 7 percent, but by 1960 they accounted for approximately 27 percent of the value of farm output.

The rising importance of purchased inputs makes net farm income increasingly sensitive to variations in input prices relative to product prices. Rising input prices during the 1950's, combined with declining or stable product prices, meant a rapid transfer of the gains in farm productivity to the non-farm sector.

The labor market has increasingly become the primary channel through which local and regional variations in nonfarm developments are transmitted to agriculture in most regions. It has been possible to realize the full potentials for rapid growth in agricultural productivity and income per farmworker only when local or regional economic growth has been rapid enough to absorb both the new entrants from the farm sector and the farmworkers released from productive employment in agriculture by advancing technology into the local nonfarm labor force.

By and large, interregional migration, in the absence of growth of local industrial and urban employment, has not been sufficient to narrow income differentials between agricultural and nonagricultural employment in localities or among the regions. Failure to achieve rapid growth in employment opportunities in the local nonfarm economy therefore has resulted in failure to achieve the adjustment necessary to bring about higher levels of productivity and income of the farm-worker.

ANNUAL AVERAGE RATES OF CHANGE IN TOTAL OUTPUT, INPUTS, AND TOTAL PRODUCTIVITY IN AMERICAN AGRICULTURE, 1870–1961

	Percentage per year			
	1870–1900	*1900–25*	*1925–50*	*1950–61*
Farm output	3.2	0.9	1.5	2.0
Total inputs	2.0	1.0	.4	.0
Total productivity	1.1	− .0	1.2	2.0

Source: *Changes in Farm Production and Efficiency, A Summary Report, 1962,* U.S. Department of Agriculture, Statistical Bulletin No. 233, Washington, September 1962.

The changes of the past several decades have set the stage for the development of several additional changes in the relationship between the agricultural and nonagricultural parts of the economy.

First of all, it is clear that agriculture in the future is likely to make an even smaller contribution to foreign exchange earnings than at present.

Rising agricultural productivity in Europe and the emerging structure of world trade will make it difficult for agriculture to maintain the position it has occupied as a source of approximately 20 percent of the foreign trade earnings.

Furthermore, agriculture will not provide an important source of growth in the nonfarm labor force, even if farm employment continues to decline relatively rapidly. The decline of farm employment and the rising rate of new entrants to the nonfarm labor force as a result of the high nonfarm birth rates of the 1940's and 1950's has reduced farm employment to less than 8 percent of the labor force.

Within the next decade, farm employment will fall below the number of unemployed workers in the United States economy even during periods of prosperity. (Two earlier benchmarks in agriculture's changing role in the national labor force were 1880, when the nonagricultural employment first exceeded agricultural employment, and 1929, when employment in manufacturing alone exceeded agricultural employment.)

A continuation of the rapid technological change of the past decade can permit agriculture to retain its role as a source of restraint on the American consumer's cost of living if appropriate farm price and income policies are developed.

Lower prices for farm products will not be able to exert as significant an impact on the consumer price index in the future as in the past, however. Food items were given a weight of 28.1 percent and apparel a weight of 8.8 percent in the consumer price index in 1961. Since the farmer receives less than 40 percent of the consumer's food dollar and an even smaller share of the consumer's clothing dollar, the farm component of the cost-of-living index was only 12 percent in 1963. I expect it to decline further.

A continuation of technological change also can permit agriculture to make a contribution to the national economic growth by releasing land for nonagricultural uses during the next several decades. We expect that extensive acreages will be released for urban development, transportation, forestry, and recreational uses at little real sacrifice in output.

Changes in the nonfarm economy will continue to influence the farm sector strongly through the labor market and the market for purchased inputs. Rapid and continuous nonfarm economic growth nationally and locally will remain a necessary condition for agricultural prosperity.

The farmworkers released from productive agricultural employment and the new entrants to the labor force from rural areas can find productive nonfarm employment most readily when employment opportunities are expanding rapidly. Annual net migration from farms since the war has typically been above 5 percent of farm population at the beginning of the year during periods of high-level economic activity. During each recession since the war, net migration has fallen to below 3 percent of the farm population.

The gains to agriculture from rapid economic growth in the nonfarm sector will be greatest if this growth is achieved without inflation in the general price level. The impact of moderate inflation has been transmitted to agriculture primarily through the market for manufactured inputs. Rising input prices and declining or stable prices of products have reduced farmers' gains from productivity increases in agriculture below the level that could have been achieved with stable input prices.

In summary, then, I foresee a national economy in which the urban-industrial sector is the dominant generator of economic change, but in which agriculture continues to make an important contribution through further gains in production efficiency.

The Family Farm, 1963

From Howard L. Hill and Frank H. Maier, "The Family Farm in Transition," U.S. Department of Agriculture, *Yearbook*, 1963 (Washington, 1963), pp. 166–74.

As farming has become more closely related to urban occupations and life, the rural tradition of the family farm has been changing and is being challenged.

The farm population has declined. Farm production has become specialized and mechanized. Most of the descriptive characteristics of the family farm system have changed. Occasionally it is suggested that the tradition of the family farm is no longer relevant to the realities of American agriculture in the sixties. What does it mean?

The ideal of the family farm had its roots in the colonial past, when land was abundant relative to labor. Early efforts to establish feudal systems of land tenure failed, because unsettled and unclaimed land was generally available to farmers of moderate means who depended on family labor. Thus, during the colonial period, settlers developed strong sympathy for the idea of individually owned and operated farms.

Thomas Jefferson's exposition of what we now call the family farm was nurtured in this soil. In his view, an agriculture of owner-operated farmers was desired as the means to a good society rather than being an end in itself. He held that the basis of enlightened self-government was the independence and self-reliance of the individual. Self-reliance rested on social equality and economic security, which could best be achieved through a system of individually owned and operated family farms. Individual ownership of farms thus provided the foundation for civic virtue and for social and political stability.

This preference for the family farm in turn produced land policies during the next century that further reinforced the ideal, and, because agricultural lands were abundant, the Federal land policies during the 19th century gave it strong support. Although few Federal restrictions were placed on the transfer of lands once title was granted, the coincidence of abundant land and lenient land disposal programs assured wide distribution of ownership of farmland over much of our country.

Even during Jefferson's lifetime, though, the role of agriculture began to change as the percentage of the total work force that was employed in agriculture began to decline — 72 percent in 1820, 59 in 1860, 38 in 1900, 27 in 1920, 12 in 1950, and 6 in 1960.

However important the family farm is as a system of agriculture, the small-ness of the farm sector means that the family farm cannot be relied upon as the only source of civic virtue and social and political stability.

Even before large-scale disposal of public lands ended, farm tenancy was increasing. As this trend progressed, the concept of the agricultural ladder emerged as an explanation for the existence of tenancy in a system that cherished the goal of owner-operatorship. A farm boy could climb up the agricultural ladder step by step — a worker on his parents' farm, a hired farmworker, renter of a farm, the owner of a mortgaged farm, and finally, owner of a debt-free farm.

Improving the operation of the agricultural ladder was seen as a way to preserve the system of owner-operated family farms. Such programs as publicly supported credit, research, and extension were also expected to assist family farmers.

Later, programs for conservation and for production control and price support that were developed gave further support to the idea of individually owned and operated farms. The right to participate in these programs, however, for the most part is not limited to family farms. Whether or not these programs tend to strengthen a family farm system of agriculture is not evident.

Discussions of how to maintain and strengthen our system of family farms are no longer concentrated primarily on the issues of security of tenure and the rights of tenants and sharecroppers.

Important changes in the tenure structure have taken place, and the inferior status sometimes associated with tenancy has changed.

The proportion of all farmers who are tenants (who operate only rented land) has declined, but the amount of land that is leased has been fairly stable — about one-third. In areas of commercial farming, with their increasing size of farms and higher farm income, the proportion of farmland under lease is high; land is commonly leased both by full tenants (who rent all the land they farm) and by part owners (who own some land and rent additional land). In most of the low-income farm sections, however, the proportion of full owners is relatively high.

For the country as a whole, the shift to fewer and larger farms has been accompanied by a rise in part ownership and increased use of such devices as vertical integration and land purchase contracts to gain control of the resources needed for larger operations. Farm operators seemingly have a basic interest in income levels and a secondary interest in tenure status.

Now the major concern is whether the trend toward the larger and more specialized farming operations is compatible with a family-farm system. As a goal or an ideal of farm organization, the family farm has changed little. But the actual conditions on what is commonly thought of as family farms have undergone continuous change, both in organization and in relation to other sectors of the economy.

Nevertheless, a study by Radoje Nikolitch, of the Economic Research Service of the Department of Agriculture, showed that in numbers of farms, the family farm overwhelmingly prevailed in 1949 and 1954 in all parts of the country and for most of the census types of commercial farms.

In that study, as in this paper, family farms were recognized as businesses in which operating families are risk-taking managers who do most of the work. The labor supply of the usual farm family is equivalent to 1.5 man-years.

Ninety-six percent of all farms and 94 percent of all commercial farms were classed as family farms in 1954. Moreover, these percentages seem to have increased slightly between 1949 and 1954, even though the average size of all commercial farms increased from 276 to 310 acres.

The 1959 Census of Agriculture disclosed a situation not greatly different.

In 1959, for the whole country, 5.6 percent of all census farms reported annual expenditures on hired labor in excess of 2,500 dollars a year. A hired vage expenditure of 2,500 dollars is roughly equivalent to 75 man-weeks of hired labor — slightly in excess of 1.5 man-years of hired labor.

The variation among regions, however, was considerable. In the Northeast, 11.1 percent of all census farms spent 2,500 dollars or more for hired labor in 1959; the Corn Belt, 3.2 percent; Lake States, 2.9; Northern Plains, 3.3; Appalachian, 2.5; Southeast, 5.0; Delta States, 4.6; Southern Plains, 8.0; Mountain, 12.7; Pacific, 19.6. The average in 48 States was 5.6 percent.

Census data on farm expenditures for hired labor also were analyzed for commercial farms by type of farm. The percentage of commercial vegetable producers who reported expenditures of 2,500 dollars or more for hired labor was 36.8; fruit and nut growers, 38.0; cotton, 12.0; tobacco, 2.1; cash grain, 4.9; miscellaneous, 28.1; other field crops, 25.4; poultry, 9.4; dairy, 7.9; livestock ranches,

16.6; other livestock, 5.4; general, 6.4. The figure for all commercial farms was 8.5 percent. Moreover, within each of the types of farm, regional variation was great.

Another way of looking at the position of the family farm is to look at the composition of the farm labor force between family workers and hired workers. This measure has the advantage of reflecting the tenure status of all the members of the farm labor force, whereas consideration of the proportion of family farms among all farms obscures the statistical weight of hired workers on the relatively few larger-than-family farms. For commercial farms for the country as a whole, Mr. Nikolitch found man-years of hired labor to have been 25.4 percent of all farm labor in 1954, having decreased from 27.8 percent in 1949. Not surpisingly, he also found that hired labor as a percentage of all labor varied considerably by type of commercial farm.

Regional variation also was great within each of the types of farm. For example, on vegetable farms in 1954, the relative importance of hired labor varied from 20 percent in the Northern Plains and 29 percent in the Delta States to about 80 percent in the Southeast and Pacific regions. On cash-grain farms in 1954, hired labor as a percentage of all farm labor ranged from 10 percent in the Lake States to 56 percent in the Delta States.

These data indicate that the ideal of the family farm as one relying primarily on family labor is more relevant and more easily attainable in some types of farming and regions than in others.

But what are the long-term trends in the family and hired worker composition of the farm labor force?

We obtained data from the Statistical Reporting Service of the Department of Agriculture on the annual average of monthly numbers of farm family workers and hired farmworkers by regions from 1929 to 1962. During the depressed years of the thirties, all region experienced at least some drop in the relative importance of hired workers in the farm labor force, very likely because of an accumulation of family labor on farms as the rate of off-farm migration slowed.

During the period of the Second World War, another drop in the proportion of hired workers in the farm labor force occurred in all regions except the Pacific States — probably a result of the retention of family workers on farms under Selective Service procedures, the general wartime scarcity of hired labor, and the limited mechanization of farm operations because of the planned wartime production of farm machinery.

In the period after 1945, however, several different patterns may be observed among the geographic regions. Only slight year-to-year changes and no trends have been evident in four regions — Middle Atlantic, East North Central, West North Central, and Mountain.

Moderate but fairly steady increases in the proportion of hired workers in the farm labor force after 1945 appear to be the pattern in the other five areas. Our data provide only inconclusive evidence of the relative position of the family farm in these areas.

In the Pacific region, an increase in hired labor probably resulted from increases in total production of specialty crops, which require much labor, and from farm enlargement. In this region, with by far the largest percentage of hired workers, the family farm has never dominated the farm scene as completely as in most other regions and could be declining further.

In New England, the increase in the hired-labor portion of the farm labor force has probably resulted in large part from a sharp drop in the number of smaller farms. This may actually represent little or no loss in the relative position of family farms.

In the South Atlantic, East South Central, and West South Central regions, the increasing proportion of hired workers is explained partly by sharp decreases in numbers of sharecropper units (whose family members are counted as family rather than hired workers) and reductions in numbers of low-production and subsistence farms. In all three of these regions, the decline in the number of small farms (including sharecropper units) was much sharper than for the Nation as a whole, so that between 1945 and 1962 the number of family workers fell by about one-half. Meanwhile, hired workers increased slightly in the South Atlantic region and decreased slightly in the other two regions. The resulting increasing proportion of hired labor in the farm work force, however, may not constitute an actual weakening of what our country desires as family farms, because sharecropper and other small, low-productive farms are usually not considered to be family farms.

Land tenure arrangements of farm operators take on particular importance in any appraisal of the family farm. The traditional tenure goal of full ownership has continued to hold a strong attraction for many farm people, yet it has been undergoing modification.

The percentage of all farm operators classed as full owners has been unchanged since 1950 at 57 percent — a higher proportion than any other period since 1900. At the same time, however, the proportion of land in full-owner farms declined from 53 percent of all land in farms in 1910 to 31 percent in 1959.

The proportion of full tenancy declined from a high point of 42 percent in 1930 to 20 percent in 1959, and the land area tenants operated decreased from 31 to 15 percent.

A significant tenure trend with reference to ownership of farms is the rise in part ownership — that is, farms made up of both owned and rented land. This tenure class since 1940 has increased steadily in relation to other tenure classes, comprising 23 percent of all farm operators in 1959. Part owners operated 45 percent of all land in farms.

Although a sharp drop in tenancy occurred after 1950, there was little decline in the total area leased. Two factors are responsible. Renting by part owners has increased. Part owners in 1963 operated 219 million acres under lease — more, in fact, than the 163 million acres rented by tenants. The other factor is the increase in average size of tenant farms. This has been due to the decline in the numbers of sharecropper farms, which are comparatively small, and of other small, tenant-operated farms.

Large declines in numbers of small- and medium-sized farms have occurred among tenant farms and among all categories of tenure. The number of farms from 10 to 500 acres declined by 1,467,000 between 1950 to 1959, while the number of farms with 500 acres or more rose by 33 thousand.

As one would expect, the dropout of farms was higher among smaller ones. Disappearance of farms of 260 to 499 acres accounted for less than 1 percent of the total decline. Seventy-two percent of the total decline consisted of farms of fewer than 100 acres. Exceptions to the overall pattern were the East North Central and West North Central States, where the heaviest dropout was in the 100- to 179-acre group, amounting to 36 and 44 percent, respectively, of the total decline in numbers of farms larger than 10 acres.

Rising land values permit comparatively few farmers to purchase enough land for large-scale operation. Many farmers with small acreages and excess machine capacity attempt to purchase more land and thereby contribute to upward pressure on land prices. Many other farmers choose to invest their limited capital in machinery or livestock and to rent some or all of their land. Thus only a fifth of all farms of 2 thousand acres or more are operated by full owners, while three-fifths are operated by part owners.

Farmers who prefer to rent (rather than purchase land) avoid paying high prices for land, but they probably pay higher rents. Their efforts to lease land have bid up effective rental rates. Moreover, higher rental returns also indirectly contribute to the upward pressure on prices of farmland because the higher rental returns make investment in farmland more attractive to farm and non-farm people alike.

The amount of capital required for farming poses serious problems for many persons who wish to get established on farms of adequate size.

A 1962 report by the Economic Research Service, "Farm Costs and Returns, Commercial Farms by Type, Size, and Location," showed a large variation in total capital investments per farm. These investments range from 13 thousand dollars per farm on small tobacco farms of the North Carolina Coastal Plain — which had an annual net farm income of 2,500 dollars — to nearly 1 million dollars per farm for large cotton-general farms in the San Joaquin Valley of California, where net farm incomes amounted to nearly 80 thousand dollars annually.

Of 39 types of farms in 21 major farming areas reported in these studies, 25 had a total capital investment in 1961 of 50 thousand dollars or more, and 11 types exceeded 100 thousand dollars. Typical dairy farms had total capital investments ranging from 30 thousand to 60 thousand dollars, and Corn Belt farms ranged from 50 thousand to 100 thousand dollars.

The lowest capital requirements were on farms in the Southeastern States that were representative of most cotton-, tobacco-, and peanut-producing farms in the region. But net farm incomes there were also low in relation to most typical farms in other areas.

The farm types selected for the annual costs and returns studies of the Economic Research Service are important, typical operating units in different farming areas, and in most instances they are the most common unit. They are representative of commercial farms. Thus their capital requirements and other organizational characteristics would be expected to differ from part-time or other farms, where the sale of farm products is not the major source of family income. Such part-time and residential farms are not family farms as the term is commonly understood.

All of the types of farms studied showed substantial increases since 1950 in their total capital requirements, reflecting increases in the amount and value of resources used. With few exceptions, the investment in land and buildings increased at a greater rate than total farm investment. Moreover, the investment in land and buildings makes up a sizable portion of the total capital investment, amounting to 80 percent or more on 18 of the typical commercial farms. Farms in these groups were primarily producers of cash crops, including cash grain, tobacco, and cotton farms, and ranged from small family units to highly capitalized, large-scale farms.

Overall, the asset position of commercial agriculture is good. At the beginning of 1962, the equities of farm operators and other owners of farm resources were nearly 87 percent of the value of farm assets. This ratio was 81 percent in 1940 and 91 percent in 1950. Capital assets of agriculture in 1962 were 207.3 billion dollars, compared to 131.6 billion dollars in 1950 and 52.9 billion dollars in 1940.

Increases in the sixties in the capital assets of agriculture resulted chiefly from rising prices of farmland. The increase in the level of capital assets and in prices of farmland has had an adverse effect on beginning farmers who are without substantial family assistance and on established farmers who need to enlarge if they are to meet minimum standards of farm income.

For farmers in these two kinds of situations particularly, means other than ownership must be used to some extent to gain control over resources needed to attain adequate levels of farm production.

In specific instances and on some types of farms, operators rely heavily on nonfarm sources to provide some of the farm resources. Livestock-share leases, farm partnerships, and producer-processor contracts are examples of this type of agreement. Each of these potentially provides that the person who supplies the farm operator with outside capital also participates actively in making some or all of the management decisions. Just how much the use of various arrangements to acquire more capital has diminished farmers' rights to make major management decisions is difficult to determine.

This matter has great significance, because the terms under which a farmer acquires land and capital resources determine whether he actually makes important management decisions, shares these decisions with someone else, or even largely turns them over to someone else. But even where farm management decisions rest mainly with farm operators, their decisions more and more must be coordinated with the operation of farm suppliers and processors, and adjusted to the requirements of government agricultural programs.

We have traced the development of the family farm tradition and described significant changes in agriculture that have transformed the organization of farms.

Still other changes, less apparent in their effect on farm organization, have direct meaning for the family farm tradition. Of particular importance are the declining need for land in crop production, reduction locally in land available for farming as a consequence of growth in urban and other nonfarm uses of land, and the increasing reliance of the farm people on nonfarm employment.

From 1950 to 1959, the acreage used for crop production in the United States declined from 377 million acres to 358 million, and the acreage harvested from 336 million acres to 317 million. The decline of about 6 percent in cropland harvested was more than offset by a 27-percent increase in the average productivity of harvested acres.

The increase in production per harvested acre has been attributed largely to increased use of fertilizer. Some of the increase is also due to concentration of production on better lands, as farmland is transferred to other uses such as to woodland and pasture. This is shown by the regional differences in the patterns of declining cropland and shifts of cropland to other uses.

Relatively large declines in the acreage of cropland harvested occurred from 1950 to 1959 in four regions — Southeast (23 percent), Appalachian (18 percent), Delta (16 percent), and Northeast (12 percent). The Northern Plains, Southern

Plains, and Corn Belt all had a decrease of about 8 percent in crop acreage harvested. Slight increases occurred in the Mountain and Pacific regions.

The effect on farming opportunities of a continued drop in the use of land for crop production will depend on whether land taken out of production is suitable for farming and is actually needed for agricultural production. Attention was given to these points in a publication in 1962 of the Department of Agriculture, "Land and Water Resources, A Policy Guide."

According to projections it reported, the national need for harvested crop acreage by 1980 to supply domestic and export needs for food and fiber would be 291 million acres, or 26 million fewer acres than the acreage harvested in 1959. By 1962, the combined operation of the Feed Grain and Conservation Reserve programs were instrumental in reducing harvested crop acreage to 288 million acres — 3 million fewer acres than the projected needs by 1980.

Upon the completion of Conservation Reserve and Feed Grain contracts, a major problem relating to the family farm will be to find uses for this land that are compatible with production needs and also take account of the needs of farm families for adequate income. In the absence of continued payments for land diversion, it can be expected that the incentive to return land to crop production will be great, unless profitable alternative uses for diverted land are developed.

Urban and other nonfarm uses for land have had important effects on farming in many localities through a reduction in the acreage locally available for farming. The reduction is not great nationally, although the effects on individual farmers are sometimes serious and may necessitate relocation or continued operation with a reduced acreage. About 1 million acres a year were required for urban and industrial growth, highways, airports, and the like from 1950 to 1961. This land was classed as rural before its conversion to urban use, and some of it had not actually been in farm use. A problem that is more serious locally is the disruptive effect on farms of land speculation extending beyond the area of imminent urban expansion.

Off-farm employment is an important source of income for many farm people. Thirty-four percent of all commercial farm operators reported some off-farm employment in 1959, compared to 27 percent in 1950. Off-farm employment of 100 days or more was reported by 15 percent of the commercial farm operators in 1959, compared to 9 percent in 1950.

A number of factors contributed to this trend. Urban and industrial expansion have multiplied the number of employment opportunities available to farm people. Decentralization of factories and businesses into rural areas and improvement in roads have made nonfarm job opportunities more accessible. A third consideration is the increased desire of farm people generally for higher incomes. Some farmers, with too little capital or credit to enlarge their farm, actively seek outside employment and make their farming a "moonlight" operation.

The combination of off-farm employment and farm operation is sometimes pointed to as being at variance with the family farm tradition, according to which a farm should be capable of providing adequately for a farm family and of utilizing fully its labor. More and more farms, however, have failed to meet one or both of these conditions, as the cash income needs for modern living standards continue to rise and as mechanization further reduces the time for farm operations.

Realistically, the alternatives to the combination of farming and off-farm employment may be much less desirable, from both an individual and community point of view. The alternatives, broadly speaking, are to continue as full-time farmers but to be underproductive, or to discontinue farming and seek full-time nonfarm employment.

To implement either alternative in a way that benefits the families concerned requires specific and sometimes difficult measures. For many such operators, a shift to full-time farming would involve the acquisition of additional land. Within limits, this could be done through the use of credit. But to try to achieve this on a large scale would seriously bid up prices of farmland.

Farm families who rely in part for their income on nonfarm work often are reluctant to seek full-time nonfarm work if it involves relocation to urban areas. Even those who would like to leave may lack the skills needed to get employment at a wage that would cover their relocation costs and exceed their present incomes, including the value of food produced for home consumption and housing.

One measure that may ease the problem of some farm people in shifting to full-time nonfarm employment is the assistance provided by the Manpower Development and Training Act of 1962. Farmworkers with less than 1,200 dollars of annual net family income are eligible for assistance under the act, which provides financial assistance for training and relocation and allowances while training. The net income limit on eligibility, however, would eliminate from participation many farmers who still operate inadequate-sized farms and rely in part on off-farm employment for their income. Some young adults, however, may be able to qualify for training and allowances under the youth provisions of the act.

Probably the most serious challenge to the family farm ideal is the difficulty of entry into farming at a level that holds promise of economic progress for the farm family.

It spells a serious inequality of opportunity between young farm people who do and who do not inherit a substantial interest in a profitable and well-organized farm or otherwise benefit from family assistance. (It must be conceded, of course, that such inequalities of opportunity are not unknown in other economic activities.)

The difficulty of becoming a successful family farmer is made more serious by the fact that farm people, historically, have had high birth rates, so that each generation of farm children is more than sufficient to replace the preceding generation.

Furthermore, the actual numbers of opportunities for employment in agriculture have been declining steadily. The results are evident in nearly every rural community where pressure of economic and technological change in farming have brought about a sharp reduction in farm numbers and farming opportunities for rural youths.

Without doubt, migration from agriculture over the decades has benefited many of those who left and has exposed new opportunities outside agriculture to their descendants. Important benefits have accrued to agriculture also, for the decline in the farm population is one of the factors that underlie the great improvements in agricultural productivity.

The family farm has adjusted to many stresses, but when we focus attention on some of its characteristics we may overlook the significance of other important trends in the structure of agriculture.

The high capital needs and the more specialized management ability needed for modern commercial farming could lead in the direction that farms become quite dependent on outside financing, with farm operators divested of an ever larger share both of ownership of farm resources and of decisionmaking.

Furthermore, some types of farms may become sufficiently large and specialized that both their management and labor force are hired employees. Finally, farming opportunities more and more may come to be hereditary, so that farms are transferred within families from generation to generation.

Any of these developments could take a direction sharply contrary to the ideal of the family farm.

Health Trends, 1963

From Helen L. Johnston, "Health Trends in Rural America," U.S. Department of Agriculture, *Yearbook*, 1963 (Washington, 1963), pp. 189–97.

Hundreds of small, new, modern hospitals everywhere in rural America attest the changes in conditions and attitudes that affect the health of individuals and communities. The changes may have both positive and negative effects. They include the hospitals themselves, the readiness of rural people to use them, a modification of the rural living and working environment, and changes in the rural population itself.

Rural outmigration, for example, has relieved overpopulation and stabilized the economic level of some communities. It has also left behind a disproportionate share of the young and the old — the age groups with the greatest relative need for health care. It has made the support of needed health services increasingly difficult in some small communities. The overall rural economy has improved, but one-third of the Nation's rural families still have incomes of less than 2 thousand dollars.

The urbanizing and broadening influences of radio, newspapers, telephones, highways, and automobiles, moreover, touch even the most remote farm family and tend to reduce old rural-urban differences in health needs, attitudes, and behavior. Visiting and shopping in nearby towns and cities have become a part of daily living, rather than a rare occurrence, and the visits to town often become the occasion for seeking medical or dental care as well.

Especially among farm residents of metropolitan counties, the rural-urban contacts have increased through off-the-farm employment. Off-the-farm work helps to stabilize farm income and makes possible improved nutrition, clothing, and shelter; greater use of medical, dental, and hospital care; and more enrollment in health insurance plans, often in connection with industrial employment.

Offsetting those advantages to some degree, however, are the lack of anyone at home to care for sick or injured family members when the homemaker is employed elsewhere, less close supervision of the health of school and pre-school children, less time devoted to the preparation of nutritious meals, and more eating away from home. Cafes and restaurants in small towns, moreover, are less likely than those in urban centers to be well equipped, have well-trained workers, and be supervised by agencies to protect the public health.

Where surburban sprawl has encroached on farm communities with little forethought or planning, the haphazard use of land for farming and nonfarm purposes may lead to health and safety risks for farm and nonfarm residents alike. Farm families may have substantial sums invested in their own water supplies and septic tanks; they may resist taxation for public improvements even after increased density of population threatens contamination of their own wells.

Both farm and nonfarm residents may also be subject to the risks involved in the drift of poisonous sprays from aerial spraying equipment, the use of crowded highways for slow-moving farm equipment, and other hazards arising from rapidly increasing population in a previously rural community.

Machines have greatly eased the burden of farmwork. They also have made the character of work hazards more and more like those of industry, but with far fewer controls. Safety devices may be lacking or misused. Overfatigue may result from long hours of work during peak seasons. Mechanized equipment may be used by young people or temporary workers who lack adequate supervision.

Expanded farm operations made possible by the use of machines have created new needs in some communities for short-term workers from outside the county or even outside the State. Such measures as the provision of field toilets, safe drinking water, handwashing facilities, and a safe means of preserving food for field lunches become increasingly important as larger numbers of fieldworkers are employed. Adequate temporary housing for workers and families from outside the area is also important.

Bypassed by economic and social change, some rural people continue to live at a depressed level. They may live in the midst of relative prosperity, but are themselves handicapped by farm units that are too small to provide an adequate family living; by age, which may force them into retirement without adequate resources to support a satisfactory level of living, including adequate health care; or by other economic, or social, or maybe physical disabilities.

Other communities have become stranded where farmland has been depleted or forests and mines have been exhausted. The people live in dilapidated homes with few conveniences. They have little access to health or other community services.

Some of these handicapped rural people, with incomes far below a taxable level, take refuge in city slums. Some become migrant farmworkers. Some deteriorate in a steadily more hopeless setting. The greatest concentration of the deteriorating rural communities is in the Southeastern and Southwestern States. Others are scattered throughout the country.

Rural people of the Great Plains, on the other hand, share in general rural economic and social improvements. Nevertheless, they suffer a growing handicap in their efforts to maintain adequate community health services as the population of the Great Plains counties continues to decrease. Speed and ease of transportation compensate to some degree by enabling the average family to reach physicians and hospitals even at distances of 50 miles or more. For the less mobile aged or chronically ill, especially those who live alone, distance may be an insurmountable barrier to obtaining needed health care. Moreover, the typical lack or arrangements to meet unexpected health emergencies affects all families of the Great Plains region.

Infant mortality is among the indexes of the health status of a population. During most of the years since 1928, infants born to urban families had the best chance of survival. Rural people have now regained a slight advantage over urban people, according to 1959 infant mortality rates (infant deaths under a year per thousand live births).

Comparisons of infant mortality according to residence, however, show that babies born outside metropolitan counties had a poorer chance to survive in 1959 than babies born to residents of metropolitan counties. Small places of 2,500 to 10 thousand in non-metropolitan counties had the highest infant mortality rates. The rural non-white infant mortality rate in nonmetropolitan counties was nearly twice the national average.

Regional differences also appear in infant mortality rates. Although the situation in the South has inproved greatly since 1928, mortality rates for both rural and urban infants in the South have continued to average higher than those for any other region.

Most deaths of infants 1 to 11 months old are considered preventable. The Children's Bureau reported for 1959 that infants of that age have the best survival chances if they belong to white families living in metropolitan counties. The mortality rate for all infants aged 1 to 11 months *declined* by 21 percent during the decade to 1960. During the same period, the mortality rate for nonwhite rural infants living outside metropolitan counties *increased* by 5 percent.

Data on injuries in accidents during work and on chronically disabling conditions provided by the National Health Survey of the Public Health Service offer other clues to rural-urban differences in health status. Fifty-six per thousand persons in farm sections and 46 per thousand city persons were hurt in work accidents each year in 1960 and 1961.

For all ages, the percentage of rural persons who have some degree of activity-limitation due to chronic conditions exceeds that of urban people.

Because many farm operators are over 50 years old, it is significant that 24 percent of the rural farm people 45 to 64 years old were limited in their activity by some type of chronic condition, compared with 20 percent for rural nonfarm and 16 percent for urban residents.

More than half of the rural farm people over 65 reported some degree of activity-limitation from a chronic condition, compared with less than 40 percent of the urban and 46 percent of the rural nonfarm people of that age.

Among the chronic conditions reported oftener among rural farm than among nonfarm and urban residents were hernia, heart conditions, high blood pressure, as well as arthritis and rheumatism.

The number of days spent in bed as a result of disability was about the same among urban and rural residents. But after age 65 rural nonfarm and rural farm people reported an average of 17 days spent in bed during a year, compared with 16 days reported for urban persons.

Regional differences appear in the number of days of bed disability. For all rural farm people in the South, regardless of age, an average of 9 days of bed disability was reported — the highest for any residence group. Rural residents of both the West and the North Central States, on the other hand, reported lower rates of bed disability than other population groups by residence in their respective regions.

Only a few clues exist to the relative health disability among especially disadvantaged rural groups. In 102 low-income rural counties designated by the Department of Agriculture as pilot counties for the Rural Areas Development program during the fifties, infant mortality averaged 31 deaths under a year per thousand live births, compared with 27 for the Nation as a whole. The pilot counties were concentrated in the Southeastern States.

A study of the California Vocational Rehabilitation Service in 1955–1958 assessed the seriousness of disability among seasonal farmworkers in that State. About one of five adults had a physical handicap that affected earning capacity.

Rural health facilities have improved measurably since the Second World War.

The Hill-Burton Hospital Survey and Construction Act of 1946 had provisions to equalize the distribution of modern hospitals so that all people, regardless of where they lived, may have ready access to general hospital care.

Up to 1962, two-thirds of the beds in general hospitals built with Hill-Burton aid were in small towns and cities. Nine hundred new hospitals — nearly one-third of the total built with Federal aid — were in communities of less than 2,500. About one-fifth were in communities of 2,500 to 50 thousand.

Besides the general hospitals, about half of the public health centers built with Hill-Burton aid are located in small communities. Small communities have been able also to qualify for assistance in the construction or improvement of nursing homes and diagnostic and treatment centers.

A study by the Public Health Service suggested that income level, rather than rurality, is a governing factor in the location of health facilities. Metropolitan and nonmetropolitan counties of comparable per capita income had comparable numbers of beds in general hospitals and nursing homes in relation to their population.

Continuing regional disparities appear when data on the distribution of physicians, dentists, and nurses per 100 thousand of population are examined by year and by region.

Throughout 1921–1960, the South's supply of physicians, dentists, and nurses was at a lower level than that of any other geographic region.

Metropolitan counties in 1940 had 153 physicians per 100 thousand residents, compared with 90 per 100 thousand in bordering counties and 79 in all other counties. Twenty years later — in mid-1959 — the physician-population ratios for each group of counties had *decreased*. Highly urbanized counties continued to have about twice as many physicians per 100 thousand people as isolated counties. Specifically, in mid-1959, metropolitan counties had 146 physicians per 100 thousand persons; bordering counties, 77; and isolated counties, 75.

Establishing functional relationships between health personnel and facilities in small communities and those in urban centers is viewed by many health experts as a way to maintain quality of rural health care.

They cite as some of the advantages the opportunity for physicians to maintain the contacts that contribute to professional growth; easier referrals without loss of patients; and provision of a wide range of diagnostic and treatment services for rural residents without costly duplication of facilities.

The number of formalized relationships between health facilities in small and large population centers is still negligible, although one of the initial objectives of the Hill-Burton program was to facilitate such relationships.

Less formal and extensive relationships, on the other hand, have increased. They involve such arrangements as the new establishment of preceptorships by medical schools, which assign graduate students to physicians in smaller centers, and periodic institutes given by teaching hospitals or other institutions for practitioners from the area.

A report in 1962 of an experiment in Michigan in establishing relationships among small and large health centers suggested that the difficulty of implementing regionalization in the health field has corollaries in library, school, and other fields. Small institutions desire autonomy and self-sufficiency. They fear being swallowed up by larger institutions if they establish working relationships with them.

Group practice, in which several physicians representing different specialized interests work together, also is viewed as a means of improving and stabilizing rural health services. It helps "put the patient together," in that a single group of individuals takes responsibility for his medical care in much the same way as the old-fashioned country doctor took responsibility for total health care of his patients.

Formalized group practice has grown in number of units and in number of physicians associated with group practice organizations since 1940. The Public Health Service reported a threefold increase between 1946 and 1959. Of the 1,200 groups in 1959, more than one-third were in isolated counties.

In addition to these formalized groups, which usually share facilities, equipment, and income, informal referral arrangements apparently have increased between the physicians of small and large communities.

Services for rural groups having special needs because of age, health condition, or income status are minimal in most small communities.

Homemaker and home nursing services are least well developed in the small community and the sparsely settled farming areas, despite growing needs because of the increasing employment of homemakers away from the farm home.

Physiotherapy services can greatly relieve the suffering of some chronically ill and aging persons; they seldom are found outside of major urban centers.

School health services, if they exist at all, are usually inadequate.

Health services especially geared to meet the needs of a temporary influx of farmworkers and their families seldom exist. Psychiatric service for the mentally ill is almost entirely lacking, and so is counseling for families of former mental patients on their return to the community.

The continuing rural shortages of health personnel to some extent are accentuated by increasing demands for some types of health service. The use by rural people of hospitals for maternity care has risen sharply. Only 45 percent of rural mothers in 1940 were hospitalized at childbirth, compared with more than 90 percent in 1959. Urban births in hospitals have increased also but at a less rapid rate; 97 percent now take place in hospitals.

Overall rates of utilization of hospitals by rural people, on the other hand, remain little changed since about 1930. The Committee on the Costs of Medical Care reported at that time that 4.6 percent of the residents of small towns and rural sections had some hospital experience in an average year, compared with 7.1 percent of large city residents. In 1957–1958, the National Health Survey reported, 5 percent of open-country residents were hospitalized, compared with 10 percent of the residents of cities of 100 thousand or more. The average length of stay for rural farm and nonfarm residents was 7 to 8 days, compared with 9 for urban residents.

The use of physicians' and dentists' services by rural people has increased, but continuing disparities exist between rural and urban levels of use.

Rural farm people averaged 3.8 visits annually to physicians, compared with 4.9 for rural nonfarm and 5.3 for urban residents in 1957–1959. People of the rural South reported the fewest visits, although the South had the greatest proportion of rural farm people with limitation of activity resulting from chronic conditions.

Rural people are also less likely to use dental care. When they do, more likely it is for extractions rather than for fillings or other remedial services. One-fourth of the rural farm people reported never having visited a dentist, compared with 20 percent of the rural nonfarm and 16 percent of urban people.

Geographic proximity makes less difference than in the past in the distances people go for health care.

Residents of a county in the Great Plains region — Kit Carson County in Colorado — used more than 200 different physicians in 1958. Seven physicians practiced in the county at the time. Most of the out-of-county physicians consulted were specialists, nearly one-half of whom practiced in Denver, more than 150 miles from Burlington, the county seat.

Studies in Mississippi, Connecticut, and New York counties indicated that the proximity of a doctor or hospital does not determine where people will purchase medical or hospital care. The increasing mobility of the population makes the majority of rural people far less dependent than in the past on nearby resources, except for emergency cases.

Medical folkways, including the use of old home remedies and folk practitioners, still compete with more sophisticated methods of treatment, especially among the low-income rural minorities.

The use of midwifery, for example, has almost disappeared among rural families in general. Nonwhite rural families, however, continue to use midwives, especially in some of the more isolated rural communities of the South.

Health neglect also is common among low-income rural groups. Physicians in California, who studied the reasons for failure to use prenatal care, even when it was offered through free clinics, found that major obstacles included inadequate understanding, dissatisfaction with the services made available to indigent persons, or failure to qualify for indigent care because family income was too high — even though marginal — or because residence requirements could not be met.

For the migratory farm family, lack of residence status is likely to bar the use of community services offered to others of similar income, even in the place they call home.

Not only purchasing power but also perceptions of health needs and appropriate means of care affect rural families' demand for the community health services. Differences among rural people in their awareness of need and proper care

are associated with differences in education and level of participation in community affairs, as well as differences in occupation and income.

Rural family health expenditures in 1955 averaged about 63 dollars a person — more than double those in 1941, in terms of dollars of constant purchasing power. They were about 80 percent of the health expenditures of urban families in 1955, compared with less than half the urban expenditures in 1941. In both years, the variations in expenditures may in part be accounted for by differences in levels of charges between rural and urban areas. As data as to utilization show, however, there are also real differences between the two population groups in use of care.

The medical expenditures of farm people in families with incomes of less than 2 thousand dollars averaged 55 dollars per person and represented about 9 percent of their total outlay for family living in 1955, compared with about 5 percent in the general population for the year. For farm people with incomes between 2 thousand and 5 thousand dollars, medical expenditures averaged between 60 and 65 dollars. Expenditures rose rapidly in groups that had incomes of more than 5 thousand dollars.

The expenditures of nonwhite families tended to be lower and to represent a smaller percentage of total family outlay than among white families. This may, in part, reflect nonwhite families' lack of access to services, especially in the South.

Prepayment coverage has expanded among people in the half-dozen most rural States faster than for the United States as a whole in recent years. The National Health Survey's report on insurance coverage for rural farm, rural nonfarm, and urban people, however, shows that rural farm people continue to have less insurance coverage than other groups. They differ also in type of coverage and in the proportion of hospital bills paid by insurance.

According to the National Health Survey, one-half of rural farm residents had no insurance. About one-third of rural nonfarm and fewer than one-third of urban residents had no insurance. A smaller proportion of persons in all residence categories had surgical insurance, compared with hospital insurance; a still smaller proportion had other medical coverage.

For each type, the proportion of rural farm people having the specified coverage was smaller than the proportion of urban or rural nonfarm. Urban people were most likely to have a Blue Cross or Blue Shield type of coverage. The insurance held by rural farm people was likely to fall in the category, "other."

The proportion of the hospital bill of discharged patients paid for by insurance averaged 70 percent for urban and rural nonfarm people. For rural farm people, it averaged 55 percent. The proportion of persons discharged from hospitals with more than three-fourths of the bill paid by insurance averaged 50 percent for urban and rural nonfarm patients. For rural farm patients, it averaged 39 percent.

The rural aged — and especially those from farms — must rely on their own financial resources to pay for needed health care oftener than the urban residents.

The possible influence of method of payment on utilization of service is implied in another Social Security Administration report of the early fifties.

The rural farm population past 65 averaged 86 days of hospital care per 100 persons in comparison with 184 — more than twice as many — for urban persons. When the insured population only was considered, however, insured farm groups had high hospital admission rates accompanied by average stays only moderately less than other population groups. Their resulting average of 208 days of hospital care per 100 persons was greater than the national average.

How much farther the possibilities of rural enrollment can be stretched may be questioned under existing circumstances. National Health Survey reports show a rapid increase in the percentage of persons enrolled with increase in income. To urge individuals or families to join prepayment organizations when their income averages 2 thousand dollars or less, as is true of one-third of the Nation's rural families, would seem likely to be costly, unproductive, and questionable from the point of view of the needs of the people. The individual insurance they would be likely to purchase would be the most costly and limited in benefits. It might provide for the economic catastrophe; it would be unlikely to encourage early detection and treatment of ailments before they reach the catastrophic stage.

On the other hand, when improvements in income are made by enlargement of the farm unit, off-farm work opportunities, or other means, rural people need to continue to work with voluntary health insurers to develop new community organization techniques and to gain acceptance of existing community organizations — other than employee groups — as a basis for group insurance coverage.

Insurance purchased on a group basis has the advantages of greater benefits at lower costs than individually purchased insurance.

In the future, as in the past, rural people will need to run fast to stay in place. The relative position of rural and urban residents in the availability and use of health facilities and services has remained about the same the past two or three decades.

Personal and community economic levels continue to be important keys to levels of health and health care. Geographic accessibility of service is of somewhat less importance than formerly to the majority of rural residents. It is still of crucial importance to some of those who are most needy — the aging, the chronically ill, migratory farm families, and the indigent rural resident.

In asking how rural areas might be brought up to the standards of urban communities, a question may be raised about urban standards. Even in the city setting where medical advances have been applied most fully, services still usually represent a hodgepodge, in the midst of which the consumer finds few guidelines to tap the services best fitted to his needs.

Among the hopeful factors are some legislative developments.

The Community Health Services and Facilities Act of 1961 opened the door for rural as well as urban experimentation in methods of providing health care to fit changing needs and circumstances. Emphasis is placed on services for the chronically ill and the aged.

Some examples of activities that may be undertaken under the program are demonstrations of nursing care of the sick at home, as a means of preventing or reducing disability; demonstration of specialized services, such as physiotherapy, supplied from a central source to patients at home or in nursing homes; and development and testing of methods of recruiting, training, and using homemakers, nurses' aides, and other subprofessional personnel in home-care programs.

Groups interested in this program can obtain information from their State health departments.

Financial support to help States and communities extend services to migrant workers and their families was authorized through the Public Health Service under 1962 legislation, which provides grants to pay part of the cost of family health service clinics and other projects to improve migrants' health services or conditions.

The objectives of the migrant health legislation are to provide a setting in which migrant farmworkers and families can realistically be expected and encouraged to take responsibility for meeting their own health needs. This will require the scheduling of services to prevent and treat illness at times and places accessible to migrants and without restrictions because they lack residence. It will also require upgrading their living and working environment to make such minimal facilities as toilets, drinking water, handwashing, and bathing and laundry facilities available in order that they can observe good personal health practices. Finally, it will require interarea coordination so that the present disparities in services and the methods whereby they are provided will be minimized.

The expanded Hill-Burton program of the Public Health Service continues to facilitate the efforts of rural people to provide facilities and services for general hospital care, nursing home care, public health, and some other types of services.

The Small Business Administration also assists rural hospitals, nursing homes, and local physicians and dentists who need loans for new or expanded facilities.

The banding together of two or more counties has succeeded in extending organized public health services to some rural counties. To accomplish the same general objective, contracts for service between the State health department and rural counties without local public health organization have proved successful in California.

Continuing shortages of health workers are neither a rural nor an urban problem, but a national problem. The Public Health Service reported that ratios of physicians to population have remained practically unchanged since 1940. With dentists, as with physicians, active practitioner-population ratios were lower in the early sixties than in the prewar period. The number of professional nurses has increased, but a serious shortage existed in 1963 in relation to demand. In hospitals alone, more than twice as many professional nurses were employed in 1956 as in 1943.

To maintain medical care of high quality for rural people will require continuing study and effort to organize services effectively, especially where depopulation, poverty, interarea farm migration, or other factors create special needs.

The growth of group practice units in rural areas gives promise for the future. A small town with several physicians practicing together may be less likely to become "doctorless" than the one-doctor community.

Moreover, nearly all group practice units have a built-in method of maintaining quality care, ranging from time off to attend meetings and post-graduate courses to participation on medical school faculties.

The continuing poverty of some people and of some communities is also neither a wholly rural nor a wholly urban problem. However, rural poverty may go unnoticed until a shift to urban residence brings it to light.

As one writer commented, "Neglected health conditions in the rural area fester into dependency in the cities, as city schools and other institutions identify problems that were unnoticed before.''

A major objective for the improvement of both rural and urban health care is to plan, organize, and administer health services in a manner that will give the entire population maximum accessibility to service according to need.

To protect and maintain the health of rural people, it is necessary to:

Continue to increase knowledge of the influence on health of the changing environment of rural people; for example, the effects of mechanization and the use of toxic substances in agriculture;

Continue ''watchdog'' observation of rural-urban differences in health status and utilization of health services, in relation to economic and social as well as geographic accessibility;

Continue investigation and development of methods to overcome the ''social costs'' of distance in such areas of continuing depopulation as the Great Plains;

Continue research to determine the real roots of human health behavior, especially among the underprivileged groups whose need for health care may be especially great;

Continue application of research findings to processes of providing and financing service, methods of health education, and modification of the environment as necessary.

Women's Contributions to Cooperatives

From Joseph G. Knapp, *Women and Cooperatives* (Washington, 1965), pp. 23–25, 30–31.

I think it is important here that we recognize that farming is uniquely a family business and that women are deeply involved in its success. If the farm business prospers women are able to obtain the things that they hold dear: Education for their children, perhaps a more modern kitchen, or an automobile — not to speak of a new dress or hat. Farm women work along with men to make the farm a success. They may keep the garden, raise the chickens, care for the livestock, or work in the fields. Many wives maintain the business records for the farm — and I am informed by a friend who handles farm loans that most farmers will not dare to make a serious business decision unless it is approved by their wives.

The cooperative business organization is distinguished by the fact that it is designed to serve an end rather than be an end in itself. Its success is measured by its ability to serve the needs of its members, by performing needed services, and by making savings for them, so as to enable them to increase their incomes from farming.

In a cooperative association the savings are returned to the members in proportion to the use they make of the association. Thus, cooperatives in themselves are non-profit organizations, for everything over costs reverts back to the members in savings. Profits are not kept by the cooperative for distribution to those who supply the capital.

While I do not wish to be too technical, it is important that we do not over-simplify the cooperative method of operation. In outward appearance cooperatives may seem quite similar to other business firms. The main difference is that they serve people as members while other business firms serve them as customers.

There are three major distinguishing characteristics of a cooperative organization as compared to a general, or non-cooperative business:

1. Members of a cooperative seek to obtain services for themselves at cost — their object is not to obtain profit from providing services for others.

2. A cooperative distributes amounts remaining after payment of the costs of doing business among those who are served by the cooperative in proportion to their use of its services — whereas in a general business such amounts are paid to investors in proportion to their investments in enterprise.

3. In a cooperative the patron-members control the organization through democratic procedures — control is not exerted by owners of the capital invested in proportion to the capital they have contributed.

I have endeavored to show that a cooperative is a special type of business which has been found suited to the needs of those who wish to serve themselves. Those who benefit from its operations are the ones who control it and who provide the risk capital needed to make it a going business. It is a form of business which enables farmers to achieve advantages in better production, better purchasing, and better marketing. Cooperatives simply extend the farm business so that it becomes something more than an isolated enterprise dependent for its production, purchasing, and marketing services on other business establishments. It becomes an autonomous part of an economic solidarity.

Farmers thus have a choice in the way they carry on their business affairs. They can choose the route of self-help and create their own business organizations, or they can obtain the business services they need from others.

Farmers or others have a basic right to look out for their own welfare. They must do so to survive and prosper — and experience indicates that they will do so through the formation of cooperative organizations whenever they understand that it is to their advantage to do so. . . .

What can women do to help cooperatives which are large and complex organizations? They can see to it that the cooperative really serves their needs. They can demand that the organization not overlook the fact that the cooperative is designed to serve them, as well as the men in the family. Women can help cooperatives improve their methods.

I have found frequently that women have many suggestions for the good of an organization that would be overlooked by men. Women have something valuable to contribute, and they should demand opportunities to be helpful. Above all, women can, and should, take steps to really find out how cooperatives work for otherwise their views will have little meaning. It stands to reason that if women know how cooperatives work they will then be able to offer suggestions of a practical nature. In this connection women can demand that financial and other reports of a cooperative be presented in such a way as to be understandable to them. In too many cases cooperative reports are presented in technical language that is not understandable even to those who have management responsibilities. Women can help cooperatives see that the informational and educational materials issued by a cooperative have a human interest appeal.

It is my firm belief that farmer cooperatives will give increased attention to the importance of women as partners in farming in the years to come. It would be poor business practice for them not to do so. I find it very encouraging to see farm women beginning to speak up and demand that their talents be more fully used in making the cooperatives which serve their families more successful. . . .

Refrigeration

From W. T. Pentzer, "The Giant Job of Refrigeration," U.S. Department of Agriculture, *Yearbook*, 1966 (Washington, 1966), pp. 123–38.

Food habits of Americans have changed greatly since the advent of refrigeration a little over 100 years ago. We eat more perishable foods the year round, in season and out of season.

We can purchase meat, fish, poultry, eggs, milk, ice cream, lettuce, strawberries, citrus fruits, bananas, and apples, to name only a few perishable foods, almost any day of the year. The variety of fresh and frozen foods available today is truly amazing.

Less than 100 years ago many persons in small cities and villages in America kept a milk cow as the only way to have fresh milk.

Meat came from cattle slaughtered locally, driven or shipped to where they were needed. In those days there were no refrigerated vehicles for shipping dressed carcasses. The mainstays in the diet then were bread and cured meats.

Development of railroads, waterways, and roads brought city and country closer together. Refrigeration made it possible for even perishable foods to be shipped long distances.

Today, a New York City housewife shopping for food may purchase citrus fruits that came from Florida or California, carrots from Texas, lettuce from Arizona, potatoes from Idaho, meat from Iowa, poultry from Delaware, and apples from Washington.

Some of these perishable foods travel 2,000 to 3,000 miles to reach the New York market and are a week or more on their journey. This is time enough for the food to spoil from microbial action or become overripe and worthless. Here is where refrigeration plays its role, arresting the processes that can lead to deterioration.

Ice provided the only practical means of keeping large quantities of perishable foods cool in warm weather until approximately 1880.

Today ice is still used in great quantities by the food industry for cooling fish, poultry, dairy products, fruits and vegetables, and beverages.

The 1963 production of ice was 20 million tons according to the National Ice Association. Ice production has decreased since World War II, when the annual value was $427 million, compared with $210 million in 1963. The decline has come about because of the replacement of iceboxes in the home and elsewhere with mechanical refrigeration equipment.

The largest use of commercial ice production today is for icing railroad cars, trucks, and the fishing fleet. About 14.5 million tons were used for these purposes in 1963. The remaining 5.5 million tons produced were used as cubed or crushed ice by restaurants, hotels, and by other institutions.

Fish was one of the first perishable foods to benefit from refrigeration. The captain of a Gloucester, Mass., smack put ice on board to preserve a catch of halibut in 1838.

In 1858 iced containers of fish were shipped from New England ports to New York City.

Fish was frozen with ice and salt as early as 1861. This may have been the beginning of the frozen food industry. Special pans for freezing the fish were developed, and the tightly filled, covered pans were packed in a mixture of ice and salt.

After freezing, the fish was coated with ice by dipping it in water.

Fish frozen in this way was held at 20° F. for 8 to 10 months. The storage rooms were refrigerated with ice and salt, later by mechanical refrigeration.

Present practices have been built on these early techniques.

Fish like haddock and cod, caught by trawl off the New England and Canadian Maritime Provinces coasts, are eviscerated, washed, and iced in pens in the vessel's hold. Other small fish, like ocean perch and whiting, are iced without eviscerating because of their small size.

Shrimp are harvested by trawl and beheaded, washed, and stored in ice in the holds.

Fish of the Pacific Northwest, like halibut and sable, are eviscerated, washed, and iced in the vessel's pens. Pacific salmon, caught by seines for use in canneries, have recently been stored whole aboard the vessel in hold tanks containing sea water refrigerated to about 30° F.

Tuna caught offshore are usually frozen at sea. Those caught inshore are often iced in the round (not eviscerated) on the vessel. Many of the small inshore tuna boats make use of refrigerated holding coils to reduce the ice losses during long trips.

Ice used on board ship must be clean and of low bacterial count, which calls for sanitary practices in manufacture, handling, and storing.

Enough ice must be used to cool the fish to about 32° and keep it cool. Ice does something else. As it melts, it washes off slime and bacteria, and prevents undesirable microbiological conditions in fish stored in the hold of the vessel.

About 1 pound of ice is required for every 2 pounds of fish.

Depending on the species, fish can be kept in ice without spoiling from 2 days to as long as 28 days.

When brought on shore, fish are stored in ice in refrigerated rooms not warmer than 35°, until they can be processed or distributed as fresh fish. Some ice meltage is desired to keep the fish washed with ice water. Ice is used to keep the packages of fresh fish chilled until they are sold.

The fishing industry uses a great deal of refrigeration, and a lot of it is in the form of ice.

Heaviest usage is by Pacific coast fishers and for shrimp.

The annual catch of fish and shellfish by U.S. vessels off our coasts and on the high seas is about 5 billion pounds valued at almost $400 million to the fishermen.

About half the catch is used for food, and the balance principally for fish meal and oil.

If ice was used on board vessel at the ratio of 1 pound per 2 pounds of fish, the 2.6 billion pounds of food fish would have required 650,000 tons of ice.

Loss of ice from melting on board the vessel before use, and other refrigeration required would increase the refrigeration to perhaps 1 million tons. Another 400,000 tons of ice would be needed during distribution.

The refrigeration for food fish would then total approximately 1.4 million tons of ice. (A ton of refrigeration represents the cooling obtained from melting a ton of ice and is equal to 288 thousand British thermal units.)

To freeze fish on board ship, as in the tuna fleet, about 44,500 tons of refrigeration would be needed. To supply refrigeration to the holds of the albacore fleet would require 1,500 tons.

To cool precooked tuna prior to cleaning and packing canned tuna would require more than 600,000 tons of refrigeration.

About 285 million pounds of fish, crab, and shrimp are frozen annually, requiring approximately 145,000 tons of refrigeration.

Without counting refrigeration required to store the frozen product, an estimate can be made that the fishing industry uses 2.2 million tons of refrigeration annually to protect fish from spoiling and convert it into a less perishable frozen or canned product.

The meat industry as we know it today could not have developed without refrigeration. Prior to the Civil War, meat slaughtering houses used little refrigeration. They were located in the centers of cities where the meat could be consumed.

As livestock production along the Atlantic seaboard proved inadequate for eastern cities, animals were driven on the hoof to markets. Cattle and sheep withstood this method of transport better than hogs.

When railroads were built, connecting the West with the East, a heavy traffic developed in freighting live animals in stock cars to the East.

Fresh meat could be shipped considerable distances in the winter, but summer temperatures were too high even for curing meat. Curing everywhere was a winter operation. Ice was being experimented with to permit summer curing, but refrigeration was not practiced until the early 1870's for this particular purpose.

The Pennsylvania Railroad in 1857 insulated 30 boxcars with sawdust and installed iceboxes in the doorways. These cars were later remodeled by suspending the iceboxes overhead at either end, and they were used for transporting meat.

The Davis Refrigerator Car was patented in 1868 and 1869. It was cooled by ice and salt in tanks which could be refilled from the roof. It became one of the most widely used cars of the early days. Successful shipment of fresh meats from

Chicago to Boston in 1869 in the Davis car inaugurated the dressed beef industry.

The Michigan Central Railroad experimented in the early 1860's in transporting fresh meat from Chicago to the East, using boxcars with ice bins built above the floor at each end.

Experimentation with refrigerator cars on a commercial basis was to a large extent by meatpackers and fruit shippers and receivers.

The meat business was growing fast, and Swift had moved his New England packing business to Chicago. Railroads were not anxious to build refrigerator cars for dressed meat. They were satisfied with the returns from transporting live animals in stock cars.

Meatpackers were forced to purchase their own cars, and even today they own a small fleet of refrigerator cars. Improvements were made to provide lower temperatures in the cars.

By 1881 the business of shipping dressed beef from Chicago to the East had become well established.

Ice refrigeration was nowhere more important between 1860 and 1890 than in meatpacking.

Ice was used in transporting meat and to cool it as well as to preserve it in the packing plant.

Some meat was frozen using ice and salt mixtures.

The meatpacking industry, concentrated in Chicago, brought the cold storage warehousing industry there also. They developed together, making the transfer from ice refrigeration to mechanical refrigeration about 1890.

Today, the same requirements for the refrigeration of meat prevail as did 100 years ago.

Body temperature of a beef animal at slaughter is around 102° F. After slaughter and continuing for 30 hours or more, changes occur that generate heat.

Temperature of the deep round part of the carcass is about 105° F. when the carcass enters the chiller. To prevent spoilage the carcass should be reduced to 35° F. as rapidly as possible. In practice, after 20 hours of cooling, surface of the carcass will be 35° to 45° F. and the deep round about 60° F. Cooling will be completed in the holding cooler.

Beef is chilled in rooms held at 32° to 34° F., at 90 to 95 percent relative humidity. About 25,000 British thermal units (B.t.u.'s) would be required to cool a beef carcass of 500 pounds from 102° to 35° F. (A ton of ice, in melting, produces a ton of refrigeration, absorbing 288,000 B.t.u.'s.) This calcuation is based on the average specific heat — heat capacity compared with water as 1.0 — of meat as 0.75.

With other sources of heat to be considered, like heat leakage and heat generated by fan motors, the refrigeration requirement could well be 20 percent greater or 30,000 B.t.u.'s. This would amount to about 60 B.t.u.'s per pound of meat cooled.

Chilling of hog carcasses follows much the same pattern as beef. The specific heat of pork is somewhat less, 0.57 instead of 0.75, and the carcasses smaller, averaging 180 pounds compared with 560 for beef.

Present practices require chilling to an internal ham temperature of 37° to 39° F. overnight. Temperature at time of slaughter varies from 100° F. to considerably higher. The refrigeration requirement may not differ much from beef in view of possibly higher initial temperatures.

In cooling lamb carcasses, the objective is to reduce slaughter temperatures of 98° to 102° to 34° to 36° F. in 12 to 14 hours, and to hold the carcass at these temperatures until shipped. Approximately the same chilling procedures are followed for calf cooling.

Humidity and air circulation are controlled in meat cooling to avoid drying the carcass too much and to avoid forming moisture on the carcass, which promotes bacterial growth.

The packinghouse may provide refrigeration for holding the beef carcasses for aging or the hog carcasses for cutting.

Total slaughter of meat in 1964 as reported by *The National Provisioner* was 31.8 billion pounds.

The breakdown by species was cattle, 16.4 billion pounds; hogs, 14.1 billion; calves, 600 million; and sheep and lamb, 700 million.

Total dollar sales of meat was about $14.6 billion.

The 1963 census records 2,992 meat slaughtering and processing plants to handle the 31.8 billion pounds of meat. . . .

William Taylor in the 1900 Yearbook of Agriculture traces development of the fruit industry in this country and in other parts of the world with the coming of refrigerated transport.

In 1800 there was no important fruit industry in the world other than growing grapes in Europe for making wine. As late as 1871 there were only a half dozen fruiterers in London and all they offered for sale were lemons and oranges and local fruit in season.

The potential in climate and soil for fruitgrowing was the same as today. But rapid and regular transportation and refrigeration were lacking.

As steam was applied to ocean transport and railroads during the middle 1800's, orchards and vineyards expanded. Railroads penetrated the interior of North America and Australia and opened up new fertile regions. California became perhaps the most conspicuous example in history of the rapid growth of a fruit and vegetable industry.

One of the first cold storages built in this country was for fruit. It was constructed in 1856 by the Rev. Benjamin Nyce, preacher, teacher, and chemist of Decatur County, Ill.

Ice was placed overhead in an insulated bunker with a metal floor which made the ceiling of the room. Warm air rising from the product was cooled by the cold ceiling and became heavier, providing air circulation by gravity. Calcium chloride was placed in the room to lower the humidity.

A ventilating fan was installed to bring in outside air. It was powered by a windmill.

Later, Nyce abandoned the idea of ventilation and made the rooms as tight as he could, using metal lining and beveled, tight doors. He had the idea, then considered foolish, that a buildup of carbon dioxide given off by the fruit would make apples keep for a longer period.

Use of airtight storages for apples was not perfected until many years later, in England by Kidd and West in the 1920's and in this country in the 1940's. In fact, the bringing in of outside air to provide ventilation had a heavy following in the early 1900's, and several systems were developed to gain benefits credited to fresh air.

By 1878 there were several commercial fruit storages. One in New York City and another in Chicago were chilled with ice.

The Western Cold Storage Co. of Chicago converted to a semimechanical system in 1866, using coils in the room through which ice-cooled brine was circulated. An ammonia compressor was installed in 1890 to cool the brine.

By 1901 there were 600 cold storage plants for fruits and other produce, using mechanical refrigeration and totaling 50 million cubic feet. All classes of cold storage space, including meat, amounted to 150 million cubic feet.

Refrigeration in transit was also developing fast in the late 1800's.

The first carlot shipments of fruit from California were made in 1869, consisting of 33 tons of pears, apples, grapes, and plums. The shipments were in nonrefrigerated, ventilated cars. These shipments were successful, thanks to carefully selected fruit from the foothill districts.

All shipments prior to 1888 were made in nonrefrigerated cars.

Refrigerator cars available in 1868 were intended for meat. They had about a 3,000-pound ice capacity. This was enough refrigeration for prechilled meat carcasses but not for warm loads of fruit. Early attempts to use these cars for peaches and berries failed because of decay development.

Parker Earle, by cooling strawberries before loading them into the car, was successful in shipping fruit from southern Illinois to Chicago, Detroit, and other northern cities in 1878.

Earle and Thomas in 1886 set up a business of fresh fruit transportation with 50 cars owned by the Detroit Refrigerator Car Co. operated over the Michigan Central Railroad.

The California Fruit Transportation Co. was subsequently organized to operate these cars. By 1891 they had about 600 cars operating in all parts of the United States.

The car was known as the Hutchins Refrigerator and was the first with ice bunkers holding 4 to 5 tons. Well constructed, the car had 4 inches of wool insulation, and was equipped with overhead ice tanks as well as end bunkers.

Other carlines were soon formed. Armour Packing Co., which had specialized in equipment for fresh beef, entered the fruit transportation field and became the dominant car owner.

There was no construction standard for refrigerator cars at this time and many were poorly made and gave poor results. Georgia peachgrowers in desperation appealed to the U.S Department of Agriculture for assistance. G. Harold Powell was placed in charge of investigations on picking, packing, cooling, and temperatures in transit in 1903.

Out of these studies came recommendations for a standard refrigerator car. The recommendations were put into effect in 1918 while the carriers were under Government control. The standards were updated after World War II, as a result of joint studies by the Agriculture Department and the Association of American Railroads.

Early work conducted by Powell in California with citrus fruits showed that careful handling during harvest and packing plus good refrigeration would prevent excess loss from decay.

Similar studies were made with Florida citrus and with peaches, apples, plums, pears, sweet cherries, and cantaloups as well as with other fruits and vegetables.

Intensive investigations also were made on precooling.

A precooling unit mounted on a railroad car that was owned by the Agriculture Department was sent into fruit districts to demonstrate how to prevent decay and overripeness by means of prompt cooling.

As a result of these studies and demonstrations, precooling plants were built by the fruit industry and the refrigerator car companies.

Later, portable fans were developed for car precooling. Still more recently, cars equipped with fans were built to use for precooling and to insure air circulation in transit.

Research was conducted on cold storage to determine the best temperatures and humidities for storing each kind of fruit and vegetable.

Diseases that cause serious losses in shipping and storing fruits and vegetables were studied. Market pathology laboratories were established in Chicago and in New York City to help the industry and the inspection agencies recognize the cause of losses.

Current research includes studies on controlling the proportion of oxygen and carbon dioxide in the storage atmosphere.

Today almost 1½ million carloads (30 million tons) of fresh fruits and vegetables are shipped each year by rail and truck in the United States.

About 35 percent are shipped by rail and 65 percent by truck.

It is difficult to find a fruit or vegetable among the 85 kinds listed in the United Fresh Fruit and Vegetable Association's guide to monthly availability that would not be refrigerated at some time of the year or at some step in moving it from the farm to the consumer.

The 20 most important fruits and vegetables are shown in an accompanying table. They differ in the temperature that is required for storing and shipping.

Bananas, lemons, unripe pineapples, tomatoes, sweetpotatoes, and winter squash suffer chilling injury if stored at temperatures below 56° F.

Avocados, some grapefruit, cucumbers, snap beans, and sweet peppers are injured by holding at temperatures which are below 45°.

Cranberries, potatoes, watermelons, ripe cantaloups, and some varieties of apples and oranges keep best in the range of 36° to 40° F. At 32° they are injured by chilling.

Florida-grown grapefruit, tangerines, and tangelos are stored at 32° F. even though some chilling injury may occur as a result.

This injury is preferable to decay that will develop at higher temperatures. Symptoms of chilling injury are pitting, internal discoloration and softening, off-flavors, and susceptibility to the development of decay.

Fruits and vegetables listed in the table that are not marked as susceptible to chilling injury keep best at 32° F. or at slightly lower temperatures. . . .

The commercial frozen pack of fruits during 1964 was approximately 702,000 tons, with citrus juices and strawberries the most important items. Frozen vegetables amounted to 1,320,000 tons. Potato products made up more than a third of the total. Peas, corn, broccoli, and spinach were other important items.

Over 2 million tons of refrigeration would be required to freeze 2,022,000

Annual Supply of Major Fresh
Fruits and Vegetables

Million Pounds

Fruits

*Apples	3,875
*Bananas	3,824
*Oranges	3,478
*Peaches	1,796
*Grapefruit	1,758
*Grapes	699
*Lemons	548
*Pears	529
*Plums, prunes	265
*Strawberries	265
*Tangerines	246
*Avocados	113
*Nectarines	95
*Pineapples	93
*Tangelos	81
*Cherries	76
*Apricots	38
*Cranberries	38
*Coconuts	35
*Blueberries	31
Total	17,883

Vegetables

*Potatoes	15,970
*Watermelons	3,119
Lettuce	2,921
*Tomatoes	2,400
Onions, dry	2,211
Cabbage	1,928
*Cantaloups	1,607
Corn	1,550
Celery	1,470
Carrots	1,304
*Sweetpotatoes	1,210
*Cucumbers	529
*Snap beans	473
*Sweet peppers	454
Radishes	350
*Squash	310
Greens, miscellaneous	253
Turnips, Rutabagas	233
Cauliflower	227
Onions, green	187
Total	38,706

*Suspectible to chilling injury.

tons of frozen fruits and vegetables. A rough estimate then for cooling, storing, shipping, and freezing fruits and vegetables would be 6 million tons.

The poultry industry is another very large user of refrigeration.

The Agriculture Department carried on extensive investigations to improve practices of handling and storing poultry, beginning about 1910. Miss Mary Pennington was one of the pioneers in this early work. Methods of killing, dressing, and refrigeration were gradually worked out.

Cooling in air and nonevisceration, or "New York dressed," was favored. Later, evisceration under careful sanitation practices and cooling in ice water became the accepted practice.

Broilers today are shipped thousands of miles from the large production areas of Georgia, Arkansas, Delaware, Maryland, Alabama, North Carolina, and Mississippi.

Poultry cooled quickly in special cooling equipment, packed in ice, and transported in refrigerated trucks and cars can be delivered in good condition more than a week after killing. The poultry will still have several days of shelf life if it is refrigerated in the retail store.

In the last 18 years the broiler business has shown a remarkable growth. Production in 1945 was 350 million birds and by 1964 it was 2.16 billion birds, amounting to about 7.5 billion pounds. Broilers are produced throughout the year in this country. Over 90 percent are not frozen.

The primary problem in refrigerating broilers is microbial deterioration. Lowering the meat temperature as near freezing as possible is the best protection against growth of microorganisms and chemical changes in the meat and the fat that affect color and flavor of the birds.

Internal temperature of the chicken after feather removal and evisceration is 70° to 90° F. The poultry should be chilled quickly to about 35° F.

Very few birds are chilled today in air. Cooling in a slush of ice and water under agitation is common, and several kinds of coolers are available to speed up the process. Water in the chill tanks and in the chillers must be kept clean.

Prolonged holding in chill tanks is avoided to keep the meat from absorbing large amounts of water.

The refrigeration requirement for poultry is about 0.7 to 1.5 pounds of ice per pound of poultry processed, with poultry chilling taking 0.4 to 1.0 pound, icing the shipping crates 0.25 to 0.35 pound, and icing trucks and trailers 0.05 to 0.15 pound.

A rough estimate of refrigeration used by the broiler industry to protect this perishable food would be about 7.5 billion pounds or 3.75 million tons of ice.

Most of the turkeys, ducks, and geese produced are marketed frozen and, of course, chickens are also frozen.

Freezing is the best method of preserving poultry meat for any long time, and excellent practices have been developed for fast freezing, packaging, storing, and distributing. Freezing in air at − 30° F., or in brine or other liquid at − 20°, and holding at 0° or below are recommended practices.

It is estimated that about 2.3 billion pounds of poultry are marketed frozen, with turkeys more than half the total. Frozen meals containing poultry are not included in this figure.

Using the rough estimate of a ton of refrigeration to freeze a ton of poultry meat, 1.15 million tons of refrigeration would be required for the frozen poultry business, not counting storage and transport requirements.

Eggs were preserved — although not very well — in water glass (sodium silicate), limewater, or by some other chemical means before refrigeration was available. In the 1880's ice refrigerated rooms began to be used for the storage of eggs.

Quality of storage eggs was not very dependable, for most came from small flocks on the farm. The farmer sold them to grocers. Egg merchants bought them from the grocers, often several weeks later.

The egg business continued to grow despite lack of quality control. By 1917, cold storage of eggs amounted to 7 million cases of 30 dozen each.

The Agriculture Department in 1913 installed a refrigerated egg packing establishment on wheels and sent it on long trips to the Midwest where farmers and dealers were shown how to care for eggs. They were encouraged to produce infertile eggs of lower perishability. Shippers were urged to chill eggs to 50° F. before loading into refrigerator cars.

Eggs were frozen commercially, beginning about 1900. After 1930 when cold storage holdings were 11 million cases, storage of shell eggs declined because of year-round production by commercial flocks. Frozen eggs came into greater use because of the growth of commercial bakeries and less baking in the home.

Annual production of eggs today is about 5¼ billion dozen. About 85 percent or 149 million cases are consumed as shell eggs. Cold storage of eggs is no longer large, seldom exceeding several hundred thousand cases. About 15 million cases of the total production of 175 million cases are broken commercially for frozen and dried egg products. Six percent of the production is used for hatching purposes.

Deterioration in shell eggs results from decomposition by molds and bacteria, changes due to chemical reactions, and absorption of flavors and odors from the environment.

If eggs are fertile, serious chemical changes take place at temperatures above 85° F. Commercially produced market eggs are infertile. As the egg ages, the white thins and the yolk flattens. Many different kinds of mold attack eggs.

Oil coatings are often applied to eggs within 24 hours after laying, to entrap the natural carbon dioxide in the egg. This helps retard aging and the loss of moisture.

Prompt cooling at the farm to 29° to 30° F. would give maximum protection, but condensation and resultant mold then is a problem. Cooling to 50° to 60° F. in air of 70 to 80 percent relative humidity is recommended.

Cold storage at 29° to 30° F. and at humidities of 85 to 90 percent are recommended, using the lower humidity if the eggs have been oiled.

Cooling 149 million cases of eggs consumed as shell eggs would require approximately 484,000 tons of refrigeration, if all the eggs were cooled 20°, say from 80° to 60° F.

About 360 million pounds of liquid eggs are frozen annually. Using again a rough estimate of a ton of refrigeration to freeze a ton of product, 181,000 tons of refrigeration would be required for this purpose.

The refrigeration required by the poultry industry is estimated as 3.75 millions tons for cooling broilers, 1.15 million tons for freezing poultry, and approximately 700,000 tons for cooling and freezing eggs, making a total of about 5.5 million tons.

Milk producers in colonial times knew milk would sour quickly in warm weather, but they did not know why.

Sultry weather and thunderstorms were directly associated with souring. Not much could be done to protect the milk except keep it in a cool place such as the well, cellar, or spring. About 1860 ice came into general use to preventmilk from souring.

As early as the 1840's milk was shipped from upstate New York by rail into the city. The Erie Railroad transported 3 million quarts of milk in 1842–1843.

Some farmers in 1849 were cooling milk in cans by stirring it with a tin tube filled with ice. In 1851 butter was shipped by rail in small iced containers. Ice refrigerated rooms were to be found in well equipped dairies in the Northern States in the 1880's.

Long distance shipment of butter and cheese to eastern markets from the Midwest began about the time refrigerator cars became available in the early 1880's.

On-the-farm cooling of milk, placing the cans in cold water or flowing the milk over cold metal surfaces, began to be practiced in the late 1800's and early 1900's as it became generally understood that low temperatures checked the multiplication of bacteria in the milk.

The Agriculture Department advised producers in the Northern States to harvest a crop of ice each winter for the summer cooling of milk.

Some cities prohibited entry of milk warmer than 60° F. Insulated jackets over milk cans helped prevent warming during the trip by wagon to the railroad receiving station. When milk reached the city for bottling, it was cooled to 45° to 50° F.

Butter churning moved from the farm to creameries where a more uniform, higher quality product could be made, largely through better sanitation and controlled temperature.

By 1915 mechanical refrigeration had replaced ice refrigeration in the large creameries. Butter storage became quite extensive.

During 1915, the first year for cold storage statistics, a total of 100 million pounds of butter were in storage by September 1, the peak of production.

Cold storage warehousing stabilized the dairy industry.

Cheese manufacturers found controlled temperatures the answer to the problem of curing cheeses of various kinds that had specific temperature requirements.

The present era of the dairy industry has seen the once widely used milk can replaced by stainless steel tanks, at the farm and on trucks and rail cars, for the bulk handling of milk.

Total milk production in 1964 was 126.6 billion pounds. Factory products accounted for 64.1 billion pounds, with butter, cheese, and ice cream the most important. Consumption of fluid milk off the farm was 52.9 billion pounds. Farm consumption made up most of the rest of total production.

Present day practices call for cooling milk to 38° F. within an hour after it is produced. Milk is kept cool in refrigerated holding tanks or cans at the farm and during its transport to the milk plant.

Since the plant seldom has capacity to pasteurize milk at the rate it is delivered, holding tanks often equipped with refrigeration are used. Some plants cool all milk received to about 36° F. before the milk is transferred to the holding tanks.

Before pasteurization, milk is separated and blended to provide the butterfat content which is desirable in fluid milk.

After standardizing, the milk is pasteurized by heating it to 145° F. and holding it at that temperature for 30 minutes. High-temperature-short-time pasteurization is now commonly used. In this method the milk is heated to 161° F. and held at this temperature for 15 seconds. It is then cooled to 40° F. or lower.

Cold milk to be pasteurized may be passed through a heat exchanger in which the cold milk is heated and the warm pasteurized milk is cooled. About 70 to 80 percent of the refrigeration which otherwise would be needed to recool the teurized milk can be saved in this manner.

From the pasteurizer, the cooled milk is passed to bottles or cartons. They are held in a storage room at 34° to 40° F. until loaded into refrigerated trucks for delivery.

If we assume that 80 percent of the milk production of 126.6 billion pounds is cooled from 90° to 50° F., and assign a specific heat of 1.0 to milk to allow for some inefficiencies in cooling, the refrigeration load would be approximately 14.1 million tons.

Milk marketed as fluid milk — about 52.9 billion pounds in 1964 — is heated to 145° or 161° F., depending on the pasteurizing process, and then it must be cooled to 40° F. or lower.

Assuming the milk is cooled a total of 100° F. and that the regeneration process of heating-cooling was 80 percent efficient, there would still remain about a 20° F. temperature reduction for which refrigeration would be required. This would take approximately 3.7 million tons of refrigeration, making a whopping total of 17.8 million tons for the milk cooling job before and following pasteurization.

Refrigeration is used in churning and storing butter, curing cheese, and to make ice cream, harden it, and transport it. These processes fall more into the field of manufacture and are not included in this chapter on how refrigeration protects the food supply.

Among the industries that developed to take care of the expanding perishable food business was the refrigerated warehousing industry.

By 1891, the industry had become large enough to have a trade association. The American Warehousemen's Association was formed in Chicago that year, consisting of 29 companies.

The U.S. Department of Commerce and Labor was requested to make a survey of cold storage plants. This was the forerunner of the report issued monthly since 1915 by the Agriculture Department on cold storage holdings of major perishable commodities.

Refrigerated warehouse capacity in 1963 was 1.1 billion cubic feet, excluding Alaska and Hawaii, representing a gain of 84 million cubic feet over the 1961 survey. Freezer capacity was 52 percent of the total. Per capita availability of space in 1963 of 5.88 cubic feet represented a gain of approximately 23 percent over 1943.

The perishable food industry depended on transportation and refrigeration for its development, with the refrigerator car playing an essential role. But the total number of refrigerator cars available has declined in recent years because much traffic has moved to trucks.

As of July 1, 1965, the breakdown of the refrigerator car fleet was 65,020 ice bunker cars of all types; 10,945 mechanically refrigerated cars of all types; and 2,360 express refrigerator cars. This makes a total of 78,325 refrigerator cars.

In addition, there are 32,645 insulated bunkerless cars for transporting canned goods and other commodities that don't require refrigeration but do require protection from freezing during cold weather.

About 5,000 mechanically refrigerated cars are on order, which will soon make a fleet of almost 16,000 cars of this type.

Refrigerated trailers transported on flatcars are also owned by the railroads. The total is 5,451 regular service trailers, 728 meat trailers, and 1,499 insulated containers.

Perishable freight traffic of foods and beverages for the railroads in 1963 amounted to 1.4 million carloads, totaling 34.7 million tons.

The 1963 Census of Transportation indicates that 1.2 percent of all motor trucks registered were refrigerated, or 152,700 vehicles.

About 20,000 were classed as 35 feet or larger, and 17,000 as 25 to 34.9 feet. These are the size used for between-city carload traffic.

Many of the smaller refrigerated trucks are used primarily for in-city delivery service. The most popular size was 10 to 15.9 feet, with some 73,000 vehicles representing about 48 percent of the total.

Trucks carry 65 percent of the frozen food traffic, and about the same percentage of fresh fruit and vegetables.

Most broiler production is transported in trucks, and most milk.

Refrigerated trucks probably move more than 65 percent of perishable foods from farm to market. Long distance hauling is more likely to be by rail than by truck.

A highly essential part of the cold chain for food is refrigeration in the retail store. Without it, there would be little business in perishable foods.

Most of the retail food business is done in supermarkets in this country. The United States has approximately 28,000 supermarkets.

A well equipped market has refrigerated display cases for frozen foods, meats and dairy products, fruits and vegetables, and a battery of reach-in refrigerators of milk, cheese, and other refrigerated products. It usually has a produce cooler and a meat cooler near the preparation areas for these commodities where the reserve supplies can be held.

The store is air-conditioned for the comfort of the customers and this, too, is beneficial to the perishable foods.

Temperatures recommended for display cases used for meat are 28° to 38° F. and for produce and nonfrozen dairy products, 35° to 45° F. Frozen food cases should maintain 0° F. and ice cream cabinets −12° F.

Restaurants and other firms that provide food services to the public have estimated sales of $20 to $26 billion, and rely heavily on refrigeration.

One meal in four is eaten away from home. Commercial restaurants make up 76 percent of the total annual sales. Clubs, airlines, schools, hospitals, and other institutions take care of the rest.

There are about 530,000 eating establishments in the Nation.

Recent surveys by *American Restaurant Magazine* indicated that all medium- to large-volume restaurants, serving 500 meals or more a day, had two reach-in refrigerators. Fifty-six percent had two walk-in coolers and 71 percent had ice cream cabinets. In addition, many had refrigerated beverage dispensers.

There were approximately 40,000 restaurants of this size. If each had two reach-in refrigerators of ½-horsepower size, a walk-in cooler of 1-horsepower size, and ice cream cabinets, milk cooler, and other fractional horsepower equipment that totaled 1 horsepower, a total of 3 horsepower or approximately 3 tons of refrigeration would be used. This would add up to just about 120,000 tons for medium to large restaurants.

The last link in the cold chain is the home refrigerator and freezer. The estimate for 1965 sales of new farm and home freezers is 1.1 million.

The 1960 census counted 9.8 million freezers in the 53 million households included in the census. This represented 18.4 percent of all the households. In the 5 years since 1960, with sales averaging over 1 million per year, consumers must have acquired almost 5 million homefreezers, making the total now over 14 million.

There are 9,900 commercial locker plants that are primarily engaged in provisioning homefreezers. The total 0° F. storage space controlled by consumers in locker plants and homefreezers is estimated at over 200 million cubic feet, capable of holding 6.5 million pounds of food.

It was expected that 4.7 million new household refrigerators would be sold in 1965. There is no current census estimate for home refrigerators in use. The last figure was in 1950 when the market was 80 percent saturated. In 1960 when the household market was estimated to be 90 percent saturated, there would have been 47.7 million refrigerators. Today the number is probably well over 50 million.

Manufacturers of refrigeration equipment have worked closely with the food industry, making improvements and supplying new kinds of equipment as the need arose. Requirements of the food and beverage industry once dominated the market and they still do if household equipment is included.

The value of total shipments manufactured by the refrigeration equipment industry in 1963 was $1.9 billion. This figure did not include household refrigerators or home and farm freezers. Packaged air conditioning made up $611 million of the total. It is not possible to determine how much equipment in the remaining $1.3 billion is used for food refrigeration.

If you take only commercial refrigerators and related equipment, $279 million, and add to it household refrigerators, $688 million, and home and farm freezers, $143 million, the total would be approximately $1.1 billion for food refrigeration equipment manufactured in 1963. This is almost twice as much as the value of packaged air conditioning equipment.

This is the story of the food refrigeration industry in the United States.

Links in the chain of refrigeration reaching from farm to kitchen are ice manufacturing plants, icemaking machines, milk coolers, vacuum coolers, hydrocoolers, poultry coolers, refrigerated warehouses, refrigerated trucks, refrigerated rail cars, walk-in and reach-in refrigerators, refrigerated display cases, locker plants, household refrigerators, and home and farm freezers.

The food industry uses over 20 million tons of refrigeration to chill and freeze fish, meat, fruits and vegetables, poultry, and eggs. The dairy industry uses an estimated 18 million tons just for cooling milk alone.

This country has 1.1 billion cubic feet of cold storage space, amounting to 5.88 cubic feet per capita.

The refrigerator car fleet totals 78,325 cars and 7,678 trailers for flatcar transport. There are approximately 152,700 refrigerated trucks.

Household refrigerators total about 50 million and home and farm freezers 5 million. There are 9,900 commercial locker plants. Manufacturing of refrigeration equipment for food is big business, amounting to an estimated $1.1 billion during 1963.

The future will bring new foods and new ways of refrigeration. Fresh quality will be captured by virtually instant cooling and freezing. It will be retained by continuous low temperature refrigeration. The variety of foods will continue to grow as fast transportation and refrigeration bring exotic foods to our markets from far-off places.

Food Marketing

From National Commission on Food Marketing, *Food from Farmer to Consumer* (Washington, 1966), pp. 91–103.

This chapter begins by identifying important factors influencing the behavior and structure of the food industry, for these are basic to explaining changes in the industry and its economic performance. The chapter then takes up topics particularly relevant to the Commission's assignment. It ends by appraising the industry's efficiency and progressiveness, farm-retail price spreads, the positions of farmers and consumers, and regulatory policies.
policies

The Market Orientation of the Food Industry

The Food industry and the agriculture that supplies it form a highly productive system in which obtaining raw materials or processing and distributing them ordinarily are not major difficulties. Efficiency in performing these functions is essential to business success, but increasingly the ability to develop and hold markets determines growth and profits of individual firms.

This shift of emphasis from production to selling is accentuated by the changing nature of the consumer market. As family incomes rise, consumers are less influenced by price and are better able to indulge their individual tastes, liking for variety, and desire for services. Changes in the role of women and in family living accentuate the importance of convenience in food preparation. The appeals that can be made to consumers in such a market are much more complex than offering basic foods at minimum prices. Skill in making successful appeals and in shaping consumer preferences is an important determinant of business success in several branches of the food industry.

Although other characteristics often are more important in determining conduct and performance in the food industry, the influence of the industry's market orientation is nevertheless extensive. It helps to explain why farm-retail price spreads for numerous foods are wide and increasing; why firms grow, often by merger and acquisition, beyond the size necessary to produce efficiently; the relative market power of various groups in the industry; the high rate of product innovation; and the survival of distribution methods that use labor and equipment wastefully.

Product Differentiation

Product differentiation is a leading means of gaining and holding a preferred market position. To the extent that a seller can convince consumers that his product is distinct from and in some respects superior to others, he has an element of monopoly in its sale. Successful product differentiation eases the necessity of competing strictly on a price and quality basis with competitors of approximately equal production efficiency.

Among manufacturers, brands backed by extensive advertising and sales promotion are the most common means of gaining access to consumers. New products are an effective form of differentiation, especially if they are genuinely original, useful, and not easily duplicated by competitors. But really new products are not easily created, and much product differentiation consists of minor variations in ingredients, shape, color, or the like.

Food retailers strive to differentiate their services from competitors' by advertising, giving trading stamps, offering prizes, or conducting games. Special sales at featured low prices are essentially promotions that tell little about the prices a consumer will pay for a week's food supply. Parking space, air conditioning, and attractive stores are examples of differentiating devices that, when widely adopted, provide useful services to the public. Retailers' brands succeed primarily because of their price appeal, but many retailers also regard private label as a means of differentiating their stores.

Advertising and Sales Promotion

Advertising and sales promotion are a significant reason for the substantial spread between farm and retail prices. In 1964, food corporations spent $2,172 million for advertising ($1,400 million on domestically produced farm products), and retailers spent $680 million for trading stamps. For the industry as a whole if not for each firm in it, these amounts were added to processing and distribution costs and became part of the food bill.

Amounts so added to the food bill were not entirely wasted. Consumers received premiums and other things of value for trading stamps and some other forms of sales promotion. Advertising helped to pay for television, newspapers, and magazines — and made publications costlier to produce. Whether this way of supporting the communications industry is good economic and social policy is outside the scope of a study of the food industry; but the costs added to the food bill are a reason for the size of the bill.

An unknown but substantial portion of advertising and sales promotion serves only to urge consumers to patronize firm A instead of B, or to buy brand C instead of D. It is highly unlikely that costs thus incurred add value to goods purchased by consumers. From the standpoint of the individual firm, however, the expenditures are warranted to hold or expand sales against competitors' similar efforts.

One function of advertising is an appropriate charge to the food bill — dissemination of information about products and prices. Consumers benefit from knowing what products are available, where they are for sale, and at what prices. A particularly significant case is the introduction of new products, discussed in the following section.

Two restraining influences on high selling costs tend to be generated within the food industry. One is the sale of retailers' label products, which are merchandised within the store rather than by extensive advertising. Retailers frequently are able to offer comparable quality under their own brands at lower prices and with more margin for themselves. Competition thus given to advertised brands is keen for staple, fairly homogeneous products, but has not been effective for a number of highly processed products.

The second restraining influence is the discount food store, which commonly gives no trading stamps and eliminates some services and amenities usually offered by supermarkets. Discount stores, operated both by chains and independents, are important in some local markets but have little influence in others.

Consumer grades, and to some extent standards of identity, are another restraining influence, although not one arising within the industry. The widespread use of Government grades in the retail sale of beef has been an important reason for the small amount of product differentiation. Consumer grading of foods is much less extensive than would be feasible.

New Products

The food industry has developed and successfully introduced many new products of undisputed value to consumers. The costs going into market testing and initial promotion for some new products have been high, as chapter 9 makes clear. Gaining rapid acceptance of a useful new product is beneficial to consumers and hastens the development of sufficient volume for low production costs.

There is a tendency for some new products to pass from an early stage in which prices and promotion are high to a later stage in which promotion and prices are lower. The second stage is reached when similar products are put on the market by other manufacturers and by retailers under their own brands. Then the product becomes a staple food, and consumer grading often would be feasible.

If price competition fully asserted itself at the second stage, the overall performance would be good. But some products show little tendency to pass from the first stage to the second. Even for products long on the market, prices of advertised brands often remain well above private label prices. In a Commission study of 10 such well-established foods as canned peas and frozen orange juice concentrate, retail prices of advertised brands averaged 21 percent higher than retail prices of retailer brands of generally comparable quality. Means of heightening price competition at the second stage, as by consumer grading, are desirable.

The proliferation of new products indicates that ample incentives exist for product innovation. The opportunity to differentiate products and to participate in a rapidly growing branch of the food industry has been a powerful magnet inducing firms to staple food fields — dairy products, flour milling — to diversify into convenience foods of all kinds.

The changing nature of the consumer market both invites and makes possible a gradual shifting from staple, fairly homogeneous foods to highly differentiated foods. Emphasis on advertising and sales promotion and new products will continue to increase. Retailers may use their own brands less exclusively for price competition and begin to adopt some of the brand promotion devices of the leading food manufacturers. Total selling costs will be a rising part of the food bill.

Concentration

Preceding chapters reveal high concentration in some segments of the food industry, especially in the various subdivisions of dry grocery manufacturing, and growing concentration in much of it. (High concentration is used to describe a situation in which the four largest firms in a field have more than 50 percent of the business.) Concentration would have increased more than it did in the past two decades if antimerger action had not been taken by the regulatory agencies. This is one reason why the increase in concentration has been greater when measured by the market shares of the top 20 firms than when measured by 4-firm shares.

Exceptions to the Rule

Growing concentration appears to be a dominant trend under ordinary circumstances, at least until the market share of the four or five largest firms becomes very large. The trend can be reversed for a time by major developments that shake up a branch of the industry or otherwise create unusual conditions. The meat packing industry provides an example. Plant location in the 1930's was uneconomic in light of truck transportation and the changing sources of livestock. Technology permitted new medium-sized plants to be more efficient than old, large ones. This opened opportunities for new entrants, who built plants in the livestock supply area, outcompeted some of the established giants (as meat packers' profit data show), and reduced the former high concentration in the industry. But once the industry has adjusted to this major upset, increasing concentration can be expected.

Concentration in poultry slaughtering apparently diminished in the 1950's as the poultry industry was reorganized and relocated by changes springing from new supply possibilities. But in the 1960's, concentration increased, and further concentration is likely in the future. Concentration in the freezing of fruits and vegetables declined while this industry was growing rapidly in the 1950's. In contrast, fruit and vegetable canning, a long-established industry, became slightly more concentrated during the same period.

Declining concentration in butter manufacture in the 1950's apparently had related, but somewhat different, explanations. Farmers' cooperatives are important in butter and have aimed at low margins; demand for butter has suffered from competition from vegetable fats; and the large dairy companies have shifted their investments to greener pastures. Even so, concentration increased slightly between 1958 and 1963.

In food retailing, the adoption of the supermarket has been substantially completed. The unaffiliated, one-store operators who were a source of new entrants into supermarket merchandising have greatly diminished in numbers. Although internal growth of the largest chains may not increase their market shares, incentives to grow by merger and acquisition are likely to lead to higher concentration in selling. Concentration of purchasing by retailers and wholesalers seems certain to rise.

Economies of Size

The smallest firms in most branches of the food industry, as in farming, are severely handicapped by inefficient size of operation. Continued decline in their numbers will contribute to higher concentration among remaining firms. But medium-sized firms commonly are, or can be, about as efficient in processing or physical distribution as the largest firms. They usually are entitled to cost-justified discounts for large-volume purchases. Little social gain in these respects is realized by replacing such firms by larger ones.

Advantages in selling — advertising, sales promotion, a sales force — frequently are gained by very large firms. National advertising is extremely expensive, and substantial discounts to large advertisers increase the difficulties faced by smaller competitors. Such advantages of large size do not have corresponding value to the public at large and are not persuasive reasons for accepting high concentration in the food industry.

Internal Growth Versus Merger

Growth through internal expansion and growth through merger or acquisition may have entirely different meanings for society. A firm that grows through superior efficiency, service to customers, or innovation, and which does not engage in predatory practices, has demonstrated a public benefit even though the benefit may not outweigh all other considerations. Mergers and acquisitions, however, do not necessarily demonstrate merit in the same sense. Important efficiencies may be gained, especially if both merging firms were inadequate in some way as originally constituted. But the merger or acquisition may represent the joining of two viable firms for reasons of little or no public benefit. Significantly, many of the small retailers taken over by the largest chains in the past 20 years were growing rapidly when acquired.

Effects of High Concentration

High concentration in the food industry is undesirable because it weakens competition as a self regulating device by which the activities of business firms are directed toward the welfare of the public at large. When a few large firms dominate a field, they frequently forbear from competing actively by price; competition by advertising, sales promotion, and other selling efforts almost always increases; and the market power inescapably at the disposal of such firms may be used to impose onerous terms upon suppliers or customers. The breakfast cereal field provides one of the clearest examples in the food industry: Four firms have 85 percent of the business; advertising and sales promotion amount to 19 percent of manufacturers' sales; retail prices of cereals rose more than other retail food prices between 1954 and 1964;[1] profits are nearly double the average for all food manufacturing; and entry of a new competitor would be extremely difficult.

Rising concentration of purchases by chain retailers, wholesalers, and buying groups of retailers limits the alternatives available to suppliers, induces suppliers to make inequitable concessions in order to get business, and makes competition among independent firms a less satisfactory way of organizing the supply industries.

Concentration among buyers tends to beget concentration among sellers. In fluid milk marketing, where the local nature of the market accentuates problems of concentration, dairy firms believe they must expand to bid for the business of large buyers — and then become bigger still, and more diversified, to bear the risk of losing a large customer.

High Concentration Not Essential

The food industry can have both high efficiency and reasonably low levels of concentration in national and regional markets. High concentration probably cannot be avoided in some local market situations. Even there, results can be generally satisfactory if other sellers or buyers can move in from adjacent markets to correct monopolizing tendencies.

Mergers among small firms, or by small with medium-sized ones, will often be necessary for efficiency and to maintain viable competitors. But if competition is to be an effective regulator of the food economy, high concentration must be prevented even in instances where specific, immediate restraint of trade cannot be identified. The most essential requirement for competition throughout the industry is to assure that a large number of substantial retailers compete in national markets for suppliers' products. Preventing horizontal mergers and acquisitions by the largest firms in each concentrated branch of the food industry is a minimal policy to assure that competition will produce results in the public interest.

Vertical Integration and Diversification

Much of the vertical integration in the food industry has had some basis in economies achieved by the new arrangement. This was true years ago when chains integrated retailing and wholesaling. Retailer integration into baking and fluid milk processing apparently has reduced costs of distributing these products from plants to retailers' shelves. Feed companies and processors that integrated into broiler production made savings by coordinating formerly independent operations and by rapidly exploiting new production methods. Feeding some cattle has helped packers to even out daily slaughter schedules, and savings in procurement costs may be significant.

In some instances, retailers have integrated into processing — or threatened to do so — to pressure other groups with substantial power into meeting retailers'

[1]Retail prices per pound increased 45 percent (A.C. Nielsen Co.), while the Bureau of Labor Statistics index of retail food prices rose 12 percent.

demands for changes in distribution methods or for private label products. Integration by suppliers into retailing has been attractive only in special circumstances, parly because a supermarket must handle a much wider range of products than any one supplier manufacturers.

Farmers' marketing cooperatives, a form of forward integration by producers, are especially important in fruit, vegetable, and dairy marketing. Farmers also have taken on marketing functions as individuals: Some fruit and vegetable growers have become shippers, some dairymen have gone into fluid milk distribution, and a few cattle feeders are full or part owners of packing plants.

Integration by marketing firms into farm production has been a factor — but not the most important factor — in shifting agriculture away from the family farm. Most fruit and vegetable production has moved out of the family farm class, but the ownership of some production by canners and shippers has had only an incidental part in the transition. The principal threat to the family farmer who feeds cattle is the large commercial feedlot, whether or not operated by a packer. The poultry industry has been the most dramatic example of a change in agriculture induced by vertical integration; but poultry production as it was before World War II would have been drastically altered in one way or another by the technology developed in postwar years.

Conglomerate Firms

Growth through diversification has been an outstanding trend in foods. Manufacturers have sought to get into the most rapidly growing parts of the industry by branching out into frozen foods, prepared foods, and convenience products in general. Manufacturers in the dry grocery field have developed highly sophisticated selling techniques and have sought to apply them to a widening range of products. The fact that unrelated foods — as well as soft drinks, detergents, etc. — were all sold through grocery stores and often could be handled by the same sales force or distribution facilities meant that some advantages could be gained by combining them in one firm.

Much of the diversification has been acheived by merger or acquisition, frequently of firms capable of competing on their own. Firms in such established fields as dairy manufacturing, meat packing, and bread baking have diversified into other lines more frequently than firms from other fields have diversified into theirs.

Table 20 shows the sharp rise in conglomerate-type acquisitions by large food manufacturers in the past two decades. Both food and nonfood firms were acquired. Acquisitions of firms engaged in later stages of processing or in distribution also increased; the relative importance of horizontal acquisitions declined. The data are especially influenced by the merger activities of dairy firms.

The size and diversity of the large food conglomerate give it great ability to survive its own mistakes or intense competitive struggles in particular product fields. It can engage in reciprocal trading arrangements not available to conventional firms. Food conglomerates are likely to grow, to reduce the number of independent competitors in the industry as a whole, and to lace the various segments of the industry more nearly into a single system characterized by the kind of nonprice competition in which they excel.

The highly diversified firm is often suspected of drawing upon earnings in one field to sustain losses in another until weaker competitors there are displaced.

The fact that firms are not required to report financial data by fields of operation gives conglomerates some advantage over their specialized competitors, and questions about playing one field against another go unanswered.

Market Power

Market power is the ability to influence prices or other terms of trade in a way favorable to the business firm. It may be gained through a firm's own strong position or conferred upon the firm by the weakness of those with which it deals. Two groups in the food industry appear to have substantial market power: retailers, including many of the small chains; and large manufacturers, usually diversified, with strong national brands.

Table 20. – *Number of acquisitions by type, 50 largest food manufacturers, 1948–65*[1]

Period	Total number of acquisitions	Horizontal	Vertical backward	Vertical forward	Conglomerate food	Conglomerate nonfood	Nonclassifiable
Number of acquisitions:							
1948–53	250	191	11	12	17	8	11
1954–59	434	254	13	36	77	39	15
1960–65	301	103	12	36	92	51	7
Total	985	548	36	84	186	98	33
Percent:							
1948–53	100.0	76.4	4.4	4.8	6.8	3.2	4.4
1954–59	100.0	58.5	3.0	8.3	17.7	9.0	3.5
1960–65	100.0	34.2	4.0	12.0	30.6	16.9	2.3
Total	100.0	55.6	3.7	8.5	18.9	9.9	3.4

[1]All acquisitions of firms in the same 3-digit SIC grouping as the acquiring firms were classed "horizontal." Probably this overstated the frequency of horizontal acquisitions.

Source: Records of the Federal Trade Commission.

Retailers

The most important source of retailers' market power is their direct contact with consumers. The retailer controls the shelves from which consumers make selections; when he acts as buyer, he is, in a sense, the purchasing agent for a large number of consumers. Because of the high productivity of agriculture and the food processing industries, eager suppliers press an abudance of products upon the retailer, and he is in a strong bargaining position.

The retailer's position is further enhanced by the great diversity of the items he handles. He must make a good impression with consumers on fastmoving, price-comparison foods, but he has some freedom to play down or do without items which he cannot buy on terms he considers satisfactory. Moreover, his inventory commitment is low relative to most suppliers'; only temporarily and selectively is he likely to have to cut prices to correct an overstocked position. Some suppliers, in contrast, carry large inventories and are weak bargainers when stocks prove excessive.

Large chain retailers gain strength from the number of stores they operate and the diversification of their business over many local markets. A difficulty in one store or one market will not be serious to the firm as a whole; price wars in single markets will be survived easily.

High concentration in a local market does not by itself give a retailer market power when he buys a product in the national market. But competitors in a concentrated local market are likely to adjust their respective selling prices so that costs they have in common are recovered in their gross margins. This is an important reason why retailers seldom absorb for long any large part of the nationwide prices increases or decreases for the products they handle.

The high concentration of purchases in national markets for retail sale is an important source of market power for chain retailers and group wholesalers. As the number of buyers is reduced, suppliers are under greater pressure to avoid losing the favor of their customers. But national concentration alone is not necessarily decisive in determining the relative bargaining power of buyers and sellers. For example, concentration among meat packers is higher than concentration among buyers of meat; yet retailers often seem to have more bargaining power than packers in transactions between them. The retailer's direct contact with consumers and his other advantages outweigh the difference in concentration.

Manufacturers With Strong Brands

The substantial market power of large, diversified manufacturers also stems in considerable part from their access to consumers. These manufacturers have gained their position by establishing strong consumer preferences for their brands by effective advertising and sales promotion. Consumer demand so generated often requires retailers to carry the manufacturers' products.

The size and diversity of many of these manufacturers give them the strength derived from large resources and the advantages of conglomerates in general. They have the ability to exploit developing market opportunities in a wide range of fields, can risk costly product innovation, and often can acquire small firms that seem in a good position to grow rapidly.

Other Market Power

Large size creates power for any food firm, at least power against exploitation by others. Firms that normally have no special bargaining power will acquire such strength if suppliers have excess capacity and are struggling for sales outlets at any price exceeding their direct costs. Small retailers frequently get free loans and similar concessions from fluid milk processors caught up in intense competition in local markets.

Unorganized farmers have no positive market power at all and depend upon competition among buyers to obtain the full value that market conditions justify for their products. Especially when products must be sold to buyers in a local market and the local buyers are few, competition may not be fully effective in achieving this result.

Trade Practices

A number of trade practices in the food industry are sources of conflict between buyers and sellers and sometimes become means of exploitation of one by the other. Price discrimination by sellers among customers is a persistent problem. Discriminations induced by buyers apparently are numerous, but are difficult to detect and to prove against the buyer. Discrimination among market areas is especially troublesome in the dairy and bakery fields. The dairy field is notorious for the frequency with which companies use loans, equipment, and less defensible inducements to obtain retailers' business; such practices are by no means confined to markets in which resale price fixing under State marketing orders prevents price competition.

Unwarranted rejections by buyers of fresh meat, fruits, and vegetables are frequently alleged. Rejections without cause do not seem to be widespread in meats, but the situation in fresh fruits and vegetables warrants concern. Rejection as a means of price renegotiation appears to be common.

In some producing areas, grower-shippers of fruits and vegetables handle other growers' produce under agency arrangements that are shot through with conflict of interest. Trading agreements are informal, and records are frequently poor. Situations may be complicated further by indebtedness by the grower to the shipper. Close supervision of trading practices is needed more in this segment of the food industry than in any other.

There is some evidence of abuses of buying power by distributors in procurement of private label merchandise. Small processors frequently are the principal private label sales. Buyers have succeeded in transferring costs and risks of carrying inventories to some processors without firm commitments to purchase. Costs of labels and special packs may also be absorbed by the processor. The low profits of the smaller fruit and vegetable canners partly reflect such pressures.

Kickbacks, special favors to buyers, and other forms of commercial bribery occur, although there is no way to measure their frequency. The Commission has had one glimpse of labor racketeering in the food industry.

Instances of deceptive advertising unfortunately offset some of the real information value to consumers that advertising should have. Packages, together with the pictorial and descriptive material on them, are sometimes misleading about the contents. Odd weights make price comparisons difficult more frequently than technical reasons justify. Reduction of package size is a common means of increasing price.

Except in sales to consumers, questionable trade practices almost always reflect the greater strength of buyers over sellers. This is one objective indication of the existence of market power and the direction in which it runs.

Changes in Marketing Channels

Direct movement of products through marketing channels has reduced the use of — and in some cases eliminated — terminal wholesale markets for fruits and vegetables and for livestock. Economies achieved by direct marketing have been the principal incentive for the change; further shifts toward direct sales are likely.

In livestock marketing, the system replacing terminal market selling itself seems to need revision. The number of local buying and selling establishments in the midwest is unnecessarily large and expensive to maintain; trading practices are difficult to regulate. Avoiding the cost of maintaining packer buyers may be one reason for more cattle feeding by packers in the future.

Terminal markets for livestock now have much more competition from other marketing methods than they did when present regulation under the Packers and Stockyards Act was developed. Some aspects of current regulation appear to be impeding their ability to compete. Changes in the act probably are needed to permit more flexibility in its administration.

The Pricing System

The classic function of price is to coordinate the activities of independent firms so that resources are used to satisfy the demands of consumers as expressed in the market place. While this role is still important, it is being modified in many significant ways; and the problem of getting adequate information about market prices is increasing.

In food retailing, the practice of offering items at special prices confuses consumers about what prevailing prices are, and some of the costs of retailing are shifted from frequently specialed foods to others. One-stop shopping by consumers reduces their sensitivity to prices of individual foods (unless featured), and weakens the pressure on retailers to keep every retail price aligned with the corresponding wholesale price. Higher incomes make consumers less willing to vary purchases in response to moderate price changes.

In the sale of meats, poultry products, and some other foods within the marketing system, buyers and sellers have gone increasingly to the use of formula pricing. The greater the volume sold under formula pricing, the less volume there is on which to establish genuine market prices. Vertical integration also draws volume out of price-making channels. Prices of products purchased on buyers' specifications sometimes are not quotable. The problem of "no price to quote" has reached a critical stage in broilers and eggs and is increasing in turkeys and dressed meat.

Prices of some manufactured foods, especially dry groceries, are strongly administered by sellers and play a minor role, as compared with that of advertising and sales promotion, in determining the volume of sales.

The decline of terminal markets has seriously detracted from their usefulness as sources of price information for fresh fruits and vegetables and for livestock. Livestock traders are paying increasing attention to dressed meat prices, but these markets, also, may become too thin to be reliable.

The widening price spread between farmers and consumers means that a given change in the farm price of a product has a smaller proportionate effect than formerly on the retail price. And consumers are becoming less responsive to changes in retail prices. Thus, a small oversupply at the farm must drive the farm price down sharply before consumers are induced to use the greater supply. Conversely, an undersupply at the farm, as for pork in 1965, will force farm prices to high levels.

As a result of closer trading relationships between producers and processors, together with unsatisfactory price information, some prices are being established well in advance of delivery in poultry and egg marketing. The use of forward pricing and production-period contracts may develop rapidly.

The shift from terminal markets to other distribution channels increases the difficulty of obtaining adequate price information for the Market News Service operated by the U.S. Department of Agriculture. More complete and reliable data could be obtained in some instances, and at lower cost, if buyers and sellers of substantial volume routinely reported prices and quantities to a Market News Office for prompt collation and publication.

Efficiency, Progressiveness

The food industry has been, and remains, progressive in most respects. Many new and useful products have been developed; processing methods have been improved in most branches of the industry. Physical distribution and warehousing of many foods have capitalized upon innovations in these fields. Management has been generally progressive in adopting new methods of inventory control, accounting, and the like. Retail stores are attractive, convenient, and afford a wide range of choice to consumers.

Change has left in its wake a number of firms that no longer have a place in food processing and distribution. They are too small for efficient operation, their plants and equipment are obsolete or poorly located, or changes in marketing channels have left them stranded. Some retail markets have more store space than the local volume of business justifies. As a broad generalization, however, the food industry does not appear to have more difficulties of this kind than might reasonably be expected in an industry serving a changing market, achieving progress, and thus undergoing constant reorganization.

Of the specific inefficiencies in the manufacture and handling of goods, several involve the distribution of products from the production plant to retail store shelves. Distribution of bread seems to be inordinately costly. A more efficient distribution system is resisted by most bakers and their driver-salesmen, which has been one reason for vertical integration into baking by large retailers. A somewhat similar situation exists in some fluid milk markets and for much the same reasons; resale pricing of milk under State marketing orders may also retard adjustments. Rack service for foods such as crackers and cookies is an expensive form of distribution. Involved in all of these is the desire of the supplier to manage the display of his product in the retail store to increase sales of his product.

A great deal of bone, fat, and waste meat is still shipped from packing plants to distributors' warehouses at unnecessary cost. Meat cutting in the backrooms of retail stores is more expensive than centralized cutting would be. If full economies were to be gained in this area, consumers would have to accept frozen meat, and some minor technological difficulties would have to be worked out. Field or central prepackaging of fresh fruits and vegetables is a similar potential improvement.

The substantial costs built into the price of food as a result of various forms of selling effort — advertising, sales promotion, expensive packaging, salesmen — are an important inefficiency in the food industry. Some of the costs are warranted for the introduction of new products and for providing consumers with information about conventional ones. But the only value received by consumers for most of these costs is the indirect benefit of premiums for trading stamps, free television programs, and the like. The power of such selling efforts reduces the role of price competition and thus moderates pressures on the industry to cut costs of other functions.

The industry is expected to be innovative in the future, as in the past. Inefficient distribution methods probably will give way irregularly to less costly ways of handling and delivering goods between the processing plant and store shelf.

Numerous painful adjustments lie ahead as inefficient or bypassed firms, many of them small, leave the field. While efficiency in performing physical functions increases, however, increased emphasis on most forms of selling effort will offset some of the effects of more efficient distribution on costs and prices.

Profits

Profits in the food industry were approximately in line with average profits in the economy at large in 1964. Corporate profits after taxes averaged 11.4 percent of stockholders' equity in all of private manufacturing, 11.3 percent in nondurable goods manufacturing, and 9.8 percent in the manufacture of food and kindred products. The First National City Bank tabulations for 1964, based on the larger corporations in industry, show profit rates of 12.1 percent for total trade, 12.5 percent for retail food chains, 12.7 percent for total manufacturing, and 10.7 percent for public utilities. Profits in food manufacturing rose between 1960 and 1964 but declined slightly in retailing.

Profit rates in 1964 in some branches of the food industry, especially in certain dry grocery lines, were well above average — large enough to indicate high barriers to entry and substantial ability to administer prices. The rate of return obtained by the 50 largest retailers was excellent for a low-risk field; the large food retailers almost never lose money.

Profits before taxes, as a percentage of sales, were about 4.7 percent in food manufacturing and about 2.3 percent in food retailing in 1964. Profits were not a large component of sales prices to consumers but were good in relation to stockholders' equity.

Farm-Retail Price Spreads

Three questions raised in chapter 3 were: Are the functions for which marketing costs are incurred necessary? Are the functions efficiently performed? Are profits reasonable? The foregoing discussions of efficiency and profits deal with these questions.

Unnecessary functions in the physical processing and distribution of foods are rarely performed. The major steps in moving products from farmer to consumer must be done, whether by a series of independent firms or one integrated firm. Usually the functions require labor, equipment, and other resources that can be obtained only by substantial cost outlays.

While some of the selling function — advertising, sales promotion, salesmen — is socially productive, most of the costs incurred to sway consumers toward one seller or product rather than another add little of value to the food consumers buy. The selling function could not be eliminated in most instances, but in principle, it might be substantially reduced without impairing the value of final products to consumers. This is the chief respect in which the necessity for an important function can be questioned.

Most functions are efficiently performed, if realistic standards are used as criteria. The inefficiencies of too-small operations usually reduce the earnings of the owners rather than adding to the farm-retail price spread. The chief example of functions inefficiently performed include the distribution of bread and, in less degree, milk; rack service for several grocery items; and the lack of centralized cutting of meat.

Profits are higher in some branches of the food industry than necessary to obtain capital. If the average rate of profit on net worth had been the same for the larger food corporations as for public utilities in 1964, however, the difference would have amounted to somewhat less than 1 percent of the retail value of total food.

Lower farm-retail price spreads would be possible (though means of doing this might be very difficult) without reducing services to consumers or unreasonably lowering earnings of the food industry. This is particularly true of a few products for which specific inefficiencies or unusually high selling costs have been noted. But farm-retail price spreads would remain high because processing and distribution are costly even when efficiently performed.

The manner in which a reduced farm-retail price spread might affect producers and consumers varies by product. When farm prices rest on price supports, as is currently true of grains used for bakery and cereal products, benefits would go largely to consumers. For products not price-supported, such as beef, eggs, or lettuce, benefits would be shared by producers and consumers.

Other Topics in Brief

The adjustment between domestic production and imports of food is constantly in flux, and the effects of imports are sometimes upsetting to the domestic industry. The most notable recent example was the increase of beef imports in the early 1960's, which reached a peak in 1963 when domestic production was rising sharply. Other examples are provided by the fruit and vegetable industry — mushrooms from Taiwan and early season vegetables and strawberries from Mexico. Investment of American capital in Mexican production has played an important role in the latter example. Except for such special situations, however, food imports have recently made a substantial contribution to the American food supply while creating only moderate and short-lived disturbances in the domestic market.

The effects of the termination of the bracero labor program at the end of 1964 were studied briefly but inconclusively. Data from published reports and Commission sources suggest that: (1) Labor difficulties and higher labor costs were encountered by numerous producers of the eight crops formerly most dependent on bracero labor; (2) farm marketings in principal States affected were lower and prices higher in 1965 than in 1964 for six of these eight crops; (3) the total farm value of the eight crops in these States declined 7 percent; (4) producers collectively received somewhat lower net income; (5) employment and earnings of domestic harvest workers rose; (6) secondary effects on processors and shippers occurred where volume or quality of production was materially reduced; and (7) the price, production, and income effects varied widely among crops, areas, and producers. Social effects were important but were not studied. Viewed in a longrun context, the termination of the program is hastening trends already underway — less use of foreign agricultural labor, mechanization of the fruit and vegetable harvest, and development of agricultural resources in Mexico. An industrial, high-income economy can best assure itself of remaining competitive in agriculture in the long-run by emphasizing what it does most effectively — the mechanization of production.

Demands for individual foods have been increasingly affected by public opinion concerning the healthfulness of particular ingredients and about insecticides, radioactive fallout, and similar matters. As the residual claimant to the consumer's food dollars, the producer is much affected by any changes in demand. Accurate information about the significance of food to health, and responsible dissemination of such information, is in the best interests of all concerned.

Position of Consumer

Much of what has been said about efficiency, progressiveness, and profits in the food industry applies to the position of the consumer. The principal criticism of the efficiency of the industry, in the broad sense of the term, is the cost devoted to selling efforts that yield little value to consumers. This point is closely related to the other principal criticism of the food industry from the standpoint of consumers: the difficulty they encounter in trying to buy so as to get the most for their money.

The difficulty takes numerous forms. Some advertising is misleading or downright deceptive; some package sizes and designs exaggerate the contents; essential information that should be contained in labels is often hard to find, illegible, or even missing; package contents may be in odd or nonstandard amounts for no technical reason, making price comparisons difficult; per-pound prices of the "large economy size" occasionally are higher than per-pound prices of smaller sizes; "cents-off" labels proclaim price reductions that may not be genuine; special prices create confusion as to what the going price is; not all products advertised as weekend features are sold at special prices; consumer grades are confined to a few products and are by no means uniformly used even for those; and standards of identity are lacking for many products. At little or no extra cost, consumers could be given more information; and the more skillful shopping this would make possible would more than offset any costs of providing additional information.

But consumers, themselves, must accept a measure of responsibility for the prices they pay and for the objectionable practices observed in the sale of food. Consumers are powerfully influenced by advertising and persistently pay premium prices for much-advertised brands when products of similar quality — sometimes the identical product — are available at lower prices. Impulse buying is common. For some, novelty is an end in itself. Children make a number of purchasing decisions.

Consumer education may modify buying behavior and deserves support. If consumers became highly skilled buyers, many of the objectionable sales practices would lose their effectiveness and disappear. Renewed emphasis on price competition would bring about further economies. The consumer is, indeed, a sovereign; but she is not, as she is so often told, an all-knowing, all-powerful, and fully-served sovereign.

Position Of Producer

Agriculture is in the midst of sweeping changes that exceed those occurring in food processing and distribution. Most of the changes originate within agriculture itself or arise from sources other than the food marketing system. Prominent among these is the technological revolution that is replacing manpower with machinery and equipment, raising crop yields per acre, and developing more productive livestock. Such changes are reducing the number of workers required in agriculture, increasing the efficient size for a farm, and transforming the farm into a business requiring skillful management, high technical competence, and large investment. The bulk of agricultural production still comes from family farms (in the sense that they employ no more hired than family labor), but some types of production, especially fruit and vegetable production, have moved, to a large extent, out of the family farm class. Probably a selective shift will continue, with the types of farming predominating in the midwest, east, and parts of the south being among the last to make the shift.

Impact of Marketing Changes

Procurement methods growing out of mass merchandising and substantial concentration of distributors' purchases have brought increasing demands to tailor farm production to particular standards, to produce in large volume, and to maintain a steady flow of products. These demands have added to forces already at work to increase the size of farms. In addition, they have brought many farmers into contractual or less formal arrangements with buyers who seek production to meet their specifications. Some farm production has been brought under the ownership of food industry firms partly for this reason — for example, some cattle feeding and egg production.

Integration into farm production by feed manufacturers, meat packers, fruit and vegetable processors, and other nonfarm firms has injected new capital into farming and hence has served to maintain or increase production. The effect has been to reduce or hold down prices and to intensify competition in agriculture. In some instances, the bargaining power of farmers may have been reduced by buyers' access to captive production.

Farmer Bargaining Power

Unorganized and unsupported farmers have had to depend upon the competitive bidding of buyers to receive the full market value for their products. If costs rose in the marketing system, the farm price usually was depressed until reduced production in relation to demand lifted prices at all levels of distribution.

Food industry developments pose more clearly than ever before the question of how farmers can obtain sufficient bargaining strength to defend their prices and other terms of sale. Group action is needed if any substantial changes in sales arrangements are to be made. But the scope and effectiveness of group action will be limited unless the groups have the means of planning production in advance, controlling the rate of their own marketing, and negotiating about price.

Farmers' cooperatives are already extensively engaged in marketing farmers' products. But, with some exceptions, cooperatives are not likely soon to be strong enough to make effective pricing and production decisions. Some form of governmental sanction for collective action will be needed, at least for a substantial period of time. Federal and State marketing orders and agreements are longstanding examples of instruments of this kind, although as conceived and administered they often have been weak or subject to serious shortcomings. But they provide a beginning for a more adequate means of firming up the market structure of agriculture where and while it is needed. One might regard such a device as a bridge on which portions of agriculture can cross from a state of disorganized production to a sufficiently firm structure that no further support is necessary.

Possibilities for effective group effort under the most favorable of circumstances appear to be restricted to the more specialized products — or, like fluid milk, ones sold in local markets. The widely grown basic crops, such as wheat and soybeans, are produced over so large an area by so many farmers that effective group action will be difficult to achieve.

Regulatory Practice and Policy

Controlling concentration in the various branches of the food industry is essential to maintaining a competitive environment favoring an acceptable distribution of market power and a socially useful employment of resources. A horizontal merger or acquisition by a large firm in an already concentrated field tends to break down conditions necessary for effective competition — perhaps in purchasing as well as in selling — even when specific restraint of trade cannot be demonstrated. An effective policy to limit concentration requires acceptance of the view that such general impairment of competition is a sufficient reason for vigorous antimerger action.

Further developments in the food industry are likely to strengthen further the position of retailers. Maintaining numerous competitive alternatives throughout the marketing system crucially depends on having a large number of significant buyers in national markets for farm and processed products. Thus, it is especially important to prevent further concentration of purchases by chain retailers, retailer buying groups, or wholesalers.

A second broad regulatory need is in the field of discriminatory practices. The availability of the "meeting competition" defense sometimes permits discrimination by sellers to continue even when serious injury is being done to the competitive position of one customer vis-a-vis another. Price discrimination often seems to be induced by buyers, but effective means of dealing with the problem remain to be developed. Discrimination through services given to customers is another area in which enforcement is difficult.

Trading in perishable farm foods, especially at early stages in marketing, needs special supervision because of the speed necessary in transactions, deterioration of products, and the frequent great disparity of bargaining power between buyer and seller. The U.S. Department of Agriculture is a reasonable place to locate responsibility for regulation of trade in these products, but administration of regulatory activities should be separate from the other activities of the Department. Most market structure and trade practice problems arising in markets for meats and dressed poultry, however, are of the type that the Federal Trade Commission and Department of Justice are best prepared to handle.

Regulatory agencies labor under handicaps of timing in dealing with mergers and trade practices. Firms need not give notice of forthcoming mergers or acquisitions. Temporary cease and desist orders cannot be issued to hold in abeyance proposed mergers or unfair trade practices. Both deficiencies should be overcome.

The various statutes — both general and specific — dealing with market power in the food industry collectively seek an equitable and workable distribution of power by restraining concentrations of great strength and by lending support to the weak. Antitrust laws are in the first category; the Capper-Volstead Act and the Federal marketing order program are in the second. Extension of policy in both respects appears desirable; but the policy should be conceived as an impartial effort to achieve an appropriate distribution of power rather than as a commitment for or against any group.

A Note on the Future

Prospective trends and developments are discussed at several points in this report. The implicit assumption in all cases is that food and agriculture in the future will operate in an economic setting developing naturally out of the recent past. But in mid-1966, two other possibilities cannot be ignored.

The first is that much expanded food aid to underdeveloped nations will place considerably heavier demands on the food production capacity of the United States. Carried far enough, this could relieve the chronic oversupply situation for agriculture, increase farm prices, and reduce the need for helping farmers to gain bargaining power. The impact presumably would be greatest on foods most needed for export. Vertical integration into agriculture might increase as food firms tried to assure themselves of supplies.

The second possibility is inflation arising out of high domestic demands on the economy plus demands growing out of the troubled foreign situation. In this case, costs of processing and distributing food would be caught up in the general advance of labor and materials costs. Probably farm food prices would advance as well. Consumers' concern about the food industry would focus even more sharply upon rising prices.

Neither development would substantiallly modify the need for the changes in policies, statutes, and services discussed in the following chapter, but the priorities to be given to them might change greatly.

The Broiler Industry

From H. R. Bird, "Chicken in Every Pot — the Broiler Bonanza," U.S. Department of Agriculture, *Yearbook*, 1968 (Washington, 1968), pp. 37–41.

Suppose you went to your favorite market to get a ready-to-cook broiler and found that it was marked 62 cents per pound instead of the customary 33 or 35. What would your reaction be? Astonishment? Unbelief? Rage? Yet 62 cents is about the "normal" price one would expect if broilers had followed the general trend of consumer prices in the last 25 years.

Why didn't they follow the general trend? Research has changed the broiler's genes, diet, family life, physical environment, life expectancy, and even his personality.

The young chicken may well be the most researched animal in this much-researched world.

Research workers and growers have done great things to the broiler, but they have not always been very successful in predicting what the broiler would do next. In 1938, I first visited the Delmarva Peninsula and became acquainted with broilers and broilermen. Every conversation eventually got around to "overproduction" and "low prices." Where would they find the people to eat all the broilers that they were producing?

Well, the total number produced in the United States in 1938 was 82 million. In 1966 it was 2.5 billion. The average price of live broilers was 17 cents per pound in 1938. It was 15 cents per pound in 1966.

In 1953, I served with a committee appointed by the American Feed Manufacturers' Association to estimate livestock numbers and feed use for the next year. The statistics indicated that broiler numbers in 1954 should be about 987 million. One member of the committee suggested we could get some publicity by being the first to predict a one-billion-broiler year. We squelched our colleague. We were interested only in an accurate prediction, not in publicity. But he had the last laugh. There were 1,048 million broilers in 1954.

In 1938, there was one major broiler area, the Delmarva Peninsula of Delaware, Maryland, and Virginia. In 1964, the 10 leading States in order of importance were Georgia, Arkansas, Alabama, North Carolina, Mississippi, Texas, Maryland, Delaware, Maine, and California.

In Delaware I was told that a major factor in the beginning of the industry in the 1930's was the success of Mrs. Wilmer Steele in growing broilers for the New York market. Wilmer Steele retired from the Coast Guard to join his wife in the broiler business and went on to become a leader in feed manufacturing, poultry processing, and banking in his area.

The low cost of modern broilers is not the sole reason for the great increase in consumption. There have also been major improvements in quality. About 1940, one writer stated: "A broiler is a scrawny, blue-looking object that tastes good in spite of its unfortunate appearance."

Why were they blue looking? Partly because they had no fat and therefore no yellow pigment in the skin. It was considered impossible to put fat on a young chicken. The other reason for the blue look was dark pigment in the skin of the dark-feathered broilers.

All the early broilers were Barred Plymouth Rocks, with black-and-white barred feathers. Then the general-purpose red-feathered New Hampshire breed was developed by Andrew Christie and other New England poultrymen. These birds excelled in growth rate and efficiency, but the industry still clung to barred feathers. They crossed Barred Rock males with New Hampshire females to produce fast-growing barred-cross birds. But the New Hampshires were big boned and angular, and even well-fleshed birds sometimes looked scrawny when they were dressed.

The big increase in consumption of broilers during World War II convinced industry leaders that there were still greater opportunities for expansion if better quality birds could be produced. Under the leadership of Howard Pierce of the Great Atlantic & Pacific Tea Co., Inc., a series of Chicken-of-Tomorrow Contests was held, with the financial support of the A. & P. Co. Breeders submitted samples of eggs which were hatched at a central point. The chicks were reared to broiler weight, slaughtered, dressed, and scored for growth rate, efficiency, viability, fertility, hatchability, and dressed grade, including a grade for conformation (shape or build).

The New Hampshire could provide everything except conformation. The Chicken of Tomorrow had to have a broad breast and thick drumsticks. One needed only to look in the Standard of Perfection to find the model with the right conformation. It was the Cornish. But for years the Cornish were reputed, more or less accurately, to grow slowly and inefficiently, to feather slowly, to lay poorly, and to have low fertility and hatchability. A combination of the good qualities of New Hampshire and Cornish seemed like a good approach to the Chicken of Tomorrow.

However, some breeders concentrated on improving the White Plymouth Rock from the standpoint of growth rate and conformation.

National contests were held in 1948 at the University of Delaware and in 1951 at the University of Arkansas. For the award ceremony in 1951, the principal address was given by Vice President Alben W. Barkley. Dr. Lewis Webster Jones, president of the University of Arkansas, presided, and Governor Sid McMath welcomed the visitors — including a congressional delegation. But the man of the hour was Charles Vantress of Live Oak, Calif. His Cornish-New Hampshire crosses had won the first national contest in Delaware, and they repeated their victory in the second. In 1940, the Vantress Poultry Breeding Farm was almost unknown beyond the boundaries of its own community. With the impetus of the two victories, it quickly grew into one of the largest international poultry breeding operations.

Today's broilers are produced with maximum efficiency by crossing two strains having different characteristics. The strain furnishing the female parents must lay well and hatch well to produce broiler chicks efficiently. Of course, its growth rate and conformation are important, too. In the strain furnishing the male parents, the breeder puts primary emphasis on growth and conformation, letting egg production and hatchability be secondary.

Male broiler lines derive mostly from Cornish and New Hampshires. The female lines are derived mostly from White Rocks.

But even a modern broiler, with his genes all properly arranged, doesn't grow very well on an old-fashioned diet. We tried this at the University of Wisconsin in 1957, feeding male broiler chicks a diet that was recommended in 1907, one that was recommended in 1932, and one that was recommended in 1957. At 9 weeks of age, the average weights of the three lots of chickens were 0.6, 2.0, and 3.2 pounds, respectively. The pounds of feed required per pound of gain for the three groups were 5.2, 3.0, and 2.0. In the 1930's, broilers reached 3 pounds in 14 weeks on 4½ pounds of feed for each pound of gain. Now 3-pound broilers are grown in 8 weeks with 2.25 pounds of feed per pound of gain.

Research on vitamin D by Hart, Halpin, and Steenbock at the University of Wisconsin in the 1920's made production of poultry independent of sunshine and permitted it to move indoors. The Wisconsin investigators developed feeds containing corn, wheat byproducts, meat meal, milk byproducts, alfalfa meal, minerals, and cod liver oil. Early broiler feeds were of this type, and most of the time they were satisfactory. But knowledge of the chick's requirements was sketchy, and nobody knew much about the normal variation in vitamin content of feedstuffs. Vitamin deficiencies were rather commonplace.

Information on nutritive requirements accumulated rapidly, and in 1947

Scott, Singsen, and Matterson developed the Connecticut Broiler Formula, based largely on research on the requirements published by the Universities of California, Cornell, Texas A. & M., and Wisconsin and the U.S. Department of Agriculture. By using synthetic vitamins, the Connecticut investigators were able to reduce the levels of wheat byproducts and increase the corn, thus raising the energy content of the feed. Higher energy levels made it possible to put some fat and yellow color into the skin.

Broilers need protein, too, but we never had enough protein to feed our livestock properly until 1957. We achieved sufficiency by an enormous increase in production of soybeans and soybean meal. Formerly, soybean meal was considered unsuitable for chickens, but research revealed how to supplement it with vitamins and minerals, and it is currently our major source of protein.

The last step in supplementing soybean meal was taken in the USDA laboratories at Beltsville in 1946 when we showed that soybean meal plus an unidentified vitamin from cow manure was as effective as animal proteins. The unknown vitamin was shown to be formed in manure by fermentation. In 1948, vitamin B_{12}, isolated in the laboratories of Merck and Co., proved to be identical with the "cow manure vitamin." Soon it was being produced in large quantities by more esthetic fermentations.

In 1950, Stokstad and Jukes of American Cyanamid Co. were experimenting with a fermentation residue from the production of the antibiotic, chlortetracycline, to determine its effectiveness as a B_{12} supplement. They found B_{12}, but they also found another growth-promoting substance which turned out to be the residual antibiotic which had not been completely removed in processing. Low levels of antibiotics in feeds improve growth and conversion of feed to broiler. Use of anitbiotics since 1950 has saved an estimated 3 million tons of broiler feed. Even with use of the most sensitive methods available, no antibiotic can be found in the meat of broilers fed low levels of antibiotics.

Before World War II, broilermen tried to keep the death loss below 10 percent. Today a grower can't stay in business unless he can keep death loss below 5 percent. Lloyd and D'Armi of the University of Delaware showed that average mortality in commercial flocks in Delmarva in 1952 was 7.2 percent. In 1962, it was 3.67 percent. Formerly, the biggest killer was the group of diseases called coccidiosis, caused by several species of microscopic parasites that attack the chicken's intestinal tract. These diseases are still a problem, but they are quite effectively controlled by drugs called coccidiostats. Other important developments in disease control were vaccines against fowl pox, Newcastle disease, and laryngotracheitis.

Since 1950, antibiotics have been used to control Mycoplasma infections. Progress is being made in eliminating these diseases by testing breeding stock and slaughtering reactors.

Through a similar testing program, carried on by the National Poultry Improvement Plan, pullorum disease was largely eliminated from chickens even before the broiler industry began its rapid growth.

In 1938, in order to minimize infections, most broilers were grown in houses that were 20 by 20 feet. Such a house accommodated about 500 broilers. As methods of disease control improved, producers began to experiment with larger houses. Now most broiler houses are 40 or 50 feet wide. Ventilation is more difficult if they are wider. Length seems to be limited only by the amount of money the builder has or can borrow. Some new houses are windowless with "controlled environment," including heating and cooling systems.

So today's broilers have different genes, different diets, different family life, different life expectancy, and different environment than their predecessors. I mentioned earlier that the broiler's personality also has changed. Growers used to explain the 20 by 20 house partly as a disease-control measure and partly as a means of preventing piling up and minimizing cannibalism. An unaccustomed noise might cause a whole population of broilers to pile up in a corner with many deaths resulting, or an epidemic of cannibalism might occur; and the greater the number of birds per unit, the greater would be the losses.

Today's large broiler houses may have a few partitions or they may not. I have seen at least 40,000 broilers in one pen. Neither the 40,000 broilers nor their owners seemed concerned about piling up or cannibalism.

Perhaps the geneticists, besides getting rid of the scrawny blue look, have also eliminated some of the broiler's antisocial tendencies.

Or perhaps the better diet and better physical environment have reduced tension and frustration.

Broilermen worry about prices, about the number of chicks the competitors are starting, about viruses, about feed supplies, and about the merits of different coccidiostats, and ventilation systems.

The broilers just keep rolling along, increasing in numbers, and producing tastier drumsticks and white meat faster and more efficiently.

Mechanized Tomato Production

From Raymon E. Webb and W. M. Bruce, "Redesigning the Tomato for Mechanized Production," U.S. Department of Agriculture, *Yearbook* (Washington, 1968), pp. 103–07.

A redesigned tomato plant and its fruit have played a highly significant part in streamlining the mechanization of tomato production, harvesting, and handling.

Development of tomato varieties suited to mechanized harvesting was concurrent with harvester design and development. G. C. Hanna and associates at the University of California, Davis, first conceived the idea that tomatoes would some day be harvested by machine. In 1947, Hanna began developing a variety able to withstand the rigors of machine harvesting and bulk handling.

Early efforts indicated no current variety possessed the relatively small-vine stature, concentrated fruit set and ripening period, and pliability of fruit needed to pass through a machine with little or no fruit breakage. Fruit of the large-vined variety, San Marzano, withstood simulated machine harvesting and was used as a parent in combination with early-maturing, soft-fruited, small-vined varieties. The small pear-type variety, V Red Top–9, was developed. Though of little commercial value, it was useful in performance trials of the machine.

By 1959, Hanna had developed for simulated harvest by machine numerous strains sufficiently uniform in vine type, concentrated profuse fruit set, maturity, resiliency of fruit, quality characteristics, and ability to "hold" for 30 days or more on the vine without deterioration. A large number of these were harvested by the prototype mechanical harvester in 1960.

From similar trials with the harvester in 1961, varieties, VF 145A and VF 145B, were released to seedsmen and growers. These two varieties, and subsequently selected varieties, are the foundation on which California tomato growers of about 180,000 acres have been able to almost entirely mechanize harvesting and handling of the crop.

Strains of the VF 145 group and the variety with elongated fruit, VF 13L, released in 1963, comprise almost 90 percent of the acreage planted to tomatoes in California in 1967.

A few years after Hanna started working on varieties that might be mechanically harvested, C. Lorenzen of the University of California initiated work on a tomato harvester. By 1962, both the machine and the plant were ready to go. Subsequently, the U.S. Government in 1964 refused to extend the provision of Public Law 78 by which foreign nationals were allowed to come into this country to help with crop production and harvesting.

As a result, tomato harvesting machines became all important almost overnight. The harvested acres of tomatoes for processing, which had dropped more than 20 percent in 1963 due primarily to a labor shortage prediction, began to regain these losses and to show some increase. By 1966, the tomato harvester had eliminated about 3.5 million man-hours of labor annually.

There is considerably more to mechanizing tomato production than just the harvester. Like all crops that are successfully mechanized, the real success of the project must go back to the plant, and indeed, even back to the seed from which the plant comes and the soil in which it grows. Machines are not made to harvest crops; in reality, crops must be designed to be harvested by machines.

It is the plant breeder, working with the engineer and many other agricultural scientists, that makes for a completely mechanized crop production system. There are few instances of completely mechanized crops where breeding and cultural practices have not had a hand in the venture's success. And there are no instances where the system cannot be improved upon by a step-by-step analysis and evaluation of each variable in the system by all branches of agriculture that are concerned.

Generally, the pressure is almost wholly on the engineer at the start to design a machine to harvest a given crop. However, in the case of tomatoes, Hanna had foreseen the need for tomato varieties that would lend themselves to mechanical harvesting and handling several years prior to any design work on the harvester. He envisioned a small, tough-skinned tomato whose plant would "set" a majority of its fruit over a short period of time, but that would hold the fruit while waiting for harvest. To a remarkable extent, these goals have been accomplished although, as with all crops, improvements will continue.

Nor has quality been forgotten during this period. Today there are many plant breeders crossing and recrossing lines to produce that one perfect product. Such a perfect product is a goal and is not envisioned in the immediate future.

However, in the newer varieties, breeders have maintained at a high level such quality factors as flavor, color, acidity, and product properties. Improvements are anticipated in the overall quality of tomatoes and their products that will be measured with more sophisticated equipment and techniques. Thus, fruit from large numbers of breeding lines will be rapidly evaluated for the many traits that influence quality and consumer acceptance.

Breeders and horticulturists alike have had a hand in increasing yields. In 1940, the average yield of tomatoes for processing in California was between 6 and 7 tons per acre. More prolific strains and better fertilization and cultural practices have raised this average to over 20 tons per acre, and fields that yield over twice that much are not uncommon.

In commercial practice today, fields are largely planted with seed directly and generally thinned to the desired plant spacing. However, there are some cases when precision seeding has minimized the need for extensive thinning.

The seedbed must be carefully prepared to avoid clods, allow for irrigation, and present a level bed under the plant for best harvesting results.

Plant population is a major factor affecting yield. In some California studies, 30,000 to 50,000 plants per acre have given good results although many plantings are in single rows 4½ to 5 feet wide, spaced 6 to 9 inches in the row, resulting in populations of 12,000 to 20,000 plants per acre. Twin-row production, or the planting of two rows close together, requires more precision and closer management; however, the results of skips and blank areas are minimized, giving a better utilization of cropland. This method is usually recommended where soil and weather conditions account for smaller plants.

Fertilization and irrigation are important for successful mechanization of the harvest. Both materially affect the "machinability" of the crop, bulk handling capability of the fruit, and the quality of the product for processing. Growers have learned the need of a fertilization program based on an extensive soil-testing program.

All the phosphorus and potash where needed are either spread uniformly on the soil surface and worked in as the soil is prepared for planting or placed in the early active root zone at planting time. Nitrogen is either applied at seeding time or a portion applied then and the remainder in a band below the soil surface and between the rows just prior to plant thinning. This program of fertilization insures an optimum supply of nutrients for early seedling vigor and continuous growth through the fruit setting and subsequent development period. An oversupply of nutrients, particularly of nitrogen, will cause excessive vine growth, cyclic setting and ripening periods, lower fruit quality, and will increase certain fruit disorders.

Irrigation practices have been developed that insure continuous growth of the tomato seedlings through the fruit-setting stage. Once the crop potential has been established, irrigation is used only to size the fruit and maintain plants in a healthy condition until 3 to 5 weeks before harvest.

Through this general procedure, growers have been able to maximize the percentage of ripe fruit in a harvestable condition at the time the field is scheduled for picking.

Handling tomatoes from the harvester and transfer to over-the-road trucks still constitutes a production bottleneck. Lugs that held approximately 30 pounds each and served as picking containers, as well as containers for over-the-road transportation, are no longer economically feasible. Even pallet boxes holding approximately 25 lugs that are transferred from field conveyances to over-the-road transportation are being replaced by over-the-road trucks that are field going also. There is less handling of the individual tomato by this method, and transfer stations are no longer needed. The firm, tough-skinned tomatoes, a product of advanced breeding developments, take such treatment with little damage so long as the proper depth allowances in the container are not violated and hauling distances are not too great.

And yet tomato harvesting machines and techniques are still in their infancy. Improved machines are coming off the assembly line each year. In 1966, some 800 machines picked almost 70 percent of the California crop. With four major manufacturers now producing machines, and others entering the field so fast it is hard to keep up with them, it is expected that more than 80 percent of tomatoes grown in the United States for processing will be harvested by machine in 1968.

Still, the job is far from finished. When tomatoes start coming off these machines in such profusion, bottlenecks occur which were never dreamed of when the bracero (imported field-worker) was spending long backbreaking hours at this dirty, menial, and seasonal task. Moving the tomatoes from the harvester, transporting them to the processing plant, and handling the increased volume at the plant over a shorter period of time are examples of problems that have yet to be solved. Add to this machinery breakdowns and newly introduced cultural practices which are parts of the same problem and you get a picture of a new concept in farm production requiring laborers with higher skills, entirely new lines of machinery, and growers who are not just agriculturists, but farm managers in every sense.

So, with the momentous start that has been made toward streamlining tomato production and harvesting through the foresight of two investigators at the University of California in the late forties and early fifties, immeasurably helped by a labor shortage and a demand for increased production, necessity has again become the mother of invention.

With these developments have come problems as well as benefits that will employ the best minds of plant breeders, horticulturists, and engineers for many years to come.

The New Wheats

From Louis P. Reitz, "Short Wheats Stand Tall," U.S. Department of Agriculture, *Yearbook*, 1968 (Washington, 1968), pp. 236–239.

Short wheats have brought new hope to millions who depend upon this time-honored food grain.

The opportunity for increased production associated with this new plant type has had a worldwide impact upon wheat breeding, management, and production.

World War II was over. The Nation had performed valiantly in producing food to support the war and the peoples of ravished countries. But crop yields remained low. Additional use of fertilizer was one of the key yield stimulants. How could fertilizers be used to stimulate wheat yields in the United States and abroad? Fertilizer made the plants grow taller, but the plant's energy "went to straw" — not to grain. Their support structure collapsed, and yields were often depressed rather than stimulated.

S. C. Salmon, an Agricultural Research Service scientist helping Japan get back on her feet, observed in 1946 that Japanese farmers were growing a number of remarkably stiff, short-stemmed wheat varieties. These, when fertilized heavily, remained erect to maturity and gave excellent yields. Dr. Salmon first saw Norin 10 at the Morioka Branch Station in northern Honshu and tells about it this way:

"It had been seeded in rows approximately 20 inches apart in accord with the Japanese practice and on land that had been heavily fertilized and irrigated. In spite of these very favorable conditions for vegetative growth, the plants were only about 24 inches high, but stood erect. They produced so many stems and there were so many heads, a second look was necessary to verify the fact that the rows were 20 inches apart instead of the common 6 to 10 inches in the United States."

He brought 16 varieties of this plant type to the United States, and, through the Department's regular seed introduction and evaluation program, they were made available to breeders at seven locations in 1947–48. One called Norin 10 is the best known and most widely used in breeding programs. Orville A. Vogel, ARS wheat breeder in Washington State, was the first to recognize its worth and to use it in a breeding program.

Norin 10 was an odd dwarf. The stems were very short, scarcely half as tall as most of our varieties, but the heads where the grains form were normal in size. On such short stems the heads appeared large indeed. The plants had as many leaves as normal plants. The straw was very strong. Norin 10 was unsatisfactory for direct use on farms outside of Japan. However, successful use of it in crossbreeding work triggered a revolution in wheat culture which has reached clear around the earth.

The word "Norin" is an acronym made up of the first letter of each word in the romanized title of the Japanese Agricultural Experiment Station. The numerals are selection numbers; hence, we have Norin 10, Norin 33, etc.

We have recently learned more about the pedigree of Norin 10 from Dr. Torao Gotoh, Ministry of Agriculture and Forestry, Japan. It includes two varieties introduced from the United States: Turkey Red and Fultz. The original cross was Fultz x Daruma which hybrid in turn was crossed to Turkey Red. Daruma means a kind of tumbler doll in Japan, and the name was applied to a group of several varieties native to the country. The final selection from the last cross was made at the Iwate-Ken local wheat-breeding station located in the northeast section of Japan. Norin 10 was registered in 1935.

Crossing this dwarf with the U.S. varieties posed problems. Many of the flowers were male sterile and crossed promiscuously with adjacent plants. Timing mechanism of the wheat sprout was triggered wrong; it began unfolding before it reached the surface of the warm loose soil of the Palouse area. Norin 10 seemed susceptible to all of our diseases. Years of intensive selection and development were needed. When at last the most serious problems were solved, a new variety, Gaines, a winter wheat, was developed which, in its habitat of the Northwest, has set world record yields — one of 209 bushels to the acre. Fertilizer could be applied, and the plants would remain erect.

Long before Gaines was born, news of the new short-strawed germ plasm reached Norman E. Borlaug, a Rockefeller Foundation research scientist in Mexico. He obtained some of the early crosses and breeding lines from Vogel in 1953. Crossing these lines with Mexican and Colombian wheats, he combined the required adaptation and disease resistance with the short straw. A series of spring wheat varieties were developed including Pitic 62, Penjamo 62, Sonora 63, Sonora 64, Lerma Rojo 64, and Mayo 64. A semidwarf durum variety, Oviachic 65, has been released.

Certain of these varieties and related ones from Colombia and Chile are also adapted to similar latitudinal zones in many countries. They are being used in Afghanistan, Bolivia, Paraguay, Guatemala, Ecuador, Peru, Tunisia, Libya, Sudan, Kenya, Rhodesia, Jordan, Pakistan, India, Turkey, Israel, Nepal, and the United States. Perhaps 14 million acres were seeded to the Mexican wheats in the 1967–68 crop year. They are furnishing breeding stock to many countries to develop varieties more perfectly adapted to local needs. Improvement programs in some countries have reached a point where Mexico is now receiving new varieties from them. If current plans succeed, Pakistan, for example, will be self-sufficient in wheat production by 1970. Vast potentialities are available to those countries that wish to capitalize on short wheats.

Gaines and a similar improved variety called Nugaines, both bred by Vogel, produce straw as much as 18 inches shorter than standard varieties in the Pacific Northwest. In low rainfall areas, the difference may be only 4 inches. The grain yield records made by these two wheats have broken all those previously established; hence, to exceed 100 bushels to the acre is commonplace in Washington, Oregon, and Idaho where the varieties are best adapted. About 2¼ million acres were seeded to these varieties in the United States for harvest in 1968.

Vogel finds semidwarf varieties use nutrients and moisture more efficiently than other wheats. Applications of nitrogen fertilizer 25 percent higher than normally used give good results. He says they have a higher yield potential because they respond to higher moisture and nutrient situations, and they produce more seeds per plant than other varieties. He is not sure whether this is because more stems are formed or because more seeds are in each head. Several plant characters need to be in balance.

When one looks at a field of Gaines, the crop appears thick on the ground, and the heads are heavy with grain. Even longtime wheatgrowers are surprised by the outpouring of grain from the combine when Gaines wheat is being threshed.

Gaines and — to a lesser extent — Nugaines have been tested in all parts of the United States and in the major wheat areas of the world. They have limitations in many areas because they are winter wheats and may not head out unless the seedlings are subjected to a period of cool weather. They are late in maturity and suffer attacks from some diseases, insects, and severe winter cold. Even in their home territory, all is not always favorable. The thick canopy of growth creates a good environment in the field for development of rusts, mildew, leaf spots, and, worst of all, foot and root rots.

Vogel and his colleagues have taken up the challenge and are searching the world's wheats for resistant kinds to use in stabilizing the new level of productiveness found in the semi-dwarf wheats. Until they succeed in their breeding work, or find some other means of control, producers will not consistently realize from their efforts the maximum potential in the semidwarfs.

It took 20 years for Borlaug and his colleagues to do the impossible. Results of the research done by this Mexico-U.S. team enabled Mexican farmers to treble their country's average wheat yield and boost their total tonnage sixfold. Mexico became self-sufficient in wheat production. The separate factors making this happen were rust-resisting new varieties including semidwarfs, new land brought into productivity under irrigation, vastly extended use of fertilizer, weed and insect control, timely tillage, and proper seeding methods. The most important factor was the will of the research team and cooperating farmers.

Within the 20-year period, more than 30 new varieties were bred and released to Mexican farmers. Three phases can be seen here on variety development:

● Early success in stem and stripe rust control in more or less traditional types of varieties. This "control" was and continues to be a tenuous matter because rust races may change in an area. In Mexico, a change in stem rust races occurred six times between 1943 and 1965, and each required new varieties with necessary resistance.

● Shorter, stiffer-strawed wheats based upon minor genetic factors accumulated from many sources to reduce the straw length was the second phase of development.

● Semidwarfs based on Norin 10 which were both shorter stemmed and more responsive to chemical fertilizer than any varieties ever observed before was the third and climactic phase. Three years after semidwarfs were widely distributed, 95 percent of the acreage in Mexico was seeded to them.

Among the semidwarfs, and some other wheats also, it was discovered that an important new dimension had been obtained. Some of these varieties were very widely adapted. They grew well in Mexico where days were about 12 hours long year around; they also grew well where days were 15 hours long. No wheat grows well in the humid tropics; however, the Mexican and Colombian wheats have turned in superb performances around the world in the drier and irrigated portions of the equatorial latitudes to about 40° N. and 40° S. These wheats have little or no frost hardiness so they cannot be safely used as a fall-seeded crop where winterkilling is a factor as, for example, in Kansas or Virginia.

What of other areas in the United States? Semidwarf germ plasm has been included in wheat breeding projects in all parts of the United States. Arizona workers developed the semidwarf Maricopa variety for the irrigated areas of the State. In New York, workers at Cornell developed a short-straw white winter wheat called Yorkstar. In North Carolina, Blueboy, a soft red winter wheat variety, was bred. Utilizing a Korean short parent, Seu Seun 27, Texas workers developed Sturdy, a semidwarf hard red winter wheat for use in the irrigated and high rainfall area. Semidwarf durum wheats are being experimented with in North Dakota. Semidwarfs have been tried in other States, but they have been found deficient in several vital properties including hardiness, disease resistance, or grain quality.

It is incorrect to imply that the Japan-Korean germ plasm is the only source of shorter, stiffer straw. Monon, Lee, Wells, Parker, and Ramona 50 are improved short wheats that have been developed, respectively, in Indiana, Minnesota, North Dakota, Kansas, and California.

And perhaps nowhere in the world have stiff, short-strawed wheats been developed which surpass the Italian wheats. Some of these, incidentally, have Japanese wheats in their ancestry.

The short wheats from Vogel's and Borlaug's breeding programs did something to people that was perhaps more important than mere development of plant forms: They challenged men to hope for and achieve new plateaus of food production. The specter of hunger was dimmed yet a little while. They showed that entrenched conservatism can be swept away, that people do change, and that war, pestilence, famine, and disease are not man's only recourse to bringing food production and population into balance.

Frozen Foods

From J. G. Woodroof, "Frozen Foods — New Techniques," U.S. Department of Agriculture, *Yearbook*, 1968, (Washington, 1968) pp. 267–71.

From field to dinner table, frozen foods have won a place for themselves. Farmers grow varieties of plants just for freezing. Equipment has been developed exclusively for harvesting, handling, processing, storing, and hauling frozen foods. Eating establishments routinely use hundreds of frozen food items. The housewife uses frozen foods in most of her meals.

One of the secrets in frozen food quality is quick freezing. The trend in preparing, storing, and using frozen foods has been to use lower and lower temperatures. This increases the rate of freezing, reduces labor costs, better retains the quality of food, and adds certain conveniences to using.

Before 1928, meats, fish, strawberries from the Northwest, and a few other foods were bulk "sharp frozen." The washed and graded products were packed in barrels or other large containers and placed at 0° F. until they froze. This kept them from spoiling and preserved the "freshness" fairly well — that is, better than heat-processed foods and those that laid on the fresh produce counter for several days. From many hours to a week was required for the foods to freeze solid. Much of the processing took place after the product was thawed.

"Quick freezing" was applied to products frozen in a half hour or less and was begun about 1929. This required smaller containers and closer contact of the food with the refrigerant. For quick freezing, foods were prepared for the table, frying pan, or broiler before being packaged. This eliminated waste and added maximum convenience.

The most commonly used quick-freezing method is by placing filled consumer-size containers of food between metal plates at −40° F. Freezing begins almost immediately and is complete in an hour.

A second way is by placing consumer-size containers of food on trays and subjecting them to a blast of air at 0° to −40°F. About twice as long is required to freeze packages by air-blast as on cold plates, yet the difference in quality of product frozen by the two methods is not great.

In the homefreezer, prepackaged foods are quick frozen on cold plates in the freezing compartment and in cold air in the storage compartment. Here again, the difference in quality is negligible for either method.

A third way of quick freezing is spreading such products as peas, beans, berries, diced carrots, and shrimp on a wire mesh belt and slowly moving them through a freezing tunnel at about $-40°$ F. The individually frozen product is scraped off the belt and packaged in bulk or in consumersize containers.

An improvement of "belt freezing" is "fluidized freezing" in which a current of cold air is passed upward through the metal belt, lifting the product off the belt, and causing it to tumble and freeze in air. This not only produces quick freezing, but prevents the individual pieces from sticking together and allows each piece to freeze equally from all sides. Freezing is so quick there is little drying.

Cryogenic freezing is freezing with liquid nitrogen ($-320°$ F.), liquid or solid carbon dioxide ("dry ice" at $-109°$ F.), liquid air, or other low-temperature refrigerants. These refrigerants have been used for holding and shipping frozen foods in a limited way since about 1928, though the product seldom reached the refrigerant temperature.

However, about 1960 commercial installations for cryogenic freezing became available. And since 1965, fleets of trailers on the highways, "piggyback trailers" on railway flatcars, and insulated railway cars have been equipped with liquid nitrogen facilities. Operational installations tripled in each succeeding year.

Increased experience, widening availability of liquid nitrogen and carbon dioxide, rapidly dwindling costs, and more stringent laws regulating the temperature of frozen foods favor cryogenic freezing. Besides freezing foods rapidly, it quickly reduces the temperature of entire loads of foods while in transit.

Freezing foods very quickly has several advantages qualitywise. Succulent vegetables like green beans, asparagus, and okra, and fruits with delicate texture like whole strawberries and sliced pineapples and peaches, have much firmer texture with greatly reduced leakage of juices when frozen very rapidly. Freezing by cryogenics produces qualities in most frozen foods that are closer to the fresh state than any other process now being used commercially. This applies to the appearance, color, and palatability of these foods. Nitrogen is inert and does not react with the product or with its constituents.

These advantages make it practical to freeze many products previously considered unsuitable for freezing. Products that are or may be frozen by this method include such hitherto unlikely candidates as whole peeled bananas, avocados, pineapples, fresh mushrooms, green peppers, onion rings, watermelon, and tomatoes as well as a wider variety of seafoods including lobster, scallops, flounder fillets, and raw and cooked shrimp. One plant in Florida froze more than 15 million pounds of shrimp with liquid nitrogen in 1966 and an even larger quantity in 1967.

Shrinkage during freezing by cryogenics may be under 1 percent, less than with any other freezing method.

The cost of freezing with liquid nitrogen or carbon dioxide is initially 3 to 5 cents per pound, which is high compared with 1 cent for sharp freezing. But an advantage is being able to save a shipment from possible total loss while in transit.

With cryogenics, freezing may be complete or just "case frozen" (freezing the outside very quickly and allowing the inside to freeze more slowly). Complete freezing, by reducing the temperature in the center of each piece to that of the freezing medium, is seldom accomplished. This is because more time would be required, no appreciable difference in quality would result, and the berries, peas, or other particles would likely break due to the sudden expansion of the centers.

Possibly the highest quality frozen produce is produced at the lowest cost by "case freezing" the outside of each piece with liquid nitrogen, and allowing the inside to freeze by a slower and cheaper method, such as fluidizing.

Liquid nitrogen systems have almost entirely eliminated potential hazards from mechanical failure in transportation. Special trailers are designed to handle four tanks of liquid nitrogen. These are serviced from 500-gallon supply stations across the Nation. This system provides delivery of frozen foods to any point in the country in the best condition at the lowest cost. In many cases, mechanical units on trailers supply the regular needs while liquid nitrogen is used for quick cooling purposes.

Some foods do not require instant freezing. The differences in quality due to method of freezing vary with the products.

For many, and perhaps most products, the physical differences between instant and slower frozen products is not markedly apparent.

In products such as candies, fruit cakes, precooked meats and vegetables, and prepared meals, the differences are virtually nonexistent. In candies, there are no cells to rupture, and in precooked products, the cells have already been altered by cooking. In fruit cakes, the high sugar concentration protects the tissues from damage.

One may not need to go to "instant" freezing to obtain all the quality improvement practical in the home or commercial operations. In most cases, an excellent product can be had by using a generally available freezing temperature ranging from $-10°$ to $-40°$ F. and giving more attention to other factors relating to quality.

Often more important than the method of freezing are factors like variety, maturity, method of preparation and packaging, and kind and shape of package.

One of the main reasons for freezing foods quickly is to minimize microbial spoilage. This is especially true with precooked foods that must pass through a warm zone between cooking and freezing. Fruits that are not heated may mold or otherwise deteriorate if freezing is delayed. Quick freezing is very important in preventing microbial spoilage of cooked foods like meat pies, fowl stuffing, and meat and vegetable dishes.

In freezing, the rate of heat removal is important, not the temperature of the freezing medium. Widely different rates of freezing may occur at a given temperature, depending upon whether the product is packaged or is loose, the density of the product, the rate of the airflow, and the amount of metal contact.

Because of the short harvesting season for peas, green beans, corn, lima beans, and diced carrots, large amounts of these vegetables are frozen loose and bulk packaged in portable bins (tote boxes) holding about 1,300 pounds. The bins are made of corrugated fiber or plywood boards and lined with polyethylene film sheets. They are placed close to the freezer, and the frozen vegetables travel directly from the freezer to the bins through 6- to 8-inch tubes. The plastic sheets are folded over the product, which is stored for later packaging into consumer-size packages. Some plants freeze up to 10,000 pounds of vegetables per hour, for holding in portable bins.

During the slack season, peas and green beans from the Northwest, corn from the Midwest, carrots from Texas, and lima beans from California can be packaged together. Strawberries, cherries, and raspberries are sometimes repackaged also.

Advantages of bulk freezing are:

● The products are hurriedly prepared and frozen at the peak of the season and stored for subsequent packaging.

● Packaging and labeling are done at slack seasons, thereby equalizing the labor load.

● Special packs of mixed vegetables or mixed fruits can be prepared throughout the year on demand.

● The transportation of bulk frozen products from one section of the country to another is cheaper and requires less space.

● The same grade of frozen products can be packed and distributed under separate labels.

A disadvantage in bulk freezing and storage is that double handling into and out of storage is required.

Low labor and costs are provided by frozen prepared entrees packed in 12- by 20-inch disposable aluminum steamtable pans. Each pan holds 18 pounds of food. Shipped two pans per carton, they are the same size as conventional steamtable pans and can be set right on the serving line. Entrees include chicken fricassee, turkey a la king, sliced turkey and gravy, sirloin tips and gravy, individual meat loaves, beef stew, sliced beef and gravy, and spaghetti sauce with meat.

In a few hours, one or two persons can prepare and set up for serving enough food for hundreds of customers.

Small freezers with as little as 6 cubic feet of storage space and requiring floorspace of 27 by 27 inches are available in stainless steel, maple-top, or under-counter models. They operate on 115 volts, but have no moving parts.

More than 2,000 frozen food items are on the market, and they are increasing constantly. Where formerly each kind of vegetable, fruit, meat, or fish was frozen separately, they are now cooked and combined into many dishes, dinners, or trays. There seems no end to the possible combinations of frozen foods.

Some of the frozen prepared dishes that have recently appeared on the market are crabsticks, cocktail deviled crabs, deviled crabs, fried clams, fried soft-shell clams, stuffed flounder, stuffed peppers, whipped sweetpotato casserole, apple crisp, 1-, 2-, and 5-pound packs of meat loaf, macaroni and cheese, oven-baked beans, barbecued beef, beef stew, sliced roast beef with gravy, Italian beef, sage dressing, meat ravioli, veal parmigiana, pork liver, chop suey, and chili con carne.

In addition, there are dozens of kinds of pies such as chicken, meat, turkey, cherry, apple, apricot, and others.

Containers for frozen foods must protect the product from drying out (freezer burn) and discoloring by oxidation. They must also be of suitable material for cooking and serving the food in the package. Most vegetables are frozen in boil-in bags that can be cooked and served directly from the bags. Meat pies, TV dinners, and casseroles are completely prepared, seasoned, and frozen in metal trays so they can be cooked and served from the freezing containers. Ease of cooking without waste, and convenience of serving without leftovers, is accomplished by innovations in frozen food containers. . . .

Farming by Regions, 1969

From Donald D. Durost, "Where Food Originates: The Farmer and His Farm," U.S. Department of Agriculture, *Yearbook,* 1969 (Washington, 1969), pp. 8–14.

Few of us ever stop to think about how much food we eat in a year. And, probably, even fewer of us ever consider how much our more than 200 million Americans eat. You may find it hard to believe, yet each of us eats nearly three-quarters of a ton every 365 days! This amounts to nearly 3 tons a year for a family of four and a whopping 150 million tons to feed us all. It's the job of our farmers and commercial fishermen to provide most of this. The rest, around 10 percent of our total food, is imported from countries around the world. . . .

Production of all this food is not planned by some central agency. It is the result of 3 million sets of decisions made by 3 million farmers. It is they who decide what crops and how many acres of each will be produced. And a declining number of our farmers have been able to supply ample food for a constantly increasing population.

Our 50 States have a total area of nearly 2.3 billion acres, with about half of this taken up as farms. Forests and rangeland take another third and parks and wastelands, such as the western desert, about a sixth. The rest, only about 55 million acres, or a mere 4 percent, is used for our cities, towns, roads, and airports. Although farms take up a fair share of our land, there's still enough left that can be used for producing more food when it's needed.

Our farms come in different sizes, produce different kinds of food, and are managed in different ways. They fall somewhere between the extremes of small family farms with a few cows and chickens, a pig or two, a garden, and a few acres to raise food to sell, and the very large farms of a thousand acres or more, owned by individuals, cooperatives, or corporations and operated by managers and hired labor.

Accordingly, a farmer may run his own small farm or a 320 acre spread where he raises grain and livestock. He may be a cattleman who owns a small farm and rents a thousand acres of range country. He may be a man who operates a big farm for someone else, or a sharecropper with a few acres. Yet in our country, farming is the only major industry where family groups make up the largest share of the labor force. Farmers and their unsalaried family members constitute almost three-fourths of the 5 million workers on farms. Only about a million are paid workers.

In addition to differences in size and the kind of employees, farms also differ in what they produce. Some grow fruits and vegetables, some produce livestock and poultry, and still others produce cotton and tobacco. Though some crops and live-stock are produced in all parts of the country, the kinds and amount vary somewhat be region. Soil conditions, climate, and even how far it is to the nearest or best market influence decisions on what and how much to grow.

If we travel around the country, we find that the Northeastern States — from Maine to Maryland — and those bordering on the Great Lakes — from New York out to Minnesota — are the Nation's principal milk-producing areas. Climate and soil in these States are suited to raising grains and forage for cattle and for providing pastureland for grazing. Broiler farming has become important in Maine — and from New Jersey to Maryland. The half million farms in the Northeast and Lake States, which average about 190 acres each, provide 17 percent of our farm products.

The some half million farms a little farther south in the Appalachian region — West Virginia to North Carolina, Kentucky, and Tennessee — are somewhat smaller in size, averaging only 122 acres. Though these farms produce commodities such as peanuts, cattle, and milk, their main product is tobacco.

Going still farther south along the Atlantic Coast, farms start getting a little larger again. About a quarter of a million farms averaging 220 acres each are important for cotton and broilers. Some vegetables, such as sweetpotatoes, are grown in this area along with peanuts. And, of course, there are the big Florida citrus groves.

Traveling west to the Southern Delta States — to Mississippi, Louisiana, and Arkansas — we find another quarter of a million farms about the same size as in Appalachia, that concentrate on raising cotton. Some rice and soybeans are also grown and livestock is being produced in larger numbers than formerly.

As we turn and go north, we come to what is frequently called the "bread-basket" of America. The eastern part of this is known as the Corn Belt and the area a little farther west as the Great Plains.

The Corn Belt, extending from central Ohio to the Nebraska border, is a region with rich soil, good climate, and sufficient rainfall for excellent farming. And, its 643,000 farms provide nearly one-fourth of our food supply — corn, beef, and pork as well as soybeans and some wheat.

The Great Plains, which extend north and south from Canada to Mexico and from the Corn Belt on the east to the Rocky Mountain States on the west, are quite different in character from the Midwest corn country. Here the one-half million farms, averaging 680 acres in size, supply a fifth of our food. The flatness of the land and the small amounts of rain in this area, greatly influence what can be produced. In addition, in the northern part — in the Dakotas and as far south as Kansas — winters are cold and snowy so the growing season is relatively short. Nevertheless, nearly 60 percent of our wheat is produced in the Great Plains. In the southern part — Oklahoma and Texas — cotton and cattle are important.

The Mountain States — from Idaho and Montana to New Mexico and Arizona — provide us with a still different terrain. Vast areas of this region are particularly suited to raising cattle and sheep. Irrigation in the valleys provides water for such crops as sugar beets, potatoes, fruits, and vegetables. The 134,000 farms and ranches in these States are the largest in the country as they average over 2,000 acres in size.

In our trek across the country, we now reach the West Coast. Farms are smaller here than in the Mountain States, but still large by most standards. The 151,000 farms in our Pacific Coast States average about 500 acres in size. Those in the south specialize in raising fruits and vegetables; wheat and fruit are important in the northern part. Cattle are raised throughout the entire region.

Finally, we come to the newest States in the Union, Alaska and Hawaii. These States provide only a small part of our total farm output. Dairy and poultry products are the major foods produced upon the 300 Alaskan farms. The long summer days make possible Alaska production of potatoes, lettuce, carrots, and cabbage. Hawaii has 4,700 farms. Pineapples and sugarcane are the major crops. The mild climate makes possible the production of bananas, coffee, macadamia nuts, and papayas.

This takes us around the country — showing us where most of our food comes from and why. Now let's take a closer look at our farms and farmers.

Our world has been changing fast and most of us have felt the impact of the changes that have taken place. Farmers are no exception. Probably no other major group in our society has had to deal with so much change in so short a time.

At one time, farming was a way of life; now it's a mighty serious business. Before World War II, farmers made up a large share of our population. Since then, more people have left the farms than now are living on them. Today, only one in 20 Americans lives on a farm. In the years gone by, a father could expect a son to take over his farm when he was too old to run it. Today, sons and daughters seek better jobs in the city and are likely to sell the farms they inherit to someone else who needs more land.

Since 1950, the number of farms has gone down significantly, but the amount of land being farmed has changed little. Today there are around 3 million farms, about half as many as in 1950. During these same years, the size of the average farm increased from 225 to 360 acres. And more than half of the farms sold in recent years were bought by farmers to enlarge their own holdings.

Though we have far fewer farmers today than what seems like only yesterday, those who have stayed have more than met the needs of a growing population. Since 1950, our population has increased 32 percent; our food supplies have gone up 41 percent. In addition, agricultural exports have nearly doubled.

All this has come about because farmers have adopted new technologies, mechanized their farms, and improved their management operations. It has been achieved because they have better seeds, insecticides, and fertilizers. They use more tractors, trucks, and harvesting machines. With this greater mechanization of their work, they plant and harvest more acres with fewer hired hands.

Family farms continue to be the backbone of our Nation's agriculture. These may vary considerably in size. On a family farm, more than half the work is done by the farmer and his family. According to this definition, 95 percent of all our farms are family farms. And they account for 65 percent of the products going to market.

But we have other kinds of farms, too — the large, commercial farms. These, larger-than-family-size, have an almost factory-type system of operation. Most of them are in California, Arizona, southern Texas, and Florida.

The decrease in the number of our farms and the increase in size doesn't necessarily mean that this trend will continue at the same pace as in the recent past.

When a farmer increases the size of his farm to take advantage of new technologies, he also increases his investments and costs. Today, if farming is his only source of income, he must sell products worth at least $10,000 to provide his family with a minimum level of living.

Not all farms produce enough to bring in $10,000 a year. Many do not even try or want to do so. Some are meant to be part-time or retirement farms only.

On the other hand, some factory-type farms can produce enough to bring in hundreds of thousands of dollars a year.

About 43 percent of our farms have sales amounting to less than $2,500 a year. These account for only about 3 percent of our food. Some are retirement farms; others are subsistence farms where family members are underemployed. On the average, those living on farms with sales falling in this dollar range receive more than five times as much income from off-farm work as from farming.

About one-fourth of the farms sell between $2,500 and $10,000 worth of products and account for about 12 percent of all sales. Few of these will provide a satisfactory level of living unless supplemented by other income.

The rest of our farms, now less than 1 million, but gradually increasing in number, have gross sales of $10,000 or more and provide 85 percent of our farm products. Among these, however, are more than 30,000 farms with sales of at least $100,000 a year. Though such big operations represent only about 1 percent of all farms, they account for almost a fourth of all sales — over 60 percent of our vegetables; 45 percent of the fruit and nuts; and 35 percent of all poultry and poultry products.

To sum up, the average size of our 3 million plus farms is 360 acres; farmers sell livestock and crops valued at $14,000 per farm; and their average net income is $4,500 a year. As mentioned earlier, some farmers have regular work off the farm; others may take jobs during slack periods. Even families on farms with $40,000 or more sales average $5,000 a year from nonfarm sources.

Farmers are specialists, too. A major change that has taken place in farming is the trend toward greater specialization — raising fewer kinds of crops or live-stock, buying more of the seeds and feed, and using more mechanical equipment — tractors and milking machines, and so on. Today, the average farm has between three and four major enterprises, compared with over five before World War II. Though there still are some advantages to diversified farming — raising more kinds of products — there are important reasons for specializing. It takes a high degree of skill and knowledge to compete successfully in producing one farm product. A farmer who does well uses knowledge of genetics, land and water conservation, and business management. He performs many jobs with complex tools and machines. He combines science and machine power with the ancient arts of tilling the soil.

A farmer must consider costs when deciding what to produce, and costs that must be met before he receives a return on his investment vary greatly by crops. For example, the cost per acre for the better-than-average farmer is $18.20 for wheat, $47.25 for corn, and up to $103.50 for cotton.

On the average, farmers spend 70 cents out of every dollar of sales for production expenses. This varies by size of farm, ranging from about 50 cents per dollar sales by small farms to 80 cents by farms with sales of more than $40,000 a year. As the size of a farm increases, farmers must purchase more fertilizers, pesticides, gas and oil, and other nonfarm goods. And the larger the farm, the more hired workers there are to pay.

Farmers are large purchasers of tractors, trucks, automobiles, and other equipment. They buy about one of every eight trucks that are sold. In a recent year, they spent over $1 billion for tractors, $1.3 billion for automobiles, and $2.5 billion for machinery like plows, planters, and harvesting machines. And, of course, as with other industries, as the years go by these wear out or become obsolete and have to be replaced.

Most crops have benefited from the use of new and improved technologies. For example, since 1950 corn yields have more than doubled — from 38 to 79 bushels per acre. Cotton yields also have nearly doubled, going from 269 to 511 pounds. Wheat yields went from 16.5 to 28.4 bushels an acre and soybeans edged up from around 22 to 27 bushels.

A major problem for a farmer, however, is the variability in prices he gets for his products. His income can fluctuate widely from year to year — and even within a season. Farm production is not a continuous process. Usually it covers a period of only a few months. During this time, crops can be badly damaged by weather, insects, or disease. And unlike most manufacturing industries, a farmer has almost no control over how much his farm will produce once the crop is planted — how many bushels of wheat per acre, for example. Wide swings in prices are common. In 1964, farmers received $14.80 for hogs, per 100 pounds. This rose to $22.80 in 1966 and then dropped back to $18.63 in 1968. The same and sometimes even greater ups and downs occur in prices of other commodites as well.

At the same time that prices may fluctuate widely, the things a farmer has to buy may be going up steadily in price. This increases his risk, already great. Some farmers, in an effort to reduce their risk, enter into informal or formal agreements with other agricultural-related businesses like feed dealers and processors. Such an agreement may let the related business share in management decisions. These arrangements are referred to as coordinated farming.

Various forms of farm and business arrangements have existed for a long time in commercial fruit and tree nut production. Contract farming now accounts for about two-thirds of the vegetables produced for canning and freezing. Most of today's broiler production is a joint undertaking between farmers and processors. Men employed by the processor do much of the poultry farm management. Production is concentrated in operations that make the fullest use of labor-saving equipment. In this way, poultry raisers reduce their risks and get a guaranteed income for themselves.

The sugar beet industry is another example of contract farming. Nearly all sugar beet growers have contracts with processors to insure a market. Sugar beets are heavy, bulky, and perishable. They are grown under contracts which guarantee a market for farmers and supplies for the processor. Negotiated contracts tie the price of the sugar beets to that of sugar. These specify the acreage to be planted, seeds and growing methods to be used, dates beets are to be delivered to the processor, marketing practices to be used, and even when the farmer will be paid.

All these changes calling for larger investments and more specialization have resulted in an increase in efficiency. Farmers have made the best record in this respect of all our industries. Since 1950, the amount of work, per man, per hour, working in agriculture has increased at a rate of nearly 6 percent a year compared with 2.5 percent for all other industries. In other words, one farmer now produces enough food for almost three times as many persons as he did back in 1950.

The share of workers employed on farms provides a good measure of a nation's productivity. In our country, only 6 percent of the total labor force works on farms. This compares with 10 and 18 percent in developed countries like West Germany and France. About 40 percent of all Soviet Union workers are on farms. In less developed countries such as India and Pakistan approximately three-quarters of the labor force works on farms.

What does all this mean to those of us who live in cities?

This abundance has helped raise our standard of living and to provide us with an unprecedented quantity, quality, and variety of food at the lowest cost in relation to our take-home pay in this Nation's history. This has left us more income for other things — houses, cars, college educations.

A second contribution of the continuing rise in agricultural productivity is the release of manpower to other sectors of the economy where they can make significant contributions in industry, the professions, and in the defense efforts of our country.

The release of manpower from our farms had its social and economic costs, however. Many of the released workers are poorly equipped in terms of skills, education, and personal resources for nonfarm occupations. As workers move from the farm to the city, some find the city has little to offer except unemployment or low paying, insecure jobs. They simply add to the already existing problems of unemployment and poverty.

A third benefit has been the creation of many jobs in the nonfarm section of the economy. Farmers spend more than $34 billion a year for goods and services to produce crops and livestock. Added to this, about $15 billion goes for the same things that city people buy — food, clothing, and other consumer products and services.

Every year farmers purchase products containing about 5 million tons of steel and some 320 million pounds of rubber — enough to put tires on nearly 6 million automobiles.

They use more petroleum than any other single industry — and more electricity than all of the people and industries in Chicago, Detroit, Boston, Baltimore, Houston, and Washington, D.C., combined.

These are today's farms and farmers.

But what about the future? What is being predicted for farms and farmers?

It is forecast that by the turn of the century the American farmer will be freed from the arduous and time-consuming demands of planting and harvesting. Some see him sitting in an air-conditioned farm office, scanning a printout from a computer center. This computer center will help him decide how many acres to plant, what kinds of seeds to sow, what kind and how much fertilizer to apply, exactly what his soil composition is, and even what day to harvest each crop.

They foresee other things as well:

Automated machinery directed by tape-controlled programs and supervised by television scanners mounted on towers.

Robot harvesters to carry out high speed picking, grading, packaging, and freezing.

Crop yields per acre double and triple those of 1969.

Farmers Look at Farming, 1970

From Wayne D. Rasmussen and Gladys L. Baker, "The Farmer Speaks for a Way of Life," U.S. Department of Agriculture, *Yearbook,* 1970 (Washington, 1970), pp. 25–31.

Farmers today cherish traditional rural values, yet feel they are victims of the economic system. The cardinal points of the agrarian creed — independence, the belief that agriculture is man's fundamental employment upon which other economic activities depend, and the conviction that farming is a natural life and therefore a dood life — are held by many farm people, and, as a 1969 study shows, by many city dwellers as well.

Farmers stress freedom of action; freedom from the crime, noise, and traffic of the cities; a healthier environment, and the farm way of life as reasons why they want their children to stay in the country. But, they say, large capital requirements, low farm prices, high prices for everything needed for production, and long hours and hard work are discouraging young people from staying in farming.

The idea that agriculture has a basic value of itself was strongly expressed by a farmwoman of Briscoe County, Tex., on September 18, 1969, at a "listening conference" held by the Secretary of Agriculture. She said: "I only want to remind you that when the farmer falls, the Nation falls!"

Another farmwoman, Mrs. E. C. Goza of Mayesville, S.C., spoke at a similar conference of the difficulties faced by the farmer: "I think that farmers are more or less called to the profession or they would never be able to withstand the strain and 'wear and tear' — and it seems as though this strain has grown greater each year for the past decade due to the everincreasing price squeeze and labor shortage in farming."

The belief that agriculture is the base upon which the Nation's economy rests was expressed by S. J. Grahmann, farmer of Hallettsville, Tex.: "With agriculture accounting for 75 percent of our nation's new creative wealth, consistently low agricultural prices will eventually reduce everyone to poverty."

Farmers today, for the most part, are convinced that they are adding to the wealth and well-being of the Nation. Yet they are just as convinced that their relative position in the economy is declining.

During the 1930's, parity prices — that is, fair prices for farm products in relation to the prices farmers paid for goods, looking back to the 1910–14 period — became a goal for farmers, farm organizations, and Congress. Parity prices were to be both the measuring rods and the means of securing for the farmers a fair share of national income and national wealth.

The present parity ratio, which is the ratio of the index of prices received to the index of prices paid, based upon 1910–14, is not an accurate measure of farm income because it does not reflect increases in productivity, returns on investment, or direct government payments. Farmers express concern both that the parity ratio is about 74 percent and that the income to each person in farming is only about 73 percent of what the nonfarmer receives. The parity index was at or above 100 from 1942 through 1952, but has been falling since.

Farmer after farmer at the "listening conferences" expressed dismay that in a period of general prosperity, their relative position as measured by parity was declining.

In 1953 and 1955, when extensive field hearings were held by agriculture committees of the Congress, farmers also expressed concern at how things were going.

Orville C. Russell of Muncie, Ind., called himself an "old fashioned dirt farmer." He spoke about the interdependence of agriculture, industry, and labor, and of the need for farmers to organize because of their minority status. In testimony of Oct. 19, 1953, he said:

"Agriculture today through organization should, and now is, recognized as a basic factor in our national economy. . . .

"In these United States there are three groups, indispensable to each other — agriculture, industry, and labor. Neither one can successfully survive without the others, and neither one should usurp power over the others. . . .

"I would like to speak of the place of agriculture in Government. Industry and labor are both organized. They put forth every effort to gain power in Government. Agriculture should be on an equal basis in Government, if Government by all people is for all people."

Three years of declining farm prices brought back disturbing questions concerning fundamental agrarian values. Were farmers being punished for producing abundantly? Instead of economic rewards, did hard work, efficiency, and technological progress bring lower farm prices and income? Could agriculture be considered the fundamental industry when farm prices were falling while other segments of the economy were relatively prosperous?

Kenneth Fridley, operator of a 640-acre Oregon farm, stated the dilemma:

". . . Late events have created doubts and a feeling of despair in the mind of the farmer. . . . It is a strange paradox that the American farmer should be treated as an economic delinquent when he has responded in every crisis in the past two decades to expand and produce to feed his countrymen and the rest of the free world."

Helge Nygren, President of the Morton County (N. Dak.) Farmers Union, stated that as a family farmer he was probably one of the most important men in America. He deplored what he considered unfair treatment given the family farmer "who founded the country." Was it just for those responsible for the American way of life to be blamed rather than rewarded for their efficiency, he asked.

"I am sure if we want to be honest, we must all admit that the family farm is the American way of life; this, I am sure, everyone knows. Still nearly every paper today has articles telling us that we must do something to do away with the inefficiency in agriculture and by that statement we all know that they mean the family farmer, and in the same article they holler about the burdensome surpluses.

"Let us check this for one moment. Does it make good sense to say to a man you are inefficient, but still you produce too much? . . .

"Are we willing to do away with our American family farmer because of this cry of efficiency? If we do, we must be willing to do away with not only the family farmer but also with the small towns and all small business, all our country schools and churches, and all social and civic functions in our rural and urban areas, and in its place what would we have?"

Other farmers discussed the unfairness of a system which failed to reward those who had provided the base for the economy and the country's most cherished institutions. One farmwoman asked how family farmers could "enjoy the beauties of nature with rumblings of a mortgage foreclosure overhead?" Farm people, she said, "were honest, kind, generous, hard working and long suffering." She felt if the farm way of life were to disappear the strength and security of the Nation would go with it.

In a 1955 statement, Lynn Bowe, owner of 400 acres of Minnesota land, who had started farming after World War II, discussed some of the difficulties and gave the following explanation of why he continued to farm:

"I suppose the reason why I farm, I farm because, well, with practically any other area I believe I could go into, I could with the same ability and energy make double the income, but I farm because I like the soil and I have fundamental respect for it, and I believe it clothes and feeds me, and that one day I will become a part of it.

"I enjoy working with growing crops and with livestock; and I believe I can understand why since time immemorial people have lived with that intimate contact with growing things, as an important asset and as an indispensable part of the heritage of man.

"Thirdly, and last but not least, I should say that farming offers a large amount of personal freedom in planning and operating, and under no conditions do I want to trade off this freedom of choice for anyone telling me what I can and cannot do on my own farm."

Farmers continue to enjoy farming as a way of life but surveys show they are becoming discouraged with farming as a way of making a living. A survey for the *Wisconsin Agriculturist* in 1966 found that 44 percent of those participating felt sure they would farm if they were starting over again while 14 percent were sure they would not, and another 17 percent doubted if they would choose farming. Those who were not sure or were undecided constituted 25 percent.

Of those who would not choose farming, 55 percent gaveas one of their reasons that it required too much money for land and equipment. Too low income was given as a reason by 49 percent. Preference for town or city life was given by only 2 percent. Too long hours was given by 38 percent while 13 percent said the work was too hard. Six percent said people look down upon farmers.

A study of dryland grain farms in Montana published in 1963 indicated that most farmers would still choose farming if they were starting over again. They would continue to farm even if it meant a lower standard of living, but some of those interviewed would not recommend farm life for a son or daughter. Farming was preferred as an occupation because of the independence it provided.

An Iowa farmwoman, interviewed in 1969, said the only way a boy could become a farmer was to inherit his father's farm. She said there is "no chance for anyone to become a new farmer." A recent college graduate who was farming with his father said, "I like the farm but it costs too much to start farming."

Donald Kaldor, a professor of economics at Iowa State University, began in 1959 a study of the long range occupational plans of 870 Iowa farm boys in their senior year of high school. At that time, 38 percent indicated they wanted to farm. A followup study of the boys in 1962 showed that only 14.3 percent of them were actually farming. Studies in 1964 and 1966 indicated that 24 percent were in farming, but those working in nonfarm occupations had risen from around 35 percent in 1962 to 64 percent in 1966.

Some farmers' sons who preferred farming as a way of life as well as a way of making a living, were discouraged by what has been labeled the corporate invasion of American agriculture. Corporations, with their large economic resources, could afford to take a loss for a number of years, if necessary. They could use losses in farming to offset capital gains in other corporate operations. They could and did often bid up the price of land in their purchases of large tracts.

Corporations which weren't interested in accumulating farmland of their own could through contracts control the marketing of large segments of the industry, making "factories in the field." Farmers would lose their independence. Corporations, it was felt, were not interested in farming as a way of life. They had no ties to the rural community. Local communities and local government, as farmers had known them, would disappear and with them the basis for the democratic way of life.

Robert W. Scott, then Master of the North Carolina State Grange, in a May 31, 1963 letter to a Congressional Committee, stated the corporate threat to the family farm. He wrote:

"The family farm is in grave danger unless steps are taken to provide it with the same degrees of competitiveness enjoyed by corporate farming, contract farming, and other types of farming operations.

"Given the same tax advantages and the same opportunities to buy needed supplies and to market farm products and an access to adequate resources through credit, I am confident that the family farm system can prove its superiority as the most efficient, the most economic, and the most satisfying operation in a prosperous agriculture. . . .

"If agriculture becomes centered in the hands of a few giant corporations vertically integrated from the field to the table and able to fix prices, then food costs would likely be greater, rural community life as we know it today would disappear, and the attitudes of self-reliance, social responsibility, individual incentive, and tolerance would be lost to America. . . . "

Farmers who are concerned over corporation farming favor legislation to bar or impede it. Twenty-seven United States Senators sponsored a bill in 1969 to prevent tax-loss farming. Bills were also introduced to ban feeding of livestock by packers with more than $1 million in annual gross sales.

A poll taken by *Wallaces Farmer* indicated that 78 percent of Iowa farmers favored national legislation to prevent packers and chain stores from operating feedlots. One farmer said, "We need legislation to prevent big chains from crushing the farmer."

However, farmers who marketed more than 500 hogs a year were less favorable to national legislation. One said, "Although I don't like large companies in competiton with me, we live in a free country, anyone has a right to operate feedlots.''

All farm organizations have not agreed on the need for federal regulation. The American Farm Bureau Federation called the idea of limiting the flow of a certain type of capital into farming and of demarcating who is and who is not a farmer ''unacceptable.''

Agrarian traditions have been called upon by farm people to support diverse positions on many issues. Even the perils of the nuclear age were mentioned in an agrarian context in a letter from an Alabama farmer published in the August 1968 issue of the *Progressive Farmer*. He wrote:

''This farm to city migration has got to be stopped and reversed if we are to survive as a nation in this nuclear age. With the ever menacing threat of nuclear war, what would be a better guarantee or defense than self-sustaining, self-supporting farm families as far back in the country away from towns and cities as possible.

''The morale and morals of the masses would be much improved if millions of our children were reared in the clean pure air where they could learn of God and Mother Nature.''

The idea of encouraging a different distribution of population — encouraging more people to stay in or return to the country — is being studied by American leaders as a means for improving the environment. Some of the arguments presently advanced by urban-oriented people for such a program go back to the point of the agrarian creed that the country provides a natural and therefore a good life.

A series of informal surveys made in the summer of 1969 showed that most commercial farmers and farm families now enjoy many of the amenities of city life — running water, electricity, telephones, television, radios, and access to shopping and cultural centers. At the same time, farmer after farmer cited traditional agrarian values as their reasons for staying in farming.

A successful commercial farmer in southwestern Iowa, Ernest Baker, stated that he had been discouraged, but really never dissatisfied, with farm life. He liked farming, and believed that a farm was a wonderful place to raise a family.

As far as basic satisfactions were concerned, he saw little difference between his father, himself, and his three sons. So far as farm life was concerned, it differed little from that in town, but crime, traffic, and particularly noise, would keep him from ever liking the city.

Commercial farmers, though, are still dependent upon weather, market prices, credit availability, increasing production expenses, and other things over which they have no control. An unfortunate series of disasters, combined with high costs of production and credit, led Willis Hansen to leave the farm in Solano County, Calif., that had been homesteaded by his great-grandmother in the 1860's.

He bought a trailer in town and sold his home place, which is no longer in commercial farm production. Yet Mr. Hansen still believes that farming is a good way of life. He prizes his independence, and likes the open spaces and the freedom from the traffic and dangers of city life.

The commercial farmer today is economically interdependent with the industrial city — the inevitable result of modern technology. His way of living, so far as physical conveniences and social and cultural life are concerned, is not obviously different from that of the city man. But he has made only minor modifications in the beliefs that have made up the agrarian tradition — independence, the importance of agriculture in the economy, and the value of farm life.

A Better Life on the Great Plains

From Elmer A. Starch, "A Better Life on the Plains," U.S. Department of Agriculture, *Yearbook*, 1970 (Washington, 1970), pp. 197–204.

My own humble opinion is that, with the exception of a few favored localities, the whole Great Plains region is already a desert that cannot be reclaimed through the plans and labors of men.

With these words, written in 1938, Lawrence Svobida closed his book entitled *An Empire of Dust*. Yet before the next decade had passed, the area was an abundant supplier of food to "win the war and write the peace."

What brought about the change? It was a unique combination of science, economics, engineering, and the resilient resourcefulness of the people on the land which reversed Svobida's evaluation of the future of the Plains.

Svobida was a young farmer who had come to Meade, Kans., in 1929 and after 9 years of hardship in the heart of the dust bowl, it was only reasonable that he should sum it up as he did. Elsewhere in the region the experiences were also extremely distressing — not as completely devastating but more prolonged.

The future seemed to hold little promise for those who had lived through the 10 years which Svobida described in his book. Adverse climatic forces had joined with a nationwide economic debacle to make the thirties a decade of disaster for America's semi-arid agriculture.

It must be recognized that the situation was not altogether the product of sudden disaster. As a matter of fact, symptoms of distress were plain during the early twenties. By the early thirties, the Great Plains was recognized to be a major problem area. The economic and physical decline which preceded the dust storms was caused, in large part, by lack of information about dealing with a semi-arid environment.

Theoretically, if the scientists and the economists of a later day could have preceded the frontiersmen into the semi-arid zones, many mistakes could have been averted.

The scientist could have worked out production methods which were compatible with the soil and climatic characteristics of that newly-occupied region.

The economist could have advised the settlers as to how much land and what types of equipment were needed to sustain a family. Also, he could have told all the members of the new community that variable income from year to year would put an unusual strain on the local financial and commercial structure.

And, of course, if there had been such a thing as a modern-day sociologist, the problems of community organization, such as public and commercial services and neighborhood relationships, could have been put into better perspective.

In actual experience, however, the adversities encountered by the settler far outran the accumulation of scientific and economic knowledge. However, the researchers were by no means idle. In fact, research in the physical sciences was begun before the turn of the century by experiment stations in most of the Great Plains States. The work was augmented by special dryland experiment stations, which were established through funds authorized in 1906 by Congress. But not until after World War I did the findings become available and begin to be taken seriously.

By that time, the scientists were suggesting some startling changes in crop production methods in a moisture-deficient environment. For instance, they said "don't plow." Plowing turns under trash which ought to stay on the surface. The practice exposes too much soil to rapid evaporation and worst of all, it is too slow. This, they said, is in itself a handicap to good farming where timeliness of operation is a very critical factor.

The soils scientists found that unleached dryland soil was a great reservoir of plant food. They said that lack of moisture rather than fertility was the limiting factor. Therefore, moisture preservation should be the prime objective of dryland cultural practices. These were only some of the findings which would make life in critical moisture areas unique.

Taking note of the scientific discoveries and of the farmers' experiences, some leaders thought there was need for a revised system of management. M. L. Wilson of Montana State College pointed this out in a management survey published in 1923. Wilson's findings were carried further by the Montana Experiment Station through a most unusual system of research.

This new research approach was made possible by a reorganization of the work of Montana's Agricultural Economics Department in 1926 under M. L. Wilson's direction and two new sources of funds.

The first source was Federal funds provided under the Purnell Act adopted by Congress in 1925. Purpose of the legislation was to stimulate economic research for agriculture. The second source was a grant by the Laura Spelman Rockefeller Foundation in 1924, for establishment of a special research unit looking toward agricultural recovery.

The special research unit was called the Fairway Farms Corp. It worked on farm financing, farm reorganization, and farm management, and facilitated adoption of new developments in science, engineering, and other areas.

Under the aegis of Fairway Farms' experimentation in the economic area, findings of the physical sciences were also brought together so that the pieces could be assembled into an effective whole. The testing period for bringing everything together into a scheme of operation was short, but the work was intensive. It began in 1924 and by the end of the 1928 cropping season, a set of revised principles of management had been developed as a standard procedure for semi-arid agriculture.

The experimental processes which preceded the rewriting of the rules of management were preceded by projections. A series of theoretically constructed farm and ranch organizations was designed, and an operational formula fitting the physical environment was outlined.

An assumption was made that specialization and mechanization would be the dominating features of an agricultural renaissance. The formula also had to meet the stresses and strains which were occasioned by the rapidly changing economic situation following World War I. For example, wheat would probably be sold for 80 cents a bushel. The old standard had been one bushel — one dollar.

The management research of Fairway Farms from 1924 to 1928, which incorporated the findings of the scientists and the experience of farmers into an operating unit, proved that both mechanization and specialized production would play a big part in making the farms and ranches of the Plains country viable. After 1928, complete reorganization of spring wheat farms was recommended by the Montana Extension Service.

Today, a visitor to the semi-arid zones of America will find an almost universal adjustment of farm operation in accordance with the criteria upon which the recommendations of 1928 were based. It is remarkable that so much adaptation could take place within one man's lifetime.

There are thousands of the new Great Plains farms which one could visit to see the change. However, the farm of George Rubin of Whitetail, Mont., is a good illustration.

Rubin began farming in 1928. His community was subject to dust storms and distress but it did not suffer the complete devastation of Svobida's community. For that reason, recovery could come more rapidly in his area than in other places, but the principles underlying the recovery and redevelopment are similar for the entire area.

Rubin and most of his Plains neighbors began adjusting their operations according to the new rules set forth by the Montana Extension Service by specializing in what they could produce to best advantage, increasing the productivity per man by mechanization, protecting the land surface through suitable methods of cultivation, trying to level off year to year variation of yields through land management practices, and other adaptations.

It is the product of these multiple adaptations that one sees within relatively prosperous semi-arid zones today.

The adaptations are in turn the product of science, economics, invention, and the refinement of the people's own experience.

The reorganization of farms and better individual management alone could not restore the economy of the semi-arid portions of the country.

Needed was a broad scale and thorough reassessment of the entire problem area and also a practical land utilization strategy. Prolonged drought and depression had greatly accentuated a situation of maladjustment which existed from the days when the new settlers had rushed into an unknown environment.

On September 17, 1936, President Roosevelt appointed the Great Plains Committee to draw up a "long term program for the efficient utilization of the resources of the Great Plains." Its report went beyond the management of the individual unit and included suggestions for a broad, land use type of approach.

The President, in transmitting the report to Congress on February 10, 1937, urged that "a new economy must be developed — which represents generally a more rational adjustment . . . to natural conditions." He emphasized the need for cooperation between Federal and State governments, and individual citizens of the region.

He concluded: "A policy should be determined, a long-run program formulated, and execution begun without undue delay."

The development of a sustained land use pattern for the Great Plains required a thoroughgoing assessment of factors which caused development of the maladjusted situation.

It was fortunate that some members of the scientific, administrative, and economic communities had been studying the situation for a decade before the drought, political unrest, and depression struck in full force in the early thirties. They were convinced that if a successful congenial habitat was to be built to survive, it was necessary to ask questions everywhere and of everyone and then look ahead to see what could be done. What they had learned formed a background for the long-term program such as the President had asked of the Committee.

The facts had to be made available to as many people as possible. Most of all, it was necessary that the people accept the hard fact that the Plains country lay in a critical climatic zone and had to be handled accordingly.

To effectively implement a redevelopment program, it was obvious that special care should be taken to correlate the efforts of the citizenry and the Government agencies. The President's Committee suggested a local coordinating effort where the Federal and State agencies would join in shaping programs to the needs of the situation.

During the months following the President's message to Congress on February 10, 1937, arrangements were worked out in the Plains States whereby the local people would analyze their own situation and work out the means for improvement.

As soon as a general consensus had been attained, the Under Secretary of Agriculture, M. L. Wilson, met with representatives of the Land Grant Colleges to formalize the understanding. Shortly thereafter, he assigned a representative of his office to each section of what came to be known as the Great Plains Agricultural Council.

The work program as set out by the group was correlated with the suggestions as outlined by the President's Committee, among these being:

● A problem-oriented research schedule for the next 9 years carried forward by the Federal and State research agencies.

● A policy and a program to shift lands to their most effective use, like moving marginal lands to grazing.

● An outline of policy affecting land and water use, systematic land management, restoration of tax delinquent land to systematic management, and steps for conserving resources.

● Encouragement to the individual manager to bring his operations into harmony with climatic realities, to create feed balances, and to adopt all feasible soil and moisture conservation practices.

It was a program designed to bring about adaptations which would enable citizens of the area to evolve a lasting and satisfactory environment in which to learn, earn, and live.

It may well be that it was because of common goals that the Great Plains community became an outstanding example of development. It is a case where the people took hold of an ineffective and declining economy and drew on the ingenuity of experience, used science, absorbed automation, reorganized resource usage, and revised public service in order to make a more viable and more congenial environment.

With the limited information at hand the people within each locality did the very best they could. They mobilized their resources, made decisions, shaped plans, and entered into an effort to put productivity and well-being on a higher plane.

The Great Plains became a laboratory in which the many elements of adjustment were measured and where development principles were tested. The adjustments were not without great cost to the people involved. Out of the wreckage of the depression, the drought, and maladjustment, a fairly strong economy and a reasonably good place to live has been rebuilt.

Even though not everything was as effective as it was hoped and even though the cost to the people was great, local planning and concerted effort have brought a higher standard of well-being to America's semi-arid zone than exists in any similar climatic area in the world.

It is a significant note in the history of the world that arid and semi-arid agriculture have given major support to the growth of civilization. Our recorded history shows this in more detail for the eastern Mediterranean areas than it does for Mexico and other parts of the world. The ancient sources of food supply have remained in a more or less traditional status over the centuries while areas of more abundant rainfall became the major suppliers of food and fiber.

An altogether new impetus was given to semi-arid agriculture through a revised system of management which was developed during the second quarter of the twentieth century.

A very distinct set of cultural practices has been added to the world of agricultural production. The discoveries in science and in economics, as well as the products of engineering, have had a worldwide influence.

Use of the agricultural resources of the Great Plains has been improved very markedly. There is much less likelihood of serious soil erosion since millions of acres of sensitive land have been returned to permanent grass cover, and a large percentage of the cultivated land is being surface cultivated to insure trash cover for wind protection.

Some areas of the wheat producing country are being protected by strip cropping. The techniques of production and the quality of the varieties of wheat have been improved. Yields have increased to the point where one of the States has almost doubled its predrought volume of cereal production.

The skills and the facilities for productive use of the scarce water resources are now such that millions of acre-feet are being beneficially retained. Part of it is in ground storage through the practice of summer fallow. Part is in very small reservoir and diversion installations. Part is in more than a million stockwater reservoirs distributed quite densely over the Plains.

Also, the water available to irrigated land is much more efficiently used because of land preparation and farm layout. Striking laborsaving has been introduced into irrigation farming as a result of research work done on a group of pilot projects established in 1937.

Uncertainty of income and variability in production have been reduced through techniques of tillage, cropping sequence, and timeliness of operation. Security of tenure has been practically assured by adaptations in financing. Volume of production per farm or ranch unit has been made more adequate through increased productivity per capita, as a result of labor distribution, mechanization, and specialization of production.

Fifteen to 20 percent more livestock is being carried on the grasslands because of improvements made in the range itself by management practices such as seeding selected grass varieties and rotated grazing. The 1,000,000 stockwater reservoirs have also improved grazing efficiency.

The semi-arid Plains now enjoy reasonable stability in sustained production capacity instead of being a serious problem area.

This stability was made possible by a number of interrelated factors, not the least of which are U.S. Department of Agriculture programs. Long-term credit, cost sharing to install needed conservation practices, and related agency programs teamed up with economic and agricultural research to help make needed changes.

A unique program of long-term cost sharing, through contractual arrangements with farmers and ranchers, was authorized by Congress in 1956. These contracts, based on conservation plans for entire operating units, help bring about needed stability through the planning and application of desirable land use changes, needed changes in cropping and grazing systems, and the installation of conservation practices.

The Great Plains Conservation Program has thus far contracted for complete conservation treatment on more than 36,000 farms and ranches covering nearly 65 million acres.

The quality of living has been raised in many respects and is no longer that of an impoverished community. Housing has been decidedly improved because the economy has been reorganized to bring a better income. The Rural Electrification Administration has brought electricity and telephones even to the sparsely-located farmsteads, reducing drudgery and enhancing livability. Roads have been improved selectively and maintenance of unneeded roads has been discontinued.

However, some aspects of well-being have not yet been brought up to the highest American standard. Creative or even suitable criteria have not been found for providing adequate health facilities or school systems. Recreational and community activities suffer from lack of innovations. The trade and commercial structures have not been revamped to give as much service as would be expected in a genuinely modernized era.

The purpose of improved efficiency and stabilized organization must surely be that of an optimum environment and adequate opportunity for personal growth and expression. Now, since drudgery, isolation, and poverty have been reduced, there can be a commensurate enhancement of the means which allow for the optimum usefulness and enjoyment of a span of life.

Changes in Farm Production and Efficiency

From *Changes in Farm Production and Efficiency: A Summary Report*, 1970. U.S. Department of Agriculture Statistical Bulletin no. 233, pp. 16–17.

TABLE 20. — *Persons supplied farm products by one farmworker, United States, selected years, 1820–1969*[1]

Year	Persons supplied per farmworker[2]			Total farm employment[3]	Total United States population July 1[4]
	Total	At home	Abroad		
	Number	*Number*	*Number*	*Millions*	*Millions*
1820	4.1	3.8	0.3	2.4	9.6
1830	4.0	3.8	.2	3.3	12.9
1840	3.9	3.7	.2	4.4	17.1
1850	4.2	4.0	.2	5.7	23.3
1860	4.5	4.0	.5	7.3	31.5
1870	5.1	4.6	.5	8.0	39.9
1880	5.6	4.5	1.1	10.1	50.3
1890	5.8	4.7	1.1	11.7	63.1
1900	6.9	5.2	1.7	12.8	76.1
1910	7.1	6.1	1.0	13.6	92.4
1920	8.3	6.9	1.4	13.4	106.5
1930	9.8	8.8	1.0	12.5	123.1
1940	10.7	10.3	.4	11.0	132.1
1950	15.5	13.8	1.7	9.9	151.7
1951	15.8	14.0	1.8	9.5	154.3
1952	16.4	15.0	1.4	9.1	157.0
1953	17.2	15.8	1.4	8.9	159.6
1954	18.1	16.2	1.9	8.7	162.4
1955	19.5	17.3	2.2	8.4	165.3
1956	21.7	18.5	3.2	7.9	168.2
1957	22.7	19.8	2.9	7.6	171.3
1958	23.2	20.6	2.6	7.5	174.1
1959	24.5	21.4	3.1	7.3	177.1
1960	25.8	22.3	3.5	7.1	179.9
1961	27.6	23.6	4.0	6.9	183.0
1962	28.6	24.7	3.9	6.7	185.8
1963	30.7	25.8	4.9	6.5	188.6
1964	33.2	27.9	5.3	6.1	191.3
1965	37.0	30.8	6.2	5.6	193.7
1966	39.6	33.6	6.0	5.2	196.0
1967	42.1	36.0	6.1	4.9	198.2
1968	43.4	37.9	5.5	4.7	200.2
1969[5]	45.3	39.1	6.2	4.6	202.2

[1]Annual data for 1941–49 in 1964 issue of Statistical Bulletin 233.
[2]Persons supplied include the farmworker. Thus in 1820, the average farmworker supplied himself and 3.1 other persons.
[3]Includes farm operators, unpaid family workers, and hired workers. From Farm Labor, Statistical Reporting Service.
[4]Includes persons in our military forces in this country and abroad.
[5]Preliminary.

TABLE 21. — Index numbers of total farm inputs, and inputs in major subgroups, United States, selected periods and years, 1910–69[1]
(1957–59 = 100)

Year	Total inputs		Purchased[3]	Farm labor	Farm estate	Mechanical power and machinery	Fertilizer and liming materials	Feed, seed, and livestock purchases[4]	Miscellaneous
	All	purchased[2]							
1910–14	85	167	47	217	89	22	14	15	59
1920–24	92	165	57	217	90	32	14	25	71
1930–34	93	165	58	210	88	35	15	24	76
1940–44	99	140	76	191	90	47	35	55	75
1950	101	119	91	142	97	86	68	72	85
1951	104	121	94	143	98	92	73	80	88
1952	103	120	94	136	99	96	80	81	88
1953	103	118	94	131	99	97	83	80	91
1954	102	114	95	125	100	98	88	82	91
1955	102	111	97	120	100	99	90	86	94
1956	101	108	98	113	99	99	91	91	98
1957	99	101	97	104	100	100	94	93	95
1958	99	99	100	99	100	99	97	101	100
1959	102	100	103	97	100	101	109	106	105
1960	101	95	105	92	101	104	111	109	106
1961	101	92	106	88	101	101	117	111	109
1962	101	90	108	84	103	100	125	117	113
1963	104	89	112	81	104	104	141	123	117
1964	104	85	115	77	106	102	155	126	120
1965	104	82	117	73	106	105	162	127	120
1966	107	82	122	69	107	110	182	136	123
1967	110	78	128	68	107	114	204	144	128
1968	111	77	130	66	107	114	214	143	130
1969[5]	112	75	133	64	107	115	224	148	133

[1] Annual data for 1910–49 in 1964 issue of this publication.
[2] Includes operator and unpaid family labor, and operator-owned real estate and other capital inputs.
[3] Includes all inputs other than nonpurchased inputs.
[4] Nonfarm portion of feed, seed, and livestock purchases.
[5] Preliminary.

TABLE 22. — *Index numbers of farm output, inputs, and productivity, United States, selected periods and years, 1870–1969*[1]
(1957–59 = 100)

Year	Farm output	Production inputs	Productivity[2]
1870	20	41	49
1880	31	53	58
1890	37	63	59
1900	48	73	66
1910–14	52	85	61
1920–24	57	92	62
1930–34	60	93	65
1940–44	78	99	79
1950	86	101	85
1951	89	104	86
1952	92	103	89
1953	93	103	90
1954	93	102	91
1955	96	102	94
1956	97	101	96
1957	95	99	96
1958	102	99	103
1959	103	102	101
1960	106	101	105
1961	107	101	106
1962	108	101	107
1963	112	104	108
1964	111	104	107
1965	114	104	110
1966	113	107	106
1967	118	110	107
1968	120	111	108
1969[3]	121	112	108

[1] Annual data for 1910–49 in 1964 issue of this publication.
[2] Output per unit of input.
[3] Preliminary.

The Future of Agriculture

Decline of Rural Institutions

From James T. Bonnen, "The Decline of the Agricultural Establishment," in Karl A. Fox and Harry G. Johnston, eds., *Readings in the Economics of Agriculture*, pp. 495–509. Homewood, Ill.: Richard D. Irwin, Inc. 1969. Reprinted by permission of the author.

What is the present state of agricultural policy? Understanding the present state of affairs always involves knowing some previous state. What policy decision makers are doing today is not only conditioned but also predetermined in a major degree by the successes and failures of time past — as well as by the changing structure of our political, economic, and social institutions. I want to look at each of these matters in turn. But first, where are we today and how did we get there?

Clearly we are at another node in agricultural policy. Over the decade ending in 1963 two alternative approaches to the farm problem were attempted. Both failed for lack of political acceptance. During the Eisenhower years, Secretary Benson made a valiant attempt, as he would put it, to return the farmer to the free market. Following that, the Kennedy Administration attempted to implement a system of government-run supply management using mandatory controls. Both of these approaches are now denied us. What is left?

One must look at the successes of these two administrations to answer this. The Eisenhower Administration presided over the creation of PL 480, the Soil Bank, and a great enlargement of domestic supplemental and special food programs. The Soil Bank was not an unalloyed success, but it was the experiment from which we have learned much of what we know today about how to withdraw land from farm production. The Kennedy Administration passed an emergency feed grain bill in 1961 which is genuinely popular with farmers and which contains several ideas since extended to wheat and now extended to cotton in the 1965 Omnibus Farm Bill. Briefly the feed grain program, as fully developed, 1) requires farmers to divert some minimum acreage in order to be eligible for price supports, 2) provides payments for diverting the minimum acreage and for the voluntary diversion of additional acreage, and 3) prohibits the use of diverted acreage for planting to other major crops. This weds price supports to land withdrawal and keys acreage diversion to a specific commodity acreage allotment.

The price-support payment and the diversion-payment techniques tend to separate the income-support operation from the pricing mechanism. This gives one a fighting chance to maintain farm income while cutting surplus stocks and letting prices move toward a level that reduces the incentive for overproduction and allows the farmer to compete in world markets without export subsidies.

The final innovation of the Kennedy years was the application of the two-price certificate plan to wheat, which transfers part of the program cost from taxpayers to consumers.

These successful innovations of the past decade will be important pieces of any answer to the problems we now face.

Policy Problems and Alternatives

In the short run our choices amount to an economic and political dilemma. With voluntary programs, the unrelenting pressure of significant annual increases in yields means that budget costs go up each year — even if you are only maintaining the same level of farm income. Each year politicians are faced with a "Hobson's choice" between greater budgetary costs or higher prices to the consumer (via certificate-type systems), and — failing increases in either budget or prices — lower total farm income. If in the process of making political choices it is decided that farm-program budgets must be reduced, then total farm income (though not necessarily average per-farm income) must fall as a direct consequence, unless the costs of these programs can be transferred to the consumer. This is the economic dilemma. It is also a political dilemma, since each of these variables — budget, consumer costs, and farm income — involves politically potent interests.

Over the longer run we are faced with additional problems and alternatives. In trade policy shall we focus exclusively on our domestic markets and continue to play the role of the world market's high-priced residual supplier or shall we lower our prices to the level of the world market, negotiate some changes in the rules, and compete?

The future growth in world food and fiber markets will be that generated primarily by the economic growth of the developing nations. Yet many of these nations are now apparently losing in the race between population growth and food production. Crisis or no, under grossly inconsistent political demands, we allow PL 480 to fritter away its potential trying to be all things to all men. Should we continue to use PL 480 as an instrument of trade expansion, hardening the terms of aid until it becomes trade? Should we in agriculture continue to look at PL 480 as a "rat hole" down which to shove farm products or should we assume some responsibility for tying it to economic development in a more meaningful manner?

When are we, in program design, going to face up to the asset inflation-income paradox with its implications for the soundness of the farm financial structure, the process of intergenerational transfer of farms, the question of factor returns and the ownership and organization of the factors of production?

Related is the question of when we are going to do something about the problems of people in rural life. As T. W. Schultz has pointed out repeatedly, the behavior of rural people, their representatives, and their institutions implies a materialistic bias in favor of plants, land, and animals and against people. Our farm programs are specifically designed to do things to improve the value of plants, land, and animals. Even from the point of view solely of the farmers' welfare — to say nothing of the rest of the rural community or society as a whole — we have underinvested in rural health, education, and the other social services which develop the potential and productivity of people. It is hardly surprising that the primary result of our rural public-investment policy has been an inflation in farm-asset values while the returns to the human factor in rural life have fallen further and further behind those to the urban community.

Will we continue to ignore the mounting problems and social ills associated with race, with rural poverty — with hired farm labor including migratory labor?

All of these matters are involved in some degree and manner in the public policy choices which commercial agriculture will be asked to make over the next few years in farm programs. They also are related to the choices with which the USDA and the colleges are faced in deciding the focus of their research.

The reason we have many of our present problems is that commercial farmers, their leaders, the USDA, the colleges, and other rural institutions have done very badly in making these choices. In part they have not always faced the facts of life honestly. But the real explanation lies in a single-minded pursuit of self-interest made lethal by inaccurate perception of where self-interest lies.

I wish to devote the rest of this article to the behavior of these institutions. I shall argue that the key problem of U.S. agriculture, present or prospective, is its own behavior, which is distorting and disordering the decision-making processes in which it is intimately involved.

The Decision-Making Structure of Agriculture

Four developments dominate any realistic description of the policy scene today.

1. The general power structure of this society has been transformed. But the political leadership of agriculture has either not awakened to this fact or it is trapped by its own past policies and mythologies, unable — even unwilling — to adapt organization, policies, and tactics to be effective in the new *realpolitik*.
2. The commercial agricultural power structure has reached a state of extreme organizational fragmentation, and its leadership is so engrossed in internecine warfare that these fragmented elements of commercial agriculture are themselves contributing greatly to a general erosion of the political power which together they exert.
3. The entire web or rural organizations had an original common goal of the economic development of American agriculture. Thus, no matter how diverse in origin they may have been, as a result of having a common general goal, they evolved into an *interdependent* set of organizations. Today this underlying complex of *interdependent* commercial, govern-

mental, political, and educational organizations in the service of agriculture is changing, and no longer is as effective as once it was in identifying and solving the problems of rural life. The organizational system in agriculture is becoming socially disfunctional.

4. With few exceptions, in any direction you look, there are rising levels of conflict, destructive tension, and mounting evidence of what can only be described as a spectacular failure of leadership combined with "organizational dry rot." The generation of individuals who now man as well as lead these organizations do not understand their dependence one upon another; nor do they perceive the changing situation of their sister institutions well enough to be able to relate themselves in a manner that avoids unnecessary conflict. They are thus led into mutually self-destructive patterns of behavior.

The vitality of these rural institutions should be a matter of concern not just for its contributions to farmers or to rural life but for its continued potential contribution to the growth of the economy and the welfare of the American consumer.

I shall call this web of rural institutions the Agricultural Establishment.

The Disintegrating System

Over the last half of the nineteenth century and the first quarter of this century, we built a series of institutions to serve and transform agriculture from a traditional subsistence farming to a technologically progressive production process capable of sustaining higher levels of rural and national welfare. The functions of some of these institutions are now at least partially obsolete; others are so completely realized that the institutions, in order to survive, are looking for new roles. In other cases, where the old role may still be viable, the environmental facts of life have changed so greatly that the institution is under pressure to perform new functions (some not even related to rural life); and, finally, many of the old organizational forms are no longer effective. As a consequence, while the institutions survive the system is failing.

The land grant colleges and the USDA were created as research and educational organizations for the purpose of generating and extending new technologies to farming and generally aiding rural people in attaining higher level of living. Originally their organizations were strikingly similar. Today both have changed. The primary role of the USDA has been entirely transformed. Its research functions now account for less than 4 percent of its budget; about 85 percent of its budget is now devoted to gigantic programs of farm income support, conservation, and credit. As a consequence, it now is organized very differently and its decision-making structure is no longer dominated by researchers and academically oriented people. Thus, it no longer behaves (nor is it free to behave) as the university-like organization it was until the late 1930's — but many land grant universities complacently presume on their relationship with the USDA as if nothing had changed and as if the USDA were a large philanthropic foundation on the banks of the Potomac devoted to being kind to friendly and deserving colleges of agriculture. Needless to say, the USDA has failed to act in this image and the level of tension and misunderstanding between the colleges and USDA has risen greatly.

The land grant university has changed also. It was once exclusively devoted to the affairs of rural life and farming. Now, however, it is under the most intense pressure to become a full-scale, high-quality institution of higher learning. It is in the process of extending its teaching, research and public service functions not only to the rest of our society but into the international area as well.

Caught in the middle of this transformation of his university, the Dean of Agriculture finds his college beleaguered within the University by these new growing and competitive functions, abused and often abandoned by his clients and allies in agriculture, and in many ways less able to control his college's destiny than at any time since the early unsettled days of the land grant system. But the USDA, and farm people, and their representatives resent and do not understand the causes of these changes in the role, and therefore, the behavior of "their college."

Let me provide a few examples of specific attitudes and behavior that are destroying the fabric of the relationship between the USDA and the colleges of agriculture.

1. Many department heads and professors in the agricultural colleges willingly take any USDA money, if it supports their programs, but have such a negative attitude toward the USDA as a scientific environment that they would encourage their better students to seek employment in almost any place rather than the Department. Yet without the high quality national research program of the USDA and its many services, these agricultural college professionals and their departments would have only a fraction of their present capacity.

2. Similarly, many USDA research administrators frequently express deep resentment that any of "their money" goes to the colleges, most of which they view as competitive and generally inadequate research organizations with high overhead costs. Indeed, many have come to believe that scientific progress will be achieved only by the establishment of large specialized USDA-operated laboratories. Yet many of these same administrators expect the agricultural colleges to "produce" for them high-quality, well-trained talent to man the research and action organs of the Department. They refuse to believe they have any responsibility for the human investment process from which they drew much of their trained personnel.

3. Most Secretaries of Agriculture tend to view Extension as their personal field staff for *selling* new policies and action programs. Since Extension must (or should) maintain the politically neutral position of an educational agency, this expectation can only lead to frustration and recrimination.

4. There is another set of attitudes that is eroding the once close relationship of the colleges and the Department. Originally the Extension Services of the land grant colleges were intimately associated with their state Farm Bureaus. In more recent decades in practically all states this direct linkage has been broken or substantially weakened. At the same time agricultural politics has become polarized and the American Farm Bureau has aligned itself with the conservatives on all issues and with the Republican Party on most political matters. The USDA, however, whether run by

Democrats or Republicans, continues generally to regard the colleges as monolith of conservatism and often the personal property of the Republican Party. The general farm organizations share this attitude toward the colleges, and the more liberal organizations either refuse to support or directly attack the colleges of agriculture. While this characterization of the colleges is accurate for some states it is not true for the system as a whole. Rarely do the farm organizations or the USDA recognize that changes have occured or that the states and their colleges vary in their behavior, nor do they bother to test the colleges' current patterns of behavior. This attitude has had unfortunate effects on many actions of the Department. Where the colleges and their extension services actually commit themselves to a partnership with any political party or even to a distinct political philosophy, they discredit themselves and destroy the national character of the Extension system.

One could go on at length to other attitudes and behavior which are eroding the relations between the colleges and the USDA, in mutually self-destructive patterns. I do not mean to imply that these attitudes do not reflect some real problems, but, because of a mutual failure to understand the other's situation, we are letting them become destructive of the fabric of our institutions. These examples are only symptoms of the problem — which is that *the roles we play have changed.*

I submit that if these two very interdependent organizations, the colleges of agriculture and the USDA, do not understand each other's modern roles and behavior any better than this, then they cannot really understand their own very well. The same kind of evidence of mutually destructive behavior is to be found in the relationships of practically all rural institutions: the colleges, the USDA, local rural community organizations both public and private, and the many organizations that attempt to represent the various interests of the farmer including the agricultural committees of Congress.

The land grant university is no longer linked exclusively to rural institutions at either the state or the federal level. Research, teaching, and extension funds come from many sources today and not even the federal relations of the college of agriculture are predominantly or exclusively with the Department of Agriculture and the agriculture committees of Congress. The land grant university is broadening its old functions of education and service to rural America, to service and education for the whole of society. The USDA has been forced to narrow its function to service for commercial agriculture alone. The colleges of agriculture, whether they like it or not, are being forced to move in both directions simultaneously and are having a very bad time of it.

The USDA, to an even greater degree than the college of agriculture, is no longer the master of its own house to the extent that it was in the 1920's and 1930's — when it was primarily a research and educational institution. Now that it is an action agency dispensing vast sums of money which directly affect the incomes and welfare of farmers, the agricultural committees of Congress, acting as agents of the commercial interests of agriculture, have taken over a substantial portion of the Department's executive function. Until very recently the committees exercised these functions with little concern for the desires of the Secretary of Agriculture or even the President of the United States.

No Secretary of Agriculture in modern times has really had effective control of the Department of Agriculture. This frustration of the Secretary's function is a consequence of the near monopoly of power in agriculture exercised by commercial agricultural interests (including nonfarm interests allied with farming) and focused primarily in specialized commodity organizations and the grass roots farmer committee structures which extend to the Washington level. Operating through the committees of Congress, they have badly mauled the Department of Agriculture in the past when it has not behaved solely as the agent of the commercial and business interests in agriculture. This severely limits the Department's capacity for public consideration of broader rural interests or even the public interest in agriculture. That the USDA is made to behave so it injures not only the Department, but commercial agriculture. It tends to give the USDA and agriculture an image in government, and in the rest of the society, of little more than that of a powerful but narrow and badly behaved vested interest.

The agricultural colleges look a little better only because they do not run commodity programs. For the colleges, too, under somewhat similar pressures, have tended to narrow their focus *in agriculture* predominantly on the interests of commercial agriculture. Thus, it can be said that the Land-Grant-USDA System has lost its dedication to the welfare of the *entire* rural community. We long have talked about doing something for the noncommercial and the nonfarm sectors — the problems of rural communities and the poor — but we never really seem willing to put "our money where our mouth is." We have missed many opportunities. For example, issues in market organization and bargaining power are being posed with urgency and obvious relevance today. There is also an urgent need to take program action on the multiplex aspects of poverty. Yet in neither case have the colleges or USDA put enough resources into research in these areas to provide the analytical base. The problems have been identified for decades but little research done. In the case of poverty, this is because it does not benefit the power structure in agriculture and it also diverts resources from the research interests of commercial agriculture. In the case of market organization, this is because the research results almost invariably upset some politically potent part of the market structure. So now we must make decisions and take action without adequate knowledge.

Yet the Department of Agriculture when it focuses on the problems of commercial agriculture generally performs with more imagination, polish, and expertise than all but a few small parts of the rest of the federal executive. No executive department has *the capacity* for objective problem solving and for administration of complex programs which the Department of Agriculture has.

No executive department is as badly abused by those it serves as the Department of Agriculture. No other member of the President's Cabinet is subjected to the demeaning, public as well as private, political vituperation that is the daily fare of the Secretary of Agriculture — heaped upon him by the people he serves. His political usefulness is eroded in the vindictive cross fire leveled by the conflicting elements of the farm policy arena. He is held politically responsible for the design and execution of all policies by the very same brawling set of commercial agricultural interests who simultaneously attempt to deny him an effective role in the design of the same policies.

The result is that, in its efforts to limit or destroy the Secretary politically, commercial agriculture is destroying itself politically. This is not politics. Politics is the art of the possible — the compromise of conflicting interest. But in agriculture, many have forgotten what compromise is and are now engaged in a war, each to obtain his own ends, with no quarter given or expected and apparently with no concern for the long-run cost to agriculture — or to rural life, or to the Nation. Like the god of antiquity, Saturn, agriculture is devouring its own.

Changing Political Power Structure Of Commercial Agriculture

What has been the effect of the successful economic development of farming upon the political structure of commercial agriculture? In the process of increasing their productivity, farmers specialized in the production of one or a few commodities. The farm supply and farm product marketing systems have become highly specialized. Similarly, entire farming regions became specialized. Thus there have developed within agriculture many narrow and often conflicting economic and political interests. The conflicts grew so great over time that it became increasingly difficult for the general farm organizations to develop a national policy position, particularly on specific commmodity legislation. The old farm bloc of pre-World War II days broke up and the specialized commodity organizations began to assume the initiative and control over much of agricultural policy, particularly as it related to commodities. Other specialized farmer county committee structures, created during the 1930's in the price-support, conservation, and credit areas, developed national organizations to reflect more directly their special interests in the political process. This fragmentation of the political organization of agriculture has transformed agricultural policy from reasonably consistent legislation, with broad social purposes generally supported by the society, into a hodge-podge of narrow special-interest legislation, the value of which is increasingly questioned by society.

Agricultural policy has come to mean commodities and little else other than a slight seasoning of conservation and credit. Through commodity and other specialized farmer organizations, the larger successful commercial farmers have come to dominate if not monopolize the political power structure of agriculture. And in the pursuit of their own interests practically all other concerns have been sacrificed — including most prominently the interests of the many small struggling commercial operators and the more than a million even smaller noncommercial operators whose prospect for earning a better living from farming is quite limited. Forgotten also are the problems and concerns of the better part of the rural population, which as a result of the development of agriculture are no longer a part of farming. In ignoring these and other public claims for its concern and support, commercial agriculture has injured its own interests.

The specialized commodity groups continue to brawl incessantly with each other. But the composition of these groups is changing and their power in the aggregate is now declining. This decline appears to be due to two things. The first is the increasing fragmentation of producer interests. For example, in cotton the producers themselves cannot agree on what they want. For years they have been fragmented into the Southeast, Mississippi Delta, Texas, and California-Arizona areas. Today even these groups are seriously fragmented. The other cause for the decline in power lies in the increasing voice of interests other than the producers in any commodity decision-making process. In cotton, for example, ginners and handlers, textile mills, cotton brokers and exporters, and the cotton exchanges all have an effective political voice in the decision-making process. In addition, rural community banking and commercial interests, the manufacturers of farm inputs, and even organized labor have an influence on what happens. As a consequence, the level of conflict and disorder is so great at present that it is almost impossible to get agreement within agricultural committees on legislation for many specific commodities.

Because of this disorder, the power of political decision making for agriculture is already in the process of drifting or is being transferred from the agriculture committees to other places in the Congress and to the Executive Branch. The disorder not only makes it nearly impossible to get a major decision in an agriculture committee but now makes agricultural legislation so politically expensive that legislation cannot be pushed through Congress without a political brawl or a major assist from the White House or both. Indeed, agricultural legislation of the present social outlook has grown to be the single, most politically expensive part of the legislative program of any President and his party. Political capital used to push the farm program through represents a reduction in the amount of political capital available to push the rest of the program through. It would be remarkable in such a situation if the majority party and the White House did not desire a reduction both in budgetary and political costs of farm legislation.

Agriculture and the Changing Power Structure of the Society

But before farm legislation can be made more acceptable and thus lower in political cost, the leaders of farm organizations and commercial agriculture will have to do a better job of relating themselves to the present power structure of this society. The political power structure which rural America helped to create many decades ago is gone forever. Gone, too, are the days of rural dominance in the political affairs of national, state, or local government. Rural leadership shows little sign even yet of understanding that it no longer leads a political majority. If rural people and their organizations are to have any continuing major role in determining agricultural and rural policy, their minority position must be faced honestly and they must learn how to work with and influence the new power structure.

Agriculture's Political Life Style

A minority must develop leverage far beyond its own direct impact if its is to exercise any effective political power. In the U.S. political structure, minority groups have the greatest potential advantage *today* in the political process that focuses on the capture of the executive organs of government. Holding or losing the political support of minority groups can mean the difference in a party's success or failure in capturing the executive branch. Thus, to maximize their power, minority groups must focus on the political party, the instrument that focuses on the capture of the executive branch. Rural people and their leaders will have to involve themselves actively in the partisan political process, and in both parities, if they are to generate enough political power to insure a continuing major role in agricultural and rural public-policy problems.

Farm-organization leaders and rural politicians, to be effective, must back away from their traditional hard-nosed Neanderthal style and from their prepackaged ideologies to combine in a politically pragmatic manner with whomever they can. Unlike a majority group, a minority to succeed must be prepared to recognize the most urgent or reasonable objectives of others. Majority groups tend to respond only to the demands of other majority groups or coalitions, and do not need to concern themselves greatly with the claims of minorities or even with the public interest. Rural and agricultural leaders must be so concerned if they are to survive. It is the obstinate refusal of the Agricultural Establishment to accommodate itself to the major and urgent problems of urban life that has generated the present intense hostility toward all things rural or agricultural. This hostility is most evident in the urban press and the political behavior of labor, among the frustrated political leaders of the urban metropolitan complexes, and in the intellectual community of scientific and professional people, many of whom are not only opinion makers, but also integral members of the present power structure.

The Rise of Urban Fundamentalism

It is almost cosmic irony that just as rural fundamentalism is clearly losing its influence outside rural life, an urban fundamentalism of equal irrationality and virulence has risen to replace it. It now infests the seats of power like rural fundamentalism before it, disordering and distorting private, political, and bureaucratic decision-making processes. By urban fundamentalism, I understand a closed attitude of mind which asserts that urban society, its culture, and its values are intrinsically superior and should be the dominant mold in which all society is cast and the measure against which social decisions are made. This disdain of everything outside of metropolitan urban culture, like its mirror image, rural fundamentalism, is predicated on a contemptuous ignorance — a disdain for and a fear of what is not understood or not experienced. Urban fundamentalism is the result of the increasing incidence of an exclusively urban cultural experience reinforced by fifty bruising years of urban intellectual and political frustration with the political and cultural imperialism of rural life. The Agricultural Establishment has been casting its fundamentalist bread upon the waters for decades. It is now being returned, multiplied many fold.

Conclusion

The entire web of rural institutions, which I have called the Agricultural Establishment, had an original common goal of the economic development of American agriculture. Thus, no matter how diverse in origin they may have been, as a result of having a common general goal they evolved into an *interdependent* set of institutions. To be interdependent is to depend in a mutually constructive tension one on another for continued effectiveness and even existence. This common goal of the economic development of agriculture has now been substantially obtained.

As a result of the effect of this success and the impact of the economic and social forces generated by an industrializing society, this interdependent web of institutions.

1. is now developing multiple goals, many of which are in conflict;
2. is becoming ineffective in the pursuit of its goals as a result of its failure to adjust rapidly enough to the realities of its new nature and new environment;
3. is failing to understand its basically interdependent nature, and thus is in serious danger of destroying itself as an effective instrument of rural public life; and finally
4. the odds for failure are even longer for there is the clear evidence that we are in the middle of a general failure of leadership, which while common to all institutions is *particularly critical in commercial agriculture,* where the power of political decision has been vested in the recent past. The leadership in moving their own institutions today must contend with professionalized bureaucracies that show growing signs of rigidity and organizational dry rot.

The *system* of organizations in the service of agriculture is disintegrating because of a lack of breadth and flexibility of view. This system was once reasonably self-contained. It is not now. It is now dependent upon, and must now be related to, a broad range of social and economic institutions and problems that go well beyond the experience and immediate interests of commercial agriculture.

Despite many changes leading toward conflict, the fundamental institutions of agriculture are still bound together in a common destiny. This system still has great potential. However, the leaders as well as the members of these institutions have failed to understand each other's changing situation and roles, and now abuse each other for failing to behave in the old patterns. The people and institutions of agriculture — whether farmers, their organizations, the colleges, the USDA, the agriculture committees and members of Congress, and our state legislatures, or others — must learn to tolerate multiple goals in the institutions with which they must cooperate. They must accept a looser sort of partnership in working toward their goals. They must learn to be more pragmatic. They must combine on those matters where they can agree. They must not refuse to cooperate to one end just because they cannot agree on another.

The role of leadership in agriculture has grown to be nasty, brutish, and frustrating — whether one speaks of the Secretary of Agriculture, the dean of the college of agriculture, the head of a farm organization, the chairman of a congressional agriculture committee, or any other agricultural leader. This fact of life is not well appreciated even in these leaders' own organizations. Even so, the major conclusion one must draw from the self-destructive behavior of the Agricultural Establishment is that there has been a general failure of leadership in the institutions underlying the policy process.

Rural leaders have isolated themselves from the present power structure and have yet to learn that they must adapt their own position to that of various groups in the power structure if successful coalitions are to be formed and if they are thus to obtain farm or rural minority objectives in the public and private decision-making processes.

The recent Omnibus Farm Bill passed Congress in part because of the support of labor, which was obtained by the Northern rural congressmen who voted for labor's major 1965 legislative objective, repeal of Section 14b of the Taft-Hartley Act. Rural leaders and politicians will have to have the support of just such groups if rural problems are to be solved in the future in a manner generally acceptable to rural people.

It is in the self-interest of the Agricultural Establishment not only that it change its political style of life, but also that it face its past errors honestly and subject its organizational form and programs, which are increasingly difficult to rationalize or defend, to the searching gaze of objective analysis and intelligent adjustment. It is already late. If the Agricultural Establishment fails to face the facts of its existence honestly and with intelligence, many of the institutions of agriculture will continue down their present unconscious path toward social irrelevance and oblivion. If the Agricultural Establishment continues, as it often has in the past, to prevent or discourage its educational and research arms from fully servicing this function of objective analysis, or if the land grant colleges and the USDA do not have the courage to fulfill this role, the Establishment will be finished as a socially useful system in a few years in any case. And the individual institutions, while surviving any of us here, will live out their organizational lives in socially diminishing roles of rising frustration and futility. The time that remains to put agriculture's house in order may not be long.

I like the way John Steinbeck described one of his characters as possessing "a fine steel wire of truthfulness — that cut off the heads of fast traveling lies." The great strength of the Agricultural Establishment in prevailing in the policy process in the past depended not only on political power but also on a dedication to the broad objectives of society and on the Land-Grant-USDA System's capacity to "cut off the heads of fast traveling lies."

As the direct political power of the Agricultural Establishment declines or becomes diffuse, it must increasingly depend on such "fine steel wires" and a clear recognition that, to survive, it must exhibit far more relevance to the broader objectives of society.

If the Agricultural Establishment cannot develop the leadership that is capable of seeing the situation as it really is and adjusting to it, it not only will fail to survive in any systemic and socially meaningful form but the system will deserve its death. And the headstone erected by an urban society will read:

> The Agricultural Establishment of the United States:
> Its Promise Exceeded its Performance,
> And Falling into Social Irrelevance
> It Took Its Own Useless Life.
> R. I. P.

Technology, 1970

From T. C. Byerly, "Systems Come, Traditions Go," U.S. Department of Agriculture, *Yearbook*, 1970 (Washington, 1970), pp. 31–39.

Revolution has been the order of business in agriculture, and it still is. During the past hundred years, output from farming has increased about six times, measured in constant dollars. During that same period, productive farm supplies of all types have increased less than three times. Thus efficiency of production, measured in dollars has doubled.

Productivity, measured in terms of output per acre, per animal breeding unit, per man-hour, has increased steadily since the difficult days in the 1930's. Then, the land was tired and wearing out; drought beset the Plains and with it dust storms; and prices of farm and forest products hit the floor.

Through all our previous history, pioneers put new land to the plow as old lands wore out. Yields changed but little. Finally, in the thirties, the era of exploitation began to give place to the current era of conservation — of the land, water, air, and finally of our communities, of our whole environment.

Farm production now consists of the managed use of purchased materials, know-how, land, and livestock, to obtain high yields of high quality plant and animal crops. Superior seed — superior breeding stock — protection against insects, diseases, parasites, and weeds — fertilization, reproduction, planting, tillage, and harvest aided by tireless machines — water management — formulated livestock feeds — are used in effective systems.

Some of the facts of the matter are indicated in the trend in productivity for selected farm commodities during the period 1935–1967, using 1967 values as 100 percent. The number of cattle fed increased four times during this period. Production of soybeans increased 20 times. Production of broilers increased more than 50 times. Production of oranges more than doubled. Potato yield per acre trebled. Production of sweet corn for the fresh market increased four times. Corn yield trebled.

How about the other side of the coin? Farm population has dropped from 32 million in 1935 to 11 million in 1967 while the total population increased from about 125 million to about 200 million. The equivalent of almost eight million full-time jobs in farming have disappeared.

People continue to leave the farm. More farm wage workers live off the farm than on the farm. Increasingly, farmers are moving to town.

Fewer farm families keep cows and chickens; and fewer nonfarm rural families, too. Many families that move to the city don't eat as well as they were able to do in the country — no garden, no cow, no pig. National food surveys in 1965 showed that more people were ill fed then than in years earlier; and rural-urban migration was a factor.

Mechanization is a basic component of the mechanical and scientific revolution. Tractor horsepower available on farms in 1967 was more than five times greater than in 1935. In 1935, about 2 to 3 horsepower from tractors was available to each farmworker; in 1967, more than 40 horsepower per farmworker was available. Expenditures for power and repairs increased about six times over the 1935 base during the 1935–67 period.

Why have these great changes occurred? Causes are diverse. Consider broilers and eggs here from the science standpoint. Genetic improvement, nutritional information, especially vitamin D and development of means for eradicating pullorum disease, made possible the shift from a small flock, highly seasonal type of enterprise to the industrialized, highly integrated, large scale enterprises we now have.

The change to ready-to-cook chilled or frozen broilers and the sharp change in price concomitant with production efficiency have kept volume increasing steadily.

Thousands of people contributed to the growth of the broiler industry. Processing technology provided the equipment for on-line picking, eviscerating, and inspection capability at a rate of thousands of broilers per hour. Successively, the market changed from live to New York dressed — head and feet on, guts in — to the present fresh, chilled, or quick-frozen, ready-to-cook product.

In the days of the live market, barred feathers were a mark of quality. As soon as the shift to dressed marketing got into full swing, the black pin feathers of barred birds became a blemish to appearance and caused increased processing costs.

Nutrition research during the 1930's and 1940's added one vitamin after another, knowledge of essential trace minerals, and amino acids. At the end of the 1940's vitamin B 12 was discovered. It was the final link needed to complete the shift from meat, milk, and fish meals to soybeans as a principal source of protein to supplement corn for poultry and pigs—and people, too, for that matter. For B_{12} must be provided in the food of these one-stomach species while cows and sheep and other ruminants depend on bacterial production of B_{12} in their paunches.

White feathers became desirable — white feathers coupled with plump breasts and rapid growth and high feed efficiency. A great search took place in the late 1940's under the "Chicken of Tomorrow" slogan. Government, marketers, processors, and poultry breeders participated.

The search was successful. Breeding stock with the needed white feathers, plump breasts, hybrid vigor, and rapid growth and feed efficiency were found in California, in Connecticut, and other places. Commercial producers quickly changed to white feathered broilers.

Egg production has undergone changes almost as dramatic as those in the broiler industry, but by a somewhat different road. While hybrid corn was getting under way in the 1920's, a geneticist, L. C. Dunn, at the Storrs Agricultural Experiment Station in Connecticut tried inbreeding chickens.

He didn't have much luck. The stock went to pot pretty fast. So did stock in similar research in England under Michael Pease. But Morley Jull came to USDA's Agricultural Research Center in Beltsville, Md., in 1924 and started inbreeding afresh. That stock wasn't too good, either. C. W. Knox came to Beltsville in the thirties and he did some more work on inbreeding.

These and other early researches laid the foundation for production of commercial hybrids. At long last the possibility of chickens bred like corn took hold, first in the hands of hybrid seed corn companies with know-how in large-scale search and test and exploitation of superior hybrids. Now these incrossbreds compete with crossbreds, strains, and strain crosses.

The feed industry, marketing outlets, and poultry men have worked together to industrialize egg production. Confined flocks of many thousands of layers are commonplace, and egg production per hen at twice the rate of the 1930's are necessary for survival. Oh, yes, vitamin D, discovered by E. V. McCollum at the University of Wisconsin in the 1920's, is still an essential to winter egg production.

From grocery money for farm families to a business for a few thousand entrepreneurs, that's the story of poultry. So, too, from chicken on Sunday to an alternate to hamburger.

And as efficiency of the broiler industry increased, the margin per bird over production cost decreased and forced further efficiencies, increase in size of enterprise, or its abandonment.

Broiler production is highly integrated with the supply of feed, credit, and processing, and marketing of the finished product. There are, of course, analogous and older integrated systems, such as beet sugar, and fruits and vegetables for processing.

In these integrated systems, and in others now developing, computer technology will provide a new tool for greatly increasing efficiency of production, marketing, processing, and distribution.

The stress of the 1930's, necessity for increased efficiency, the search for new crops, and need for added income made farmers receptive to change. As broilers began in the thirties, soybeans started their change from a minor crop to a major one. During the 1935–67 period, soybeans have displaced oats in many Corn Belt farms and provided a new crop for acres no longer needed for cotton.

Science made adaptation of the soybean to a wide north-south range easier through the research on photo-period to which H. A. Allard and W. W. Garner of the U.S. Department of Agriculture contributed so substantially. Breeders selected soybeans for day-length flowering suited to each latitude from Louisiana to Minnesota, and soybean production increased by 20 times from 1935–1967.

Orange production increased three times during the period. Helped by research to find virus-free stock, production has grown despite freezes and diseases. It could grow because research on better concentrates and better juices, in the Utilization Research Laboratories of the U.S. Department of Agriculture, kept the demand for orange products expanding.

Corn yield increase started in the 1930's when hybrid seed became available. The scientific demonstration of hybrid vigor in corn by E. M. East at Harvard, G. F. Shull at Princeton, and D. M. Jones at the Connecticut Agricultural Experiment Station before 1920 was not put to work until the 1930's. Traditional corn breeding methods based on selection of open pollinated corn stood in the way.

Since inbreds so obviously were inferior, it took bold, young breeders and seedmen to produce and demonstrate the superiority of hybrid corn seed.

Stress of the 1930's started adoption of hybrid seed on the way; it was complete by the middle 1950's as seed adapted to the various latitudes was developed. Adoption of hybrid seed was accompanied by about a 60 percent increase in acre yield.

Hybrid seeds alone are not enough. These plus fertilizer are not enough. Add pesticides and still the story is imcomplete. The capability of the soil, estimated by a soil survey, with soil amendment by technology based on research of soil scientists and plant physiologists, are needed, too. So saline and sodic soils are made productive because L. A. Richards and other scientists at the U.S. Salinity Laboratory at Riverside, Calif., taught us and the world how to do it.

Interaction, the theme song of Charles Kellogg of the Soil Conservation Service, is the road to sustained productivity. Good seed, sufficient, well-managed water, fertilizer, and pesticide chemicals as needed, planted at the right time — not by the phase of the moon but by soil temperature and moisture in the right seedbed — and hope the rains come at the right time — all these are needed.

Corn yield has doubled since 1955, largely due to fertilizer nitrogen in the context of all the interacting factors just named — and more plants per acre, too. Basic discoveries on fixation of atmospheric nitrogen were made by the German chemist Fritz Haber and others before World War I.

Since that time the chemical industry has developed and adopted technology in the manufacture and delivery and application of anhydrous ammonia to the field that makes generous application of nitrogen profitable to the grower at current corn prices. Increased use for other crops including forest crops is also occurring.

There is some concern that excess nitrogen from fertilizer will contaminate our wells, lakes, and streams. Further technological improvements are needed so that nitrogen, whether from fertilizer, soil reserve, or manure, becomes available to crop plants as needed without excess which may be leached or volatilized from the soil.

The quadrupling of feedlot cattle is technologically based on engineering and management systems for delivering feed to large lots of cattle and establishing a continuous flow of slaughter cattle of uniform quality.

Because of its suitability for automated feeding systems, grain and other feed concentrates comprise an increasing portion of feedlot cattle diets. For the first 20 years of the 1935–67 period, beef cows replaced horses; since then, they have replaced dairy cows as milk production per cow increased through general use of tested, superior sires by artificial insemination.

Increased beef production parallels consumer income, because beef is a status meat. Increased production can bring lower prices to consumers only as technology — a higher percent calf crop and improved feed efficiency — makes it possible.

Large feedlots — especially those near cities, large dairy farms, egg, swine, turkey, and broiler enterprises bring problems of waste disposal paralleling the Augean stables. But there is no Hercules to turn an Alpheus river through them to disperse the filth, nor any river the public will long permit to be used for this purpose.

Indeed, it is our dependence on outmoded means of waste disposal, or our tendency to ignore the matter that comprises one of our most urgent problems in farm technology. A billion tons of animal wastes must be moved; hopefully to the land where their value as fertilizer and enhancing soil condition is large — but perhaps not large enough to cover handling and transportation costs to take a billion tons of wastes from feedlots, dairy, egg, and broiler facilities to croplands.

The increase in irrigated acreage is based on the wide adoption of pump irrigation in the Plains States and on the development and use of additional water supplies in the Western States. The very large increases in crop yields accomplished by irrigation and fertilization have made it profitable at current cotton, grain, and other crop prices, and at current water costs.

A dropping water table in the Texas High Plains makes future increase in water cost and ultimate decrease in supply inevitable there.

Irrigated acreage has more than doubled since 1935. Irrigated land, under proper management, yields far more than dryland. Kansas and Nebraska, which increased their irrigated acreage from about a half million acres to 3.5 million, trebled their acre yield of corn, much of which is now irrigated in these States.

As stress in the 1930's forced change, so the stress of World War II forced change. DDT was found to be a lifesaver for our troops in the tropics. It freed them of lice, fleas, mosquitoes, vectors of disease. At war's close, it became available for agricultural use. Since it was not protected by patent, chemical companies quickly came up with their own effective pesticides — the chlorinated hydrocarbons, carbamates, and organophosphates.

Weed killers that will destroy weeds without injury to crop plants came at the close of World War II and partly due to wartime research.

Dramatic increases in potato yields, and in production of sweet corn — available now year around without earworms, occurred between 1945–50. Other crops responded, too. But resistant pests soon renewed pressure for more effective pesticides.

Damage by pesticides to bees, other beneficial insects, and to fish, birds, and other wildlife have so challenged the use of chemical pesticides as to make urgent the need for new, more specific chemical pesticides, less toxic for birds and bees and fish — and people, too.

We must increase our efforts to find new and more effective cultural and biological control methods which may be integrated with minimal effective use of chemical pesticides.

Our present and prospective abundance of food, fiber, and forest products rests on the application of technology. We in the United States can look forward to vast areas of wooded lands and grassy ranges, teeming with wildlife, because technology has made our cultivated acres so productive. So, too, can all other developed countries.

Continuing development and application of technology in production of food, fiber, and forest products can supply the next generation abundantly. It can enable them to take the actions necessary to have clean air, sparkling water, and a green and pleasant world in which to live. Will the world's peoples take this course?

Assessment of the benefits of these great changes in agriculture, even in retrospect, is difficult. Assessment of current changes and those in prospect is even more difficult.

The first test, of new technology generally depend on the old, hard, questions: Will it work? Will it pay? Inherent in these questions, but seldom clear, is, Will the new technology benefit the user? the supplier of materials and equipment required? other people in the same part of agriculture? the public?

The corollary, what damage will the technology do and to whom, has lately been emphasized — especially with respect to use of pesticides, hormones, antibiotics, and fertilizer.

There is an increasing trend to monoculture and specialization, away from "general" diversified farming.

Mechanization of some operations — land preparation, planting, cultivation, even harvesting — shortens the season when extra help is needed but does not eliminate it. We have a substantial migratory farm labor force. Mechanization has not eliminated it; in fact, monoculture has aggravated the problem.

Technology is based on scientific discovery, chance discoveries, experience, invention, ingenuity, hard work, and motivation. Men seek profit; they seek recognition of their peers for their achievements; they seek opportunities for themselves, their families, their communities. They seek to reduce the burden of stoop labor. They seek the satisfaction of service.

And, finally, farmers, scientists, industrialists, everyone seeks to satisfy an insatiable curiosity. Jules Verne said, "What the mind of man can imagine, some man will do."

Technology is based on the exploitation and adaptation of discovery and invention in practice. Its application is assumed to convey benefits to the user; this is often the case. Technology is increasingly based upon a complex and systematic application of processes and equipment based on scientific information resulting from research in many scientific disciplines.

Our newly applied technology has brought indirect and sometimes unforeseen costs. Pesticides have been dispersed throughout our environment. Crop adjustments have left people without work or means of self support. Our abundance has cost the taxpayer in funds for supply management and the producer in depressed prices.

But these costs are small in comparison to the very large benefits in abundance of food, fiber, and forest products of land and other resources available for non-agricultural uses in moderate cost to consumers of products of the land, and the benefits to our friends in other lands from the materials and skills we share with them.

Future Needs for Grains

From Don Paarlberg, Changing World Needs for Grains in the 1970's. U.S. Department of Agriculture, Press release 191–73, Jan. 22, 1973.

Last year, the Soviet Union experienced a severe shortfall in its wheat crop and subsequently made unusually large grain purchases on the world wheat market, especially from the United States. In India, late and insufficient monsoon rains caused a sharp decline in grain production. In much of Southeast Asia the rice harvest was reduced by adverse weather. Drought also cut Australian wheat output.

This situation, with accompanying high prices and distorted trade patterns, has resulted, I think, from unusually poor weather. We don't know enough about the weather to engage in long-run predictions with any accuracy. It appears that weather is not a random variable. Good years show some tendency to cluster, and so do bad years. When the weather is better than average in one area it appears likely to be better than average in other areas; the same thing appears to be true when weather is bad. The recent past is not likely to be the new normal. Much work needs to be done in studying weather as related to crop yields.

I say all this in order to counter a new and growing belief that there has been a fundamental deterioration in the world food situation. Disappointing crops and high food prices are headline grabbers. For example, in the December 11 Washington Post we read "Specter of Famine Looms Over India." The same issue proclaimed "Indonesia Facing Crisis Because of Rice Shortage." There are plenty of such headlines but relatively few that call attention to the very real strides made in recent years in establishing a solid base for long-run increases in productivity in agriculture in many countries.

Some critics seem to believe that these recent events prove the Green Revolution has failed. Moreover, many are indicting technology itself, the very basis of the Green Revolution. Some ecologists, sociologists and economists say that the most important effect of improved technology is to make us worse off by accelerating imbalances in our economic structure, our social patterns, and our relationships with nature. Fortunately, people of this kind were not calling the shots during the Industrial Revolution or, more recently, the Agricultural Revolution in North America. If they had been, the world food situation would be more precarious than it is now.

World agricultural production declined slightly in 1972. Although world grain output was down from 1971, the 1972 crop was still the second largest on record. And we can expect efforts to expand grain production in 1973 as farmers and governments respond to high prices. Of course, weather and other crop conditions will be major factors in determining the success of these efforts.

Great variations in food availabilities bring about problems and real hardships, but the record indicates that there is a lot of stability in the long-run trends in food and grain production. For the world as a whole, and even for the poor countries as a group the production of food per capita has shown a rising trend, according to USDA indices dating back to 1954.

Over the period 1954–1972, there was an upward trend in the per capita production of food throughout most of the world. Africa is the exception. Food production per capita in developed regions increased about 1½ percent annually, while the less developed regions experienced a much slower rate: less than ½ of 1 percent. But the difference was less a function of food production than of the very rapid pace of population growth in the less developed world.

Our food production indices indicate an overall, long-run improvement in the world food situation. Admittedly, for the less developed countries, this improvement is from a very low level.

But these indices do not tell us all we would like to know about nutrition levels around the world. For individual countries, only the annual changes in the output of edible products are measured. The indices cannot tell us whether the products were consumed in the producing country or exported or fed to livestock or eaten by rats and mice.

Even if we had current statistics on the available supplies of food, those statistics would not tell us how many hungry people there are. For many reasons, including poverty, inadequate distribution facilities, persistence of traditional habits, tastes and taboos, some people have inadequate diets, even in a rich country with abundant food. Our indices are averages and do not pinpoint many special problems. As has been pointed out, one would not be comfortable with a hand on a hot stove and a foot in the icebox. Yet, statistically speaking, the temperature might be fine, on the average. Despite their limitations, I think these indices do point to the general direction in which we are headed, a course of improvement in diets around the world.

Most of the world's population relies upon high carbohydrate foods — cereals, sugar, roots, tubers and plantains — for a major share of its diet. Cereals are the most important food staple group, directly accounting for almost two-thirds of the average per capita calorie intake in the Far East and nearly half of the calorie value of the diet in the Soviet Union and Eastern Europe. Rice and wheat are consumed in the largest quantities, but corn is the principal cereal in much of Africa and Latin America.

Cereals are also the major protein source. Even in areas where animal products are relatively plentiful, cereals still furnish a large part of the total protein supply. In less developed areas, dependence on cereals for protein is especially important.

Cereals, however, are more than foodstuffs. Less than half of the cereals produced (outside Communist Asia) are used for directly consumed food. According to FAO food balances for 1964–66, 48 percent of the cereals was used for food, 38 percent for animal feed, and 14 percent for seed, starch, liquor and other uses.

We can expect the direct food use of cereals to rise as population grows. But the relative importance of the direct food use of cereals will decline. We have comparable statistics for the OECD countries for the 1954–56 and 1964–66 average periods. The total quantity of cereals used for food went up slightly but per capita use fell 10 percent. However, non-food use of cereals per capita went up 24 percent in the decade.

When we look at the total production of grain over the last two decades, we see a great difference in the performance of the developed and the less developed regions. Developed countries increased their total production of grains more than 60 percent with hardly any increase in the total area planted to grains; thus all the increases came from higher yields. On the other hand, the less developed countries, while increasing their production by about three-fourths, expanded their total area in grains by about one-third. Over this period the average yield per hectare of grains in the developed countries increased twice as fast as the average yeilds in the less developed countries. Current overall average grain yields in the less developed regions are only about 60 percent of those in the developed countries.

Wheat and rice yields have increased dramatically in particular less developed areas and even in particular countries, largely as a result of the pioneering work done at this institution. Average yields are increasing in the less developed countries as a group. But there is as yet little evidence of revolutionary change on a broad basis. While astonishing progress has been made in developing new grain technology, the general adaptation of these advances still has a long way to go. The upward trend in average rice yields in the less developed countries has not accelerated in recent years. Since the early 1960's average wheat yields have been increasing faster than before, but not so fast as in the developed countries.

This in no way denies the great importance of the technological changes which have been labeled the Green Revolution. The general adoption, or rather adaptation, of these improved practices remains to be accomplished. And, of course, continued and expanded research work is needed to hold the ground that has been gained and to achieve the additional gains that are needed.

Recently there have been reports of a number of problems associated with the implementation of the new technology. These problems include:

1. The need for better water control systems to permit more efficient irrigation.
2. Salinity and water logging — old problems that are being aggravated by new irrigation development and unlined canals.
3. Land fragmentation, which increases the difficulty of implementing the technology of the Green Revolution.
4. Insufficient capital to meet the increased requirements for purchased inputs.
5. Inadequate extension education to inform farmers of the best use of machinery and agrichemicals.
6. Inadequate pest control.
7. Inadequate food storage, along with rodent and vermin control.
8. Insufficient farm-to-market transport.
9. Excessive reservoir siltation due to lack of proper watershed protection.

Admittedly there are these problems. Most of them can be alleviated by additional and improved technology. But criticism of the Green Revolution comes also from another source — from those who challenge technology itself. Undeniably, there are extremely important economic, ecological and social problems associated with technological change and economic growth. They must receive attention, more than they have had. But to stop all change and growth is not the proper solution. I agree with Rene Dubos, who said in a recent address to the American Association for the Advancement of Science: ''The human use of natural resources and of technology is compatible with ecological health.''

I know that this conference is focused on food production, not on population growth. Nevertheless, I want to comment on the population problem. Unless the rate of growth in the world's population is checked there is no solution to the world food problem. The agronomists do not have the solution, the plant breeders do not have it, nor do the plant pathologists have it; it does not exist. Long range projections of present rates of population growth simply run off the chart and beyond the range of agricultural solutions that are either possessed or conceivable. For some decades agriculture can meet the needs of a population growing at present rates. But time will run out. By the extraordinary accomplishments of agricultural scientists both here and elsewhere, valuable time has been bought with which to check the rate of population growth. That time should be used to good advantage. There is heartening progress in certain countries.

The rapid expansion in population not only places great stress on the food supply; it also brings social unrest, political disturbance, and environmental degradation. Unchecked population growth may encounter these latter problems before the food supply becomes severely limiting. There may be limitations on population growth that are more critical than the one on which Malthus focused.

With rising incomes, people consume more food and particularly higher quality and more expensive foods, which require greater agricultural resources for their production. Rising demand for animal products generates a demand for grain for feed. In societies which have moved away from a subsistence orientation, prices largely determine what food is produced, how much, and to whom it is distributed. Social welfare programs to feed particularly disadvantaged groups make important contributions to the nutrition of some.

Economists have devoted considerable attention to measuring the relation of income to the demand for food. It is generally agreed that the proportion of income spent on food changes greatly as the level of income changes, but there is uncertainty as to the magnitude and rapidity of the changes. Most studies of the relations between per capita incomes and food consumption have measured food by monetary value. But this is a deceptive measure. Poor people will eat a larger amount of their accustomed diet if they can afford it. But the main way in which the value of food consumed increases is through changes in the number of different foods consumed and substitution of higher unit value foods for lower value ones. Even more important in the richer countries is the increase in expenditures on the services to related marketing and processing foods as incomes increase.

People with higher incomes generally buy more meat, dairy products, fruits, vegetables and sugar. Since most of these foods are nutritionally desirable, an improved diet is to some extent selected by consumers as their incomes rise. For large groups of people, when diets in which animal protein is important are compared to diets based mainly on cereals and to diets consisting largely of roots and tubers, the protein content of the former tends to be greater, and the quality of the protein nutritionally better.

While increased consumption of animal protein usually provides a nutritionally improved diet, it is now recognized that combinations of fish and vegetable protein can also provide an adequate balance of amino acids. Fortunately, good nutrition can be obtained by a very wide variety of combinations of foods, with consequent great spread in cost. Pulses can be very helpful in providing a diet nutritionally adequate in protein at much lower cost than animal products. For example, protein from beef usually costs many times as much as protein from soybeans.

Fortification of foods by adding missing elements and special feeding programs for groups such as school children and pregnant women can help to overcome the income constraints to improved nutrition. Within the next decade substantial progress will be made in the breeding of staple crops with more and better protein. This can be an excellent way of improving diets in the poor countries.

Scientific and technological progress in agriculture must be accelerated, especially in the poor countries. Expanding needs for food and the limitations of land make it clear that technological developments to increase pre-hectare crop yields are essential. Those affluent people from the advanced countries who recommend a slowdown in the rate of economic growth are acting with propriety when they advocate this for themselves. They are in a less defensible position when they recommend this for others in other countries, who are less fortunate.

Usually, until economic developments gets well underway, agricultural methods change only slowly. To a large extent agricultural production increases through expansion onto additional land and by use of traditional methods. Most developing countries have been able to expand their cultivated area by putting crops on land formerly unused or occupied by pasture or forests.

However, good unused land is becoming less readily available throughout the poor countries, and especially in a number of countries in Asia, Central America, the Near East, and Northwest Africa. In much of Africa south of the Sahara and in South America, the man-land ratio is less adverse. But, to make use of much of the large reserves of land not now cultivated would require large expenditures for clearing jungles, establishing soil conservation programs, building irrigation systems, controlling malaria and tsetse flies, and building new settlements for colonizers. For these and other reasons, the moving of large numbers of people to remote new areas is difficult and usually has not been very successful.

Multiple cropping and inputs such as fertilizer, insecticides, herbicides, and improved seed are, in a real sense, substitutes for land. Although, of course, these inputs must be applied to land, they make the land so much more productive that less land is needed or the shortage of land becomes a much less restricting element on agricultural production. The increasing use of improved seed, chemicals, and machinery not only has been the main factor in increasing agricultural output in the rich countries, but has necessarily led to a greater commercialization of farming, a since more and more of the inputs come from outside agriculture and require money outlays.

Substitution of machinery, and especially large-scale machinery, for labor is one of the most significant characteristics of agriculture at the stage of development reached in Western Europe and the United States. However, in many of the poor countries, because of the rapid increase of population in rural areas, the farm labor force will grow at a very fast rate for a good many years. Thus, the problem will tend to be more in the direction of finding productive work on the farm or in farm-related activities rather than in supplanting farmers with machinery.

There will need to be further developments and changes in technology, the marketing situation, availability of credit, and other aspects of agriculture. Research should continue to develop still better varieties of grain and other crops.

The title of my talk refers to the 1970's. I am well aware of the hazards of trying to look ahead so many years. I have already said that the weather cannot be predicted with accuracy so far into the future. There are other important forces that cannot be predicted. One such is government policy with respect to agricultural production and trade. Another is the rate of development and spread of new technology, such as are involved in the new varieties of grain. Another is the rate of increase in the population and of income, which are the main factors on the demand side. The income effects on the demand for food grains and for livestock products (and thus for feed grains) may be greater than we had thought.

The central question is: Is the recent shortfall in world grain production simply a fluctuation around the long-run trend; or does it indicate a major change in the trend itself? Let's look at what the experts have said about the trends and about the future for world grains. The main producers of long-run projections of world production, utilization and trading of agricultural commodities are the FAO and the Economic Research Service of the USDA.

In 1971, FAO published a major two-volume set of agricultural commodity projections for the period 1970–1980. This study was a continuation of previous FAO studies of the outlook for agricultural commodities. The data used generally extended through 1969 or 1970. The study concludes that by 1980 the average "shortage" of food will be somehwat less than at present, but that "the absolute number of people short of food may be much the same as today." The study also concludes that the outlook for protein nutrition is better than was believed on the basis of earlier studies. In fact, "diets would become more diversified in both high income and developing countries with a continuing shift to animal products, fruit and vegetables from cereals and roots." The study also concludes that substantial world "surpluses" are likely for wheat, rice, and coarse grains, as well as for other products.

I would like to add a parenthetical comment here. I think the terms "surplus" and "shortage" can be misleading when we are talking about long-run projections. In a sense, there never are "surpluses" or "shortages" of food; everything gets used up and no one is able to subsist on unproduced food. When food is abundant there is an improvement in diets. When crops are poor diets deteriorate.

In 1971 the U.S. Department of Agriculture also published projections of the agricultural commodities to 1980. These projections are being revised. I have some preliminary results. The Department also concludes that per capita nutritional levels of the LDC's are likely to improve. Their projections suggest that under normal weather conditions the world's capacity for production of cereals will increase faster than consumption and that thus there will likely be a rebuilding of wheat stocks, downward pressure on prices, and possibly programs to restrict production in the major grain exporting nations. These projections do not take into account unusual years such as the poor year 1972, or some of the exceptionally good years we have had in the past.

Looking at the separate cereal markets, the analysts still expect consumption and trade of wheat and rice to grow less rapidly than that of coarse grains. The growing need for feed for livestock and poultry improves the outlook for coarse grains.

The projections suggest that countries in the developed and in the centrally-planned parts of the world will continue to be the major producers and consumers of wheat and coarse grains. Trade will continue to flow from the five or six major developed exporters to other developed and developing countries. The LDC's will continue to import wheat and coarse grain despite substantial increases in grain production. China will likely import wheat and export rice. The potential trade levels of the USSR and Eastern Europe remain a mystery, but these projections suggest that the USSR and Eastern Europe will be close to self-sufficiency in grains by 1980. Obviously policy decisions and trade relations could change this. Decisions regarding levels of stocks needed, and amount of animal products to be produced or a series of years with bad weather could significantly change the trade picture.

The projections suggest that consumption of wheat will grow about as fast as production in the LDC's. Per capita consumption of both wheat and coarse grains in 1980 in the LDC's will generally increase but the levels are low compared with the rest of the world. A more rapid increase in production in many of the LDC's could easily be consumed at home. On the other hand the major exporters of wheat and coarse grains will likely find domestic consumption and exports growing slower than production.

Rice trade is small relative to total consumption of rice in the major rice producing and consuming regions. The projections indicate that trade will remain small. Major increases in rice consumption in Asia will more likely come from larger domestic production than from larger trade. Appended tables give these projections.

There are many factors which could significantly change this picture of the future world grain situation. In addition to the possible changes mentioned earlier, the following factors need to be watched carefully.

1. The petroleum-producing regions of Latin America and West Asia could decide to produce or import more animal products in order to upgrade their diets. This would increase the need for feed grains.

2. The liberalization of world trade could alter production and trade patterns, especially for the developed nations.

3. Major breakthroughs or even continued steady progress in the work you all are doing could increase crop yields, change production patterns, change production costs, and boost nutritional values of cereals. These changes would send us back to our computers for a reassessment of the world grain picture.

In the nineteen-sixties, when there were several bad crop years and the mood of the world food supply turned pessimistic, our analysts in the Department of Agriculture continued to project an increase in the per capita supply of food. They were right. Now, in the 'seventies, the mood has again turned pessimistic and again our analysts project improvement in dietary levels. Let us hope they are right again. Whether they are right or wrong depends in large measure on the scientists and technologists in this audience and in other research centers around the world.

TABLE 1 — World production, consumption and net trade of grain, 1964–66 and 1969–71 with projections for 1980[1]

Commodity and Item	Developed countries[2]			Central plan countries[3]			Developing countries[4]			World		
	1964–66	1969–71	1980	1964–66	1969–71	1980	1964–66	1969–71	1980	1964–66	1969–71	1980
	Million metric tons											
Wheat												
Production	109.1	112.2	130.8	122.8	142.7	176.3	47.2	63.0	91.1	279.1	317.9	398.2
Consumption	78.7	87.8	96.2	136.9	147.1	181.3	66.1	82.7	120.4	281.7	317.6	397.9
Net trade[5]	32.9	29.2	34.3	−14.1	−4.4	−5.0	−17.8	−21.8	−29.3	−1.0	−3.0	0
Coarse grains												
Production	222.2	274.4	349.0	163.1	194.5	244.8	108.0	123.5	160.1	493.3	592.34	753.9
Consumption	235.9	272.7	339.7	163.1	198.0	245.9	103.1	118.2	163.7	502.1	588.9	749.3
Net trade[5] (Low)	−3.4	−0.9	4.8	0	−3.5	−1.1	4.9	5.9	−3.6	1.5	1.5	0.1
(High)			17.5			−10.0			−7.5			0
Milled rice[6]												
Production	15.0	16.7	15.9	64.4	63.8	78.2	93.0	114.5	155.4	172.4	195.0	249.5
Consumption	14.3	13.7	14.1	64.0	63.5	77.5	94.3	116.4	157.7	172.6	193.6	249.4
Net trade[5]	0.4	1.8	1.8	0.4	0.3	0.7	−1.1	−1.9	−2.3	−0.3	0.2	0.1
Total grains												
Production	346.3	403.3	495.7	350.3	401.0	499.3	248.2	301.0	406.6	944.8	1,105.3	1,401.6
Consumption	328.9	374.2	450.0	364.0	408.6	504.7	263.5	317.3	441.8	956.4	1,100.1	1,396.6
Net trade[5, 7]	29.9	30.1	40.9	−3.7	−7.6	−5.4	−14.0	−17.8	−35.2	0.2	−1.3	0.1

[1]Preliminary projections, minus indicates net imports.
[2]Includes United States, Canada, Western Europe, Japan, Australia, New Zealand and South Africa.
[3]Includes Eastern Europe, USSR and the People Republic or China.
[4]Includes rest of world.
[5]Some regions do not balance because of stocks.
[6] 1969–71 column is an average centered on 1969.
[7]Low net trade alternative.

TABLE 2 — World per capita consumption of grains, 1964–66, and 1969–71 with projections for 1980[1]/

	Wheat	Coarse grains	Milled rice[2]	Total grain
		Kilos per person		
Developed countries[3]				
1964–66	118	352	21	491
1969–71	125	387	20	532
1980	123	433	18	574
Central plan countries[4]				
1964–66	306	298	3	607
1969–71	323	344	4	671
1980	352	397	6	755
Developing countries[5]				
1964–66	42	66	60	168
1969–71	46	66	66	178
1980	51	69	66	186
World				
1964–66	86	153	52	291
1969–71	87	162	54	303
1980	89	168	56	313

[1]Preliminary projections.

[2]1969–71 for rice is an average centered on 1969.

[3]Includes United States, Canada, Western Europe, Japan, Australia, New Zealand and South Africa.

[4] Eastern Europe and USSR only. Projected per capita consumption for the Peoples Republic of China in 1980 for wheat is 42 kilos, for coarse grains 93 kilos and for milled rice 84 kilos.

[5] Includes rest of world.

Future Structure of Agriculture

From Harold F. Breimyer, Structure of Agriculture: The Policy Issue. Paper delivered before the Southern Agricultural Economics Assn., Feb. 7, 1973.

Each generation believes it has a monopoly on crises. Its spokesmen declare how exceptional are the perils of its day. Crossroads are invariably said to loom ahead.

It is therefore with diffidence that I declare my uneasy feeling that our nation is approaching a crisis decision as to the kind of economy and kind of government that are to prevail through ending years of our century. I am not timid to the point of silence because I have not customarily played a Cassandra role. My direst warnings have been of prospective demise of central markets for setting cattle prices.

I cannot here relate all the factors that contribute to my anxiety. Nor does my topic accommodate such a confessional. I will touch on a few developments that disturb me. The purpose of this sobering introduction is to justify treating my subject not in agricultural chauvinism, nor as microdecisions such as whether a hog farmer ought to accept sows on lease. The issue of the future structure of agriculture is part and parcel of more comprehensive issues as to the structure of the economy and therefore also of the structure of the government that necessarily gives direction to the economy.

In brief summary, I am apprehensive on the following grounds:

1.   A retarding rate of growth of the economy, due to declining birth rate and increasing tightness of resources including the cost of cleaning up those we still have and disposing of their refuse.

2.   A highly skewed distribution of wealth that was tolerable during an expanding economy but is fraught with social chaos when that expansion slows.

3.   Imminent scarcity and eventual exhaustion of some of our essential mineral resources. This ties back not only to item 1 but to item 2 also, for the monopoly value of the remaining reserves will be astronomical.

4.   A system of government that probably will not prove adequate to the task ahead. Our governmental system, like our economic system, was well suited to an economy of relative plenty. It is not designed for the forthcoming economy of scarcity. In particular, our forefathers, for reasons that were appropriate to the time, were fearful of overcentralization of power. They relied heavily on dispersed balance of power. Balanced power works best when not too much exercise of it is required. In wartime we almost abandoned the principle. We are now seeing a trend toward centralization, not only in abdication by the Legislative to the Executive but in promised reorganization of the Executive Branch which would transform that branch from a gravitational federalism that resembles our solar system to a direct command organization.

5.   Accretions of private power, primarily in the conglomerates and above all the multi-national conglomerates. These not only interfere with the workings of a competitive enterprise system but seriously weaken the capacity of government. The old kings knew better than to let any noble acquire power greater than theirs. Modern democracies aren't that smart.

6.   A reorientation of moral values and social structures. This last reason for my concern is hardest to phrase. It relates to the conventions of our society, which has abandoned religion as the central moral code and weakened the family as the mutual support unit. Reliance is placed instead on secular science for our philosophical underpinning and on private and public bureaucracy as the support institutions.

Each of these points is perhaps debatable, and customary language is scarcely adequate for capsule communication. But if even a few of them possess partial validity, they suffice to put the structural issue in agriculture into a catholic or even cosmic context.

How indeed shall the resources for producing life-sustaining food and fiber be organized? Who shall own the physical component, and who control? What shall be the role of the human participant, and what combination of incentives and sanctions shall guide his efforts?

These are timeless questions. On other occasions I have pointed out that our prevailing agricultural system in the U.S., the market proprietorship, is rare both historically and geographically. Not often in time and space has the precious resource of the land been held in small units, and even more rarely have those units been operated by freeholders. What shall be the organizational answer for the future?

Goals; 1. High farm productivity. The policy issue posed before us has two prongs. One relates to our goals as to the kind of food-and-fiber system we want. The second concerns the policy instruments we might be willing to apply in order to get what we want. These are just the familiar ends and means; but as every philosopher declares, democracy must consider both ends and means and can scarcely distinguish between the two. That is, we are selective not only as to goals but as to devices for pursuing them.

Some of the goals for our food-and-fiber system are well known. Perhaps the first is high farm productivity, though why we should go wild about that goal when we subsidize resource idleness I cannot quite explain.

In the North Central Extension project of which I have been a member, and to which I will refer later, the unanimous judgment was that productivity will not differ enough under various forms of organization to be worth a moment's worry. Let's dismiss that one.

Traditionally, we have been concerned for the income and material level of living for those who remain on land. To our credit, we give first attention to the operators — the people who plow the furrow and feed the hogs — as contrasted with absentee owners. But only with the surviving operators. We abandon the displaced; that is to say, the rejected. This theme has been developed often, and needs no elaboration here.

It has been a long, hard fight to win sympathetic attention for hired farm laborers.

Other goals merit equal billing. Let me mention a few that I believe to belong on the roster of goals, or at least potential goals, of policy for structural organization of agriculture.

2. *Social stability.* This is the general term that cloaks many issues in socio-economic class relationships. Our object is a system of relationships that meets our moral standards and thereby yields an acceptable degree of stability. We reject repression as a substitute for stability.

For some reason economists shy away from this consideration in agricultural policy. How can any student of history do so? The record of the ages is replete with social conflict stemming from rigid and exploitive class distinctions in agriculture. Make no mistake, agriculture lends itself readily to a highly stratified social system.

Social stability is ordinarily considered alongside concepts of status. Certainly our farmer-forbears' dreams combined a personal status free of feudal bonds with hopes for stable communities. Those dreams led to a small unit freehold system of farming. To be sure, limitless expanse of land made it easy for them to indulge their ideology.

Early American farmers wanted proprietary status, which includes the managerial prerogative. So do Missouri farmers today.

3. *Optimum performance in food production and distribution.* Objective performance norms must be set for the food distribution system, however it be organized. As inherent productivity of the land resource is about the same in any system, and economy of size or scale does not characterize farming as it does manufacturing, the target of concern is those twin companions of imperfect compe-

tition, (1) monopolization (really, oligopolization) and (2) excessive costs of non-price competition.

Few sectors of the economy are so fertile with possibilities for exploitive monopolization as is the farming of land. Even when atomistically organized, farming can generate enormous returns to land as the fixed but vital factor of production. Because aggregate demand for food is so inelastic, any successful effort to create scarcity would yield an enormous additional profit. The possibility of doing so is attractive!

Raw farm products are now sold with a minimum of promotion, advertising, new product development. A few economists deplore this fact but most consumers seem to glory in it. Non-price competition with its costs is confined to the later stages in distribution, and is much more elaborate for certain food products than others.

In all the opinion surveys I have seen, urban consumers show sharp sensitivity to how alternate kinds of agriculture would affect the cost of food.

4. *Conservation of resources, environmental protection.* In A.D. 1973 one goal, and therefore one test, for any organizational system for agriculture must be how well it conserves resources and protects the environment.

5. *Development of rural communities.* If we assume that the rhetoric about wanting to protect and develop our rural communities is not entirely idle, this must be a factor that enters into any policy for the organization of agriculture. The various forms of organization do differ in this regard. This consideration is readily accepted in policy circles — until it is converted into goal number 6 calling for increased employment in farming.

6. *Opportunities for employment.* Should the effect on employment be a consideration in a choice among systems for organizing agriculture?

If we are sure we will always have full employment in the economy, this can be disregarded. If chronic unemployment is our destiny, while urban ghetto enclaves become both symbol and substance of what we do *not* want, it is conceivable that we will stop applauding how fast we kick people out of agriculture, and begin to search for more opportunities there.

Categories of Organizational Structure

If the preceding statement of goals is approximately accurate, we next ask how various kinds of organization of agriculture rate when measured against them. What is the scorecard of each?

I will necessarily condense my remarks, and will draw heavily on the work of a group of extension economists in North Central States. We have published one report and a second, a set of pamphlets, is due off the press soon. When we began our study we discovered quickly that our profession is handicapped in treating the subject by the absence of a generally accepted system or framework for analysis. We drew up our own. More accurately stated, we drew up two. In our 1972 publication we explained how the organization of agriculture is determined by:

Access to farmland
Access to technical knowledge
Access to commercial inputs
Access to markets

Rules and laws affecting such factors as risk abatement, income tax rates, pollution control, land retirement payments, etc.

In our pamphlets we are describing four "pure" farming systems plus a combination:

Dispersed open market

Corporate

Cooperative

Government-administered

Combination

The corporate includes both contractual and giant-corporation operatorship. The cooperative is no innocuous voluntary unit but a full-contract set-up. . . .

Selective Comparisons

The digest that follows will relate to only three departures from traditional U.S. agriculture: absentee landholding of family sized farms; giant-unit operatorship; contractual integration.

Absentee landholding. This would put land in the hands of a large *rentier* landholding class. The principal consequences would affect, obviously, the role and status of farmers, and income distribution.

All super-marginal land generates unearned income and as land becomes scarcer that capacity multiplies. If a separate social class gets hold of most of the land, it can live in luxury on its *rentier* income.

Such a social system violates all our tenets of democracy. It has been the scourge of nations in the past and continues so for many today. Our development counsellors exhort nations so burdened to undertake agrarian reform. Fine; but we ought also be mindful of our own state of affairs.

However, to date we have not violated this tenet extensively. Many of our landlords are retired farmers or widows of farmers. They are not a vested-interest social class. Perhaps the paramount trend is to make absentee landlords out of over-paid city lawyers, doctors, and university professors.

Giant-unit landholding. This not only puts ownership into non-operator hands but employs industrial techniques, particularly job specialization, in managing farms. As in industry, there is a layer-cake hierarchy of supervision and tasks. Persons who work on land or in feedlots are simply wage laborers.

The owner may be a non-farm corporation or a very large farmer (almost always incorporated).

Obviously, not a penny of the unearned income from land normally goes to farm workers. Presumably it would go to stockholders, although the suspicion circulates that officers of the firm might latch on to a few shekels. Moreover, that return to land would be not only the familiar rent but capital gains also. A vice president of Tenneco was candid when he declared that his company did not expect to make any profit from its current immense farming operations; it was banking on inflationary rise in price of its land.

Insofar as this system widens the income gap between workers and owners it jeopardizes social stability. Even more unsettling is the likelihood that farm workers would themselves adopt the ways of industry and organize to add to their income.

Neither the strike that often accompanies negotiation nor any policy of suppression is very appealing.

Contractual integration. Closely related is contractual integration, a system that lets the operator keep his land but removes part of the capital-supplying and much of the managerial role. The degree of transfer to management varies according to terms of contracts. Implications of a contractual agriculture have been reviewed often. Scattered islands of integration are inconsequential. On the other hand, when a commodity goes entirely contractual, as broilers have done, there is danger of circumscribing farmers' opportunities. Aside from the effect on income distribution, itself hard to predict (though greater inequity is likely), integration like giant farming breeds class division and invites collective organization and action. We don't have good experience models for predicting how an organized contractual agriculture would perform.

For other performance tests contractual and giant-unit agriculture can be considered together. Both are marked by concentrated economic power. For most tests we lack reliable evidence. Much doubtless would depend on how large the firms might become. If big enough, they could invoke some of the monopoly power that is a fright to all consumers. Granted, the public might use its own political power to put them all under a strict price-control blanket. It *might*; the obstacles to doing so are formidable.

Effect on rural community? My extension colleagues are virtually unanimous in believing that this test is about the easiest to apply. Giant and contractual agriculture would do it harm.

Conservation of resources and environmental protection? Here again, we have little to go by. If the coal companies of Missouri provide our example, we should worry. Except when subjected to vigorous public pressure their score seems to be exploitation 100, conservation 0.

On the other hand, an agriculture organized in large units might apply pollution control laws more effectively than family farms do. The reason is that industrial-type firms have an administrative mechanism for doing that sort of thing. One big plus for corporate style management is that it is experienced in applying rules, especially fine print rules.

Dispersed Open Market Proprietorships

Finally we must ask, what about dispersed open market proprietary farming — the so-called family farm? Have our forefathers' ideas been disproved? Have their dreams vanished?

First, let it be clear that our present farming is by no means all family farm. My estimates are that 5 to 7 percent of all marketings come from giant-unit farms, and another 12 to 15 percent from contractual integration. Not more than 80 percent is family farm; and this figure is receding.

Far from being the uniform, almost idyllic sector that Jefferson envisaged, U.S. farming has as sharp divisions *relatively* as do most industrial and commercial parts of the economy. Tom Stout at Ohio State has long nagged us with data supporting that allegation.

For my part, I am generally partial to traditional farming, yet I am somewhat ambivalent. On the one hand, I am confident that status is an important considera-tion, as it relates to human values and motivation and also to the strength of our social institutions. Further, the combining of several roles in the family farmer reduces the danger of social conflict. It is hard to stir up a capital-labor or landlord-tenant conflict if the same person is capitalist, laborer, and land-owner. As there is no compelling technological reason for denying farmers a proprietary status, much is to be said for granting it to them.

On the other hand, a seminar speaker at Missouri reminded us recently that small farmers are the epitome of the *petite bourgeoisie,* with all their pretenses and prejudices.

When addressing the independent bankers of our nation I put my mixture of feelings into these words:

The family farm . . . strengthens the family as an institution. It generates various desirable personal qualities. It breeds a sense of responsibility that is absent in obscure posts in corporate bureaucracy. But the rural community has its social class lines and its discrimina-tion. Large farmers, however sterling their personal qualities, often are more interested in squeezing the smaller farmers out of farming than in helping them stay in. Established families sometimes treat newcomers as interlopers . . .

I could add to compelling evidence that political failures of agriculture to organize for cooperation or bargaining are chargeable not to farmers' minority status — their favorite plaint — but to divisiveness within the farming community. The Farm Bureau's ambitious American Agricultural Marketing Association offers a good example. When it begs other farm groups to help it firm up a legal base for bargaining it encounters cold shoulders. But it also has trouble with its own parent organization. Its original drive to organize broiler growers was resisted not only by integrated processors, but by some Farm Bureau scions who identified more with those integrators than with obscure hill farmers who tend fowl for a living.

Structure of Agriculture and the Perils of Our Times

It is time to go back to the opening theme.

Slowdown of economic growth, incipient scarcity of mineral resources, alarming inequity in distribution of wealth, untested capacity of government: these will live with us, or we with them, in decades ahead. In two short centuries we have devastated a continent. Science aided the process; worse, it gave us a meretricious ideology, a faith

. . . that if the man-hour efficiency of all industries could be increased so greatly as to bring the world into a period of *abundance,* in place of the medieval, feudal, of mercantile . . . *scarcity,* then all the conflicting disagreements and class conflicts . . . would sink to insignificance . . .

The trust probably was never justified, but in any event it becomes a misplaced trust as the resource base for abundance erodes away. A new day of reckoning now appears before us. The reckoning will include a choice as to our system for organiz-ing our agriculture.

So I say, let's don't reckon for an agriculture that: (1) speeds depletion of resources; (2) worsens distribution of wealth; (3) adds to accretions of private power; (4) makes food unnecessarily costly; (5) reduces opportunities for employment; (6) puts undue strains on exercise of government; (7) depreciates the status of the individual; (8) erodes moral values; (9) weakens the fibre of the community.

My argument points toward a decentralized agriculture. My main tenets are to avoid bringing farmers into mass organization and mass contest, and land into monopoly control. But this is not a plea for the *status quo*. Any agriculture of the future must help relieve the perils of our times and pursue the goals set for it.

One thing more remains. If my apprehensions as to our future are correct, agriculture, recently relegated to the shadows, will move front and center. Reasons are two. First, under stress the public reasserts its concern for fundamentals to existence such as the source of its food supply. And second, as shortage of energy presses upon us we will re-learn that the only renewal supply on this planet is solar energy converted by the biological process of photosynthesis. The economics and sociology and political science of the organization of those processes that alone can convert rays from the sun into protein and vitamins and fiber and timber — this will be the heart of the issue of what kind of agriculture we are going to have, who will control it, and who will get the benefit of its magic productivity.

Index

System'' (Ezekiel), 2328–2333
"Agriculture and Soils of California,
  The'' (Hilgard), 1478–1509
"Agriculture in the Tropical Islands of the
  United States'' (Cook), 1723–1739
Agriculture in an Uneasy World,
  3029–3054
*Agriculture of the United States in 1860;
  Compiled from the Original Returns
  of the 8th Census* (Kennedy),
  913–962
Aircraft
  and introduction of new plant pests,
    2791–2792
  uses in agriculture, 3455–3462
"Aircraft in Agriculture'' (Isler),
  3455–3462
Akikiyu tribe, 3259–3260
Alabama, 4-H clubs in, 2508
Alabama Agricultural Experiment Station
  Corn, Cotton, Rye Chufas, 1250–1258
Alaska
  agriculture in, 3353–3373, 3374–3390
  Matanuska colony in, 3358–3373
  reindeer in, 1640–1645, 2541–2544,
    2755–2756
Alaska Agricultural Experiment Station,
  3380
  Metanuska Valley Memoir, 3353–3373
Alaska College of Agriculture, 2756
Albany, New York, 206
Albumen, 1689
Alcohol, and farm labor, 1890–1891
Alderney cows, 1085, 2834
Alfalfas
  blight-resistant, 2526, 2527
  in California, 1492
  Colorado Station work in 1898 with,
    1310
  cultivation in New Jersey, 464–465
  on dairy farm, 1772
  and fertilizers, 2727
  in Kansas, 1276–1277
  in New Mexico, 1656–1657
  on sheep farm, 1772–1773
Alfalfa wilt, controlled by breeding, 2532
"Alfalfa Wilt Control by Breeding
  Making Remarkable Progress''
  (Tysdal), 2532
Algerian flint wheat, 828
Alkali soil, 1271–1273, 1487–1488
  crops for, 1273
  and irrigation, 1420–1421
Allan, William, 926
Allen, John, 872, 879
Allen, Jonathan B., 1719
Allen, R.L., 764, 765
Alliance Exchange, opening of,
  1605–1606
Alligator pear, in American tropics, 1728
Allis-Chalmers Manufacturing Co., 3422,
  3426, 3432
Almond trees, 297, 300
Alsacian cabbage, 835
Alsyke clover, 838
Aluminous earth, 737
Alurel tulip tree, 141
Alvarado Company, 1139

Alvord, Henry E., 1676–1690
Annin, William E., 1722
"Anniversary Oration of the Agricultural
  Society of South Carolina''
  (Hammond), 709–714
Annual Fairs of Monroe county
  Agricultural Society in 1863, 667
American Academy of Arts and Sciences,
  274
American Agricultural Association, 567
American Agricultural Editors'
  Association, 2054
American agricultural revolutions. *See*
  Agricultural revolution, first;
  Agricultural revolution, second
American agriculture
  and agribusiness, 3408–3413
  attractions of, 1449–1450
  and bread crops, 847–853
  and changes in farm size and type,
    2922–2928
  changes in productivity and efficiency
    of, 3557–3559
  and Civil War, 672–674, 685–692
  commercialization of. *See*
    Commercialization of agriculture
  and decline of rural institutions,
    3560–3571
  deficiencies of, 1866–1872
  English traveler's view of, 426–436,
    438–446
  and farm life in 1862, 1035–1039
  and farm management in 1902,
    1759–1774
  future outlook for, 2920–2921,
    3560–3593
  and government policies from 1920 to
    1940, 2440–2468. *See also*
    Government agricultural policies
  historical development until 1899,
    1658–1676
  leaders in, 3267–3275
  poetry on, 1430–1431
  and post-World War I depression,
    2645–2648, 2651–2658, 2684–2686
  regional shifts in, 2784–2787
  by regions in 1969, 3540–3546
  related to business prosperity,
    2641–2645
  and Report of Country Life
    Commission, 1875–1906
  and rural disorganization in 1913,
    1949–1964
  Secretaries of Agriculture speak on,
    3029–3054
  and subsistence farming, 2810–2814
  and technology, 3572–3577
  and tractors, 3414–3434
  types of, 1833–1846
  U. S. Census Bureau report of 1870 on,
    1150t–1159t
  and weed problem, 2623–2629
  during World War I, 2585–2602
  during World War II, 3817–3237
  from 1783–1840, 273–517
  in 1840, 500–517
  in 1869, 913–962
  in 1908, 1833–1846

from 1914 to 1940, 1993–2913
  in 1970, 3546–3551
American Agriculture, 764, 973
American Agriculturist, 279, 522,
  560–561, 609–611, 2817–2818
  on Agricultural Department of Patent
    Office, 594–597
  on agricultural implements in 1867,
    1981
  call for agricultural schools and
    colleges, 565–567
  on experimental farms at agricultural
    colleges, 646
  on goals for Department of Agriculture,
    624–626
  on the Grangers, 1447–1449
  on need for agricultural colleges,
    561–565
  on results of Homestead Act, 553–554
American Archives (Force), 241–244,
  244–246, 247, 248–249, 249–250,
  251–252, 252–253, 255–256
American Association for the
  Advancement of Science, 1329
American Association of Farmers'
  Institute Managers, The, 1312–1313
American Association of Land-Grant
  Colleges 3281–3283
American colleges, educational resources
  of, 643t
American Council of Agriculture, 2451
American Courier, 776–779
American Farm Bureau, 2324
American Farm Bureau Federation, 1996,
  2155
  Bulletin on cooperative Marketing,
    2639–2640
  establishment of, 2637–2638,
    2884–2888
  program of 1939, 2888–2892
American Farmer, 279–280, 437–438,
  446–447
  beginnings of, 446–447
  call for agricultural state university,
    579–583
  on founding of Maryland Agricultural
    College, 585–587
  on new reaper, 865–866
American Forestry Association, 2054
American Gardener, The, 2733
"American Gardener's Calendar,'' 2733
American Guernsey Cattle Club,
  2836–2837
American Historical Review, 355–361
American Husbandry, 204–226, 229
American Jersey Cattle Club, 2834, 2836
American Medical Association, Council
  on Foods and Nutrition, 3261, 3262
American National Red Cross
  and distribution of stabilization
    supplies, 2233
  and wheat distribution, 2214–2215
"American Orchardist'' (Thacher), 2733
American Philosophical Society, 274
American Railway Development
  Association, 2054
American Restaurant Magazine, 3507
American Revolution

Bolley, H. L., 2826
Bollworm, 3313
Bomberger, Wight & Co., 932
"Bonanza" farm idea, 1774–1775
Bone meal, 810, 1114
Bonesteel, Otto & Co., 1137
Bonnen, James T., 3560–3571
Borah, William, 1197–1204, 1205, 2219
Bordeaux mixture, 1247–1248
    and downy mildew, 1302
    as fungicide, 1248–1249
    and potato blight, 2863
    removal from fruit, 1250
Border States, during Civil War, 663–664
Borlaug, Norman E., 3534
Borrison, B. Y., 2529
Boston, milk shipments to, 1443–1445
Boston Gazette and Country Journal,
    203–204
Bounties
    for corn-growing in Utah Territory,
        1552
    for killing wolves and foxes, 100
    for silk culture, 1329, 1330
Bourbon sugar cane, 772
Boussingault, Jean, 3250
Bovine tuberculosis, 2520
Bow and arrow, for killing crows, 16, 19
Bowdoin, 316
Bowl making, from calabashes, 180
Bowles, Chester, 3228
Boyd, John, 248
Boyd-Orr, Lord John, 3259–3260
"Boys' Agricultural Clubs" (Crosby),
    1338–1344
Boys' corn clubs, 1375, 2547
    and hog raising, 2609
    during World War I, 2589–2590
"Boys and Girls' Clubs Do Pioneer Work
    in Improving Farm Life" (Hill),
    2507–2510
Bracero labor program, 3521
Brackenridge, H. M., 487
Braconnot, M. H., 3250
Bradford, William, 94, 95
Bradfute, O. E., 2180–2187, 2888
Brandy making, 1787–1788
Brannan, Charles F., 3040–3042, 3047,
    3048, 3050, 3053
Brannan Plan, 2952–2959
Bread, 37
    of American Indians, 73–74
    for Confederate Army, 655
    enrichment of, 3262
    grain growing for, 847–853
    and pure food laws, 2979–2980
"Bread Crops," 847–853
"Breaking Prairie" (May), 804–806
"Breeding and Genetics in Potato
    Improvement" (Stevenson and
    Clark), 2860–2863
Breimyer, Harold F., 2920, 3586–3593
Brennen, C. A., 2796–2805
Brewer, William H., 1216–1227, 1235
Brewing, *See* Beer brewing
Brick work, 284
Brickmaking, in colonial North Carolina,
    158
Bridlington fair, 119, 120

Briggs, Albert, 668
Briggs, G. G., 1784
Bright, V. S., 1803–1805
Brine, salt made from, 664–665
"Brinley Eagle," 1062
British Cyclopaedia, 904
Broccoli, 835
Broiler industry, 3525–3529, 3573
Brookhart, Smith, 2157
Brooks, W. P., 2855
Brown, Elisha, 872, 873
Brown, Frank B., 1458
Brown, George Rothwell, 1831–1833
Brown, H. B., 2845
Brown, John, 250
Brown, Joseph E.
    on conditions of Confederate soldiers,
        675–676
    on impressment of supplies, 678–680
Brown Swiss cattle, 2835, 2837
Brown-tail moths, control with parasites,
    2497–2499, 2782–2784
Browne, Daniel J., 596–597, 827–846
Browne, William Hand, 256–257,
    262–263
Bruce, W. M., 3529–3532
Brussels sprouts, 835
Buchanan, George, 848–849, 853
Buchanan, James, and veto of Morrill Bill,
    587–594
Buchanan, Smith & Co., 792
Buchman, Kenneth L., 2922–2928
Buckwheat
    in colonial New Jersey, 180
    in colonial New York, 207
    in colonial North Carolina, 151
    as fertilizer, 292
    in Highlands, 889
    in Maine, 870
    threshing, 427, 803
    See also Buckwheat production
Buck-wheat cakes, 180
Buckwheat production
    in Census of 1870, 1154t–1155t
    in U.S. Patent Office *Annual Report* of
        1840, 505
Buel, Judge, 903
Buffalo
    domestication of, 604–605
    extermination of, 1640
Bulkley, C., 935
Bull associations, 2695
Bull-plough, 927
Bull Tractor Co., 3422–3423
Bulletin (University of Idaho, Agricultural
    Experiment Station), 1270–1274
Bungay, George W., 973–974
Burd, Richard, 81
Burdick, R. T., 3296–3299
Bureau of Agricultural Economics, 2457,
    3223
    Division of Cotton Marketing, 2841
Bureau of Animal Industry, 1358
    and enforcement of pure food laws,
        2982
    and eradication of Texas fever,
        1304–1309
    establishment of, 1164, 1228–1230
    and foot-and-mouth disease, 2753–2754

    fundamental research done in,
        2519–2522
    and Meat Inspection Act, 1351–1357,
        2988
    on varieties of dairy products,
        1672–1673
    work of, 1230–1232
Bureau of Biological Survey, 2133, 2134
Bureau of Entomology and Plant
    Quarantine, 2814–2816, 3326
Bureau of Indian Affairs, 2934–2935
Bureau of Mines, 2071
Bureau of Plant Industry, 1936, 2545
    and alfalfa wilt control, 2532
    county demonstration work, 2548
    Division of Mycology and Disease
        Survey, 2862–2863
    Division of Vegetable Physiology, 2515
    and Farmers' Cooperative
        Demonstration Work, 1371–1372
    and hybrid corn experiments,
        2820–2821
    and industry, 2645
    insect resistance studies, 2777–2778
Bureau of Plant Quarantine, 2791–2792
Bureau of Reclamation, 2053, 3348
Bureau of Statistics, on wage rates of farm
    labor, 1925–1929
Burgundy grapes, of Kentucky, 377
Burials, of Grange members, 1430
Burke, Bertha, 3260
Burke, Edmund, 769–776
Burling, Walter, 2842
Burnet grass, 839
Burnett, Edmund C., 254, 258, 261, 262,
    264, 265, 266–269, 314–318
Burnett, G. P., 1596
Burnett, Micajah, 808–809
Burnett, S. P., 1099
Burrill, T. J., 1301
Burton, Richard F., 1031–1034
Bushland, R. C., 3284
Business, relation to agriculture,
    2641–2645, 2779–2782
Business Men's Commission on
    Agriculture, 2454
Bussey, Benjamin, 1235
Butchering, 430, 466, 468, 469. *See also*
    Slaughterhouses
Butchers, and beef prices, 776–779
Butler, Antony, 1610
Butte, Montana, 1595
Butter
    exports of, 1669
    prices of, 670, 809
    regional production of, 2691
    sale of, 31
    varieties, of, 1672–1673
    See also Butter making
Butter making, 34, 120
    changes in, 1688–1689
    in Confederate States, 659–660
    establishment of factories for,
        1679–1680, 2694
    European, and World War I, 2604
    in Kentucky, 795
    in Maine, 871–872
    by tenant farmers, 536
Butter tests, 2835–2836

reduction in number of, 2026–2027
routes for, 1850–1851
in South, 523
in Southern states, 522–523
in Tennessee, 1805
transporting of, 1846–1860
types of, 1762, 1841–1844
on Virginia farm in 1809, 409–410
during World War II, 3231
See also Cattle; Ranching
Livestock associations, 2764
Live-stock cars, on railroads, 1855–1856
Live-stock trails, 1847–1848
Livingston, 1217–1218
Livingston, Walter, 244
Lloyd, W. A., 2547
Loans
and Agricultural Adjustment Act of
1938, 2385–2415, 2461–2462
on agricultural commodities,
2390–2392
and Drought Relief Act of 1930,
2213–2214
to ex-soldiers for land settlement in
1926, 2024
to farmers. *See* Agricultural credit
by Federal Farm Board, 2207–2208
for rehabilitation of tenant farmers,
2115–2117
to tenant farmers, 2121–2133
Lobsters
in Indian Americans diet, 71
and Plymouth colonists, 96
Local government, in Great Plains,
2072–2073
Locust trees, premiums for, 395
Logan, General Ben, 790
Logan, William, 181–183
Logwood seed, 489
Lombard, Alvin O., 3416
London cauliflower, 835
London Company, 1779
London Society of Arts, 927
London purple, 1246–1247
London short, prickly cucumber, 836
Long, Robert, 248
"Long Fight for Pure Foods, The"
(Crawford), 2979–2989
Long-horned cattle, imported to
Kentucky, 791, 793–794
Long Island, 206
Long-podded or butter bean, 830
Long, thick, smooth cucumber, 836
Long, violet-colored egg-plant, 836
Long white cucumber, 836
Longevity, and diet, 3260–3261
Longworth, Nicholas, 2734, 2865–2866
Longworthy, C. F., 1816–1823
Look, Allen, 1460
Loomis, Arthur Perkins, 1517–1525
Loomis, Frances, 1517–1525
Loomis, James W., 1517–1525
Loomis family, 1166
Loomis Family Farm Diaries (Loomis),
1517–1525
Lorain, John, 280
Lord, Russell, 2477–2478
Lord Bacon watermelon, 1655

Lorenzen, Coby, 3449
Louisiana
architecture in 1874 in, 756–761
rice culture in, 815
sugar cultivation and manufacture in,
742–752, 769, 1105
varieties of sugar cane cultivated in,
772–774
Lovejoy, Owen, 613
Lovett, Benjamin T., 1443
Loving, George B., 1553
Lowe, E. N., 2033
Lowell, S. J., 2156–2157
Lowndes, Rawlins, 258, 261
Lubin, David, 2877
Lucerne, 186, 427, 877–878, 901–902
in Confederate States, 659, 671
and rye grass, 905
See also Alfalfa
Lunin, Nicolai, 3252
Lupine, 34, 899
Lux, Darby, 248
Lux, George, 248
Lyceum of Natural History, New York,
485
Lyman, Charles A., 2157
Lytle, J. K., 1936

Macaroni, and durum wheat, 1978
Machen, A. W., 1722
"Machinery Plays a Vital Role in Making
Agriculture Efficient" (Cooper),
2768–2770
Macocks, 68–69
Macoupin County Farmers' Institute,
1338–1344
"Mad itch," 796
Madder, 247, 760
Maddeson, Captain, 81
Madeira grapes, 801
of Kentucky, 377
Madison, James, 1225
letter to Edmund Randolph, 316–317
letter to Thomas Jefferson, 317
Madison, Ohio. 445
Magendie, Francois, 3250
Maguey, 488. *See also* Pulque
Mail delivery, rural, 1606–1607,
1712–1723
"Mail Delivery in the Country"
1606–1607
Maine
agriculture in 1857 in, 866–876
agriculture in 1868 in, 1118–1122
agriculture in 1874 in, 1454–1455
fences of, 1390
plans for agricultural college in, 644
Maine Board of Agriculture, *Annual
Report, 1857*, 866–876
Maine potatoes, 762
Maison Rustique or *The Country Farme*
(Stevens and Liebault), 32–39
Maize
in California, 1501
in colonial New Jersey, 177–178
in colonial New York, 207
in colonial North Carolina, 150
in Louisiana, 758–759

in U.S. Patent Office *Annual Report* of
1840, 505
See also Indian corn
Malaria, in American tropics, 1724
Mallory, C. F., 851
"Management of Tribal Lands, The"
(Goding), 2929–2935
Mango, in American tropics, 1732
Mangold wurzel, 834
Manila hemp, in American tropics,
1732–1733
Mann, Dr. H. C. Corry, 3259
Manning, William, 930, 931
Manpower Development and Training Act
(1972), 3482
Manual labor
in agricultural college curriculum, 612,
635–639
and education, 886–888
Manufacturers
of mowers and reapers, 932
of scythes, 934
of tractors, 3431–3433
Manufacturing
and agriculture, 1509–1514
encouragement of by Virginia
Convention of 1775, 241–244
Jefferson on, 294
related to agriculture, 2641–2645
and supply of farm labor, 1579
See also Industry; Manufacturers
"Manufacturing and Agricultural Interests
Inseparable" (Seward), 1509–1514
Manures
calcareous, 735–742
clover as, 720–723
and corn culture, 421
and cotton cultivation, 790
on dairy farm, 1772
and extension work, 1374
and grass culture, 897–898
and Indian corn, 417
made with vegetable and animal matter,
715–716
and moveable pens, 409–410
and non-grazing of stock, 716–717
putrescent, top dressing with, 723–725
rotting, 404–405
See also Fertilizer; Manuring
Manuring, 729, 916–917, 1041
with dung, bones and guano, 811–812
of sugar cane, 776
and wheat raising, 979–980
Manchester, Job, 250
Manhattan Island
population in 1646, 106
purchase of, 104
Manorial system, 1949–1950
Manning, Robert, 2734
Maracocks, 66, 69
Marbut, Curtis Fletcher, 3271–3272
Marcellus, H., 879
Marchal, Dr. Paul, 2497
Mare, advertisement for lost or stolen, 203
Mareuil, Baron de, 471
Marglobe, 2505–2506
Marine, David, 3258
Mark Lane Express, 916, 1035

Moha de hongie, 836–837
Mohawk (ship), 792
Mojave Desert, soils of, 1487
Molasses
  for Confederate Army, 655
  production in Census of 1870,
    1158t–1159t
Moline Plow Company, 1994
Monckton, 1135
Monetary policies, People's Party
  platform on, 1646–1647
Money orders, rural free-delivery routes,
  1717
Monopoly
  and agricultural statistics, 500–502
  of beef market, 778
  and Capper-Volstead Cooperative
    Marketing Act, 2153
  of cattle market, 1595
  in food industry, 3511–3513
  and organization of National Grange,
    2877–2881
  and public lands, 1192–1193
  of Texas cattle transportation, 1145
  of water rights, 1879–1882
Monroe, James, 334–335
  letter from William Grayson to, 318
Monroe County Agricultural Society, 667
Montague, Robert, 785
Montana
  pioneer ranching in 1882–83 in,
    1530–1549
  ranching in, 1554, 1592–1593,
    1594–1600
Montgomery, James S., 849
Montgomery Ward & Co.,
  Catalogue, 1875, 1474–1475
Monthly Report, January, 1867 (U.S.
  Department of Agriculture),
  1068–1081
Monticello, 273
Moody, John W., 1610
Moon, and January farming tasks, 33
Moore, Francis, 140–142
Moore & Haskell, 930
Morales, Julio A., 3400–3408
"More Sugar Beets, Wheat, Barley and
  Vegetables — Colorado's Postwar
  Goal" (Burdick), 3296–3299
Morgan, Gideon, 3415
Morgan, Justin, 384, 388
Morgan horse, origin of, 384–389
Morgan Horses (Linsley), 385–389
Morgenthau, Henry, 2324, 2326–2327
Mormons, 1032–1033
  on farm size, 1065–1068
  and irrigation, 1179–1180, 1832
  and Utah Territory, 1551–1552
Morocco dressers' sumach, 846
Morrill, Justin S., 522
Morrill Land Grant College Act (1862),
  522, 616–618, 1164
  and differences between grants to states,
    643–644
  and mechanic arts training, 645
  Presidential veto of, 587–593
  and requirements of agricultural
    colleges, 630–632

support for, 593–594
Morrill Act (1890), 3287, 3289
  and Negro land-grant colleges, 2557
Morse, W. J., 2629–2636, 2854–2859
Morton, George, 95–97
Morton, John C., 620
Morton County Farmers' Union, 3547
Mosaic diseases
  and potato breeding, 2862
  research on, 2521–2522
Mosquito, and malaria, 1724
Motor Carrier Act, 2913
Movable Schools, 1378–1379, 2511–2513
Moveable pens, 409–410
Mowers
  development of, 1662–1663
  and hay making, 2724–2725
  history of, 929–933
  at New York State Fair of 1858, 879
  See also Mowing; Reapers
Mowing, 35
  of barley, 28
  of hawme, 28
Moyer, A. J., 3265
Mrs. Motte (cow), 794
Mud-sill, 886–887
Muir, F., 2495–2496
Mulberry scale, introduction of parasite
  of, 2499
Mulberry trees, 141, 298
  planting, 34
  in 16th century Virginia, 64
  wild, 760
Mulder, Gerrit Jan, 3250
Mules
  in Confederate States, 658–659
  and farm implements, 2793–2795
  in Highlands, 889–890
  raising of, 279, 1844
  replaced by tractors, 2918–2919,
    3337–3340
Murphy, George, 3097–3098
Murray, Phillip, 3225
Muscat grapes, 800
Muscatels, 1784
Musser, John, 854
Mustard seed, 27
Musquit grass, 906
My Diary North and South (Russell),
  668–669
My Farm of Edgewood (Mitchell),
  1035–1039
Myatt, 2866
Myers, Albert Cook, 117–118, 119–121
Myers, Albert Cook, 122–127, 128–130
Myers, William I., 2324

Nairne, Thomas, 159–160
*Narratives of Early Maryland,
  1633–1684* (Hall), 109–116,
  148–150
*Narratives of Early Pennsylvania, West
  Jersey and Delaware 1630–1707*
  (Myers), 117–118, 119–121,
  122–128, 128–130
*Narratives of New Netherlands
  1609–1664* (Jameson), 105–108
Narrow-leaved plantain, 900

National Academy of Sciences — National
  Research Council
  Committee on Food and Nutrition, 3261
  Food and Nutrition Board of, 3263
National Agricultural Advisory
  Commission, 3006–3019
National Agricultural Conference of 1922,
  2443–2444, 2445
National Agricultural Society
  formation of, 501
  proposals for, 556–559
  purposes of, 502
National Board of Agriculture (Great
  Britain), 291
National Broadcasting Company,
  agricultural program, 2516–2517
National Conference on Land Utilization
  (1931), 2053–2054
National farm organizations
  American Farm Bureau Federation,
    2884–2892
  development of, 2874–2876
  legislative and educational work of,
    2893–2895
  National Farmers' Union, 2881–2884
  National Grange, 2876–2881
National Farmers' Union, 3272
  legislative recommendations of,
    2882–2884
  origins and development, 2881–2882
National Gallery, 501
National Grange, 1951
  and Agricultural Adjustment Act, 2324
  historical background, 2876–2881
  organization of, 524
  role of, 1370, 1893
National Industrial Conference Board,
  2454
National Industrial Recovery Act, 2477
National Intelligencer, 647, 783–785
National Inventory of Soil and Water
  Conservation Needs, 2946, 2948
National Livestock Association, 2054
National Nutrition Conference for Defense
  (1941), 3261, 3262
National Park Service, 2133
National Sheep and Wool Growers
  Association, 2054
National Thresher Reunion, 3417
National Tractor Demonstration (1918),
  3422
National Wool Act (1954), amendments
  to, 3058–3059
Native breed cows, 826–827
Natural History of Carolina (Catesby),
  160–161
Natural resources
  in Alaska, 3374–3390
  call for development of, 757
Natural selection theory, and wheat
  improvement, 2514–2516
Nauman, E. D., 1719
Navajo Indians, 2934
  and dry farming, 1917
Navigation Act (1660), 161–168, 231
Navy, Jefferson calls for formation of, 295
Neapolitan clover, 900
Nebraska

of dye plants, 247
of farm labor, 1928–1929
and farm problems of 1922, 2684
and farm-retail spread, 3520–3521
of fencing, 1387–1389
of flour during Civil War, 654
of food during Civil War, 698
and food industry, 3518–3519
on foodstuffs during American
Revolution, 250
and government policies, 2441–2442
of grapes, 1788
of hard wheats, 1966–1968
of hemp, 1755
of hogs, 650–651
importance of publication of, 501–502
of land on borders of Ohio River, 376
and legislation, 1994
and market power of food industry,
3515–3516
in Montgomery Ward Catalog of 1875,
1474–1475
in newspaper notices in 1853, 537
and plan for equality for agriculture,
2157–2178
in post-World War I depression, 1994,
2646–2647, 2656–2657
of salt during Civil War, 655
secretaries of Agriculture on,
3029–3054
of sheep in Maine, 1121–1122
of silkworm cocoons, 1329–1330
of slaves, 863
of sorghum sugar, 1042
of supplies for Confederate Army, 693
of turkeys, 2870
of Texas cattle, 1145
in Virginia during Civil War, 670
of Western lands, 315–316
of wheat, 503–504, 850, 852, 1115,
1910–1911, 2665–2666
of wheat and rye, 302
Pride of Saline corn, 2510
Prince, W. R., 1780
Prince, William, 2734–2735
Pritchard, Fred J., 2504–2506
Private property, orders to Confederate
soldiers on, 666–667
Privies, cleaning, 25
"Proceedings of the South Carolina
Provincial Congress, 1775," 244
"Proceedings, Virginia Convention,"
241–244
Proclamation of 1763, 229, 233–236
Proclamation Line, 229–230, 233–236
Production costs
control of, 2330–2332
and farm wages, 1927
of sugar-beets, 1136
for wheat, 983–984
See also Costs; Productivity
Productivity
and agribusiness, 3410
and agricultural implements, 919–920,
924–925
changes between 1820 and 1969,
3557t–3559t
of Chilean wheat seed, 461

in Colorado after World War II,
3296–3299
cost of, and agricultural implements,
1675–1676
and drought, 2807–2808
in Europe and United States, 1659
and farm size, 2924–2925
of farm workers, 521
impact of World War II on, 3229–3237
legislation encouraging, 2570–2573
Lincoln on, 882–883
of Maine Agriculture, 869–871
in Maryland and New England States
compared, 861
and mechanization, 2769
and national economy, 3470–3471
in New England, 1453–1454
and new technology, 2919–2021
per farm worker, 3008, 3557t
and percentage of tenant farmers,
2007–2008
of slave labor, 494–495, 863–864
in South, 894
of tenant farmers, 536
and tenant farming, 2006
total value of, in Census of 1870, 1150t
in 1863, 682
See also Agricultural
productivity
Profits
of cotton cultivation, 784–785
of cotton vs. sugar cane in South,
1105–1106
of dairying, 823–824, 1772
and farmers' institutes, 1277–1278
of food industry, 3520
from grape culture, 1784
of Missouri Farmers' Association,
2686–2687
and New England farming, 1452–1464
of range cattle business, 1553–1554
of sale of slaves, 862
of sheep vs. cattle raising, 1118–1120
of sheep farm, 1773
of tenant farmer, 1528
of truck farming, 1831
from Virginia agricultural investment,
300–301
and wheat growing, 1910–1911
See also Accounts
"Progress of Agriculture in the United
States" (Holmes), 1658–1676
"Progress in Economic Entomology in the
United States" (Howard), 1288–1290
"Progress in Research on Cotton Insects",
(Rainwater), 3313–3317
"Progress in the Treatment of Plant
Diseases in the United States"
(Galloway), 1299–1303
Progressive Farmer, 3550
on land use planning, 2949–2951
Protein
in Americans' diet, 1819, 1820t, 1821
nutritional research on, 3254–3256
Prout, William, 3250
Prouty, Winston L., 3097–3098
Providence Gazette, 250
Provisions

recommended for settlers, 127
recommended for settlers of Maryland,
113–116
recommended for settlers of North
Carolina, 158–159
Prowlers, 18
Prune of Agen, 842
Prune Sainte Catherine, 842–843
Prunes
drying of, 843
harvesting machines for, 3450
marketing of, 2639–2640
Pruning
of fruit trees, 34, 35–36, 410
of grapes, 1783
Public Health Service, 3486, 3487
Public lands
after American Revolution, 275
availability, and tenant farming, 2006
and Commutation Clause of Homestead
Act, 1189–1190
disposition of, 1186–1193
future use of, 2949–2951
and grazing, 1190–1192, 1806–1807
in Hawaii, 3396–3397
laws limiting entries on, 1174–1175
legislation on, 1172–1173, 1173–1175
and monopoly, 1192–1193
People's Party platform of 1896 on,
1647–1648
proposed legislation on, 2186
protected of, 2803–2804
and ranching business, 1555–1556,
1701–1702
sale of timber on, 1188–1189
Senate debate on, 1197–1205
and Taylor Grazing Act, 2055–2060
in Virginia colony, 84–91
after World War I, 1993
See also Land distribution
Public Land Law Review Commission,
2036–2945
Public Law 272, 2966
Public Law 480, 3031, 3124, 3172
*Public Range and the Livestock Industry
of Nevada, The* (Nevada Agricultural
Experiment Station), 2796–2805
Puddling, in irrigation, 1410–1411
Puerto Rico
agriculture in, 3400–3408
Mexican pochote tree, 2528
See also American tropics
"Puerto Rico; Chjange and Progress"
(Morales), 3400–3408
Pugh, Dr. E., 612
Pulse, 112
in colonial North Carolina, 151–152
Pumps, for irrigation, 1628–1630
Pungnough, 68
Purdie, Alexander, 243
Pure food laws, 1164
Food and Drugs Act of 1906,
1346–1351
history of, 2979–2989
and inspection of meats for export,
1242–1245
Meat Inspection Act of 1906,
1351–1357

Semolina, durum-wheat, 1978
Seneca, 995
September, farmer's chores during, 12–13, 15–18
Sequoias, 1480
Servants, in colonial Maryland, 116, 148, 149–150
Settlement
  and government land policy in 1930's, 2052–2053
  of Great Plains, 2065–2067, 2070–2071
  of submarginal lands, 2134–2135
  during World War I, 2600–2602
  in 1926, 2021–2024
  See also Settlers
Settlers
  advice from Plymouth colonists to, 97
  in California in 1855, 854–855
  in Colorado Territory, 1147–1149
  effect on economy of Great Britain, 131–137
  in Kentucky, 790
  in Matanuska colony, 3361–3364
  new, 432–433
  provisions needed by, 113–116
  provisions recommended for, 127, 158–159
  types of, 118
  in Utah Territory, 523, 1551–1552
  in 1926, 2021–2024
Seward, W. B., 1509–1514
"Seward's Folly Can Be a Great Land" (Johnson) 3374–3390
Seymour, Morgan & Allen, 932
Shade trees, new varieties of, 2773
Shannon, O. K., 1758
Sharecropping, 1096–1097
  contracts, 1582–1585
  in Puerto Rico, 3406
  See also Tenant farming
Sharnel, A. D., 2820
Sheeley, Ross L., 3365
Sheep
  ban on export of, 231, 239–240, 241
  ban on slaughtering of, 242
  in California, 1494
  Columbia type, 2767–2768
  cross breeding of, 392–393
  digestion experiments with, 1310
  on general livestock farm, 1771
  in Highlands, 889–890
  in Kentucky, 378
  on Nevada public ranges, 2800–2802
  at New York State Fair of 1858, 878
  and poisonous weeds, 2624
  shearing of, 34
  See also Sheep raising
"Sheep of the Columbia Type Well Adapted to Intermountain Region" (Cooper), 2767–2768
Sheep farm, management of, 1772–1774
"Sheep Industry, The" (Spencer), 2703–2710
Sheep raising, 3463
  and American Revolution, 232
  and breeding, 2709–2710
  vs. cattle raising, 1118–1120
  during Civil War, 668, 689–691

in colonial Virginia, 172
and Columbia sheep, 2767–2768
development in United States of, 2704–2709
and dogs, 658, 730–731
encouragement of during American Revolution, 252–253
and introduction of Merino sheep, 414–416
in Iowa, 970–971, 1044–1045
in Maine, 876
in post-Civil War South, 1106
regional distribution of, 2706–2707
in Rhode Island, 1797
in Somerset County, Maine, 1868, 1120–1122
types of, 1842
in Utah, 1047, 1552
in 1923, 2703–2710
Sheep's fescue, 838
Sheepshead (fish), 124
Sheet-iron shovel, 935
Sheets, E. W., 2674–2679
Sheffield Scientific School, 1236
Shelby, Isaac, 462
Sheppard, Morris, 1256
Sherer, R., 1605–1606
Sheridan, Major-General, 697
Sherman, Henry C., 3257, 3260–3261, 3263
Sherman horse, 388
Sherrard, Lon, 1520
Shoemaker, E., 848
Shoes, in Confederacy, 661
Short, R. E., 2888
"Short Wheats Stand Tall" (Reitz), 3532–3536
Shorthorn cattle, 279
  importation of, 437–438, 1085
  See also Durham cattle
Shotwell, R. L., 3321
Shovel-plough, 927
Shovels, history of, 935–936
Shrubbery
  implements for, 768
  seeds from, 840–846
Shubert, W., 358
Shull, G. F., 3574
Shull, G. H., 2819, 2820
Siberia domestic reindeer in, 1642, 1643–1644
Siberian crab apple, 872
Siberian wheat, 284
Sickels, T. E., 1144
Side-hill plough, 927
Sierra Nevada, climate of, 1483–1484
Silage, on dairy farm, 1771
Silicious earth, 736–737
Silk, importation of in 1892–1902, 1336t–1337t
Silk cocoon production, in U.S. Patent Office *Annual Report* of 1840, 510–511
Silk-culture, 34
  in California, 1497
  in Census of 1870, 1158t–1159t
  during Civil War, 660
  in colonial South Carolina, 159–160

in colonial Virginia, 175
experiments with in 1903, 1327–1337
in Georgia, 141, 147, 223
historical background, 1327–1330
in Louisiana, 760–761
in Maryland, 112
in Northern states, 1009
prospects for, 1335–1337
Silk trade
  and settlement of Georgia, 138–139
  and slavery in Georgia, 145–146
  in Virginia, 64
Silos
  construction of, 1600–1601, 1603–1604
  filling of, 1602
"Silos and Ensilage" 1600–1605
Silver, Gray, 2157
Silver buckwheat, 830
Silver fox farming, 1845
Simmons, W. H., 530–531
"Simple Plumbing Repairs," 2744
Sims, Grover J., 3210–3220
Sinclair, Sir John, 271, 287–288, 291, 302, 722, 723, 903, 996, 997
Sinclair, Upton, 1164, 2981
Single-crop systems, 1836–1838
Single line selection, 2827
Sisal hemp
  in American tropics, 1735–1736
  cultivation in Florida of, 476, 482–489
  propagation of, 497
Sisk, W. S., 1757
Skeleton plough, 804
Sketch of the Life and Times and Speeches of Joseph E. Brown (Fielder), 675–676
Skills, of laborers, 430
Skinner, John Stuart, 279–280, 814
Skiprow planting, 3172
Slade, S. W., 1936
Slaughter, G. W., 1143
Slaughterhouses, 23
  during Civil War, 656
  federal subsidies during World War II to, 3214–3216
  See also Butchering
Slave children, 170
Slave-quarters, in Virginia, 169, 814
Slave trade, 185
  and colonial Virginia, 169–170
  in Georgia in 1750, 142–146
  See also Slavery
Slavery
  and agriculture of seaboard states, 809–821
  and American Revolution, 278
  and cotton production, 522–523, 714
  European view of, 860–865
  growth of, 815
  and land values, 892–894
  Lincoln on, 885–887
  in Northwest Territories, 323
  opposition to, in 1782, 351–352
  and overseers, 992
  See also Slave trade; Slaves
Slaves
  advertisement for sale of, 204
  breeding, 862

boys' agricultural club movement in, 1342
cattle trade in 1870 in, 1141–1146
grain crops in, 849
home economics education in, 2489–2491
invasion by cotton-boll weevil, 1739–1740
land requirements for grazing in, 1553
soil erosion in, 2033
as supplier of cattle to Northern ranges, 1554–1555
Texas Agricultural Experiment Station, 3345
Texas Commissioner of Agriculture, *Annual Report, 1916,* 2489–2491
Texas fever, 1064–1065
cattle tick and, 2519
control of, 1286–1288
definition of districts of, 1282–1283
dissemination of, 1283–1286
history of, 1279–1281
investigations by Department of Agriculture and Board of Health, 1281–1282
Textile manufacture
in American colonies, 242
and American Revolution, 252–253
premiums for, 402–403
Thacher, James, 2733
Thanksgiving, first, 95
Thatcher, R. W., 2180–2187
Thayer, F., 604
Thirty-fifth Annual Report, 1911–12, (North Carolina Agricultural Experiment Station), 1379–1380
"Thirty Million Customers for the Surplus" (Perkins), 2468–2472
Thistles
and land quality, 19–20
plantings of, 34
Thomas, John J., 2734
Thomas, Karl, 3255
Thompson, George F., 1304–1309
Thompson, Hugh M., 1039–1041
Thompson, S. H., 2888
Thoreau, Henry David, 803
Thorne, C. E., 1763
Three-share plow, 764–765
Threshing, 23, 470
accidents during, 24
corn, 35
cost of, 427
preparations for, 35
of rice, 161, 820–821
Threshing machines, 279, 284–285, 727, 933, 998
Wheeler's, 797–798
Thwaites, R. G., 438–446
Ticonderoga, New York, 244–245
Tillage, 39–43, 188–203, 1368
arguments against, 200–202
in colonial North Carolina, 150
for tobacco culture, 362–363
See also Hoeing; Soil preparation
Timber
and acorn sowing, 21

of colonial New York, 207–208
of colonial North Carolina, 155
of colonial Virginia, 170
of Georgia, 221
of Hawaii, 3395–3396
of Maine, 867
on public lands, 1188–1189
and September chores, 18
of Utah Territory, 1033
See also Forests
Timber Culture Act (1873), 1163–1164, 1167–1168
Timber and Stone Act (1878), 1164
and public lands, 1187
Timothy, 903, 1039–1040
and crop rotation, 1768
and hay-making, 2723
on livestock farm, 1769
See also Herds grass
Tinkham, Samuel W., 1121
Tiremakers, and tractors, 3425–3426
Tisdall, Dr. Frederick, 3260
Tobacco
botanical definition of, 361
cowpen, 171
exports of, 1669
as insecticide, 1247
marketing quotas on, 2393–2396
used as payment during American Revolution, 251–252
See also Tobacco culture
Tobacco culture, 361–373, 1838
by American Indians, 74
in American tropics, 1737–1738
in Census of 1870, 1154t–1155t
during Civil War, 682
in colonial Virginia, 78–79, 80
and conveying to market, 371–373
cutting and gathering, 366–367
and "firing," 366
in Georgia, 223
hanging, 369–370
harvesting, 3455
hoeing, 364
and housing, 367–369
by Indians, 1659
land preparation for, 361–363
planting methods, 363–364
and preparations for cutting, 369
and price supports, 2955
in Puerto Rico, 3404
and ripening, 366
and season for planting, 363
and slavery, 864–865
and smoking crop, 370
and soil depletion, 200, 279
in South Carolina, 381
and stemming, 270–271
and stripping, 466
and suckering, 365
and topping, 364
in U.S. Patent Office *Annual Report* of 1840, 508
in Virginia, 171
and worming, 365–366, 468
from 1850 to 1890, 1668
in 1920, 2645
Tobacco houses, 367–369

Tobacco laws, in colonial Virginia, 80, 83, 92–93, 173, 1631–1632
Tobacco worms, 365–366
Tobey, W., 879
Todhunter, Elizabeth Neige, 3246–3263
Tolley, Howard Ross, 3273
Tomato culture
mechanization of, 3529–3532
and truck farming, 1830
and wilt resistant varieties, 2504–2506
"Tomato Varieties Developed for Wilt Resistance" (Pritchard), 2504–2506
Tools
of Indians, 72
recommended for settlers, 115
Topography, farm income and, 2603t
Topping tobacco plants, 364
Torrey, Bradford, 803
Towns
of colonial Pennsylvania, 122
of colonial Virginia, 169
of Georgia, 142
Townsend, C. H. T., 1740
Tractors
and animal power, 2923
and changes in agriculture, 3572–3573
replacement of horses and mules by, 2918–2919, 3337–3340
and second agricultural revolution, 2919
and world agricultural production, 2606
Trade
and Agricultural Trade Development and Assistance Act of 1954, 2973–2979
British restrictions against, 515
in colonial Pennsylvania, 128
and cotton production, 509–510
and farm wages, 1927
with Indians, 79, 119
and Navigation Act of 1660, 161–168
from New Netherlands, 104–105
between North Carolina and Virginia colonies, 156–157
restrictions on American colonies, 176, 230–231, 237–240
of South Carolina and Georgia, 137–140
taught to slaves, 170
of United States during Civil War, 686–687
Transactions (Illinois State Agricultural Society)
1861–64, 695–696
1865–66, 1053–1060
Transactions (Iowa State Agricultural Society), 1863, 1039–1041
Transactions (New York Society for the Promotion of Agriculture, Arts and Manufactures), 1218
Transactions (Society for Promoting Agriculture in the State of Connecticut), 1219–1220
Transactions (Wisconsin State Agricultural Society)
1851, 804–806
1858–59, 881–888
1861–68, 1113–1118

Wilson & Armstrong, 648, 652, 656
Wilson & Johnson, 652, 656
Winder, William, Jr., 256
Windmills, and irrigation, 1404–1405, 1630–1631
Winds, on Great Plains, 2083
Wine-making, 34, 35, 1787–1790
  in American colonies, 1611
  in California, 1260–1268, 1431–1432, 1505–1509
  in colonial New York, 216–217
  in colonial North Carolina, 158
  in colonial Pennsylvania, 123
  in colonial Virginia, 174
  and colonial women, 37
  in Confederate States, 661–662
  in Europe and U.S. compared, 1790
  growth of, 1781
  in Maryland, 112
  in Ohio, 431
  in U.S. Patent Office *Annual Report* of 1840, 511
Wing, De Witt C., 2874–2895
Wing, Joseph E., 1772–1774
Wing-dams, 1406
Winlaw, 284–285
Winn, Colonel, 1466
Winnemore, J. T., 678
Winslow, Edward, 95–97
Winter, preparations for, 29–31
Winter-killing, 980–981
Winter melon, 836
Winter plantings, 15–19
Winter vetch, 302
Winter wheat
  and crop rotation, 1710–1711
  hard, 1968–1972
Winters, R. Y., 2842
Winston, Clement, 792
Wisconsin
  agriculture in 1864 in, 629–630
  agriculture in 1868 in, 1113–1118
  agricultural experimentation in, 1380–1383
  breaking prairie of, 804–806
  marketing in, 1381–1383
Wisconsin Agricultural Experiment Station, *Annual Report, 1913,* 1380–1383
Wisconsin State Agricultural Society *Annual Report, 1864,* 629–630
Wisconsin State Agricultural Society *Transactions,* 1851, 804–806
  Transactions, 1858–59, 881–888
  Transactions, 1861–68, 1113–1118
Wisconsin Agriculturalist and Farmer, 3227
Wise, William, 256
Woad, 247, 760
Woburn hogs, 1129
Wodrow, Alexander, 247
Wolf, O. O., 2888
Wollaston, William, 3250
Wolves, bounty for, 100
Wolves (Indians), 107–108
Women
  and berry plantings, 17

in colonial Maryland, 148–149
contributions to cooperatives made by, 3492–3494
and dietary habits, 1821–1823
as farm laborers, 1923–1924
and farming in New Netherlands, 102
in home demonstration clubs, 3019
and home economics education, 2489–2491
and mustard seeds, 27
in Pennsylvania colony, 120
and public lands, 530–531
and pure food laws, 2981
See also Farmers' wives
Women's Land Army, 3204
Women's Progressive Farm Clubs, 2688
Women's Progressive Farmers' Association, 2688
Wood, Jethro, 278, 459, 560, 928
Wood, William, 69–71, 97–99, 111
Wood, 879
  cutting, 36
  gathering, 30
  prices during Civil War, 670
  prices in 1819, 431
Woodcroft, Bennett, 931
Woodland Ditch Company, 1416
Woodman, Jason, 1719
Woodpecker (horse), 793
Woodroof, J. G., 3536–3540
Woods, A. F., 2513–2516
Wool, of Barbary sheep, 392–393
Wool industry
  and Agricultural Act of 1958, 3026
  and Agricultural Act of 1970, 3108
  and Agriculture and Consumer Protection Act of 1973, 3159
  during Civil War, 682
  encouragement of during American revolution, 252–253
  exports of, 1669
  and Food and Agriculture Act of 1965, 3058–3059
  and sheep raising, 2705–2706
  in South during Civil War, 657
  in Utah Territory, 1552
Woolford, Levin, 256
Woolsey, Bishop S. A., 1552
Work hours, of farm laborers, 430
Workshops, at agricultural colleges, 645
World Agriculture
  and Agricultural Trade Development and Assistance Act of 1954, 2973–2979
  and grain needs, 3578–3586
  during World War II, 2917
  effect of World War I on, 2604–2607
  and soybeans, 2855–2856
World food supply, 2920–2921
  and grains, 3577–3586
World War I
  Department of Agriculture during, 2598
  farm acreage during, 2595
  farm labor during, 2590–2591
  and farm production, 2570–2573
  food controls during, 2573–2584
  home gardens during, 2590

impact on agriculture, 2604–2607
and sheep raising, 2708–2709
small vegetable garden during, 2590
tenant farmers during, 2601–2602
yields during, 2595–2596
World War II
  and agriculture, 3187–3237
  agricultural production during, 3195–3209
  and changes in farm productivity, 3229–3237
  farm labor during, 3203–3206, 3477
  and farm life, 3294–2559
  farm price policies during, 3220–3228
  food program during, 3188–3193
  and insecticides and pesticides, 2986
  land settlement during, 2600–2602
  meat supplies during, 3210–3220
  and second American agricultural revolution, 2917
  and War Food Administration, 3194
"World's Agriculture Much Changed by the War and the Results" (Stine), 2604–2607
Worm-fence, 1390–1392
Wormwood seed, and fleas, 26
Writings of Henry David Thoreau, Journal, III, Sept. 16, 1851–April 30, 1852 (Torrey), 803
Wyoming, ranching in, 1554

Yale College, 1234
  agricultural department, 569
Yearbook (U.S. Department of Agriculture). *See* U.S. Department of Agriculture *Yearbook*
Yeardley, Sir George, 83–91
Year's Residence in the United States of America, A (Cobbett), 426–436
Yellow fever, 378
  in American tropics, 1724
  control of, 2519
Yellow lupine, 832
Yellow trefoil, 838
Yellowstone Journal, 1592–1593
Yerkes, J. D., 851
Yield, 882–883
  and agricultural education, 563
  of corn, 1804
  of corn and cotton in South, 1093–1094
  of cotton, 2681–2682
  and extension work, 1374
  of dates, 2751–2752
  on Great Plains, 2084
  and guano, 811, 813–814
  of hay, 2726–2728
  of hemp, 1755
  and irrigation, 1416–1418
  methods of increasing, 1804
  of Negro farmers, 1936
  in New England, 1453
  and potato breeding, 2862
  of potatoes, 3576
  and prices, 2567–2569
  of rice, 821
  of soybeans, 2859
  of sugar beets, 3300